McDougal Littell
CLASSZONE

Visit **classzone.com** and get connected.

ClassZone resources provide instruction, planning and assessment support for teachers.

Help with the Math

- @Home Tutor enables students to focus on the math and be more prepared for class, using animated examples and instruction.

Games and Activities

- Crossword puzzles, memory games, and other activities help students connect to essential math concepts.
- Math Vocabulary Flipcards are a fun way to learn math terminology.

Animated Math

- Engaging activities with animated problem-solving graphics support each lesson.
- Online resources include direct correlations to hands-on games and activities at the SHODOR website.

You have immediate access to the the online version of the textbook and ClassZone resources at **www.classzone.com**

MCDTANTZM8ZZ

Use this code to create your own user name and password.

D1444764

McDougal Littell
Where Great Lessons Begin

McDougal Littell

MathThematics

NEW EDITION

Senior Authors

Rick Billstein
Jim Williamson

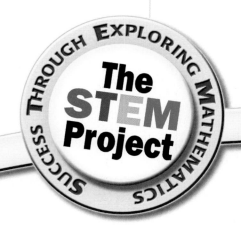

SUCCESS THROUGH EXPLORING MATHEMATICS

The **STEM** Project

BOOK 3

AUTHORS

SENIOR AUTHORS

Rick Billstein   Department of Mathematical Sciences, The University of Montana, Missoula, Montana

Jim Williamson   Department of Mathematical Sciences, The University of Montana, Missoula, Montana

REVISION WRITERS Lyle Andersen, Jean Howard, Deb Johnson, Bonnie Spence

MATHEMATICS CONSULTANTS Dr. Ira Papick, The University of Missouri, Columbia, Missouri; Dr. David Barker, Illinois State University, Normal, Illinois

PROJECT EVALUATOR Dr. Ted Hodgson, Montana State University, Bozeman, Montana

CONSULTING AUTHORS Perry Montoya, Jacqueline Lowery, Dianne Williams

STEM WRITERS Mary Buck, Clay Burkett, Lynn Churchill, Chris Clouse, Roslyn Denny, William Derrick, Sue Dolezal, Doug Galarus, Paul Kennedy, Pat Lamphere, Nancy Merrill, Perry Montoya, Sallie Morse, Marjorie Petit, Patrick Runkel, Thomas Sanders-Garrett, Richard T. Seitz, Bonnie Spence, Becky Sowders, Chris Tuckerman, Ken Wenger, Joanne Wilkie, Cheryl Wilson, Bente Winston

STEM TEACHER CONSULTANTS Melanie Charlson, Polly Fite, Jean Howard, Tony Navarro, Paul Sowden, Linda Tetley, Marsha Vick, Patricia Zepp

PHOTOGRAPHY ACKNOWLEDGEMENTS

Cover: Anasazi Ruin in Alcove Zion National Park © Tom Till/Alamy; *Cross Section of Chambered Nautilus Shell* © Josh Westrich/zefa/Corbis; *Canal Bridge in Magdeburg, Germany* © Eckehard Schulz/AP Images.

Pages T1–T73: **T4** *both* RMIP/Richard Haynes/McDougal Littell/Houghton Mifflin Co., **T6** © Don Mason/Corbis; **T7** © Richard Chung/Reuters/Corbis; **T8** © Craig Lovell/Corbis; **T9** © John D. Russell/AP Images; **T10** © Eckehard Schulz/AP Images; **T11** © Firefly Productions/Corbis; **T12** © BSIP/Photo Researchers, Inc.; **T13** © Josh Westrich/zefa/Corbis; **T57** Jorge Alban/McDougal Littell/Houghton Mifflin Co.

Further acknowledgements for copyrighted material can be found at the end of the book and constitute an extension of this page.

THE STEM PROJECT   *McDougal Littell Math Thematics*® is based on the field-test versions of The STEM Project curriculum. The STEM Project was supported in part by the

 NATIONAL SCIENCE FOUNDATION

under Grant No. ESI-0137682. Opinions expressed in *McDougal Littell Math Thematics*® are those of the authors and not necessarily those of the National Science Foundation.

ISBN-13: 978-0-618-65611-0   123456789-VJM-11 10 09 08 07
ISBN-10: 0-618-65611-1

Internet Web Site: http://www.mcdougallittell.com

McDougal Littell
Math*Thematics*

BOOK 3

The STEM Project

SUCCESS THROUGH EXPLORING MATHEMATICS

TEACHER'S EDITION

Table of Contents

Promoting Student Success

The *Math Thematics* program is a complete mathematics curriculum that promotes student success and engages students in learning by using a thematic approach, active learning, and varied practice and assessment.

- **Thematic Approach** Students learn mathematical concepts and skills through thematic modules that connect mathematical concepts to real-world applications and students' interests.

- **Active Learning** Students are actively engaged in learning as they explore, model, and communicate mathematical ideas using a variety of tools. Direct instruction is also included when appropriate.

- **Varied Practice and Assessment** Teachers and students have a variety of practice and assessment tools that can be used to assure development and mastery of important concepts and skills. Students also learn to assess their own progress.

Unifying Concepts

Four key unifying concepts are used throughout the *Math Thematics* curriculum to make mathematical connections and increase understanding.

- **Proportional Reasoning** The ability to reason proportionally provides the basis for understanding concepts of ratio, rate, percent, proportions, slope, similarity, scale, linear functions, and probability.

- **Multiple Representations** Multiple representations of concepts help students see the connections between topics such as coordinate systems and functions, fraction-decimal-percent representations, and geometric representations of arithmetic concepts.

- **Patterns and Generalizations** Identifying and describing numeric and geometric patterns and making, testing, and applying generalizations about data are tools that students use to develop concepts and construct mathematical thinking.

- **Modeling** By expressing real-world problems using mathematics, finding solutions, and then interpreting the solutions in a real-world context, students become confident problem solvers.

Organization of the Student Edition

The mathematics content for each grade level is presented in one book containing eight thematic modules that connect the mathematical ideas to real-world applications.

Each module contains four to six sections, an *Extended Exploration,* a *Module Project,* and a *Review and Assessment.* A typical module takes about 4 weeks to complete.

The organization of the material in a module is described below.

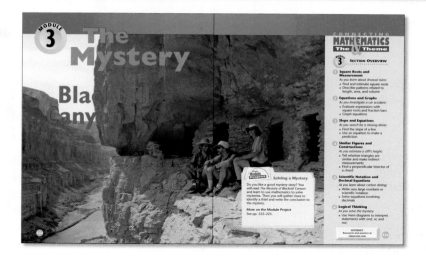

Module There are 8 modules in each book.

Section Each module has 4 to 6 sections. A section contains 1 to 3 explorations and typically requires 1 to 3 days to complete.

Section   Section   Section   Section   Section   Section
①   ②   ③   ④   ⑤   ⑥

Exploration There are 1 to 3 explorations per section. An exploration typically takes 1 day to complete.

Exploration 1   Exploration 2

Key Concepts The *Key Concepts* gives the main ideas and new terms of the section.

Key Concepts

Practice & Application Exercises Homework exercises are assigned at the end of each exploration. *Practice & Application Exercises, Spiral Review,* and *Extension* reinforce and extend learning.

Practice & Application Exercises

Extra Skill Practice The *Extra Skill Practice* provides additional exercises for students who need more practice.

Extra Skill Practice

T5

Mathematics Students Will Be Learning

Section 1
- finding and using rates and equivalent rates
- creating and interpreting histograms and circle graphs

Section 2
- making and analyzing back-to-back stem-and-leaf plots
- creating and interpreting box-and-whisker plots
- choosing an appropriate data display

Section 3
- writing and solving equations
- identifying like and unlike terms
- simplifying expressions
- applying the distributive property over addition and subtraction

Section 4
- making and interpreting scatter plots
- fitting a line to data points on a scatter plot and using it to make predictions

Section 5
- using a 4-step approach to problem solving
- using tables, graphs, and equations to model relationships

MODULE 1

AMAZING FEATS and FACTS

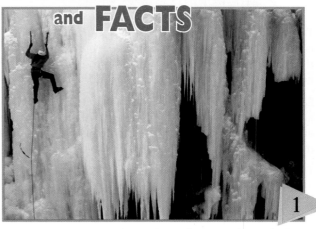

Connecting the Theme *Towering talents and amazing facts will capture your imagination, as you see how mathematics can be used to describe incredible accomplishments and surprising relationships.*

AT THE MALL

MODULE 2

76

Connecting the Theme *Malls combine shopping with entertainment. Mathematics helps store owners plan inventory, and helps shoppers compare prices. You'll learn the mathematics that operates behind the scenes.*

Module Features

MODULE PROJECT
Designing a Game, pp. 77 and 150–151

CAREER CONNECTION
Business Owner, p. 148

EXTENSION
Absolute Value Equations, p. 90
Sampling Methods, p. 137
Percent of Profit, p. 148

Assessment Options

PORTFOLIO ASSESSMENT
  EXTENDED EXPLORATION (E²):
  Is It a Boy or a Girl?, p. 121
  REFLECTING ON THE SECTION:
  pp. 90, 103, 119, 136, and 147

ONGOING ASSESSMENT
  CHECKPOINTS: pp. 80, 81, 82, 85, 94, 96, 98, 99, 108, 110, 113, 124, 126, 127, 128, 130, 131, 142, and 143
  KEY CONCEPT QUESTIONS: pp. 86, 87, 100, 114, 115, 132, 143, and 144
  STANDARDIZED TESTING: pp. 91, 104, 120, and 149

MODULE ASSESSMENT
  REVIEW AND ASSESSMENT: pp. 152–153
  REFLECTING ON THE MODULE: p. 153

Mathematics Students Will Be Learning

SECTION 1
- adding, subtracting, multiplying, and dividing integers
- finding opposites and absolute values
- translating figures on a coordinate plane

SECTION 2
- adding and subtracting positive and negative fractions
- adding and subtracting positive and negative mixed numbers

SECTION 3
- finding experimental and theoretical probability
- recognizing equally likely, independent, and dependent events
- using tree diagrams to model the outcomes of an experiment and to find theoretical probabilities

SECTION 4
- estimating a percent of a number
- using proportions and equations to find percents and solve problems
- developing the meanings of population, sample, and representative sample
- summarizing and interpreting survey results

SECTION 5
- using estimation and mental math to find percents
- using percents to solve problems
- finding percent of increase or decrease

Mathematics Students Will Be Learning

SECTION 1
- finding and estimating square roots
- relating length, area, and volume

SECTION 2
- evaluating expressions containing square roots and fraction bars
- graphing equations
- using graphs to solve problems

SECTION 3
- finding the slopes of linear graphs
- using equations and graphs to model situations
- finding the equation of a fitted line and using it to make predictions

SECTION 4
- applying the properties of similar figures including similar triangles
- solving indirect measurement problems
- constructing the perpendicular bisector of a chord of a circle

SECTION 5
- writing large numbers in decimal and scientific notation
- solving equations involving decimals

SECTION 6
- interpreting statements with *and, or,* or *not*
- organizing information in Venn diagrams

Module Features

MODULE PROJECT
Solving a Mystery, pp. 155 and 222–225

STUDENT RESOURCE
Circles, p. 197

EXTENSION
Making a Conjecture, p. 202

Assessment Options

PORTFOLIO ASSESSMENT
EXTENDED EXPLORATION (E²):
Mystery State, p. 191
REFLECTING ON THE SECTION:
pp. 166, 178, 189, 201, 212, and 220

ONGOING ASSESSMENT
CHECKPOINTS: pp. 160, 162, 170, 171, 174, 182, 183, 185, 193, 195, 197, 206, 208, and 217
KEY CONCEPT QUESTIONS:
pp. 163, 175, 186, 198, 209, and 217
STANDARDIZED TESTING:
pp. 179, 190, 203, 213, and 221

MODULE ASSESSMENT
REVIEW AND ASSESSMENT:
pp. 226–227
REFLECTING ON THE MODULE:
p. 227

The MYSTERY of BLACKTAIL CANYON

154

Connecting the Theme *Be on the lookout as a mystery unfolds. As you read, you'll rely on mathematics to help you piece together clues to catch a thief. Then, you'll use rules of logic to try solving the mystery.*

T8

INVENTIONS

228

Connecting the Theme *How do inventors get new ideas? They brainstorm, experiment, and carefully calculate. You'll see how mathematics has helped in perfecting inventions from the tin can to the Braille alphabet to the combination lock.*

Module Features

MODULE PROJECT
Building a Ramp, pp. 229 and 304–305

EXTENSION
Maximum Efficiency, p. 255
Repeating Decimals, p. 281
Pascal's Triangle, p. 295

Assessment Options

PORTFOLIO ASSESSMENT
 EXTENDED EXPLORATION (E²):
 Getting the Most Out of a Can, p. 257
 REFLECTING ON THE SECTION:
 pp. 243, 254, 268, 280, 295, and 302

ONGOING ASSESSMENT
 CHECKPOINTS: pp. 232, 233, 236, 247, 249, 260, 262, 263, 273, 276, 287, 290, and 299
 KEY CONCEPT QUESTIONS:
 pp. 238, 239, 251, 264, 265, 277, 291, 292, and 300
 STANDARDIZED TESTING:
 pp. 244, 269, 282, 296, and 303

MODULE ASSESSMENT
 REVIEW AND ASSESSMENT:
 pp. 306–307
 REFLECTING ON THE MODULE:
 p. 307

Mathematics Students Will Be Learning

SECTION 1
• finding the circumference and area of a circle
• finding the volumes of prisms, cylinders, spheres
• exploring the effect of changing a linear dimension has on area or volume

SECTION 2
• finding the surface area of a cylinder
• finding and interpreting the surface area to volume ratios

SECTION 3
• finding and interpreting slopes
• identifying the slopes of horizontal and vertical lines
• identifying the y-intercept of a line
• writing the equation of a line in slope-intercept form

SECTION 4
• identifying rational numbers
• using repetend notation for repeating decimals
• solving equations containing rational numbers

SECTION 5
• using the counting principle
• finding permutations
• finding combinations

SECTION 6
• using the counting principle to find probabilities

Mathematics Students Will Be Learning

SECTION 1
- finding the volume and surface area of figures built with cubes
- drawing three-dimensional and flat views of figures

SECTION 2
- naming congruent figures
- applying the triangle inequality
- creating nets for polyhedrons
- identifying the faces, vertices, and edges of a polyhedron
- constructing angle bisectors
- applying the side-side-side and side-angle-side rules for triangle congruence

SECTION 3
- using side lengths to classify triangles
- using the Pythagorean theorem to find an unknown side length in a right triangle

SECTION 4
- finding surface areas of prisms and pyramids
- finding volumes of prisms, pyramids, cones, and composite figures

SECTION 5
- identifying pairs of angles formed by intersecting lines
- determining the measures of angles formed by parallel lines and a transversal
- identifying complementary and supplementary angles

SECTION 6
- making scale drawings
- determining relationships between side length and perimeter and between side length and area for similar figures

T10

 Table of Contents

ARCHITECTS and ENGINEERS

308

Connecting the Theme *From blueprint to model to construction site, a structure takes shape. As you give form to your own constructions, you'll see how measurement and mathematics are tools of the construction trade around the world.*

VISUALIZING CHANGE

MODULE 6

390

Connecting the Theme *It may be impossible to see the future. Still, many professionals need to predict coming trends. From economics to environmental science, you'll learn how mathematical models can help people see patterns of change.*

Module Features

MODULE PROJECT
Modeling Change in a Story, pp. 391 and 452–453

CAREER CONNECTION
Wildlife Veterinarian, p. 430

EXTENSION
Exponential Decay, p. 430
Finding the Vertex, p. 450

Assessment Options

PORTFOLIO ASSESSMENT
EXTENDED EXPLORATION (E²):
Choosing the Right Plan, p. 419

REFLECTING ON THE SECTION:
pp. 404, 417, 429, 440, and 449

ONGOING ASSESSMENT
CHECKPOINTS: pp. 396, 399, 409, 410, 411, 412, 423, 425, 434, 435, 445, and 446

KEY CONCEPT QUESTIONS:
pp. 400, 401, 413, 414, 426, 436, and 447

STANDARDIZED TESTING:
pp. 418, 431, 441, and 451

MODULE ASSESSMENT
REVIEW AND ASSESSMENT:
pp. 454–455

REFLECTING ON THE MODULE:
p. 455

Mathematics Students Will Be Learning

SECTION 1
- using tables and graphs to model change in data
- using tables, graphs, and equations to identify and model functions

SECTION 2
- using tables, graphs, and equations to solve problems about linear change
- using the distributive property to combine like terms and solve multi-step equations

SECTION 3
- using tables, graphs, and equations to model exponential change
- using equations to model compound interest

SECTION 4
- writing an algorithm to describe a series of transformations
- reflecting geometric figures over the *x*- or *y*-axis

SECTION 5
- using equations to predict the shapes of parabolas
- recognizing and graphing quadratic equations
- simplifying quadratic expressions

Mathematics Students Will Be Learning

Section 1
- multiplying and dividing powers
- simplifying powers with zero and negative exponents
- representing small numbers in decimal and scientific notation

Section 2
- identifying irrational numbers
- simplifying square roots
- simplifying radical expressions

Section 3
- writing, graphing, and solving simple multi-step inequalities

Section 4
- multiplying binomials
- factoring quadratic expressions

MODULE 7

Module Features

MODULE PROJECT
Math and Careers, pp. 456 and 512–513

CAREER CONNECTION
Scientist, p. 468

EXTENSION
Extending the Properties of Exponents, p. 468

Assessment Options

PORTFOLIO ASSESSMENT
EXTENDED EXPLORATION (E²):
Sum Fun!, p. 481
REFLECTING ON THE SECTION:
pp. 467, 479, 493, and 510

ONGOING ASSESSMENT
CHECKPOINTS: pp. 460, 461, 462, 463, 472, 473, 475, 476, 485, 487, 488, 498, 499, 500, 503, and 505
KEY CONCEPT QUESTIONS:
pp. 464, 477, 489, 506, and 507
STANDARDIZED TESTING:
pp. 469, 480, 494, and 511

MODULE ASSESSMENT
REVIEW AND ASSESSMENT:
pp. 514–515
REFLECTING ON THE MODULE:
p. 515

 Table of Contents

The ALGEBRA CONNECTION

456

Connecting the Theme *Algebra plays and important role in the world both inside and outside of the classroom. You will see algebra at work in the careers of scientists, mathematicians, engineers, and artists from ancient times to the present.*

MATH-THEMATICAL MIX

516

Connecting the Theme *In this module, you will connnect and expand mathematical topics you studied in earlier modules. You will use mathematics to find, describe, and compare patterns, relationships and measurements.*

Module Features

MODULE PROJECT
Looking for Patterns, pp. 517 and 574–575

CAREER CONNECTION
Digital Artist, p. 529

EXTENSION
The Koch Snowflake, p. 529

Assessment Options

PORTFOLIO ASSESSMENT
  EXTENDED EXPLORATION (E²):
  Changing Shape, p. 531
  REFLECTING ON THE SECTION:
  pp. 528, 540, 552, 560, and 572

ONGOING ASSESSMENT
  CHECKPOINTS: pp. 520, 521, 524, 534, 536, 543, 546, 548, 557, 566, and 567
  KEY CONCEPT QUESTIONS:
  pp. 525, 537, 550, 558, and 568
  STANDARDIZED TESTING:
  pp. 541, 549, 553, 561, and 573

MODULE ASSESSMENT
  REVIEW AND ASSESSMENT:
  pp. 576–577
  REFLECTING ON THE MODULE:
  p. 577

Mathematics Students Will Be Learning

SECTION 1
- identifying arithmetic and geometric sequences
- writing an equation for finding any term in a sequence
- finding terms of the Fibonacci sequence

SECTION 2
- finding the sum of the measures of the interior angles of a convex polygon
- describing rotational symmetries

SECTION 3
- classifying quadrilaterals
- finding the distance between points on a coordinate grid
- finding the coordinates of the midpoint of a segment

SECTION 4
- finding probabilities using areas

SECTION 5
- using the tangent ratio to find unknown side lengths in right triangles
- using the sine and cosine ratios to find unknown side lengths in right triangles

STUDENT RESOURCES

NCTM Standards and Focal Points

The charts below give information about the NCTM Principles and Standards for School Mathematics (2000) and the NCTM Curriculum Focal Points for Prekindergarten through Grade 8 Mathematics (2006).

NCTM Principles and Standards for School Mathematics

CONTENT STANDARDS	PROCESS STANDARDS
1. NUMBER AND OPERATIONS Understand numbers, ways of representing numbers, relationships among numbers, and number systems; understand meanings of operations and how they relate to one another; compute fluently and make reasonable estimates.	**6. PROBLEM SOLVING** Build new mathematical knowledge through problem solving; solve problems that arise in mathematics and in other contexts; apply and adapt a variety of appropriate strategies to solve problems; monitor and reflect on the process of mathematical problem solving.
2. ALGEBRA Understand patterns, relations, and functions; represent and analyze mathematical situations and structures using algebraic symbols; use mathematical models to represent and understand quantitative relationships; analyze change in various contexts.	**7. REASONING AND PROOF** Recognize reasoning and proof as fundamental aspects of mathematics; make and investigate mathematical conjectures; develop and evaluate mathematical arguments and proofs; select and use various types of reasoning and methods of proof.
3. GEOMETRY Analyze characteristics and properties of two- and three-dimensional geometric shapes and develop mathematical arguments about geometric relationships; specify locations and describe spatial relationships using coordinate geometry and other representational systems; apply transformations and use symmetry to analyze mathematical situations; use visualization, spatial reasoning, and geometric modeling to solve problems.	**8. COMMUNICATION** Organize and consolidate their mathematical thinking through communication; communicate their mathematical thinking coherently and clearly to peers, teachers, and others; analyze and evaluate the mathematical thinking and strategies of others; use the language of mathematics to express mathematical ideas precisely.
4. MEASUREMENT Understand measurable attributes of objects and the units, systems, and processes of measurement; apply appropriate techniques, tools, and formulas to determine measurements.	**9. CONNECTIONS** Recognize and use connections among mathematical ideas; understand how mathematical ideas interconnect and build on one another to produce a coherent whole; recognize and apply mathematics in contexts outside of mathematics.
5. DATA ANALYSIS AND PROBABILITY Formulate questions that can be addressed with data and collect, organize, and display relevant data to answer them; select and use appropriate statistical methods to analyze data; develop and evaluate inferences and predictions that are based on data; understand and apply basic concepts of probability.	**10. REPRESENTATION** Create and use representations to organize, record, and communicate mathematical ideas; select, apply, and translate among mathematical representations to solve problems; use representations to model and interpret physical, social, and mathematical phenomena.

NCTM Curriculum Focal Points

GRADE 6 FOCAL POINTS	GRADE 7 FOCAL POINTS	GRADE 8 FOCAL POINTS
1 NUMBER AND OPERATIONS Developing an understanding of and fluency with multiplication and division of fractions and decimals	**1 NUMBER AND OPERATIONS and ALGEBRA and GEOMETRY** Developing an understanding of and applying proportionality, including similarity	**1 ALGEBRA** Analyzing and representing linear functions and solving linear equations and systems of linear equations
2 NUMBER AND OPERATIONS Connecting ratio and rate to multiplication and division	**2 MEASUREMENT and GEOMETRY and ALGEBRA** Developing an understanding of and using formulas to determine surface areas and volumes of three-dimensional shapes	**2 GEOMETRY and MEASUREMENT** Analyzing two- and three-dimensional space and figures by using distance and angle
3 ALGEBRA Writing, interpreting, and using mathematical expressions and equations	**3 NUMBER AND OPERATIONS and ALGEBRA** Developing an understanding of operations on all rational numbers and solving linear equations	**3 DATA ANALYSIS and NUMBER AND OPERATIONS and ALGEBRA** Analyzing and summarizing data sets

SCOPE AND SEQUENCE

The Scope and Sequence chart below correlates *Math Thematics* objectives to the NCTM Principles and Standards for School Mathematics (2000) and to the NCTM Curriculum Focal Points (2006). *Math Thematics* objectives appear as bulleted items beneath each bold-faced NCTM Standard. Columns for the three student editions indicate where an objective is covered and correlate the objective to the relevant NCTM grade-level focal point, as shown in the key to the right.

Key to Focal Points		
Grade 6:	**Grade 7:**	**Grade 8:**
Focal Point 1	Focal Point 1	Focal Point 1
Focal Point 2	Focal Point 2	Focal Point 2
Focal Point 3	Focal Point 3	Focal Point 3

Number and Operations

	Math Thematics Book 1	Math Thematics Book 2	Math Thematics Book 3
Students should work flexibly with fractions, decimals, and percents to solve problems.			
• Write a fraction or mixed number to compare part of a set or object with the whole.	**1** 1.4.1 *		
• Identify and find equivalent fractions.	**1** 1.5.1, 1.5.2	3.3.1	
• Write fractions in lowest terms.	**1** 1.5.2, 3.3.1	3.3.1, 4.1.1	
• Write a fraction greater than one as a mixed number, and vice versa.	**1** 1.4.2	3.4.1	
• Write a quotient as a mixed number and decide when a mixed number quotient is appropriate to solve a problem.	**1** 1.4.2		
• Write fractions and mixed numbers as decimals, and vice versa.	**1** 3.1.1, 4.2.3, 6.6.1	2.1.1, 4.3.3	4.4.1
• Understand decimal place value and read and write decimal numbers.	3.1.1	2.1.1	
• Round decimals.	4.2.3, 5.1.2		
• Use notation for repeating decimals.		**3** 4.3.3	4.4.1
• Identify rational and irrational numbers.			4.4.1, 7.2.1
• Write fractions and decimals as percents, and vice versa.	6.6.1	**1** 5.5.1	2.4.1
• Use mental math, common fraction/percent equivalents, or percent bar models to estimate percents.	6.6.2	**1** 5.4.1, 5.5.2	2.5.1
• Use mental math to write ratios as percents.		**1** 5.5.1	2.5.2
• Use equations to find the percent, the part, or the total.		**1** 5.5.2, 5.5.3, 8.3.1	2.4.3
• Use a fraction to find a percent of a number.	6.6.2	**1** 5.5.2	2.4.2, 2.4.3
• Estimate a percent of a number.	6.6.2	**1** 5.4.3	2.4.2
Students should compare and order fractions, decimals, and percents efficiently and find their approximate locations on a number line.			
• Compare fractions by writing equivalent fractions with a common denominator, converting to decimals, or by using number sense.	5.1.1, 5.1.2	3.3.1	
• Compare and order decimals.	3.1.2	2.1.1	

* The reference 1.4.1 means Module 1, Section 4, Exploration 1

Number and Operations (continued)

	Math Thematics Book 1	Math Thematics Book 2	Math Thematics Book 3
Students should develop meaning for percents greater than 100 and less than 1.			
• Recognize that the whole is 100%.	6.6.1		
• Find percents greater than 100% and less than 1%.		5.5.3	2.4.3
Students should understand and use ratios and proportions to represent quantitative relationships.			
• Use ratios, rates, and unit rates to compare quantities.	**2** 6.1.1, 6.2.1, 6.3.1, 6.3.2	**1** 2.2.1, 5.1.1	1.1.1
• Express a ratio three ways: using the word *to*, a colon, or fraction form.	**2** 6.1.1	**1** 2.2.1, 5.1.1	
• Recognize and write equivalent ratios and rates.	**2** 6.1.1	**1** 5.1.1	1.1.1
• Use the decimal form of a ratio to make comparisons.	**2** 6.3.1, 6.3.2	**1** 2.2.1	
Students should develop an understanding of large numbers and recognize and appropriately use exponential, scientific, and calculator notation.			
• Write integral powers of 10 in exponential and standard form.	**1** 8.6.1	2.1.2	
• Identify powers and convert between standard and exponential form.	3.3.3	1.1.3, 2.1.2	**3** 6.3.1, 6.3.2
• Write powers with negative exponents in fraction form.		2.1.2	**3** 7.1.2
• Simplify powers with zero and negative exponents.		2.1.2	**3** 7.1.2
• Write numbers in scientific notation.	8.6.1	2.1.3	**3** 3.5.1, 7.1.1, 7.1.2
• Write numbers that are in scientific notation in standard form.	8.6.1	2.1.3	**3** 3.5.1, 7.1.2
Students should use factors, multiples, prime factorization, and relatively prime numbers to solve problems.			
• Use divisibility tests for 2, 3, 5, 9, and 10.	3.3.1	**3** 3.2.2	
• Find all the factors of a number.	3.3.1	**3** 3.2.1	
• Find the greatest common factor (GCF) of two or more numbers.	3.3.1	**3** 3.2.2	
• Identify prime and composite numbers.	3.3.2	**3** 3.2.1	
• Find the prime factorization of a number.	3.3.2	**3** 3.2.1, 3.2.2, 3.2.3	
• List the multiples of a number.	3.4.1	**3** 3.2.3	
• Find the least common multiple of two or more numbers.	3.4.1	**3** 3.2.3	
Students should develop meaning for integers and represent and compare quantities with them.			
• Use integers to represent real life situations.	7.5.1	**3** 1.2.1	
• Compare integers.	7.5.1	**3** 1.2.1	

Number and Operations (continued)

	Math Thematics Book 1	Math Thematics Book 2	Math Thematics Book 3
Students should understand the meaning and effects of arithmetic operations with fractions, decimals, and integers.			
• Use the order of operations to evaluate numerical expressions.	**1** 1.1.1	**3** 1.1.3, 4.5.2	3.2.1
• Interpret the remainder in a division problem.	**1** 1.4.2		
• Interpret division with zero.		4.3.3	
• Use measurement, area, and number-line models to interpret addition, subtraction, and multiplication of fractions and mixed numbers.	**1** 3.5.1, 5.3.1, 5.4.1, 5.4.2	3.3.2	
• Use measurement models and partitioning to interpret division of fractions.	**1** 5.6.1	**3** 4.1.2	
• Interpret the remainder when dividing by a fraction.	**1** 5.6.1		
• Use set union and take-away models to interpret addition and subtraction of decimals.	3.2.1, 3.2.2		
• Use area models and partitioning to interpret multiplication and division of decimals.	**1** 3.6.1, 4.3.1, 4.4.2		
• Multiply decimals by powers of 10.	**1** 3.6.2, 8.6.1	2.1.3	
• Understand the effect of multiplying a positive number by 0, by a number between 0 and 1, and by a number greater than 1.		**3** 4.3.1	
• Understand the effect of dividing a positive number by 1, by a number between 0 and 1, and by a number greater than 1.		**3** 4.3.3	
• Use a chip model to interpret integer addition and subtraction.	8.3.1, 8.3.2		
• Use a number-line to model addition and subtraction of integers.		**3** 1.3.1, 1.3.2, 1.3.3	
• Apply addition properties of 0 and opposites to integer addition.		**3** 1.3.2, 1.5.2, 1.5.3	
• Use repeated addition and a number-line to model and interpret multiplication of integers.		**3** 4.5.1	2.1.3
• Use the missing factor model to interpret division of integers.		**3** 4.5.1	2.1.3
Students should use the associative and commutative properties of addition and multiplication and the distributive property of multiplication over addition to simplify computations with integers, fractions, and decimals.			
• Use the distributive property to multiply a mixed number by a whole number or a fraction.	**1** 3.5.2	4.1.1	
• Apply the commutative and associative properties to integer addition.		**3** 1.3.2	
• Apply the commutative and associative properties to integer multiplication.		**3** 4.5.1	

Number and Operations (continued)

	Math Thematics Book 1	Math Thematics Book 2	Math Thematics Book 3
Students should understand and use the inverse relationships of addition and subtraction, multiplication and division, and squaring and finding square roots to simplify computations and solve problems.			
• Use the inverse relationships between addition and subtraction or multiplication and division to solve equations.	**3** 4.3.3, 5.5.3	**3** 1.5.3, 4.6.6	1.3.2
• Use the inverse relationship between multiplication and division to develop an algorithm for decimal division.		**3** 4.3.2, 4.3.3	
• Multiply by the reciprocal to solve multiplication equations.	**3** 5.5.3		
• Find the reciprocal of a number.	**3** 5.6.1	4.1.1	
• Find principal and negative square roots of perfect squares.		6.3.1	**2** 3.1.1
• Estimate and find square roots.		6.3.1	**2** 3.1.1
• Simplify square roots and expressions involving square roots.			**2** 7.2.1
Students should select appropriate methods and tools for computing with fractions and decimals from among mental computation, estimation, calculators or computers and pencil and pencil, depending on the situation, and apply the selected methods.			
• Decide when to use estimation, mental math, paper and pencil, or a calculator.	**1** 1.1.3		
• Use mental math to find a fraction of a whole number.	**1** 1.5.3		
• Multiply mentally by special multipliers like 0.001 and 1000.	**1** 3.6.2		
Students should develop and analyze algorithms for computing with fractions, decimals, and integers and develop fluency in their use.			
• Use compatible numbers to find sums and products mentally.	**1** 1.1.3		
• Use trading off to find a whole number or decimal sum.	8.2.1		
• Add and subtract fractions and mixed numbers.	5.3.1, 5.4.1, 5.4.2	**3** 3.3.2, 3.4.2	2.2.1, 2.2.2, 2.2.3
• Multiply and divide fractions and mixed numbers.	**1** 1.5.3, 3.5.1, 3.5.2, 5.6.1, 5.6.2	**3** 4.1.1, 4.1.2	
• Add and subtract decimals.	3.2.1, 3.2.2		
• Multiply and divide decimals.	**1** 3.6.1, 4.3.1, 4.4.2	**3** 4.3.1, 4.3.2, 4.3.3	
• Add and subtract integers.	8.3.1, 8.3.2	**3** 1.3.2, 1.3.3	2.1.1, 2.1.2
• Multiply and divide integers.		**3** 4.5.1	2.1.3
• Multiply and divide powers.		2.1.3	7.1.1

Number and Operations (continued)

	Math Thematics Book 1	Math Thematics Book 2	Math Thematics Book 3
Students should develop and use strategies to estimate the results of rational-number computations and judge the reasonableness of the results.			
• Estimate sums, differences, and products of whole numbers by rounding.	1.1.2		
• Use front-end estimation to approximate a whole number or decimal sum.	8.2.1		
• Estimate mixed number sums.	5.4.1		
• Use compatible numbers to check the reasonableness of decimal quotients.	**1** 4.3.1		
• Estimate decimal products and quotients.	**1** 3.6.1, 3.6.2, 4.3.2	4.3.1, 4.3.2	
Students should develop, analyze, and explain methods for solving problems involving proportions, such as scaling and finding equivalent ratios.			
• Make tables of equivalent rates and use patterns to make predictions.	**2** 6.2.1		
• Find unit rates and use them to make predictions.	**2** 6.2.1	**1** 5.1.1	1.1.1
• Use cross products to identify equivalent ratios.	6.4.1	**1** 5.3.1	
• Find equivalent ratios to solve a proportion.	**2** 6.1.1, 6.2.1	**1** 5.1.1	
• Use "nice" fractions to approximate ratios and make predictions.	**2** 6.3.2		
• Use cross products to find a missing term in a proportion.	6.4.1, 6.4.2	**1** 5.3.1, 5.4.2	
• Write and use proportions to solve problems and make predictions.	**2** 6.4.2	**1** 5.1.1, 5.3.1	2.4.2
• Recognize when using a proportion is or is not appropriate.	**2** 6.4.2		
• Use the scale of a drawing or model to find unknown measures.	**2** 6.5.2	**1** 6.5.1, 6.5.2	5.6.1
• Use proportions to find the percent, the part, or the total.		**1** 5.4.2, 5.4.3, 5.5.3	2.4.2
• Use percents to make predictions and solve problems.		**1** 5.5.2	2.5.1, 2.5.2
• Find percent of increase or percent of decrease.		**1** 8.3.1	2.5.2

Algebra

	Math Thematics Book 1	Math Thematics Book 2	Math Thematics Book 3
Students should represent, analyze, and generalize a variety of patterns with tables, graphs, words, and, when possible, symbolic rules.			
• Analyze patterns and find rules to extend patterns.	**3** 1.2.1, 1.2.2, 1.3.3, 2.2.3, 3.4.1	2.3.1	8.1.1, 8.1.2
• Model a number sequence with a verbal rule, a table, a graph, or an equation and predict the nth term.	**3** 1.2.1, 1.2.2, 1.3.3, 2.2.3, 3.4.1, 4.4.3	2.3.1	**1** 8.1.1, 8.1.2
• Identify arithmetic and geometric sequences.			**1** 8.1.1

Algebra (continued)

	Math Thematics Book 1	Math Thematics Book 2	Math Thematics Book 3
Students should relate and compare different forms of representation for a relationship.			
• Use coordinates to identify and plot points in a coordinate plane.	4.4.3, 6.3.3, 7.5.2	1.2.2	2.1.1
• Use exponents to write products and to evaluate expressions.	3.3.3	1.1.3	6.3.1, 6.3.2
• Graph equations and formulas.	4.4.3	**1** 1.4.2, 2.2.1,	**1** 3.2.2, 6.2.1
• Use tables, graphs, and equations to model relationships.		**1** 1.4.1, 1.4.2, 1.5.1, 2.2.1, 4.6.3	**1** 1.5.1, 3.3.1, 3.3.2, 6.2.1
Students should identify functions as linear or nonlinear and contrast their properties from tables, graphs, or equations.			
• Identify linear functions from their graphs.	4.4.3	1.4.2, 2.2.1	**1** 3.2.2, 6.2.1
• Use tables and graphs to model and interpret changes in data.			**1** 6.1.1, 6.3.1, 6.3.2
• Interpret coordinate graphs without scales or labels.			**1** 6.1.1
• Use tables, graphs, and equations to model exponential change.			**1** 6.3.1, 6.3.2
• Use equations to predict the shapes of parabolas.			6.5.1
• Recognize quadratic equations.			**1** 6.5.2
• Use equations, tables, and graphs to represent and identify functions.		1.4.1, 1.4.2	**1** 6.1.2, 6.3.1, 6.5.1
Students should develop an initial conceptual understanding of different uses of variables.			
• Use a variable to represent an unknown value or a quantity that can change.	**3** 1.2.2	**3** 1.4.1	1.3.1
• Evaluate expressions containing variables.	**3** 1.2.2, 4.4.3	**3** 1.4.1, 4.5.2	1.3.1, 3.2.1
• Use opposites to evaluate $-x$.			2.1.1
Students should explore relationships between symbolic expressions and graphs of lines, paying particular attention to the meaning of intercept and slope.			
• Use graphs to explore and compare linear functions.		1.4.2, 2.2.1	**1** 2.1.3, 3.3.1, 4.3.2, 6.2.1
• Find the slope of a line.		**1** 2.2.1, 5.3.2	**1** 3.3.1, 4.3.1, 6.2.1
• Recognize how the slope of a line and its equation are related.		**1** 2.2.1	**1** 2.1.3, 3.3.1, 3.3.2
• Identify slopes of horizontal and vertical lines.			**1** 4.3.1
• Write equations in slope-intercept form.			**1** 3.3.2, 4.3.2, 6.2.1

Algebra (continued)

	Math Thematics Book 1	Math Thematics Book 2	Math Thematics Book 3
Students should use symbolic algebra to represent situations and to solve problems, especially those that involve linear relationships.			
• Write addition and subtraction equations.	**3** 4.3.2	**3** 1.5.1	1.3.1
• Write multiplication and division equations.	**3** 4.4.3	**3** 1.4.1, 1.5.1	1.3.1
• Write two-step equations involving integers, fractions, or decimals.	4.4.3	**3** 4.6.3	1.3.1, 3.5.2, 4.4.2
Students should recognize and generate equivalent forms for simple algebraic expressions and solve linear equations.			
• Model and solve equations using algebra tiles.	**3** 4.3.2, 4.3.3	1.5.2, 1.5.3	
• Use inverse operations to solve one-step equations.	**3** 4.3.3, 5.5.3	**3** 1.5.3	**1** 1.3.2
• Solve two-step equations involving integers, fractions, or decimals.		**3** 4.6.3	**1** 1.3.2, 3.5.2, 4.4.2, 6.2.2
• Solve equations with variables on both sides or that involve simplifying.			**1** 6.2.2
• Solve equations graphically.			**1** 6.2.1
• Solve systems of linear equations graphically and algebraically.		1.4.2	**1** 6.2.1, 6.2.2
• Identify like and unlike terms.			**1** 1.3.3
• Use properties to simplify expressions.		**3** 2.3.2	**1** 1.3.3, 6.2.2
• Solve equations involving absolute value.			2.1.1
• Simplify quadratic expressions.			6.5.2
• Use algebra tiles to model polynomials.			7.4.1
• Use algebra tiles and tables to multiply binomials.			7.4.1
• Multiply binomials.			7.4.1
• Use algebra tiles to factor quadratics.			7.4.2
• Factor quadratics.			7.4.2
• Simplify radical expressions.			7.2.2
Students should model and solve contextualized problems using various representations, such as graphs, tables, and equations.			
• Use tables, graphs, and equations to model situations and solve problems.	**3** 4.3.3	**3** 1.4.2, 1.5.1	**1** 3.2.2, 3.3.1, 3.3.2, 6.3.1, 6.3.2
• Use equations in slope-intercept form to model real-world situations.			**1** 3.3.2, 4.3.2, 6.2.1
• Write exponential equations to model situations and solve problems.			6.3.2
• Write, graph, and solve inequalities.		6.1.1, 7.3.2	7.3.1, 7.3.2, 7.3.3

Algebra (continued)

	Math Thematics Book 1	Math Thematics Book 2	Math Thematics Book 3
Students should use graphs to analyze the nature of changes in quantities in linear relationships.			
• Interpret the slope of a line.		**1** 2.2.1, 2.2.2, 5.3.2	**1** 3.3.1, 4.3.1
• Use equations, tables, and graphs to solve problems involving linear change.			**1** 3.3.1, 3.3.2, 6.2.1, 6.2.2

Geometry

	Math Thematics Book 1	Math Thematics Book 2	Math Thematics Book 3
Students should precisely describe, classify, and understand relationships among types of two- and three-dimensional objects using their defining properties.			
• Identify, draw, and name basic geometric figures (point, line, segment, ray, angle, etc.)	2.3.1, 2.3.3	1.1.1	
• Recognize parallel and perpendicular lines in a plane.	2.3.1	1.2.2, 3.1.2	
• Identify pairs of angles formed by intersecting lines.		6.4.1	**2** 5.5.1
• Determine the measures of angles formed by parallel lines and a transversal.		6.4.1	**2** 5.5.1
• Classify angles as acute, obtuse, right, or straight.	2.3.3	1.1.1	
• Identify and find the measures of complementary and supplementary angles.		1.1.2	**2** 5.5.1
• Know the characteristics of a polygon.	2.4.1	6.1.2	
• Identify regular polygons.	2.4.1	6.1.2	
• Recognize concave and convex polygons.		6.1.2	8.2.1
• Find the sum of the measures of the interior angles of a convex polygon.		6.4.2	**2** 8.2.1
• Use the sum of the measures of the angles to find unknown angle measures in polygons.		6.4.2	**2** 8.2.1
• Classify triangles as equilateral, isosceles, or scalene.	2.3.2	3.1.2	
• Classify triangles as right, obtuse, or acute.	2.3.3	3.1.2	
• Classify polygons by the number of sides.	2.4.1		
• Classify quadrilaterals.	2.4.1	6.1.2, 8.4.1	8.3.1
• Identify, draw, and name prisms and distinguish between right and oblique prisms.	7.1.1	**2** 6.3.2	4.1.2, 5.1.1
• Identify and count the vertices, edges, and faces of a polyhedron.	7.1.1	**2** 6.3.2	5.2.2
• Identify parts of a circle.	7.3.1	3.1.1, 6.3.3	3.4.2
• Identify cylinders.	7.4.2	**2** 7.2.1	4.1.2
• Recognize a cone.		7.2.1	

Geometry (continued)

	Math Thematics Book 1	Math Thematics Book 2	Math Thematics Book 3
Students should understand relationships among the angles, side lengths, perimeters, areas, and volumes of similar objects.			
• Identify similar and congruent figures and their corresponding parts.	6.5.1	**1** 4.6.2, 6.5.1	**2** 3.4.1, 5.2.1
• Understand and apply properties of similar figures.	6.5.1	**1** 6.5.1, 6.5.2	**2** 3.4.1
• Find unknown measures in similar figures.	**3** 6.5.2	**1** 6.5.2	**2** 3.4.1
• Find perimeters and areas of similar figures.			**2** 3.1.2, 5.6.2
• Recognize the effects of linear dimension changes on area or volume and solve problems involving the relationships.			**2** 3.1.2, 4.1.2
• Find and interpret surface area to volume ratios.			4.2.2
Students should create and critique inductive and deductive arguments concerning geometric ideas and relationships, such as congruence, similarity, and the Pythagorean relationship.			
• Apply the triangle inequality.	2.3.2	3.1.2	5.2.1
• Demonstrate that figures are or are not similar.	6.5.1	**1** 6.5.2	3.4.1
• Apply the side-side-side and side-angle-side congruence rules.			**2** 5.2.1, 5.2.3
• Identify triangles by their side lengths (converse of the Pythagorean theorem).			**2** 5.3.1
• Use the Pythagorean theorem to find an unknown side length of a right triangle.			**2** 5.3.2
Students should use coordinate geometry to represent and examine the properties of geometric shapes.			
• Use coordinates to describe translations and reflections and locate an image after a transformation.		4.6.1	2.1.2, 6.4.1
Students should use coordinate geometry to examine special geometric shapes, such as regular polygons or those with pairs of parallel or perpendicular sides.			
• Use coordinate geometry to identify quadrilaterals and explore the properties of figures.			8.3.2
Students should describe sizes, positions, and orientations of shapes under informal transformations such as flips, turns, slides, and scaling.			
• Identify and perform translations, rotations, and reflections.	8.5.1, 8.5.2	4.4.1, 4.4.2, 4.6.1	2.1.2, 6.4.1
• Use coordinates to describe a stretch or squash transformation of a figure.		4.6.2	
• Write an algorithm to describe a series of transformations.			6.4.1

Geometry (continued)

	Math Thematics Book 1	Math Thematics Book 2	Math Thematics Book 3
Students should draw geometric objects with specified properties, such as side lengths or angle measures.			
• Use a compass to draw a circle.	7.3.1	3.1.1	
• Construct triangles.		3.1.2	5.2.1
• Construct perpendicular bisectors of segments.		3.1.2	3.4.2
• Construct angle bisectors.			5.2.3
Students should use two-dimensional representations of three-dimensional objects to visualize and solve problems such as those involving surface area and volume.			
• Create and explore nets for three-dimensional figures and predict the shape a net will form.	7.1.1, 7.1.2	2 6.3.2	5.2.2
• Use nets for polyhedra to explore surface area.		2 6.3.2	5.4.1
• Use isometric dot paper to draw figures made with cubes.			5.1.1
• Explore volumes and surface areas of figures made with cubes.	3 7.1.2	2 7.1.1	5.1.1
• Draw different views of three-dimensional figures.		2 7.1.3	5.1.2
Students should use visual tools such as networks to represent and solve problems.			
• Sort data and organize information using arrays and Venn diagrams.	2.4.1, 4.1.1		3.6.1
Students should use geometric models to represent and explain numerical and algebraic relationships.			
• Use geometric models to model fractions and mixed numbers.	1.4.1		
• Use geometric models to model multiplication of fractions.	3.5.1		
• Construct geometric models for the terms of a sequence.	3 1.2.2	2.3.1	
• Use geometric models to illustrate the expression for the general term of a sequence.	3 1.2.2	2.3.1	
• Use geometric models to model equivalent expressions.		1 2.3.1	
• Use base-ten blocks to model decimal place value.	3.1.1		
• Use base-ten blocks to add and subtract decimals.	3.2.1, 3.2.2		
• Use geometric models to model decimal multiplication.	1 3.6.1		
• Use a geometric model to interpret and find probabilities in a multistage experiment.		6.2.2	
Students should recognize and apply geometric ideas and relationships in areas outside the mathematics classroom, such as art, science, and everyday life.			
• Use transformations to make designs.	8.5.2		
• Create a tessellation.		8.4.2	
• Make a scale drawing.			2 5.6.1
• Solve indirect measurement problems.			2 3.4.1

Measurement

	Math Thematics Book 1	*Math Thematics* Book 2	*Math Thematics* Book 3
Students should understand both metric and customary systems of measurement.			
• Select appropriate metric units to measure length and mass.	4.1.2	4.2.2	
• Choose an appropriate customary unit or combination of units to measure length and weight.	5.2.1, 7.2.1		
Students should understand relationships among units and convert from one unit to another within the same system.			
• Convert between metric units of measure.	**2** 4.1.3, 8.1.2	**1** 4.2.2, 7.1.2	
• Use the relationship among metric units of volume, capacity, and mass.	**2** 8.1.2	**1** 7.1.2	
• Convert between customary units of measure.	**2** 5.2.2, 7.2.1, 8.1.1	**1** 3.4.3, 7.3.1	
• Convert between units of area in the same measurement system.	**2** 5.5.1		
Students should understand, select, and use units of appropriate size and type to measure angles, perimeter, area, surface area, and volume.			
• Measure lengths in metric units.	4.1.2	4.2.2	
• Measure lengths in customary units.	5.2.1		
• Select appropriate customary units to measure area.	5.5.1		
Students should use common benchmarks to select appropriate methods for estimating measurements.			
• Use benchmarks to estimate metric length, mass, and capacity.	4.1.2, 8.1.2	4.2.1	
• Use benchmarks to estimate customary length, weight, and capacity.	5.2.1, 7.2.1, 8.1.1		
• Use models to estimate area in customary units.	5.5.1		
• Use benchmarks to estimate Celsius and Fahrenheit temperatures.	7.5.1		
Students should select and apply techniques and tools to accurately find length, area, volume, and angle measures to appropriate levels of precision.			
• Measure lengths in metric units.	4.1.2	4.2.1	
• Measure the length of an object in customary units.	6.5.2	3.4.3	
• Add and subtract lengths measured in customary units.	5.2.2		
• Use customary units to estimate and measure area.	5.5.1		
• Use a protractor to measure and draw angles.	2.4.2	1.1.1	
• Use an equation to find a missing dimension.	**3** 6.5.2		

Measurement (continued)

	Math Thematics Book 1	Math Thematics Book 2	Math Thematics Book 3
Students should develop and use formulas to determine the circumference of circles and the area of triangles, parallelograms, trapezoids, and circles and develop strategies to find the area of more-complex shapes.			
• Develop formulas to find the area of a parallelogram and a triangle.	5.5.2, 5.5.3	**2** 6.1.2	
• Find the areas of parallelograms and triangles.	**3** 5.5.2, 5.5.3	**2** 6.1.2	
• Develop formulas to find the area of a trapezoid.		**2** 6.1.3	
• Find the area of trapezoids.		**2** 6.1.3	
• Find the area of composite shapes.		**2** 6.1.2	
• Develop a formula for finding the circumference of a circle.	7.3.2	**2** 3.1.1	
• Find the circumference of a circle.	**3** 7.3.2	**2** 3.1.1	4.1.1
• Develop a formula for finding the area of a circle.	7.4.1	**2** 6.3.3	
• Find the area of a circle.	**3** 7.4.1	**2** 6.3.3	4.1.1
Students should develop strategies to determine the surface area and volume of selected prisms, pyramids, and cylinders.			
• Understand the concept of volume.	7.1.1, 7.1.2	**2** 7.1.1	3.1.2
• Develop a formula for finding the volume of a prism.	7.1.2	**2** 7.1.1	
• Find the surface area of a prism.		**2** 6.3.2	5.4.1
• Find the volume of a prism.	**3** 7.1.2	**2** 7.1.1	3.1.2, 4.1.2, 5.4.2
• Find the surface area of a cylinder.			4.2.1
• Find the volume of a cylinder.	**3** 7.4.2	**2** 7.2.1	4.1.2
• Find the volume of a cone.		7.2.1	5.4.2
• Find the surface area of a pyramid.			5.4.1
• Find the volume of a pyramid.		7.2.2	5.4.2
• Find the volume of a sphere.			4.1.2
• Find volumes of composite figures.			5.4.2
Students should solve problems involving scale factors, using ratio and proportion.			
• Apply similarity to solve problems involving scale drawings, scale models, and map scales.	6.5.2	**1** 6.5.1, 6.5.2	
• Use sine, cosine, and tangent ratios to find side lengths in a right triangle.			8.5.1, 8.5.2
Students should solve simple problems involving rates and derived measurements for such attributes as velocity and density.			
• Solve problems involving rates.	6.2.1	**1** 1.4.1, 1.4.2, 5.1.1	**1** 1.1.1

Data Analysis and Probability

	Math Thematics Book 1	Math Thematics Book 2	Math Thematics Book 3
Students should formulate questions, design studies, and collect data about a characteristic shared by two populations or different characteristics within one population.			
• Design and conduct a survey.		**1** 5.2.1	2.4.1
• Identify and correct biased survey questions.			2.4.1
Students should select, create, and use appropriate graphical representations of data, including histograms, box plots, and scatterplots.			
• Construct line plots (dot plots).	4.2.1, 4.2.2		
• Construct stem-and-leaf plots and back-to-back stem-and-leaf plots.	4.4.1	5.1.2, 5.2.2	1.2.1
• Make a line graph.	4.5.1	2.2.2	
• Make circle graphs.	6.6.3	**1** 7.4.2	1.1.2
• Choose a scale for a graph and determine how the scale affects the appearance of a graph.	4.2.1, 4.5.1, 6.3.3	1.4.2, 2.2.1, 2.2.2	1.4.1
• Construct a scatter plot.	6.3.3	5.3.2	**3** 1.4.1, 3.3.2
• Construct histograms.		**1** 5.2.2	1.1.2
• Construct box-and-whisker plots.		7.4.1	**3** 1.2.2
• Choose an appropriate data display.		5.2.2	**3** 1.2.3
Students should find, use, and interpret measures of center and spread, including mean and interquartile range.			
• Find the mean, median, mode, and range of a data set.	4.2.1, 4.2.2, 4.2.3, 4.5.2	5.1.2	**3** 1.2.1
• Choose an appropriate average.	4.2.3, 4.5.2	5.1.2, 5.3.3	**3** 1.2.1
• Find and interpret quartiles and the interquartile range.		5.3.3, 7.4.1	**3** 1.2.2

Data Analysis and Probability (continued)

	Math Thematics Book 1	Math Thematics Book 2	Math Thematics Book 3
Students should discuss and understand the correspondence between data sets and their graphical representations, especially histograms, stem-and-leaf plots, box plots, and scatterplots.			
• Interpret data displayed in line plots (dot plots).	4.2.1		
• Interpret data displayed in stem-and-leaf plots and back-to-back stem-and-leaf plots.	4.4.1	5.1.2	1.2.1, 1.2.3
• Interpret data displayed in line graphs.	4.5.1	2.2.2	1.2.3, 4.3.1
• Interpret data displayed in circle graphs and use percents and fractions to estimate angle measures in a circle graph.	6.6.3	**1** 7.4.2	1.1.2, 1.2.3
• Interpret data displayed in a scatter plot.	6.3.3	**1** 5.3.2	**3** 1.2.3, 1.4.1, 4.1.1
• Understand the difference between data displayed in a bar graph and in a histogram and interpret data displayed in histograms.		**1** 5.2.2	1.1.2, 1.2.3
• Interpret data displayed in box-and-whisker plots.		5.3.3, 7.4.1	**3** 1.2.2, 1.2.3
• Recognize trends and identify correlations in data from a scatter plot.			**3** 1.4.2, 4.4.1
Students should use observations about differences between two or more samples to make conjectures about the populations from which the samples were taken.			
• Understand the meanings of population, sample, and representative sample.	1.5.3		**3** 2.4.2
• Summarize and interpret survey results.	6.6.1	**1** 5.2.1	**3** 2.4.2, 2.4.3
• Make predictions from samples.	1.5.3		**3** 2.4.2, 2.4.3
Students should make conjectures about possible relationships between two characteristics of a sample on the basis of scatterplots of the data and approximate lines of fit.			
• Make a scatter plot, fit a line to the data, and use the line to make predictions.	6.3.3	5.3.2	**3** 1.4.2, 3.3.2
• Use an equation of a fitted line to make predictions.			**3** 3.3.2
Students should use conjectures to formulate new questions and plan new studies to answer them.			
• Design and conduct a survey or a study and analyze the results.	4.Project, 6.Project	**1** 2.Project, 5.Project, 8.Project	
Students should understand and use appropriate terminology to describe complementary and mutually exclusive events.			
• Find probabilities of complementary events.	8.4.1	6.2.1	8.4.1

Data Analysis and Probability (continued)

	Math Thematics Book 1	Math Thematics Book 2	Math Thematics Book 3
Students should use proportionality and basic understanding of probability to make and test conjectures about the results of experiments and simulations.			
• Identify outcomes of an experiment.	2.1.1	2.5.1	2.3.1
• Find experimental and theoretical probabilities.	2.1.1, 2.1.2	**1** 2.5.1, 2.5.2	2.3.1, 2.3.2
• Compare the experimental and theoretical probabilities of an event.	2.1.2	**1** 2.5.2	2.3.3
• Use numbers from 0 through 1 to estimate probabilities and identify impossible and certain events.	2.1.1, 2.1.2	**1** 2.5.1	2.3.1, 2.3.2
• Determine if outcomes are equally likely.	2.1.1	**1** 2.5.2	2.3.1, 2.3.2
• Use probabilities to predict.	2.1.1, 8.4.1	**1** 2.5.1, 2.5.2	2.3.1, 2.3.2
• Plot probabilities on a number line.	2.1.2	2.5.1	
• Identify dependent and independent events.			2.3.2
Students should compute probabilities for simple compound events, using such methods as organized lists, tree diagrams, and area models.			
• Find geometric probabilities.	8.4.1	**1** 6.2.1	8.4.1
• Find theoretical probabilities for a multistage experiment.		**1** 6.2.2	2.3.3
• Find all possible arrangements of items.		8.1.1	4.5.1
• Use tree diagrams to model the outcomes of an experiment and to find theoretical probabilities.		6.2.2	2.3.3
• Use the counting principle and tree diagrams to find the number of permutations of a group of items.		8.1.2	4.5.1
• Use the counting principle to determine the probability of an event.			4.6.1
• List and find the number of permutations when items repeat.		8.2.1	
• Use tree diagrams and listing to find the number of combinations of items chosen from a group of items.		8.2.2	4.5.2
• Distinguish a combination from a permutation.		8.2.2	4.5.2

Summary of Assessment

As shown below, *Math Thematics* provides a variety of assessment tools, many of which are built into the student edition. The *Teacher's Edition* and other teaching resources offer additional assessment tools.

Assessment in the Student Edition

Tool	Used to Assess	Purpose	Book 3 Examples
Discussion Questions	• understanding of a concept	• **student** uses for self-assessment	Question 14, p. 173
Checkpoint Questions	• mastery of a skill	• **teacher** assesses student proficiency in content area and makes instructional decisions	Question 9, p. 171 Question 16, p. 174
Try This as a Class Questions	• understanding of a concept or an algorithm • application of concepts and skills	• **student** uses for self-assessment • **teacher** assesses student proficiency in content area and makes instructional decisions	Question 15, p. 173
Practice & Application Exercises (See the *Section Planner* pages in the *Teacher's Edition* for each module.)	• understanding of a concept • mastery of a skill • application of concepts and skills	**teacher** • assesses student proficiency in content area and makes instructional decisions • monitors student progress in problem solving, reasoning, and communication • uses for grading	Exercises 10, 12, 18, 20, 21 and 24, pp. 176 and 177
Reflecting on the Section Questions	• understanding of a concept • application of concepts and skills • problem solving, reasoning, and communication	• **student** uses for self-assessment • **teacher** monitors student progress in problem solving, reasoning, and communication • **teacher** uses for grading	Exercise 29, p. 166 Exercise 34, p. 178 Exercise 14, p. 189 Exercise 19, p. 201 Exercise 26, p. 212
Extended Explorations (E²s)	• problem solving, reasoning, and communication • application of concepts and skills	• **student** uses the *Student Self-Assessment Scales* for self-assessment • **teacher** monitors student progress in problem solving, reasoning, and communication • **teacher** uses the *Teacher Assessment Scales* for grading	"Mystery State," p. 191
Module Projects	• mastery of specific content • problem solving, reasoning, and communication • application of concepts and skills	• **student** uses the *Student Self-Assessment Scales* for self-assessment • **teacher** monitors student progress in problem solving, reasoning, and communication • **teacher** uses the *Teacher Assessment Scales* for grading	See pp. 155, 222–225.

Assessment in the Student Edition *continued*

Tool	Used to Assess	Purpose	Book 3 Examples
Module Review and Assessment	• mastery of specific content • problem solving, reasoning, and communication • application of concepts and skills	**teacher** • assesses student proficiency in content area and makes instructional decisions • monitors student progress in problem solving, reasoning, and communication • uses for grading	See pp. 226 and 227.

Assessment in the Teaching Resources

Tool	Used to Assess	Purpose	Resource
Warm-Ups	• prerequisite skills and concepts for a section	• **teacher** assesses student proficiency in content area and makes instructional decisions	See *Teacher's Resource Books.*
Pre-Course Test	• prerequisite skills and concepts for a course	• **teacher** assesses student proficiency in content area and makes instructional decisions	See the student edition (pp. xxii–xxiii) and the *Teacher's Resource Books.*
Module Diagnostic Tests	• skills and concepts to be taught in a module	• **teacher** assesses student prior knowledge of content and makes instructional decisions	See *Teacher's Resource Books.*
Module Tests, Standardized Tests, Performance Assessments, Cumulative Tests, Mid-Year Test, End-of-Year Test	• mastery of specific content • problem solving, reasoning, and communication • application of concepts and skills	**teacher** • assesses student proficiency in content area and makes instructional decisions • monitors student progress in problem solving, reasoning, and communication • uses for grading	See *Teacher's Resource Books.*
Portfolios	• growth over time and perseverance in problem solving, reasoning, and communication	**teacher** • assesses student proficiency in content area and makes instructional decisions • monitors student progress in problem solving, reasoning, and communication • reports to parents	See *Teacher's Resource Books.*
Test Generator	• mastery of specific content • problem solving, reasoning, and communication • application of concepts and skills	**teacher** • assesses student proficiency in content area and makes instructional decisions • monitors student progress in problem solving, reasoning, and communication • uses for grading	Test Generator CD-ROM

The *Math Thematics Assessment Scales* are designed to help students answer the question "How can I improve my performance in problem solving, reasoning, and communication?" There are five scales—Problem Solving, Mathematical Language, Representations, Connections, and Presentation—which together provide a generalized rubric that defines the various dimensions of mathematical investigation.

The scales can be applied to open-ended questions, *Module Projects*, *Reflecting on the Section* questions, and especially *Extended Explorations (E²s)*. Students are encouraged to write their solutions to these items using appropriate language and representations to communicate how they solved the problem, the decisions they made as they solved it, and any connections they made.

The key to improving student performance is to actively involve students in assessing their own work. As students become familiar with the *Student Self-Assessment Scales*, they understand what they need to do to improve their problem solving, reasoning, and communication. Teachers assess students' work using the same scales written from a teacher's point of view. The combination of student and teacher assessment provides important feedback to help students improve.

If used consistently, the *Math Thematics Assessment Scales* have the potential to raise the level of students' performance. However, you and your students will not master the use of the assessment scales immediately. This is okay—the more work you and your students assess, the better and more confident you will be with the assessment process. Keep in mind that learning to use the scales is like learning a new language. It requires time and patience. In the end, the effort will pay off, and students' higher-order thinking skills will improve as a result of using the *Math Thematics Assessment Scales*.

Copies of the *Teacher Assessment Scales* and the *Student Self-Assessment Scales* can be found in the *Teacher's Resource Book* for each module. The *Student Self-Assessment Scales* are also shown on page 599 of the student edition.

Descriptions of the scales and facsimiles of the *Teacher Assessment Scales* are provided below. For a detailed discussion of how to interpret each scale, see *The Teacher's Resource Book* for Modules 1 and 2.

Problem Solving Scale

The *Problem Solving Scale* assesses the student's ability to select and use appropriate mathematical concepts and problem solving strategies (guess and check, make a model, look for a pattern, and so on) to solve a problem. The scale emphasizes and reinforces the steps in the *4-Step Approach to Solving Problems*—Understand the Problem, Make a Plan, Carry out the Plan, and Look Back. The related Teacher Assessment Scale gives a range of criteria used for problem solving.

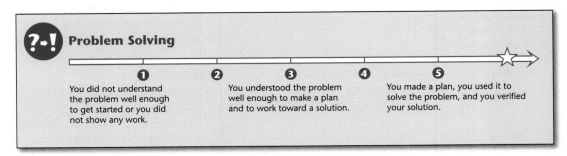

? → ! Problem Solving

① You did not understand the problem well enough to get started or you did not show any work.

③ You understood the problem well enough to make a plan and to work toward a solution.

⑤ You made a plan, you used it to solve the problem, and you verified your solution.

Mathematical Language Scale

The *Mathematical Language Scale* assesses the student's use of mathematical vocabulary, notation, and symbols. The scale encourages consistent and accurate use of mathematical language.

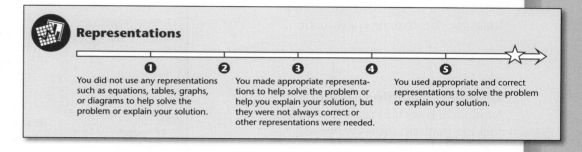

Mathematical Language

❶ You did not use any mathematical vocabulary or symbols, or you did not use them correctly, or your use was not appropriate.

❸ You used appropriate mathematical language, but the way it was used was not always correct or other terms and symbols were needed.

❺ You used mathematical language that was correct and appropriate to make your meaning clear.

Representations Scale

The *Representations Scale* assesses the student's use of graphs, tables, models, diagrams and equations to solve problems. The scale looks specifically at whether the representations are accurate and appropriate.

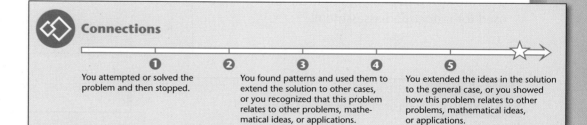

Representations

❶ You did not use any representations such as equations, tables, graphs, or diagrams to help solve the problem or explain your solution.

❸ You made appropriate representations to help solve the problem or help you explain your solution, but they were not always correct or other representations were needed.

❺ You used appropriate and correct representations to solve the problem or explain your solution.

Connections Scale

The *Connections Scale* assesses the student's ability to make connections within mathematics, to real-world situations, and to other disciplines. This scale emphasizes and reinforces the Look Back step in the 4-Step Approach to Solving Problems.

Connections

❶ You attempted or solved the problem and then stopped.

❸ You found patterns and used them to extend the solution to other cases, or you recognized that this problem relates to other problems, mathematical ideas, or applications.

❺ You extended the ideas in the solution to the general case, or you showed how this problem relates to other problems, mathematical ideas, or applications.

Presentation Scale

The *Presentation Scale* assesses the student's ability to reason logically and to communicate ideas effectively. This scale assesses why students did what they did to solve the problem. Evidence of reasoning is shown by making and testing conjectures, formulating models, explaining why, and gathering and presenting evidence. The differences between levels on the scale reflect both the correctness and the clarity of reasoning.

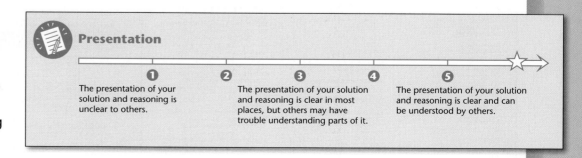

Presentation

❶ The presentation of your solution and reasoning is unclear to others.

❸ The presentation of your solution and reasoning is clear in most places, but others may have trouble understanding parts of it.

❺ The presentation of your solution and reasoning is clear and can be understood by others.

The *Teacher's Edition* provides complete planning support and point of use support.

Point of Use Support

Suggestions are given for helping students understand new concepts and avoid common errors. Other features include classroom examples, classroom management ideas, and ideas for differentiating instruction.

Complete Planning Support

Module and section planning guides include mathematical overviews, day-by-day planning guides, and homework assignments. Section objectives are keyed to exercises that can be used for embedded assessment.

Exploration 2 *continued*

COMMON ERRORS
For **Question 20(d)**, if students have difficulty understanding the concept that subtraction can be written as addition of the opposite, do more examples of changing translations from subtraction form to addition form. For example, $(x - 4, y - 1)$ becomes $(x + (-4), y + (-1))$. Show how this results in the same move on the coordinate grid.

DEVELOPING MATH CONCEPTS
Through movement on a coordinate grid, **Question 20** is designed to help students see that subtracting an integer is the same as adding the opposite of that integer. To aid in developing the concept from the **Example**, make sure students notice that the first addend is not changed when written as an addition problem and that the second addend is changed to its opposite.

CLASSROOM EXAMPLES

Find the difference: $-14 - 9$

Answer: Rewrite subtraction as addition. $-14 - 9 = -14 + (-9)$
$= -23$

Find the difference: $5 - (-11)$

Answer: Rewrite subtraction as addition. $5 - (-11) = 5 + (-(-11))$
$= 5 + 11$
$= 16$

✓ **QUESTION 22**
...checks that you can subtract integers.

DIFFERENTIATED INSTRUCTION
Visual Learners For students who have difficulty with the concept of changing subtraction to addition, encourage them to use a number line and to move in the opposite direction they would move if the problem was addition.

82 **Module 2** At the Mall

---

19 This table shows the coordinates of several points and their images after a translation.

Coordinates of the point	(3, 2)	(5, −7)	(0, −3)	(−5, 6)	(x, y)
Coordinates of the image	(2, 5)	(4, −4)	(−1, 0)	(−6, 9)	?

  a. Describe the translation using the form $(x + \underline{?}, y + \underline{?})$.
  $(x + (-1), y + 3)$
  b. Suppose the same translation is used on the point $(-45, -105)$. What are the coordinates of the image? $(-46, -102)$

20 **Try This as a Class** Suppose you are programming a video game in which a jester is located at point (x, y).

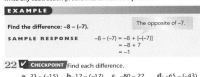
(x, y)

  a. Write a translation in the form $(x + \underline{?}, y + \underline{?})$ that will move the jester to the right 2 units and up 1 unit. $(x + 2, y + 1)$
  b. Use the form $(x - \underline{?}, y - \underline{?})$ to write a translation that will move the jester to the left 3 units and down 5 units. $(x - 3, y - 5)$
  c. Rewrite the translation in part (b) in the form $(x + \underline{?}, y + \underline{?})$.
  $(x + (-3), y + (-5))$
  d. Explain why any subtraction expression can be written as an addition expression.

20. d. Sample Response: Adding the opposite moves the figure the same as subtracting the original amount, so you can rewrite subtraction by adding the opposite of the number after the subtraction sign.

21 Suppose the jester in Question 20 is at point $(1, 1)$ and that the translation $(x - (-3), y - 4)$ is used to move him.

  a. Write $1 - (-3)$ as an addition expression. $1 + 3$
  b. What is the jester's new position after the translation $(x - (-3), y - 4)$? $(4, -3)$
  c. Describe this translation in words.
  Move right 3 units and down 4 units.

▶ **Subtracting Integers** As you saw in Questions 20 and 21, you can write any subtraction problem as an addition problem.

EXAMPLE

Find the difference: $-8 - (-7)$.   The opposite of −7.

SAMPLE RESPONSE $-8 - (-7) = -8 + [-(-7)]$
$= -8 + 7$
$= -1$

22 ✓ **CHECKPOINT** Find each difference.
  a. $23 - (-15)$ **b.** $12 - (-12)$ **c.** $-80 - 22$ **d.** $-65 - (-43)$
  38   24   −102   −22

HOMEWORK EXERCISES ▶ See Exs. 26–35 on pp. 88–89.

Section 1   Operations with Integers

Section 1 Planner

Section Objectives

Exploration 1
• Add integers
• Use opposites to evaluate $-x$
• Evaluate absolute values and solve equations involving absolute value

Exploration 2
• Subtract integers
• Perform translations in the coordinate plane

Exploration 3
• Multiply and divide integers

Days for Section 1

First Day
Setting the Stage, p. 78

Second Day
Exploration 1 through Question 9, pp. 79–80

Third Day
Exploration 1, pp. 80–81

Fourth Day
Exploration 2, pp. 81–82

Fifth Day
Exploration 3 through Question 28, pp. 83–85

Sixth Day
Exploration 3, p. 85
Key Concepts, pp. 86–87

Teaching Resources

Teacher's Resource Book
• Warm-Up
• Labsheets 1A, 1B, 1C, and 1D
• Practice and Applications

Materials List

Exploration 1
• Labsheets 1A and 1B
• 2 colored number cubes per group
• colored disks

Exploration 2
• Labsheet 1C
• tracing paper

Exploration 3
• Labsheet 1D and ruler

Practice and Applications
• Labsheet 1B and graph paper

Assessment Options

EMBEDDED ASSESSMENT
• Add integers
  Exercises 1, 2, 3
• Use opposites to evaluate $-x$
  Exercise 17
• Evaluate absolute values
  Exercise 16
• Subtract integers
  Exercises 26, 27, 30, 31
• Peform translations
  Exercise 35
• Multiply and divide integers
  Exercises 39, 40, 41

PERFORMANCE TASK/PORTFOLIO
• Exercise 25 on p. 88 (challenge)
• Exercise 33(b) on p. 88 (writing)
• Exercise 55 on p. 90 (visual thinking)
• Standardized Testing on p. 91 (open-ended)

QUIZZES/TESTS
• Section 1 Quick Quiz

TEST GENERATOR

Section 1 Overview

In this section, students will explore how mathematics is used to play and program video games.

Exploration 1
Students play a game in which they plot points on a coordinate plane by modeling integer addition. In a variation of the game, students use equations to solve for one of the coordinates and identify quadrants. Students develop strategies and formulate rules for adding integers. The concepts of opposite and absolute value are introduced and developed.

Exploration 2
Students use subtraction to translate an object on a coordinate plane. Students recognize that for any subtraction problem there is an equivalent addition problem and learn to rewrite subtraction expressions as addition expressions.

Exploration 3
This exploration leads students to discover the way in which multiplication and division are used to create a line on a coordinate plane. They look for patterns in linear equations and recognize how the coefficients affect the slope of a line. Students build strategies for multiplying and dividing integers and develop understanding of the relationship between the two operations.

Guide for Assigning Homework

REGULAR SCHEDULING (45 MIN CLASS PERIOD)			EXERCISES TO NOTE		
Section/ P&A Pages	Core Assignment	Extended Assignment	Additional Practice/Review	Open-ended Problems	Extended Problems
1 pp. 88–91	**Day 1:** SR 56–65 **Day 2:** 1–6 **Day 3:** 7–24 **Day 4:** 26–33, 35 **Day 5:** 36–39, 48–52 **Day 6:** 40–47, 53, ROS 55	SR 56–65 1–6 13–25 26–27, 30–35 38–39, 48–52 40–41, 44–47, 53–54, ROS 55, 66–69	TB, p. 590 EP, p. 91	ST 1, 2	Ext 66–69 Challenge, PA 25, 54

Key: PA = Practice & Application; ROS = Reflecting on the Section; SR = Spiral Review; TB = Toolbox; EP = Extra Skill Practice; Ext = Extension; ST = Standardized Testing

Math Background and Teaching Strategies

Classroom Notes

Bulletin Board display ideas for this section include:

• pictures of malls, stores, and sale advertisements

Visitors might include:

• mall video game designer

Math Strands

Topic Spiraling and Integration

Exploration 1
Students should be familiar with

follow in building a table of x and y values lay a foundation for graphing equations. In Module 1, graphing of equations and data was limited to the first quadrant. Now, with the inclusion of integers, writing and graphing equations will be extended into all four quadrants. Students will apply and expand these skills in Modules 3, 4, and 6. The absolute value of a number is an important concept for students to understand. It is needed in order to define integer addition, and is used extensively when simplifying the square roots of algebraic expressions in Module 7.

Exploration 2 uses translations to write subtraction expressions. Exposure to translations and writing the related expression for an image will be important for graphing linear and quadratic functions in Modules 4 and 6. Using a parent equation such as $y = x^2$, students will be able to identify how the transformation represented by $y = x^2 + 3$ affects the image of the parent equation.

Exploration 3
Multiplication and division of integers in Exploration 3 completes the calculations with integers. Students will be expected to have

Using the Teaching Resources

The *Teacher's Resource Books* contain a variety of resources for each module:

- *Teaching tools*, including section warm-up exercises, labsheets, additional practice and application exercises, study guide materials, and parent newsletters
- *Assessment tools*, including quizzes, module tests, cumulative tests, pre-course, mid-year, and end-of-year tests, standardized tests, and performance assessments

Teacher's Resource Book for Modules 1 & 2

The **Student Workbook** contains labsheets, additional practice and application exercises, and study guide materials.

The **Spanish Resources** book includes practice and applications exercises, assessment, and parent newsletters translated into Spanish, as well as a Spanish glossary.

The **Technology Book** provides alternative technology-based explorations designed for use with the modules of *Math Thematics*.

Student Workbook

Spanish Resources

Technology Book

Technology Resources

A variety of technology resources are designed for use with *Math Thematics*.

- **Test Generator (CD-ROM)**
- **@Home Tutor (CD-ROM and online)**
- **Activity Generator (CD-ROM)**
- **Professional Development DVD**
- **ClassZone.com**

CLASSZONE.COM

Professional Development DVD

@Home Tutor

Activity Generator

Test Generator

The *Math Thematics* program was originally developed using National Science Foundation funding over a five-year period that involved extensive field testing. The new edition was developed over a four-year period, and reflects recent thinking from the National Council of Teachers of Mathematics (NCTM) including the Curriculum Focal Points, results from the National Assessment of Educational Progress (NAEP), new state standards, feedback from teachers, and additional field-test results. The *Math Thematics* curriculum has been shown to be particularly effective in promoting strong communication skills and problem solving abilities, as well as positive student attitudes about mathematics.

An Instructional Approach that Works

Research shows that students learn best when they play an active role in instruction. With this observation in mind, *Math Thematics* helps teachers provide a learning environment in which students model real-world situations and see mathematics as a way of thinking about real-world problems. The *Math Thematics* program's hands-on, exploratory approach, combined with its strong offering of varied practice, ensures that students will have a solid underpinning for the concepts and skills they learn. The program's emphasis on problem solving helps students become strong mathematical thinkers. Its use of cooperative learning techniques promotes discussion, so that students learn to justify their thinking. Its use of multiple entry points for mathematical content addresses the needs of all students. And its innovative approach to assessment, which involves not only teacher assessment tools but also student self-assessment tools, encourages students to become active participants in their own progress.

> *During initial development, the* Math Thematics *materials underwent extensive field testing by more than 250 teachers with over 35,000 students.*

Development and Field Testing

The *Math Thematics* curriculum was developed using an iterative process that involved many stages of field testing and revision. The writing team consists of mathematics educators from mathematics departments and schools of education as well as mathematicians from departments of mathematics. In addition, many of the *Math Thematics* writers are actual classroom teachers. These teachers were able to provide valuable feedback on their students' success with field-testing materials.

> *Many of the* Math Thematics *writers are actual classroom teachers.*

Program Development During initial development, the *Math Thematics* curriculum materials and instructional strategies underwent five years of extensive field testing by more than 250 teachers in 25 states with over 35,000 students. An outside evaluator chose sites to assess the effectiveness of the materials in different types of schools—urban, suburban, and rural—as well as in a variety of classroom settings. *Math Thematics* program staff made frequent visits to field-test sites to observe classes and consult with teachers. Formative evaluation data was collected from the sites by the evaluator, and the teachers met in the summer to give feedback on materials and to prepare for the use of upcoming modules. Data and teacher feedback were used to revise, edit, and rewrite the materials.

Program Evaluation To assess the impact of the *Math Thematics* program, evaluators conducted research on *Math Thematics* students and on control groups of students using other textbooks. At the end of sixth- and seventh-grade field tests, criterion referenced tests (CRTs) were administered to both groups. The CRTs were designed to assess student achievement on content-specific learner outcomes related to one of twelve NCTM Curriculum Standards (2000) for Grades 5–8. (Standard 4: Mathematical Connections was excluded.) The test for each grade level consisted of a combination of short-answer and open-response items, as well as essay questions designed to measure students' ability to communicate with and about mathematics, to do arithmetic, and to solve problems.

The results from the CRTs, which included traditional objectives, showed that sixth-grade students who used *Math Thematics* for one year significantly outperformed control-group students on 11 of the 40 CRT objectives. The control group did not significantly outperform the *Math Thematics* group on any objectives. At the seventh-grade level, *Math Thematics* students achieved a significantly greater mastery level on 12 of the 42 CRT objectives. These results occurred after a statistical correction was applied to make significance more difficult to obtain, thus giving more meaning to the differences.

> *For students who had used* Math Thematics, *the research showed positive shifts in attitude towards problem solving abilities, interest in mathematics, and the perception of the importance of mathematics for their future.*

Student Attitudes The outside evaluator also collected and analyzed data about students' attitudes. For students who had used *Math Thematics*, the research showed positive shifts in attitude toward problem solving abilities, interest in mathematics, and the perception of the importance of mathematics for their future. These shifts were found among both boys and girls and there was evidence to show that *Math Thematics* may have benefited girls by closing a "gap" in attitudes that was evident before the students started using the program.

Other Studies Recent research studies confirm that the *Math Thematics* program is successful when it comes to teaching students basic skills, mathematical concepts, and problem solving approaches. Researchers have compared student performance in school districts using *Math Thematics* for at least two years with the performance of students from similar backgrounds in districts using other materials. The findings indicate that students using *Math Thematics* scored as well as or significantly higher than students using other materials. The *Math Thematics* students scored higher than the control groups in number; geometric and spatial sense; discrete mathematics; algebra; and data analysis, probability, and statistics; as well as on the nationally norm referenced Terra Nova assessment. The researchers also note that, in terms of open-ended problem solving, *Math Thematics* students were both more likely to earn partial credit for each subscale and to excel at the highest level of achievement. These results were consistent across all subgroups of students.

In this study, the control group's eighth graders in all districts studied were enrolled in prealgebra or algebra and most used algebra textbooks. It is worth noting that significant differences occurred across the groups on the algebra portion of the Missouri Assessment Program (MAP) test. In every case, students using *Math Thematics* scored significantly higher on the cluster of algebra items than their comparison groups, a result that demonstrates the effectiveness of the program on students' understanding of algebra.

The *Math Thematics* curriculum was written for a broad range of academic abilities and learning styles, and the goal of the program is to reach all students. This goal is accomplished through the use of cooperative-learning groups, visual representations, manipulatives, discovery learning, and teaching the mathematics content in context. Pages T34–T35 and T48–T54 of the Teacher's Edition describe how the student edition, Teacher's Edition, and ancillary materials support the learning of all students.

Understanding more about the different types of teaching challenges you may have in your classroom, such as working with students who are learning English, students with learning disabilities, or students needing additional challenge, can help you adapt instruction to accomodate all students. The following section identifies areas in which teachers can adjust their teaching method or the curriculum to accommodate all students.

Learning Styles

Students learn by seeing, hearing, and doing. Knowing that some students learn best by one of these means can help you adjust your teaching style to accommodate all learners. The learning styles associated with seeing, hearing, and doing are described in the book *Marching to Different Drummers* (Guild, P. and S. Garger. Alexandria, VA: Association for Supervision and Curriculum Development, 1985).

Visual learners use illustrations, diagrams, tables, and charts to help them understand and remember information. They like to follow what a teacher is presenting with an advanced organizer that outlines the presentation. To accommodate the visual learner, key terms and steps students are to follow are bolded in color within the *Math Thematics* student edition. Written directions are often further supported by photos of students shown engaged in an activity during various steps of a process. In addition, many of the text *example boxes* include visuals of manipulatives and written explanations for each step of a problem. The *Math Thematics* materials also include labsheets where students can record their work during an exploration or activity. Through introduction of *multiple representations*, students are encouraged to record their work in tables, charts, and diagrams.

Auditory learners love class discussion. They understand by working and talking with others, and they appreciate a teacher taking time to explain something to them. They want to talk through a problem that is difficult to understand. To accommodate the auditory learner, *Math Thematics* materials include embedded *discussion questions* and questions that are worked together as a class (*Try This As a Class*). *Reflecting on the Section* questions and *Module Projects* provide opportunities for oral reports or presentations. In addition, students frequently work in pairs or small groups where discussion is essential.

Kinesthetic learners want to act out a situation or make a product. They find that when they physically do something, they understand it and they remember it. To accommodate the kinesthetic learner, *Math Thematics* materials incorporate games, manipulatives, and other hands-on activities to introduce and teach mathematical concepts. In addition to the exploration activities, the *Module Projects* often allow students to physically construct models related to the mathematics of a module. The active approach in *Math Thematics* promotes "doing" math in place of passively receiving information.

Being aware of your students' learning styles and your teaching method can help you reach all students. Think about these questions as you prepare or teach a lesson:

- Do I write down important ideas as well as say them aloud?
- Do my students have opportunities to act out situations in addition to reading about them?
- Are there other ways I can present this material to appeal to different learners? For example, can I use video or audio tapes, speakers, field trips, plays, skits, poems, stories, or art work?

Instructional Levels

Students at middle-school age, even those at the same grade level, are at a variety of operational levels. Some students are at a concrete level, some at an abstract level, and some at a connecting level. At the connecting level, students begin to write symbols for the physical situation. Students at a concrete level for one concept may be at an abstract level for another concept. To accommodate these various levels, *Math Thematics* uses hands-on, concrete models whenever possible and appropriate. Pictures and symbolic representations are also shown to help students make the transition from the concrete to the symbolic.

For example, in Book 3, students use algebra tiles to multiply binomials and to combine like terms within the product. The algebra tile model is then paralleled with the use of a table. The table helps students transition from the physical model to the symbolic representation while informally applying the distributive property. An example from the student pages showing part of this development is shown at the right.

Language and Cultural Diversity

Students who are learning English can enhance self esteem and build friendships in cooperative-learning groups. There are several ways to actively engage students in the learning process. The following suggestions apply to all students, but they are especially helpful for linguistically or culturally diverse students.

- Encourage students to discuss how the module theme relates to their lives. Many of the *Practice & Application Exercises* can be used to address cultural diversity.
- The hands-on work in *Math Thematics* allows students to explore concrete models. You may want to have manipulatives available for use at home or in later modules.

---

10 How would you write $(x + 2)(2x - 1)$ without subtraction signs?

11 Use Labsheet 4A. Follow the directions for *Multiplying Binomials* to find the product $(x + 2)(2x - 1)$.

12 Try This As a Class

  a. Use algebra tiles to model $(x - 2)(x - 3)$.

  b. In which situations does a negative tile appear in the product?

  c. In which situations does a positive tile appear in the product?

13 ✔ CHECKPOINT Use algebra tiles to find the product of the binomials. Combine like terms.

  a. $(x - 2)(x - 1)$ **b.** $(2x - 1)(x + 3)$

▶ The example below shows how you can multiply binomials using algebra tiles and a table.

EXAMPLE

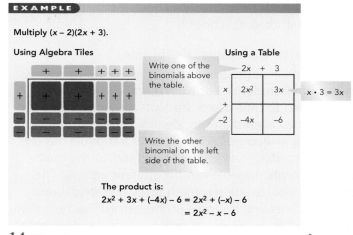

Multiply $(x - 2)(2x + 3)$.

Using Algebra Tiles

Write one of the binomials above the table.

Write the other binomial on the left side of the table.

Using a Table

	$2x$	$+$	3
x	$2x^2$		$3x$
$+$			
-2	$-4x$		-6

$x \cdot 3 = 3x$

The product is:
$$2x^2 + 3x + (-4x) - 6 = 2x^2 + (-x) - 6$$
$$= 2x^2 - x - 6$$

14 Discussion

  a. Explain how the table was used to find the product. Compare this model to the algebra tile model.

  b. Did you have to rewrite the product in descending order of exponents? Explain.

- Create a poster of troublesome mathematical words or English phrases. Review these terms often and try to anticipate other difficult words students may encounter. Try to give a translation of the word or phrase in one of the languages spoken in your class. For Spanish speaking students, see the Spanish Glossary in the *Spanish Resources* book. For speakers of other languages, you may want to use the *Multi-Language Visual Glossary*, also published by McDougal Littell.

Be sure to involve parents through letters or conferences. Clearly state your expectations for your students and describe ways parents can help students succeed in school. The *Math Gazette* parent letter for each module is available in both English and Spanish. The activities and information provided in the newsletter allow parents to communicate with their children about the mathematics that is being studied at school.

Students with Learning Disabilities

The *Math Thematics* program offers many ways to address the needs of all students. For each module, a diagnostic test is provided to help assess students' understanding of concepts to be covered and to identify gaps in students' background knowledge. Each section in a module has an accompanying *Study Guide* which summarizes the mathematical concepts presented in the student edition. The guides give steps, examples, math facts, and definitions necessary for meeting the goal of the lesson. Teachers may use the guides as replacement sections or as reinforcement and review of the section covered in class. Each *Study Guide* comes with its own exercise set. Also, in the student edition, the additional practice provided in the *Spiral Review* and *Extra Skill Practice* help solidify understanding of mathematical concepts for all students, and are extremely helpful for students with learning disabilities.

Some characteristics of students with learning disabilities are hyperactivity, attention deficit, impulsiveness, and reading difficulties. Specific suggestions for these behaviors follow.

Hyperactivity The hands-on activities in *Math Thematics* work well with hyperactive students, but establishing well-defined goals and expectations for the activity and a student's behavior will help the hyperactive student channel his or her energy. Consider posting a class-generated list of rules and goals.

Attention Deficit Students with attention deficit are often distracted by superfluous pictures, designs, or other problems. If students have trouble focusing on one problem at a time, you may want to have them create a "window," as shown below. Students with attention deficit may have less trouble concentrating with such a tool, since all other problems are blocked from view.

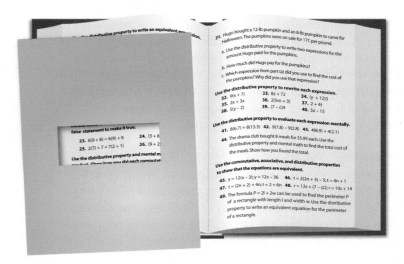

Materials used for activities can also be distracting to students. Materials needed for an activity, such as labsheets, number cubes, pattern blocks, and so on, should be distributed only when students need them.

Students with attention deficit may need to sit in a low-traffic area. Additionally, you may want to seat these students away from bulletin boards or display centers.

Impulsiveness Students who hastily begin activities, games, homework assignments, or tests without reading or listening to directions may need assistance. One technique is to have students read the directions and explain the directions in their own words before you provide the materials for an activity or game. You may also want to go over the directions for tests or homework with students before distributing or assigning them.

Reading Difficulties The reading level in *Math Thematics* is at or below grade level. *Setting the Stage* readings have the flexibility to be read aloud as a class, while the *Think About It* questions give students the opportunity to reflect on a reading. Similarly, students working in small groups can read the directions or instructions for an activity aloud and confirm their understanding before beginning the activity. *Student Resource Pages* as well as step-by-step photos for completing an activity help students understand written instructions.

In *Math Thematics*, key terms and goals are listed at the beginning of each exploration so that students are aware of the main ideas and terms. The *key terms* are bolded within the text and then defined again along with the main ideas of the section in the *Key Concepts Pages*. An organized display of mathematical vocabulary on a wall chart or in a student-created math dictionary can also be helpful.

Gifted Students

Math Thematics provides teachers with many projects and exercises to enrich the learning of gifted students. These projects and exercises can be used in place of, or in addition to, the regular coursework. For each module, teachers are provided with a diagnostic test for assessing students' knowledge of upcoming content, suggestions for extended homework assignments, and a list of open-ended and extended problems. A description of the enrichment and extended learning problems in the *Math Thematics* student edition follows.

- *Challenge* exercises in the *Practice & Application Exercises* are a source of enrichment. Often these exercises build students' problem-solving skills.
- *Open-ended* exercises in the *Practice & Application Exercises* engage students in working on problems that do not have predetermined solutions, thereby encouraging in-depth responses and exploration.
- *Create-your-own* exercises in the *Practice & Application Exercises* encourage student creativity and ingenuity by providing the opportunity to develop unique diagrams, artwork, or problems related to a given math concept.
- *Extensions* take students to a deeper level of understanding of the mathematics in a section or connect to other branches of mathematics.
- *Extended Explorations* (E^2s) may be completed by all students but provide rich opportunities for gifted students. Because most E^2s are open-ended, gifted students can develop creative approaches and solutions to the problem. One component of an E^2 is the presentation of the solution. Gifted students can use their expressive talents to present the solution.
- *Module Projects*, which vary in math content and theme, can be a creative release for many gifted students. Music, artwork, and drama can be incorporated, and creativity and divergent thinking will help students devise unusual solutions. The projects can also be used in place of regular coursework for students who may already have an understanding of material within a module.

A Final Note

Adjusting for students' special needs takes a team of people: the student, parents, general classroom teacher, and possibly the resource teacher, speech therapist, physical therapist, counselor, and others. The suggestions given in this section are limited and do not encompass all special needs cases. We recommend that you consult with your team to decide which teaching ideas are appropriate for your students.

Teachers who use cooperative learning in their classrooms have reported that it produces higher levels of achievement than competitive or individualistic learning.

The Four Parts of Cooperative Learning

Cooperative learning is based on ideas defined by Johnson and Johnson (1984).* These ideas include positive interdependence, individual accountability, cooperative skills, and assessment. Some of these ideas are clearly embedded in the *Math Thematics* curriculum, while others are achieved by teaching students appropriate social skills.

We're All In This Together!

Positive interdependence is sometimes communicated to students as "together you must attain this goal." Fundamentally, it means the group cannot succeed unless all members of the group succeed.

Sometimes positive interdependence means that students need each other to complete a task or understand a concept. Other times it means sharing materials or information.

To help students develop positive interdependence, you can assign a task or role to each group member. The list below gives some ideas for assigning tasks. Remember that not all roles are applicable for all situations.

Roles and Tasks for Group Members

- **Record Keeper** Records the data for the group.
- **Writer** Writes or edits the final report to be turned in.
- **Materials Dispatcher** Gathers and distributes materials needed by the group. This student may also put away all materials at the end of the period.
- **Encourager** Encourages everyone to participate and notes when members have done a good job. (We recommend that you assign this job to all students.)
- **Reader** Reads the directions, story, or problem out loud.
- **Spokesperson** Reports on the group's progress or results.
- **Time Keeper** Monitors how much time the group has left to complete the task.
- **Noise Monitor** Reminds group members to keep the noise level within an acceptable range.

- **Ideas Generator** Asks questions using words like *how*, *why*, and *what else* to help the group come up with ideas.

You Are Responsible

One criticism of cooperative learning is that one student does the work for everyone. In reality, if cooperative learning is implemented correctly, all students are accountable for their learning and for the group results. Individual accountability can be fostered in a number of ways.

- Give points to individuals who demonstrate good social and group skills.
- Test students individually on what they have learned instead of giving a group test.
- Randomly select one group member to explain the problem and solution to the class.
- Give points to groups that demonstrate exceptional cooperation.

Getting Along

An important aspect of cooperative learning is teaching students the social skills needed for interaction. One way to encourage students to think about these skills is to have the class generate a list of behaviors that are acceptable when working within a group. Students should include rules of conduct for listening, talking, giving help, and checking others' work.

Group size and group selection also contribute to the success of cooperative learning. Even the set up of the desks and tables can influence the outcome of group learning. Below are suggestions for each of these concerns based on our work with *Math Thematics* teachers and students.

Group Size In the *Math Thematics* curriculum, groups either have two, three, or four students. Although groups of five or six can use cooperative learning effectively, we feel that teachers and students perform better with smaller groups. We recommend that you use groups of four, and have students pair up with the person on their right or left for partner work. Most activities designed for three students have three obvious roles for students to play. If your class is already set up for groups of four, use one or more of the roles previously listed for the fourth person.

Group Selection At the beginning of the school year, it may be best to have students write down one person they would like to have in their group. You can then randomly select pairs of students to create groups of four. As you get to know your students, you may want to choose the groups. Some things to consider are students' instructional levels, gender ratio, learning disabilities, and behavioral concerns. It is important to remember that some groups work well together and others do not. The personalities of the students will play a major role in how well groups work together.

Classroom Set Up The arrangement of desks or tables should be considered as you implement cooperative learning. Students should be close enough to each other to quietly discuss the problem at hand. The noise level can be an issue if students are too far away from each other or are too close to other groups. Try to have desks or tables situated so that all students can see the overhead or board easily.

How Did We Do?

At various times during a module, students should reflect on how well their group has worked together, both academically and socially. These reflections can take the form of a journal entry or a group discussion. A checklist like the one shown at the right is another way students can assess their group's progress.

You should also give feedback to students on the social interaction you observe. Making the class aware of superior behavior helps all students model appropriate conduct. Many teachers employ a point-reward system when students work in cooperative groups. These points can be added to a test score or counted as a component of the final grade.

Other Common Concerns

How often should I use cooperative groups?

The *Math Thematics* curriculum clearly states when group work is most appropriate. The remaining activities can be done in a variety of ways and their structure is left to the teacher. Although cooperative learning is an excellent teaching tool it should not be used to the exclusion of whole class or individual work.

Should students stay in the same groups for the entire semester?

Students should have a chance to interact with others in the class, so new groups should be formed every 4 weeks or so. Since a typical module in the *Math Thematics* curriculum is approximately 4 weeks long, new groups should be organized for each module.

Take It Slow

There are many facets and layers to cooperative learning, and it may take time to fully incorporate the philosophy into a classroom. When introducing cooperative learning to your class, you may want to focus on one part of cooperative learning, such as positive interdependence, and later bring in the other aspects.

* Johnson, D., R. Johnson, E. Holubec, et al. *Circles of Learning: Cooperation in the Classroom*. Association for Supervision and Curriculum Development, 1984.

Cooperative Learning Evaluation Form

Comment	Always	Sometimes	Never
Everyone in our group is given a chance to talk.			
My opinions are valued by others in my group.			
I listen to others in my group without interrupting.			
Our group is able to finish the task or solve the problem in the given time.			
I understand the mathematics I learn in my group.			
Other comments:			

Extended Explorations (E^2s) are open-ended, problem solving tasks designed to be completed independently. Many E^2s can be assigned to pairs or groups of students. An E^2 should take one or two weeks to complete.

Introducing the E^2

Some class time should be used to introduce and begin working on the E^2. Consider the suggestions at the right as you introduce the E^2 to the whole class.

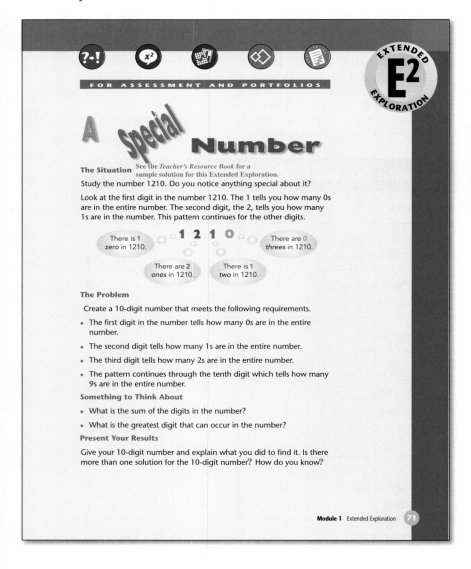

- Discuss the due date. You have some flexibility as to when you assign E^2s. If you have five classes, do not have all the E^2s due the same day.
- Use the *Format for an E^2 Solution* in the *Teacher's Resource Book* for Module 1 to explain to students what is expected in the solution of an Extended Exploration.
- Make sure everyone understands the problem. Discuss what students know about the problem and what they do not know.
- Brainstorm possible approaches to the problem.

As you read through the following discussion, try answering the questions in the shaded boxes. For answers to the questions see the Additional Answers beginning on page A1.

> **1.** How might you introduce the E^2 shown here?
>
> **2.** What approaches do you think would work best?
>
> **3.** Suppose you are a student. Solve the *A Special Number E^2*.

Monitoring Student Progress

Students often do not fully comprehend a task until they start it. Thus, it is important to discuss the E^2 after students have had a day or two to think about it. If students have difficulty getting started, you may want to:

- Make sure they have identified and collected the information needed to solve the problem.
- Give clues about appropriate problem solving strategies.
- Provide prompts about possible connections.

To help students organize their thinking, you may want to have them turn in an outline of what they plan to do before they venture off on their final product. You may also want to offer to look at students' work in progress.

Before collecting the E^2, have students assess their own work using the *Student Self-Assessment Scales*. After they have assessed their work, you may want to:

- Have students share parts of their solutions with the class.
- Give students a chance to rework parts of their solution before turning it in.

> **4.** Suppose you are a student. Use the *Student Self-Assessment Scales* in the *Teacher's Resource Books* to assess your work on *A Special Number.*

Assessing Solutions

The following are tips for assessing student work on an *E²* using the *Math Thematics Assessment Scales.*

- Give yourself the same amount of time to evaluate the solutions as you gave the students to work on them. Read an entire solution before you begin to assess it.

- Look at the sample solution in the *Teacher's Resource Book* to get ideas about what scales to use and what a solution might contain. Use this information and the *Teacher Assessment Scales* to get an idea of what you might expect a student to do to score at each level on each scale.

- Do not spend too much time deliberating over the scoring on a scale. Use your best judgment and move on. If you are not sure which level a solution scores at on a scale, score it between two levels.

- Be sure to record the mathematical content used and note any calculation errors on the bottom of the *Teacher Assessment Scales.*

- Students are not going to score high at first, but they will improve. The goal is that the final level reflect the student's highest potential.

- Students' solutions give you information about their conceptual understanding. When you recognize a misconception, have a conference with the student to clear it up.

> **5.** Read over the sample solution to *A Special Number* given in the *Teacher's Resource Book* for Module 1. How would you score your solution now?

Grading Solutions

The reason for assessing an *E²* is to give students an indication of their current problem solving ability, how it has changed over time, and what they can do to continue to improve. Simply giving each solution a grade based on the total of the ratings on the scales does not achieve this

goal. Instead, we recommend using scoring profiles like the ones in the *Teacher's Resource Book* for Module 1 to help assign grades.

The line on a profile indicates the minimum level a student should score at on each scale for each response. The *Excellent* response is a composite of the abilities the *Math Thematics* curriculum strives to develop. The *Good* response reflects the primary objective of the curriculum; most students should eventually reach this level. The *Developing* response indicates progress toward an acceptable level. Anything below the *Developing* level reflects little effort or understanding.

Keep the following in mind as you convert scores into students' grades.

- Be flexible. The profiles are only suggestions. You must determine which procedure is best for converting your students' assessment data into grades.

- If you use the profiles, familiarize your students with them so they know how their grades were determined and what goal to work toward.

> **6.** Read the Student Sample *E²* Solutions in the *Teacher's Resource Book* for Module 1. Use the *Teacher Assessment Scales*. Read, assess, and grade the students' sample work.

Follow-Up

You may want to spend some class time letting students share their results and strategies for solving the problem. You may want to display solutions on a bulletin board.

With the class as a whole you might want to:

- Discuss universal misunderstandings or misconceptions regarding a problem or a mathematical idea.

- Illustrate a variety of solutions, approaches, and connections and highlight exceptional responses.

With the individual student, you may want to:

- Monitor individual growth on the scales.

- Compare the *Student Self-Assessment* with the *Teacher Assessment.*

- Give help or explanations regarding the student's individual solution.

Research has shown that students perform better when there is a strong parental involvement program that includes communicating with parents and other family members on a regular basis. Communication can be achieved through individual conferences, letters to parents, newsletters, and parent workshops. We recommend that you use a variety of methods to reach parents, but adjust the content or delivery to best suit your community.

Letters to Parents

Most parents remember mathematics classes as hours spent doing endless arithmetic problems. Although this teaching strategy is viable for a small number of students, it does not address the learning styles of most students, nor the intellectual needs of our society. It is important to share information about changes in mathematics education and about the advantages of using a program like *Math Thematics*. One way to apprise parents is to send out a general letter describing the textbook their students will be using and the philosophy of the curriculum. A sample letter is shown below.

Dear Family Members,

This year we'll be using the *Math Thematics* curriculum. This curriculum is designed to help all students develop their mathematical understanding and ability. The materials stress not only key mathematical skills, but also the importance of problem solving, reasoning, and critical thinking. One component of this approach is that students will spend time discussing and writing about mathematics.

Math Thematics uses a variety of instructional techniques, including discovery learning and real-world problems, to motivate students. Because the program allows students to discover the mathematics, you will see few step-by-step procedures. This does not mean that students are completely on their own. There are many examples and pages in the textbook that will help you and your child identify the content that is most important. These examples include:

• **Key Concepts pages** that summarize what students have learned in each section.

• **Student Resource pages** that appear throughout the book and give detailed guidance on various mathematical skills, such as using fraction-percent relationships and using a protractor.

• The **Toolbox** at the end of the book to help students review essential skills they need this year but may have forgotten.

You should expect to see homework assignments at least three nights each week. Some of these problems reinforce skills while others require more thought and effort. As part of your child's homework, you may be asked to help conduct an experiment, answer questions for a survey, or play a math game.

I have planned a Math for Parents meeting to familiarize you with the text and to answer questions. The first session will be held on (date). Additional information about this session will be sent home with your child.

Sincerely,

Newsletters

For each module of *Math Thematics*, the *Teacher's Resource Book* includes a *Math Gazette*. This newsletter informs parents about the mathematics, activities, and real-world situations their children will explore in the coming weeks. Questions are provided to help parents discuss the mathematics and themes with their child. The newsletter also lists several activities parents can do at home with their child, and it describes the *Extended Exploration* (*E²*), and the *Module Project*. We encourage you to copy and distribute these newsletters on a regular basis.

Math for Parents Meetings

Meetings with parents provide an opportunity to discuss the concerns of parents and to explore the pedagogical approaches in *Math Thematics*. Depending on the needs of your community, your math department may want to hold a "Math for Parents" meeting or several such meetings throughout the year. For example, four meetings could be scheduled as follows:

- **Meeting 1:** two weeks into the school year
- **Meeting 2:** one month into the school year
- **Meeting 3:** halfway through the school year
- **Meeting 4:** at the end of the school year

For meeting 1, you could give an overview of the *Math Thematics* curriculum and philosophy, emphasizing that it is a challenging curriculum that addresses the needs of a broad range of students, and pointing out that its theme-based approach engages students and encourages them to become expert problem solvers. To introduce the program's hands-on, discovery philosophy, you could have parents work in cooperative groups to complete an exploration that students will be doing in class. For example, they could try doing the activity involving foot-to-height ratios in Module 3, Section 3.

At other meetings, you might want to focus on a particular topic such as "learning the basics," so that parents will understand that each book in the *Math Thematics* program explores and reviews basic computation, mental math, estimation, number ideas, and measurement. Pre-Algebra and technology are other topics that may be of interest to parents.

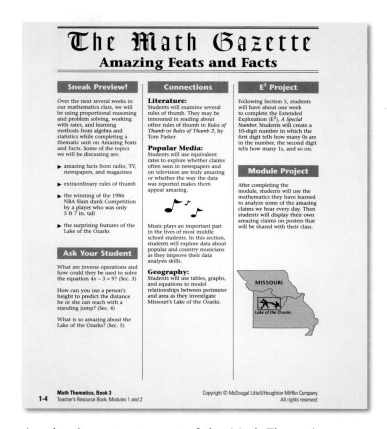

Another important aspect of the *Math Thematics* curriculum that you may want to discuss at a parent meeting is assessment. (See the articles on pages T30–T33.) You might want to have parents try solving an *Extended Exploration*, such as "Changing Shape" in Module 8. Consider having parents use the assessment scales to critique their own work.

Parent meetings are also a good opportunity to talk about how to help students with homework. You may want to point out textbook features such as the *Key Concepts* pages and the *Toolbox*, which are intended to help students and parents review concepts.

The last meeting of the year could be an orientation for parents of students now in an earlier grade who will be using the *Math Thematics* curriculum in the coming year.

To ensure that all parents hear the same message, we suggest that the entire math department organize and participate in Math for Parents meetings.

ORGANIZATION OF THE BOOK

This book contains eight modules. To get an overview of the modules and their themes, look at the Table of Contents starting on p. iv.

THEMATIC APPROACH

MODULES:
8 per book

MODULE **1**

MODULE **2**

MODULE **3**

MODULE **4**

MODULE **5**

MODULE **6**

MODULE **7**

MODULE **8**

SECTIONS:
4–6 per module

Section ①
Section ②
Section ③
Section ④
Section ⑤
Section ⑥

EXPLORATIONS:
1–3 per section

Exploration 1
Exploration 2

PRACTICE:
for each exploration

Practice & Application Exercises

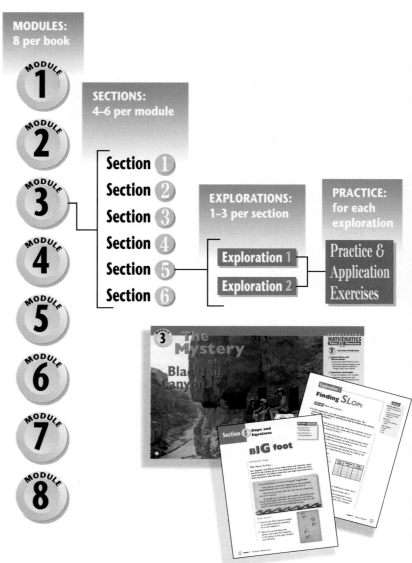

MODULE THEME & PROJECT

Each module's theme connects the mathematics you are learning to the real world. *The Mystery of Blacktail Canyon* is the theme of Module 3. At the end of each module is a Module Project that relates to the module theme.

Connecting Mathematics and the Theme
The math topics you'll be learning and the settings in which you'll be learning them.

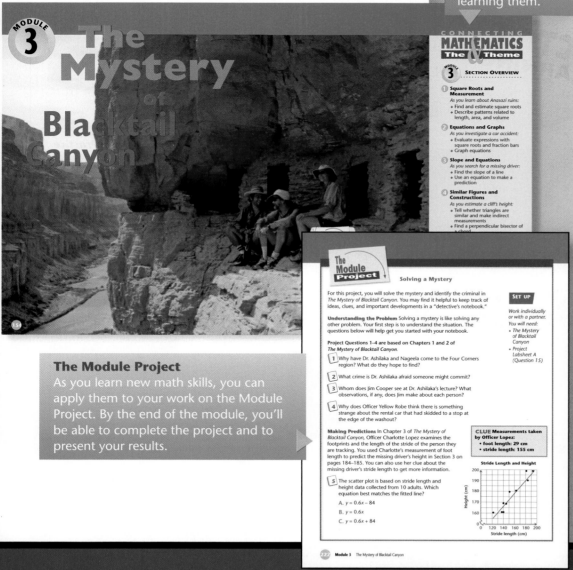

The Module Project
As you learn new math skills, you can apply them to your work on the Module Project. By the end of the module, you'll be able to complete the project and to present your results.

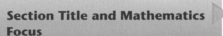

SECTION ORGANIZATION

The diagram below illustrates the organization of a section:

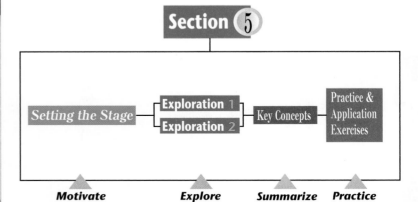

Section 5

Setting the Stage → Exploration 1 / Exploration 2 → Key Concepts → Practice & Application Exercises

Motivate   **Explore**   **Summarize**   **Practice**

Section 5 Scientific Notation and Decimal Equations

IN THIS SECTION
EXPLORATION 1
• Using Scientific Notation
EXPLORATION 2
• Equations with Decimals

Section Title and Mathematics Focus
The title of Section 5 is *Forgotten Bones*. Its math focus is *Scientific Notation and Decimal Equations*.

Forgotten BONES

·Setting the Stage

SET UP *You will need Labsheet 5A.*

The Story So Far...

▶ Nageela visits Dr. Beatrice Leschensky, a s... analyzing the bones found at the site. Dr... how she uses *carbon dating* to estimate th...

Setting the Stage
begins with a reading, graph, activity, or game to introduce the section.

"Every living creature contains a certain amount of a radioactive substance known as *carbon-14*. After a plant or an animal dies, the carbon-14 decays, so that there is less and less carbon-14 over time. After about 5730 years, only half the carbon-14 remains. After another 5730 years or so, only one fourth the carbon-14 remains. After each additional 5730 years, only half the previous amount of carbon-14 remains. By measuring the amount of carbon-14 in these bones, I was able to estimate their age. That's all there is to it."

Think About It

1 Scientists say that carbon-14 has a half-life of 5730 years. Why is *half-life* a good term to use?

2 What fraction of carbon-14 is left in an 11,460-year-old bone? in a 17,190-year-old bone? How do you know?

3 **Use Labsheet 5A.** Use a table and a graph to model the *Half-Life of Carbon-14*.

▶ In this section, you will use mathematics to find out more about the bones found in the cliff dwelling in *The Mystery of Blacktail Canyon*.

xiv

EXPLORATIONS & KEY CONCEPTS

In the explorations you'll be actively involved in investigating mathematics concepts, learning mathematics skills, and solving problems.

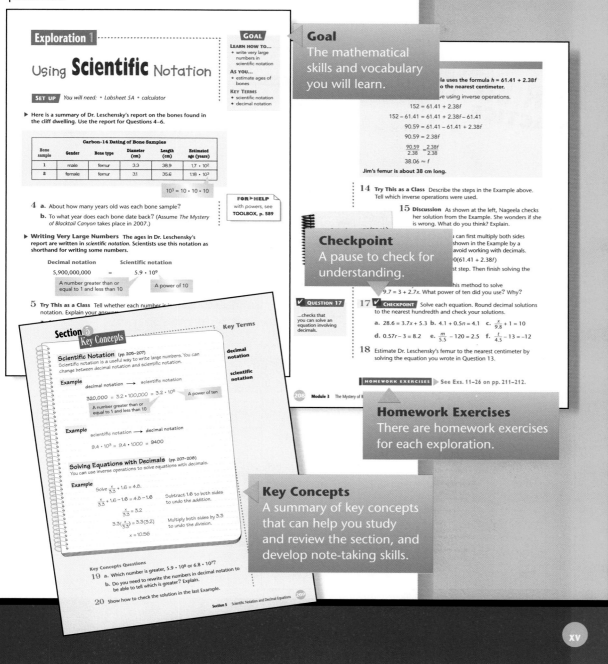

Goal
The mathematical skills and vocabulary you will learn.

Checkpoint
A pause to check for understanding.

Homework Exercises
There are homework exercises for each exploration.

Key Concepts
A summary of key concepts that can help you study and review the section, and develop note-taking skills.

SECTION OVERVIEW

PRACTICE & APPLICATION

Practice and Application Exercises will give you a chance to practice the skills and concepts in the explorations and apply them in solving many types of problems.

VARIED PRACTICE

Balanced Practice
These exercises develop algebra, geometry, numerical, and problem solving skills and help you communicate mathematical ideas.

Section 5
Practice & Application Exercises

YOU WILL NEED
For Ex. 7:
♦ calculator

For Exercises 1–4, write each number in decimal notation.

1. Approximate age of Earth: at least $4.5 \cdot 10^9$ years

2. The distance from Earth to the sun: about $9.3 \cdot 10^7$ mi

3. Speed of light: about $1.86 \cdot 10^5$ mi/sec

4. Distance light travels in a year: about $5.88 \cdot 10^{12}$ mi

5. Which numbers below are written in scientific notation? Explain.
   A. $7.987 \cdot 10^2$ B. $3.57 \cdot 10^{99}$ C. $82.1 \cdot 10^3$ D. $5.13 \cdot 2^{10}$

Astronomy A *light-year* is the distance that light travels in a vacuum in one year. One light-year ≈ $5.88 \cdot 10^{12}$ miles. Use this fact and the bar graph below for Exercises 6–8.

Approximate Distances to Galaxies Near Earth

Cloud of Magellan	165,000
l Cloud of Magellan	195,000
Ursa Minor dwarf	240,000
Draco dwarf	260,000
Sculptor dwarf	280,000
Fornax dwarf	420,000
Leo II dwarf	750,000
Leo I dwarf	750,000
Barnard's Galaxy	1,700,000

0   500,000   1,000,000   1,500,000   2,000,000   2,500,000

The Mystery of Blacktail Canyon

25. **Open-ended** If you buy shoes from another country, you may need to know your European shoe size. The formulas below relate European size *e* to United States size *u*. Write a word problem that can be solved by using one or both of the formulas.

Men's shoes	Women's shoes
$e = 1.29u + 30.8$	$e = 1.24u + 28.7$

RESEARCH

Exercise 26 checks that you know how scientific notation is applied.

Reflecting ◆ on the Section

26. Find three large numbers in a newspaper or encyclopedia. Write them in scientific notation and add labels that explain what the numbers mean.

Spiral ◆ Review

27. $\triangle ABC \sim \triangle ADE$. Find the length of $\overline{DE}$.
    (Module 3, p. 198)

[figure: triangle with C at top, E interior, 7.1 m on right side, A—6 m—D—B along base, 14 m total]

Find each sum or difference. (Module 2, p. 86)

28. $-8 + 7$ 29. $6 - (-11)$ 30. $92 + (-2)$ 31. $-15 - (-21)$

32. $-50 + 50$ 33. $0 - (-12)$ 34. $-18 - (-5)$ 35. $3 - 5 + 8$

Use the box-and-whisker plots. (Module 1, p. 23)

Second Period Test Scores

50 55 60 65 70 75 80 85 90 95 100

⟵———————————⟶ Module 1
⟵———————————⟶ Module 2

36. Estimate the median score on the Module 2 test.

37. Estimate the high score on the Module 1 test.

Reflecting on the Section
exercises help you communicate ideas through oral reports, journal writing, visual thinking, research, and discussion.

Spiral Review
exercises help you maintain skills by revisiting material from previous sections in the book.

ADDITIONAL PRACTICE

At the end of every section, you will find Extra Skill Practice. If needed, you can use these exercises for extra practice on important skills before you begin the next section.

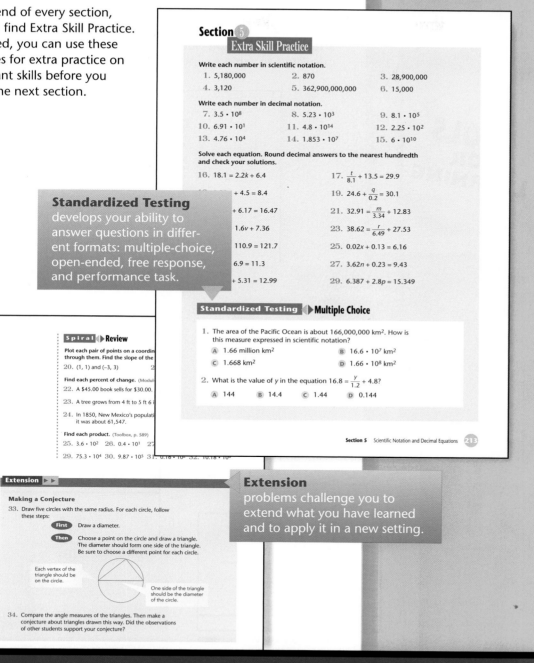

Section 5
Extra Skill Practice

Write each number in scientific notation.

1. 5,180,000   2. 870   3. 28,900,000

4. 3,120   5. 362,900,000,000   6. 15,000

Write each number in decimal notation.

7. $3.5 \cdot 10^8$ 8. $5.23 \cdot 10^3$ 9. $8.1 \cdot 10^5$

10. $6.91 \cdot 10^1$ 11. $4.8 \cdot 10^{14}$ 12. $2.25 \cdot 10^2$

13. $4.76 \cdot 10^4$ 14. $1.853 \cdot 10^7$ 15. $6 \cdot 10^{10}$

Solve each equation. Round decimal answers to the nearest hundredth and check your solutions.

16. $18.1 = 2.2k + 6.4$ 17. $\frac{t}{8.1} + 13.5 = 29.9$

 $+ 4.5 = 8.4$ 19. $24.6 + \frac{q}{0.2} = 30.1$

 $+ 6.17 = 16.47$ 21. $32.91 = \frac{m}{3.34} + 12.83$

 $1.6v + 7.36$ 23. $38.62 = \frac{r}{6.49} + 27.53$

 $110.9 = 121.7$ 25. $0.02x + 0.13 = 6.16$

 $6.9 = 11.3$ 27. $3.62n + 0.23 = 9.43$

 $+ 5.31 = 12.99$ 29. $6.387 + 2.8p = 15.349$

Standardized Testing ▶ Multiple Choice

1. The area of the Pacific Ocean is about 166,000,000 km². How is this measure expressed in scientific notation?

  Ⓐ 1.66 million km²   Ⓑ $16.6 \cdot 10^7$ km²

  Ⓒ 1.668 km²   Ⓓ $1.66 \cdot 10^8$ km²

2. What is the value of y in the equation $16.8 = \frac{y}{1.2} + 4.8$?

  Ⓐ 144   Ⓑ 14.4   Ⓒ 1.44   Ⓓ 0.144

Section 5 Scientific Notation and Decimal Equations   213

Standardized Testing develops your ability to answer questions in different formats: multiple-choice, open-ended, free response, and performance task.

Spiral ▶ Review

Plot each pair of points on a coordin... through them. Find the slope of the ...

20. (1, 1) and (–3, 3)   2

Find each percent of change. (Modul...

22. A $45.00 book sells for $30.00. ...

23. A tree grows from 4 ft to 5 ft 6 i...

24. In 1850, New Mexico's populati... it was about 61,547.

Find each product. (Toolbox, p. 589)

25. $3.6 \cdot 10^2$ 26. $0.4 \cdot 10^1$ 27...

29. $75.3 \cdot 10^4$ 30. $9.87 \cdot 10^5$ 31...

Extension ▶▶

Making a Conjecture

33. Draw five circles with the same radius. For each circle, follow these steps:

  First   Draw a diameter.

  Then   Choose a point on the circle and draw a triangle. The diameter should form one side of the triangle. Be sure to choose a different point for each circle.

Each vertex of the triangle should be on the circle.

One side of the triangle should be the diameter of the circle.

34. Compare the angle measures of the triangles. Then make a conjecture about triangles drawn this way. Did the observations of other students support your conjecture?

Extension problems challenge you to extend what you have learned and to apply it in a new setting.

TECHNOLOGY OVERVIEW

CALCULATORS & COMPUTERS

There are many opportunities to use calculators, as well as mental-math and paper-and-pencil methods. Online resources and a Technology Book provide opportunities to use computers and calculators to explore concepts and solve problems.

TOOLS FOR LEARNING

Using Calculators
Calculators can be especially useful as a problem solving tool. The questions on this page help make calculator use meaningful.

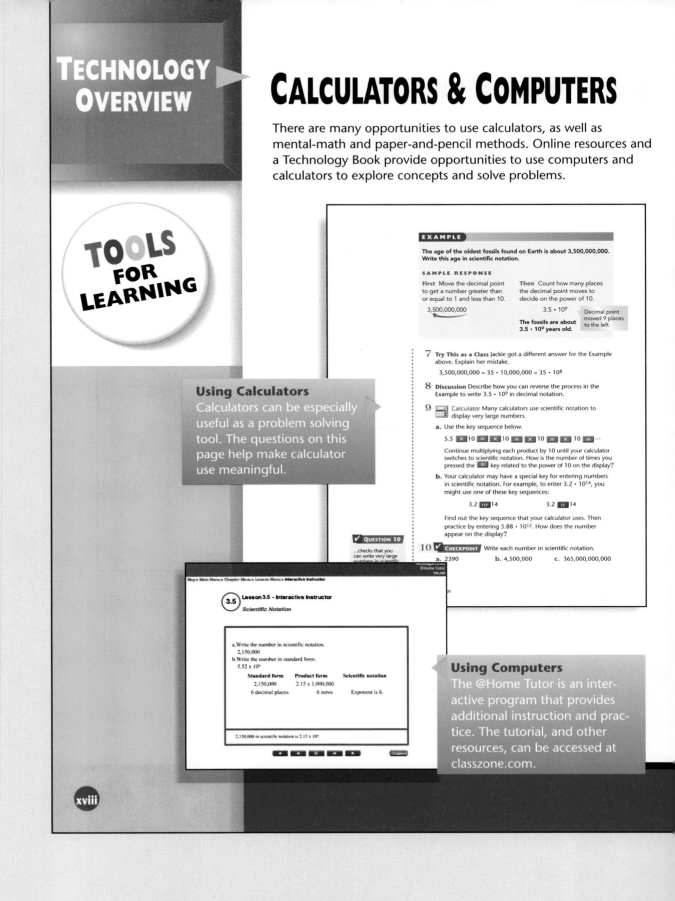

EXAMPLE

The age of the oldest fossils found on Earth is about 3,500,000,000. Write this age in scientific notation.

SAMPLE RESPONSE

First Move the decimal point to get a number greater than or equal to 1 and less than 10.

3,500,000,000

Then Count how many places the decimal point moves to decide on the power of 10.

$3.5 \cdot 10^9$

The fossils are about $3.5 \cdot 10^9$ years old.

Decimal point moved 9 places to the left.

7 **Try This as a Class** Jackie got a different answer for the Example above. Explain her mistake.

$3,500,000,000 = 35 \cdot 10,000,000 = 35 \cdot 10^8$

8 **Discussion** Describe how you can reverse the process in the Example to write $3.5 \cdot 10^9$ in decimal notation.

9 Calculator Many calculators use scientific notation to display very large numbers.

a. Use the key sequence below.

5.5 × 10 = × 10 = × 10 = × 10 = ···

Continue multiplying each product by 10 until your calculator switches to scientific notation. How is the number of times you pressed the = key related to the power of 10 on the display?

b. Your calculator may have a special key for entering numbers in scientific notation. For example, to enter $3.2 \cdot 10^{14}$, you might use one of these key sequences:

3.2 EXP 14   3.2 EE 14

Find out the key sequence that your calculator uses. Then practice by entering $5.88 \cdot 10^{12}$. How does the number appear on the display?

✓ QUESTION 10
...checks that you can write very large numbers in scientific

10 ✓ **CHECKPOINT** Write each number in scientific notation.
a. 2390   b. 4,500,000   c. 365,000,000,000

McDougal Littell
@Home Tutor
ONLINE

Map > Main Menu > Chapter Menu > Lesson Menu > Interactive Instructor

3.5 **Lesson 3.5 - Interactive Instructor**
Scientific Notation

a. Write the number in scientific notation.
2,150,000
b. Write the number in standard form.
5.52×10^6

Standard form	Product form	Scientific notation
2,150,000	$2.15 \times 1,000,000$	
6 decimal places	6 zeros	Exponent is 6.

2,150,000 in scientific notation is 2.15×10^6.

Using Computers
The @Home Tutor is an interactive program that provides additional instruction and practice. The tutorial, and other resources, can be accessed at classzone.com.

xviii

T54

ASSESSMENT & PORTFOLIOS

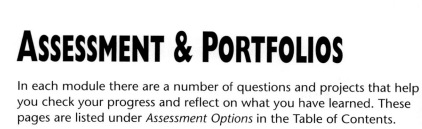

In each module there are a number of questions and projects that help you check your progress and reflect on what you have learned. These pages are listed under *Assessment Options* in the Table of Contents.

E^2 stands for Extended Exploration— a problem solving project that you'll want to add to your portfolio.

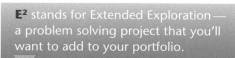

FOR ASSESSMENT AND PORTFOLIOS

Mystery State

The Situation

Try the following puzzle. Is mystery or mathematics at work?

- Pick an integer between 1 and 10.
- Multiply your number by 6.
- Add 12.
- Divide by 3.
- Subtract 4.
- Divide by your original number.
- Add 4.
- Match the number with the corresponding letter of the alphabet (1 = A, 2 = B, *and so on*).
- Think of a state in the United States that begins with that letter.
- Look at the third letter of the name of the state. Think of a fruit that begins with that letter and grows in that state.
- Turn your book upside-down and look at the bottom of the page to complete the mystery.

The Problem

Explain why the mystery puzzle works. Then create a puzzle of your own and explain why it works.

Something to Think About

- How might examining a mystery puzzle with fewer steps help you?
- Does this puzzle work for any positive integer? Would it work for negative integers? decimals? fractions?

Present Your Results

Write your puzzle on a sheet of paper. Include the solution on the back. Explain why the puzzle above works, and why your mystery puzzle works.

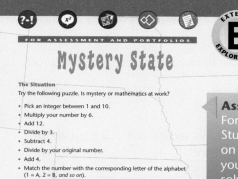

Student Self-Assessment Scales

Assessing Problem Solving
For each E^2, you can use the Student Self-Assessment Scales on page 599. They will help you become a better problem solver.

MODULE 3 — **Review and Assessment**

Module Review and Assessment
Each module ends with exercises to help you review and assess what you've learned.

You will need • *graph paper* (Exs. 9–12) • *compass, ruler, and Review and Assessment Labsheet* (Ex. 18)

Find each value. Describe your method. Tell whether your answer is exact or an estimate. (Sec. 1, Explor. 1)

1. $\sqrt{0.09}$ 2. $\sqrt{16{,}000}$ 3. $-\sqrt{96}$ 4. $\sqrt{\dfrac{4}{81}}$

5. Keith claims that the large can will hold twice as much as the small can. Is he correct? Explain. (Sec. 1, Explor. 2)

Find each value. (Sec. 2, Explor. 1)

6. $\dfrac{3(4) + 21}{\sqrt{102} + 19}$ 7. $\sqrt{\dfrac{8(3) + 2(-4)}{36}}$ 8. $\dfrac{5^2}{4(-3) + 87}$

Graph each equation. Tell whether the graph is *linear* or *nonlinear*. (Sec. 2, Explor. 2)

Scavenger Hunt

1. In this book mathematics is learned through thematic modules that connect mathematical concepts to real world applications related to a module theme.

The following resources will help you on your Scavenger Hunt:
- Table of Contents
- Test-Taking Skills
- Toolbox
- Tables
- Glossary
- Index
- Selected Answers

3. Amazing Feats and Facts, At the Mall, The Mystery of Blacktail Canyon, Inventions, Architects and Engineers, Visualizing Change, The Algebra Connection, MATH-Thematical Mix

Your textbook will be an important tool in your study of mathematics this year. Complete the scavenger hunt below to learn more about your textbook and its various resources.

1. Why do you think the title of the book is *Math Thematics*?

2. According to the book, what does STEM stand for? **Success Through Exploring Mathematics**

3. What are the titles of the eight modules you will be studying?

4. In which module and section will you learn about "Slope-Intercept Form"? **Module 4 Section 3**

5. In Module 7 Section 3, what math will you be learning? **graphing and solving inequalities**

6. a. On what page does the Student Resources section begin? **page 602**

   b. What is the eighth math topic that is reviewed in the Toolbox? **adding and subtracting fractions**

   c. Use the Table of Symbols to find the meaning of the symbol $\approx$. **is approximately equal to**

   d. In which of the Student Resources can you find the definition of independent events? **glossary**

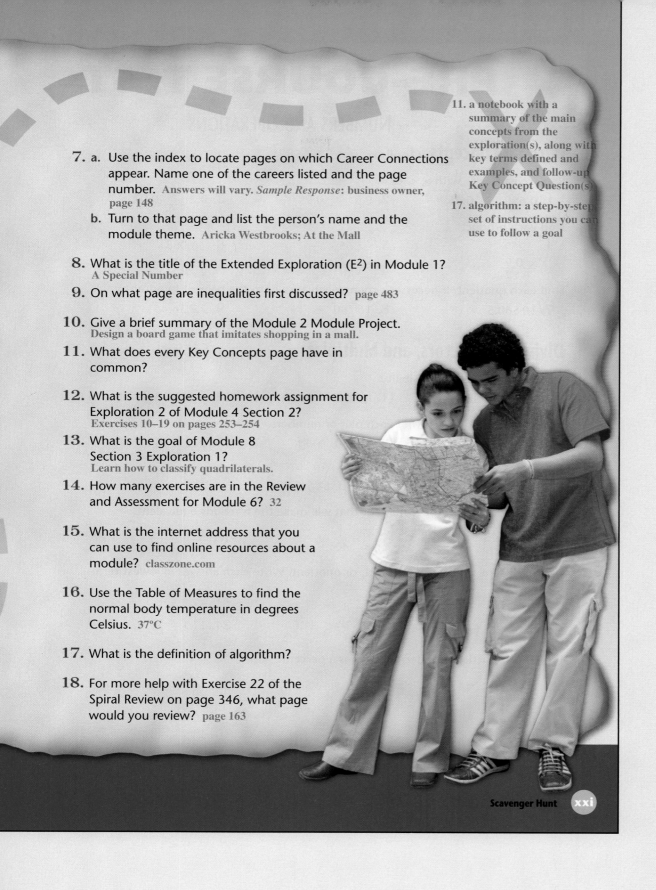

7. a. Use the index to locate pages on which Career Connections appear. Name one of the careers listed and the page number. *Answers will vary.* *Sample Response*: business owner, page 148

   b. Turn to that page and list the person's name and the module theme. Aricka Westbrooks; At the Mall

8. What is the title of the Extended Exploration (E²) in Module 1?
A Special Number

9. On what page are inequalities first discussed? page 483

10. Give a brief summary of the Module 2 Module Project.
Design a board game that imitates shopping in a mall.

11. What does every Key Concepts page have in common?

12. What is the suggested homework assignment for Exploration 2 of Module 4 Section 2?
Exercises 10–19 on pages 253–254

13. What is the goal of Module 8 Section 3 Exploration 1?
Learn how to classify quadrilaterals.

14. How many exercises are in the Review and Assessment for Module 6? 32

15. What is the internet address that you can use to find online resources about a module? classzone.com

16. Use the Table of Measures to find the normal body temperature in degrees Celsius. 37°C

17. What is the definition of algorithm?

18. For more help with Exercise 22 of the Spiral Review on page 346, what page would you review? page 163

11. a notebook with a summary of the main concepts from the exploration(s), along with key terms defined and examples, and follow-up Key Concept Question(s)

17. algorithm: a step-by-step set of instructions you can use to follow a goal

Scavenger Hunt **xxi**

T57

PRE-COURSE TEST

Decimal Concepts (Toolbox, pp. 579–582)

Replace each ___?___ with >, <, or =.

1. 0.650 __?__ 0.65 =

2. 0.9 __?__ 0.99 <

3. 0.2 __?__ 0.02 >

Find each product.

4. $\begin{array}{r} 251 \\ \times\ 0.9 \\ \hline 225.9 \end{array}$

5. $\begin{array}{r} 7.65 \\ \times\ 1.2 \\ \hline 9.18 \end{array}$

6. $\begin{array}{r} 0.088 \\ \times\ 0.06 \\ \hline 0.00528 \end{array}$

Find each quotient. If necessary, round each answer to the nearest hundredth.

7. $10\overline{)560.5}$ 56.05

8. $16\overline{)780}$ 48.75

9. $2.7\overline{)26.46}$ 9.8

Divisibility, Factors, and Multiples (Toolbox, pp. 583–584)

Test each number for divisibility.

10. Is 636 divisible by 4? yes

11. Is 3852 divisible by 6? yes

12. Is 52,418 divisible by 8? no

Find the GCF and the LCM of each pair of numbers.

13. 18, 45 9; 90

14. 17, 50 1; 850

15. 225, 240 15; 3600

Fraction Concepts (Toolbox, pp. 585–588)

Replace each ___?___ with the number that will make the fractions equivalent.

16. $\frac{5}{9} = \frac{?}{18}$ 10

17. $\frac{7}{8} = \frac{?}{40}$ 35

18. $\frac{12}{56} = \frac{?}{14}$ 3

Find each sum, difference, product, or quotient. Write each answer in lowest terms.

19. $\frac{1}{8} + \frac{2}{5}$ $\frac{21}{40}$

20. $\frac{4}{7} - \frac{3}{8}$ $\frac{11}{56}$

21. $\frac{7}{15} + \frac{1}{3}$ $\frac{4}{5}$

22. $\frac{1}{7} \cdot \frac{7}{8}$ $\frac{1}{8}$

23. $\frac{3}{5} \div \frac{6}{25}$ $\frac{5}{2}$ or $2\frac{1}{2}$

24. $1\frac{1}{8} \cdot \frac{5}{9}$ $\frac{5}{8}$

Write each fraction as a decimal and as a percent.

25. $\frac{3}{25}$ 0.12; 12%

26. $\frac{9}{10}$ 0.9; 90%

27. $\frac{17}{20}$ 0.85; 85%

T58

Order of Operations and Integers (Toolbox, pp. 589–590)

Find each answer.

28. $70 - 20 \cdot 3 + 5$ 15

29. $50 - 4^2 \cdot 2$ 18

30. $2(3 + 2)^2$ 50

Use a number line to write each group of integers in order from least to greatest.

31. 2, 1, –2 –2, 1, 2

32. 0, 6, –5, 3 –5, 0, 3, 6

33. 4, –5, 3, –3 –5, –3, 3, 4

GEOMETRY AND MEASUREMENT

Locating Points in a Coordinate Plane (Toolbox, p. 591)

Use the diagram at the right. Give the coordinates of each point.

34. A (–4, 1)

35. B (0, 2)

36. C (4, –4)

37. D (–2, –3)

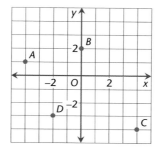

Angles and Triangles (Toolbox, pp. 592–594)

Tell whether each triangle is (a) *acute, right,* or *obtuse* and (b) *scalene, isosceles,* or *equilateral.*

38.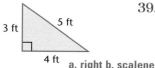
3 ft, 5 ft, 4 ft

a. right b. scalene

39.
96° 42° 42°

a. obtuse b. isosceles

40.
60° 60° 60°

a. acute b. equilateral

41. Explain why the figure in Exercise 40 is a regular polygon.

Using Formulas from Geometry (Toolbox, p. 595)

Find the volume of each right rectangular prism.

42. base length: 7 m, base width: 3 m, height: 4 m 84 m³

43. base length: 5 cm, base width: 4 cm, height: 8 cm 160 cm³

DATA ANALYSIS

Finding the Mean, Median, Mode, and Range (Toolbox, p. 596)

Find the mean, the median, the mode(s), and the range of each set of data.

44. 20, 18, 7, 18, 20, 13, 16 mean: 16; median: 18; modes: 18 and 20; range: 13

45. 56, 51, 47, 61, 58, 59, 48, 60 mean: 55; median: 57; mode: none; range: 14

41. The figure is a polygon because it is a plane figure that is closed and that is formed by (three) segments that do not cross each other. It is a regular polygon because all the angles are of equal measure and all the sides are of equal length.

TEST-TAKING SKILLS

Reading a Word Problem

Before you can solve a word problem, you have to understand the information being given and the question being asked.

- Read quickly through the problem once to get a general sense of what the problem is about.

- Read carefully through the problem a second time, focusing on those things that relate to solving the problem.

Problem

Anna is planning a vegetable garden. She wants the garden to be 6 ft wide and in the shape of a rectangle that is not a square. She paid $144 for fencing that cost $4 per linear foot, and she plans to use all of it to fence her garden. If Anna decides to make a square garden wider than 6 ft, how much more or how much less area will the garden cover?

Solving a Word Problem

- Underline, jot down, and/or make a quick sketch of any information that can be used to solve the problem.

- Decide which math topic(s) relate to the problem. Think of procedures, formulas, and definitions related to that topic that can be used to solve the problem.

- Solve the problem, making sure that the question answered is the question asked. If the problem asks more than one question, make sure you answer every question

Fencing: Total cost = $144
Cost = $4 per foot

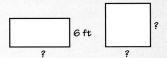

Total feet = total cost ÷ cost per foot
Perimeter = sum of the side lengths
Area = length x width

Total feet = 144 ÷ 4 = 36 feet

The two lengths of the garden use 36 ft – 12 ft = 24 ft of fencing. So, the garden's length is 24 ft ÷ 2, or 12 ft.

Area of rectangle = 12 ft x 6 ft = 72 ft²

Area of square = 9 ft x 9 ft = 81 ft², because one side is 36 ft ÷ 4, or 9 ft.

The area of the square garden is greater by 9 square feet, because 81 – 72 = 9.

$4 x (6 + 6 + 12 + 12) = 4 x 36 = 144$ ✓
$4 x (9 + 9 + 9 + 9) = 4 x 36 = 144$ ✓

- Check your work.

T60

Keep up with the course.

Ask questions about things you don't understand. Take advantage of extra-help sessions. If you get a problem wrong on a test or on your homework, try to figure out why you got it wrong. If you are absent, find out what material you missed and make up the work.

Become familiar with the test.

Make sure you know the answers to the following questions before you take the test:

- How much time do I have to complete the test?

- How many points are assigned to each type of question?

- About how much time should I spend answering a multiple choice question? a short response question? an extended reponse question?

- If I can't answer a multiple choice question, is it better to guess, or to leave a blank?

- Am I better off answering the easy, or the more difficult questions first, or should I just answer the questions as they come?

- Is paper provided for scrap work, or should it be done in the white space of the test booklet?

- On which, if any, parts of the test may I use a calculator?

During the Test

- As soon as the test begins, jot down on scrap paper or in the white space of the test booklet any formulas or procedures you're afraid you'll forget.

- Quickly scan the entire test to get an idea of which problems will probably take you the most time to do. Some people prefer to do those problems first. Others do them last.

- Skip over any question you are stuck on. Make a mark next to the question in your test booklet so that you can go back to it later if you have time. Be sure to leave a blank on your answer sheet for the answer to the question.

- Read an entire problem carefully before you start to answer it. Don't assume you know the question that will be asked.

- When answering a multiple choice question, don't assume your answer is correct because it is one of the choices. Always double check your work.

- If you think you can't do a multiple choice question, try substituting each choice back into the problem to see if it is the correct choice.

- If you must guess on a multiple choice question, first try to eliminate any choices that are obviously wrong because they have the wrong units or sign, for example.

- As you write the answer to an extended or short response question, imagine that you are writing an explanation for a fellow student who doesn't know how to solve the problem.

- If you can do part, but not all, of an extended or short response question, write down what you can do. Something written may receive partial credit. Nothing written definitely receives no credit.

Test-Taking Skills xxv

Strategies for Answering

Multiple Choice Questions

You can use the 4-step approach to solving problems on page 64 to solve any problem. If you have difficulty solving a problem involving multiple choice, you may be able to use one of the strategies below to choose the correct answer. You may also be able to use these strategies and others to check whether your answer to a multiple choice question is reasonable.

Strategy: Estimate the Answer

Problem 1

The table shows how many nickels you save each day. If the pattern continues, what is the first day you will save more than fifty dollars' worth of nickels?

●---- You need 1000 nickels to equal fifty dollars.

Day	1	2	3
Nickels	$3^1 = 3$	$3^2 = 9$	$3^3 = 27$

A. day 5

B. day 6

C. day 7 ●----

D. day 8

Estimate: $3^5 = 27 \times 3 \times 3 \approx 27 \times 9$. A low estimate is $25 \times 8 = 200$. A high estimate is $30 \times 10 = 300$. So 3^5 is between 200 and 300. Since $3^6 = 3^5 \times 3$; 3^6 is between 600 and 900. Since $3^7 = 3^6 \times 3$, 3^7 is between 1800 and 2700. The correct answer is C.

Strategy: Use Visual Clues

Problem 2

How many feet of fencing do you need to enclose the square dog pen shown?

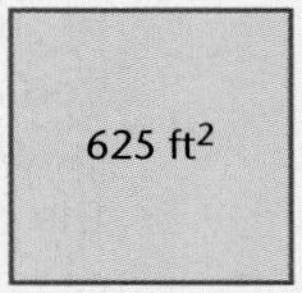

625 ft²

●---- The dog pen's area is 625 square feet. Use the guess and check strategy to find the length of one side of the pen. Each side of the pen is 25 feet long.

F. 25 ft

G. 50 ft

H. 75 ft

I. 100 ft ●----

Multiply the side length by 4 to find the total amount of fencing needed. To enclose the dog pen, you need 100 ft of fencing. The correct answer is I.

Strategy: Use Number Sense

Problem 3

When multiplying a positive fraction less than one by a positive mixed number, the product is __?__.

- A. greater than the mixed number
- **B. less than the mixed number**
- C. less than the fraction
- D. equal to the fraction

Think of some examples of a fraction less than 1 times a mixed number, such as $\frac{1}{3} \cdot 1\frac{1}{2}$.

A positive fraction less than 1 times any positive number is less than the number, so the correct answer is B.

Eliminating Unreasonable Choices

The strategies used to find the correct answers for Problems 1–3 can also be used to eliminate answer choices that are unreasonable or obviously incorrect.

Strategy: Eliminate Choices

Problem 4

A bicycle helmet is on sale at 25% off the original price. The sale price of the bicycle helmet is $48. What was the original price?

Read the problem carefully. The *discount* is 25%, so the sale price is 75% of the original price, not 25%.

- F. $12 ----- *Not* the correct answer: the original price must be greater than the sale price.
- G. $56.25
- H. $64 ---- 48 = 0.75(64). The correct answer is H.
- I. $192

Watch Out!
An answer that appears to be correct may be an incorrect answer that you get if you make a common error.

TRY THIS

Explain why the highlighted answer choice is unreasonable.

1. The length of the rectangular top of a picnic table is twice the width. If the perimeter of the table is 18 feet, what is the length?

   A. 3 ft   B. 6 ft   C. 7 ft   ✗ **D. 9 ft**

   Sample Response: 9 ft is half of the perimeter, so it can't be the length.

2. A bathrobe originally priced at $60 is now on sale for $24. What is the percent of decrease in the price?

   ✗ **F. 40%**   G. 52%   H. 55%   I. 60%

   Sample Response: The discount price is more than half off the original price, so the percent of decrease must be greater than 50%.

3. What is the product −3(−7)(−18)? *Sample Response:* The product of three negative integers is negative.

   A. −378   B. −278   ✗ **C. 378**   D. 421

Multiple Choice

1. Mary runs 3.5 miles in 28 minutes 42 seconds. What is her average time per mile? **B**

   A. 14 min 21 sec   B. 8 min

   C. 9 min 14 sec   D. 8 min 12 sec

2. The stem-and-leaf plot shows the number of minutes Sasha spent talking on her cell phone on each of 15 days. What is the mode of the data? **I**

0	0 5 7 7
1	2 7 7
2	1 2 2 2
3	5 6 9
4	0

   Key: 3|5 represents 35 minutes.

   F. 7   G. 12   H. 17   I. 22

3. You are drawing a circle graph to display the results of a survey. Which angle measure would you use for a sector that represents 55% of the data? **D**

   A. 55°   B. 99°   C. 180°   D. 198°

4. The amount that Pria made life-guarding this week is $5 less than twice the amount she made baby-sitting. If Pria made $185 life-guarding this week, which equation can be used to find the amount she made baby-sitting? **F**

   F. $185 = 2b - 5$ G. $185 = 2b + 5$

   H. $185 = 5b - 2$ I. $185 = 5b + 2$

5. In a survey of 96 randomly selected students at a high school, 12 said that they took art. If there are a total of 642 students enrolled at the high school, how many would you expect take art? **C**

   A. 7   B. 12   C. 80   D. 90

6. The translation $(x + 2, y + 3)$ is applied to a figure with vertices $A(4, 5)$, $B(2, 6)$, $C(0, 3)$, and $D(6, 0)$. Which point is *not* a vertex of the image? **G**

   F. (4, 9)   G. (–2, 6)

   H. (6, 8)   I. (8, 3)

7. Which expression has the greatest value? **C**

   A. 24% of 752

   B. 49% of 398

   C. 67% of 315

   D. 79% of 240

8. The class treasurer records the amount of money spent and made at the school dance. His notes are shown below. What is the sum of the amounts? **H**

Ticket Sales	+$423
Disc Jockey	–$349
Decorations	–$65

   F. –$9   G. $7

   H. $9   I. $74

9. Six red marbles and 4 blue marbles are in a bag. A marble is randomly drawn from the bag. What is the probability that it is a blue marble? **B**

   A. $\frac{1}{4}$ B. $\frac{2}{5}$

   C. $\frac{3}{5}$ D. $\frac{2}{3}$

Strategies for Answering

Short Response Questions

Scoring Rubric

FULL CREDIT
- answer is correct, *and*
- work or reasoning is included

PARTIAL CREDIT
- answer is correct, but reasoning is incorrect, *or*
- answer is incorrect, but reasoning is correct

NO CREDIT
- no answer is given, *or*
- answer makes no sense

A *short response* question should take about five minutes to answer. A solution should always include the work or reasoning that leads to a correct answer. The three ways a solution can be scored are listed above.

Problem

Your father hires you to work in his store after school. He pays you $35 the first week. You can then choose from 2 payment plans. With Plan A, you earn a 10% raise each week. With Plan B, you earn a $4 raise each week. Which plan is a better deal?

FULL CREDIT SOLUTION

Week	1	2	3	4	5	6
Plan A pay	$35.00	$38.50	$42.35	$46.59	$51.25	$56.38
Plan A total	$35.00	$73.50	$115.85	$162.44	$213.69	$270.07
Plan B pay	$35.00	$39.00	$43.00	$47.00	$51.00	$55.00
Plan B total	$35.00	$74.00	$117.00	$164.00	$215.00	$270.00

●--- Data are used to justify the solution.

If you work 5 weeks or less, Plan B is better. If you work more than 5 weeks, Plan A is better, because the total pay is greater and the 10% weekly raise will continue to be more than $4.

●--- The question is answered clearly and in complete sentences.

PARTIAL CREDIT SOLUTION

Week	1	2	3	4	5	6
Plan A	$35.00	$38.50	$42.35	$46.59	$51.25	$56.38
Plan B	$35.00	$39.00	$43.00	$47.00	$51.00	$55.00

●--- The calculations are correct.

Plan B is better if you work 4 weeks or less, but Plan A is better if you work more than 4 weeks.

●--- The reasoning is faulty, because the total amount earned was not considered.

Test-Taking Skills xxix

Plan B is the better plan. The table shows that more money is earned with Plan B in each of the first 4 weeks. •---- The table does not include data past week 4. So, the answer is incorrect.

Week	1	2	3	4
Plan B	$35.00	$39.00	$43.00	$47.00
Plan A	$35.00	$38.50	$42.35	$46.59
Difference	$0	$1.50	$0.65	$0.41

•------------ The calculations are correct.

NO CREDIT SOLUTION

Plan B is the better plan. •----------------------------- The answer is incorrect.

Week	1	2	3	4	5
Plan A	$35.00	$38.50	$42.00	$45.50	$49.00
Plan B	$35.00	$39.00	$43.00	$47.00	$51.00

•--- The calculations are not done correctly.

TRY THIS

Score each solution to the short response question below as *full credit, partial credit,* or *no credit.* **Explain your reasoning.**

Watch Out!
Be sure to explain your reasoning clearly.

Problem

You have a set of glasses. Each glass has the shape of a cylinder with a diameter of 6 cm and a height of 6 cm. You have a 1750 cm^3 bottle of juice. About how many glasses can you fill to the brim? Explain.

1. $V = 2\pi rh \approx 2(3.14)(6)(6) \approx 108$, so the volume of the glass is about 100 cm^3 and $2000 \div 100 \approx 20$; 20 times. No credit; the formula and calculations are wrong and the answer is incorrect.

2. $V = \pi r^2 h \approx (3.14)(9)(6) = 169.56 \approx 170$, so the volume of the glass is about 170 cm^3. Because $1750 \div 170 \approx 10$, I can fill about 10 glasses. I rounded the actual volume up and the quotient $1750 \div 170$ down, so I'm sure I have enough juice to fill 10 glasses. Full credit; the answer is correct and the work and reasoning are included.

Short Response

1. If the side length of a square is doubled, by what factor does the perimeter increase? By what factor does the area increase? Explain your reasoning. **The perimeter is doubled; the area is multiplied by 4;**

2. Jen works as a waitress. During one shift, Jen kept track of the total bill (rounded to the nearest dollar) for each customer and the corresponding tip she received. The data are shown below. Make a scatter plot of the data. Estimate Jen's tip for a total bill of $40.00. Explain your method. **about $7.00**

Bill	Tip	Bill	Tip
$13.00	$2.00	$24.00	$4.50
$72.00	$13.00	$30.00	$4.00
$51.00	$10.00	$31.00	$6.00
$44.00	$7.00	$63.00	$9.50

3. Sheri is buying a square tarp for a camping trip. The package says that the tarp has an area of 182 square feet. What is the approximate side length of the tarp? Show your work. **about 13.5 ft**

4. Glen used fencing to enclose a rectangular garden that is 40 feet long and 25 feet wide. He wants to take down the fencing and enclose a square garden. What are the dimensions of the largest square garden he can build using the existing fence? Explain your method. **about 11.4 ft by 11.4 ft**

5. There are a total of 39 girls on the soccer and lacrosse teams. Seven of the girls play both sports. There are 2 more girls on the soccer team than on the lacrosse team. Make a Venn diagram that shows the relationship between the members of the soccer and lacrosse teams. Then tell how many girls play lacrosse, but not soccer. **15**

6. The radius of Cylinder A is half that of Cylinder B. The height of Cylinder A is twice that of Cylinder B. Which cylinder has greater volume? Explain your reasoning. **Cylinder B**

7. Clarice asked a group of 112 students which of two televised sports they had watched in the last week. The number of students who watched neither was twice the number who watched both. The rest of the results are shown in the Venn diagram. To the nearest whole percent, what percent of the students surveyed watched both sports? Show your work. **11%**

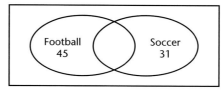

8. The figure shows the floor of one room in a house under construction. The builder is having a hardwood floor installed in the unshaded region at a cost of $16 per square foot, and ceramic tile installed in the shaded region at a cost of $10 per square foot. Find the total cost of installing the floors. Show your work. **$4560**

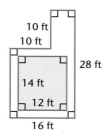

Strategies for Answering

Context-Based Multiple Choice Questions

Some of the information you need to solve a context-based multiple choice question may appear in a table, a diagram, or a graph.

Problem 1

You made an angel food cake. The cake is approximately cylindrical, with a cylindrical hole through the center. If you want to frost the top and side of the cake, what is the surface area you need to frost?

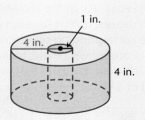

1 in.
4 in.
4 in.

A. 47 in.^{2} B. 101 in.^{2}

C. 148 in.^{2} D. 179 in.^{2}

Solution

1) To find the area of the top of the cake, you first need to find the area of the outer circle and the area of the inner circle.   ●--- Read the problem carefully. Decide what calculations you need to make to solve the problem.

   Area of outer circle: Area of inner circle:

   $A = \pi r^2$ $A = \pi r^2$

   $= \pi \cdot 4^2$ $= \pi \cdot 1^2$

   $= 16\pi$ $= \pi$

2) Area of top of cake = Area of outer circle − Area of inner circle   ●--- Use the areas of the outer and inner circles to find the area of the top of the cake.

   $A = 16\pi - \pi = 15\pi$

3) Area of cake side = 2π • Radius of outer circle • Height of cake

   $A = 2\pi \cdot 4 \cdot 4 = 32\pi$

4) Add the area of the top of the cake and the area of the side:

   $A = 15\pi + 32\pi = 47\pi \approx 148$

   The surface area you need to frost is about 148 square inches.
   The correct answer is C .

5) Check to see that the answer is reasonable. Estimate the area of the top of the cake: $\pi \cdot 4^2 - \pi \cdot 1^2 \approx 3 \cdot 16 - 3 \cdot 1 = 48 - 3 = 45$. Estimate the area of the cake side: $2\pi \cdot 4 \cdot 4 \approx 96$. Since $96 + 45 \approx 140$ square inches, C is the most reasonable choice.

Problem 2

Vanessa has paced off her distance from a clock tower she knows to be 48 feet high. Her eye is 5 feet above the ground, and she is standing about 30 feet from the base of the tower. About how long is the line of sight from her eye to the top of the tower?

F. about 13 feet G. about 52 feet

H. about 57 feet I. about 73 feet

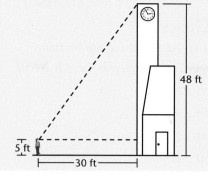

Solution

1) Find the height of the tower above Vanessa's eye level: ●--- Subtract the height of Vanessa's eye level from the height of the clock tower.

$48 - 5 = 43$ ft

2) Let x = the length of Vanessa's line of sight. ●

$x^2 = 30^2 + 43^2$

$x^2 = 900 + 1849$

Use the Pythagorean theorem to write and solve an equation.

$x^2 = 2749$

$x \approx 52.4$

Vanessa is about 52 feet from the base of the clock tower.
The correct answer is G.

TRY THIS

1. In Problem 2, if Vanessa were 35 feet from the tower, how long would her line of sight be?

A. about 8 ft B. about 55 ft

C. about 59 ft D. about 78 ft

> **Watch Out!**
> Be sure that you know what question you are asked to answer. Some choices given may be intended to distract you.

In Exercises 2–3, use the spinner shown.

2. What is the probability of spinning an even number?

F. 0.125 G. 0.25

H. 0.375 I. 0.625

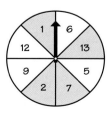

3. What is the probability of landing on a shaded section?

A. 0.375 B. 0.4

C. 0.5 D. 0.75

PRACTICING TEST-TAKING SKILLS

Multiple Choice

In Exercises 1 and 2, use the diagram below.

1. Which angles are supplementary? B

   A. ∠1 and ∠2

   B. ∠2 and ∠3

   C. ∠1 and ∠3

   D. ∠2 and ∠4

2. Which angles are vertical angles? I

   F. ∠1 and ∠2   G. ∠2 and ∠3

   H. ∠1 and ∠3   I. ∠2 and ∠4

3. A can of soup is shown. Which are reasonable dimensions for the label? A

   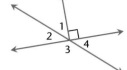

   8.5 cm

   SOUP

   11 cm

   A. 27 cm by 11 cm   B. 27 cm by 14 cm

   C. 54 cm by 11 cm   D. 54 cm by 14 cm

4. A bagel shop offers the bagel and cream cheese choices shown below. How many different bagel and cream cheese combinations are possible? H

Bagels	Cream Cheese
plain	plain
poppy seed	chive
onion	smoked salmon
sesame seed	

   F. 7   G. 9

   H. 12   I. 16

5. Carmen and Joey each buy notebooks at an office supply store. Information about their purchases is shown in the table. If the data were graphed and connected with a line, what would the slope of the line be? B

Number of notebooks, x	3	7
Total cost, y	$8.25	$19.25

   A. 2.25   B. 2.75   C. 4.75   D. 11

In Exercises 6 and 7, use the diagram below. In the diagram, lines *m* and *n* are parallel.

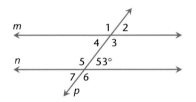

6. What is the measure of ∠7? G

   F. 37°   G. 53°

   H. 127°   I. 143°

7. What is the measure of ∠3? C

   A. 37°   B. 53°

   C. 127°   D. 143°

8. A block of cheese as shown below is being cut into 4 equal pieces to be wrapped and sold at a grocery store. What is the surface area of one piece of cheese? F

   F. 408 cm²

   G. 472.5 cm²

   H. 472.5 cm³

   I. 1002 cm²

   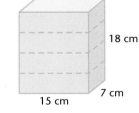

   18 cm

   7 cm

   15 cm

Strategies for Answering

Extended Response Questions

Scoring Rubric

FULL CREDIT
- answer is correct, *and*
- work or reasoning is included

PARTIAL CREDIT
- answer is correct, but reasoning is incorrect, *or*
- answer is incorrect, but reasoning is correct

NO CREDIT
- no answer is given, *or*
- answer makes no sense

Problem

In a certain city, a taxicab ride costs $2.25 for entry into the taxicab plus $1.50 per mile traveled. Make a table and draw a graph that shows the cost of a taxicab ride as the distance traveled increases. If you have exactly $9.00 to spend on the taxicab fare, how far can you travel? Explain how you found your answer.

FULL CREDIT SOLUTION

In the graph, the horizontal axis shows the miles traveled and the vertical axis shows the cost of the taxicab ride.

Miles	Cost
0	$2.25
1	$3.75
2	$5.25
3	$6.75
4	$8.25
5	$9.75
6	$11.25
7	$12.75

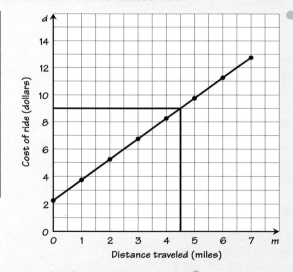

●---- The table and graph are correct and reflect an understanding of the problem.

For $9.00, you can travel 4.5 miles in a taxicab. ●------ The answer is correct.

To find my answer, I found $9.00 on the vertical axis of the graph. ●--- The reasoning
I then looked across and saw that where the line has a y-value of $9.00, behind the answer
the corresponding x-value is 4.5. is explained clearly.

Miles	Cost
0	$2.25
1	$3.75
2	$5.25
3	$6.75
4	$8.25

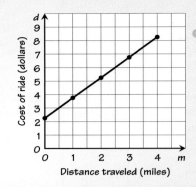

● - - - - - - - - - The table and graph
are correct.

The taxicab costs $1.50 per mile. Since $9.00 ÷ $1.50 = 6, ● - - - The answer is incorrect.
you can travel 6 miles for $9.00.

Miles	0	1	2	3	4
Cost	$2.25	$3.75	$5.25	$6.75	$8.25

● - - - The table is correct, but there is no
graph.

You can travel 5 miles for $9.00. ● - - - The answer is incorrect, and there is no explanation.

TRY THIS

Watch Out!
Scoring is often based on
how clearly you explain your
reasoning.

1. A student's answer to the problem on the previous page
   is given below. Score the solution as *full credit*, *partial
   credit*, or *no credit*. Explain your choice. If you choose
   partial credit or *no credit*, explain how you would change
   the answer to earn a score of *full credit*. **Full credit; the answer is correct and the reasoning is correct.**

Miles	0	1	2	3	4	5
Cost	$2.25	$3.75	$5.25	$6.75	$8.25	$9.75

You can travel 4.5 miles in a taxicab for $9.00.

The table shows that for $8.25 you can travel
4 miles, and for $9.75 you can travel 5 miles.
Since $9.00 is halfway between $8.25 and $9.75,
the distance you can travel for $9.00 must be
halfway between 4 miles and 5 miles. Since
4.5 miles is halfway between 4 miles and 5 miles,
you can travel 4.5 miles.

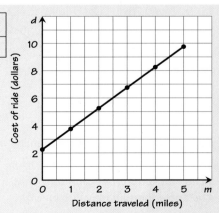

Extended Response 1–5. See Additional Answers for explanations

1. You are deciding which of two gyms to join. Gym A has a membership fee of $75 and a monthly fee of $45. Gym B has no membership fee and has a monthly fee of $60. Write an equation for each gym that models the cost of the gym in terms of the number of months you go to the gym. Graph each equation in the same coordinate plane. What is the point of intersection and what does it represent? Describe under what conditions you would choose to join each gym. **(5, 300)**

2. Describe how to move triangle *ABC* to triangle *A′B′C′* using a series of transformations that includes a reflection, a rotation, and a translation. Tell what the new coordinates of triangle *ABC* are after each transformation. **Answers may vary.**

3. Adrianne has $50 to put in a savings account or to buy a savings bond. With $50, she can buy a savings bond that will be worth $100 in 20 years. With the savings account, Adrianne's money will earn 3% interest compounded annually. With which option will Adrianne have more money in 20 years? About how long will it take for the money in the savings account to equal $100? Explain your reasoning. **the savings bond; between 23 and 24 years**

4. The table below gives the population of a town from 1995 to 2004. Make a scatter plot of the data. Does the data have a *negative correlation*, a *positive correlation*, or *no correlation*? What do you predict the population of the town will be in 2007? Explain how you made your prediction.

Year	1995	1996	1997	1998	1999
Population	11,750	11,850	11,800	11,320	11,290
Year	2000	2001	2002	2003	2004
Population	11,500	11,290	11,150	10,900	10,780

5. The stem-and-leaf plot shows the ages of fans in the front row of a concert. Use the data to make a histogram, a box-and-whisker plot, and a circle graph. Which of the four displays would you use to find the median of the data? Which of the displays would you use to find the mode? Which of the displays would you use to find the numerical interval containing the greatest number of data? Explain your choices. **the box-and-whisker plot**

Ages of Fans in the Front Row of a Concert

```
1 | 6  6  8  9  9  9
2 | 0  2  3  3  5  7  8
3 | 4  6  6
4 | 0  5  8
5 | 1
```

Key: 3|4 represents 34.

Amazing Feats and Facts

Module 1 Overview

Rates, constructing and using data displays, solving equations, graphing equations, and problem solving are developed and applied as students take a closer look at some "incredible" accomplishments and records. Amazing claims, the music industry, and athletic achievements are explored using the tools of measurement, algebra, and statistics.

Module 1 Planner

Day 1: Section 1	Day 2: Section 1	Day 3: Section 1	Day 4: Section 2	Day 5: Section 2
Setting the Stage, p. 2	Exploration 2 through Question 14, pp. 5–7	Exploration 2, pp. 7–8	Setting the Stage, p. 15	Exploration 2 pp. 18–20
Exploration 1, pp. 3–4		Key Concepts, pp. 9–10	Exploration 1, pp. 16–17	
Day 6: Section 2	**Day 7: Review and Assessment**	**Day 8: Section 3**	**Day 9: Section 3**	**Day 10: Section 3**
Exploration 3, pp. 21–22	Mid-Module Quiz	Setting the Stage, p. 32	Exploration 2 through Question 15, pp. 35–36	Exploration 2, pp. 37–38
Key Concepts, p. 23		Exploration 1, pp. 33–35		
Day 11: Section 3	**Day 12: Section 4**	**Day 13: Section 4**	**Day 14: Section 4**	**Day 15: Section 4**
Exploration 3, pp. 39–41	Setting the Stage, p. 49	Exploration 2 through Question 13, pp. 53–54	Exploration 2, pp. 55–56	Exploration 1 through Question 5, pp. 64–65
Key Concepts, pp. 42–43	Exploration 1, pp. 50–52		Key Concepts, pp. 56–57	
Day 16: Section 5	**Day 17: E²**	**Day 18: Module Project**	**Day 19: Module Project**	**Day 20: Review and Assessment**
Exploration 1, from Question 6, pp. 65–66	Begin Extended Exploration p. 71	Begin Module Project pp. 72–73	Finish Module Project, pp. 72–73	Review and Assessment, pp. 74–75
Key Concepts, p. 67				
Day 21: Assessment				
Module 1 Test				

Materials List

Section	Materials
1	• Labsheets 1A–1B, compass, protractor
2	• Labsheets 2A–2B
3	• Labsheet 3A, algebra tiles (optional)
4	• Labsheets 4A–4B, masking tape, tape measure or yardstick, meter stick, ruler, graph paper, 2 colored pencils, small ball
5	• Labsheets 5A–5C, graph paper, ruler
Project	• Project Labsheet A, posterboard, markers, graph paper

Module 1 Objectives

Section	Objectives	NCTM Standards 2000*
1	• Use rates and find equivalent rates. • Write a unit rate. • Draw and interpret circle graphs. • Draw and interpret histograms.	**1, 2, 4, 6, 7, 8, 9, 10**
2	• Make and analyze back-to-back stem-and-leaf plots. • Review mean, median, mode, and range. • Construct and interpret box-and-whisker plots. • Choose an appropriate data display.	**5, 6, 7, 8, 9, 10**
3	• Write equations from words. • Solve simple one and two-step equations. • Identify like and unlike terms. • Apply the distributive property of multiplication over addition and the distributive property of multiplication over subtraction. • Simplify expressions by combining like terms.	**1, 2, 6, 7, 8, 9, 10**
4	• Make and interpret scatter plots. • Visually fit a line to data points on a scatter plot and use it to make predictions. • Recognize trends in data from a scatter plot and identify correlations.	**5, 6, 7, 8, 9, 10**
5	• Use a 4-step problem-solving approach. • Use tables, graphs, and equations to model relationships.	**2, 4, 6, 7, 8, 9, 10**

* See page T14.

Section 1 Rates and Data Displays

Section 1 Planner

Section Objectives

Exploration 1
- Use rates
- Find equivalent rates
- Write a unit rate

Exploration 2
- Draw and interpret circle graph
- Draw and interpret histograms

Days for Section 1

First Day
Setting the Stage, *p. 2*
Exploration 1, *pp. 3–4*

Second Day
Exploration 2 through Question 14, *pp. 5–7*
Key Concepts, *pp. 9–10*

Third Day
Exploration 2, *pp. 7–8*

Teaching Resources

Teacher's Resource Book
- Warm-Up
- Labsheets 1A and 1B
- Practice and Applications
- Study Guide
See page 1 for additional teaching resources.

Materials List

Exploration 2
- Labsheets 1A and 1B
- compass and protractor

Practice and Applications
- compass and protractor

Extra Skill Practice
- compass and protractor

Assessment Options

EMBEDDED ASSESSMENT
- Use rates
  Exercises 10, 11
- Find equivalent rates
  Exercises 4, 6, 9, 13
- Write a unit rate
  Exercises 1, 2
- Draw and interpret circle graphs
  Exercises 14, 17, 19
- Draw and interpret histograms
  Exercises 21, 22

PERFORMANCE TASK/PORTFOLIO
- Exercise 8 on *p. 11 (open-ended)*
- Exercise 23 on *p. 13 (writing)*

QUIZZES/TESTS
- Section 1 Quick Quiz

TEST GENERATOR

Section 1 Overview

In this section, students will use rates, circle graphs, and histograms to determine the validity of amazing claims and examine extraordinary feats.

Exploration 1
Students will use equivalent rates to explore whether claims often seen in newspapers and on television are truly amazing or whether the way the data was reported makes them appear amazing. Students will learn how reporting a rate using varied quantities can give differing impressions of the data.

Exploration 2
Students will learn how a frequency table can be used to construct either a circle graph or a histogram. Students will utilize prior knowledge of converting between fractions, decimals, and percents, as well as measuring and drawing angles. The terms, *frequency*, *frequency table*, circle *graph*, *sector*, and *histogram* are introduced in this exploration.

Guide for Assigning Homework

REGULAR SCHEDULING (45 MIN CLASS PERIOD)			EXERCISES TO NOTE		
Section/ P&A Pages	Core Assignment	Extended Assignment	Additional Practice/Review	Open-ended Problems	Extended Problems
1 pp. 10–14	**Day 1:** 1–11, 13 **Day 2:** 14–19, SR 25–29 **Day 3:** 20–23	1, 4, 6, 7–13 14–19, SR 25–29 20–23	EP, p. 14 Table of Measures, p. 601 TB, pp. 580, 585, 588, 592, 595	PA 7, 8, 22(c)	PA Challenge 12

Key: PA = Practice & Application; ROS = Reflecting on the Section; SR = Spiral Review; TB = Toolbox; EP = Extra Skill Practice; Ext = Extension; ST = Standardized Testing

Math Background and Teaching Strategies

Classroom Notes

Bulletin Board display ideas for this section include:

- newpaper or magazine ads that make amazing claims

- graphs and displays of students' work.

Math Strands

Topic Spiraling and Integration

Exploration 1

Students should be familiar with the concepts of ratio and rate as these concepts were introduced in Books 1 and 2. These concepts are developed futher in Exploration 1 where students are required to analyze rates, and write and identify equivalent rates. Students will be expected to use a variety of equivalent measures throughout this section. Although

support is provided for the student in the Table of Measures, students need to be able to distinguish between the units used to measure distance, area, volume, capacity, and time. Students will build on these concepts in Module 4 and Module 5.

Exploration 2

Constructing circle graphs and histograms from a frequency table are concepts that have been explored in Books 1 and 2. Students are expected to apply their knowlege of angle measure to determine sectors of a circle to create a graph. Once a percent of the data is determined, students translate it into the degree measure of a sector of the circle. Students will build on this skill in Module 8 where they use the angle measures of sectors to describe rotational symmetries.

Math Content

Bar graphs and histograms look similar, but are distinct types of data displays and are used in different contexts. The two graphs differ in the type of data being compared. Bar graphs compare categorical data, such as: pets, populations, heights of buildings, or favorite movies. Of those listed, only the numerical data for populations and heights of buildings could be displayed in a histogram. This data can be divided into intervals whose frequencies are then compared. Movies and pets are categories that cannot be divided into intervals.

Section 2 Displaying Data

Section 2 Planner

Section Objectives

Exploration 1
- Make and analyze back-to-back stem-and-leaf plots
- Review mean, median, mode, and range

Exploration 2
- Interpret box-and-whisker plots
- Construct box-and-whisker plots

Exploration 3
- Choose an appropriate data display

Days for Section 2

First Day
Setting the Stage, *p. 15*
Exploration 1, *pp. 16–17*

Second Day
Exploration 2, *pp. 18–20*

Third Day
Exploration 3, *pp. 21–22*
Key Concepts, *p. 23*

Teaching Resources

Teacher's Resource Book
- Warm-Up
- Labsheets 2A and 2B
- Practice and Applications
- Study Guide
See page 1 for additional teaching resources.

Materials List

Exploration 2
- Labsheets 2A and 2B
- ruler

Assessment Options

EMBEDDED ASSESSMENT
- Make and analyze back-to-back stem and leaf plots
  Exercise 1
- Review mean, median, mode, and range
  Exercise 2
- Interpret box-and-whisker plots
  Exercises 3, 6, 8
- Construct box-and-whisker plots
  Exercises 10–11
- Choose an appropriate data display
  Exercises 13, 14, 17

PERFORMANCE TASK/PORTFOLIO
- Exercise 10 on *p. 27*
- Exercise 11(c) on *p. 27 (writing)*
- Exercise 13 on *p. 28 (open-ended)*
- Exercise 15 on *p. 28 (open-ended)*
- Exercise 17 on *p. 29 (research)*

QUIZZES/TESTS
- Section 2 Quick Quiz
- Mid-Module Quiz

TEST GENERATOR

Section 2 Overview

In this section, students will investigate typical values in a set of data values. They will review how the mean, the median, and the mode all represent averages.

Exploration 1
Students will learn how the mean, median, mode, and range can be determined from a stem-and-leaf plot. After drawing and interpreting stem-and-leaf plots, students will use the plots to compare data.

Exploration 2
Students use a box-and-whisker plot to display sets of statistical data. Students will learn how these plots show the distribution of data and will examine the relationship of the quartiles to a median, and then use box-and-whisker plots to analyze and compare data.

Exploration 3
Students explore ways in which two data displays can give different impressions of the same data. As students examine data on circle graphs, stem-and-leaf plots, histograms, scatter plots, and box-and-whisker plots, they will discuss similarities and differences between the ways these graphs display data. They will also examine the type of information that is available in each of these graphs so they can understand the specific purpose of each type of data display.

Guide for Assigning Homework

REGULAR SCHEDULING (45 MIN CLASS PERIOD)			EXERCISES TO NOTE		
Section/ P&A Pages	**Core Assignment**	**Extended Assignment**	**Additional Practice/Review**	**Open-ended Problems**	**Extended Problems**
2 pp. 24–30	**Day 1:** 1–2, SR 19–29 **Day 2:** 3, 4, 7–11 **Day 3:** 13–15, 17, ROS 18, 30–32	1–2, SR 19–29 4–6, 10–12 13–17, ROS 18, 30–32	EP, p. 31 TB, p. 596	PA 4, 5, 13, 15, 17	PA Challenge 5, 12, 16 Career Connection 30–32

Key: PA = Practice & Application; ROS = Reflecting on the Section; SR = Spiral Review; TB = Toolbox; EP = Extra Skill Practice; Ext = Extension; ST = Standardized Testing

Math Background and Teaching Strategies

Classroom Notes

Bulletin Board display ideas for this section include:

- pictures of recording artists, both past and present.

Visitors/filed trips might include:

- professional musician

Math Strands

Topic Spiraling and Integration
In this section, students revisit concepts related to making and interpreting stem-and-leaf plots and box-and-whisker plots that were explored in Book 2, Modules 5 and 7.

Exploration 1
A stem-and-leaf plot displays data in an organized fashion and lists the values from least to greatest. In this exploration, students will expand on their prior knowlege by analyzing

and creating back-to-back stem-and-leaf plots. Students will recognize the value in using this method of organization as they complete Explorations 2 and 3 and use stem-and-leaf plots to build box-and-whisker plots and to compare data displays.

Exploration 2
A box-and-whisker plot is used to show how the data are distributed. Recognizing that box-and-whisker plots are useful for comparing medians and ranges of data, but have limitations in determining individual data values, will help students make appropriate selections of displays in Exploration 3.

Exploration 3
All of the displays introduced in Explorations 1 and 2, as well as those students explored in Section 1, will be revisited as students apply their

knowlege of data displays. This exploration also provides a means of assessing student understanding of the way in which each display is used, and the benefits and limitations of each of them. It may be possible to represent a set of data using a variety of different displays, but not all displays represent the data appropriately, or provide the desired information. This concept is emphasized in this exploration as students analyze a set of data represented in a variety of displays enabling them to choose displays that best represent a given set of data. Although these concepts will not be formally revisited in Book 3, students are expected to utilize their understanding of representations of data as they prepare E^2 and Module Project presentations throughout Book 3.

Section **3** Equations and Expressions

Section 3 Planner

Section Objectives

Exploration 1
- Write equations from words

Exploration 2
- Solve simple one and two-step equations

Exploration 3
- Identify like and unlike terms
- Simplify expressions by combining like terms

Days for Section 3

First Day
Setting the Stage, *p. 32*
Exploration 1, *pp. 33–35*

Second Day
Exploration 2 through Question 15, *pp. 35–36*

Third Day
Exploration 2, *pp. 37–38*

Fourth Day
Exploration 3, *pp. 39–41*
Key Concepts *pp. 42–43*

Teaching Resources

Teacher's Resource Book
- Warm-Up
- Labsheet 3A
- Practice and Applications
- Study Guide
See page 1 for additional teaching resources.

Materials List

Exploration 1
- Labsheet 3A
- algebra tiles (optional)

Assessment Options

EMBEDDED ASSESSMENT
- Write equations from words
  Exercises 2, 3, 6, 8
- Solve simple one and two-step equations
  Exercises 9(c), 9(f), 12(d), 12(f)
- Identify like and unlike terms
  Exercises 16, 18
- Simplify expressions by combining like terms
  Exercises 17, 20, 23, 25(a)

PERFORMANCE TASK/PORTFOLIO
- Exercise 13 on *p. 45 (create your own)*
- Exercise 26 on *p. 46 (geometry connection)*
- Exercise 29 on *p. 47 (visual thinking)*

QUIZZES/TESTS
- Section 3 Quick Quiz

TEST GENERATOR

Section 3 Overview

In this section, students will learn how to translate verbal statements into equations and learn how to solve simple linear equations.

Exploration 1
Students begin by writing equations for familiar rules of thumb requiring arithmetic computations. These rules of thumb are translated from words to equations by identifying the variables and constants and representing the relationship with symbols and variables.

Exploration 2
Many rules of thumb can be expressed as equations that have variables on both sides. Students explore how evaluating one side of the equation for a given value of a variable can help them to find the value of the other side of the equation. They will learn that a solution is a value of a variable that makes an equation true and will use inverse operations to solve the equations.

Exploration 3
Some of the equations in this exploration require that students simplify expressions. Algebra tiles will be used to model the process of simplifying expressions and to demonstrate how like terms can be combined, but unlike terms cannot. Students will learn the definitions of term, like terms, and coefficient. The associative, commutative and distributive properties will be used to simplify equations with like terms.

Guide for Assigning Homework

REGULAR SCHEDULING (45 MIN CLASS PERIOD)			EXERCISES TO NOTE		
Section/ P&A Pages	Core Assignment	Extended Assignment	Additional Practice/Review	Open-ended Problems	Extended Problems
3 pp. 44–47	**Day 1:** 1–8 **Day 2:** 9–10, SR 30–32 **Day 3:** 11–14 **Day 4:** 16–28, ROS 29	1–8 9–10, SR 30–32 12–15 16–28, ROS 29	EP, p. 48 TB, p. 589	PA 13	PA Challenge 15

Key: PA = Practice & Application; ROS = Reflecting on the Section; SR = Spiral Review; TB = Toolbox; EP = Extra Skill Practice; Ext = Extension; ST = Standardized Testing

Math Background and Teaching Strategies

Math Strands

Topic Spiraling and Integration

Students have been exposed to solving equations, simplifying expressions, and modeling simple equations in both Books 1 and 2. These concepts will be further developed in this section.

Exploration 1

Expressing a situation algebraically is an important skill for students to posess as they move through Book 3. They will utilize this skill throughout the book as they calculate proportions and percent of change, find unkown side lengths of triangles, and work with area, perimeter, surface area, and volume.

Exploration 2

Once students have modeled a situation with an algebraic equation, they will learn how to solve the equation using inverse operations. Since the equation $48 = 6f + 12$ utilizes multiplication and addition, the inverse operations of division and subtraction will be applied to "undo" the operations and solve for f. In this equation, the standard procedure is to first subtract 12 from both sides of the equation and then divide both sides by 6. The same result is obtained when division is performed first.

$$\frac{48}{6} = \frac{6f + 12}{6};$$
$$8 = f + 2$$
$$6 = f$$

Students will notice that, if they attempt to use this procedure for every problem, they may encounter fractions or decimals such as in the equation $2p - 7 = 15$. If division is performed first, there will be decimals on both sides of the equation making mental calculation a bit more challenging.

Exploration 3

One of the errors students make in solving equations is in the combination of terms. In this exploration students will differentiate between variable terms, distinguish variables from the numerical part of an equation, and identify like terms. This concept will be particularly important when students explore quadratic equations in Modules 6 and 7.

Differentiated Instruction

Early in Exploration 3, algebra tiles are used to model the process of combining like terms to simplify an expression. Some students may need to use algebra tiles to model simplifying expressions and to model solving equations throughout the exploration. As they record their results, they will gain confidence and become comfortable with the concept.

Section 4 Scatter Plots

Section 4 Planner

Section Objectives

Exploration 1
• Make and interpret scatter plots

Exploration 2
• Visually fit a line to data points on a scatter plot and use it to make predictions
• Recognize trends in data from a scatter plot

Days for Section 4

First Day
Setting the Stage, *p. 49*
Exploration 1, *pp. 50–52*

Second Day
Exploration 2 through Question 13, *pp. 53–54*

Third Day
Exploration 2, *pp. 55–56*
Key Concepts, *pp. 56–57*

Materials List

Exploration 1
• masking tape
• tape measure or yardstick
• ruler
• graph paper

Exploration 2
• Labsheet 4A
• ruler
• jumping data scatter plot from Exploration 1

Practice and Applications
• graph paper
• 2 colored pencils
• small ball
• yardstick or meter stick

Extra Skill Practice
• graph paper

Teaching Resources

Teacher's Resource Book
• Warm-Up
• Labsheets 4A and 4B
• Practice and Applications
• Study Guide
See page 1 for additional teaching resources.

Assessment Options

EMBEDDED ASSESSMENT
• Make and interpret scatter plots
   Exercises 1, 4
• Visually fit a line to data points on a scatter plot and use it to make predictions
   Exercise 16
• Recognize trends in data from a scatter plot
   Exercises 5, 6, 7

PERFORMANCE TASK/PORTFOLIO
• Exercise 15 on *p. 60 (challenge)*
• Exercise 17 on *p. 60 (home involvement)*
• Exercise 18 on *p. 61 (research)*

QUIZZES/TESTS
• Section 4 Quick Quiz

TEST GENERATOR

Section 4 Overview

In this section, students will continue their study of utilizing graphs for displaying data.

Exploration 1
Working in a group, students record data in a table and then use the data to make a scatter plot. The scatter plot will then be used to compare two sets of data as students look for relationships between them. Students will learn how to use the range of a data set to determine the scale of each axis of the scatter plot, and will learn to use the notation indicating when a scale does not start at zero.

Exploration 2
As students examine the data points in a scatter plot, they will look for patterns that may indicate a correlation. When the points appear to indicate a linear pattern, students will learn how to draw a fitted line through the points by visually placing the line so that about half of the points fall on one side of the line and half lie on the other side. This line will then be used to analyze data and make predictions. The terms *positive correlation, negative correlation*, and *no correlation* are introduced and developed in this exploration.

Guide for Assigning Homework

REGULAR SCHEDULING (45 MIN CLASS PERIOD)			EXERCISES TO NOTE		
Section/ P&A Pages	Core Assignment	Extended Assignment	Additional Practice/Review	Open-ended Problems	Extended Problems
4 pp. 57–61	**Day 1:** 1–4 **Day 2:** 5–14, SR 19–26 **Day 3:** 16, 17, ROS 18	1–4 5, 6, 8–15, SR 19–26 16, 17, ROS 18	EP, p. 62	PA 16(b), 18	Challenge 15

Key: PA = Practice & Application; ROS = Reflecting on the Section; SR = Spiral Review; TB = Toolbox; EP = Extra Skill Practice; Ext = Extension; *more time

Math Background and Teaching Strategies

Classroom Notes

Bulletin Board display ideas for this section include:

• Pictures of athletes and displays of sports data from media sources

• Displays of student scatter plots

Visitors might include:

• A Special Olympics athlete

Math Strands

Topic Spiraling and Integration

A scatter plot compares two sets of data to identify whether a relationship exists between them. Creating a scatter plot and fitting a line were introduced in Module 5 of Book 2. In Section 2 of this module, students compared the data in a scatter plot to other data displays. Students will continue to use this skill in Section 3 of Module 3.

Exploration 1

In this exploration, students will refine their skill of constructing a scatter plot. In some sets of data the first data point is a great distance from 0. A squiggle can be used on one or both of the axes to make the graph more manageable in size, to allow for appropriate interval selection, and for ease in reading. As students create their own graphs and determine scales, they should recognize when it is appropriate to use the squiggle to indicate that some of the scale has been omitted. They should also recognize that the scales on the two axes may use different units of measure and/or different intervals since two distinct sets of data are being recorded.

Exploration 2

In Exploration 2, students analyze scatter plots to determine whether a linear correlation exists. A correlation is a relationship between two sets of data that is either positive, negative or non-existent. In the scatter plot on the Key Concepts page 56, it appears that, generally speaking, the taller the person the higher the jump height. This correlation doesn't necessarily indicate a cause-effect relationship. The height of an individual does not cause one to have a greater jump height, nor does one's jump height determine that person's height. As in all data displays, students need to be aware of the advantages and limitations of the display so as to use it appropriately and extract accurate information from it.

Differentiated Instruction

Students may be given the opportunity to explore creating a scatter plot on a graphing calculator or by using a graphing program on the computer.

Section 5 Problem Solving and Mathematical Models

Section 5 Planner

Section Objectives

Exploration 1
- Use a 4-step problem-solving-approach
- Use tables, graphs and equations to model relationships

Days for Section 5

First Day
Exploration 1 through Question 5,
pp. 64–65

Second Day
Exploration 1 from Question 6, *pp. 65–66*
Key Concepts, *p. 67*

Teaching Resources

Teacher's Resource Book
- Warm-Up
- Labsheets 5A, 5B, 5C, and 5D
- Practice and Applications
- Study Guide
See page 1 for additional teaching resources.

Materials List

Exploration 1
- Labsheet 5A
- graph paper
- ruler

Practice and Applications
- Labsheets 5B and 5C

Extra Skill Practice
- Labsheet 5D
- graph paper

Assessment Options

EMBEDDED ASSESSMENT
- Use a 4-step problem-solving approach
  Exercise 2
- Use table, graphs and equations to model relationships
  Exercise 4
- Extended Exploration on p. 71*
* indicates a problem-solving task that can be assessed using the Assessment Scales.

PERFORMANCE TASK/PORTFOLIO
- Exercise 5 on *p. 68*
- Exercise 6 on *p. 69 (visual thinking)*
- Standardized Testing on *p. 70 (performance task)*
- Module Project on *pp. 72–73*

QUIZZES/TESTS
- Section 5 Quick Quiz
- Module Tests A and B
- Module Standardized Test
- Module Performance Assessment

TEST GENERATOR

Section 5 Overview

In this section, students will use tables, graphs, equations, and problem-solving strategies to study some amazing features of the Lake of the Ozarks.

Exploration 1
Students will use the 4-step problem-solving process as they investigate a claim. By breaking the problem down into simpler problems, and then constructing a table and graph to look for patterns, students will see how it is possible for the area of one polygon to be much smaller than the area of a second polygon even though the perimeter of the first polygon is greater than the perimeter of the second polygon. They then apply this observation to solve the problem posed at the beginning of the exploration.

Guide for Assigning Homework

REGULAR SCHEDULING (45 MIN CLASS PERIOD)			EXERCISES TO NOTE		
Section/ P&A Pages	Core Assignment	Extended Assignment	Additional Practice/Review	Open-ended Problems	Extended Problems
5 pp. 68–69	**Day 1:** SR 7–8 **Day 2:** 1–4, ROS 6	SR 7–8 1–5, ROS 6	EP, p. 70 Review & Assessment, pp. 74–75		ST, p. 70 Mod Proj, pp. 72–73

Key: PA = Practice & Application; ROS = Reflecting on the Section; SR = Spiral Review; TB = Toolbox; EP = Extra Skill Practice; Ext = Extension; ST = Standardized Testing

Math Background and Teaching Strategies

Classroom Notes

Bulletin Board display ideas for this section include:

• travel brochures or ads that make amazing claims

• a display of the 4-step problem-solving approach

Math Strands

Topic Spiraling and Integration

Exploration 1
Students have used the 4-step problem-solving process in the previous two books and will utilize these strategies throughout Book 3.

In this exploration, students see how tables, graphs, and equations can be used to study mathematical relationships. For example, after students make a table of values for the dimensions of a rectangle with a given area, and then plot the data values on a coordinate grid, they will estimate the least possible perimeter for the given area. Tables, graphs, and equations will be used throughout Book 3 to analyze situations and model relationships.

Module 1

OVERVIEW

Rates, constructing and using data displays, solving equations, graphing equations, and problem solving are developed and applied as students take a closer look at some "incredible" accomplishments and records. Amazing claims, the music industry, and athletic achievements are explored using the tools of measurement, algebra, and statistics.

PREREQUISITE SKILLS

Warm-Up Exercises for each section are provided in the *Teacher's Resource Book*. You can use these exercises to review skills and concepts students will need for each section. In addition, the Spiral Review exercises at the end of each section in the student edition provide practice on prerequisite skills.

MODULE DIAGNOSTIC TEST

The Module Diagnostic Test in the *Teacher's Resource Book* can be used to assess students' prior knowledge of skills and concepts that will be taught in each section of this module. You can use test results to help structure your teaching to meet the diverse needs of your classroom.

MODULE 1 AMAZING feats and FACTS

CONNECTING

MATHEMATICS & The Theme

MODULE 1 SECTION OVERVIEW

1 Rates and Data Displays

As you determine if facts are realistic:

- ◆ Find rates and unit rates
- ◆ Draw and interpret circle graphs and histograms

2 Displaying Data

As you compare musical performers:

- ◆ Construct stem-and-leaf plots
- ◆ Use and create box-and-whisker plots
- ◆ Choose appropriate data displays

3 Equations and Expressions

As you investigate various rules of thumb:

- ◆ Write and solve equations
- ◆ Simplify expressions

4 Scatter Plots

As you study athletic record-makers:

- ◆ Organize data in a scatter plot
- ◆ Use a fitted line to make predictions

5 Problem Solving and Mathematical Models

As you learn about the Lake of the Ozarks:

- ◆ Use a 4-step problem-solving approach
- ◆ Model relationships using tables, graphs, and equations

The Module Project

Fact or Fiction

Every day you are bombarded with claims that seem amazing or incredible. In this project, you will use mathematics to uncover the truth in some of these claims. Then you will display your own amazing claims on a poster to share with your class.

More on the Module Project
See pp. 72–73.

INTERNET
Resources and practice at
classzone.com

1

Module Resources

TEACHER'S RESOURCE BOOK
Resources
- *The Math Gazette* (parent newsletter)
- Warm-Ups
- Labsheets
- Practice and Applications
- Study Guide

Assessment
- Pre-Course Test
- Section Quick Quizzes
- Mid-Module Quiz
- Module 1 Diagnostic Test
- Module 1 Tests A and B
- Module 1 Standardized Test
- Module 1 Performance Assessment

SPANISH RESOURCES
- *The Math Gazette* (parent newsletter)
- Practice and Applications
- Assessment
- Spanish Glossary

STUDENT WORKBOOK

TECHNOLOGY BOOK

TECHNOLOGY RESOURCES
- @Home Tutor
- Test Generator
- Activity Generator
- Professional Development DVD
- Online Activities

Section ① Rates and Data Displays

It's AMAZING!?

Setting the Stage

SET UP Work in a group of 2 or 3.

Every day news reports on radio and TV, in newspapers and magazines, and online use numbers to describe the world. The facts are often phrased to make a powerful impact. Are the claims accurate? Are they really amazing? In this section, you will use rates and statistics to decide.

◄ Gentoo penguins, the fastest swimming underwater birds, can swim about 132 meters in one minute!

▲ One rapper was able to rap 723 syllables in 51.27 seconds!

On average, Americans eat 36,500 acres of pizza each year!

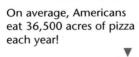

▲ In the two weeks before it leaves the nest, a baby robin may eat 14 ft of earthworms!

◄ In 2006, the record speed for typing a text message was 160 characters in 41.52 seconds!

Think About It

1 Choose one of the facts above and tell why it seems amazing.
Answers will vary.

2 How many kilometers could a Gentoo pengin swim in an hour? Does that seem more amazing? about 8; Answers will vary.

▶ In this module you will read about some amazing people and use mathematics to investigate some amazing claims.

Using /RATES

▶ A *rate* was used to describe each fact in the *Setting the Stage*. A **rate** is a ratio that compares two quantities measured in different units. Rates can be expressed in many different yet equivalent ways.

EXAMPLE

"On average, Americans eat 36,500 acres of pizza each year!"

The rate compares the number of acres of pizza to the number of years.

Other rates:

1 acre = 43,560 ft²
100 acres = 4,356,000 ft²

73,000 acres in 2 years

100 acres per day

4,356,000 ft² per day

1 year = 365 days

$$\frac{36{,}500 \text{ acres}}{365 \text{ days}} = \frac{100 \text{ acres}}{1 \text{ day}}$$

3 Try This as a Class

a. On average, about how many square inches of pizza do Americans eat each day? (1 ft² = 144 in.²) **627,264,000 in.²**

b. The population of the United States is about 300,000,000. On average, about how many square inches of pizza does each American eat per day? **about 2.1 in.²**

c. Based on your answer to part (b) do you find the amount of pizza Americans eat to be amazing? Why or why not?

For Questions 4 and 5, use the fact that a baby robin may eat 14 ft of earthworms in two weeks.

4 What two quantities are being compared in the rate? **14 feet and 2 weeks**

5 Write an equivalent rate using the given units.

a. feet per week
7 ft per week

b. feet per day
1 ft per day

c. inches per hour
$\frac{1}{2}$ **in. per hour**

6 Discussion Which of the rates from Question 5 gives you a better idea of how many earthworms a baby robin may eat? Explain.

FOR ▶ HELP
with *ratios*, see
TOOLBOX, p. 585

GOAL

LEARN HOW TO...
◆ use rates
◆ find equivalent rates

AS YOU...
◆ determine if facts are realistic

KEY TERMS
◆ rate
◆ equivalent rates
◆ unit rate

3. c. no; Sample Response: 2 in.² a day is not that much. It is about the size of a saltine cracker.

6. Answers will vary. Sample Response: $\frac{1}{2}$ in. per hr makes you realize how often a baby robin needs to eat in order to get up to 7 ft per week.

Exploration 1

TEACHING NOTES
To help students better understand how large an acre is, draw one square foot on the board, and give some benchmarks such as the area of the classroom floor, gym floor, or a football field in square feet. Then relate those benchmarks to the size of an acre.

Read through the **Example** with your students. As you do, ask them questions such as:
"How does 73,000 acres in 2 years relate to the original statement?"
"How can you get 100 acres per day from the original statement?"
"Which of the expressed rates is easiest to comprehend? Why?"

Computations in **Question 3(b)** require a calculator that will accept numbers of 9 digit length.

Question 5(c) Note that both quantities, feet and weeks, change. For students not sure how to begin this problem, suggest they change feet per day from part (b) to inches per day and then use that result to calculate inches per hour.

DEVELOPING MATH CONCEPTS
As students begin Exploration 1, emphasize that a rate is a ratio that compares two quantities measured in different units. Encourage students to write the units of measurement for each quantitiy.

FOR▶HELP

with *measures*, see
TABLE OF MEASURES, p. 601

ABOUT EXPLORATIONS

A section contains one to three explorations. In an exploration, students may work individually, in small groups, or as a class. Activities range from guided discovery to open-ended investigation, with students doing one or more of the following: collecting, generating, and presenting data; using concrete and/or visual models; applying problem-solving strategies; looking for patterns and relations; exploring alternative methods and solutions; using number sense; and applying prior knowledge. Students observe, analyze, predict, make and test conjectures, draw conclusions, and communicate their ideas orally and in writing.

TEACHING NOTES

As you work through **Question 9**, ask students which units they will have to change and what measurement facts will be needed. For example, for part (a), ask: "Which units will change from the rate given?" *(meters to millimeters)*. "What is the relationship between meters and millimeters?" *(1 meter = 1000 millimeters)*. "How will you change 132 m to millimeters?" *(Multiply by 1000; 132 m/1 sec = 132,000 mm/1 sec.* "How do you get the rate for 1 second?" *(Divide 132,000 by 60).*

DEVELOPING MATH CONCEPTS

Question 10 Point out that we often need to convert measurement units in order to make sense of a problem. Have students discuss Question 10 in groups of four prior to conducting a class discussion. They should note that rewriting a rate using units that are most familiar for a situation makes the rate more meaningful.

▶ The rates you wrote in Question 5 are *equivalent*. **Equivalent rates** are equal rates that may be expressed using different units. For example, 1 gal/sec and 60 gal/min are equivalent rates.

7 Tell whether the given rates are equivalent.

a. 50 mi/hr; 1 mi/min
not equivalent

b. 48 oz/box; 3 lb/box
equivalent

▶ **Unit Rates** To make a rate easier to understand, it may be helpful to change it to a unit rate. A **unit rate** is a ratio that compares a quantity to one unit of another quantity.

> **EXAMPLE**
>
> Change the rate to a unit rate:
>
> **A rapper rapped 723 syllables in 51.27 seconds!**
>
> **SAMPLE RESPONSE**
>
> $$\frac{723 \text{ syllables}}{51.27 \text{ sec}} = \frac{723 \text{ syllables} \div 51.27}{51.27 \text{ sec} \div 51.27}$$
>
> $$\approx \frac{14.1 \text{ syllables}}{1 \text{ sec}} \text{ or } \textbf{14.1 syllables per second}$$

For Questions 8–10, use the fact that a Gentoo penguin can swim 132 m in 1 min.

8 Explain why it might be difficult to picture this rate.
Sample Response: A person may not be able to visualize 132 m.

9 **Try This as a Class** Write the rate using the given units.

a. mm/sec
2200 mm/sec

b. cm/min
13,200 cm/min

c. km/hr
7.92 km/hr

10 Discussion

a. Which of the rates from Question 9 gives you a better idea of how fast a Gentoo penguin can swim? Explain. Answers will vary.

b. Which rate would you use to amaze someone? Why?

10. b. Sample Response: 132 m/min; A Gentoo penguin can swim more than 2.5 times the length of an Olympic swimming pool (50 m) in 1 minute.

✔ QUESTION 11

...checks that you can use equivalent rates.

11 **✔ CHECKPOINT** At top speed, a cheetah, the fastest animal on 4 legs, can run about 2060 yd in 1 min.

a. Write an equivalent rate that makes it easier to understand how fast a cheetah can run. Sample Response: about 70.2 mi/hr

b. Explain why the rate in part (a) makes it easier to understand how fast a cheetah can run. This rate can be compared to a car on a highway at 70 mi/hr, the fastest human runner at 27 mi/hr, or the average grizzly bear at 35 mi/hr.

HOMEWORK EXERCISES ▶ See Exs. 1–13 on pp. 10–11.

Exploration 2

 **Circle Graphs** and **HISTOGRAMS**

GOAL

LEARN HOW TO...
- draw and interpret circle graphs
- draw and interpret histograms

AS YOU...
- examine facts about computer usage and access to the Internet

KEY TERMS
- frequency table
- frequency
- circle graph
- sector
- histogram

SET UP *Work with a partner. You will need:* • *Labsheets 1A and 1B*
• *calculator* • *compass* • *protractor*

▶ The rapid increase in Internet use is one of the most amazing phenomena of our time. In the year 2003, more than 3 in 5 U.S. households had Internet access—over three times the number that had access in 1997, the first year the Census Bureau kept records on Internet access. The number of adults who used the Internet at home in 2003 is displayed below using a *frequency table* and a *circle graph*.

Frequency Table

Adults Who Used the Internet at Home in 2003	
Age Group	**Number**
18 to 24	16,438,000
25 to 34	23,951,000
35 to 44	29,391,000
45 to 54	27,563,000
55 and over	28,413,000
Total	125,756,000

Circle Graph

Adults Who Used the
Internet at Home in 2003

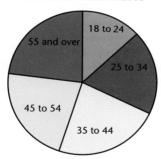

A **frequency table** shows the **frequency**, or number of items in each category or numerical interval.

A **circle graph** shows the division of a whole into parts, each represented by a slice called a **sector**.

12 **Use Labsheet 1A.** The Labsheet shows a larger version of the *Circle Graph* above. **a–b. See margin.**

　a. Follow the directions to complete the table on the labsheet.

　b. **Discussion** Describe how you can make a circle graph from a frequency table.

FOR▶HELP
with *writing percents*, see
TOOLBOX, p. 588
with *measuring angles*, see
TOOLBOX, p. 592

Exploration 2

ABOUT LABSHEETS
All labsheets for *Math Thematics* are copymasters in the *Teacher's Resource Book* for the given module.

TEACHING NOTES
Review what students know about the way data is displayed in circle graphs and their uses. Students should remember that a circle graph divides data into portions or percents and is used to compare the percent of data in each category.

Labsheet 1A To build estimation skills have students estimate the percent that each of the sectors in the circle graph represents prior to completing the table. Estimates can then be compared with the actual percent after the table is completed.

Question 12, You may find it necessary to have students complete the first row across the table and then read out loud the correct answers, so students can check their work before completing the remainder of the table. If necessary, you might have to work through the first line of the table to review how to find a percent, how to measure angles, and how to find the percent of a total measure.

TECHNOLOGY
For a related technology activity, see the *Technology Book*.

12. See Additional Answers beginning on page A1.

Exploration 2 *continued*

TEACHING NOTES
Question 13 Refer students to the Example. Note that the percents add up to 100 and the degrees to 360. Due to human error in measurement and because of rounding, the sums in other circle graphs will not always be exactly 100% or 360°. Let students know they should question any amounts that are off by more than 1 or 2 units.

ALTERNATIVE APPROACH
Students may use a computer program to create each graph and then be asked to explain how the sectors of the circle graph were determined. Most programs allow students to determine the scales used for a histogram and to add a title and labels to all graphs. A computer program should not, however, completely replace the students' construction of each graph in the section.

Computer generated graphs can also be used to explore the way data looks in varied displays.

DIFFERENTIATED INSTRUCTION
Students with limited fine motor dexterity may find drawing graphs challenging. If computer programs are not available, these students should be provided with a template of the graph on which to work.

EXAMPLE

A software company asked 60 computer owners what they use their computers for most. Of these owners, 21 said Internet access, 18 said word processing, 6 said spreadsheets, and 15 had other responses. Use a circle graph to display these results.

SAMPLE RESPONSE

Step 1 Organize the data in a table. Find the percent of computer owners giving each response. Use these percents to find the angle measures of the sectors of the circle graph.

FOR ▶ HELP
with *multiplying decimals*, see
TOOLBOX, p. 580
with *writing fractions, decimals, and percents*, see
TOOLBOX, p. 588

Response	Number	Percent	Angle measure
Internet access	21	$\frac{21}{60} = 35\%$	$0.35 \times 360° = 126°$
word processing	18	$\frac{18}{60} = 30\%$	$0.30 \times 360° = 108°$
spreadsheets	6	$\frac{6}{60} = 10\%$	$0.10 \times 360° = 36°$
other	15	$\frac{15}{60} = 25\%$	$0.25 \times 360° = 90°$

Step 2 Use a compass to draw a circle. Then use a protractor to draw sectors having the angle measures found in Step 1.

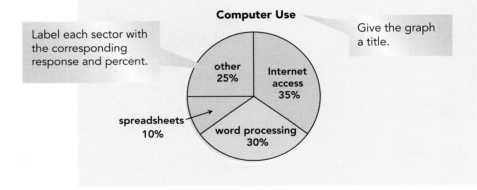

Label each sector with the corresponding response and percent.

Give the graph a title.

Computer Use

13 Find the sum of the percents and the sum of the angle measures in Step 1 of the Example. How does this help you check your work when making a circle graph? **The percents should add up to 100%, and the angle measures should equal 360°. If the sums do not make these amounts, there is an error in calculations. Minor differences may be due to rounding and are acceptable.**

6

14 ✔ **CHECKPOINT** Children are also using the Internet at home. Draw a circle graph of the data in the frequency table to compare the number of Internet users in each age group.
See margin.

Children Who Used the Internet at Home in 2003	
Age Group	Number
3–9	17,493,000
10–14	14,407,000
15–17	9,023,000
Total	40,923,000

✔ **QUESTION 14**

...checks that you can draw a circle graph.

▶ To measure demand for Internet access at school, the computer club at Garfield Middle School asked 50 students to estimate the number of times per month they access the Internet at home. The results are displayed below in a frequency table and a *histogram*.

Frequency Table

Internet Access at Home	
Times per Month	Frequency
0–4	3
5–9	5
10–14	9
15–19	7
20–24	14
25–29	12

Histogram

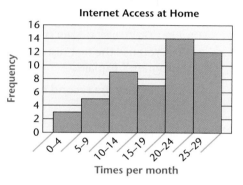

A **histogram** shows the frequencies of numerical values that fall within intervals of equal width.

15 **Discussion** How are bars in the histogram related to the frequencies in the table? **The heights of the bars correspond to the frequencies in the table.**

16 How is a histogram like a bar graph? How is it different?

17 Can you tell from the histogram exactly how many students said they access the Internet 10 times per month? Explain.

18 **a.** Draw a circle graph that displays the data in the frequency table. What does each sector of the circle graph tell you?
See margin.
b. How does the information given by the histogram differ from the information given by the circle graph? **The histogram gives the number of students who fall within particular intervals of Internet usage, not the percent.**

FOR ▶ HELP
with *bar graphs*, see
STUDENT RESOURCE, p. 597

16. Both use bars of varying heights to display data; Each bar in a histogram represents the data for an interval. Each bar in a bar graph represent the data for a single value or category. The bars in a histogram touch each other. In a bar graph there are gaps between the bars.

17. No; A frequency is given for the interval 10–14 times per month, but not for a specific value within that interval.

TEACHING NOTES
In completing **Checkpoint Question 14**, some students may need to create a chart, as in the Example, prior to drawing their graph.

TEACHING NOTES
This portion of the exploration is devoted to histograms. The main focus in the discussions during the section should concentrate on how histograms are different from bar graphs and circle graphs, and how the interval sizes can affect the appearance of the graph.

COMMON ERROR
Students may fail to recognize that a histogram and a bar graph are different in ways other than the linking of the bars. For *Checkpoint Question 24* they will need to recognize that a histogram shows frequencies within intervals while a bar graph compares categorical data. You may ask the students if it is possible to display the results of a survey of the class about favorite pets in a histogram. If they reply that it is possible, ask them to show what the intervals and frequencies would be.

14. Children Who Used the Internet at Home in 2003

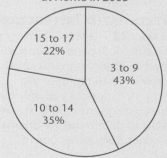

18. a. See Additional Answers beginning on page A1.

Exploration 2 *continued*

TEACHING NOTES

As a class, look at the *Data for Internet Usage* and decide what intervals would be appropriate for making a histogram. Compare the class's ideas to those used in the histograms on **Labsheet 1B**. If the ideas generated by the class are different than what is on the labsheet, you might assign a group of students to draw a histogram of the data using the class intervals and then compare it to those on the labsheet.

Make sure students understand how the intervals selected affect the shape of a graph. You may ask students questions such as, "How does the size of the interval affect the way the graph looks?" (The smaller intervals have fewer data points included so the bars are shorter than the bars of larger intervals.) "Which of the histograms that you created gives you a more accurate view of the data? Why?" (The hisogram with smaller intervals; In the graphs using larger intervals it is difficult to tell if data points fall all at one end of the interval or the other, or if they are evenly distributed. Therefore, they don't provide as accurate a picture of the actual results as a graph using smaller intervals.)

DIFFERENTIATED INSTRUCTION

Question 23 The word *recover* may be difficult for Second Language Learners to interpret in this context. You may want to rephrase the quesion as, "Suppose you only had the two histograms to look at. Are you able to determine the original data values from either one of them?"

19., 24. a. See Additional Answers beginning on page A1.

---

22. a. Yes; The frequencies of the first 2 bars in the first histogram can be combined to give the frequency of the first bar in the second histogram; the frequencies of the next 2 bars in the first histogram can be combined to make the second bar in the second histogram, and so on.
    b. No; There is no way of knowing how the frequencies of the 0–9 bar should be distributed over the 0–4 and 5–9 bars.

✔ **QUESTION 24**

...checks that you know how to use a histogram to display data.

▶ The Garfield computer club raises money to pay a provider for Internet access. Then the club monitors the number of times students access the Internet at school. The numbers of students who access the Internet at school each day for 30 days are shown.

> 16, 27, 26, 5, 11, 33, 23, 17, 15, 20, 3, 14, 29, 21, 23,
> 31, 16, 8, 14, 28, 19, 20, 24, 35, 7, 12, 22, 27, 18, 20

Use Labsheet 1B for Questions 19–23.

19 Follow the directions on the Labsheet to complete the *Frequency Tables* and draw the *Histograms*. **See margin.**

20 Compare the shapes of the two histograms you drew.

  a. How are they alike? The heights of the bars increase and then decrease.
  b. How are they different? The bars of the second histogram are fewer and broader.

21 Which histogram gives more information? Explain. The first; The frequencies are given for a greater set of intervals.

22 a. Can you use the first histogram to make the second histogram? Explain.

  b. Can you use the second histogram to make the first histogram? Why?

23 Can you use either histogram to recover the original data values? Why or why not? No; The frequencies of individual data values are not shown.

24 ✔ **CHECKPOINT** Tell whether each data set can be displayed using a histogram. If it can, draw a histogram of the data. If it cannot, explain why not.

  a. weekly high temperatures (in °F) for 20 consecutive weeks: See margin.
     15, 18, 30, 22, 25, 37, 33, 35, 40, 47,
     38, 49, 52, 59, 51, 62, 68, 65, 70, 74

  b. days on which weekly high temperatures occurred for 20 consecutive weeks:

     Wed, Sat, Mon, Fri, Wed, Sun, Mon, Thurs, Thurs, Fri, Tues,
     Fri, Wed, Sat, Sun, Fri, Mon, Tues, Sat, Sun
     No; The data are not numerical.

HOMEWORK EXERCISES ▶ See Exs. 14–23 on pp. 12–13.

Section 1
Key Concepts

Key Terms

Rates (pp. 3–4)
A rate is a ratio that compares two quantities measured in different units. A unit rate gives an amount per one unit.

rates

Example Suppose you pay $24 for 4 movie tickets. You can convert this rate to a unit rate of $6 per ticket. Both rates describe how the amount of money you pay depends on the number of tickets you buy.

unit rate

Equivalent Rates (pp. 3–4)
Equivalent rates are equal rates that may be expressed using different units. You can use equivalent rates to make a rate easier to understand or to make a more powerful impact.

equivalent rates

Example Each person in the United States eats an average of 3 oz of sugar per day. To impress upon someone how much sugar this is, you might convert to pounds per year.

$$\frac{3 \text{ oz}}{\text{day}} = \frac{3 \text{ oz}}{1 \text{ day}} \cdot \frac{1 \text{ lb}}{16 \text{ oz}} \cdot \frac{365 \text{ days}}{1 \text{ year}} \approx 68.4 \text{ lb/year}$$

Circle Graphs (pp. 5–6)
A circle graph shows the division of a whole into parts. Each part is represented by a slice, or sector, of the circle graph.

circle graph

sector

Example
This circle graph compares the number of adults with access to the Internet by different household incomes.

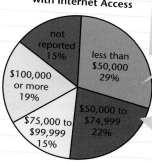

Household Income of Adults with Internet Access

not reported 15%
less than $50,000 29%
$100,000 or more 19%
$50,000 to $74,999 22%
$75,000 to $99,999 15%

The angle measure of this sector is 29% of 360°, or 104.4°.

If the percents have not been rounded, their sum should be 100%.

25 **Key Concepts Question** Use a rate other than ounces per day or pounds per year to specify the average amount of sugar eaten by each person in the United States. Describe a situation where it would make sense to use the rate you chose. **Sample Response: 1 oz/meal; An ad campaign is being developed to encourage people not to worry about eating too much sugar.**

Key Concepts

ABOUT KEY CONCEPTS
Students can use the *Key Concepts* to review for a test or as a reference when they have missed a day of class. The *Key Concepts* are also a resource for parents who are helping their child with homework. These pages give a quick overview of the content, illustrate the content with examples, highlight the most important content, and provide a reference to the applicable pages in the explorations. The *Key Concepts* questions reinforce the main ideas from the section.

ABSENT STUDENTS
For students who were absent for all or part of this section, the blackline Study Guide for Section 1 may be used to present the ideas, concepts, and skills of Section 1.

CLOSURE QUESTION
Explain why you could not write an equivalent rate about the speed of your reading using the rates *words/min* and *words/page*.

Sample Response: The rates do not refer to similar units of measure. Words per minute refers to the speed at which words are read and words per page refers to the number of words that a page contains. Words per page cannot be used to measure speed since there is no time element involved. To write an equivalent rate for words/min another rate involving time would need to be used such as words/sec or words/hr.

Key Concepts *continued*

CLOSURE QUESTION
A survey was conducted to see which of six different drinks was preferred by a class of eighth grade students. Which display, a circle graph or histogram, would be best to use to display this data? Explain.

Sample Response: The circle graph would be the better way to display this data since a circle graph shows the percentages of students that chose each of the drinks in the survey. A histogram displays the frequency of data within intervals. There are no intervals within which the frequency of responses could be compared.

Practice & Applications

SUGGESTED ASSIGNMENTS

Core Course
Day 1: Exs. 1–11, 13
Day 2: Exs. 14–19, 25 –29
Day 3: Exs. 20–23

Extended Course
Day 1: Exs. 1, 4, 6, 7–13
Day 2: Exs. 14–19, 25–29
Day 3: Exs. 20–23

Note: Extended Course assignments can be used to differentiate within the regular classroom. In classrooms where students are grouped homogeneously, the material might be covered in fewer days. In this case assignments may be combined.

Section 1
Key Concepts

Key Terms

histogram

frequency

frequency table

Histograms (pp. 7–8)
A histogram shows the frequencies of numerical values that fall within intervals of equal width.

Example The histogram below displays the test score data given in the frequency table.

The height of each bar is the frequency of test scores in the corresponding interval.

Test Scores	
Score	Frequency
51-60	3
61-70	6
71-80	10
81-90	8
91-100	4

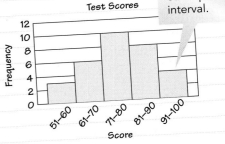

26 Key Concepts Question Refer to the circle graph in the Example on page 9. Tell whether the data displayed in the graph can be displayed in a histogram. If it can, explain how to do so. If it cannot, explain why not. No; the values do not occur in intervals of equal width.

Section 1
Practice & Application Exercises

YOU WILL NEED

For Exs. 1–8:
◆ Table of Measures on p. 601

For Ex. 17:
◆ compass and protractor

Name the units in each rate. Then write a unit rate.

1. 360 mi in 6 hr
   miles and hours; 60 mi/hr

2. 1.5 lb for $3.00
   pounds and dollars; $2/lb

Copy and complete each equation.

3. 8000 lb/min = _?_ lb/hr
   480,000

4. 60 in./year = $\frac{?}{5}$ in./month

Tell whether the given rates are equivalent.

5. 5 cars/min; 300 cars/sec
   not equivalent

6. 20 lb/day; 3.65 tons/year
   equivalent

7. **Open-ended** Use an equivalent rate to rewrite this statement so that it makes a more amazing fact: "A person must consume about 2.5 quarts of water per day in order to survive."

8. **Open-ended** Use an equivalent rate to rewrite this statement so that it is easier to understand: "The three-toed sloth moves along the ground at an average speed of about 0.07 mi/hr." Explain why you chose the rate.

9. **World Records** California middle school teacher Constance Constable set a footbag record for women's singles in 1998 in Monterey, California, with 24,713 kicks in about 4 hr 9 min.

   a. Find Constance's "kick rate" in kicks per minute. Round to the nearest whole number. **about 99 kicks/min**

   b. The overall open singles record set in 1997 is 63,326 kicks in about 8 hr 51 min. Compare this kick rate with Constance Constable's kick rate. **At about 119 kicks/min, this rate is greater than Constance Constable's.**

Write a word problem for each calculation. Solve the problem.

10. 55 mi/hr • 8 hr

11. $0.99 per oz • 6 oz

12. **Challenge** A light-year is the distance light travels in one year. Light travels at a speed of 186,282 mi/sec.

   a. Change the rate 186,282 mi/sec to mi/hr. **670,615,200 mi/hr**

   b. How fast does light travel in mi/day? **16,094,764,800 mi/day**

   c. How far does light travel in one year? **5,874,589,152,000 mi**

   d. The sun is about 93 million miles from Earth. Estimate the amount of time it takes light from the sun to reach Earth. **about 8 min**

13. It took about 21 months for the space probe Pioneer 10 to travel from Mars to Jupiter. This distance was about 620,000,000 mi. Write Pioneer 10's average speed using the given units.

   a. miles per month **about 29,523,810 mi/month**

   b. miles per day (Assume an average of 30.4 days per month.) **about 971,178 mi/day**

   c. miles per hour **about 40,466 mi/hr**

   d. Which rate gives you the best sense of how fast Pioneer 10 was traveling? Explain. **Sample Response; miles per hour; It is more common to measure speed in miles per hour.**

11. **Sample Response: The unit price given for cinnamon is $0.99 per ounce. What is the cost of 6 oz? Answer: $5.94**

The modern game of *footbag* is based on an old Native American game. The game involves keeping a small stuffed cloth bag in the air by kicking it with your foot. ▼

7. **Sample Response: A person must consume about 80 fluid oz of water per day in order to survive.**

8. **Sample Response: The three-toed sloth moves along the ground at an average speed of about 6 ft/min; it is easier to visualize 6 feet than 0.07 mile.**

10. **Sample Response: The Taylor family drove on interstate highways at a rate of 55 mi/hr for 8 hr. How many miles did they travel? Answer: 440 mi**

ADDITIONAL PRACTICE
See the *Teacher's Resource Book* for additional practice and application exercises for this section.

ABOUT PRACTICE & APPLICATIONS
The questions in the *Practice and Applications* exercises range from skill to application and open-ended to single answer. A wide variety of topics are covered, and students may explore how the content relates to other areas of mathematics or other subject areas. The exercises can be used to assess how well students comprehend the content. See the section planner page that appears in the *Teacher's Edition* before each module for a list of exercises that can be used as embedded assessment. (For Module 1, Section 1, see page 1C.)

EXERCISE NOTES
In **Exercise 2** on page 10, the form of student responses may vary. They may express the unit rate as 0.5 lb/dollar or $2/lb.

Exercises 10–11 Encourage students to be creative in writing situations for the calculations. Looking back at the situations in Exploration 1 may give them some ideas and help them write interesting problems.

Exercise 17 Students with limited fine motor dexterity may be allowed to use a computer program to construct the graph. You may also have a circle template available for the student so only the sectors need to be constructed.

COMMON ERROR
Exercises 18–19 Students may think the percents shown in the graph are not correct. Tell them to assume the percents are correct but the graph is not.

18. The sizes of the sectors do not correspond to the percents they represent.

19. The sum of the percents is only 90%.

For Exercises 14–16, use the circle graph below.

Cost of Computer Joysticks

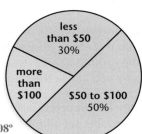

14. What percent of computer joysticks cost more than $100? How do you know?
 20%; 100% − (30% + 50%) = 20%

15. Ten joysticks were reviewed. How many cost $100 or less? 8

16. Without measuring, give the angle measure of the sector for joysticks that cost less than $50. 108°

17. **Social Studies** The gross domestic product (GDP) of a country is the total market value of all the goods and services produced by the country in a given year. For each country in the table, draw a circle graph that shows the sources of the country's GDP in 2004.
See margin.

Source of GDP in 2004 (in billions of U.S. dollars)			
Country	Agriculture	Industry	Services
a. China	1,000	3,842	2,418
b. India	783	883	1,682
c. Pakistan	78	84	185

Tell what is wrong with each circle graph.

18. **Favorite Subject**

other 12% | English 28% | science 15% | history 26% | math 19%

19. **Favorite Color**

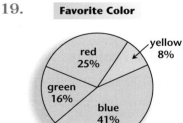

red 25% | yellow 8% | green 16% | blue 41%

17. See Additional Answers beginning on page A1.

Psychology In 1978, D. H. Foster performed an experiment to see how people process visual patterns. Participants were shown 96 pairs of patterns like those at the left. They were asked if the two patterns contained the same number of dots. The numbers of correct responses from the 24 participants are given below.

> 55, 60, 58, 50, 57, 59, 61, 59, 65, 58, 49, 63,
> 54, 55, 56, 48, 50, 62, 66, 55, 51, 54, 62, 61

20. a. Using intervals of 2, make a frequency table of the data. The first interval should be 48–49, then 50–51, and so on. See margin.
b. Draw a histogram of the data using the intervals of 2 from your table in part (a). See margin.

21. Draw a histogram of the data using intervals of 5. See margin.

22. a. Explain how you can draw a histogram with intervals of 10 using only the histogram from Exercise 20.

b. Explain how you can draw a histogram with intervals of 10 using only the histogram from Exercise 21.

c. Open-ended Use one of the methods you described in parts (a) and (b) to draw a histogram with intervals of 10. See margin.

23. Writing Explain why you cannot use the histogram from Exercise 20 to draw the histogram from Exercise 21. See margin.

Reflecting ◀▶ on the Section

Be prepared to discuss your response to Exercise 24 in class.

24. Suppose you are writing an article for a science magazine and need to describe the distance from Earth to Mars. Look up the distance from Earth to Mars. To make this fact as interesting as possible, you may want to compare the distance to Mars to distances that are familiar to most people. **Sample Response: The distance from Earth to Mars is 35,000,000 mi, which is equivalent to about 6000 round-trip flights across the United States.**

Spiral ◀▶ Review

25. Find the mean, median, mode(s), and range of the ice skater's competition scores shown below. (Toolbox, p. 596)

> 10, 10, 9.8, 9.8, 10, 9.9, 9.7, 9.8, 9.6
> mean: about 9.84, median: 9.8, modes: 9.8 and 10; range: 0.4

Write each percent as a fraction in lowest terms. (Toolbox, p. 588)

26. 40% $\frac{2}{5}$ **27.** 80% $\frac{4}{5}$ **28.** 20% $\frac{1}{5}$ **29.** 35% $\frac{7}{20}$

▲ Without counting, can you tell which card shows two patterns with the same number of dots?

22. a. Use the intervals 40-49, 50-59, and 60-69. To find the frequency within each interval, add the frequencies of the intervals from Exercise 20 that fall within the range of the new intervals.

RESEARCH

Exercise 24 checks that you can use rates.

22. b. Use the intervals 40-49, 50-59, and 60-69. To find the frequency within each interval, add the frequencies of the intervals from Exercise 21 that fall within the range of the new intervals.

Extra Skill Practice

About Extra Skill Practice

The first part of the *Extra Skill Practice* reinforces the concepts students investigated in the section. The exercises are usually skill-based, but sometimes are application-based. The last part of the page usually provides *Standardized Testing* questions relating to the section content. Sometimes an important study skill is presented.

Teacher Notes

For each Exploration, the corresponding Extra Skills Practice Exercises are noted.

Exploration 1: Exs. 1–2
Exploration 2: Exs. 3–7

Extra Help

Teacher's Resource Book
- Practice and Applications
- Study Guide

Technology Resources
- @Home Tutor
- Test Generator

Assessment

- Section 1 Quick Quiz
- Test Generator

6. See Additional Answers beginning on page A1.

Section 1 Extra Skill Practice

You will need: • *compass* (Ex. 7) • *protractor* (Ex. 7)

Tell whether the given rates are equivalent.
You may need to use the Table of Measures on page 601.

1. \$365,000/year; \$100/day
   not equivalent
2. 15 gal/min; 2 pt/sec
   equivalent

For Exercises 3–5, use the circle graph at the right.

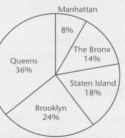

Calorie Sources

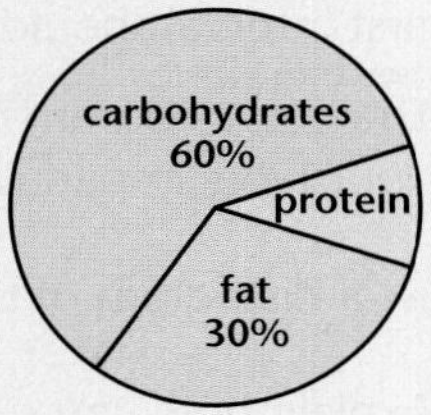

3. What percent of calories should come from protein? How do you know? 10%; The circle graph represents 100%; 100% – (60% + 30%) = 10%
4. Without measuring, give the angle measure of the sector that represents fat. How did you get your answer?
   108°; 30% of 360° = 108°
5. John takes in about 2000 calories each day. How many of these calories should come from carbohydrates? 1200 Cal
6. The record low temperatures (in °F) for each month in Phoenix, Arizona, are 17, 22, 25, 32, 70, 50, 61, 60, 47, 34, 25, and 22. Draw a histogram of the data using intervals of 10.
   See margin.
7. Draw a circle graph that compares the areas of the five boroughs of New York City.

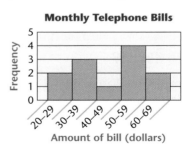

Borough	Area
Manhattan	23 mi²
The Bronx	41 mi²
Staten Island	56 mi²
Brooklyn	73 mi²
Queens	110 mi²

Standardized Testing ▶ Multiple Choice

The histogram shows a person's monthly telephone bills for one year.

Monthly Telephone Bills

1. Which interval contains the greatest frequency of the data? C
   - (A) \$30–\$39
   - (B) \$40–\$49
   - (C) \$50–\$59
   - (D) \$60–\$69
2. How many bills are for at least \$40? B
   - (A) 6
   - (B) 7
   - (C) 10
   - (D) 12

Section 2 Displaying Data

IN THIS SECTION

EXPLORATION 1
◆ Stem-and-Leaf Plots

EXPLORATION 2
◆ Box-and-Whisker Plots

EXPLORATION 3
◆ Choosing a Data Display

Amazing Musicians

Setting the Stage

How would you like to have a hit song at the age of 13? Stevie Wonder had a #1 hit single at only 13. He ranks in the top four of solo pop artists for 1955-1999.

How unusual is it for a musician to have a #1 single at age 13? One way to answer this question is to look at the ages of musicians when they had their first #1 single.

**Age of Top 20 Solo Pop Artists
When They Had Their First #1 Singles**

21, 25, 26, 13, 14, 29, 20, 25, 21, 20,
29, 22, 26, 18, 26, 29, 21, 31, 25, 21

▲
Stevie Wonder was 13 when his song *Fingertips Pt 2* made it to the #1 position on *Billboard's* Top 40 chart in July, 1963.

Think About It

1 For the data above, find each average.

   a. mean 23.1   **b.** median 23.5   **c.** mode 21

2 Which average do you think best represents the data? Explain.
See margin.

3 How do you think the data above would compare to data about musicians of this millennium? Why? See margin.

> **FOR ▶ HELP**
> with *mean, median, and mode,* see
> **TOOLBOX, p. 596**

In this section you will learn how to represent data in both *stem-and-leaf* and *box-and-whisker plots.* Then you will create different displays for musical accomplishments in the current decade.

Setting the Stage

ABOUT THE THEME

Music plays an important part in the lives of most middle school students. In this section, students will explore data about popular and country musicians as they improve their skills with stem-and-leaf plots, box-and-whisker plots, and scatter plots.

Because of the rapidly changing music industry, students will study record holders from the 20th century and early 21st century. In the Practice & Application Exercises, students will have the opportunity to create their own data display of popular musicians in the current decade. They may be surprised to find that few have been able to challenge the records set by less recent artists such as the Beatles and Elvis Presley.

GETTING STARTED

Module 1, Section 2 *Warm-Up* assesses student ability to order a set of values and to find the median.

Students should read the introduction and photo captions prior to discussing **Think About It Questions 1–3**. Ask students if they know the approximate age of any other musician when his/her first song was recorded.

TECHNOLOGY

For a related technology activity, see the *Technology Book.*

2., 3. See Additional Answers beginning on page A1.

Exploration 1

TEACHING NOTES

Point out to students that the stem-and-leaf plot shown is an *ordered* plot. Often stem-and-leaf plots are first constructed with the leaves recorded in the order they occur in the data list. Then the plot is rewritten to put the leaves in order. Remind students it is important always to have a title for a table or a graph. For a stem-and-leaf plot, students also need to include a legend or a key to illustrate what the numbers in the stems and leaves represent.

Note that in **Question 4(a)**, there is no way to distinguish which of the two leaves representing 20 is the one recorded for Mariah Carey's age, or which of the three leaves representing 26 is the one recorded for Prince's age.

LEARN HOW TO...
- make and use stem-and-leaf plots

AS YOU...
- analyze the ages of famous pop and country musicians

KEY TERMS
- stem-and-leaf plot
- stem
- leaf

Exploration 1

STEM and LEAF Plots

▶ One way to organize data is in a **stem-and-leaf plot**. The stem-and-leaf plot below shows the ages of the top 20 solo pop musicians when they had their first #1 singles. These musicians were rated as the top artists from 1955 to 1999.

Ages of Top 20 Solo Pop Artists When They Had Their First #1 Singles

```
1 | 3 4 8
2 | 0 0 1 1 1 1 2 5 5 5 6 6 6 9 9 9
3 | 1
```

The **leaves** are written in order from least to greatest.

Each **stem** represents a tens digit.

1 | 3 represents the data item 13.

4. a. Observe students or ask them to show you how they found the ages.

4 a. The table at the right lists the names and ages of three musicians from the stem-and-leaf plot. Find their ages in the plot.

Pop Artist	Age
Elton John	25
Prince	26
Ricky Nelson	18

b. Mariah Carey's age is listed right after Ricky Nelson's. Find Mariah's age at her first #1 single. **20**

c. Of the artists in the plot, Billy Joel was the oldest when he had his first #1 single. How old was he when he had his first #1 hit? **31**

5 Try This as a Class Use the stem-and-leaf plot above.

a. How were the numbers for the stems chosen? The stems are the tens digits of the numbers in the data set.

b. How were the numbers for the leaves chosen? The leaves are the ones digits of the numbers in the data set.

FOR ▶ HELP
with *range*, see
TOOLBOX, p. 596

c. Find the range of the data in the stem-and-leaf plot. 18

d. Which averages (mean, median, and mode) can be found easily using the stem-and-leaf plot? Explain. Median, because the numbers are already in order from least to greatest, and mode because the numbers that are the same are placed together in the plot.

▶ **Comparing Data** You can use back-to-back stem-and-leaf plots to compare two sets of data.

EXAMPLE

The back-to-back stem-and-leaf plot below compares the ages when the top 10 solo pop musicians of the 1950s and the top 10 of the 1980s had their first #1 record.

Age at First #1 Hit Single for Top 10 Musicians

of the 1950s		of the 1980s
	0	
8 5	1	4
6 4 1 1 1 1	2	1 5 6 6
9	3	0 1 2 3 5
5	4	

5 | 4 | represents
an age of 45.

| 3 | 2 represents
an age of 32.

6 Discussion Use the example above.

  a. How old was the youngest musician in the 1950s? in the 1980s?
  15; 14

  b. How do the oldest musicians' ages in each decade compare?

  c. Based on the plot, what statements could you make to compare the ages of the musicians in the 1950s to those in the 1980s?

7 The ages of the top 20 solo country artists of the 1900s when they had their first #1 records are 28, 27, 24, 34, 29, 30, 24, 30, 30, 42, 33, 36, 27, 28, 21, 28, 30, 31, 32, 27.

Make a back-to-back stem-and-leaf plot of the ages of the top 20 country artists and the ages of the top 20 pop artists on page 15. (Be sure to put the same amount of space between the leaves.)
See margin.

8 ✔ **CHECKPOINT** Use the back-to-back stem-and-leaf plot you created in Question 7.

  a. What does the plot tell you about the two groups of musicians?
  See margin.

  b. Compare the ranges of the two sets of data. What do the ranges tell you about the ages of the two groups of musicians?
  See margin.

  c. One artist, Linda Ronstadt, had her first #1 pop hit and her first #1 country hit when she was 28. Is this age unusual for pop musicians? for country musicians? Explain. Yes, No; Her age is near the high end for pop artists and near the middle for country artists.

HOMEWORK EXERCISES ▶ See Exs. 1–2 on p. 24.

6. b. The oldest musician listed for the 50s was 10 years older than the oldest musician listed for the 80s. (45, 35)

c. Most of the musicians listed for the 1980s were in their 20s and 30s when they had their first #1 single with a fairly even distribution among those two groups. With the exception of two musicians, the musicians of the 1950s were all 26 years old or younger when they had their first #1 single, and more than half were 21 or younger (only two during the 1980s were 21 or younger).

✔ **QUESTION 8**

...checks that you can interpret stem-and-leaf plots.

Several key terms are introduced in the box-and-whisker plot in **Question 9**. After students complete Question 9, review all the new vocabulary, asking students to describe each term in their own words. Students will be expected to understand these terms which are used in the instructions for constructing their own box-and-whisker plots. Later in the section they will be asked to describe the plots using these vocabulary terms.

DEVELOPING MATH CONCEPTS
Students should recognize that individual data values can be found in the stem-and-leaf plot, however, the box-and-whisker plot shows only a range and distribution of data values.

GOAL

LEARN HOW TO...
◆ use box-and-whisker plots to analyze and compare data

AS YOU...
◆ investigate the achievements of famous musicians

KEY TERMS
◆ box-and-whisker plot
◆ lower extreme
◆ upper extreme
◆ lower quartile
◆ upper quartile

Exploration 2
BOX and WHISKER Plots

SET UP *You will need Labsheets 2A and 2B.*

▶ Age is only one way that artists may be deemed amazing. Another way is to examine how many of their songs were popular. The stem-and-leaf plot and the **box-and-whisker plot** below both show the number of Top 40 singles each of the top 25 artists of the 1960s had during that decade.

Number of Top 40 Singles Each Artist Had from 1960–1969

During the 60s, two artists stood out among the top 25 of the decade, Elvis Presley who produced 51 Top 40 hits and the Beatles who produced 44.

```
1 | 7 7 7 7 8 8 8 9
2 | 0 1 2 2 3 4 5 5 5 6 7 7 7 7 9
3 |
4 | 4
5 | 1
```

2 | 1 means 21 Top 40 singles.

Number of Top 40 Singles Each Artist Had from 1960–1969

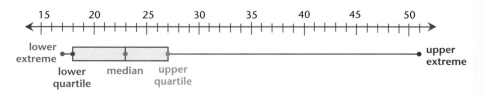

9 **a.** Find the least and greatest data items in the stem-and-leaf plot. How are these shown in the box-and-whisker plot and what are they called? least 17; greatest 51. Each of these points appears as a point at the end of each whisker and are labeled lower extreme and upper extreme.
b. Use the stem-and-leaf plot to find the median of the data. How does the box-and-whisker plot show the median? 23, it is marked by a point with a vertical line passing through it inside the rectangular box.

10 Use the box-and-whisker plot on page 18.

    a. The upper whisker extends from 27 to 51. What are possible values in the lower whisker? *17 or 18*

    b. About what fraction of the data lies in the box between the lower and upper quartiles? What percent is this? $\frac{1}{2}$, *50%*

▶ **The steps for constructing a box-and-whisker plot are given below. You will use them to construct a box-and-whisker plot of the number of Top 40 hits each of the top 25 artists of the 90s had during that decade.**

Creating a Box-and-Whisker Plot

The **upper quartile** is the median of the data values that occur after the median in an ordered list.

Step 1 Put the data in order from least to greatest.

Step 2 Find the upper and lower extremes of the data.

Step 3 Find the median.

Step 4 Find the lower quartile and the upper quartile.

Step 5 Plot the lower extreme, lower quartile, median, upper quartile, and upper extreme below a number line. Use these values to draw the box and the whiskers.

Use Labsheet 2A for Questions 11–14.

11 **Discussion** Use the *Top 40 Hits Stem-and-Leaf Plot* on the Labsheet to answer the following questions.

    a. How do you calculate the lower quartile?

    b. What differences do you notice between the data for the 1960s and the data for the 1990s? *Sample Response: The data values for the 1960s seem to be much greater than those for the 1990s.*

    c. How do you think the differences you noticed in part (b) will be represented in the box-and-whisker plots? *The upper extreme for the 1990s will not be as great and the upper whisker might be shorter.*

12 **Try This as a Class** Use the steps for creating a box-and-whisker plot and the instructions on the Labsheet to complete the *Top 40 Hits Box-and-Whisker Plots*. *See margin.*

11. a. Arrange the data in order from least to greatest. Find the median, then find the median of only those data values that occur between the lowest value and the median in the ordered list. This value is the lower quartile.

Exploration 2, *continued*

TIPS FROM TEACHERS
Graph paper is helpful in making box-and-whisker plots.

TEACHING NOTES
Remind students that organizing the data in stem-and-leaf plots (or one back-to-back stem-and-leaf plot) or organized lists will help in locating the extremes, quartiles, and median necessary for constructing the plots.

TIPS FROM TEACHERS
You may find it helpful to make an overhead of the labsheet to project while going through the steps with students.

14. Answers will vary. Sample Response: The musicians of the 1960s far outshine those of the 1990s when it comes to number of Top 40 Hits they had. All of the musicians during the 60s had more Top 40 Hits than $\frac{3}{4}$ of the musicians of the 90s. Over 25% of the musicians during the 1960s surpass the top musician of the 1990s. You can see this by looking at the upper extreme of the 90s and the upper whisker of the 60s. Plus the extreme of the 60s (51) Top 40 singles is about double of the extreme of the 90s (26).

15. a. See Additional Answers beginning on page A1.

---

13. a. 25% in each whisker, 25% in the box below the median, 25% in the box above the median, and a total of 50% in the entire box.

✔ QUESTION 14

...checks that you can use box-and-whisker plots to compare data sets.

13. c. For the 1960s the middle 50% of the range of the data was fairly evenly divided between the lower and upper portions of the box, but for the 1990s the range of the data in the lower portion of the box is very small. Since 25% of the data falls between 9 and 10, the values are all very close.

---

13 **Discussion** The box-and-whisker plot is divided into four regions. Each of these regions represents about the same number of data items.

  a. About what percent of the data fall into each region of the box-and-whisker plot?

  b. Why is the upper whisker longer than the upper portion of the box? **The data values in the upper whisker are more spread apart and have a greater range than the ones in the upper portion of the box.**

  c. Consider the two box-and-whisker plots. For the 1960s the median lies close to the center of the box, but for the 1990s it does not. Explain what this means about the two sets of data.

14 **✔ CHECKPOINT** Which group of musicians do you think is more amazing? Use the box-and-whisker plots from the Labsheet to support your choice. *See margin.*

▶ **Comparing Data** As you have seen, a box-and-whisker plot can stand alone to report data or be used with other box-and-whisker plots on the same number line to compare data.

15 **Use Labsheet 2B.** Box-and-whisker plots can be used to compare other musicians of the 1960s to those of the 1990s.

  a. Follow the directions on Labsheet 2B. *See margin.*

  b. Use the plots from part (a) to write a short article about how the winners of the 1960s and 1990s compare. *Answers will vary. Check students' work.*

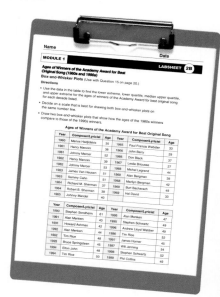

HOMEWORK EXERCISES ▶ See Exs. 3–12 on pp. 25–28.

Exploration 3

Choosing a Data Display

At age 14, Rachel Barton was the first American, and the youngest artist ever, to win the gold medal at the Quadrennial J.S. Bach International Violin Competition in Leipzig, Germany. Rachel is from Chicago, where at age 10, she performed with the Chicago Symphony. Because she was home schooled, Rachel had many hours to practice the violin.

Research has shown that practice can make the difference between good violinists and the best violinists. The displays below represent the number of hours per week different students might say they practice.

Weekly Hours of Practice

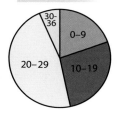

Weekly Hours of Practice

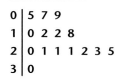

0	5 7 9
1	0 2 2 8
2	0 1 1 1 2 3 5
3	0

1 | 2 means 12 hours.

Weekly Hours of Practice

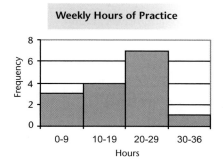

16 Which display best shows that almost half the students practice an average of 20–29 hours a week? **the circle graph**

17 a. How are the histogram and the stem-and-leaf plot alike?
Both show the frequencies of practice hours within intervals of 10.
b. How are they different?
The histogram does not show the individual practice hours.

18 Which display gives you the actual hours? **the stem-and-leaf plot**

19 Given the actual hours of practice, can you make a histogram different from the one above? a stem-and-leaf plot different from the one above? Explain. **Yes; You could make a histogram with different intervals. No; if using integer values for the stems, this is the only possible plot.**

Section 2   Displaying Data   **21**

Exploration 3

TEACHING NOTES

Question 19 The answer key states that it is not possible to make a different stem-and-leaf plot. Based on what students have learned, this is true. There are, however, conventions for constructing the plot with further intervals as shown below. You may decide to share this with students.

0	
•	5 7 9
1	0 2 2
•	8
2	0 1 1 1 1 2 3
•	5
3	0

1|2 is read 12
•|8 is read 18

Ask students in what situation it might be useful to have this information. (*When leaves get extremely long they can be divided into ranges, 0–4 and 5–9 for each stem. The repeated stem is indicated by •. Dividing the leaves is also useful in comparing the upper and lower half of each group of 10.*)

Exploration 3 *continued*

TEACHING NOTES

Question 20 Refer students to Section 1 where they saw how data can be used to give a false impression. Ask students what impressions they may get from the data on page 21. Then ask questions such as:

"Do you think the inferences you made are accurate?"

"Based on this data, would it be fair to say that a 12-year-old who practices an instrument 20 hours a week will be a better musician than someone who only practices 10 hours a week?"

"Could you infer from this data that someone who practices the same number of hours as a professional musician did at that age will grow to be a professional musician?"

"What other factors might affect an individual's future success as a musician?"

DEVELOPING MATH CONCEPTS

Question 25 Students may be led to recognize key words that help determine the type of display to use. Ask, "What word in **part (a)** gives you a clue as to the type of graph you may want to create? (*compare*)

"In **part (b)**, asking for the median eliminates what kinds of graphs?" (*circle graph, scatter plot, bar graph*)

You might have students discuss in groups the word or words in **parts (c–e)** that cue them to the type of graph(s) they might consider using. (*part c, key word relationship - scatter plot; part d, key word percentage - circle graph; part e, key words show that four - bar graph or stem-and-leaf plot.*)

22. See Additional Answers beginning on page A1.

---

20. Sample Response: whether students are female or male, the ages of the students, whether those who practice more are enrolled in special music schools, whether the amount of practice affects their performance.

21. median = 20, lower extreme = 5, upper extreme = 30, lower quartile = 10, upper quartile = 22, range = 25

---

20 What information might you want that the displays do not give?

21 Use the box-and-whisker plot below to find the median, the quartiles, the extremes, and the range of the data.

Weekly Hours of Practice

22 Can you find the information in Question 21 using each data display? Explain. **a–c. See margin.**

  a. circle graph   **b.** stem-and-leaf plot   **c.** histogram

23 **Discussion** What information can you estimate quickly from the circle graph, stem-and-leaf plot, or histogram that the box-and-whisker plot does not show? Sample Response: You can see which interval of hours (20-29) is most common for music students to practice in a week, and you can compare that to the other intervals of weekly hours of practice.

▶ The data displays you have seen so far display singular numerical data. *Scatter plots* like the one shown below display *paired* numerical data. You will learn more about scatter plots in Section 4 of this module.

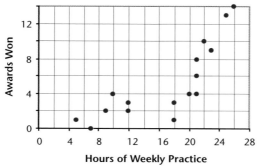

Hours of Practice and Awards Won

24 What does the data point (20, 4) on the scatter plot represent? a musician who practiced 20 hours per week and won 4 awards.

25 ✔ **CHECKPOINT** Use the Student Resource on page 597. Tell which type of display would best do each of the following.

  a. Compare the ages at which artists began playing a musical instrument. table or stem-and-leaf

  b. Give the median age at first performance in Carnegie Hall. box-and-whisker plot

  c. Show the number of Grammys earned and the yearly income for various musicians. scatter plot

  d. Show the percentage of artists who had only one hit this year. circle graph

  e. Show that four musicians made the cover of *Rolling Stone Magazine* at age 18. stem-and-leaf plot

✔ **QUESTION 25**

...checks that you understand when to use different types of displays.

HOMEWORK EXERCISES ▶ See Exs. 13–18 on pp. 28–29.

Section 2
Key Concepts

Stem-and-Leaf Plots (pp. 16–17)

A stem-and-leaf plot displays data in an organized format. The data items are usually ordered from least to greatest.

John Lennon's Top 40 Singles:
Highest Position Reached on the Top 40 Charts

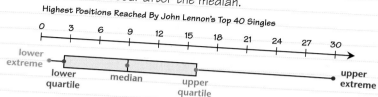

stem

```
0 | 1 1 2 3 3 5 9
1 | 0 1 4 8          leaf
2 | 0
3 | 0
```

1|8 represents #18 on the Top 40 chart.

Box-and-Whisker Plots (pp. 18–20)

A box-and-whisker plot shows how data are distributed by dividing the data into 4 groups. Each group contains about 25% of the data items. The lower quartile is the median of the data values that occur before the median in an ordered list. The upper quartile is the median of the data values that occur after the median.

Highest Positions Reached By John Lennon's Top 40 Singles

```
0   3   6   9   12   15   18   21   24   27   30
```

lower extreme

lower quartile   median   upper quartile   upper extreme

Choosing a Display (pp. 21–22)

You can use bar graphs, histograms, box-and-whisker plots, stem-and-leaf plots, scatter plots, line graphs, and circle graphs to display data. When deciding what type of display to use, consider the type and number of data sets you have as well as what aspect of the data you want to emphasize.

Key Terms

stem-and-leaf plot

stem

leaf

box-and-whisker plot

lower extreme
upper extreme
lower quartile
upper quartile

26 Key Concepts Question   Use the displays above.

a. How many #1 singles did John Lennon have? Which display doesn't give you this information?
two #1 singles; the box-and-whisker plot

b. Which display(s) can you use to find the mean of the data? the median? the modes? Find each of these averages.

c. About what percent of John Lennon's Top 40 singles made it to the 16th through 30th positions of the charts? 25%

d. What other displays would be appropriate for reporting the given data about John Lennon's music?

26. b. stem-and-leaf
plot; both; stem-
and-leaf plot;
mean = about
9.8, median = 9,
modes = 1 and 3

d. A histogram or
possibly a circle
graph divided
into sectors that
represent percent
of Top 40 singles
that reached
positions 1-10,
11-20, 21-30,
31-40. Neither
a line graph
nor a scatter
plot would be
appropriate.

Key Concepts

ABSENT STUDENTS

For students who were absent for part or all of this section, the blackline Study Guide for Section 2 may be used to present the ideas, concepts and skills of Section 2.

CLOSURE QUESTION

Explain how you would choose a display to represent data values.

Sample Response: I would first decide what values or aspects of the data I want to emphasize. Then I would select a type of display that best illustrates those values.

Practice & Applications

SUGGESTED ASSIGNMENTS

Core Course
Day 1: Exs. 1–2, 19–29
Day 2: Exs. 3, 4, 7–11
Day 3: Exs. 13–15, 17, 18, 30–32

Extended Course
Day 1: Exs. 1–2, 19–29
Day 2: Exs. 4–6, 10–12
Day 3: Exs. 13–18, 30–32

Note: Extended Course assignments can be used to differentiate within the regular classroom. In classrooms where students are grouped homogeneously, the material might be covered in fewer days. In this case assignments may be combined.

ADDITIONAL PRACTICE

See the *Teacher's Resource Book* for additional practice and application exercises for this section.

1. a. See Additional Answers beginning on page A1.

1. b. Sample Response: Ages of country winners are much more spread out than pop winners, although the greatest numbers of winners for both pop and country are in their 30s.

2. a. Country:
mean $\approx$ 37.7,
median = 33.5,
mode = 33,
Pop:
mean $\approx$ 28.6,
median = 30,
modes = 23, 30

c. It lowers the mean slightly since her age is 10 years less than the next youngest female artist. The mean of the other artists' ages without LeAnn is about 39.8, but with her age included the mean is 37.7.

Section ② Practice & Application Exercises

1. The table lists the Grammy Award winners for best female vocal performance for both country music and pop music from 1995–2006. The table also shows the artists' ages when they received the award.

Age when Awarded Grammy for Best Female Vocal Performance				
Year Awarded	**Country**		**Pop**	
	Name	**Age**	**Name**	**Age**
1995	Mary Chapin Carpenter	37	Sheryl Crow	33
1996	Alison Krauss	24	Annie Lennox	41
1997	LeAnn Rimes	14	Toni Braxton	30
1998	Trisha Yearwood	33	Sarah McLachlan	30
1999	Shania Twain	33	Celine Dion	30
2000	Shania Twain	34	Sarah McLachlan	32
2001	Faith Hill	33	Macy Gray	30
2002	Dolly Parton	56	Nelly Furtado	23
2003	Faith Hill	35	Norah Jones	23
2004	June Carter Cash	74	Christina Aguilera	23
2005	Gretchen Wilson	31	Norah Jones	25
2006	Emmylou Harris	48	Kelly Clarkson	23

a. Use the data to make a back-to-back stem-and-leaf plot that compares the ages by type of music. **See margin.**

b. Compare the shapes of the two stem-and-leaf plots. What do the shapes tell you about the ages of the best female vocal performance Grammy winners for country music and pop music?

2. a. Find the mean, the median, and the mode for each data set.

b. How does LeAnn's age compare with the ages of the other country winners? **She is younger than all the rest, and is not representative of the median, mean or mode of female ages.**

c. How does LeAnn's age affect the mean for the country winners?

d. Which average from part (a) do you think best represents each data set? Explain your thinking. **Sample Response: All three values are reasonable representations of the data for either group.**

24

The table shows history test scores for two classes. The data were used to make the box-and-whisker plots. Use the table and the box-and-whisker plots for Exercises 3–6.

History Test Scores			
Class A		Class B	
66	100	78	64
54	90	76	77
68	72	87	93
86	64	45	47
100	59	78	80
59	100	76	76
68	84	90	100
85	100	45	83

History Test Scores

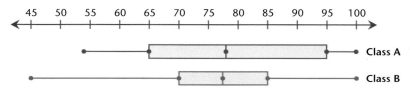

3. For each box-and-whisker plot, find the values below.

   a. the lower extreme
   Class A: 54, Class B: 45
   b. the upper extreme
   Class A: 100, Class B: 100
   c. the lower quartile
   Class A: 65, Class B: 70
   d. the upper quartile
   Class A: 95, Class B: 85

4. a. **Writing** Explain how to use the box-and-whisker plots to compare the median test scores for the two classes.

   b. Find the mean test score for each class. Which class had at least 50% of its test scores greater than its mean?
   Class A: about 78.4; Class B: about 74.7; Class B

5. **Challenge** Diana says that you can tell from looking at the box-and-whisker plots that the mean test score for class A is higher than the mean test score for class B. Do you agree? Explain.

6. a. About what percent of each class's test scores are included in the box portion of each box-and-whisker plot?   50%

   b. What do the sizes of the box portions tell you about the test scores for each class?

EXERCISE NOTES

For **Exercise 5**, students may need help in understanding that you cannot predict where the mean will be located in a box-and-whisker plot. Remind them that extreme values pull the mean away from the median. For example, for the data set 1, 12, 12, 13, 14, 15, 16 the mean is 12, which is the same as the first quartile.

4. a. Sample Response: Find the median for each plot. The one that is drawn farther to the right is greater.

5. Sample Response: No; Box-and-whisker plots do not show the mean because they do not show all the numbers in the data set or how many times each number occurs.

6. b. The size of the box portion shows the range of the middle 50% of the data. Class A had a larger range of scores among the middle half of its students than did Class B.

Practice & Applications

EXERCISE NOTES

In **Exercise 7**, remind students that in this box-and-whisker plot, a lower number is more desirable on the Top 40 charts, since a #1 single is at the top of the chart and a #40 is at the bottom.

In discussing **Exercise 8**, ask students to explain how the lower quartile for the Beatles can be a decimal number when hits can only stay at #1 for a whole number of weeks, such as 1, 2, 3,... weeks. Students should realize that the values of LQ, UQ, and median are not always a value from the data, but instead can be the mean of two data values.

9. a. These are the data values that range from the line inside the box (the median) to the end of the upper whisker (the upper extreme).

   b. Answers will vary. Sample Response: Elvis because more than $\frac{1}{2}$ of his hits stayed at #1 for 4 or more weeks, whereas the Beatles had less than 25% of their #1 hits stay for 4 weeks or longer. The median is greater for Elvis, and for the Beatles, the median is equal to Elvis's lower quartile value showing that only about 50% of the Beatles' hits were at #1 for 2 weeks or more while about 75% of Elvis's hits were at #1 for 2 weeks or more.

7. a. lower extreme = 1, upper extreme = 40; the range of the data. You know Elvis had at least one hit make it to #1 and at least one make it only to #40 on the charts.

---

7. Elvis Presley had 104 singles make the Top 40 charts. The box-and-whisker plot below shows data about the highest position reached on the Top 40 charts by those singles.

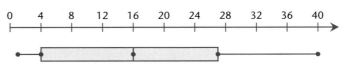

Highest Positions Reached By Elvis Presley's 104 Top 40 Singles

   a. Identify the lower extreme and the upper extreme. What information do these values give you about the data?

   b. Find the median of the data. **16**

   c. About what percent of Elvis Presley's Top 40 singles reached positions 1 though 16? **about 50%**

8. Use the box-and-whisker plots below.

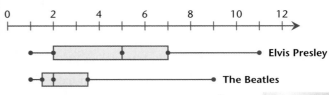

Number of Weeks at the #1 Position on the Chart

Elvis Presley

The Beatles

> The Beatles hit "Hey Jude" stayed #1 for 9 weeks.

   a. What is the range for each data set?
   Presley: 10; Beatles: 8

   b. About what percent of the Beatles' #1 hit singles stayed at the #1 position for two weeks or less?
   about 50%

   c. About what percent of Elvis Presley's #1 hit singles stayed at the #1 position for two weeks or less? **about 25%**

   d. For each set of data, about what percent of the data items are represented by the box portion of the box-and-whisker plot?
   about 50%

   e. Why are the sizes of the boxes different?
   The ranges of the data within the middle 50% of the data vary.

9. a. About 50% of Elvis Presley's #1 hit singles stayed at the #1 position for 5 to 11 weeks. About 50% of the Beatles' #1 hits stayed at the #1 position for 2 or more weeks. How do the box-and-whisker plots above show this information? **See margin.**

   b. Who do you think is more amazing, Elvis Presley or the Beatles? Use the box-and-whisker plots above to support your choice. **See margin.**

10. By the end of the 1900s Mariah Carey ranked #3 to the Beatles and Elvis Presley in most #1 singles.

    a. Using the clues below, sketch a box-and-whisker plot to represent the number of weeks Mariah Carey's hits held on to the #1 position. **See margin.**

- All but one of her songs remained in the #1 position for more than a week.
- 50% of the songs were hits for 3 weeks or longer.
- Her longest running hit, "One Sweet Day," sung with Boyz II Men topped the charts for 16 weeks.
- 5 of her 14 #1 hits stayed at #1 for 2 weeks.
- 25% of the hits remained at #1 for 4 weeks or longer.

    b. Compare your sketch to the box-and-whisker plots in Exercise 8. What part of the plot could you use to convince someone that Mariah Carey is more amazing than the Beatles or Elvis Presley?

11. a. Use the data in the table below to construct a box-and-whisker plot of the number of times a composer's work was performed by American orchestras during the 2005–2006 season. **See margin.**

Number of Times a Composer's Work Was Performed by American Orchestras			
Name (year of birth)	Performances	Name (year of birth)	Performances
Handel (1685)	163	Mahler (1860)	226
Bach (1685)	201	Strauss (1864)	325
Haydn (1737)	249	Sibelius (1865)	251
Mozart (1756)	1453	Rachmaninoff (1873)	270
Beethoven (1770)	948	Ravel (1875)	277
Mendelssohn (1809)	220	Bartok (1881)	161
Schumann (1819)	196	Stravinsky (1881)	227
Brahms (1883)	495	Prokofiev (1891)	248
Tchaikovsky (1840)	581	Copland (1900)	201
Dvorak (1841)	302	Shostakovich (1906)	314

    b. Use the same number line to create two more box-and-whisker plots for the data in the table: one for the composers born before 1850 and one for composers born after 1850. **See margin.**

    c. **Writing** Use the box-and-whisker plots along with related vocabulary such as extreme, quartile, percent, and median to write a summary comparing the data for the two groups. **See margin.**

10. b. The upper extreme shows that Mariah Carey had a single that stayed at #1 longer than any of the singles of Elvis Presley or the Beatles.

Exercise Notes

In **Exercise 10**, students should recognize that the statement "5 of her 14 #1 hits stayed at #1 for 2 weeks" represents about 36% of the data. Since there is a cluster of 2s, this data is divided between the lower whisker and the lower box rather than all falling in the same section of the graph.

11. c. The data show that during the 2005–2006 season, American orchestras tended to perform works by composers born before 1850 more often than they performed works by composers born after 1850. About 50% of the composers born before 1850 had their works performed about 275 times or more, while 75% of the composers born after 1850 had their works performed 277 times or less. The upper quartile and upper extreme for the composers born before 1850 are much greater than those for the composers born after 1850. The lower extreme, lower quartile, and median are similar for both plots.

10. a., 11. a–b. See Additional Answers beginning on page A1.

27

Practice & Applications

EXERCISE NOTES

Exercise 12 If students are having difficulty answering the question, suggest they make a set of data that fits the plot as well as the facts given. By doing this they will see that because there are so many 1s in the data, the lower extreme and lower quartile are both 1.

13. a. the number of grizzly bears sighted during each decade for the past 9 decades
    b. heights or weights of champion show horses
    c. how income is spent
    d. hours of sleep before a test and grade made on the exam

15. a. Sample Response: How many days during the month do you ride your bike? 0 to 7? 8 to 15? 16 to 23? 24 to 31?
    b. Sample Response: How often do you ride your bike? Never? Every day? A few times a week? A few times during the month?
    c. Data for a bar graph is given in categories. Data for a histogram is given in intervals.

12. **Challenge** The Beatles had 50 singles that made the Top 40 charts. Of these hit singles, 20 made it to the #1 position. How does this fact explain why there is no lower whisker on the box-and-whisker plot below?
The lower extreme and the lower quartile are the same.

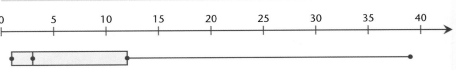

Highest Position Reached by the Beatles' Top 40 Singles

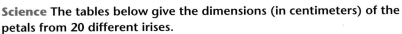

13. **Open-ended** Describe a data set that can be shown using the given type of display. **Sample Responses are given.**

    a. histogram
    b. stem-and-leaf plot
    c. circle graph
    d. scatter plot

Science The tables below give the dimensions (in centimeters) of the petals from 20 different irises.

Length	Width	Length	Width	Length	Width	Length	Width
4.7	1.4	4.5	1.3	3.5	1.0	4.4	1.4
4.5	1.5	4.7	1.6	4.2	1.5	4.5	1.5
4.9	1.5	3.3	1.0	4.0	1.0	4.1	1.0
4.0	1.3	4.6	1.3	4.7	1.4	4.5	1.5
4.6	1.5	3.9	1.4	3.6	1.3	3.9	1.1

14. For each statement below, make a display that shows the information specified. Tell why you chose that type of display.

    a. the number of irises whose petals are 4.0–4.1 cm long
    See margin.
    b. the percent of irises whose petals are 1.3 cm wide
    See margin.
    c. the median petal length compared to the median petal width
    See margin.

15. **Open-ended** Suppose you conduct a survey to find out how often people ride bicycles during the month of July. You decide to give sample responses for people to choose from.

    a. What are four sample responses you could give if you want to display your survey results in a histogram?

    b. What are four sample responses you could give if you want to display your survey results in a bar graph?

    c. Why must your sample responses for part (b) be different from your sample responses for part (a)?

14. See Additional Answers beginning on page A1.

16. Challenge

a. Given a stem-and-leaf plot of a data set, can you always make a box-and-whisker plot? Explain.

b. Given a box-and-whisker plot of a data set, can you always make a stem-and-leaf plot? Explain. No; Since individual data values are not shown in a box-and-whisker plot, it cannot be used to construct a stem-and-leaf plot.

17. Research
a–c. Check students' work.

a. Research data about musicians in the current decade.

b. Decide upon two different appropriate displays and use them to present the findings of your research.

c. Discuss an advantage that each display has over the other.

Reflecting ◀▶**on the Section**

Be prepared to discuss Exercise 18 in class.

18. Aretha Franklin is another amazing musician. During a career that spans five decades, she has won nearly twenty Grammy Awards and she is known as the "Queen of Soul." The stem-and-leaf plot below shows data about her singles that reached the top 40 on the U.S. Hot 100 chart as of 2007.

Highest Positions Reached by Aretha Franklin's Hits on the U.S. Hot 100 Chart

```
0 | 1 1 2 2 2 2 3 3 3 4 5 5 5 6 6 7 7 8 9 9
1 | 0 1 3 3 4 6 6 7 8 9 9 9
2 | 0 1 2 3 4 6 6 6 8 8 8
3 | 1 3 7 7
```

3|1 represents position number 31.

a. Suppose a box-and-whisker plot was constructed from the data above. What value would be the lower extreme? the upper extreme? the median?
1; 37; 13

b. Where would the data value 11 be on the box-and-whisker plot? For example, would it be on the lower whisker? It would be in the lower box.

c. Which whisker would be longer, the upper whisker or the lower whisker? Explain. upper whisker; The lower whisker runs from 1 to 5 and the upper whisker runs from 23 to 37.

d. Use the data to create another type of display. Describe the advantages this display has over the stem-and-leaf and box-and-whisker plots. Check students' work. Students may choose to create a histogram or circle graph.

16. a. Yes; Since individual data values are given in a stem-and-leaf plot, the extremes, quartiles, and median can be calculated using the plot.

Discussion

Exercise 18 checks that you can interpret stem-and-leaf plots and box-and-whisker plots.

Section 2 Displaying Data

EXERCISE NOTES
Exercise 17 Have current magazines, encyclopedia yearbooks, websites, or other resources available for students to use in locating this data.

Exercise 18 You might suggest that students divide the data into four equal parts before answering parts (a–d).

Practice & Applications

Exercise Notes

You may want to ask students what occupations require understanding the appropriate use of graphs to be successful. (*Responses may include: newspaper or magazine editor, financial advisor, store manager, research analyst.*)

Spiral ◀▶ Review

Copy and complete each equation.
(Module 1, p. 12; Table of Measures, p. 601)

19. 4.8 m/min = __?__ m/hr
    288

20. 55 mi/hr = __?__ mi/min
    about 0.92

21. 8 lb/ft² = __?__ lb/in.²
    about 0.06

22. $0.75 per day = $ __?__ per week
    $5.25

Test each number for divisibility by 2, 3, and 5. (Toolbox, p. 583)

23. 615
    3 and 5 only

24. 2189
    none

25. 41,852
    2 only

26. 111
    3 only

Replace each __?__ with > or <. (Toolbox, p. 590)

27. −6 __?__ −10
    >

28. 3 __?__ − 4
    >

29. −12 __?__ −22
    >

Career ▪ Connection

Career Counselor: Charles Cunningham

School counselors like Charles Cunningham may use a box-and-whisker plot to help you understand your score on a standardized test such as the SAT. A counselor can help you find where your score falls in comparison to the scores of the other students.

2006 SAT Mathematics Test Scores

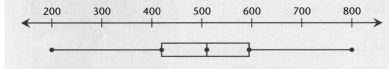

▲
Charles Cunningham helps students research college options.

30. Would a score of 550 qualify you for an honors program that requires you to score in the top 25% of those who took the exam? Explain.

31. Give three sample scores that would lie in the lower 50%.
    Sample Response: 230, 350, 490 (any score below the median which is about 510)

32. About what fraction of the data values are in the interval from 510 to 595? 25%

30. No; 550 is in the box between the median and the upper quartile. To be in the upper 25% of the data, the score would need to fall between the upper quartile and the upper extreme.

Section 2

Extra Skill Practice

Use the data in the table for Exercises 1 and 2.

1. a. Make a back-to-back stem-and-leaf plot for Best Actor and Best Actress ages. See margin.

   b. What do the shapes of the stem-and-leaf plots tell you about the ages of female award winners and male award winners? See margin.

   c. Find the mean, the median, and the mode(s) for each data set. Which average best represents each data set? Why? See margin.

Ages of Academy Award Winners, 1980–2003	
Best Actor ages	**Best Actress ages**
43, 26, 47, 36, 40, 46, 60, 45, 31, 38, 37, 52, 57, 42, 32, 54, 43, 61, 35, 45, 52, 39, 76, 37	28, 35, 33, 33, 25, 25, 34, 39, 49, 45, 35, 33, 29, 42, 80, 26, 41, 21, 61, 38, 49, 33, 74, 31

2. Using one number line, create two box-and-whisker plots to represent the data in the table. See margin.

3. Jessica Tandy was 80 years old when she received the Best Actress Award. How unusual is it for an 80-year-old actress to receive this award? Explain. Sample Response: Very unusual; Among the actors and actresses listed, she is the only person in her 80s to receive an academy award, and only 1 of 3 actresses over the age of 49.

Tell which type of display best does each of the following. Explain your thinking.

4. Shows the relationship between height and shoe size.
   scatter plot; A scatter plot shows a relationship between two sets of data.

5. Compares the populations of New York, Los Angeles, and Chicago.
   bar graph; A bar graph compares data items grouped into categories.

6. Shows that a company's profit has increased each year since 1992.
   line graph; A line graph shows how data values change over time.

7. Tells what percent of the United States population is self-employed.
   circle graph; A circle graph shows the division of a whole into parts.

Standardized Testing ◀▶ Multiple Choice

1. Tell which values *cannot* be found using a box-and-whisker plot. **D**

   Ⓐ range   Ⓑ extremes   Ⓒ median   Ⓓ mean

2. Tell which display does *not* indicate the range of a data set. **A**

   Ⓐ histogram   Ⓑ table

   Ⓒ stem-and-leaf plot   Ⓓ box-and-whisker plot

Section 2   Displaying Data   **31**

Extra Skill Practice

TEACHER NOTES

For each Exploration, the corresponding Extra Skill Practice Exercises are noted.

Exploration 1: Ex. 1
Exploration 2: Exs. 2–3
Exploration 3: Exs. 4–7

EXTRA HELP

Teacher's Resource Book
• Practice and Applications
• Study Guide

Technology Resources
• @Home Tutor
• Test Generator

ASSESSMENT
• Section 2 Quick Quiz
• Mid-Module Quiz
• Test Generator

1. b. With the exception of a few actresses, the actresses were mainly in their 20s, 30s or 40s when receiving an Academy Award. For men, the awards were earned at slightly older ages, mainly 30s, 40s and 50s. Only one actor was in his 20s as compared to six actresses.

1. a., 1. c., 2. See Additional Answers beginning on page A1.

31

ABOUT THE THEME

Rules of thumb are used in our daily lives as a means for easily estimating measurements. A seamstress may use a rule of thumb to estimate the number of yards of fabric needed for a piece of clothing, or a farmer may use a rule of thumb to estimate the yield of his wheat crop.

In this section students will use some "rules" to explore how a simple statement can be written as an equation that can be evaluated or solved to make an estimate.

GETTING STARTED

Module 1, Section 3 *Warm-Up* assesses students' facility with mental calculation using variables, and checks their ability to simplify expressions using order of operations. These skills will be developed throughout this section. Students who struggle with the *Warm-Up* may benefit from additional practice as the Section progresses.

Read the *Rules of Thumb* together as a class. Explain to the students that many rules of thumb are really informal equations, but they are different from exact relationships expressed by standard formulas or equations in that they are often based on an "average" standard of measure, such as an average adult height, or an average distance that will give a reasonable approximation or estimate. More rules of thumb can be found in several of Tom Parker's books, *Rules of Thumb, Rules of Thumb 2,* or on the internet.

Section ③ Equations and Expressions

Extraordinary Rules of Thumb

- - - *Setting the Stage*

Rules of thumb have been passed from one generation to the next for hundreds of years. These rules help people estimate things like the temperature outdoors. Many rules are about ordinary events, but they seem extraordinary because someone noticed patterns and made connections.

Rule 1

Your adult height will be twice your height at age 2.

Rule 2

You can tell how many miles you are from a thunderstorm by counting the seconds between the lightning and the thunder and dividing by five.

Rule 3

To estimate the temperature outdoors in degrees Fahrenheit, count the number of times one snowy tree cricket chirps in fifteen seconds and add thirty-nine.

Think About It

1 Suppose your height at age 2 years was 2 ft 10 in. How tall should you be as an adult? 5 ft 8 in.

2 How many miles are you from a thunderstorm if you count 25 sec between the lightning and the thunder? 5 mi

Exploration 1

Writing **E**=**quations**

SET UP *You will need Labsheet 3A.*

GOAL

LEARN HOW TO...
- write equations from words

AS YOU...
- investigate rules of thumb

KEY TERMS
- variable
- constant

▶ Many rules of thumb can be written as mathematical formulas or equations using *variables*. A **variable** is a symbol used to represent a quantity that is unknown or that can change. For example, the rule of thumb for finding your adult height from your height at age 2 can be represented as an equation.

EXAMPLE

Write an equation for predicting a person's height from his or her height at age 2.

First Choose a variable to represent each of the quantities that are unknown or may change.

Let c = height at age 2.   Let a = adult height.

Then Represent the word relationships with symbols and variables.

Your adult height is equal to twice your height at age 2.

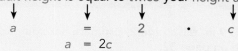

$$a \quad = \quad 2 \quad \cdot \quad c$$
$$a = 2c$$

3 **Discussion** Refer to the example above.

   a. Why is each height represented by a variable?
   These quantities will change for different people.
   b. How is *twice* represented?
   multiply by 2
   c. For any height, toddler or adult, what will always remain the same in the equation? the number 2

▶ Any quantity that does not change is a **constant**.

4 When buying the right size refrigerator for your family, one rule of thumb states that you need about 10 cubic feet of fresh food space for two people, plus 1 cubic foot for each additional family member.

   a. Which quantities in this rule are unknown or might change?
   number of family members, size of refrigerator needed
   b. Which quantities in this rule are constants? 10 cubic ft, 1 cubic ft

---

Exploration 1

TEACHING NOTES
Students should know that a variable can be denoted using any letter of the alphabet. Ask them why they think a "*c*" and "*a*" were used in the example. (*possible answer: A c was used for a child's height, and a for an adult's height because the letter association makes it easier to remember what each variable represents.*)

The example along with **Questions 3 and 4** are important in ensuring students understand how to identify the variables and constants when translating a word sentence into an equation. Following Question 3, you might ask what the equation $2a = c$ would represent using the description of the variables in the example.

Question 4 Encourage visual thinking and estimation by asking for the dimensions of a 10 cubic foot refrigerator. (Most refrigerator-freezers are more than 20 cubic feet in size.)

Exploration 1 continued

TIPS FROM TEACHERS

Make an overhead of **Labsheet 3A** for working **Question 6** as a class, asking students to come forward to underline variables, circle operations, etc.

TEACHING NOTES

Question 6 Help guide the students in the steps for translating the first 4 statements, and then allow them to complete the last two on their own before reviewing them as a class.

Checkpoint Question 7
Encourage students to use the steps practiced on Labsheet 3A to help them write each rule as an equation.

DEVELOPING MATH CONCEPTS

For the **Example**, point out to students that, for ease in calculation, 9 inches was converted to 0.75 ft $\left(\frac{9}{12} = 0.75\right)$ before multiplying. The answer, 5.5 ft, was then converted back to feet and inches to be consistent with the original question.

HOME INVOLVEMENT

Students are encouraged to find out the size of the refrigerator they have at home and use the formula in **Question 5** to determine whether the rule of thumb in Question 4 was used in making the purchase of their refrigerator. They might also want to determine how big their refrigerator would be if it was purchased based on this rule of thumb.

6. See Additional Answers beginning on page A1.

---

5. choice a: $r = 10 + 1f$; r = refrigerator size and f = number of additional family members.

✔ **QUESTION 7**

...checks that you can translate a word sentence into an equation.

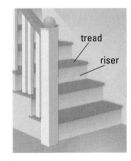

tread

riser

▲
The Council of American Building Officials recommends that risers be not more than $8\frac{1}{4}$ in. and treads not less than 9 in.

FOR ▶ HELP
with *order of operations*, see
TOOLBOX, p. 589

---

5 Which of the equations below can you use to represent the rule of thumb in Question 4? Explain your choice and what the variables r and f represent.

a. $r = 10 + 1 \cdot f$ **b.** $r = 10f$ **c.** $f + r = 10$ **d.** $r = 1 + 10f$

Use Labsheet 3A for Question 6.

6 Try This as A Class Follow the directions on the labsheet to practice translating various rules of thumb into equations. See margin.

7 ✔ CHECKPOINT Write an equation for each rule of thumb. Be sure to tell what each variable represents.

a. The highest price you should pay for a car you are buying with a car loan is one-half your annual salary.
$p = 0.5s$, where p is the highest price you should pay and s is your yearly salary
b. To estimate the surface area of your body, multiply the surface area of the palm of your hand by 50. $b = 50p$, where b is the surface area of your body and p is the surface area of your palm
c. A set of steps will be comfortable to use if two times the height of one riser plus the width of one tread is equal to 25 in.
$2h + w = 25$, where h is the height of the riser, and w is the width of one tread
d. Separate a calf from its mother when the calf has gained 15 lb over its birth weight. $w = b + 15$, where w is the weight at which a calf should be separated from its mother and b is the calf's weight at birth

▶ For an equation like $a = 2c$, you can find the value of a if you know the value of c.

EXAMPLE

Trinja was 2 ft 9 in. tall at age 2. Estimate her adult height using the rule of thumb on page 32.

SAMPLE RESPONSE

Write the rule of thumb as an equation.	$a = 2c$
	$= 2(2.75)$
	$= 5.5$

2 ft 9 in. = 2.75 ft
Substitute 2.75 for the variable c.

Trinja's adult height would be 5.5 ft, or 5 ft 6 in.

8 a. To find h, the equivalent human age for a 6-year-old dog, substitute 6 for d in the equation $h = 15 + 4d$. $h = 15 + 4(6)$

b. To evaluate $15 + 4d$ when $d = 6$, which operation is performed first, addition or multiplication? Why?
multiplication; order of operations is followed
c. What is the equivalent human age for a 6-year-old dog? 39 yr

d. What is the equivalent human age for an 11-year-old dog? 59 yr

9 ✓ **CHECKPOINT** **Use Labsheet 3A.** Use an equation from the Labsheet to estimate each quantity.

a. A pilot is at an altitude of 24,000 feet. How far from the landing point should the pilot begin to descend? *about 80 nautical miles*

b. The temperature is 15°C. What is it in degrees Fahrenheit? *about 60° F*

c. How many pounds of gravel should be in a 55 gallon aquarium? *about 82.5 lb*

HOMEWORK EXERCISES ▶ See Exs. 1–8 on pp. 44–45.

Exploration 2

Solving E=quations

10 a. Face one wall of your classroom directly and hold your thumb at arm's length. Focus on the wall. Now close one eye and open the other. Switch eyes and estimate how far left or right your thumb jumped along the wall.
Check as students perform estimations.

b. Multiply the estimated distance by 10. This is the approximate distance from you to the wall.
Answers will vary based on distance from the wall.

▶ This rule of thumb for estimating distances can be represented by the following equation.

Let *d* = the distance from you to the object.

Let *e* = the estimated distance that your thumb moved.

$$d = 10e$$

11 Discussion Suppose the distance from you to an object is 25 ft. How far should you expect your thumb to appear to move when you view it through one eye and then the other? *2.5 ft*

▶ When you answered Question 11, you *solved the equation* 25 = 10*e*. The value of a variable that makes an equation true is a **solution** of the equation. The process of finding solutions is called **solving an equation**.

GOAL

LEARN HOW TO...
◆ solve equations

AS YOU...
◆ work with rules of thumb

KEY TERMS
◆ solution
◆ solve an equation
◆ inverse operations

TEACHING NOTES
Checkpoint Question 9 Check to see that students first write the equation for the rule, then substitute the information from the statement, complete the indicated operations, and, finally, state the solution.

Exploration 2

TEACHING NOTES
Question 10 is a good self-starting activity for the students to do while the teacher is taking attendance. Students sitting nearby each other can compare their estimates. If the approximate distances students get in **part (b)** are too short, check that they focused their eyes on the background wall, not on their thumb. If they focus on their thumb, it will always jump the same amount, regardless of their distance to the wall because the length of their arm does not change.

Exploration 2 *continued*

TEACHING NOTES

Question 12 Point out to students that the equation $n = 15 - 6$ in folder 1 shows an unsimplified solution. This is done deliberately to help students answer part (c) for folders 3 and 4, where the operation is not as obvious as in folders 1 and 2. To help students see the connection, have them state the second equation in folder 1 more simply and then ask, "If the second equation in folders 3 and 4 had been written in an unsimplified form, how would they be written?" (*folder 3: $y = 21 + 7$; folder 4: $a = 6 \cdot 3$*)

Questions 14 and 15 Solving 1-step equations using inverse operations is treated as a quick review. This will accelerate the development of 2-step equations.

Remind students that an equation uses the "=" sign to show that both sides of the equation represent the same value. In order to maintain this equality, or "balance," an operation performed on one side of the equation must also be performed on the other side of the equation.

DIFFERENTIATED INSTRUCTION

For students who benefit from concrete models, algebra tiles may be used to model the equations.

EXTRA HELP

Students should feel comfortable solving 1-step equations before completing the remainder of this section. For those students who require additional practice with 1-step equations you can assign **Practice & Application Exercise 9 (a–f)** on page 45.

---

12 Try This as a Class Each folder contains a pair of equations.

1	2	3	4
$6 + n = 15$	$2w = 7$	$y - 7 = 21$	$\dfrac{a}{3} = 6$
$n = 15 - 6$	$w = \dfrac{7}{2}$	$y = 28$	$a = 18$

  a. Do the equations in each pair have the same solution? How do you know? **Yes; When the solution of the second equation on each card is substituted in the first equation, it makes the equation true.**

  b. Which operation (addition, subtraction, multiplication, or division) is used in the first equation in each box? **1: addition, 2: multiplication, 3: subtraction, 4: division**

  c. Which operation can you use to get from the first equation to the second equation in each box? **1: subtraction, 2: division, 3: addition, 4: multiplication**

13 Addition is the *inverse operation* of subtraction. **Inverse operations** are operations that undo each other.

  a. What is the inverse operation of multiplication? **division**

  b. How were inverse operations used in Question 12? **Sample Response: They were used to rewrite the equation with the variable on one side.**

▶ The Example below shows how to use math symbols and inverse operations to solve the equation $23 = t + 18$.

EXAMPLE

Solve $23 = t + 18$ using math symbols and inverse operations.

SAMPLE RESPONSE

$$
\begin{aligned}
23 &= t + 18 \\
23 - 18 &= t + 18 - 18 \\
5 &= t + 0 \\
5 &= t
\end{aligned}
$$

$t + 0 = t$

14 Discussion When you solve an equation the expressions on both sides must remain equal. Sometimes this is referred to as keeping the equation balanced.

  a. What inverse operation was used in the Example? **subtraction**

  b. How is the equation kept balanced when this inverse operation is used? **The equation remains equal since 18 is subtracted from both sides of the equation.**

15 Solve each equation. Show your work as in the Example above.

  a. $19 + x = 31$ **b.** $87 = y - 4$ **c.** $36w = 144$ **d.** $\dfrac{r}{6} = 13$
      12   **91**   **4**   **78**

▶ **Two-Step Equations** Some equations use more than one operation. For example, the rule of thumb for calculating the recommended amount of kitchen cupboard space for a family is given by the formula $c = 6p + 12$, where c is the number of square feet of cupboard space and p is the number of people in the family. The formula uses both multiplication and addition.

16 Copy and complete the following to express the rule of thumb in words.

To find the number of square feet of kitchen cupboard space recommended for a family, …
Multiply the number of family members by 6 and add 12.

▶ To find the recommended amount of kitchen cupboard space for a family of 3, you can evaluate the expression $6p + 12$ for $p = 3$. The order of operations tells you how to evaluate an expression.

FOR ▶ HELP

with *order of operations*, see

TOOLBOX, p. 589

EXAMPLE

Evaluate the expression $6p + 12$ for $p = 3$.

p	Start with the number.	3
$6p$	Multiply by 6.	$6 \cdot 3 = 18$
$6p + 12$	Add 12.	$18 + 12 = 30$

17 Examine the Example above.

a. How much cupboard space is recommended for a family of 3?
30 ft²

b. Which operation was performed first, addition or multiplication? Why?
multiplication; order of operations was followed

▶ A real estate agent is writing an ad for a house she is selling and has calculated the kitchen cupboard space to be about 48 ft². The storage needs of how many people can be met by the given amount of space?

18 **Try This as a Class**

a. Substitute 48 ft² for the cupboard space in the equation $c = 6p + 12$. $48 = 6p + 12$

b. Which variable should the real estate agent solve for to find the number of people whose storage needs can be met? p

Section 3 Equations and Expressions 37

TEACHING NOTES
Explain to students that when there are two variables as in the formula $c = 6p + 12$, knowing the value of one of the variables will help to find the value of the other. You might ask questions such as: "In the example, what does the 3 represent?" "Why is it used to replace the p?"

For **Question 18** ask, "Why was the "c" in the equation replaced with a value rather than the p?"

Students should realize that the variable left in the equation represents the information we don't know, therefore they need to solve for that variable.

Assist students in reading the **diagram on page 38**. The left arrow indicates how the expression was built around p and the order in which operations would appply when evaluating the expression. Read this arrow from the bottom up. The right arrow shows the order of steps to "undo" the operations. Note that inverse operations are listed directly across from each other inside the arrows.

Exploration 2 *continued*

USING MANIPULATIVES

You may want to model or have students model the equation in the example using algebra tiles. If more practice is needed, you may pose another problem to the students to work independently or as a class.

CLASSROOM EXAMPLE

Use a model and math symbols to show how to use inverse operations in solving the equation $3h + 8 = 14$.

Answer:
Using a Model

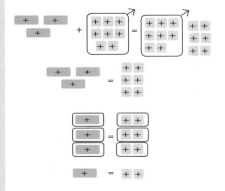

Using Math Symbols

$$3h + 8 = 14$$
$$3h + 8 - 8 = 14 - 8$$
$$3h = 6$$
$$\frac{3h}{3} = \frac{6}{3}$$
$$h = 2$$

TEACHING NOTES

You may want to review **Question 19** with students to be sure they understand the process of using inverses to solve 2-step equations. Remind them that working backwards means that they reverse the order of operations.

38

▶ The diagram below shows how to use math symbols and inverse operations to solve the equation $48 = 6p + 12$.

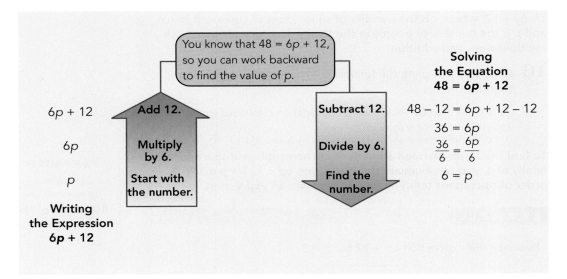

---

19 The diagram above shows the steps for solving the equation $48 = 6p + 12$.

a. What inverse operation is used to undo the multiplication $6p$? **division**

b. Why do you *subtract 12* before you *divide by 6*?
Because you are working backwards to find the value of p.

c. How do you know in what order to use the inverse operations to solve an equation? Reverse the order of operations that were performed on the variable.

d. The storage needs of how many people can be met by the given amount of space? **6 people**

e. Check the solution by substituting it into the original equation. $48 \stackrel{?}{=} 12 + 6(6)$
$48 = 48$

✔ QUESTION 20

...checks that you can use inverse operations to solve equations.

20 ✔ **CHECKPOINT** Solve each equation. Show your work and check your solutions.

a. $8y + 16 = 24$ **1** **b.** $2p - 7 = 15$ **11** **c.** $4a = 10$ **2.5**

d. $\frac{n}{2} = 9$ **18** **e.** $\frac{x}{2} + 3 = 11$ **16** **f.** $\frac{r}{5} - 1 = 6$ $r = 35$

HOMEWORK EXERCISES ▶ See Exs. 9–15 on pp. 45–46.

Exploration 3

Simplifying EXpressions

▶ The average person in the United States does an amazing 8493 loads of laundry in a lifetime! A rule of thumb states that the typical adult generates one load of laundry per week, while athletes, outdoor workers, and children generate two loads per week.

"MAYBE WE SHOULDN'T HAVE LET THE LAUNDRY PILE UP FOR A YEAR."

21 Write an expression that represents the number of loads of laundry generated in x weeks.

    a. by one child $2x$ **b.** by one typical adult x

    c. by the child and the adult together $3x$

22 Evaluate your expression in Question 21(c) when $x = 4$. 12

▶ Consider a family with one child and two adults where one of the adults is an outdoor worker. An expression for the number of loads of laundry generated by the family in x weeks is shown below.

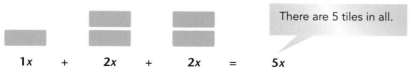

    $1x$ $+$ $2x$ $+$ $2x$

▶ The parts of an expression that are added are called **terms**. Each of the three terms in the expression $1x + 2x + 2x$ contains the variable x, which can be represented by the tile 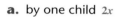. You can use algebra tiles to model an equivalent expression.

There are 5 tiles in all.

    $1x$ $+$ $2x$ $+$ $2x$ $=$ $5x$

After discussing **Question 24**, practice using the term, *coefficient* by asking students to name the coefficient of various terms in the table.

DEVELOPING MATH CONCEPTS
For **Question 25** you may want to have each student or group of students choose a different value for x, evaluate the expressions, and share their results. Make sure that students try a wide variety of numbers, including decimals, fractions, and the number 1. Point out that expressions that are equivalent for all values of a variable are *equivalent* expressions.

When combining like terms it is not necessary for students to show how the distributive property is used, but they should understand why $6x - x$ can be combined to equal $5x$. In the definition on this page and the example on page 41, these steps are shown for the purpose of teaching the the *distributive property of multiplication over addition* and the *distributive property of multiplication over subtraction*.

23. b. Sample Response: $5x$ is easier because you only have to do one operation, whereas for $1x + 2x + 2x$ you must do three multiplication operations and two additions.

24. The pairs of terms in the left column either have no variable, the same variables, or the same variable with the same exponent. The pairs of terms in the right column do not.

23 **a.** How many loads of laundry will this family generate in $1\frac{1}{2}$ years, which is 78 weeks? **390 loads of laundry**

b. Did you use $1x + 2x + 2x$ or $5x$? Why? **see margin**

▶ The terms $1x$, $2x$, and $2x$ are *like terms*. **Like terms** have identical variable parts and can be combined by adding *coefficients*. The **coefficient** is the number part of the term.

24 **Discussion** Use the table. Explain why the terms in the left column are *like* terms and the terms in the right column are *unlike* terms.
see margin

Like terms	Unlike terms
1, 13	4, 13x
2y, 8y	2y, 8y²
3rs, 4rs	3r, 4rs
$\frac{1}{4}m^2$, $7m^2$	$\frac{1}{4}m^2$, $7p^2$

25 **Try This as a Class**

a. Choose a value for x and substitute it in the expressions $2x + x$, $3x$, and $2x + 1$.
Answers will vary. Check students' work.
b. For which values of x does $2x + x = 3x$? **all values of x**

c. Are there values of x for which $2x + 1 = 3x$? If so, which ones?
Yes; when $x = 1$
d. Explain why $2x + x$ can be combined and written as $3x$, but $2x + 1$ cannot. **$2x + x = 3x$ for all values of x, whereas $2x + 1$ is only equal to $3x$ when x equals one specific value (when $x = 1$).**

▶ You can use the *distributive property of multiplication over addition* to write the expression $1x + 2x + 2x$ in another way.

The **distributive property of multiplication over addition** says that for all numbers a, b, and c:

$a(b + c) = ab + ac$ and $ab + ac = a(b + c)$

Examples:

$$7(5 + 2) = 7(5) + 7(2)$$
$$= 35 + 14$$

$$6 + 24 = 6(1) + 6(4)$$
$$= 6 (1 + 4)$$

$$8(x + 3) = 8x + 8(3)$$
$$= 8x + 24$$

$$5x + 15 = 5x + 5(3)$$
$$= 5(x + 3)$$

You can use the distributive property of multiplication over addition to simplify the expression $1x + 2x + 2x$ to $5x$.

$$1x + 2x + 2x = (1 + 2 + 2)x$$

$$1x + 2x + 2x = \quad 5x$$

26 **Try This as a Class** Use the distributive property of multiplication over addition to simplify the expression $2y + 11 + 4y - 2$. $6y + 9$

27 **Discussion** Michael says there is also a distributive property of multiplication over subtraction because for all numbers a, b, and c,

$$a(b - c) = ab - ac \text{ and } ab - ac = a(b - c).$$

Do you agree? Use examples to support your answer.

28 ✔ **CHECKPOINT** Combine like terms to simplify each expression.

a. $2w + 3w$ $5w$
b. $2b^2 + b^2$ $3b^2$
c. $3y + 7y - 6$ $10y - 6$

d. $4x - x + 1 + 3$ $3x + 4$
e. $5mn + 6mn$ $11mn$
f. $9q^2 + 7 - 2 - 3q$ $9q^2 - 3q + 5$

✔ **QUESTION 28**

...checks that you can combine like terms.

▶ Sometimes you can combine like terms to solve an equation.

EXAMPLE

$$6x - x + 3 = 18$$
$$(6 - 1)x + 3 = 18$$
$$5x + 3 = 18$$
$$5x + 3 - 3 = 18 - 3$$
$$5x + 0 = 15$$
$$5x = 15$$
$$\frac{5x}{5} = \frac{15}{5}$$
$$x = 3$$

Use the distributive property of multiplication over subtraction.

27. Sample Response: Yes; I tried several examples and found them to give the same result whether I followed the order of operations or the distributive property. For example, I tried $3(9 - 2)$ and $3 \cdot 9 - 3 \cdot 2$, both equaled 21.

29 Show that 3 is a solution of the original equation $6x - x + 3 = 18$.
$6(3) - 3 + 3 = 18 - 3 + 3 = 18$

30 ✔ **CHECKPOINT** Solve each equation. Group and combine like terms if possible to simplify the equation before solving.

a. $3m + 5 + 10 = 45$ 10
b. $12t - 4t + 2t = 30$ 3

c. $21 = 5 + x + x$ 8
d. $5p - 3p + 7 - 2 = 27$ 11

✔ **QUESTION 30**

...checks that you can combine like terms to solve an equation.

HOMEWORK EXERCISES ▶ See Exs. 16–29 on pp. 46–47.

TEACHING NOTES

Question 26 Explain to students that changing the order of 11 and $4y$ does not affect the value of the expression because the commutative property is being applied. It does, however, make it easier to see how to apply the distributive property.

Go through the steps in the **Example** with students. Students should notice that simplifying an equation makes it easier to solve since all like terms are combined.

You may want to go through another classroom example before allowing students to complete **Checkpoint 28** independently.

CLASSROOM EXAMPLE

Combine like terms to simplify the left side of the equation $12y - 14 - 7y = 1$.

Answer:

$$12y - 14 - 7y = 1$$
$$12y - 7y - 14 = 1$$
$$(12 - 7)y - 14 = 1$$
$$5y - 14 = 1$$

COMMON ERROR

In regrouping to combine like terms as in the **Classroom Example**, students should remember that since addition is commutative and subtraction is not, they must rewrite (or think of) each term as "plus the opposite of" before rearranging.

Key Concepts

ABSENT STUDENTS

For students who were absent for part or all of this section, the blackline Study Guide for Section 3 may be used to present the ideas, concepts and skills of Section 3.

CLOSURE QUESTION

Use the equation $3p - 4 = 8$. Explain why it is desirable to perform addition before division to solve for p.

Sample Response: It is possible to solve by either performing addition first or division first. When performing addition first,

$3p - 4 + 4 = 8 + 4$

$3p = 12$, then divide by 3,

$\frac{3p}{3} = \frac{12}{3}$

$p = 4$.

Checking this solution,

$3(4) - 4 = 8$

$12 - 4 = 8$

$8 = 8 \checkmark$

In performing division first,

$\frac{3p - 4}{3} = \frac{8}{3}$

$p - \frac{4}{3} = \frac{8}{3}$, then add $\frac{4}{3}$,

$p - \frac{4}{3} + \frac{4}{3} = \frac{8}{3} + \frac{4}{3}$

$p = \frac{12}{3} = 4$.

As shown in the check above, 4 is the solution to the equation. In this problem, either way works, however, the result of performing the division first is a fraction which is more difficult to calculate. It is also possible to fail to include the 4 when performing the division resulting in an incorrect solution.

Key Terms

variable

constant

solution of an equation

solve an equation

inverse operations

Writing Equations (pp. 33–35)

To write an equation for a word sentence, choose a variable to represent each of the quantities that are unknown or that may change. Any quantities that do not change are constants. Use symbols to repreent the relationships between the quantities.

Example

According to a rule that some caterers use, you should prepare 3 appetizers for each person at a party.

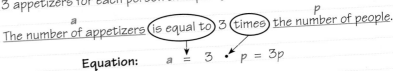

The number of appetizers (is equal to) 3 (times) the number of people.

Equation: $a = 3 \cdot p = 3p$

Solving Equations (pp. 35–38)

A value of a variable that makes an equation true is a solution of the equation. The process of finding solutions is called solving an equation. One way to solve an equation is to use inverse operations. Inverse operations are operations like addition and subtraction that undo each other.

Example

Solve: $\frac{y}{3} + 6 = 30$

$\frac{y}{3} + 6 - 6 = 30 - 6$

$\frac{y}{3} = 24$

$\frac{y}{3} \cdot 3 = 24 \cdot 3$

$y = 72$

Check: $\frac{y}{3} + 6 = 30$

$\frac{72}{3} + 6 \stackrel{?}{=} 30$

$24 + 6 \stackrel{?}{=} 30$

$30 = 30$

31 Key Concepts Question Explain how inverse operations were used to solve the equation in the second example.

6 was subtracted from each side of the equation since it is the inverse of adding 6. Then since y had been divided by 3, each side of the equation was multiplied by 3.

Section 3
Key Concepts

Simplifying Expressions (pp. 39–41)

The parts of an expression that are added are terms. Terms with identical variable parts are like terms. To simplify some expressions and to solve some equations you can combine like terms by adding coefficients.

Example

Solve: $41 = 5x - 3x - 1$

$41 = 2x - 1$

$41 + 1 = 2x - 1 + 1$

$42 = 2x$

$\dfrac{42}{2} = \dfrac{2x}{2}$

$21 = x$

Check: $41 = 5x - 3x - 1$

$41 \overset{?}{=} 5 \cdot 21 - 3 \cdot 21 - 1$

$41 \overset{?}{=} 105 - 63 - 1$

$41 \overset{?}{=} 42 - 1$

$41 = 41$

Distributive Property (pp. 40–41)

The distributive property of multiplication over addition says that for any numbers a, b, and c:

$$a(b + c) = ab + ac \qquad \text{and} \qquad ab + ac = a(b + c)$$

The distributive property of multiplication over subtraction says that for any numbers a, b, and c:

$$a(b - c) = ab - ac \qquad \text{and} \qquad ab - ac = a(b - c)$$

The distributive property allows you to combine like terms to simplify expressions and equations.

Examples

$4(x + 8) = 4x + 4 \cdot 8$

$= 4x + 32$

$5x - 3x = (5 - 3)x$

$= 2x$

---

32 Key Concepts Question

a. Simplify and then solve the equation $3x + 5 + 5x = 51$.
$8x + 5 = 51; x = 5.75$

b. Check your solution. How do you know your solution is correct?

CLOSURE QUESTIONS

What is the goal in solving equations involving a variable? What is meant by the phrase "combine like terms?"

Sample Response: To find the values for the variable that make the equation true. "Combine like terms" means to add or subtract terms that contain identical variable parts.

32. b. $3(5.75) + 5 + 5(5.75) = 17.25 + 5 + 28.75 = 51$; The value of x makes the equation true.

Section ③

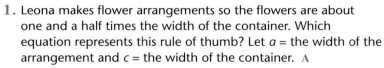

Practice & Application Exercises

1. Leona makes flower arrangements so the flowers are about one and a half times the width of the container. Which equation represents this rule of thumb? Let a = the width of the arrangement and c = the width of the container. **A**

   A. $1\frac{1}{2}c = a$ B. $1\frac{1}{2}a = c$ C. $c + 1\frac{1}{2} = a$

For Exercises 2–6, use variables to write each word sentence as an equation. Tell what each variable represents.

2. The total cost of tickets for a group of people at an amusement park is $29 per child plus $40 per adult.
   Let c = number of children, a = number of adults, t = total cost; $t = 29c + 40a$

3. The total distance of a bike trip divided by 50 gives the approximate number of days the trip will take.
   Let t = total distance of the trip, d = number of days; $\frac{t}{50} = d$

4. To estimate a yearly salary from an hourly wage, double the hourly wage and multiply by 1000.
   Let y = yearly salary, h = hourly salary; $y = 2h \cdot 1000$ or $y = 2000h$

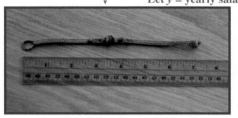

5. To estimate the beginning length of each cord needed to make a macramé bracelet, multiply the length you want the bracelet to be by 8. **see margin**

5. Let c = beginning length of cord, f = finished length of the bracelet; $c = 8f$

6. The age of a lobster can be estimated by multiplying its weight in pounds by 7. **see margin**

6. Let a = age of lobster in years, w = weight of lobster in pounds; $a = 7w$

7. In the following rule of thumb and formula, C = temperature in degrees Celsius and F = temperature in degrees Fahrenheit.

▯ 1 Rule of Thumb	▯ 2 Formula
$F = 2C + 30$	$F = \frac{9}{5}C + 32$

   a. Use the rule of thumb to convert 0°C, 15°C, and 100°C to Fahrenheit temperatures. 30°F, 60°F, 230°F

   b. Use the formula to convert 0°C, 15°C, and 100°C to Fahrenheit temperatures. 32°F, 59°F, 212°F

   c. For which Celsius temperature does the rule of thumb give the best estimate of the Fahrenheit temperature you found using the formula? 15°C

8. Your mass in kilograms multiplied by 0.08 is approximately equal to the volume of your blood in liters.

   a. Write an equation for this rule of thumb. Tell what each variable represents.
      Let m = mass in kilograms, v = volume of blood in liters; $v = 0.08\,m$

   b. According to this rule of thumb, how many liters of blood does a 50-kilogram person have? **4 L**

9. Use inverse operations to solve each equation. Check your solution.

   a. $6 + x = 31$ 25

   b. $\dfrac{x}{12} = 105$ 1260

   c. $6t = 21$ 3.5

   d. $161 = 7y$ 23

   e. $39 = \dfrac{y}{4}$ 156

   f. $y - 18 = 27$ 45

10. Check whether $x = 14$ is a solution for each equation below.

    a. $2x + 3 = 25$ no

    b. $1 = \dfrac{x}{7} - 1$ yes

    c. $x - 14 = 0$ yes

11. Which of the following is the preferred first step in solving the equation $16 = 6x - 7$? **A**

    A. Add 7 to both sides of the equation.

    B. Subtract 7 from both sides of the equation.

    C. Divide each side of the equation by 6.

    D. Subtract 16 from each side of the equation.

12. Use inverse operations to solve each equation. Check your solution.

    a. $6 + 3x = 39$ 11

    b. $\dfrac{x}{12} + 8 = 105$ 1164

    c. $6t - 8 = 154$ 27

    d. $30 = 7y - 5$ 5

    e. $3y + 5 = 11$ 2

    f. $\dfrac{y}{4} + 1 = 7$ 24

13. **Create Your Own** Write your own rule of thumb for something you estimate and then write it as an equation. Use your equation in two examples. **Answers will vary. Check students' work.**

Oceanography Ships use the speed of sound in water to help find the water's depth.

14. a. The speed of sound in water is about five times the speed of sound in air. Write an equation for this rule of thumb. Let w = the speed of sound in water, a = the speed of sound in air; $w = 5a$

    b. Assume that the speed of sound in ocean water is 1470 m/sec. At about what speed does sound travel in air?   **294 m/sec**

This sonar image shows the ocean floor off the coast of California.
▼

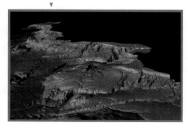

EXERCISE NOTES

For **Exercise 11** students may argue that it is possible to divide both sides by 6 first. Remind them that although it is possible, it is not the preferred method because it introduces fractions which make the calculations more difficult.

Exercise 13 It may be helpful to conduct a quick brainstorming session to help students think of ideas for writing rules of thumb. Suggest that they think of two or three rules and then select the best one to illustrate with an equation and examples.

Practice & Applications

COMMON ERROR

Exercise 16 Some students may believe x^2y and xy^2 are like terms because they both have the same variable parts and both expressions contain an exponent of 2. Point out that the exponents on each corresponding variable must be the same and that x^2y^1 is x^2 with y^1 but xy^2 is x^1 with y^2.

Exercise 26 Ask students if there are any other polygons that have similar equations to the two in **parts (a) and (b)**. *(Yes, any regular polygon.)*

15. a. The sound has traveled the distance between the ship and the ocean floor twice, so the ocean depth is half the distance traveled.

15. **Challenge** A sonar pulse from a ship is sent to the bottom the ocean. To find the distance the pulse has traveled, multiply the speed of sound in water by the amount of time it takes for the pulse to travel from the ship to the ocean floor and back to the ship. Assume that the speed of sound in water is 1470 m/sec.

 a. Suppose the sonar pulse returns in 2 sec. Explain why the ocean depth is 1470 m rather than 2940 m. (Hint: Draw a diagram of the path the sound travels.)

 b. Write a formula for finding ocean depth. Use your formula to find the ocean depth if the sonar pulse returns in 2.5 sec. $d = \frac{1}{2} \cdot 1470t;\ 1837.5$ m

16. Which of the terms below are like terms? $x^2, \frac{1}{2}x^2,$ and $2x^2$

$$x^2 \qquad \frac{1}{2}x^2 \qquad xy \qquad x^2y \qquad 2x^2 \qquad xy^2$$

If possible combine like terms to simplify each expression.

17. $17x + 4 - 3$
 $17x + 1$

18. $8rs - 6r$
 not possible, unlike terms

19. $16w + 3 + w$
 $17w + 3$

20. $3t - 2t + 9t$
 $10t$

21. $19n - 19n^2$
 not possible, unlike terms

22. $4xy + 4x - 4x$
 $4xy$

23. $12y^2 + 6x + 3y^2 + x$
 $15y^2 + 7x$

24. $f^2 + 3f + 4f - 6$
 $f^2 + 7f - 6$

25. **Geometry Connection** The perimeter of a rectangle can be represented by the equation $P = l + l + w + w$, where P = the perimeter, l = the length, and w = the width.

 a. Simplify the equation by combining like terms. $P = 2l + 2w$

 b. If $l = 10$ in. and $w = 3$ in., what is the perimeter of the rectangle? 26 in.

 c. Solve for w when $P = 50$ cm and $l = 18$ cm. 7 cm

 d. Solve for l when $P = 15$ m and $w = 3$ m. 4.5 m

26. **Geometry Connection** Write an equation for finding the perimeter of each figure. Tell what each variable represents. Combine like terms when possible.

 a. equilateral triangle
 $P = 3l$

 b. square
 $P = 4l$

27. Find the length of one side of each figure in Exercise 26 when the perimeter is 36 yd. triangle: 12 yd, square: 9 yd

28. Solve each equation. If possible, combine like terms to simplify each equation before solving.

 a. $3x + 8 - 5 = 27$
 8

 b. $72 = x + 2x + 3x$
 12

 c. $5m - 4 = 56$
 12

Reflecting ◀▶on the Section

29. The balance scales below are each balanced.

    a. What objects from Balance Scale A could be substituted for a cube on Balance Scale B?
       1 cylinder and 2 pencils can be substituted for 1 cube on Balance Scale B.

    b. Use your answer to part (a) to find how many pencils it will take to balance one cylinder. Explain how you solved this problem. How is solving it like solving an equation?

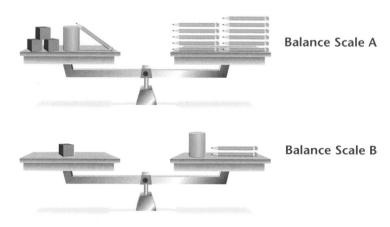

Balance Scale A

Balance Scale B

Visual THINKING

Exercise 29 checks to see if you can balance an equation.

29. b. 1 pencil; After substituting 1 cylinder and 2 pencils for each cube, Balance Scale A has 4 cylinders and 7 pencils balancing 11 pencils. Subtracting 7 pencils from each side leaves 4 pencils balancing 4 cylinders, which means 1 pencil would balance 1 cylinder. This is like solving an equation because you are doing the same thing to both sides to keep the scale balanced.

Spiral ◀▶Review

Choose a type of data display that you could use for each data set. Explain each choice of display. (Module 1, pp. 9–10)

30. the amounts of rainfall during the months of a certain year
Sample Response: a bar graph; The data fall into categories.

31. the percentages of people who voted for various candidates in a student council election
Sample Response: a circle graph; The data are given in percentages.

Science In a thunderstorm, you see flashes of lightning before you hear the thunder from the lightning. This is because sound travels much more slowly than light. (Module 1, p. 12)

32. The speed of sound through air is about 1100 ft/sec.

    a. Suppose you want to explain to a friend how the speed of sound compares to the speed of a car. What units would you use to express the speed of sound for your friend? Explain.
       Sample Response: mi/hr; The speed of a car is usually given in mi/hr.

    b. Express the speed of sound in the units you chose in part (a).
       750 mi/hr

Extra Skill Practice

Extra Skill Practice

TEACHER NOTES
For each Exploration, the corresponding Extra Skills Practice Exercises are noted.

Exploration 1: Exs. 1–4
Exploration 2: Exs. 5–10
Exploration 3: Exs. 11–19

EXTRA HELP
Teacher's Resource Book
• Practice and Applications
• Study Guide

Technology Resources
• @Home Tutor
• Test Generator

ASSESSMENT
• Section 3 Quick Quiz
• Test Generator

Section 3
Extra Skill Practice

Use variables to write each word sentence as an equation. Tell what each variable represents.

1. The camp cooks agree that the amount of hamburger they need to purchase for a trip is $\frac{1}{4}$ lb of hamburger for each camper and an extra 5 lb. Let t = total amount of hamburger used in pounds and c = the number of campers; $t = 0.25c + 5$

2. The total bus fare for a family is \$0.60 for each adult and \$0.10 for each child. Let f = total bus fare, a = the number of adults, and c = the number of children; $f = 0.6a + 0.1c$

3. To estimate the monthly rent of an apartment in her city, Jenny multiplies the area in square feet of the apartment by \$0.90. Let r = rent and a = area of the apartment; $r = 0.9a$

4. A mattress alone costs \$25 plus half the price of the box spring and mattress together. Let c = cost of the mattress alone and p = the price of the mattress and box spring together; $c = \frac{p}{2} + 25$

Use inverse operations to solve each equation. Check your solution.

5. $3j + 2 = 95$ 31

6. $5w = 30$ 6

7. $\frac{m}{52} = 4$ 208

8. $8 + 4z = 12$ 1

9. $r - 131 = 17$ 148

10. $27 = 14 + 2y$ 6.5

If possible, combine like terms to simplify each expression.

11. $1y + 6y - 2y$
    $5y$

12. $5 + 11rz - 3z$
    no like terms

13. $t + 9t - 4$
    $10t - 4$

14. $5p + 4p - 18pr$
    $9p - 18pr$

15. $18r - 18rd + 18r$
    $36r - 18rd$

16. $10v + 5k^3 - v + 20k^3$
    $9v + 25k^3$

17. $2h^3 + 4h$
    no like terms

18. $\frac{1}{2}xy + \frac{1}{4}x$ no like terms

19. $7 + 5w - 4w + w^2$
    $7 + w + w^2$

Standardized Testing ◄►Multiple Choice

1. If $\frac{x}{3} - 23 = 4$, what does $2x$ equal? D

   A 114   B 70   C 54   D 162

2. Combine like terms to simplify the expression $3x^2 + 10xy + x^2 - 7xy$. Which expression is correct? A

   A $4x^2 + 3xy$ B $3x^2 + 3xy$ C $4x^4 + 3x^2y^2$ D $6x^6y^2$

Section ④ Scatter Plots

IN THIS SECTION

EXPLORATION 1
◆ Making a Scatter Plot

EXPLORATION 2
◆ Fitting a Line

Athletic Triumphs

Setting the Stage ▶▶▶▶▶▶▶▶▶▶▶▶▶▶▶▶▶▶▶▶▶▶▶▶▶▶▶▶▶▶▶▶▶

The achievements of many athletes seem even more amazing when you think about the difficulties they have overcome.

At 5 ft 7 in., Anthony "Spud" Webb is much shorter than most National Basketball Association players. Yet he won the Slam-Dunk Competition at the 1986 NBA All-Star game.

In 1996, Lance Armstrong was given less than a 50% chance of surviving cancer. But he did survive, and in 2005 he won the grueling Tour de France bicycle race for the seventh year in a row.

Marla Runyan has been legally blind since the age of 9, but it hasn't slowed her down! She finished eighth in the 1500 m run at the 2000 Olympics and fifth in the 2002 New York City marathon. In the 2004 Athens Olympics she competed in the 5000 m run.

Think About It

1 With a running start, Spud Webb could jump $3\frac{1}{2}$ ft off the floor.
Sample Responses are given.
 a. Estimate how high Spud's hand could have reached when he jumped. **10 ft 2 in.**

 b. How did you make your estimate?

 ▾ **1. b. I measured my arm, added 5 ft 7 in., subtracted the distance from my shoulder to the top of my head, then added 3.5 ft.**

2 Shaquille O'Neal is 7 ft 1 in. tall. Do you think he could dunk a basketball without jumping? Explain your reasoning. **Sample Response: No; A basketball rim is $10\frac{1}{2}$ ft. high, so Shaquille's arm would have to extend $3\frac{1}{2}$ feet beyond the top of his head to reach the rim without jumping.**

Setting the Stage

GETTING STARTED
Module 1, Section 4 *Warm-Up* assesses whether students can write ordered pairs from a set of values.

The photo captions highlight the accomplishments of three amazing athletes. Ask what makes their accomplishments amazing. Students should relate the fact that these athletes have all overcome a disability or illness, or they have displayed extraordinary skill in reaching their full potential. You might have students discuss athletes they know of who have made amazing accomplishments.

TEACHING NOTES
Question 1 Point out that Spud Webb's reach is composed of three parts: his height, the height off the floor that he jumps, and the distance his hand reaches above his head. For the Explorations, students will conduct an experiment measuring their own heights and standing jump reaches. The scatter plot and fitted line they produce for their own data will help them appreciate Spud's amazing ability.

To answer **Question 2**, each student could measure his/her height and the distance he/she can reach above his/her head and then set up and solve a proportion involving O'Neal's height.

DIFFERENTIATED INSTRUCTION
If there are students who have mobility restrictions in your class, you may want to use an alternative to the activity in Exploration 1. A suggestion is to compare hand span from thumb to little finger to arm length from wrist to elbow. Be prepared with a set of directions for the activity you choose prior to introducing it to the students.

49

Exploration 1

CLASSROOM MANAGEMENT

Before beginning **Questions 3 and 4**, read through the directions with the students so that they are aware of the steps they will be completing to gather data from this activity. Stations set up for groups with meter sticks or measuring tapes adhered to the wall would be helpful.

Assigning roles can facilitate groups working more efficiently. Some possible roles are:

- Height Data Collector - measure the height of each group member and report it to the data recorder

- Jump Data Collector - measure the height of each group member's jump and report it to the data recorder

- Data Recorder - records the height and jump data for each group member

- Data Reporter - assists with making measurements and reports the group's final results to the class

An overhead timer will allow students to keep track of the time remaining for completing the lab.

DEVELOPING MATH CONCEPTS

Before students begin gathering and recording data in **Question 3**, review how to convert their data from their tape measure or yardstick to inches for their tables. For example, to change 5 ft 3 in. to inches, tell students to multiply 5 · 12 to get 60 in., then add the remaining 3 inches to get 63 in. You may need to do another example, converting 7 ft 5 in. to inches (*89 in.*).

50

GOAL

LEARN HOW TO...
- organize data in a scatter plot

AS YOU...
- analyze data about height and jumping distance

KEY TERMS
- scale
- interval
- scatter plot

Exploration 1

Making a scatter Plot

SET UP *Work in a group of six. You will need: • masking tape • tape measure or yardstick • ruler • graph paper*

▶ **Spud Webb's jumping ability was amazing, even for a professional athlete. How high would someone your age need to jump to be an amazing jumper? One way to find out is to gather data and use it to predict how high a 5 ft 7 in. eighth grade student might be expected to jump.**

3. a–c. Answers will vary. Check students' work.

3 **a.** Make a table like the one shown.

b. Measure the height of each person in your group. Record the heights in your table.

Jumping Data		
Student	Height (in.)	Jump height (in.)
Sarah	63	89
MIlo	61	85

c. Follow the directions given below to measure each student's jump height to the nearest inch. Record the jump heights in your table.

First

Jump near a wall. Make two standing jumps, placing a piece of masking tape as high on the wall as possible.

Then

Record your jump height. Your jump height is the distance from the floor to your higher piece of masking tape.

 Module 1 Amazing Feats and Facts

4 a. Write an *ordered pair* like the one shown for each person in your group.

a–b. Answers will vary. Check students' work.

b. Write the ordered pairs on the board so each student can record the results for the entire class.

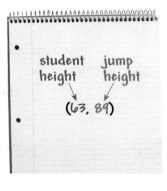

▶ Sometimes it is easier to see how data are related by graphing the data. On a graph, the numbers written along an axis are its **scale**. The numbers on the scale can increase by ones, but when the data are spread over a large range it may be better to choose a scale that increases by twos, fives, tens, or some other number.

5 **Try This as a Class** The questions below will help you plan how to graph your class's jumping data. a–d. Answers will vary according to class data collected. Check students' work.

a. The horizontal axis of the graph will show student heights in inches. What are the greatest and least student heights?

b. Use the values from part (a) to decide what range of heights to show on the horizontal axis. Explain your thinking.

c. Use the range of heights to decide how many intervals you can fit along the horizontal axis. Explain your thinking.

d. Use your answers to parts (b) and (c) to choose a scale for the horizontal axis. Explain your decision.

e. The vertical axis will show jump height in inches. Decide what values will be shown and choose a scale for the vertical axis. Explain how you made your choices.

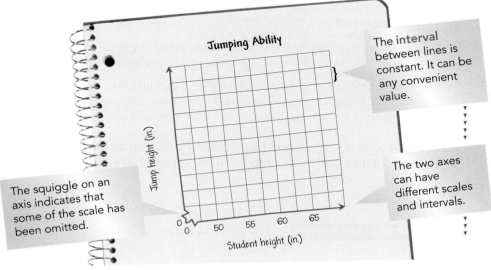

TEACHING NOTES

Question 5 Work with the whole class to determine appropriate ranges and scales for the two axes of their graphs. Encourage them to include values above the highest data value and below the lowest data value on each scale so that data points will not lie on an axis. Remind students that they can use the broken line symbol as shown in the graphic on the notebook page to indicate that a scale does not start at zero.

COMMON ERROR

Before students move on to **Question 6** on the next page, you may want to write a reminder on the board above the ordered pairs such as (student height, jump height) since the axes of their graphs should be labled with these same titles. This should prevent students from confusing the order in which they plot the ordered pair, thus needlessly erasing and replotting the points.

Exploration 1 *continued*

TEACHING NOTES
Following **Question 8**, students may benefit from working an additional classroom example together as a class.

CLASSROOM EXAMPLE

Draw a scatter plot of the numbers of at-bats and hits for the members of a softball team for one season. Use the horizontal scales for at-bats, and the vertical scale for hits.

Number of at-bats	Number of hits
32	10
35	13
33	10
21	5
32	16
40	18
37	14
22	5
19	3
29	10
27	8
36	12
20	4
24	5

Answer:

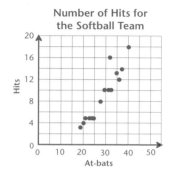

Number of Hits for the Softball Team

6 a. On graph paper draw and label the horizontal and vertical axes for your graph. Include the scale for each axis and a title for the graph. **a–b. Answers will vary according to class data collected. Check students' work.**

b. Plot the class's jumping data on your coordinate grid. You should have one point for each member of the class.

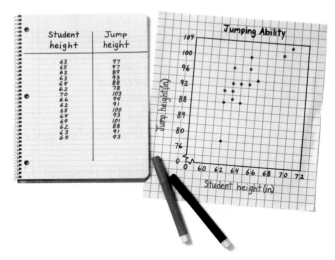

▶ The graph you created is a *scatter plot*. A **scatter plot** is the graph of a set of data pairs. A **scatter plot** can help you to recognize patterns and make predictions.

7 Discussion Use your scatter plot.

a. Looking at the scatter plot, what can you tell about the jump heights? For example, what is the greatest height reached? the least reached? the range?
Answers will vary. Check students' work.

b. What information does the graph show about the heights of the students? **Sample Response: The height of the jump increases with the height of the student.**

c. Did a student's height seem to have an effect on his or her jump height? Is this what you expected? Were there any exceptions? Explain your thinking. **Answers will vary. Check students' work.**

8 Will the scale on your scatter plot change if a new student in your class is 6 ft 1 in. and has a jump height of 9 ft 4 in.? Why or why not? **Answers will vary. Check students' work.**

HOMEWORK EXERCISES ▶ See Exs. 1–4 on pp. 57–58.

Fitting a L|NE

You will need • Labsheet 4A • ruler • your scatter plot of jumping data from Exploration 1

▶ **The scatter plot below compares the performances of the top 20 finishers in one of the Tour de France races. Each point represents a racer's time for the mountain time trial and his total time for the Tour de France.**

> **GOAL**
>
> **LEARN HOW TO...**
> ◆ use a fitted line to make predictions
>
> **AS YOU...**
> ◆ analyze data about the Tour de France and about students' jump heights
>
> **KEY TERMS**
> ◆ positive correlation
> ◆ negative correlation
> ◆ fitted line

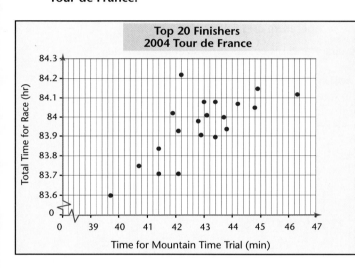

Top 20 Finishers
2004 Tour de France

Total Time for Race (hr) vs. *Time for Mountain Time Trial (min)*

9 **a.** Lance Armstrong had the fastest total time for the race and the fastest time for the mountain time trial. Find the point on the scatter plot that shows his performance. What was his total time for the 2004 Tour de France? **83.6 hr**

b. Estimate Lance Armstrong's time for the mountain time trial. **about 39.7 min or 39 min 42 sec**

c. For the top 20 finishers, the slowest time for the mountain time trial was 46.28 min and the slowest total time for the race was 84.22 hr. Did the same racer have both of these times? Explain. **No, To be the same person, there would have to be a point at (46.28, 84.22) and there is not.**

10 **Discussion** What pattern do you notice in the points on the scatter plot? **In general as times for Mountain Trials increase, so do Total Times.**

Exploration 2

COMMON ERROR

Question 9(a) Students may pick out the highest point on the graph. There is a common tendency to interpret the highest point as representing the best. Remind students that in each of these events, the shortest time represents the best performance.

TECHNOLOGY

For a related technology activity, see the *Technology Book*.

TEACHING NOTES

In **Question 11**, students may have difficulty determining a strong or weak correlation. Explain that strongly correlated data tend to fit tightly together with most of the data lying inside a long, narrow oval. Weakly correlated data seem to fall randomly inside or near an oval that is wider or more circular in shape.

Strong Positive Correlation   Weak Negative Correlation   No Correlation

Data with no correlation tend to appear randomly inside or near a circle on the graph.

CLASSROOM EXAMPLE

Draw a fitted line on the scatter plot from the Classroom Example for Exploration 1.

Sample Answer: Draw a line through the data values so that about half of the data values lie on one side of the line and about half of the data values lie on the other side of the line.

Number of Hits for the School Softball Team

TIPS FROM TEACHERS

Use a clear ruler or straightedge to draw your fitted line. Explain that it is easier to determine where the points lie when you can see them on both sides of the line you are drawing. A piece of uncooked spaghetti can also be used to draw fitted lines.

---

11. b. weak; Variation in the data means that an increase in time for mountain trials does not necessarily result in an increase in total time.

✔ **QUESTION 12**

...checks that you can determine if there is a correlation between two variables.

13. b. No, The plot does not prove that rising stock prices are the cause of more manatees being killed by boats, it only shows that the data show a positive correlation.

▶ Two variables that are related in some way are said to be correlated. There is a **positive correlation** if one variable tends to increase as the other increases. There is a **negative correlation** if one variable tends to decrease as the other increases.

11 Try This as a Class

a. Is there a *positive correlation*, a *negative correlation*, or *no correlation* between the times for the mountain time trial and the total times for the race? Explain. **positive correlation, as the Mountain Time Trials times increase so do the Total Times.**

b. If there is a correlation, would you describe it as *strong* or *weak*? Why?

12 ✔ CHECKPOINT Tell whether there is a *positive correlation*, a *negative correlation*, or *no correlation* between the two variables.

a. the height and weight of a stack of pennies **positive correlation**

b. the outside temperature and sales of hot cocoa **negative correlation**

c. an adult's salary and his or her shoe size **no correlation**

13 Try This as a Class The scatter plot below shows the number of Florida manatees killed by boats and the price of stocks as measured by the Dow Jones Industrial Average for 1983–2004.

 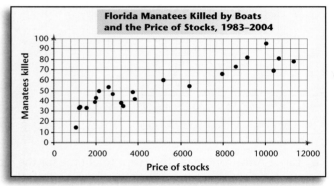

a. Is there a *positive correlation*, a *negative correlation*, or *no correlation* between the price of stocks and the number of manatees killed by boats? **positive correlation**

b. Would it be correct to say that a rise in stock prices tends to cause an increase in the number of manatees killed by boats? Why or why not?

c. If a correlation exists between two variables, does that necessarily mean there is a cause-and-effect relationship between the variables? That is, does a change in one of the variables cause the other variable to change? Explain. **No; Sample Response: It may just be a coincidence that the data show a correlation.**

▶ When the data points show a strong correlation, a **fitted line** can be drawn to show the pattern in the data and to help make predictions. An example of a fitted line is shown on the scatter plot of the Tour de France data.

EXAMPLE

A fitted line is drawn so that most of the data points fall near it. About half of the points should be above the line and about half should be below it.

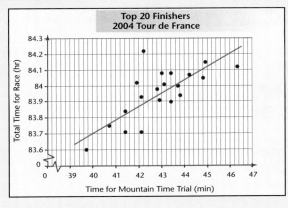

14 **Discussion**

a. How does the fitted line in the Example help you see that the racers who are faster on the mountain time trial are usually faster for the whole race?
Sample Response: The points follow an upward trend along the line.

b. Which points do not seem to follow this pattern?
Sample Response: (42.2, 84.22) and (46.3, 84.12)

c. Suppose a racer finishes the Mountain Time Trial in 41.2 min. Use the fitted line to predict his total time for the race.
83.8 hr

▶ The data points in a scatter plot do not always show a straight-line pattern. If you see a curved pattern or no pattern at all, it does not make sense to draw a fitted line.

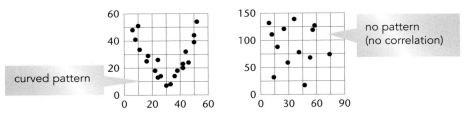

curved pattern

no pattern (no correlation)

15 **Use Labsheet 4A.** You will examine scatter plots and make decisions about *Correlations and Fitted Lines*. see margin

15. See Labsheet 4A.
   Graph on left:
   a. negative
   b. strong
   c. Check students' fitted lines.
   Graph in middle:
   a. no correlation
   Graph on right:
   a. positive
   b. weak

55

Exploration 2 *continued*

TEACHING NOTES

Question 17(a) Guide students to identify points that are well above the fitted line. These points indicate better than average jumping ability. For **part (b)**, scales on their class graphs may not extend far enough to graph a point for Spud Webb. This will confirm the unusual nature of his accomplishment.

Key Concepts

Make sure students understand that the main reason for fitting lines to data points on a scatter plot is to help identify relationships between the two sets of data and to make predictions as in **Question 18**.

ABSENT STUDENTS

For students who were absent for part or all of this section, the blackline Study Guide for Section 4 may be used to present the ideas, concepts, and skills of Section 4.

✔ QUESTION 16

...checks that you can draw a fitted line on a scatter plot and decide how well it represents the data.

17. a. Sample response: Note anyone whose jump height is markedly above the fitted line.

---

16 ✔ **CHECKPOINT** Draw a fitted line on your scatter plot from Exercise 6 in Exploration 1. Does the line represent your data well? Explain. **Answers will vary. Check students' work.**

17 **a.** How can you use your fitted line from Question 16 to decide whether your class has any "amazing jumpers"?

b. Spud Webb is 5 ft 7 in. tall. What jump height would you expect for a student as tall as Spud Webb? **Answers will vary. Check students' work.**

HOMEWORK EXERCISES ▶ See Exs. 5–18 on pp. 58–61.

Section ④
Key Concepts

Key Terms

scatter plot

scale

fitted line

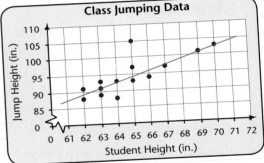

Scatter Plots and Fitted Lines (pp. 51–53 and 55–56)

You can use a scatter plot to look for patterns in paired data and make predictions. The range of each data set determines the scale of each axis of the scatter plot. Sometimes the data show a strong correlation. When they do, you can draw a fitted line to show a pattern and help make predictions.

Example The scatter plot at the right compares how high a group of eighth grade students jumped to their heights. Because the correlation is strong, you can draw a fitted line.

Class Jumping Data

18 **Key Concepts Question** Use the scatter plot in the Example.

a. Describe the relationship between the students' heights and how high they jumped.
The taller the students, the higher they jumped.

b. Predict the jump height for a 68 in. tall student. **about 99 in.**

c. Gerome's jump height was 105 in. About how tall is he? How does his jump height compare with those of other students?
65 in.; Gerome jumped much higher than expected for his height. Other students his height jumped about 95 in.

Key Concepts

Correlation (p. 54)

Two variables that are related in some way are said to be correlated. There is a positive correlation if one variable tends to increase as the other increases. There is a negative correlation if one variable tends to decrease as the other increases.

Key Terms

positive correlation

negative correlation

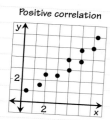
Positive correlation

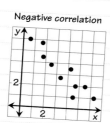
Negative correlation

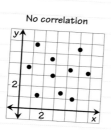
No correlation

19 Key Concepts Question

a. Describe two real-world variables that have a negative correlation. **Sample Response: Time spent e-mailing and in chat rooms and grades made on homework assignments.**

b. Does an increase in one of the variables in part (a) cause a decrease in the other variable? Explain your thinking. **Answers will vary. Check students' answers in response to variables described in part (a).**

Section 4

Practice & Application Exercises

Use Labsheet 4B for Exercises 1–3. The scatter plot shows *World Record Marathon Times* for men and women of different ages.

1. **a.** What is the approximate age and record time of the oldest female marathon runner? **92 yr, 6.5 hr**

   b. What is the approximate age and record time of the youngest male marathon runner? **6 yr, just under 5.5 hr**

2. **a.** In what 10-year age range are the record times for men fastest? **22 to 32**

   b. Does the fastest individual male time fall in this age range? **Yes**

YOU WILL NEED

For Exs. 1–3:
◆ Labsheet 4B

For Exs. 4 and 16:
◆ graph paper
◆ two colored pencils

For Ex. 17:
◆ small ball
◆ yardstick or meter stick
◆ graph paper

CLOSURE QUESTION

Describe how you can tell from a scatter plot if a fitted line could be used to represent a set of data. Then describe how to draw a fitted line.

Sample Response: If the data points appear to lie on or near a line, then a fitted line could be used. Draw a fitted line through the data points so that about half of the points are above the line and half of the points are below the line.

Practice & Applications

SUGGESTED ASSIGNMENTS

Core Course
Day 1: Exs. 1–4
Day 2: Exs. 5–14, 19–26
Day 3: Exs. 16–18

Extended Course
Day 1: Exs. 1–4
Day 2: Exs. 5–6, 8–15, 19–26
Day 3: Exs. 16–18

Note: Extended Course assignments can be used to differentiate within the regular classroom. In classrooms where students are grouped homogeneously, the material might be covered in fewer days. In this case assignments may be combined.

ADDITIONAL PRACTICE

See the *Teacher's Resource Book* for additional practice and application exercises for this section.

Practice & Applications

DEVELOPING MATH CONCEPTS

Exercise 4 Point out that because the rate of travel varies during the actual trip, it may be difficult to use the scatter plot in **part (a)** to predict the actual time required to travel a given distance. When students constructed the line graph in **part(b),** they should have discovered that the planned times all fall on a line, and that this line can be used to make fairly accurate estimates of the actual time required to travel a given distance. The line can be thought of as a fitted line and illustrates why we often fit a line to the data in a scatter plot to make predictions from it.

3. Sample Response: Marathon runners in their teens start at a relatively fast pace, peak in their 20s and 30s, then their times gradually increase over the next 30 years. Their times increase more rapidly after the age of 60.

4. c. Sample Response: Both times are within a few minutes of each other until about 14 km, when the planned time is about 10 to 15 minutes greater than the actual time.

4. d. Between the 15th and 17th km; Sample Response: I divided the number of kilometers covered in each time period by the amount of time lapsed between the two distances.

3. **Writing** Describe the pattern of the data points. Explain what it shows about the marathon runners and their times.

4. Some friends planned to travel at a rate of 12 km/hr on a 20 km bike trip. Several times during the trip they recorded the total distance traveled and the time elapsed. They also recorded the time it would have taken them at their planned rate of 12 km/hr. Their data are shown in the table below. a–b. See margin

   a. Make a scatter plot that compares distance and actual time. Put distance on the horizontal axis.

   b. On the same graph, use a different color to plot ordered pairs (distance, planned time). Use these new points to make a line graph. (In a line graph, a segment is drawn to connect each point to the next point.)

Distance	Planned Time	Actual Time
0 km	0 min	0 min
2 km	10 min	6 min
4 km	20 min	22 min
6 km	30 min	32 min
10 km	50 min	45 min
14 km	70 min	58 min
15 km	75 min	60 min
17 km	85 min	77 min
20 km	100 min	90 min

   c. How does the planned time compare with the actual time?

   d. During what stage of the trip were people traveling the fastest? Explain how you found your answer.

Tell whether each graph shows a *positive correlation*, a *negative correlation*, or *no correlation* between the two variables.

5.
Cassette and CD Sales for 1989–1996

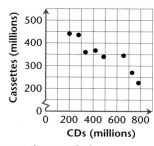

negative correlation

6.
Population Density and Area of Hungarian Counties

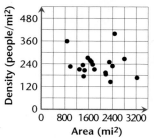

no correlation

4. a–b. See Additional Answers beginning on page A1.

7. Tell whether each scatter plot appears to have a straight-line pattern, a curved pattern, or no pattern.

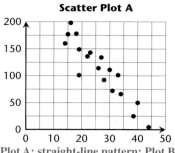

Scatter Plot A

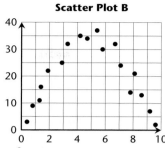

Scatter Plot B

Plot A: straight-line pattern; Plot B: curved pattern

Biology The table shows biological data for several animals.

Animal	Body weight (kg)	Brain weight (g)	Heart rate (beats/min)	Life span (years)
Mouse	0.02	0.40	630	3.2
Hedgehog	0.79	3.5	250	6.0
Kangaroo	35	56	130	16
Pig	190	180	78	27
Cow	470	420	45	30
Elephant	2500	4600	30	69

Use the table to tell whether there is a *positive correlation*, a *negative correlation*, or *no correlation* between each pair of variables.

8. brain weight, body weight
positive correlation

9. heart rate, body weight
negative correlation

10. heart rate, brain weight
negative correlation

11. life span, body weight
positive correlation

12. life span, brain weight
positive correlation

13. life span, heart rate
negative correlation

14. One rule of thumb from someone living in New York City states that to predict the day's high temperature, add 18 degrees to the temperature at 6:00 A.M.

a. Do you think this is a good rule of thumb? Explain how you can use the scatter plot at the right to convince someone you are right.

b. Does it make sense to fit a line to the data in the scatter plot? Explain your reasoning.

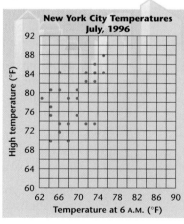

New York City Temperatures July, 1996

14. a. Sample Response: No; the temperatures found by adding 18° to the temperatures at 6 A.M. are almost always greater than the corresponding high temperatures in the scatter plot.

b. No; The correlation is weak.

EXERCISE NOTES

Exercise 7 Students may need to attempt to draw a line or a curve through the points on the graphs to visualize the shape of the graph.

Exercise 14 Some students may argue that the data in the plot is too spread out to fit a line or infer a correlation exists. By drawing an ellipse that contains most of the points, students will see that most of the data points fall near a line that has positive slope indicating a positive correlation. Those points that fall a distance away from the line may be explained by a front that moved into the area, changing the normal weather pattern.

Practice & Applications

Exercise 16 You may want to make two transparencies each containing the same scale. Prepare each scatter plot in a different color on separate transparencies. You can then overlay them to see how the data and the fitted lines compare.

15. **Challenge** Suppose there is a positive correlation between *x* and *y* and a negative correlation between *y* and *z*. What kind of correlation is there between *x* and *z*? Explain. **negative; As *x* increases, *y* increases. As *y* increases, *z* decreases. So, as *x* increases, *z* decreases.**

16. a. **History** Make a scatter plot of the female employment data below. Put population age 16 and over on the horizontal axis and the number employed on the vertical axis. Add the male employment data to your scatter plot. Draw a fitted line for each set of data points. **See margin.**

Employment Status of United States Civilian Population in millions (1960–2005)				
	Total Female Population		Total Male Population	
Year	Age 16 and over	Employed	Age 16 and over	Employed
1960	62	22	58	44
1965	67	25	62	46
1970	73	30	67	49
1975	80	34	73	51
1980	87	41	80	56
1985	94	47	84	60
1990	99	54	90	65
1995	103	58	95	67
2000	111	64	102	73
2005	117	66	110	76

b. Predict how many women will be employed when the total female population age 16 and over is 130 million.
Answers will vary. About 74 million

c. About what will the number of males age 16 and older be if 90 million of them are employed?
Answers will vary. About 123 million

17. **Home Involvement** Use a tennis ball, racquetball, or other small ball to compare drop height and bounce height. Have a friend or family member help you.
a–c. Answers will vary. Check students' work.

a. Drop the ball from five different heights. For each drop, measure the height the ball was dropped from and the height it reached on its first bounce. Record your data.

b. Use your data to make a scatter plot. Put drop height on the horizontal axis and bounce height on the vertical axis. Draw a fitted line if it makes sense.

c. Based on your scatter plot, do you think there is a relationship between drop height and bounce height? Explain.

16. a. See Additional Answers beginning on page A1.

Reflecting ◀▶ on the Section

18. Explain how scatter plots could be used in science class. Describe an actual problem or experiment where a scatter plot was used. You may want to interview a science teacher or student in your school to see how they use scatter plots. Answers will vary.

RESEARCH

Exercise 18 checks that you know how to use a scatter plot.

Spiral ◀▶ Review

Find each answer. (Toolbox, p. 589)

19. 4^2 16   **20.** 2^4 16   **21.** $3 \cdot 2^3$ 24   **22.** $3.14 \cdot 2.5$ 7.85

Find the area of each figure. (Toolbox, p. 595)

23.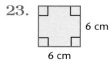
6 cm
6 cm
36 cm²

24.
4 m
9 m
36 m²

25.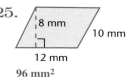
8 mm
10 mm
12 mm
96 mm²

26. Football The heaviest football players are usually defensive linemen, linebackers, and offensive linemen. The box-and-whisker plots below compare the weights of these players on an NFL team. Use the box-and-whisker plots to tell whether each statement below is true or false. Explain your thinking. (Module 1, p. 23)

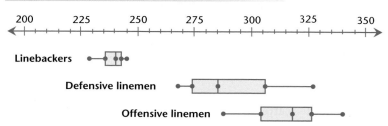

Weights (in lb) of players on an NFL team

200   225   250   275   300   325   350

Linebackers

Defensive linemen

Offensive linemen

a. All of the linebackers weigh 245 lb or less.
True; The upper extreme for linebackers is 245.
b. About half of the defensive linemen weigh less than 285 lb.
True; The median for the defensive linemen is 285 lb.
c. At least one defensive lineman weighs less than all of the linebackers.

d. About 25% of the offensive linemen weigh more than the heaviest defensive linemen.

26. c. False; The upper extreme for the linebackers is about 245 lb and the lower extreme for the defensive linemen is about 270 lb.
d. True; The upper whisker of the offensive linemen contains 25% of the data values and it begins at the same value as the upper extreme of the defensive linemen plot.

EXERCISE NOTES
While investigating the accomplishments of famous athletes, students have expanded their knowledge of scatter plots and have learned how to draw a fitted line to show a trend in a data set. History and science are other disciplines where this type of data display is commonly used. You may wish to have students share their answers to **Exercise 18** so they can observe several different applications of scatter plots in science.

Extra Skill Practice

62

Section ④
Extra Skill Practice

You will need: • *graph paper* (Ex. 3)

Interpreting Data This scatter plot shows some records for the distance traveled by a human-powered vehicle in one hour.

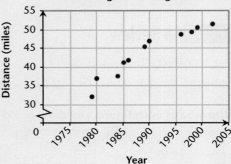

Human-Powered Land Vehicle Men's 1 Hour Records Standing Start - Single Rider

1. About how far is the longest distance record? In about what year was that record set? **52 miles; 2002**

2. Explain whether it makes sense to draw a fitted line for the scatter plot. **See margin.**

3. A snack shop owner is trying to decide how much hot cocoa to make each day. The owner records the high temperatures and cocoa sales each day for two weeks.

High temperature	77	72	75	70	71	68	69	65	64	60	55	58	54	51
Cups of cocoa sold	6	6	4	7	5	9	11	14	15	18	25	21	28	31

a. Make a scatter plot of the data. Put high temperature on the horizontal axis. Choose a scale for each axis. Explain your choices. **See margin.**

b. If it makes sense to draw a fitted line, draw one. **See margin.**

c. Suppose one pot makes 10 cups of cocoa. How many pots should the owner make when the high temperature is 50°? **3 pots**

Standardized Testing ◀▶ Free Response

Sprint times for contestants in a race at a weekend picnic are shown in the scatter plot. The contestants' ages are also shown.

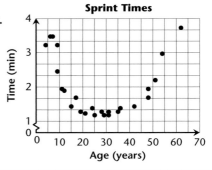

Sprint Times

1. For what ages do the times appear to be decreasing? increasing? **approximately 7 through 22; approximately 35 through 62**

2. Do the data appear to have a straight-line pattern or a curved pattern? Explain. **curved pattern; The data decreases, then levels off, then increases. This creates a curve.**

Section 5 — Problem Solving and Mathematical Models

IN THIS SECTION

EXPLORATION 1
♦ A Problem-Solving Approach

An AMAZING Lake

Setting the Stage ▸

In this module, you have explored some amazing facts. Now you will learn about a lake with some surprising features.

Lake of the Ozarks

- A lake constructed by 20,500 workers in about 2 years
- 61,000 acres (93 mi²) of water surface
- 87 billion cubic feet of water
- A shoreline almost as long as the border of the entire state of Missouri
- Located around the lake: 11 miniature golf courses, 4 underground caves, 6 go-cart tracks, and much more...

MISSOURI

Lake of the Ozarks

Think About It

1 **Discussion** Which claims on the travel brochure seem amazing? Why?

Answers will vary. Any of the claims may be listed.

Setting the Stage

GETTING STARTED
Module 1 Section 5 *Warm-Up* assesses student facility with area and perimeter of rectangles.

Your students are probably familiar with the claims of tourism brochures. You may want to have students bring in brochures from vacations, local or state tourist information agencies, or travel agencies.

The brochure shown was adapted from actual travel brochures for the Lake of the Ozarks, a popular American vacation spot.

In discussing **Question 1**, encourage students to focus on the claim that the shoreline of the Lake of the Ozarks is nearly as long as the border of the state of Missouri. As students examine the map of Missouri, they can see that the Lake of the Ozarks is contained in a small rectangle within the state. This activity should enhance their skepticism that the claim on the brochure could be true.

Exploration 1

DEVELOPING MATH CONCEPTS

Exploration 1 begins by applying problem-solving strategies to determine the validity of a claim made on the travel brochure concerning the size of the Lake of the Ozarks. Students will use a 4-step problem-solving approach to analyze this claim. You may want to go through the four steps prior to beginning this exploration or have the steps posted in the room as a reminder of a process that can be used in solving math problems.

TEACHING NOTES

Question 2(c) Each partner pair should share their rewording of the problem with another pair to see that they understand the problem.

2. a. Sample Response: The question asks us to compare the distances around objects that have different areas.

b. Sample Response: The area and perimeter of different plane figures.

3. a. Sample Response: The perimeter of a lake is the length of its shoreline. The perimeter of a polygon is the sum of the lengths on the sides of the polygon. Both perimeters are the distances around the object.

b. Sample Response: The area of a lake is the number of square units its surface covers. The area of a polygon is also the number of square units of surface the polygon encloses.

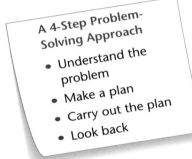
A Problem-Solving Approach

GOAL

LEARN HOW TO...
◆ use a 4-step problem-solving approach
◆ use tables, graphs, and equations to model relationships

AS YOU...
◆ learn about the Lake of the Ozarks

SET UP *Work with a partner. You will need:* • *graph paper* • *a ruler* • *Labsheet 5A*

▶ **How can the Lake of the Ozarks have a perimeter almost as long as the border of Missouri even though the area of the lake is much less than the area of the state? To answer this question, you may want to use a 4-step problem solving approach.**

> **A 4-Step Problem-Solving Approach**
> • Understand the problem
> • Make a plan
> • Carry out the plan
> • Look back

2 The first step in the 4-step approach is to *understand the problem.*

  a. What is the question asking you to compare?

  b. What information will you need to find?

  c. To show that you understand the problem, restate it in your own words.
  Sample Response: How is it possible for a figure to have a greater perimeter but smaller area than another figure?

▶ **Once you understand the problem, the next step is to *make a plan* for solving it. The plan for solving a problem often involves using problem solving strategies.**

3 Discussion

  a. How is finding the perimeter of a lake similar to finding the perimeter of a polygon?

  b. How is finding the area similar to finding the area of a polygon?

  c. How might exploring a simpler problem that involves polygons help solve the lake problem?
  Sample Response: The lake's shoreline and the state's border are both too irregular to make calculating area and perimeter feasible. Polygons are good to use since their perimeters and areas are usually easy to find.

64

4 The third step is to *carry out the plan*. Complete parts (a)–(d) to apply the *solve a simpler problem* strategy.

   a. Draw a 5-unit by 9-unit rectangle on graph paper.
   Check students' drawings.
   b. Find the perimeter and the area of the rectangle.
   perimeter: 28 units, area: 45 sq units
   c. Draw a polygon inside the rectangle that has a perimeter greater than the perimeter of the rectangle. Use only segments on the graph paper for the sides of the polygon.
   See margin.
   d. Find the perimeter and the area of your polygon.
   Answers will vary.

5 **Discussion** Explain how the Lake of the Ozarks could have a shoreline almost as long as the border of Missouri even though the area of the lake is much less than the area of state.

▶ The final step is to *look back* to see if you can verify, extend, or generalize your solution.

6 Explain how your plan helped you explain the brochure's claim about the lake's shoreline.

▶ You discovered how the Lake of the Ozarks could have a shoreline almost as long as the border of the state of Missouri. You can extend your solution by determining the greatest possible perimeter the lake could have and still enclose 61,000 acres. Start by looking at a simpler problem.

Use Labsheet 5A for Questions 7–9.

7 Follow the directions on the Labsheet to complete the *Rectangles with Area of 24 Square Units* table and graph. See margin.

8 **Try This as a Class** Use your graph on Labsheet 5A.

   a. Does your graph show the perimeter of a rectangle with a width of 10 units? Explain.

   b. Does your graph show the width of the rectangle with the least possible perimeter? Explain.

9 **a.** Draw a smooth curve to connect the points on the graph.
   See margin.
   b. Use your graph to estimate the perimeter of a rectangle with a width of 10 units. about 25 units

   c. Use your graph to estimate the width and length of a rectangle with the least possible perimeter. Draw the rectangle.
   width: 4.9 units, length: 4.9 units. Students should draw a square.

5. **Sample Response:** The shoreline could be almost as long if the lake had many inlets and still not cover the entire area of the state.

6. **Sample Response:** Carrying out my plan helped me see that to increase the perimeter, my polygon had to go in and out (be concave).

8. a. No; There is no point for width = 10. (Assuming students only drew their rectangles on the grid lines using integer values for the lengths and widths.)
   b. No; There are two rectangles with a perimeter of 20, so there is probably one with a smaller perimeter.

Question 4 is an open-ended activity with many possible solutions three of which are shown below.

Perimeter = 32 Area = 15

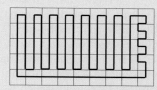

Perimeter = 76 Area = 19

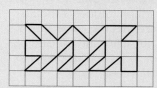

Perimeter ≈ 35.8 Area = 14

Have students share their sketches from **Question 4** and/or list their results from **part (d)** before beginning the discussion in **Question 5**.

DEVELOPING MATH CONCEPTS
Students often believe that figures with the same area must have the same perimeter and conversely, that figures with the same perimeter must have the same area. In **Question 7**, these students should notice that rectangles that have a greater number of edges of the unit squares exposed have a larger perimeter while those with more unit squares in the interior have fewer edges exposed and thus a smaller perimeter.

4. c., 7., 9. a. See Additional Answers beginning on page A1.

65

The general shape of the curve drawn in **Question 9(a)** on page 65 indicates where the perimeter reaches its minimum of a little less than 20—at the lowest point on the curve—when the width is about 5 units. Ask students to try to construct a rectangle with a width of 5 units and an area of 24 units². They will notice that the length cannot be a whole number. By dividing 24 by 5, they will find that the length will be 4.8 units making the perimeter 19.6 units which is just less than 20 units as is indicated on the graph. Students should recognize that the curve shows all the possible widths including fractional ones and rational and irrational values.

Question 10(d) The formula for finding the perimeter of a rectangle should be familiar to students. You may want to ask students to list the ways in which the formula can be expressed: $P = l + l + w + w$
$\qquad P = 2l + 2w$
$\qquad P = 2(l + w)$
Ask students which form might be considered simplest form and why.

Question 11 Make sure students understand that they have created three different models or representations for the same problem. As they respond to the questions, check to be sure they are developing a general sense of when to use an equation (when an exact answer is required and the answer is not evident in the table or graph), when to use a table (when the question matches the data in the table), and when to use a graph (when a quick estimate is required).

---

10 **a.** How can you find the length of a rectangle with an area of 24 square units and a width of 16 units? **Divide 24 by 16.**

b. What is the length? **1.5 units**

c. Write an equation that tells how to find the length of a rectangle with an area of 24 square units when you know the width. Use the variables *l* and *w* for the length and width. $l = \frac{24}{w}$

d. Write an equation for the perimeter *P* of any rectangle when you know the length *l* and the width *w*. $P = 2l + 2w$

e. Use the equations from parts (c) and (d) to find the perimeter of a rectangle with an area of 24 square units and a width of 16 units. **35 units**

▶ **Mathematical Models** Tables, graphs, and equations can be used as models to study mathematical relationships. You used them to explore relationships among the length, the width, and the perimeter of a rectangle.

11. a. Sample Response: I would use the graph because it is a faster way to find an estimate.
b. Sample Response: I would use the equations because an exact answer is needed and I could only estimate from the graph.
c. No; The graph shows that as the width gets closer to 0, the rectangle becomes long and thin so the perimeter increases.

11 ✔ **CHECKPOINT** Look back at the table, graph, and equations you made in Questions 7–10.

a. Suppose you want to quickly estimate the perimeter of a rectangle with an area of 24 square units and a width of 15 units. Which model would you use? Explain.

b. Suppose a rectangle with an area of 24 square units has a width of $\frac{1}{6}$ unit. Which model would you use to find the exact length? Why?

c. Is there a greatest possible perimeter for a rectangle with an area of 24 square units? Which model best shows this?

12 Do you think there is a greatest possible perimeter the Lake of the Ozarks could have and still enclose an area of 61,000 acres? Explain. **Sample Response: No; Based on my answers to Questions 7–11, it appears that there can be a least perimeter but not a greatest perimeter for a given area.**

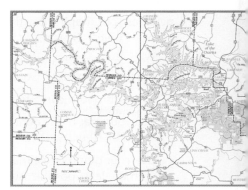

HOMEWORK EXERCISES ▶ See Exs. 1–6 on pp. 68–69.

4-Step Problem-Solving Approach (pp. 64–65)

Understand the Problem Identify the questions that need to be answered. Find the information you need to answer them. It may be helpful to restate the problem in your own words.

Make a Plan Choose a problem solving strategy such as solve a simpler problem, make a table, or use an equation. Decide what calculations, if any, are needed.

Carry out the Plan You may need to change your strategy or use a different approach, depending on how well your original plan works.

Look Back Is your solution reasonable? Could you solve the problem another way to verify your result? Can you generalize your solution or extend it to other situations or to solve other problems?

Mathematical Models (p. 66)

Tables, equations, and graphs can be used as mathematical models to study mathematical relationships.

Example Three ways to model a relationship between the perimeter P and the area A of a square with side length (s) are shown below.

Equations

$P = 4s$

$A = s^2$

Table

Perimeter (P)	Area (A)
4	1
8	4
12	9
16	16

Graph

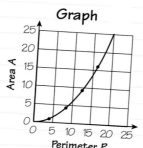

When data points fall in a curved pattern, a smooth curve can be drawn through the points as shown above.

13 Key Concepts Question

a. Explain how you could use one of the models above to find the area of a square with a perimeter 10 units long.

b. Explain how you could use a different model to estimate the perimeter of a square with area 20 square units.

13. a. Sample Response: You could use the equation $P = 4s$ to find the length of a side of the square ($10 = 4s$; $10 \div 4 = s$; $2.5 = s$). Then you could use the equation $A = s^2$ to find the area ($A = 2.5^2$; $A = 6.25$ square units).

b. Sample Response: Since you only need an estimate, you could use the graph to estimate the perimeter. Find the area 20 on the vertical axis. Move right until you hit the curve. Then move down to the horizontal axis to find the corresponding perimeter, about 18 square units.

Key Concepts

For students who were absent for all or part of this section, the blackline Study Guide for Section 5 may be used to present the ideas, concepts, and skills of Section 5.

CLOSURE QUESTION

State the 4-step approach to problem solving. Briefly explain each step.

Sample Response: (1) understand the problem, (2) make a plan, (3) carry out the plan, and (4) look back

To understand the problem, read the problem carefully and find any important information. To make a plan, select a problem-solving strategy or strategies that will help you solve the problem. To carry out the plan, solve the problem using the selected strategies along with others you may need. To look back, check that your solution is reasonable and complete and that the work done is accurate.

Practice & Applications

SUGGESTED ASSIGNMENTS

Core Course
Day 1: Exs. 7–8
Day 2: Exs. 1–4, 6

Extended Course
Day 1: Exs. 7–8
Day 2: Exs. 1–6

Note: Extended Course assignments can be used to differentiate within the regular classroom. In classrooms where students are grouped homogeneously, the material might be covered in fewer days. In this case assignments may be combined.

TEACHING NOTES

For **Exercises 1-3**, encourage students to use the 4-step problem solving approach to guide them. If students have difficulty getting started on Exercise 1, suggest that they begin with the year zero, and describe the times in years each planet completes an orbit of the sun. This should help students recognize that the problem involves least common multiples.

Exercise 5 Note that on the labsheet it is not physically possible to make a rectangle with an area of zero, therefore the points (0,14) and (14, 0) should be graphed with open circles to indicate that they are not included. Their purpose is to ensure that, when graphed, rational values less than $w = 1$ are represented.

2., 4. a., 5. a. See Additional Answers beginning on page A1.

YOU WILL NEED

For Ex. 4:
◆ Labsheet 5B

For Ex. 5:
◆ Labsheet 5C

3. a. **Sample Response:** Weigh 4 rocks on each side. Take the heavier side, divide it in half, and weigh 2 rocks on each side. Take the heavier side, divide it in half and weigh 1 rock on each side.

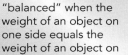

A balance scale is "balanced" when the weight of an object on one side equals the weight of an object on the other side.

4. c. **180 units; Sample Response:** the equation; An exact answer is needed. I can only estimate from the graph or the table.

d. **Sample Response:** No; As the width gets closer and closer to 0, the rectangle gets very long and thin, and I can see from the graph that this makes the perimeter greater and greater.

Module 1 Amazing Feats and Facts

Section 5
Practice & Application Exercises

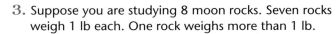

Use the 4-step problem-solving approach for Exercises 1–3.

1. Jupiter revolves around the sun about once every 12 Earth years. Saturn revolves around the sun about once every 30 Earth years. In 1982, Jupiter and Saturn appeared very close to each other. About when will Jupiter and Saturn appear together again? **2042**

2. Four different types of tents are being used on a camping trip. They include 12-person, 6-person, 5-person, and 2-person tents. Find a possible combination of tents to sleep exactly 26 people in each situation.

   a. Only one 12-person tent is used. **See margin.**

   b. The 12-person tent is not used. **See margin.**

   c. At least one 5-person tent is used. **See margin.**

3. Suppose you are studying 8 moon rocks. Seven rocks weigh 1 lb each. One rock weighs more than 1 lb.

   a. Describe how you can use a balance scale to find out which rock is the heaviest one.

   b. What is the least number of weighings you could use to find the heaviest rock? **3 weighings**

4. **Use Labsheet 5B.**

   a. Complete the table and graph on Labsheet 5B. **See margin.**

   b. Estimate the width and length of the rectangle with the least perimeter. How do the width and the length compare?
   about 5 units; about 5.5 units; They are close.

   c. Find the exact length of a rectangle with an area of 30 square units and a width of $\frac{1}{6}$ unit. Which model (*table or graph*) did you use? Why?

   d. **Writing** Is there a greatest possible perimeter for a rectangle with an area of 30 square units? Explain.

5. **Use Labsheet 5C.** Suppose the perimeter of a rectangle is 28 units.

   a. Follow the directions on the labsheet to complete the table and graph of *Rectangles with Perimeter 28 Units*. **See margin.**

   b. Determine the width and the length of a rectangle with a perimeter of 28 units and the greatest area. **The length and width of the rectangle with the greatest area is 7 units and the area is 49 square units.**

Reflecting ◀▶ on the Section

6. The polygons shown were made by placing square tiles side by side so each tile shares at least one full side with another tile. Each tile measures 1 unit by 1 unit.

a. Find the perimeter of each polygon shown. **16 units; 16 units**

b. Use 9 squares to make a polygon with a 14-unit perimeter. Sketch your result.

c. What is the least possible perimeter for a polygon made with 9 squares? **12 units (a 3 by 3 square)**

d. What is the greatest possible perimeter for a polygon made with 9 squares? **20 units (a 1 by 9 rectangle)**

Exercise 6 checks that you understand how the shape of a polygon can affect its perimeter.

6. b. Answers may vary. Sample Response:

Spiral ◀▶ Review

7. **Social Studies** Lake Baikal, located in southern Siberia, is the deepest lake in the world. At its deepest point its depth is 5371 ft. Lake Baikal is 395 mi long and varies in width from 16 mi to 50 mi. *(Module 1, p. 67)*

a. Find the area of a rectangle that is 395 mi long and 16 mi wide. **area: 6320 sq mi**

b. Find the area of a rectangle that is 395 mi long and 50 mi wide. **area: 19,750 sq mi**

c. The area covered by Lake Baikal is 12,160 mi². How does this compare with the areas you found in parts (a) and (b)? Is this what you would expect? Explain your thinking. **It is about in the middle. Sample Response: Yes; I would expect the average width to be about 33 mi which would make the area of this lake about 13,000 mi.**

RUSSIA

Bratsk Reservoir

Irkutsk •

Lake Baikal

• Ulan-Ude

Hovsgol Lake   MONGOLIA

8. a. Find the perimeter of a rectangle that is 395 mi long and 16 mi wide. *(Module 1, p. 67)* **perimeter: 822 mi**

b. Find the perimeter of a rectangle that is 395 mi long and 50 mi wide. **perimeter: 890 mi**

c. Lake Baikal has 1243 mi of shoreline. How does this compare with the perimeters you found in parts (a) and (b)?

8. c. The actual perimeter is greater than either of the two that were calculated. The shoreline must have many inlets.

Extra Skill Practice

TEACHER NOTES

All of the Extra Skills Practice Exercises correspond to Exploration 1.

EXTRA HELP

Teacher's Resource Book
- Practice and Applications for Section 5
- Study Guide
- Practice and Applications for Sections 1–5

Technology Resources
- @Home Tutor
- Test Generator

ASSESSMENT
- Section 5 Quick Quiz
- Test Generator

TEACHING NOTES

Standardized Testing

Exercise 2 If students have difficulty finding the formula, suggest that they add another row with the values of $\frac{P}{2}$ to their table. Then have them look for a formula for A in terms of $\frac{P}{2}$, and l.

3., 4., and Standardized Testing 1. See Additional Answers beginning on page A1.

You will need: • *graph paper* (Exs. 2 and 4)

Use the 4-step problem-solving approach.

1. On a hike, a climber needs to measure 5 c of water to make soup. The climber has two pots, one that holds $3\frac{1}{2}$ pt and one that holds $1\frac{1}{2}$ pt. Explain how the climber can measure exactly 5 c of water.

   1. Sample Response: Measure two $3\frac{1}{2}$ pt pots of water then remove three $1\frac{1}{2}$ pt pots of water.

Sheila was hired to organize a karate demonstration for a sports club's grand opening. She will use a space with an area of 48 square units.

2. On graph paper, draw 10 different rectangles that have an area of 48 square units. Check students' drawings. They should have 2 of each of the rectangles that are 1 by 48, 2 by 24, 3 by 16, 4 by 12, and 6 by 8.

3. Make a table for the lengths, widths, and perimeters of your 10 rectangles. See margin.

4. On a graph, plot the points for the width and perimeter of each rectangle. Put width on the horizontal axis and perimeter on the vertical axis. Draw a smooth curve to connect the points. See margin.

Write an equation or use the table or graph you made in Exercises 3 and 4 to complete Exercises 5 and 6.

5. Estimate the width and length of a rectangle with the least perimeter. Explain how you found your answer.
   about 7 units; Sample Response: I used the graph to find the least perimeter.

6. What is the exact width of a rectangle with a perimeter of 48 units and a length of 5 units? Explain how you found your answer.

   6. 19 units; Sample Response: I used the equation $P = 2l + 2w$ and substituted the values given for the variables P and l to find w.

Standardized Testing ◀▶ **Performance Task**

You will need: • *Labsheet 5D*

Pick's Formula is a formula for finding the area of a polygon drawn on dot paper. Complete the following exercises to discover Pick's Formula.

1. **Use Labsheet 5D.** Complete the table of values for the polygons drawn on the *Polygon Dot Paper*. See margin.

2. Try to guess a formula for the area A of any polygon in terms of the number of dots on its perimeter P and the number of dots in its interior I. You may want to get more data by drawing additional polygons. $A = \frac{P}{2} + I - 1$

70

FOR ASSESSMENT AND PORTFOLIOS

A Special Number

The Situation

See the *Teacher's Resource Book* for a sample solution for this Extended Exploration.

Study the number 1210. Do you notice anything special about it?

Look at the first digit in the number 1210. The 1 tells you how many 0s are in the entire number. The second digit, the 2, tells you how many 1s are in the number. This pattern continues for the other digits.

1 2 1 0

There is **1** zero in 1210.

There are **0** threes in 1210.

There are **2** ones in 1210.

There is **1** two in 1210.

The Problem

Create a 10-digit number that meets the following requirements.

- The first digit in the number tells how many 0s are in the entire number.

- The second digit tells how many 1s are in the entire number.

- The third digit tells how many 2s are in the entire number.

- The pattern continues through the tenth digit which tells how many 9s are in the entire number.

Something to Think About

- What is the sum of the digits in the number?

- What is the greatest digit that can occur in the number?

Present Your Results

Give your 10-digit number and explain what you did to find it. Is there more than one solution for the 10-digit number? How do you know?

Extended Exploration

E² NOTES

You may want to introduce the problem by discussing why the number started below cannot be a solution. (*The number of 1s would have to be at least 2.*)

Digit → 0 1 2 3 4 5 6 7 8 9
Number of → 2 1 1 0 0 ...
times digit
is used.

Then ask students to find another 4-digit number that meets the requirements. (*2020*) This will help students understand the problem and provide an opportunity to compare and discuss possible strategies for solving it.

Using an E²: Suggestions for managing and evaluating an Extended Exploration are available in the *Teacher's Resource Book* for Modules 1 and 2. See also pages T44–T45 in the *Teacher's Edition*.

ASSESSMENT SCALES

To help students assess their work on this and other Extended Explorations (E²), direct students to the Self-Assessment Scales in the Toolbox on pages 598–599. Teacher Assessment Scales appear in the *Teacher's Resource Books*.

Module Project

PROJECT NOTES

The Module Project will give students an opportunity to use the skills they have developed in his module.

Using a variety of approaches, students will analyze amazing claims and decide if the claims are fact or fiction. They will then create their own amazing claim and share the claim and analysis with the class.

As students work on the project, encourage them to use what they have learned about rates and unit measure conversions.

Labsheet: Each student needs a copy of Project Labsheet A, which is found in the *Teacher's Resource Book.*

1. **Sample Response: Find the average distance between Earth and the moon (238,857 mi). Find out how many pennies are needed to reach a height of 1 in. (17 pennies). Use this fact to determine how many pennies are needed to reach a height of 1 mi (1,077,120 pennies). Multiply this number by 238,857. (257,777,651,840 pennies) Check the answer using this method: Divide the final number of pennies by 17, then determine the number of inches in 238,857 miles. Divide the second result by the first. The results should be the same. (The answer checks.) Compare the two lengths to determine if the claim is reasonable. (It is not.)**

Fact or Fiction?

Have you ever heard or read information that seemed too unlikely to be true? For example, "the average person eats 1095 lb of food a year!" or "The surface temperature of Venus is perfect for frying eggs."

For your module project you will look at similar claims and check to see if they are true or false. Then you will do research and gather data to write your own amazing claims. Finally, you will share your claims with your class by making a poster to display the evidence that shows your claims are true or false.

SET UP

You will need:
• Project Labsheet A
• poster board
• markers

 1 **Using a 4-Step Approach** Decide whether the following claim is reasonable. Use the 4-step problem-solving approach shown below to organize your work.

A stack of 200 billion pennies would reach from Earth to the moon.

Understand the Problem	Rewrite the claim in your own words. Decide what additional information you need to prove the claim.
Make a Plan	List some problem solving strategies you can try. Decide which strategy will be best.
Carry Out the Plan	As you carry out your plan, keep careful records of everything you do and the results of your work.
Look Back	Decide whether your solution is correct. If possible, check your solution by solving the problem another way.

Using Data Displays Many "amazing claims" are based on data. You will investigate to see whether the claim below is true.

Third basemen live longer than shortstops.

Use Project Labsheet A for Questions 2 and 3.

2 Find the mean, the median, and the mode(s) of each set of data in the stem-and-leaf plots showing Baseball Players' Life Spans.

3 Tell whether you think the claim on page 72 is true. Use the data and the displays to support your answer.

Collecting Data Sometimes it may be necessary to collect information to determine if a claim is true or false.

4 Work with a partner. Have your partner count the number of times you breathe in one minute. Then use the data collected to prove whether the following claim is true.

> Human adults breathe about 23,000 times a day!

5 Choose a topic to research for your fact or fiction claim and gather data. You might want to explore the following subjects.
Check students' work.
  • Your Amazing Brain   • Extraordinary People in History

Finishing and Sharing You have written your own amazing claim and gathered data to show whether it is true or false. Now it is time to present your amazing claim to the world!

6 With a partner, create a poster showing your amazing claims. Think about interesting ways to illustrate your claims and the data you have gathered. Include enough information on the poster so that anyone reading it will be able to decide whether the claims are true or false. 6–8. Check students' claims and solutions on their posters.

7 Write the solutions for your amazing claims. Show how to determine whether your claims are true or false. You may include the solutions on your poster or keep them separate.

8 Tell where you found your information. For example, if you used a book, include the title, the author, and the page number. If you used information from a computer source, include the name of the program or website, and the name of the person or organization that created it.

"Cats: Nature's Masterwork"
by Stephen J. O'Brien
National Geographic, June, 1997

Information found:

2. Shortstops: mean: 67.4, median: 67, modes: 61, 65, and 81; Third basemen: mean: about 75.2, median: 81, mode: 77

3. Sample Response: Yes; Both the mean and the median for third basemen is higher than those for shortstops. Also, the mode for third basemen is higher than two of the modes for shortstops.

4. Measurements will vary. A person breathing 20 times in one minute would breathe about 28,800 times in a day at this rate. Taking into account increases for activity other than sitting and the slowing of breathe for 8 hours of sleep, this claim is probably reasonable.

PROJECT NOTES
Questions 2 and 3 provide a good opportunity to discuss the importance of being a critical consumer of statistics. Even though the stem-and-leaf and box-and-whisker plots confirm the statement for the baseball players listed, the data set is too small and is from a limited number of years. So, it would be risky to draw any conclusions about how long players at different positions live. Students should also notice that there is no data provided for players of other positions.

Encourage students to apply the concepts that have been covered in this module as they prepare solutions for their amazing claims. Whenever posible, they should include illustrations that highlight the amazing nature of their claims. Encourage students to use models, including tables, graphs or plots, and equations to present their solutions.

MODULE 1

Review and Assessment

4. a. Company A: lower extreme = 2
   Company B: lower extreme = 1
   b. Company A: upper extreme = 26
   Company B: upper extreme = 25
   c. Company A: lower quartile = 9
   Company B: lower quartile = 5
   d. Company A: upper quartile = 19
   Company B: upper quartile = 16

You will need: • *graph paper* (Ex. 10)

Periodical cicadas hatch at regular intervals. In Connecticut, they hatched in 1962, 1979, and 1996. (Sec. 1, Explor. 1, Sec. 5, Explor. 1)

1. The year 1996 was a leap year. Leap years generally occur every four years. When will the next hatching occur in a leap year? 2064

2. Male cicadas make a buzzing noise by using muscles to vibrate a membrane. When making this noise, the muscles move 3 times each second. How many times do the muscles move in one hour? 10,800

Two package delivery companies each have 18 airplanes. The ages of the airplanes are shown in the table. Use the table for Exercise 3 and the box-and-whisker plots for Exercises 4 and 5. (Sec. 2, Explor. 1 and 2)

Company A	2, 3, 5, 6, 9, 15, 15, 12, 13, 17, 17, 17, 19, 18, 20, 20, 21, 26
Company B	1, 2, 3, 3, 5, 8, 7, 7, 6, 9, 12, 14, 16, 16, 25, 20, 19, 16

3. a. Use the data in the table to make a back-to-back stem-and-leaf plot of the ages of the airplanes of the two delivery companies. **See margin.**

   b. What does the shape of the plot tell you about the ages of the airplanes of the two companies?

   c. Find the mean, the median, and the mode(s) of each data set and record them in a table like the one on the right.

Company	A	B
mean	?	?
median	?	?
mode	?	?

4. The box-and-whisker plots below display the data from the table. For each box-and-whisker plot, find each value. **See margin.**
   a. the lower extreme
   b. the upper extreme
   c. the lower quartile
   d. the upper quartile

3. b. Sample Response: Most of the planes owned by Company A are older than the planes owned by Company B.
   c. Company A: mean: about 14.2, median: 16, mode: 17 Company B: mean: 10.5, median: 8.5, mode: 16

Airplane Ages (years)

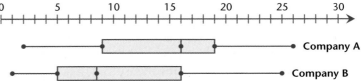

5. For which company is the statement below true? Explain how you can tell from the plots.

   At least 50% of the company's planes are less than 10 years old. Company B. The median for Company B is below 10, so more than 50% of the planes are under 10 years old.

3. a. See Additional Answers beginning on page A1.

6. What type of data display could you use if you wanted to show the number of planes in each interval by age in years: 0–5, 6–10, 11–15, 16–20, 21–25, and 26–30? (Sec. 2, Explor. 3) histogram

7. a. Admission to the 1893 World's Columbian Exposition in Chicago was $0.50 for people over age 12 and $0.25 for children aged 6–12. Children under 6 were free. Write an equation that represents the cost of tickets for any group of people attending the fair.
$t = 0.50a + 0.25c$
  b. How much would it have cost for a family of 3 adults, 1 baby, and 2 eight-year-olds to go to the Exposition? (Sec. 3, Explor. 1) $2.00

8. Use inverse operations to solve each equation. (Sec. 3, Explor. 2)

  a. $6y = 32$ **b.** $2 + 3x = 23$ **c.** $\frac{t}{4} + 3 = 9$ **d.** $3s - 16 = 11$
     $5\frac{1}{3}$ 7 24 9

9. If possible, combine like terms to simplify each expression. (Sec. 3, Explor. 3)

  a. $rs + s + r$ **b.** $3y + 6y - y$ **c.** $2t - t + 4$ **d.** $3(m + 2)$
     not possible $8y$ $t + 4$ $3m + 6$

10. Cassandra drew 6 right triangles. The perimeter of each triangle was 32 cm. She measured the base and the height of each triangle to the nearest tenth of a centimeter. Then she found the area to the nearest tenth of a square centimeter. (Sec. 4, Explor. 1 and 2)

  a. Make a scatter plot of the data in the table.
    See margin.
    • Put base length on the horizontal axis and area on the vertical axis.

    • Use a straight line or a smooth curve to connect the points.

  b. Use your graph to estimate the length of the base of the triangle with the greatest area.
    about 9 cm

Base (cm)	Height (cm)	Area (cm²)
1.5	15.2	11.4
2.9	14.4	20.9
5.9	12.4	36.6
7.9	10.8	42.7
9.3	9.4	43.7
11.9	6.6	38.7

Reflecting on the Module

11. Writing Describe a problem you solved outside of math class which involved using rates, equations, data displays, perimeter, or area. Explain how you solved the problem. Answers will vary. Check students' work.

Assessment Options

TEACHER'S RESOURCE BOOK
• Module 1 Tests A and B
• Module 1 Standardized Test
• Module 1 Performance Assessment

TEST GENERATOR

10. a. See Additional Answers beginning on page A1.

Module 2 Overview

The mall provides a context for exploring percents, sampling, probability, and integer operations. Students create numerical, statistical, visual, and algebraic representations for real-world situations, such as comparing sale prices and analyzing customer preferences.

Module 2 Planner

Day 1: Section 1	Day 2: Section 1	Day 3: Section 1	Day 4: Section 1	Day 5: Section 1
Setting the Stage, p. 78	Exploration 1, *through Question 9 pp. 79–80*	Exploration 1, *from Question 10 pp. 80–81*	Exploration 2, pp. 81–82	Exploration 3, *through Question 28 pp. 83–85*
Day 6: Section 1	**Day 7: Section 2**	**Day 8: Section 2**	**Day 9: Section 2**	**Day 10: Section 2**
Exploration 3, *from Question 29 p. 85* Key Concepts, pp. 86–87	Setting the Stage, p. 92 Exploration 1, pp. 93–94	Exploration 2, pp. 95–96	Exploration 3, *through Question 16 pp. 97–99*	Exploration 3, *from Question 17 p. 99* Key Concepts, p. 100
Day 11: Review and Assessment	**Day 12: Section 3**	**Day 13: Section 3**	**Day 14: Section 3**	**Day 15: Section 3**
Mid-Module Quiz	Setting the Stage, p. 105 Exploration 1, p. 106	Exploration 1, pp. 107–108	Exploration 2, pp. 108–110	Exploration 3, pp. 111–113 Key Concepts, pp. 114–115
Day 16: E²	**Day 17: Section 4**	**Day 18: Section 4**	**Day 19: Section 4**	**Day 20: Section 4**
Work on Extended Exploration, p. 121	Setting the Stage, p. 122 Exploration 1, pp. 123–124	Exploration 2, *through Question 12 pp. 125–126*	Exploration 2, pp. 127–128	Exploration 3, pp. 129–131 Key Concepts, p. 132
Day 21: Section 5	**Day 22: Section 5**	**Day 23: Module Project**	**Day 24: Module Project**	**Day 25: Review and Assessment**
Setting the Stage, p. 139 Exploration 1, pp. 140–141	Exploration 2, pp. 141–143 Key Concepts, pp. 143–144	Begin Module Project, pp. 150–151	Finish Module Project, pp. 150–151	Review and Assesment, pp. 152–153
Day 26: Assessment				
Module 2 Test				

Materials List

Section	Materials
1	• Labsheets 1A–1D, colored number cubes, colored disks, tracing paper, ruler, graph paper
2	• Labsheet 2A, 14 index cards, fraction calculator
3	• Labsheets 3A–3C, paper clips
4	• Labsheets 4A–4B
5	• Labsheet 5A, 4 index cards
Project	• Project Labsheets A–B, items for game pieces, markers, cardstock, scissors

Module 2 Objectives

Section	Objectives	NCTM Standards 2000*
1	• Add and subtract integers. • Use opposites to evaluate $-x$. • Evaluate absolute values and solve equations involving absolute value. • Perform translations in the coordinate plane. • Multiply and divide integers.	**1, 3, 6, 7, 8, 9, 10**
2	• Add and subtract positive and negative fractions. • Add and subtract positive and negative mixed numbers.	**1, 2, 7, 8, 9**
3	• Review probability concepts and vocabulary. • Find theorectical probabilities. • Find experimental probabilities. • Use tree diagrams to model the outcomes of an experiment and to find theoretical probabilities.	**1, 5, 6, 7, 8, 9**
4	• Estimate a percent of a number. • Use proportions to find percents and solve problems. • Use equations to find percents. • Begin to understand the meanings of population, sample, and representative sample. • Summarize and interpret survey results.	**1, 2, 5, 6, 7, 8, 9, 10**
5	• Use estimation and mental math to find percents. • Use percents to solve problems. • Find and apply percents of change.	**1, 2, 6, 7, 8, 9, 10**

* See page T14.

Section ① Operations with Integers

Section 1 Planner

Section Objectives

Exploration 1
- Add integers
- Use opposites to evaluate −x
- Evaluate absolute values and solve equations involving absolute value

Exploration 2
- Subtract integers
- Perform translations in the coordinate plane

Exploration 3
- Multiply and divide integers

Days for Section 1

First Day
Setting the Stage, p. 78

Second Day
Exploration 1 through Question 9, pp. 79–80

Third Day
Exploration 1, pp. 80–81

Fourth Day
Exploration 2, pp. 81–82

Fifth Day
Exploration 3 through Question 28, pp. 83–85

Sixth Day
Exploration 3, p. 85
Key Concepts, pp. 86–87

Teaching Resources

Teacher's Resource Book
- Warm-Up
- Labsheets 1A, 1B, 1C, and 1D
- Practice and Applications
- Study Guide
See page 77 for additional teaching resources.

Materials List

Exploration 1
- Labsheets 1A and 1B
- 2 colored number cubes per group
- colored disks

Exploration 2
- Labsheet 1C
- tracing paper

Exploration 3
- Labsheet 1D and ruler

Practice and Applications
- Labsheet 1B and graph paper

Assessment Options

EMBEDDED ASSESSMENT
- Add integers
  Exercises 1, 2, 3
- Use opposites to evaluate −x
  Exercise 17
- Evaluate absolute values
  Exercise 16
- Subtract integers
  Exercises 26, 27, 30, 31
- Peform translations
  Exercise 35
- Multiply and divide integers
  Exercises 39, 40, 41

PERFORMANCE TASK/PORTFOLIO
- Exercise 25 on *p. 88 (challenge)*
- Exercise 33(b) on *p. 88 (writing)*
- Exercise 55 on *p. 90 (visual thinking)*
- Standardized Testing on *p. 91 (open-ended)*

QUIZZES/TESTS
- Section 1 Quick Quiz

TEST GENERATOR

Section 1 Overview

In this section, students will explore how mathematics is used to play and program video games.

Exploration 1
Students play a game in which they plot points on a coordinate plane by modeling integer addition. In a variation of the game, students use equations to solve for one of the coordinates and identify quadrants. Students develop strategies and formulate rules for adding integers. The concepts of opposite and absolute value are introduced and developed.

Exploration 2
Students use subtraction to translate an object on a coordinate plane. Students recognize that for any subtraction problem there is an equivalent addition problem and learn to rewrite subtraction expressions as addition expressions.

Exploration 3
This exploration leads students to discover the way in which multiplication and division are used to create a line on a coordinate plane. They look for patterns in linear equations and recognize how the coefficients affect the slope of a line. Students build strategies for multiplying and dividing integers and develop understanding of the relationship between the two operations.

Guide for Assigning Homework

REGULAR SCHEDULING (45 MIN CLASS PERIOD)			EXERCISES TO NOTE		
Section/ P&A Pages	**Core** **Assignment**	**Extended** **Assignment**	**Additional** **Practice/Review**	**Open-ended** **Problems**	**Extended** **Problems**
1 pp. 88–91	**Day 1:** SR 56–65 **Day 2:** 1–6 **Day 3:** 7–24 **Day 4:** 26–33, 35 **Day 5:** 36–39, 48–52 **Day 6:** 40–47, 53, ROS 55	SR 56–65 1–6 13–25 26–27, 30–35 38–39, 48–52 40–41, 44–47, 53–54, ROS 55, 66–69	TB, p. 590 EP, p. 91	ST 1, 2	Ext 66–69 Challenge, PA 25, 54

Key: PA = Practice & Application; ROS = Reflecting on the Section; SR = Spiral Review; TB = Toolbox; EP = Extra Skill Practice; Ext = Extension; ST = Standardized Testing

Math Background and Teaching Strategies

Classroom Notes

Bulletin Board display ideas for this section include:

• pictures of malls, stores, and sale advertisements

Visitors might include:

• mall manager

• video game designer

Math Strands

Topic Spiraling and Integration

Exploration 1

Students should be familiar with integer addition, since the concept has been taught in both Books 1 and 2. In Book 3, the lesson for adding integers focuses on coordinate graphing and evaluating an equation to determine the y-coordinate. The steps students follow in building a table of x and y values lay a foundation for graphing equations. In Module 1, graphing of equations and data was limited to the first quadrant. Now, with the inclusion of integers, writing and graphing equations will be extended into all four quadrants. Students will apply and expand these skills in Modules 3, 4, and 6. The absolute value of a number is an important concept for students to understand. It is needed in order to define integer addition, and is used extensively when simplifying the square roots of algebraic expressions in Module 7.

Exploration 2

Subtracting fractions, which is introduced in this exploration, will be revisited immediately in Section 2 of this module as students learn to add and subtract positive and negative fractions and mixed numbers.

Exploration 2 uses translations to write subtraction expressions. Exposure to translations and writing the related expression for an image will be important for graphing linear and quadratic functions in Modules 4 and 6. Using a parent equation such as $y = x^2$, students will be able to identify how the transformation represented by $y = x^2 + 3$ affects the image of the parent equation.

Exploration 3

Multiplication and division of integers in Exploration 3 completes the calculations with integers. Students will be expected to have mastery of the four basic operations with integers when simplifying expressions, solving equations, solving inequalities, factoring polynomials, and analyzing sequences in Modules 6 and 7.

Section 2 Operations with Fractions

Section 2 Planner

Section Objectives

Exploration 1
- Add and subtract two positive fractions
- Add two negative fractions

Exploration 2
- Add and subtract positive and negative fractions

Exploration 3
- Add and subtract positive and negative mixed numbers

Days for Section 2

First Day
Setting the Stage, p. 92
Exploration 1, pp. 93–94

Second Day
Exploration 2, pp. 95–96

Third Day
Exploration 3 through Question 16, pp. 97–98

Fourth Day
Exploration 3, p. 99
Key Concepts, p. 100

Teaching Resources

Teacher's Resource Book
- Warm-Up
- Labsheet 2A
- Practice and Applications
- Study Guide
See page 77 for additional teaching resources.

Materials List

Exploration 2
- Labsheet 2A
- 14 index cards

Exploration 3
- game cards from Exploration 2

Practice and Applications
- fraction calculator

Assessment Options

EMBEDDED ASSESSMENT
- Add and subtract two positive fractions
  Exercises 1, 3
- Add two negative fractions
  Exercises 5, 6
- Add and subtract positive and negative fractions
  Exercises 12, 13, 14, 19
- Add and subtract positive and negative mixed numbers
  Exercises 23, 24, 25, 26

PERFORMANCE TASK/PORTFOLIO
- Exercise 20 on *p. 101 (writing)*
- Exercise 21 on *p. 102 (patterns)*
- Exercise 36 on *p. 103 (challenge)*
- Exercise 38 on *p. 103 (discussion)*

QUIZZES/TESTS
- Section 2 Quick Quiz
- Mid-Module Quiz

TEST GENERATOR

Section 2 Overview

In this section, students begin their work by estimating the height of an amusement park ride, as well as the speed of the *Mindbender* rollercoaster. Student will then play *Fraction Mindbender* in which they try to create the greatest sum or difference using numbers, addition and subtraction symbols, and positive and negative signs in a fraction expression. Students will see that adding two fractions will not necessarily give a greater number than subtracting the fractions.

Exploration 1
To play the *Fraction Mindbender* game students will have to apply the rules for adding and subtracting integers in order to add and subtract fractions. Exploration 1 reviews addition and subtraction of positive fractions and mixed numbers and introduces the addition of two negative fractions.

Exploration 2
As students play *Fraction Mindbender*, computation with fractions is extended to include operations with both positive and negative fractions within the same expression.

Exploration 3
Exploration 3 builds on student understanding of Explorations 1 and 2 as they focus on operations with positive and negative mixed numbers. Students will play the game *Mixed Number Mindbender* to gain more practice and understanding of these concepts.

Guide for Assigning Homework

REGULAR SCHEDULING (45 MIN CLASS PERIOD)			EXERCISES TO NOTE		
Section/ P&A Pages	Core Assignment	Extended Assignment	Additional Practice/Review	Open-ended Problems	Extended Problems
2 pp. 101–104	**Day 1:** 1–10 **Day 2:** 11–19 **Day 3:** 20–21, SR 39–43 **Day 4:** 22–35, ROS 38	5–10 11–19 20–21, SR 39–43 22–37, ROS 38	EP, p. 104 TB, p. 585		Challenge, PA 36–37

Key: PA = Practice & Application; ROS = Reflecting on the Section; SR = Spiral Review; TB = Toolbox; EP = Extra Skill Practice; Ext = Extension; ST = Standardized Testing

Math Background and Teaching Strategies

Classroom Ideas

Bulletin Board ideas for this section include:

• articles and advertisements from newspapers and magazines that use positive and negative fractions

Interest centers for this section might include:

• additional copies of the *Fraction Mindbender* game boards for additional practice

• other fraction games

Math Strands

Topic Spiraling and Integration

Exploration 1
Addition and subtraction of positive fractions and mixed numbers are treated as review topics from Book 1 and Book 2. As an alternative method to regrouping and renaming when subtracting mixed numbers, students are introduced to the method of rewriting mixed numbers as fractions. This is taught in anticipation of having to add and subtract negative and positive mixed numbers in Exploration 3.

Exploration 2
The rules for adding and subtracting integers play a key role in the methods for adding and subtracting negative and positive fractions. To build on students' understanding of integer operations the negative sign of a fraction is best allocated to the numerator so that the rules for integer operations can be applied. Conceptually students should understand that the negative sign reflects a negative fraction, but for ease of performing calculations it is carried with the numerator, since the operations of addition and subtraction involve adding/ subtracting the numerators.

Exploration 3
Rewriting mixed numbers as fractions is a preferred method for adding and subtracting mixed numbers when the signs on the numbers are not all positive. It avoids many of the errors attributed to renaming because, once the fractions have been expressed with a common denominator, students can apply the rules for integers to the numerators of the fractions. Addition and subtraction of fractions and mixed numbers will appear again when solving and graphing equations and with arithmetic sequences in Modules 3, 4, and 8.

Section 3 Exploring Probability

Section 3 Planner

Section Objectives

Exploration 1
- Find experimental probabilities
- Review probability concepts and vocabulary

Exploration 2
- Recognize independent and dependent events
- Find theoretical probabilities

Exploration 3
- Use a tree diagram to model the outcomes of an experiment and to find theoretical probabilities

Days for Section 3

First Day
Setting the Stage, p. 105
Exploration 1, p. 106

Second Day
Exploration 1, pp. 107–108

Third Day
Exploration 2, pp. 108–110

Fourth Day
Exploration 3, pp. 111–113
Key Concepts, pp. 114–115

Teaching Resources

Teacher's Resource Book
- Warm-Up
- Labsheets 3A, 3B, and 3C
- Practice and Applications
- Study Guide
See page 77 for additional teaching resources.

Materials List

Exploration 1
- Labsheets 3A–3B
- paper clip

Exploration 3
- Labsheet 3C

Practice and Applications
- paper clip

Assessment Options

EMBEDDED ASSESSMENT
- Review probability concepts and vocabulary
  Exercises 4, 5, 6
- Find experimental probabilities
  Exercises 10, 14
- Recognize independent and dependent events
  Exercise 27
- Find theoretical probabilities
  Exercises 19, 20
- Use tree diagrams to model the outcomes of an experiment and to find theoretical probabilities
  Exercises 31, 32

PERFORMANCE TASK/PORTFOLIO
- Exercise 26 on *p. 118 (open-ended)*
- Exercise 29 on *p. 119 (writing)*
- Exercise 30 on *p. 119 (challenge)*
- Exercise 33 on *p. 119 (journal)*
- Extended Exploration on *p. 121**

* indicates a problem-solving task that can be assessed using the Assessment Scales

QUIZZES/TESTS
- Section 3 Quick Quiz

TEST GENERATOR

Section 3 Overview

In this section, students learn to calculate experimental and theoretical probabilities as well as represent outcomes using a tree diagram. The section begins with a discussion of a contest at a mall in which each customer is given the opportunity to win a gift certificate by spining a spinner.

Exploration 1
By simulating the contest, students estimate the probability of winning the mall contest. In doing so, they will record the results of their experiment and then use ratios to write the experimental probability of winning. The simulation will introduce them to *experiments, outcomes, equally likely outcomes, events, probability,* and *experimental probabilities.*

Exploration 2
Students look at a different mall promotion in which the numbered spheres are not put back into the box after they are drawn. Students determine the theoretical probability of winning a gift certificate using this model. *Independent, dependent, impossible,* and *certain events* are defined.

Exploration 3
Students use tree diagrams to model the possible results of an experiment. They learn how the branches of a tree diagram represent the stages of an experiment. Then they use tree diagrams to find the theoretical probabilities of events associated with the mall contest.

Guide for Assigning Homework

REGULAR SCHEDULING (45 MIN CLASS PERIOD)			EXERCISES TO NOTE		
Section/ P&A Pages	**Core Assignment**	**Extended Assignment**	**Additional Practice/Review**	**Open-ended Problems**	**Extended Problems**
3 pp. 115–120	**Day 1:** 1–7, SR 34–44 **Day 2:** 8–16 **Day 3:** 17–27 **Day 4:** 28–29, 31–32, ROS 33	4–7, SR 34–44 8–16 17–27 28–32, ROS 33	EP, p. 120	PA 26 ROS 33	Challenge, PA 30 E^2, p. 121

Key: PA = Practice & Application; ROS = Reflecting on the Section; SR = Spiral Review; TB = Toolbox; EP = Extra Skill Practice; Ext = Extension; ST = Standardized Testing

Math Background and Teaching Strategies

Classroom Notes

Interest centers for this section might include:

- activities in which students record the experimental probabilities
- games in which students determine the theoretical probability of winning the game

Math Strands

Exploration 1
Experimental probability is the focus of this exploration. The vocabulary introduced is applicable to both theoretical and experimental probability and should continue to be used throughout the other explorations. The experimental probability of an event is defined as a ratio in fraction form. Students should be able to convert probabilities from fraction to decimal form. Since students are exposed to percents such as a 50% chance of an event occurring, they should understand that in decimal and fraction form a probability is a number from 0 through 1, yet in percent form the range is from 0 through 100% (the percent equivalent of 1).

Exploration 2
Theoretical probability allows students to figure probabilities without having to conduct an experiment. This exploration focuses on contrasts between theoretical/ experimental probability, dependent/ independent events, and certain/ impossible events.

Exploration 3
In Exploration 3 students use tree diagrams as a method for determining theoretical probabilities. Tree diagrams allow for representation of both dependent and independent events by inclusion or elimination of branches. The structure helps students organize possible outcomes and to see duplicated outcomes. Tree diagrams are seen again in Section 5 of Module 4 as a method for showing permutations and combinations and as a tool for developing the counting principle.

Throughout the explorations and practice and application exercises in this section, students are exposed to a variety of situations for which probabilities can be calculated, such as spinning a spinner, playing a game of *Rock, Paper, Scissors*, rolling 6-sided and 8-sided number cubes, drawing lettered tiles or marbles from a bag, and flipping a coin. In Module 6 students explore how probability can be related to areas of geometric figures.

Section 4 Surveys, Proportions, and Percents

Section 4 Planner

Section Objectives

Exploration 1
- Use percents, fractions, and decimals to summarize the results of a survey
- Identify and correct biased survey questions

Exploration 2
- Use proportional reasoning to estimate the percent of a number
- Identify representative samples

Exploration 3
- Write equations to solve percent problems
- Find a representative sample

Days for Section 4

First Day
Setting the Stage, *p. 122*
Exploration 1, *pp. 123–124*

Second Day
Exploration 2 through Question 12, *pp. 125–126*

Third Day
Exploration 2, *pp. 127–128*

Fourth Day
Exploration 3, *pp. 129–131*
Key Concepts, *p. 132*

Teaching Resources

Teacher's Resource Book
- Warm-Up
- Labsheets 4A and 4B
- Practice and Applications
- Study Guide
See page 77 for additional teaching resources.

Materials List

Exploration 1
- Labsheet 4A

Exploration 3
- completed Labsheet 4A
- Labsheet 4B

Assessment Options

EMBEDDED ASSESSMENT
- Use percents, fractions, and decimals to summarize results of a survery
  Exercises 14, 19
- Identify and correct biased survey questions
  Exercises 10, 12
- Use proportional reasoning to estimate the percent of a number
  Exercises 16, 17
- Identify representative samples
  Exercise 13
- Write equations to solve percent problems
  Exercises 31, 33, 35
- Find a representative sample
  Exercise 39

PERFORMANCE TASK/PORTFOLIO
- Exercise 36 on *p. 135 (writing)*
- Exercise 41 on *p. 136 (journal)*
- Exercises 50–51 on *p. 137 (Extension)*

QUIZZES/TESTS
- Section 4 Quick Quiz

TEST GENERATOR

Section 4 Overview

In this section, students will continue to explore how mathematics is used at shopping malls by looking at a teen survey.

Exploration 1
Students begin by conducting a survey and summarizing the results. During this activity students see how the way questions are asked can influence the results of a survey. Students identify and then rewrite biased questions.

Exploration 2
In this exploration, the key terms *population*, *sample*, and *representative sample* are introduced. Once a representative sample is selected, students can use the results of a survey to estimate information about the population for which the survey was intended. Two different methods for estimating a percent of a number are shown. One method focuses on use of "nice" fractions. The other on the use of multiples of 10%. A percent bar model is used to visualize the process. Using proportions to solve percent problems is also reviewed.

Exploration 3
In the context of surveys, students use equations to make predictions and calculate missing data. The equations are categorized into three types for which information is missing: the *part*, the *percent*, and the *total*.

Guide for Assigning Homework

REGULAR SCHEDULING (45 MIN CLASS PERIOD)			EXERCISES TO NOTE		
Section/ P&A Pages	Core Assignment	Extended Assignment	Additional Practice/Review	Open-ended Problems	Extended Problems
4 pp. 133–138	**Day 1:** 1–12 **Day 2:** 13–15, SR 42–49 **Day 3:** 16–26 **Day 4:** 28–37, 39–40, ROS 41	10–12 13–15, SR 42–49 16–20, 24–27 28–40, ROS 41, Ext 50–51	TB, p. 588 EP, p. 138	PA 39	Challenge, PA 38 Ext 50–51

Key: PA = Practice & Application; ROS = Reflecting on the Section; SR = Spiral Review; TB = Toolbox; EP = Extra Skill Practice; Ext = Extension; ST = Standardized Testing

Math Background and Teaching Strategies

Classroom Ideas

Bulletin Board ideas for this section include:

- a "survey says..." board of various survey results from magazines and newspaper articles

- survey results from Exploration 1

- a table with biased and unbiased columns where students can post biased questions and restate them in unbiased ways.

Math Strands

Topic Spiraling and Integration

Exploration 1
Much of information found in newspapers, magazines, and commericals, or on internet sites describes public opinion about a topic or product. The opinions often have been obtained through a survey.

The information often is summarized with ratios such as 95% who use the product saw results in 2 weeks, or 4 out of 5 teenagers prefer... . In this exploration, decimal, percent, and fraction skills are reviewed as students use these three forms of a ratio to summarize the results of a survey.

Exploration 2
After completing Explorations 1 and 2, students should become more critical readers of surveys and survey results. After learning in Exploration 1 about how the form of a survey question can affect the results obtained, students also explore how the sample selected to represent a population can create biased results. Students learn that mathematics is not just about analyzing data, but also about making sure data is collected in a solid, unbiased manner. This real world skill can help them become wiser consumers and

make them more aware of the data, samples, and survey results they use to support their mathematical solutions of problems such as E^2s. Students continue to use percent skills to make predictions about a population on the basis of results from a representative sample. Estimation skills, proportions, fractions, and solving one-step equations are applied in the context of making predictions.

Exploration 3
In Module 1 students wrote and solved simple algebraic equations. In Exploration 3, students continue to represent information as an equation and solve it to find either a percent or a number.

Section 5 Planner

Section Objectives

Exploration 1
- Use estimation and mental math to find percents
- Use percents to solve problems

Exploration 2
- Estimate and apply percents of change

Days for Section 5

First Day
Setting the Stage, *p. 139*
Exploration 1, *pp. 140–141*

Second Day
Exploration 2, *pp. 141–143*
Key Concepts, *pp. 143–144*

Teaching Resources

Teacher's Resource Book
- Warm-Up
- Labsheet 5A
- Practice and Applications
- Study Guide
See page 77 for additional teaching resources.

Materials List

Exploration 1
- Labsheet 5A
- 4 index cards labeled A, B, C, and D

Assessment Options

EMBEDDED ASSESSMENT
- Use estimation and mental math to find percents
  Exercises 1, 5, 8
- Use percents to solve problems
  Exercises 6, 7
- Estimate and apply percents of change
  Exercises 10b, 12, 15c

PERFORMANCE TASK/PORTFOLIO
- Exercise 16 on *p. 147* (home involvement)
- Exercise 17 on *p. 147* (research)
- Standardized Testing on *p. 149* (performance task)
- Module Project on *pp. 150–151*

QUIZZES/TESTS
- Section 5 Quick Quiz
- Module Tests A and B
- Module Standardized Test
- Module Performance Assessment

TEST GENERATOR

Section 5 Overview

In this section, students will extend their study of percents from the previous section to see how mental math and estimation can be used for comparison shopping.

Exploration 1
Students begin by playing the *Bargain Basement* game in which they must estimate different sale prices of an item. The strategy of the game involves determining the best buys by estimating percents or by finding a sale price when the fraction or percent of savings is given.

Exploration 2
As they work with percent discount and percent markup, students will learn how to calculate a percent of decrease and a percent of increase. They study the relationship between the new price and the old price when either percent of change is involved. In a class activity, students find an amount of decrease given the percent of decrease and the original amount. This will require them to solve a proportion.

Module Project
In the Module Project, students design a shopping game based on percents.

Guide for Assigning Homework

REGULAR SCHEDULING (45 MIN CLASS PERIOD)			EXERCISES TO NOTE		
Section/ P&A Pages	**Core Assignment**	**Extended Assignment**	**Additional Practice/Review**	**Open-ended Problems**	**Extended Problems**
5 pp. 144–149	**Day 1:** 1–9, SR 18–23 **Day 2:** 10–16, ROS 17, SR 24–30	1–9, SR 18–23 10–16, ROS 17, SR 24–30, Ext 31–32, Career 33–34	EP, p. 149 Review & Assessment, pp. 152–153	ROS 17	Ext 31–32 Career 33–34 Mod Proj, pp. 150–151

Key: PA = Practice & Application; ROS = Reflecting on the Section; SR = Spiral Review; TB = Toolbox; EP = Extra Skill Practice; Ext = Extension; ST = Standardized Testing

Math Background and Teaching Strategies

Classroom Ideas

Bulletin Board ideas for this section include:

- sales advertisements showing percents of discount and sale prices
- fraction, decimal, and percent equivalents chart

Math Strands

Topic Spiraling and Integration

Exploration 1
Applications with percents continue from Section 4, but in the context of shopping and sale prices. Students are encouraged to mentally calculate percents and to estimate percent by knowing how to find 10% of a number. Once students are able to accomplish this skill, they can find any multiple of 10%, such as 30% by tripling the result of 10%, or 90% by reducing the whole amount (100%)

by 10% to result in 90%. Teacher questioning should include asking students to develop strategies for finding 15%, which might include using the multiples to find 30% and then taking half, or finding half of 10% and adding it to 10% of the number. Discussion focuses on why two different methods for finding sale prices of items have equivalent results. The two methods discussed include finding the sale price of an item by calculating the amount of discount and then subtracting the amount of discount from the original price or by subtracting the percent of discount from 100% and then multiplying the original price by the result.

Exploration 2
Percent of increase and percent of decrease are percents of change from the original amount. The percent of decrease can be developed from students' experience in Exploration 1 where they learned that:

$$original\ amount \cdot \frac{percent\ of\ decrease}{100} =$$

amount of decrease.

Solving the equation for percent of decrease gives: *percent of decrease =*

$$\frac{amount\ of\ decrease}{original\ amount} \cdot 100.$$

Both percent of increase and percent of decrease represent percents of change. Students should be aware of whether an amount has increased or decreased when finding the percent of change.

Module 2

OVERVIEW

The mall provides a context for exploring percents, sampling, probability, and integer operations. Students create numerical, statistical, visual, and algebraic representations for real-world situations, such as comparing sale prices and analyzing customer preferences.

PREREQUISITE SKILLS

Warm-Up Exercises for each section are provided in the *Teacher's Resource Book*. You can use these exercises to review skills and concepts students will need for each section. In addition, the Spiral Review exercises at the end of each section in the student edition provide practice on prerequisite skills.

MODULE DIAGNOSTIC TEST

The Module Diagnostic Test in the *Teacher's Resource Book* can be used to assess students' prior knowledge of skills and concepts that will be taught in each section of this module. You can use test results to help structure your teaching to meet the diverse needs of your classroom.

MODULE
2
AT THE
MALL

76

CONNECTING
MATHEMATICS
The & Theme

MODULE 2 **SECTION OVERVIEW**

① Operations with Integers

As you discover how video games are created:

- ◆ Add and subtract integers
- ◆ Multiply and divide integers
- ◆ Find absolute values and opposites of integers

② Operations with Fractions

As you explore a mall:

- ◆ Add and subtract positive and negative fractions
- ◆ Add and subtract positive and negative mixed numbers

③ Exploring Probability

As you find the chances of winning a contest:

- ◆ Find experimental probabilities
- ◆ Find theoretical probabilities
- ◆ Construct tree diagrams

④ Surveys, Proportions, and Percents

As you study the use of surveys:

- ◆ Summarize and interpret survey results
- ◆ Estimate percents using "nice" fractions or multiples of 10%
- ◆ Find percents using equations

⑤ Working with Percents

As you explore shopping in malls:

- ◆ Estimate percents
- ◆ Find percents of change

The Module Project
Designing a Game

There are many games that imitate life. But who makes up these games and how much of life do they imitate? In this module you will use mathematics to create your own board game about shopping in a mall. Then you will play your game, refine it, and share it with your class.

More on the Module Project
See pp. 150–151.

INTERNET
Resources and practice at
classzone.com

77

Module Resources

TEACHER'S RESOURCE BOOK
Resources
- *The Math Gazette* (parent newsletter)
- Warm-Ups
- Labsheets
- Practice and Applications
- Study Guide

Assessment
- Section Quick Quizzes
- Mid-Module Quiz
- Module 2 Diagnostic Test
- Module 2 Tests A and B
- Module 2 Standardized Test
- Module 2 Performance Assessment
- Modules 1 and 2 Cumulative Test

SPANISH RESOURCES
- *The Math Gazette* (parent newsletter)
- Practice and Applications
- Assessment
- Spanish Glossary

STUDENT WORKBOOK

TECHNOLOGY BOOK

TECHNOLOGY RESOURCES
- @Home Tutor
- Test Generator
- Activity Generator
- Professional Development DVD
- Online Activities

Setting the Stage

ABOUT THE THEME

Students use coordinate geometry to simulate a video arcade game. Many malls contain video arcades that are popular with mall visitors.

GETTING STARTED

Module 2 Section 1 *Warm-Up* assesses prerequisite skills for plotting points on a coordinate grid.

Review the rules for *Integer Invasion I* as a group prior to play. Allow 10–15 min. for playing the game. Be sure students start from the origin on each turn, not from the location of their last marker.

ABOUT THE MATERIALS

Game disks used should be transparent or small enough so as not to cover more than one planet, comet or star at a time. Some alternatives include dried beans or one-centimeter cubes.
An overhead transparency of Labsheet 1B would be helpful for a demonstration on how to play *Integer Invasion.*

TEACHING NOTES

Question 3(b) lends itself to a review of the commutative property of addition. Students should recognize that this property applies to the set of integers.

MODULE NOTES

This first section of Module 2 includes three explorations and contains a great deal of mathematics; however, it should be review for most eighth grade students. The *Try This as a Class* and *Checkpoint* questions will allow the teacher to assess student's knowledge of mathematics concepts mastered during the previous year.

Section ① Operations with Integers

IN THIS SECTION

EXPLORATION 1
♦ Adding Integers

EXPLORATION 2
♦ Subtracting Integers

EXPLORATION 3
♦ Multiplying and Dividing Integers

The

VIDEO ARCADE

Setting the Stage

SET UP *Work in groups of two. You will need: • Labsheets 1A and 1B • 2 number cubes (red and blue) • colored disks*

Where can you go if you want to meet your friends, buy a stereo, experience virtual reality, enter a spaghetti-eating contest, or ride a roller coaster? A mall, of course!

Malls provide a wide variety of entertainment options for their visitors. Because of their popularity, many malls contain video arcades. Some arcade games require skill, others are based on chance, and some combine the two. The *Integer Invasion* games are simulations of video games similar to ones you might find in a video arcade.

Use Labsheets 1A and 1B. Play *Integer Invasion I* with a partner.

Think About It

2. a. when the greater digit is positive
   b. when the greater digit is negative
   c. when the digits are the same, but the signs are opposite

1 What operation were you performing to find each coordinate in *Integer Invasion I*? addition

3. a. Sample Response: Subtract the lesser digit from the greater and make the sign of the sum that of the greater digit.

2 Use the results in your *Recording Sheet*. When will the sum of a positive integer and a negative integer be as described?

   a. positive   **b.** negative   **c.** equal to 0

3 a. How can you find the sum of a positive integer and a negative integer without using a number line?

   b. Does the order of the addends affect the sum? Explain.

▶ **Malls have become an important part of life for many people. In this module you will explore how mathematics is used at malls. You may find that math shows up when you least expect it.**

3. b. No. Sample Response: Addition is commutative so adding 3 and −4 results in the same sum as −4 + 3. The sum is −1.

Exploration 1

Adding **INTEGERS** +

SET UP Work with a partner. You will need: • Labsheets 1A and 1B
• 2 number cubes (red and blue) • colored disks

▶ In the game *Integer Invasion I* you plotted points on a coordinate grid in an attempt to hit celestial bodies. The coordinates of these points are *integers*. The **integers** are the numbers … , –3, –2, –1, 0, 1, 2, 3, … .

Use Labsheets 1A and 1B for Questions 4–8.

4 **Try This as a Class** Use the *Integer Invasion Game Board* on Labsheet 1B. In *Integer Invasion II*, each player will roll the number cubes and add the numbers rolled to determine the *x*-coordinate. Numbers on the blue cube are positive, and the ones on the red cube are negative. The *y*-coordinate will be determined by evaluating an expression.

  a. Suppose Player A rolls a 4 and a –2 (a 2 on the red cube). Write an addition expression for the *x*-coordinate. $4 + (-2)$

  b. What is the *x*-coordinate? 2

  c. To find the *y*-coordinate, substitute the value of *x* from part (a) into the expression $x + 5$ and perform the addition. $y = 2 + 5 = 7$

  d. What are the coordinates of the point? $(2, 7)$

5 Play *Integer Invasion II* with a partner. Use the rules for *Integer Invasion I*, but evaluate the expression $x + (-3)$ to determine the *y*-coordinate. Record the coordinates in a *Recording Sheet* like the one below. **Check students' work.**

Blue	Red	x	x + (–3)	y
6	2	4	4 + (–3)	1
?	?	?	?	?

6 Use the results in your *Recording Sheet*.

  a. Is the sum of two negative integers *positive* or *negative*?
  negative

  b. How can you find the sum of two negative integers?
  Add the digits and make the sum negative.

GOAL

LEARN HOW TO…
• add integers
• find the opposite of an integer
• find absolute values

AS YOU…
• simulate a video game

KEY TERMS
• integers
• quadrant
• opposite
• absolute value

Exploration 1

TEACHING NOTES
Allow 10–15 min. for playing *Integer Invasion II*. This amount of time should allow students to complete a sufficient number of plays of the game to answer Question 6 from their *Recording Sheet*.

CLASSROOM MANAGEMENT
Be sure students are aware that they have a specific amount of time to play *Integer Invasion*. Using an overhead projector timer or announcing when half of the designated time has passed will help students manage their time as they play the game.

DEVELOPING MATH CONCEPTS
Through the game and follow-up questions students should be able to determine if a sum will be positive, negative, or zero before performing the addition. Students will also gain an understanding of how the signs of the coordinates relate to each quadrant and be able to determine in which quadrant a point will lie.

DIFFERENTIATED INSTRUCTION
Students having difficulty with integer addition may benefit from using a calculator to determine the *y*-coordinate during *Integer Invasion II*. In this way, the students can participate in the game and be able to participate in making the generalizations introduced in Question 6. These generalizations will aid students in understanding how to add integers without a calculator.

Section 1 Operations with Integers **79**

79

Exploration 1 *continued*

COMMON ERRORS

In **Questions 8(a) and 8(b)**, some students may fail to add –2 to find the *y*-coordinate. Check to insure students are focusing on the equation rather than the game board.

TEACHING NOTES

Students should be able to perform **Question 9** without the aid of a number line or a calculator. However, for those who need a number line, make one available.

In **Question 11**, students should recognize when numbers are additive inverses (opposites) of each other and that zero is its own opposite.

DEVELOPING MATH CONCEPTS

Absolute value is a difficult concept for many students. For those struggling to understand why absolute value is always non-negative, use a concrete illustration such as:

It is 3000 miles from Los Angeles to New York and it is 3000 miles from New York to Los Angeles.

The direction does not matter. Distance is always nonnegative.

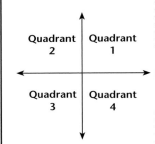

Quadrant 2   Quadrant 1

Quadrant 3   Quadrant 4

✔ **QUESTION 9**

...checks that you can add integers.

8. c. Sample Response: The value of *x* must be greater than 2 to land in the first quadrant and less than 0 to land in the third quadrant. Values of *x* between 0 and 2 will produce points in the fourth quadrant.

7 **Try This as a Class** Suppose in another game of *Integer Invasion II* the expression *x* + 2 is used to find the *y*-coordinate. For what values of *x* will the disk be placed as described?

   a. above the horizontal axis –1 and greater

   b. below the horizontal axis –3 and less

   c. on the horizontal axis –2

▶ The axes on a coordinate plane divide the grid into four sections or **quadrants**. They are numbered counterclockwise as shown.

8 **Use Labsheet 1B.** To find the *y*-coordinate, use the expression *x* + (–2).

   a. What must the value of *x* be to hit a planet in the first quadrant? 5

   b. What must the value of *x* be to hit a planet in the third quadrant? –2 or –5

   c. How does the value of *x* affect the quadrant in which the points are located?

9 ✔ **CHECKPOINT** Find each sum.

   a. –8 + (–7)   **b.** 12 + (–7)   **c.** 2 + (–6)   **d.** –7 + 7
     –15   5   –4   0

10 The numbers –3 and 3 are **opposites**. So are 7 and –7. What is true about the sum of two opposites? It always equals 0.

11 Find the opposite of each integer.

   a. –17 17   **b.** 31 –31   **c.** –215 215   **d.** 0 0

12 **Use Labsheet 1B.** A planet is located at (–5, 3) on the *Integer Invasion Game Board*. How far is the planet from each axis?

   a. the vertical axis 5   **b.** the horizontal axis 3

▶ When you found the distance from the point (–5, 3) to the vertical axis, you found the *absolute value* of –5, or |–5|. The **absolute value** of a number is its distance from 0 on a number line.

EXAMPLE

The distance from –5 to 0 is 5 units.

|–5| = 5

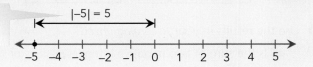

   –5 –4 –3 –2 –1 0 1 2 3 4 5

13 What other number has an absolute value of 5? 5

14 What two numbers have an absolute value of 15? 15, −15

15 Find each absolute value.

  a. $|-3|$ 3   **b.** $|0|$ 0   **c.** $|12|$ 12   **d.** $|-17|$ 17

Read −x as "the opposite of x."

16 **Try This as a Class** Suppose in a new game, *Integer Invasion III*, you are given clues to determine the location of a disk on the game board. You have these two clues about the coordinates (x, y). What are the possible positions of the disk? (5, 3) or (5, −3)

Clue 1
$-x = -5$

Clue 2
$|y| = 3$

17 ✔ **CHECKPOINT** Solve each equation.

  a. $|x| = 2$ **b.** $-y = -3$ **c.** $|a| = 7$ **d.** $-b = 12$
    2 or −2   3   7 or −7   −12

✔ **QUESTION 17**

...checks that you can solve equations with opposites and absolute values.

HOMEWORK EXERCISES ▶ See Exs. 1–25 on p. 88.

Exploration 2

Subtracting
INTEGERS

SET UP *You will need: • Labsheet 1C • tracing paper*

▶ When you played *Integer Invasion*, you attempted to hit a celestial body to score points. Game programmers may need to move these images to different locations on the grid to keep the game fresh. This type of move is a *translation*. A **translation**, or slide, moves each point of a figure the same distance in the same direction.

18 **Use Labsheet 1C.** The labsheet shows a translation on a coordinate grid. Points A', B' and C' (read "A prime, B prime, and C prime") are the **images** of points A, B, and C after the translation. Follow the instructions for *Exploring Translations* to learn more about translations.

GOAL

LEARN HOW TO...
  ◆ subtract integers
  ◆ translate figures
  ◆ define a translation algebraically

AS YOU...
  ◆ explore translations on a coordinate grid

KEY TERMS
  ◆ translation
  ◆ image

18. a. They are parallel to each other and they are congruent.
  b. Check students' work.
  c. no
  d. They are the same.
  e. $B(2, 4)$, $C(4, 5)$, $A'(7, 4)$, $B'(6, 1)$, $C'(8, 2)$
  f. $x + 4$; g. $y - 3$

Section 1 Operations with Integers

TEACHING NOTES
In **Question 16**, clarify the meaning of each equation by reading it out loud.

Read Clue 1 as, "The opposite of some number x equals negative 5." Then ask students, "What number can you take the opposite of and get negative 5?" Some students have difficulty understanding that the solution to this equation is $x = 5$ (not −5) and that it is only when 5 is substituted in place of the x that the value of the expression on the left hand side becomes negative 5. To emphasize that the negative sign is part of the expression, you can insert parentheses around the variable x and then ask students what number would have to be placed inside the parentheses for the expression on the left to match the expression on the right side of the equation.

Read Clue 2 as, "The absolute value of some number y is 3." Then ask, "What number could y be?" If students' only response is 3, draw a number line on the board and ask students to find a number that is a distance of 3 from 0. Continue to ask this question until both solutions, $y = 3$ and $y = -3$, are found.

After completing Question 16, you may want to ask the students how their answer would be different if Clue 1 had read $-x = 8$. Their responses can provide feedback as to whether students understand that −x means the opposite of x.

Exploration 2

DIFFERENTIATED INSTRUCTION
For students with limited fine motor capabilities provide a cut out or tracing of the turtle on Labsheet 1C for completing **Question 18**.

81

82

Exploration 2 *continued*

COMMON ERRORS

For **Question 20(d),** if students have difficulty understanding the concept that subtraction can be written as addition of the opposite, do more examples of changing translations from subtraction form to addition form. For example, $(x - 4, y - 1)$ becomes $(x + (-4), y + (-1))$. Show how this results in the same move on the coordinate grid.

DEVELOPING MATH CONCEPTS

Through movement on a coordinate grid, **Question 20** is designed to help students see that subtracting an integer is the same as adding the opposite of that integer. To aid in developing the concept from the **Example,** make sure students notice that the first addend is not changed when written as an addition problem and that the second addend is changed to its opposite.

CLASSROOM EXAMPLES

Find the difference: $-14 - 9$

Answer: Rewrite subtraction as addition. $-14 - 9 = -14 + (-9)$
$= -23$

Find the difference: $5 - (-11)$

Answer: Rewrite subtraction as addition. $5 - (-11) = 5 + (-(-11))$
$= 5 + 11$
$= 16$

DIFFERENTIATED INSTRUCTION

Visual Learners For students who have difficulty with the concept of changing subtraction to addition, encourage them to use a number line and to move in the opposite direction they would move if the problem was addition.

---

19 This table shows the coordinates of several points and their images after a translation.

Coordinates of the point	(3, 2)	(5, –7)	(0, –3)	(–5, 6)	(x, y)
Coordinates of the image	(2, 5)	(4, –4)	(–1, 0)	(–6, 9)	?

a. Describe the translation using the form $(x + \underline{?}, y + \underline{?})$.
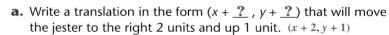
$(x + (-1), y + 3)$
b. Suppose the same translation is used on the point $(-45, -105)$. What are the coordinates of the image? $(-46, -102)$

20 **Try This as a Class** Suppose you are programming a video game in which a jester is located at point (x, y).

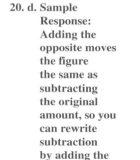

(x, y)

a. Write a translation in the form $(x + \underline{?}, y + \underline{?})$ that will move the jester to the right 2 units and up 1 unit. $(x + 2, y + 1)$

b. Use the form $(x - \underline{?}, y - \underline{?})$ to write a translation that will move the jester to the left 3 units and down 5 units. $(x - 3, y - 5)$

c. Rewrite the translation in part (b) in the form $(x + \underline{?}, y + \underline{?})$.
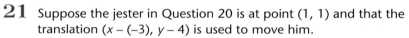
$(x + (-3), y + (-5))$
d. Explain why any subtraction expression can be written as an addition expression.

20. d. Sample Response: Adding the opposite moves the figure the same as subtracting the original amount, so you can rewrite subtraction by adding the opposite of the number after the subtraction sign.

21 Suppose the jester in Question 20 is at point (1, 1) and that the translation $(x - (-3), y - 4)$ is used to move him.

a. Write $1 - (-3)$ as an addition expression. $1 + 3$

b. What is the jester's new position after the translation $(x - (-3), y - 4)$? $(4, -3)$

c. Describe this translation in words.
Move right 3 units and down 4 units.

▶ **Subtracting Integers** As you saw in Questions 20 and 21, you can write any subtraction problem as an addition problem.

EXAMPLE

Find the difference: $-8 - (-7)$.

The opposite of –7.

SAMPLE RESPONSE $-8 - (-7) = -8 + [-(-7)]$
$= -8 + 7$
$= -1$

✔ **QUESTION 22**

...checks that you can subtract integers.

22 ✔ **CHECKPOINT** Find each difference.

a. $23 - (-15)$ **b.** $12 - (-12)$ **c.** $-80 - 22$ **d.** $-65 - (-43)$
38   24   –102   –22

HOMEWORK EXERCISES ▶ See Exs. 26–35 on pp. 88–89.

Multiplying and Dividing INTEGERS

GOAL

LEARN HOW TO...
- multiply and divide integers

AS YOU...
- explore linear equations

KEY TERM
- linear equation

SET UP   You will need: • Labsheet 1D • ruler

▶ Some video games display the path of an object such as a golf ball once it is hit or an asteroid moving through space. Programmers need to establish the paths for these visual effects. Multiplication and division may be used to create paths on a coordinate grid.

23 Use Labsheet 1D.

a. Plot points *A, B, C* and *D* on the *Exploring Multiplication* coordinate plane.   **See margin.**

b. Copy the table. Look for patterns to find the missing values.
−9, −3, 3, 12

x	−4	−3	−2	−1	0	1	2	3	4
y	−12	?	−6	?	0	?	6	9	?

c. What equation describes the relationship between *x* and *y*?
$y = 3x$

▶ **Multiplying Integers** To find the *y*-coordinate of point *A* on Labsheet 1D you must multiply the *x*-coordinate, −4, by 3. You can use repeated addition to find the product.

EXAMPLE

Use repeated addition to find 3 • (−4).

Think:
3 groups of −4.

SAMPLE RESPONSE

$$3 \cdot (-4) = (-4) + (-4) + (-4)$$
$$= -12$$

3 • (−4) can also be written as 3(−4).

Exploration 3

TEACHING NOTES

Students should be able to recognize the pattern in the table in **Question 23(b)**, however for those needing assistance, direct them to start with the positive values of *y* to complete the table and then compare the *x* and *y* values to describe a relationship in **part (c)**. Sometimes students are able to verbalize the relationship before being able to write the formal equation relating *x* and *y*. Encourage students to write the relationship between *x* and *y* in words and then guide them as to how they can transfer key words in their description into variables and symbols until they have an equation relating *x* and *y*.
Sample: The number in the second row is triple the number in the top row.
Teacher asks: "What variable are we using for the numbers in the second row?" Then have the student replace that part of their description with the variable *y*. Then use similar questioning for the remaining description (*is* translates to =, *triple* translates to 3 •, *number in the first row* translates to *x*) until reaching the equation $y = 3 \cdot x$ or $y = 3x$.

CLASSROOM EXAMPLE

Use repeated addition to find (−5) • 4.

Answer:
$$(-5) \cdot 4 = 4 \cdot (-5)$$
$$= (-5) + (-5) + (-5) + (-5)$$
$$= -20$$

23. a. See Additional Answers beginning on page A1.

83

Question 24 Students use the patterns in the table on page 83 to develop a rule for multiplying a positive and a negative integer.

In **Question 26** students develop a rule for multiplying two negative integers by using the table in **part (a)**. Encourage students to look for *when* the products in the table change from negative to positive.

TEACHING NOTES

For **Question 27**, use the same labsheet as in Question 25. Both sets of points should be plotted on the same coordinate plane for ease in comparing the two lines formed. In the **Discussion Question 27(c)** students should notice that one line has a positive slope, moving upwards from left to right on the coordinate plane, while the other has a negative slope, moving downwards left to right. Study of slope will follow in Module 3. Students may or may not use proper vocabulary at this time, so the focus should be on building the concept of slope.

DIFFERENTIATED INSTRUCTION

Points in **Questions 25 and 27** can be entered into a table and plotted using a graphing calculator or a computer graphing program.

---

25. d. Sample Response: It should fall on the line because the same equation was used for the y-coordinate.

27. b. Sample Response: It slants in the opposite direction. The line slants down from the left instead of slanting up.
   c. Sample Response: When the coefficient is positive, the line slants up to the right. When it is negative, it slants down to the right. Check students' work.

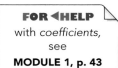

FOR ◀HELP

with *coefficients*, see

MODULE 1, p. 43

---

24 **Try this as a Class** Use your table from Question 23(b).

   a. Is the product of a positive integer and a negative integer *positive* or *negative*? negative

   b. Describe how to find the product of a positive integer and a negative integer. Sample Response: Multiply the whole number part of the integers and make the product negative.

   c. Use your method from part (b) to find the *y*-coordinate when the *x*-coordinate is –9. 3(–9) = –27

25 **Use Labsheet 1D.**

   a. Plot all the points from the table in Question 23(b) on the *Exploring Multiplication* coordinate plane. Check students' work.

   b. If you connect all the points, what figure do you think will be formed? Sample Response: a straight line

   c. Use a ruler to connect the points to see if your conjecture in part (b) was correct. Check students' work.

   d. If you plot the point from Question 24(c), how do you think it will relate to the other points you plotted? Explain.

▶ **Linear Equations** An equation whose graph is a straight line is a **linear equation**. Notice the word *line* in the word *linear*.

26 **Try This as a Class**

   a. Copy the table below. Look for patterns to find the missing values. 12, 4, –4, –16

x	–4	–3	–2	–1	0	1	2	3	4
y	16	?	8	?	0	?	–8	–12	?

   b. What equation describes the relationship between *x* and *y*?
   $y = -4x$
   c. Is the product of two negative integers *positive* or *negative*?
   positive
   d. Describe how you can find the product of two negative integers. Sample Response: Multiply the whole number part of the integers and make the product positive.

27 **Use Labsheet 1D.**

   a. Plot the points from your table in Question 26(a) on the *Exploring Multiplication* coordinate plane. Check students' work.

   b. Connect the points using a ruler. How does this line compare with the one you drew in Question 25(c)?

   c. **Discussion** How does the coefficient of *x* affect the graph of the line? Test your conjecture by graphing the equations $y = 5x$ and $y = -5x$.

28 ✔ **CHECKPOINT** Find each product.

    a. 3(–7) –21   **b.** (–8)(–13) 104 **c.** (–1)(–1) 1   **d.** 7(–9)(8) –504

▶ **Dividing Integers** In Exploration 2, you discovered that for every subtraction problem there is a related addition problem. This is also true for multiplication and division. For every division problem, there is a related multiplication problem.

29 Write a multiplication equation related to $28 \div 7 = 4$.

    $7 \cdot 4 = 28$ or $4 \cdot 7 = 28$

30 **a.** Write a multiplication equation related to $-32 \div 8 = x$. $8x = -32$

    b. What must the value of x be to make the multiplication equation you wrote for part (a) true? –4

    c. What is the quotient $-32 \div 8$? –4

31 Write and solve a related multiplication equation to find each quotient.

    a. $72 \div (-9) = x$ $-9x = 72; -8$ **b.** $-16 \div 8 = x$ $8x = -16; -2$

    c. $-9 \div (-3) = x$ $-3x = -9; 3$ **d.** $-24 \div (-6) = x$ $-6x = -24; 4$

32 **Try This as a Class** You can find quotients without using multiplication.

    a. Is the quotient $-264 \div 12$ *positive* or *negative*? Explain.

    b. Explain how to divide two integers.

33 ✔ **CHECKPOINT** Find each quotient.

    a. $-18 \div (-3)$ 6 **b.** $\dfrac{35}{-7}$ –5   **c.** $-150 \div 5$ –30 **d.** $\dfrac{-48}{-6}$ 8

34 **Discussion** Suppose you graph the equation $y = x \div (-2)$.

    a. Do you think the graph will be a straight line? Explain.

    b. Find the values of y for $x = 4, 8, 12,$ and 16 and plot the points. Then connect the points. $y = -2, -4, -6, -8$; Check students' work.

    c. How can you write the equation using a multiplication expression? $y = -\frac{1}{2}x$

HOMEWORK EXERCISES ▶ See Exs. 36–55 on pp. 89–90.

✔ **QUESTION 28**

...checks that you know how to multiply integers.

32. a. Negative. Sample Response: The product of a negative and a positive integer is negative.

    b. Sample Response: Divide the whole number parts of the integers. If both are positive the quotient is positive; if both are negative the quotient is positive; if one is positive and one is negative the quotient is negative.

✔ **QUESTION 33**

...checks that you know how to divide integers.

34. a. Sample Response: Yes, because division is related to multiplication. Dividing by –2 is the same as multiplying by $-\frac{1}{2}$.

Key Concepts

ABSENT STUDENTS

For students who were absent for all or part of this section, the blackline Study Guide for Section 1 may be used to present the ideas, concepts, and skills of Section 1.

CLOSURE QUESTION

Explain why 10 is the only solution to $|10| = n$, but 10 and –10 are both solutions to $|n| = 10$.

Sample Response: The first equation is asking for the absolute value of 10 which means the distance 10 is from 0 on a number line. 10 is 10 units from 0. Distance is always nonnegative; direction does not matter. In the second equation *n* represents any number 10 units away from zero. Since you could move 10 units in either direction, both 10 and –10 are at a distance 10 units from 0, so *n = 10 or –10.*

Key Terms

integers

absolute value

opposites

35. No. Sample Response: The absolute value of an integer is the opposite of the integer only when the integer is negative or zero.

36. a. Sample Response: The positive integer is greater than the absolute value of the negative integer.
b. Sample Response: The absolute value of the negative integer is greater than the positive integer.
c. The integers are opposites.

Adding and Subtracting Integers (pp. 79–81)

The integers are the numbers … , –3, –2, –1, 0, 1, 2, 3, … .
The sum of two integers may be positive, negative, or zero.

Examples

$$-3 + 5 = 2 \qquad -4 + 1 = -3$$
$$12 + (-12) = 0 \qquad -1 + (-9) = -10$$

The difference of two integers may be positive, negative, or zero.

Examples

$$-4 - (-6) = 2 \qquad 5 - 7 = -2$$
$$-3 - (-3) = 0 \qquad -2 - 3 = -5$$

Absolute Value and Opposites (pp. 80–81)

The absolute value of a number tells you its distance from 0.

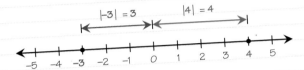

The integers 5 and –5 are opposites. To subtract an integer, add its opposite.

Examples

$$3 - 5 = 3 + (-5) = -2$$
$$7 - (-2) = 7 + (-(-2)) = 7 + 2 = 9$$

Key Concepts Questions

35 The absolute value of –12 and the opposite of –12 are both 12. Is the absolute value of an integer always its opposite? Explain.

36 A negative integer and a positive integer are added. Describe the relationship between the integers being added if their sum is as described.

a. positive **b.** negative **c.** zero

Section 1
Key Concepts

Key Terms

Translations (pp. 81–82)

A translation, or slide, moves each point of a figure the same distance in the same direction. A translation can be described by adding values to the coordinates of a point. The result of a translation is the image.

translation

image

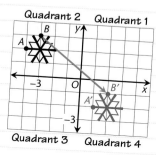

Quadrant 2 Quadrant 1

Quadrant 3 Quadrant 4

Original		Image
$A(-4, 2)$	⟶	$A'(1, -2)$
$B(-3, 3)$	⟶	$B'(2, -1)$

quadrants

Translation: $(x + 5, y + (-4))$

Multiplying and Dividing Integers (pp. 83–85)

The product or quotient of two integers is:

- positive when both integers are positive or when both are negative.

Examples $-3(-8) = -3 \cdot (-8) = 24$ $\qquad -24 \div (-8) = \frac{-24}{-8} = 3$

- negative when one integer is positive and the other is negative.

Examples $3(-8) = 3 \cdot (-8) = -24$ $\qquad 24 \div (-3) = \frac{24}{-3} = -8$

Linear Equations (p. 82)

An equation whose graph is a straight line is a linear equation.

linear equation

Examples $y = -3x$ and $y = x \div (-5)$ are linear equations.

---

37 Key Concepts Question When is the product of three integers as described?

a. positive Sample Response: The product is positive when one or three of the three integers is positive.

b. negative Sample Response: The product is negative when one or three of the three integers is negative.

c. zero The product is zero when one or more of the integers is zero.

CLOSURE QUESTIONS

Describe how to use addition and subtraction of integers to move a figure on a coordinate grid.

Sample Response: When you add a positve number or subtract a negative number from the x–coordinate of a point, the point will move to the right the number of units equal to the absolute value of the number you added or subtracted. When you add a negative number or subtract a positive number from the x–coordinate of a point, the point will move to the left the number of units equal to the absolute value of the number you added or subtracted. The effects on the y-coordinate are similar except the point moves up or down instead of right or left.

How are addition and multiplication of integers different?

Sample Response: If both numbers are negative, their sum is the negative of the sum of their absolute values, but their product is positive and equal to the product of the absolute values. If one number is positive and the other negative, the product is negative and equal to the product of their absolute values, but the sum may be positive or negative depending on which number has the greater absolute value.

Practice & Applications

SUGGESTED ASSIGNMENTS

Core Course

Day 1: Exs. 56–65
Day 2: Exs. 1–6
Day 3: Exs. 7–24
Day 4: Exs. 26–33, 35
Day 5: Exs. 36–39, 48–52
Day 6: Exs. 40–47, 53, 55

Extended Course

Day 1: Exs. 56–65
Day 2: Exs. 1–6
Day 3: Exs. 13–25
Day 4: Exs. 26–27, 30–35
Day 5: Exs. 38–39, 48–52
Day 6: Exs. 40–41, 44–47, 53–55, 66–69*

Note: Extended Course assignments can be used to differentiate within the regular classroom. In classrooms where students are grouped homogeneously, the material might be covered in fewer days. In this case assignments may be combined.
* denotes Extension Exercises

ADDITIONAL PRACTICE

See the *Teacher's Resource Book* for additional practice and application exercises for this section.

COMMON ERROR

In **Exercise 20**, students may be inclined to write the money Joe spends as subtraction. Remind them that they can also express subtraction as adding a negative number which will allow them to write all parts of the problem as addition.

YOU WILL NEED

For Ex. 25:
♦ Labsheet 1B

For Ex. 35:
♦ graph paper

Section 1

Practice & Application Exercises

Find each sum.

1. $-23 + (-8)$ –31
2. $91 + (-10)$ 81
3. $-15 + 7$ –8
4. $12 + (-12)$ 0
5. $-88 + (-12)$ –100
6. $4 + (-10) + 7$ 1

Find the opposite of each integer.

7. -15 15
8. 101 –101
9. 74 –74
10. -62 62

Find each absolute value.

11. $|-47|$ 47
12. $|53|$ 53
13. $\left|8\frac{1}{2}\right|$ $8\frac{1}{2}$
14. $|-0.43|$ 0.43

15. Find two different integers with an absolute value of 7. 7, –7

Solve each equation.

16. $|y| = 12$
    12, –12
17. $-w = 2$
    –2
18. $|z| = 0$
    0
19. $-x = -5$
    5

20. Joe earned $15 mowing lawns, then bought a radio for $11. The next day he earned $5 and spent $3 on arcade games. Write an addition expression for his income and expenses and find the sum. $15 + (-11) + 5 + (-3)$ or $20 + (-14)$; 6

Algebra Connection Find y when $x = -6$.

21. $y = x + 28$
    22
22. $y = x + (-12)$
    –18
23. $y = x + 4$
    –2
24. $y = x + 6$
    0

25. **Challenge** Suppose the value of x is –4. What equation could be used to determine the value of y so that a star is hit on the *Integer Invasion* game board? Explain how you found your equation. Answers may vary. Sample Responses: $y = x, y = x + 10, y = x + 6$

Find each difference.

26. $5 - 9$ –4
27. $18 - (-13)$ 31
28. $2 - (-11)$ 13
29. $-3 - (-3)$ 0
30. $-10 - 4$ –14
31. $-7 - (-19)$ 12

32. **Weather** Suppose the temperature is –18°F at 6:00 A.M. and 23°F at 2:00 P.M. What is the difference in the temperatures? 41°F

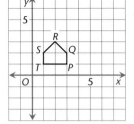

33. The translation $(x + 2, y + (-3))$ is applied to figure *PQRST*.
    a. Give the coordinates of the image points P', Q', R', S', and T'.
       $P'(5, -2), Q'(5, -1), R'(4, 0), S'(3, -1), T'(3, -2)$
    b. **Writing** Describe in words a translation that moves *PQRST* to the opposite side of the vertical axis. Sample Response: Add –4 to x and any integer to y.

34. After the translation $(x + 5, y + 2)$, the image of a point is $(12, 16)$. What are the coordinates of the original point? *(7, 14)*

35. For each pair of coordinates, describe the translation in two ways, one using only addition and one using only subtraction. Then show each translation on a graph.

	Original	Image	Translations
a.	$L(2, 4)$	$L'(1, 5)$	$(x + \underline{\ ?\ }, y + \underline{\ ?\ })$ or $(x - \underline{\ ?\ }, y - \underline{\ ?\ })$
b.	$M(0, -7)$	$M'(2, -1)$	$(x + \underline{\ ?\ }, y + \underline{\ ?\ })$ or $(x - \underline{\ ?\ }, y - \underline{\ ?\ })$
c.	$N(-6, 3)$	$N'(-10, -3)$	$(x + \underline{\ ?\ }, y + \underline{\ ?\ })$ or $(x - \underline{\ ?\ }, y - \underline{\ ?\ })$

35. a. $-1, 1; 1, -1$
b. $2, 6; -2, -6$
c. $-4, -6; 4, 6$

Find each product or quotient.

36. $8(-9)$
-72

37. $-16 \cdot 20$
-320

38. $-3(-8)(2)$
48

39. $-2(-7)(-4)$
-56

40. $-27 \div 9$
-3

41. $\dfrac{-56}{-8}$
7

42. $\dfrac{72}{-3}$
-24

43. $-48 \div (-6)$
8

Algebra Connection Evaluate each expression when $a = -16$, $b = -4$, and $c = 48$.

44. ab *64*

45. bc *–192*

46. $c \div a$ *–3*

47. $\dfrac{a}{b}$ *4*

Algebra Connection Find y when $x = -7$.

48. $y = 3x$ *–21*

49. $y = -12x$ *84*

50. $y = 9x$ *–63*

51. $y = -6x$ *42*

52. Football On each of three consecutive plays, a football team loses 5 yd. Suppose lost yardage is represented by a negative integer.

a. Write a multiplication expression that describes the total change in yardage. *3(–5)*

b. Find the total number of yards lost. *15 yards lost*

Use this information for Exercises 53 and 54: On a test, each correct answer scores 5 points, each incorrect answer scores –2 points, and each question left unanswered scores 0 points.

53. Suppose a student answers 15 questions on the test correctly, 4 incorrectly, and does not answer 1 question. Write an expression for the student's score and find the score. *15(5) + 4(–2) + 1(0); 67*

DEVELOPING MATH CONCEPTS
For **Exercise 34**, you may need to guide students to see that they can reverse the translation to find the original point. It is appropriate to use inverse operations since they are "undoing" the translation. The translation from the image point to the original point becomes $(x - 5, y - 2)$.

Exercise 35 reinforces the concept that every subtraction problem can be rewritten as an addition problem by having students write the coordinate translations in two ways and then graph each translation to see that they produce the same result.

Practice & Applications

EXERCISE NOTES

Exercise 55 Have students create a figure on graph paper and perform the transformation described. Their original figure and image can be displayed on a bulletin board along with their findings about the visual effect created by multiplying each point of a figure by –1. Some students may enjoy exploring the differences that multiplying, dividing, adding, and subtracting make on the coordinates of a figure by performing these operations with various numbers. Allow them to report their findings to the class or make a display to illustrate their findings.

DIFFERENTIATED INSTRUCTION

Extension Exercises 66–69 extend students' understanding of absolute value and provide application of algebra concepts to solving absolute value equations. **Exercises 66–68** can be used to provide challenge for students who quickly grasped the concept of absolute value and were able to solve Checkpoint Questions 17(a) and (c) on p. 81. **Exercise 69** requires the application of integer rules for multiplication or division.

54. Challenge Suppose you answer all 20 questions on the test. What is the greatest number of questions you can answer incorrectly and still get a positive score? Explain your reasoning.
14 questions; Sample Response: Use guess and check,
14(–2) + 6(5) = –28 + 30 = 2 and 15(–2) + 5(5) = –30 + 25 = –5.

Visual THINKING

Exercise 55 checks your understanding of opposites.

Reflecting ◀▶ on the Section

55. Suppose you multiply each coordinate of each point of a figure by –1. Describe the visual effect created by this operation.
Sample Response: The figure will appear to be reflected over both the vertical and horizontal axes.

Spiral ◀▶ Review

Find each quotient. Write each answer in lowest terms.
(Toolbox, p. 587)

56. $\frac{3}{8} \div \frac{1}{4}$ $1\frac{1}{2}$ **57.** $\frac{7}{12} \div \frac{5}{6}$ $\frac{7}{10}$ **58.** $\frac{33}{39} \div \frac{11}{13}$ 1 **59.** $\frac{10}{21} \div \frac{7}{9}$ $\frac{30}{49}$

Replace each ? with the number that will make the fractions equivalent. (Toolbox, p. 585)

60. $\frac{1}{5} = \frac{?}{30}$ 6 **61.** $\frac{1}{3} = \frac{?}{24}$ 8 **62.** $\frac{5}{8} = \frac{35}{?}$ 56

63. $\frac{3}{10} = \frac{?}{110}$ 33 **64.** $\frac{3}{4} = \frac{21}{?}$ 28 **65.** $\frac{9}{16} = \frac{54}{?}$ 96

Extension ▶ ▶

Absolute Value Equations

The equation $|x + 1| = 3$ includes a variable inside the absolute value bars. You can use what you know about absolute value to find the values of x that make the equation true.

$$|x + 1| = 3$$
$$x + 1 = 3 \quad \text{or} \quad x + 1 = -3$$

66. Solve each equation above to find the values of x that make $|x + 1| = 3$ true. $2, -4$

Solve each equation.

67. $|y + 2| = 8$
$6, -10$

68. $|w - 5| = 10$
$15, -5$

69. $|-2z| = 4$
$-2, 2$

Section 1

Extra Skill Practice

Find each sum.

1. $-12 + 16$ 4
2. $27 + (-49)$ -22
3. $-130 + (-65)$ -195
4. $-78 + 25 + (-4)$ -57

Find the opposite of each integer.

5. 512 -512
6. -43 43
7. -1 1
8. 38 -38

Find each absolute value.

9. $|29|$ 29
10. $|-83|$ 83
11. $\left|-3\frac{3}{4}\right|$ $3\frac{3}{4}$
12. $|-1.45|$ 1.45

Find each difference.

13. $-32 - 45$ -77
14. $26 - (-13)$ 39
15. $-16 - (-22)$ 6
16. $55 - (-55)$ 110

Find each product.

17. $-25(-10)$ 250
18. $4(-15)$ -60
19. $-7 \cdot 6$ -42
20. $-12(-5)$ 60

Find each quotient.

21. $42 \div (-7)$ -6
22. $-88 \div 22$ -4
23. $\frac{-54}{-3}$ 18
24. $\frac{95}{-5}$ -19

Simplify each expression.

25. $-14(-3)$ 42
26. $27 + (-33)$ -6
27. $-24 \div (-6)$ 4

28. $52 - (-16)$ 68
29. $\frac{-76}{19}$ -4
30. $-41 + (-11)$ -52

31. $64 \div (-4)$ -16
32. $9 \cdot (-7)$ -63
33. $-13 - 13$ -26

Standardized Testing ◀▶ **Open-ended**

1. Give an example of two numbers that fit each description below. If no numbers fit the description, explain why.

   a. Both the sum and the product of 2 numbers are negative.
      Sample Response: $-7, 5$
   b. The sum of 2 numbers is 0 and the product is positive.

   c. The sum of 2 numbers is positive and the quotient is negative.
      Sample Response: 10 and -5

   1. b. None. Two numbers with sums of 0 are opposites. The product of opposites is always less than or equal to 0.

2. A rectangle *ABCD* has two vertical sides that intersect the *x*-axis, and two horizontal sides that intersect the *y*-axis. Give a set of possible coordinates for *A*, *B*, *C*, and *D*. Then write the coordinates of *A′*, *B′*, *C′* and *D′* after the translation $(x - 4, y + 6)$.
   Sample Response: $A(-3, 2)$, $B(3, 2)$, $C(3, -2)$, $D(-3, -2)$;
   $A'(-7, 8)$, $B'(-1, 8)$, $C'(-1, 4)$, $D'(-7, 4)$

Section 1   Operations with Integers   **91**

Extra Skill Practice

TEACHER NOTES

For each Exploration, the corresponding Extra Skill Practice Exercises are noted.

Exploration 1: Exs. 1–12
Exploration 2: Exs. 13–16
Exploration 3: Exs. 17–24

Exs. 25–33 require students to perform a mixture of the operations studied in all three Explorations.

EXTRA HELP

Teacher's Resource Book
• Practice and Applications
• Study Guide

Technology Resources
• @Home Tutor
• Test Generator

ASSESSMENT
• Section 1 Quick Quiz
• Test Generator

91

92

Setting the Stage

GETTING STARTED

Module 2 Section 1 *Warm-Up* assesses prerequisite skills for adding and subtracting fractions. Students should be able to find a common denominator, write equivalent fractions using the common denominator, add or subtract the fractions, and simplify the sum or difference.

Discuss with students the top speed and G-force experienced when riding the Mindbender roller coaster. Ask them what 26.8 m/sec means. (*Answer: about 27 meters distance in 1 second of time*) You may want to compare this to running 100 m in less than 4 sec or to use a length in your school that corresponds to a distance of 27 meters so that students get an idea of how fast the coaster is traveling at top speed. G-force is the force of gravity. When you sit, stand or lie down you experience a force of 1G. The effect of 5.2 Gs is felt on a roller coaster as you try to lift your head from the back of the seat. As you experience more Gs, your weight increases correspondingly. At 5.2 Gs your 10-lb head will weigh 52 lbs! Book 2 Module 5 Section 3 has a diagram showing the relationship between G-force and roller coaster rides.

DEVELOPING MATH CONCEPTS

Students play the game *Fraction Mindbender* in Exploration 2 of this section. Exploration 1 reviews adding and subtracting positive fractions and mixed numbers and then introduces the sum of two negative fractions. In the game students will add positive and negative fractions. In Exploration 3 the game is revisited as students learn how to add and subtract positive and negative mixed numbers.

Section 2 Operations with Fractions

A WORLD CLASS W❓NDER

Setting the Stage

The West Edmonton Mall in Alberta, Canada, has over 800 stores, more than 110 eating establishments, and covers the equivalent of 48 city blocks. It is also the home of *Galaxyland*, the world's largest indoor amusement park. *Galaxyland* contains 25 rides and attractions, including the *Mindbender* roller coaster that reaches a top speed of 26.8 m/sec and a G-force of 5.2. It is easy to see why some people have called the West Edmonton Mall the eighth wonder of the world!

▲ The first descent on the *Mindbender* is 14 stories high.

Think About It

1 One story of a building is about 10 ft. Estimate the height of the *Mindbender*. **about 140 ft**

2 a. The 130-second ride covers 1280 m of track. To the nearest tenth, what is the average speed? **9.8 m/sec**

   b. If the rollercoaster ran at top speed the entire length of the ride, about how many seconds would the ride last? **about 48 sec (1280 m ÷ 26.8 m/sec)**

▶ In this section, you will play *Fraction Mindbender*, a game of quick thinking and skill.

Working with FRACTIONS

▶ In the game *Fraction Mindbender*, you will try to create the greatest sum or difference by placing numbers in a fraction expression.

3 a. Look at the *Fraction Mindbender* game board below. Find the sum and difference to determine which expression has the greater value. **Player B's expression. A:** $\frac{31}{14}$ **B:** $\frac{29}{10}$

Player A

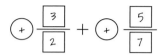

Player B

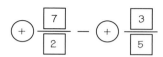

b. Rearrange the numbers 3, 2, 5, and 7 in the four boxes so Player A's sum is greater than the sum of the fractions shown. Give the new expression and the sum.

3. b. Answers will vary. Check students' work. Sample Response: $\frac{7}{3} + \frac{2}{5} = \frac{41}{15}$

c. Rewrite the new expression from part (b) using mixed numbers.
Answers will vary. Sample Response: $2\frac{1}{3} + \frac{2}{5}$

4 Try This as a Class

a. To find the difference $5\frac{3}{8} - 2\frac{7}{8}$ by subtracting the whole number and fractional parts separately, why would you need to regroup? $\frac{3}{8}$ is less than $\frac{7}{8}$, so you will need to regroup in order to subtract.

b. Regroup and find the difference. $4\frac{11}{8}$; $2\frac{4}{8}$ or $2\frac{1}{2}$

c. Change the mixed numbers $5\frac{3}{8}$ and $2\frac{7}{8}$ to fractions. $\frac{43}{8}, \frac{23}{8}$

d. Use the fractions you found in part (c) to find the difference in part (a). $\frac{20}{8}$ or $2\frac{1}{2}$

e. Which method, regrouping or changing mixed numbers to fractions, do you prefer for finding the difference? Why? Answers will vary. Students may choose to change mixed numbers to fractions when regrouping is necessary.

Exploration 1

TEACHING NOTES

Question 3(c) It is possible that the new expression students write may include only one fraction that can be expressed as a mixed number.

Question 4 provides an opportunity to review subtraction of mixed numbers where it is necessary to regroup (borrow) in order to subtract. Students learn that mixed numbers can also be changed to fractions thus eliminating the need to rename the whole number. Either method is appropriate for students to use and students may choose the method appropriate for the problem being solved. In Exploration 3, when working with positive and negative mixed number operations, changing the mixed numbers to fractions will be emphasized.

COMMON ERROR

Question 4(b) Students will often apply regrouping of the base ten system to fractions renaming $5\frac{3}{8}$ as $4\frac{13}{8}$ instead of $4\frac{11}{8}$. As you work through Question 4 as a class, emphasize the mathematics of renaming $5\frac{3}{8}$ as $4\frac{11}{8}$ by writing the steps as students help explain that $5\frac{3}{8} = 4\frac{3}{8} + 1 = 4\frac{3}{8} + \frac{8}{8} = 4\frac{11}{8}$.

Exploration 1 *continued*

TEACHING NOTES

You may want to discuss the placement of negative signs with fractions. In the **Example** the negative sign is written in front of the fraction, but during the calculations it also appears in the numerator. Connect to what students know about integer division. Remind them that the fraction bar represents division. Ask them to state each of the following as a division problem:

$-\frac{1}{2}$ (*the opposite of the quotient 1 divided by 2*), $\frac{-1}{2}$ (*–1 divided by 2*), and $\frac{1}{-2}$ (*1 divided by –2*). Then ask students if these are equal. (*Yes, all equal –0.5.*) Though all three forms are equivalent, writing the fraction with a positive denominator is usually preferred for non-calculator computations since a negative in the denominator is easily overlooked or mishandled during computations.

COMMON ERRORS

During the discussion of **Question 5**, be sure students understand that a negative fraction or a negative mixed number represents the "opposite" of the positive fraction/mixed number. Often students think that since

$1\frac{3}{5} = 1 + \frac{3}{5}$ then $-1\frac{3}{5} = -1 + \frac{3}{5}$.

In reality, $-1\frac{3}{5} = -1 + \left(-\frac{3}{5}\right)$ and $-1 + \frac{3}{5} = -\frac{2}{5}$.

---

5. a. In both you find the common denominator, write the equivalent fraction with that denominator and then add the numerators, keeping the common denominator.

d. **Sample Response:** Add them as if they were positive and then place a negative sign on the result.

▶ **Adding Negative Fractions** Sometimes during the game you may need to add two negative fractions. Look at the example below.

EXAMPLE

Find $\left(-\right)\dfrac{2}{5} + \left(-\right)\dfrac{3}{4}$

$-\dfrac{2}{5} + \left(-\dfrac{3}{4}\right) = \dfrac{-8}{20} + \left(\dfrac{-15}{20}\right)$ ◀ Rewrite each fraction with a common denominator.

$= \dfrac{-8 + (-15)}{20}$ ◀ Add the integers $-8 + (-15)$ to find the new numerator, -23.

$= \dfrac{-23}{20}$

$= -\dfrac{23}{20}$

$= -\left(\dfrac{20}{20} + \dfrac{3}{20}\right)$

$= -\left(1 + \dfrac{3}{20}\right)$

$= -1\dfrac{3}{20}$

---

5 **Discussion**

a. How is adding two negative fractions similar to adding two positive fractions?

b. How is it different? With two negative fractions the final sum is negative.

c. In the Example, when $-\dfrac{23}{20}$ was changed to a mixed number, what happened to the negative sign? The negative sign was placed in front of the whole number.

d. Explain how to add two negative fractions.

 QUESTION 6

...checks that you can add and subtract fractions and mixed numbers.

---

6 ✔ **CHECKPOINT** Find each sum or difference. Write all fractions in your answers in lowest terms.

a. $\dfrac{2}{9} + \dfrac{5}{6}$ $1\dfrac{1}{18}$

b. $\dfrac{11}{12} - \dfrac{2}{3}$ $\dfrac{1}{4}$

c. $-\dfrac{3}{10} + \left(-\dfrac{5}{6}\right)$ $-1\dfrac{2}{15}$

d. $4\dfrac{2}{9} + 1\dfrac{1}{3}$ $5\dfrac{5}{9}$

e. $-\dfrac{2}{3} + \left(-\dfrac{3}{4}\right)$ $1\dfrac{1}{3}$

f. $5\dfrac{1}{2} - 3\dfrac{3}{8}$ $2\dfrac{1}{8}$

HOMEWORK EXERCISES ▶ See Exs. 1–10 on p. 101.

Exploration 2

Fraction Mindbender

GOAL

LEARN HOW TO...
◆ add and subtract positive and negative fractions

AS YOU...
◆ play *Fraction Mindbender*

SET UP Work with a partner. You will need: • Labsheet 2A
• 14 index cards

▶ Make a deck of cards and read the directions below to prepare to play *Fraction Mindbender*. You will try to create the greatest sum or difference using numbers and symbols in a fraction expression.

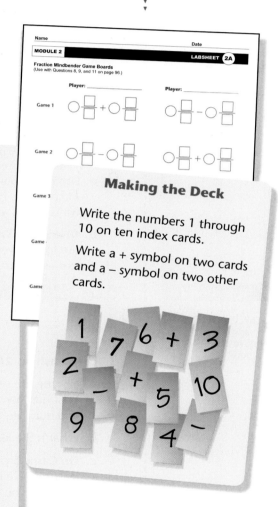

Fraction Mindbender

Playing the Game

Labsheet 2A has 5 game boards for each player. A game is completed when each player fills in one game board.

Shuffle the deck of 14 cards, place it face down on the desk, and turn over the top card.

If a number is turned over, each player must write it in one of his or her four squares on the game board. If a symbol is turned over, each player must write it in one of his or her two circles.

Turn over cards from the top of the deck and record each number or symbol until you have filled your game board. Ignore any extra numbers or symbols you turn over.

Once all the squares and circles are filled, find each player's sum or difference. The player with the greater number wins.

Making the Deck

Write the numbers 1 through 10 on ten index cards.

Write a + symbol on two cards and a – symbol on two other cards.

Exploration 2

CLASSROOM MANAGEMENT
Game partners will each need a copy of Labsheet 2A. Each player needs to record the choices of both players on the gameboards on their labsheets. Students will use their completed labsheet for Questions 8, 9, and 11.

TIPS FROM TEACHERS
Preparing the ten index cards and laminating them ahead of time will make cards useable for several years, and give you more class time for the lesson.

Exploration 2 *continued*

TEACHING NOTES

For **Questions 7 and 8** point out that in each round of the game, one player adds two fractions and the other player subtracts two fractions. Be sure students have read and understand *Adding and Subtracting Positive and Negative Fractions* at the top of the page. To answer **Question 7(a)** students will have to consider four problems: $\frac{8}{2} + \frac{6}{3}$, $\frac{8}{2} + \left(-\frac{6}{3}\right)$, $\frac{6}{3} - \frac{2}{8}$, and $\frac{6}{3} - \left(-\frac{2}{8}\right)$.

Work an example together as a class before starting Question 8.

CLASSROOM EXAMPLE

Subtract $-\frac{5}{6} - \frac{3}{10}$.

Answer: $-\frac{5}{6} - \frac{3}{10} = -\frac{5}{6} + \left(-\frac{3}{10}\right)$

$= -\frac{25}{30} + \left(-\frac{9}{30}\right)$

$= -\frac{34}{30}$

$= -1\frac{4}{30}$

$= -1\frac{2}{15}$

DEVELOPING MATH CONCEPTS

Discussion Question 9(b) Both boards have advantages depending on the symbols drawn. For example, when two (−)s are drawn, the person using the addition board has the advantage, whereas if it is two (+)s, the subtraction board is better. When one (−) and one (+) are chosen the subtraction board is only advantageous if the negative is placed in front of the first number. However, if the only available location is on the second number of the subtraction board, the person using the addition board will automatically win.

96

---

7. a. No; It depends on the next symbol turned over. If it is +, Leeza wins. If it is −, Rhea wins.

QUESTION 10

...checks that you can add and subtract positive and negative fractions.

▶ Adding and Subtracting Positive and Negative Fractions

Positive and negative fractions can be added and subtracted the same way as integers. Before adding or subtracting, you may have to rewrite the fractions so the denominators are the same.

7 **Try This as a Class** Leeza and Rhea are playing *Fraction Mindbender*. Their game board shows that they have turned over the 8, 2, +, and 3 cards. The next card is a 6.

Player: Leeza   Player: Rhea

$\left(+\right)\ \dfrac{8}{2} + \bigcirc \dfrac{\square}{3}$ $\left(+\right)\ \dfrac{\square}{3} - \bigcirc \dfrac{2}{8}$

a. Can you tell who will win? Explain why or why not.

b. On the next draw, which symbol would be best for Rhea? Explain. (−); Sample Response: She would win with a score of $2\frac{1}{4}$ over Leeza's score of 2.

Use Labsheet 2A for Questions 8 and 9.

8 Play two games of *Fraction Mindbender* with your partner. Check students' work.

9 **a.** Use a new game board. Play another game of *Fraction Mindbender*, but this time the player with the lesser number wins. Check students' work.

b. **Discussion** Which part of the board do you think is best to use for this version of the game, the part with the subtraction expression or the part with the addition expression? Explain. Answers will vary. Check students' work.

10 ✔ **CHECKPOINT** Find each sum or difference.

a. $-\frac{1}{2} + \left(-\frac{3}{4}\right)$ $-1\frac{1}{4}$ **b.** $\frac{5}{6} - \left(-\frac{4}{3}\right)$ $2\frac{1}{6}$ **c.** $-\frac{6}{10} + \frac{7}{8}$ $\frac{11}{40}$

11 **Use Labsheet 2A.** Use the remaining game boards.

a. Choose the symbols and numbers from the deck that give the least number. Fill in the boxes on Game 4 with the symbols and numbers you chose. $-\frac{9}{2} - \frac{10}{1}$

b. What is the least number? $-14\frac{1}{2}$

c. On Game 5 choose the symbols and numbers that give the least positive number. Fill in the boxes with the symbols and numbers you chose. $\frac{9}{10} - \frac{7}{8}$

d. What is the least positive number? $\frac{1}{40}$

HOMEWORK EXERCISES ▶ See Exs. 11–21 on pp. 101–102.

Working with MiXED NUMBERS

SET UP *Work with a partner. You will need the game cards from Exploration 2.*

Mixed Number Mindbender allows for mixed numbers by including a box for a whole number in front of each fraction on the game board. To play this version, you will need to be able to add and subtract mixed numbers.

▶ **Adding Two Negative Mixed Numbers** Compare adding two positive mixed numbers with adding two negative mixed numbers.

EXAMPLE

Positive Mixed Numbers

$$5\frac{1}{8} + 2\frac{3}{4} = 5\frac{1}{8} + 2\frac{6}{8}$$

$$= 7\frac{7}{8}$$

Add the absolute values of the mixed numbers and place a negative sign on the sum.

Negative Mixed Numbers

$$-5\frac{1}{8} + \left(-2\frac{3}{4}\right) = -5\frac{1}{8} + \left(-2\frac{6}{8}\right)$$

$$= -\left(5\frac{1}{8} + 2\frac{6}{8}\right)$$

$$= -7\frac{7}{8}$$

Positive Mixed Numbers

$$3\frac{3}{5} + 1\frac{4}{5} = 4\frac{7}{5}$$

$$= 4 + 1\frac{2}{5}$$

$$= 5\frac{2}{5}$$

Negative Mixed Numbers

$$-3\frac{3}{5} + \left(-1\frac{4}{5}\right) = -\left(3\frac{3}{5} + 1\frac{4}{5}\right)$$

$$= -\left(4\frac{7}{5}\right)$$

$$= -\left(4 + 1\frac{2}{5}\right)$$

$$= -5\frac{2}{5}$$

Exploration 3

DEVELOPING MATH CONCEPTS

In Exploration 1 students worked with adding two positive mixed numbers and adding two negative mixed numbers. In Exploration 2 they learned to add/subtract fractions with mixed signs. In this Exploration students combine skills learned in Explorations 1 and 2 to develop the steps for adding and subtracting any combination of positive and negative mixed numbers.

TEACHING NOTES

After reviewing the **Example** on page 97 and discussing answers to **Question 12**, use an additional example and have students explain the steps to solving it.

CLASSROOM EXAMPLE

Add $-3\frac{1}{2} + \left(-2\frac{2}{5}\right)$.

Answer: $-3\frac{1}{2} + \left(-2\frac{2}{5}\right) = -\left(3\frac{1}{2} + 2\frac{2}{5}\right)$

$= -\left(3\frac{5}{10} + 2\frac{4}{10}\right)$

$= -\left(5\frac{9}{10}\right)$

$= -5\frac{9}{10}$

In **Question 14** students are NOT to solve each expression, but to use their knowledge of addition and subtraction of positives and negatives to identify the equivalent expressions. Later they will complete the sums and differences of similar problems.

✔ QUESTION 13

...checks that you can add negative mixed numbers.

12. b. To add negative integers, you add the numbers and then apply a negative sign to the result. The same is true for mixed numbers.

c. To add two negative mixed numbers, add them as if they are positive mixed numbers. Find a common denominator if necessary. Add the whole numbers and add the numerators of the fractions. Rename or simplify if necessary and then make the sum negative.

---

12 Look at the examples on the previous page.

a. How are adding positive mixed numbers and adding negative mixed numbers alike? **You can use the same methods for each, only the sign of the sum is different.**

b. How is adding two negative mixed numbers like adding two negative integers?

c. Describe the steps for adding two negative mixed numbers.

13 ✔ **CHECKPOINT** Add each pair of mixed numbers. Write all fractions in your answers in lowest terms.

a. $-3\frac{2}{9} + \left(-1\frac{5}{9}\right)$ $-4\frac{7}{9}$

b. $-8\frac{2}{5} + \left(-10\frac{8}{15}\right)$ $-18\frac{14}{15}$

c. $-5\frac{2}{3} + \left(-3\frac{6}{7}\right)$ $-9\frac{11}{21}$

▶ **Adding and Subtracting Mixed Numbers with Different Signs** You can use your knowledge of operations with integers to write equivalent expressions with mixed numbers.

14 For each expression, choose the expression on the right that is equivalent.

a. $4\frac{2}{9} - \left(-1\frac{1}{3}\right)$ $4\frac{2}{9} + 1\frac{1}{3}$ $\qquad$ $4\frac{2}{9} + 1\frac{1}{3}$ $\qquad$ or $\qquad$ $\frac{2}{9} - 1\frac{1}{3}$

b. $5\frac{1}{2} - 3\frac{3}{8}$ $5\frac{1}{2} + \left(-3\frac{3}{8}\right)$ $\qquad$ $-5\frac{1}{2} + \left(-3\frac{3}{8}\right)$ $\qquad$ or $\qquad$ $5\frac{1}{2} + \left(-3\frac{3}{8}\right)$

▶ Some of the fractions you added and subtracted during *Fraction Mindbender* may have been greater than 1 or less than –1.

15 Discussion

a. How are fractions that are greater than 1 or less than –1 related to mixed numbers? **All fractions greater than 1 or less than –1 can be written as mixed numbers.**

b. How can fractions that are greater than 1 or less than –1 be used to add or subtract mixed numbers? **Every mixed number can be rewritten as a fraction and then added using the methods applied to fraction addition/subtraction.**

16 **Try This as a Class** In a game of *Mixed Number Mindbender*, two players have filled in the game board as shown.

Player A

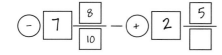

Player B

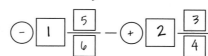

a. Change the mixed numbers to fractions to determine which player's game board has the greater value. **See margin.**

b. Describe how to add positive and negative mixed numbers using the method in part (a). **See margin.**

c. Describe how to subtract positive and negative mixed numbers using the method in part (a).

17 ✔ **CHECKPOINT** Add or subtract. Write all fractions in your answers in lowest terms.

a. $-3\frac{2}{5} + 1\frac{5}{9}$ $-1\frac{38}{45}$

b. $-4\frac{2}{5} - 5\frac{1}{10}$ $-9\frac{1}{2}$

c. $-\frac{2}{5} - \left(-3\frac{2}{3}\right)$ $3\frac{4}{15}$

d. $6 + \left(-2\frac{7}{8}\right)$ $3\frac{1}{8}$

18 Charla and Maya are playing *Mixed Number Mindbender* and trying to obtain the *least* value. Their game board is shown below.

Charla

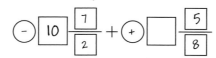

Maya

a. If the next card chosen is a 4, who will win?

b. Rewrite the expressions in part (a) as if both sign cards drawn had been negatives. How would this affect the value of each expression?

19 On your own paper, draw a *Mixed Number Mindbender* game board like the one in Question 18. Use the rules for playing the game from page 95 to play two games with a partner.
Observe students playing the game.

HOMEWORK EXERCISES ▶ See Exs. 22–38 on pp. 102–103.

16.c. Do the same as for adding, just apply the rules for subtracting integers to the numerators instead.

✔ **QUESTION 17**

...checks that you can add and subtract positive and negative mixed numbers.

18. a. Charla will win.

Charla: $-11\frac{1}{20}$,

Maya: $-8\frac{7}{8}$

18. b. $-7\frac{8}{10} - \left(-2\frac{5}{4}\right)$;

$-10\frac{7}{2} + \left(-4\frac{5}{8}\right)$;

Charla's expression would have a value of $-4\frac{11}{20}$, while Maya's expression would have a value of $-18\frac{1}{8}$.

TEACHING NOTES

The format of students' answers in **Checkpoint 17** will depend on whether students used mixed numbers or fractions to complete the operations. $\frac{14}{5}$ and $2\frac{4}{5}$ are both in lowest terms, but $1\frac{9}{5}$ and $\frac{28}{10}$ are not. Write all four problems on the board and have students explain why each is or is not in lowest terms.

In **Question 18**, fractions that are not in lowest terms may appear in the game. This is acceptable due to the board design and the nature of chance in the game, but you may want to have students rewrite the problems to show the mixed numbers with their fractional parts in lowest terms.

16. a. Player A: $-\frac{23}{5} + \frac{13}{6} = \frac{-138 + 65}{30}$

$= -\frac{73}{30}$ or $-2\frac{13}{30}$, Player A has the greater value.

Player B: $-\frac{11}{6} - \frac{11}{4} = \frac{-22 + (-33)}{12}$

$= -\frac{55}{12}$ or $-4\frac{7}{12}$

b. Change the mixed numbers to fractions. Find a common denominator and write the equivalent fractions using that denominator. Use any negative signs on the fraction with the numerator. Follow the methods for adding integers to determine the new numerator. Simplify the fractions if necessary.

99

Key Concepts

Key Concepts

ABSENT STUDENTS

For students who were absent for all or part of this section, the blackline Study Guide for Section 2 may be used to present the ideas, concepts, and skills of Section 2.

CLOSURE QUESTION

Describe the possible ways to add or subtract positive and negative fractions.

Sample Response:
Addition: If both fractions are positive, add them and the result is positive. If both fractions are negative, add the absolute values of the fractions and the result is negative. Adding and subtracting fractions with opposite signs: Perform the operations as you do with integers. Mixed numbers: Mixed numbers can be rewritten as fractions and added/subtracted using the methods for fractions.

TEACHING NOTES

Ask students to justify how they know they created the greatest number possible in **Key Concepts Question 20(a)**. Ask,"Is it possible to be sure you have the greatest result without trying every possible combination of the symbols and numbers given?" (*Yes, use the negative sign so it creates an addition problem with two positive fractions. Then only try combinations that create fractions whose values are greater than 1 by placing digits in the numerator that are greater than those in the corresponding denominator.*)

20. a. $\frac{10}{1} - \left(-\frac{5}{4}\right) = 11\frac{1}{4}$

Section 2
Key Concepts

Adding and Subtracting Fractions (pp. 93–96)

Positive and negative fractions can be added and subtracted the same way as integers. Make sure that the denominators of the fractions are the same before adding or subtracting.

Example

$$-\frac{5}{12} - \left(-\frac{1}{8}\right) = -\frac{5}{12} + \frac{1}{8}$$

Subtraction can be rewritten as adding the opposite.

$$= -\frac{10}{24} + \frac{3}{24}$$

Rewrite using the least common denominator.

$$= \frac{-10 + 3}{24}$$

$$= \frac{-7}{24} = -\frac{7}{24}$$

Example

$$-\frac{1}{5} + \left(-\frac{3}{10}\right) = \frac{-2}{10} + \left(\frac{-3}{10}\right)$$

$$= \frac{-2 + (-3)}{10}$$

$-2 + (-3) = -5$

$$= \frac{-5}{10}$$

$$= \frac{-1}{2} = -\frac{1}{2}$$

Adding and Subtracting Mixed Numbers (p. 93 and pp. 97–99)

Positive and negative mixed numbers can be added and subtracted just like positive and negative fractions once they are rewritten as fractions.

Example $2\frac{5}{8} + \left(-1\frac{7}{8}\right) = \frac{21}{8} + \left(-\frac{15}{8}\right) = \frac{21 + (-15)}{8} = \frac{6}{8} = \frac{3}{4}$

---

20 Key Concepts Question

a. Use the numbers 1, 4, 5, and 10, the symbols + and −, and the part of the game board shown at the right to create the greatest number you can.

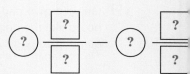

b. How would you answer part (a) if both of the symbols were −? $-\frac{4}{5} - \left(-\frac{10}{1}\right) = 9\frac{1}{5}$

Section 2
Practice & Application Exercises

YOU WILL NEED

For Ex. 30:
- fraction calculator

Find each sum or difference. Write your answer in lowest terms.

1. $\frac{4}{9} + \frac{3}{8}$ $\frac{59}{72}$

2. $\frac{1}{6} + \frac{2}{5}$ $\frac{17}{30}$

3. $\frac{5}{14} - \frac{2}{7}$ $\frac{1}{14}$

4. $\frac{5}{4} - \frac{7}{8}$ $\frac{3}{8}$

5. $-\frac{1}{12} + \left(-\frac{5}{12}\right)$ $-\frac{1}{2}$

6. $-\frac{5}{11} + \left(-\frac{3}{2}\right)$ $-1\frac{21}{22}$

7. $-\frac{4}{9} + \left(-\frac{5}{9}\right)$ -1

8. $-\frac{1}{2} + \left(-\frac{2}{5}\right)$ $-\frac{9}{10}$

9. **Sewing** A fabric store has the three pieces of scrap material shown below. An art teacher needs four pieces of material that are each $\frac{3}{8}$ yd long and 1 yd wide.

9. b. Use one piece from the $\frac{1}{2}$ yd remnant, two pieces from the $\frac{7}{8}$ yd remnant, and one piece from the $\frac{5}{8}$ yd remnant; $\frac{1}{8}$ yd; $\frac{1}{8}$ yd; $\frac{1}{4}$ yd

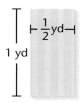

$\vdash \frac{1}{2}\text{yd} \dashv$

1 yd

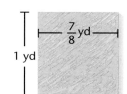

$\vdash \frac{7}{8}\text{yd} \dashv$

1 yd

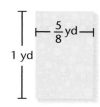

$\vdash \frac{5}{8}\text{yd} \dashv$

1 yd

a. Is there enough fabric for the teacher? **yes**

b. How should the teacher cut the material? How much material will be left over from each original piece?

10. A carpenter is making a picture frame. The width of each piece of wood is $3\frac{5}{8}$ in. The top and the bottom pieces are $15\frac{3}{4}$ in. long and the two side pieces are $23\frac{3}{8}$ in. long. When the carpenter puts it together as shown, what will the outer dimensions of the picture frame be? $19\frac{3}{8}$ **in. by 27 in.**

Find each sum or difference.

11. $-\frac{8}{12} + \left(-\frac{4}{12}\right)$ -1

12. $\frac{4}{11} - \frac{10}{11}$ $-\frac{6}{11}$

13. $-\frac{8}{15} + \frac{2}{5}$ $-\frac{2}{15}$

14. $-\frac{7}{16} - \left(-\frac{3}{8}\right)$ $-\frac{1}{16}$

15. $\frac{3}{14} + \left(-\frac{6}{7}\right)$ $-\frac{9}{14}$

16. $\frac{3}{4} + \left(-\frac{5}{12}\right)$ $\frac{1}{3}$

17. $-\frac{3}{7} - \left(-\frac{1}{6}\right)$ $-\frac{11}{42}$

18. $-\frac{2}{3} - \frac{3}{5}$ $-1\frac{4}{15}$

19. $-\frac{8}{15} - \frac{7}{20}$ $-\frac{53}{60}$

20. **Writing** Suppose your friend missed today's class. Write a letter to the friend describing how to add and subtract positive and negative fractions. Include several examples. **Answers will vary. Check students' work.**

SUGGESTED ASSIGNMENTS

Core Course
Day 1: Exs. 1–10
Day 2: Exs. 11–19
Day 3: Exs. 20–21, 39–43
Day 4: Exs. 22–35, 38

Extended Course
Day 1: Exs. 5–10
Day 2: Exs. 11–19
Day 3: Exs. 20–21, 39–43
Day 4: Exs. 22–38

Note: Extended Course assignments can be used to differentiate within the regular classroom. In classrooms where students are grouped homogeneously, the material might be covered in fewer days. In this case assignments may be combined.

ADDITIONAL PRACTICE
See the *Teacher's Resource Book* for additional practice and application exercises for this section.

DIFFERENTIATED INSTRUCTION
Exercise 10 For advanced students, replace the $3\frac{5}{8}$ width with the variable w. Then ask students to write expressions to represent the outer dimensions of a frame put together as shown using any length pieces. (*Answer:* top/bottom $w + x$, left/right $w + y$, where x is the length of each top/bottom piece and y is the length of each right/left piece) Extend the problem by asking students to find the perimeter. (*Answer:* $2(x + w) + 2(y + w)$ or $4w + 2x + 2y$)

EXERCISE NOTES

Exercises 28–30 Although stock prices represent dollars, until the latter part of the twentieth century, stock prices and the change in price were reported as mixed numbers and fractions, not decimals. Students may enjoy seeing a page of stock reports from an old newspaper. Those especially interested in the topic can make a chart showing the dollar value in decimal form of each change they see reported in the paper. This chart could then be displayed in the classroom or added to the student's portfolio.

If a fraction calculator is not available for **Exercise 30**, challenge students to find a common denominator for all the fractions in the table and find the sum or to convert each value to decimals to find the answer.

In **Exercises 34–35**, students might use guess and check, work backwards or write and solve an equation to find the fraction described by each set of clues.

21. a. $\frac{1}{2} - \frac{1}{4} + \frac{1}{8} - \frac{1}{16} + \frac{1}{32}$; $\frac{1}{2} - \frac{1}{4} + \frac{1}{8} - \frac{1}{16} + \frac{1}{32} - \frac{1}{64}$

c. Sample response: positive; The fraction to be subtracted will be smaller than the value of the twenty-ninth expression.

21. **Patterns** The expressions below are part of a pattern.

$$\frac{1}{2} - \frac{1}{4} \qquad \frac{1}{2} - \frac{1}{4} + \frac{1}{8} \qquad \frac{1}{2} - \frac{1}{4} + \frac{1}{8} - \frac{1}{16}$$

a. Write the next two expressions in the pattern.

b. Evaluate each expression above and the two that you wrote for part (a). $\frac{1}{4}, \frac{3}{8}, \frac{5}{16}, \frac{11}{32}, \frac{21}{64}$

c. Suppose you evaluated the thirtieth expression in the pattern. Do you think the result would be positive or negative? Explain.

Find each sum or difference.

22. $3\frac{2}{3} - 4\frac{1}{3}$ $-\frac{2}{3}$

23. $-1\frac{4}{5} - 6\frac{1}{5}$ -8

24. $-3\frac{1}{2} + \left(-1\frac{1}{4}\right)$ $-4\frac{3}{4}$

25. $8\frac{1}{4} + \left(-1\frac{7}{8}\right)$ $6\frac{3}{8}$

26. $-4\frac{2}{3} - \left(-7\frac{1}{6}\right)$ $2\frac{1}{2}$

27. $2\frac{5}{9} - \left(-3\frac{1}{3}\right)$ $5\frac{8}{9}$

Stock Market Until August of 2000, changes in stock prices were reported as fractions. The table at the right shows how the price of a company's stock changed during one day.

28. What was the change in the stock price from 9:30 A.M. to 11:00 A.M.? $\frac{3}{8}$

29. How much did the stock change from 12:00 P.M. to 3:00 P.M.? $\frac{3}{8}$

30. Fraction Calculator Suppose the price of the stock was $36 at 9:00 A.M. Use a fraction calculator to find the price at 4 P.M. Is the total change from the beginning of the day to the end of the day positive or negative? $36\frac{1}{8}$; positive

Time	Stock change
9:30 A.M.	None
10:00 A.M.	$+\frac{1}{2}$
11:00 A.M.	$-\frac{1}{8}$
12:00 P.M.	$-\frac{9}{16}$
1:00 P.M.	$+\frac{1}{2}$
2:00 P.M.	$-\frac{3}{8}$
3:00 P.M.	$+\frac{1}{4}$
4:00 P.M.	$-\frac{1}{16}$

Mental Math Use mental math to find each sum or difference.

31. $-2\frac{3}{5} + \left(-4\frac{2}{5}\right)$ -7

32. $4\frac{5}{6} + \left(-2\frac{5}{6}\right)$ 2

33. $1\frac{3}{8} - \left(-1\frac{5}{8}\right)$ 3

For Exercises 34–36, find the fraction described by each set of clues.

34. The fraction is between 0 and 1. If you add $\frac{2}{8}$ to it, the result is equivalent to $\frac{10}{16}$. $\frac{3}{8}$

35. The fraction is between –1 and 0. If you subtract $\frac{2}{4}$ from it, the result is $-1\frac{1}{4}$. $-\frac{3}{4}$

36. **Challenge** The absolute value of a fraction is between 1 and 2. If you add $\frac{1}{8}$ to half the fraction the absolute value of the result is equivalent to $\frac{1}{2}$. What is the fraction? $-1\frac{1}{4}$

37. **Challenge** Solve each equation for n.

    a. $-3\frac{2}{3} + n = -1\frac{3}{8}$ $2\frac{7}{24}$ b. $-5 = n - \left(-2\frac{1}{6}\right)$ $-7\frac{1}{6}$

Reflecting ◀▶ on the Section

Discussion

Exercise 38 checks that you understand operations with fractions.

Be prepared to discuss your response to Exercise 38 in class.

38. Two students each started to evaluate $-\frac{3}{10} - \left(-\frac{2}{15}\right)$ as shown.

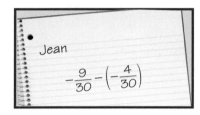

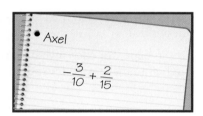

    a. Describe what each student has done so far. Then write the next step for each student. Will their answers be the same?

    b. Which method do you prefer? Explain your choice.
      Answers will vary.

38. a. Sample Response: Jean rewrote fractions with a common denominator of 30, $-\frac{9}{30} + \frac{4}{30}$; and Axel rewrote the difference as a sum, $-\frac{9}{30} + \frac{4}{30}$; yes

Spiral ◀▶ Review

Simplify each expression. (Module 2, pp. 86–87)

39. $28 + (-41)$ 40. $-12 \cdot (-8)$ 41. $72 \div (-8)$ 42. $-56 - 56$
   -13 96 -9 -112

43. The box-and-whisker plot models survey data from 16 countries. Find the lower extreme, the upper extreme, and the median of the data. (Module 1, p. 23) lower extreme = 10; upper extreme = 45; median = 20

Percent of People Who Would Like to Move to Another Country

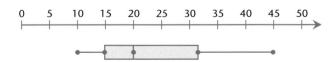

EXERCISE NOTES
Students attempting **Challenge Exercise 36** may want to refer back to solving absolute value equations in the Extension on p. 90 of Section 1.

TEACHER NOTES
The Extra Skill Practice Exercises in this Section are designed to be assigned after Exploration 3. If needed, problems could be separated as indicated below.

Exploration 1: Exs. 1, 4, 11
Exploration 2: Exs. 2, 3, 6, 8
Exploration 3: Exs. 5, 7, 9, 10, 12, 13

EXTRA HELP
Teacher's Resource Book
• Practice and Applications
• Study Guide

Technology Resources
• @Home Tutor
• Test Generator

ASSESSMENT
• Section 2 Quick Quiz
• Mid-Module Quiz
• Test Generator

HOME INVOLVEMENT
Play additional rounds of *Fraction Mindbender* at home with a family member for extra practice.

Section ② Extra Skill Practice

Find each sum or difference.

1. $\frac{3}{5} - \frac{7}{2}$ $-2\frac{9}{10}$

2. $-\frac{1}{3} - \frac{2}{7}$ $-\frac{13}{21}$

3. $\frac{4}{2} + \left(-\frac{7}{8}\right)$ $1\frac{1}{8}$

4. $4\frac{1}{9} + \frac{7}{8}$ $4\frac{71}{72}$

5. $\frac{2}{3} + \left(-1\frac{1}{3}\right) - \frac{2}{3}$

6. $-\frac{4}{9} - \left(-\frac{2}{7}\right)$ $-\frac{10}{63}$

7. $-\frac{3}{10} + 2\frac{2}{5}$ $2\frac{1}{10}$

8. $-\frac{3}{11} + \frac{2}{3} - \frac{9}{11}$ $-\frac{14}{33}$

9. $-1\frac{7}{9} - 1\frac{2}{6}$ $-3\frac{1}{9}$

10. $6\frac{7}{9} - \left(-\frac{5}{8}\right)$ $7\frac{29}{72}$

11. $\frac{5}{8} + 2\frac{1}{2}$ $3\frac{1}{8}$

12. $-\frac{4}{9} - \left(-\frac{2}{3}\right) + 1\frac{1}{6}$ $1\frac{7}{18}$

13. Johanna has decided to make her own party invitations. She has already bought the envelopes that are 7 in. long and 5 in. wide.

   a. She wants to have an extra $\frac{1}{6}$ in. of clearance around each edge of an invitation when it is placed in the envelope. What size should the invitations be? $4\frac{2}{3}$ in. by $6\frac{2}{3}$ in.

   b. What size should the paper for each invitation be? Assume she folds the paper in half to make each invitation.
   Possible answers: $4\frac{2}{3}$ in. by $13\frac{1}{3}$ in. or $9\frac{1}{3}$ in. by $6\frac{2}{3}$ in.

Standardized Testing ▶ Multiple Choice

1. Find $-7\frac{2}{3} + 5\frac{1}{5}$. D

   Ⓐ $-12\frac{13}{15}$ Ⓑ $-2\frac{13}{15}$ Ⓒ $-2\frac{3}{8}$ Ⓓ $-2\frac{7}{15}$

2. The expression $-5\frac{7}{16} - 3\frac{5}{8}$ has the same value as what other expression? A

   Ⓐ $-3\frac{5}{8} - 5\frac{7}{16}$ Ⓑ $5\frac{7}{16} + 3\frac{5}{8}$ Ⓒ $5\frac{7}{16} + \left(-3\frac{5}{8}\right)$ Ⓓ $-5\frac{7}{16} + 3\frac{5}{8}$

3. Which expression has a value that is less than $-\frac{2}{3}$? A

   Ⓐ $-\frac{3}{8} - \frac{2}{3}$ Ⓑ $-\frac{3}{8} + \frac{2}{3}$ Ⓒ $\frac{3}{8} + \left(-\frac{2}{3}\right)$ Ⓓ $\frac{3}{8} - \frac{2}{3}$

The GRAND GIVEAWAY

Setting the Stage ►►►►►►►►►►►►►►►►►►►►►►►

When a new store opens at a mall, special promotions are often used to attract shoppers. The "Grand Giveaway" is such a promotion. Each customer is given the opportunity to spin a spinner to try to win a gift certificate for purchases in the store. Nancy and Becky are waiting to take their turns to spin the spinner. Nancy is second in line and Becky is third. The first person spins a 7 and wins a $100 gift certificate.

Spin and Win $$$$$	
Spinner number	Gift Certificate Value
1	$25
2	Sorry
3	$25
4	$10
5	$10
6	Sorry
7	$100
8	$10

Think About It

1 Which of Nancy's and Becky's statements do you agree with? See margin.

2 How can you decide which comments are correct? One way to decide which comments are correct is to model the promotion by spinning a spinner.

Setting the Stage

GETTING STARTED
Module 2 Section 3 *Warm-Up* assesses student ability to write fractions in lowest terms which will be expected when reporting experimental and theoretical probabilities.

ABOUT THE THEME
The reading should provoke some lively discussion about contests, luck, and probability. Use **Question 1** to stimulate discussion about the giveaway and other games of chance. Students will probably disagree about whether Nancy should go to the back of the line. Encourage students to share their thinking about how Nancy's position in line affects her chance of winning. Students may enjoy acting out the situation to understand it better. Leave the question unresolved and tell students you will come back to the question after they have explored some similar situations using concepts about probability.

1. Sample Response: I agree with both of Becky's statements. I disagree with Nancy. Winning the greatest gift certificate prize was lucky but moving to the back of the line will not give Nancy a better chance of winning.

105

CLASSROOM MANAGEMENT

Students should work in groups of four to complete Exploration 1. For performing the experiment in **Question 5**, try to make sure all students are involved. Since students are working in a group of four have 3 students in the group spin, while 1 person records the results. If the number of students in your class is not evenly divisible by four, use some groups of three, with one of the three absorbing the job of recorder for the group.

ALTERNATIVE APPROACH

If you have a small class, you can have the groups do more than 16 trials. If the results of the combined trials are not fairly evenly distributed, you may wish to have students conduct a second set of trials and combine the resuts with their first trials. This will reinforce the notion that more trials improves the likelihood that the experimental results will be closer to the theoretical probabilities.

COMMON ERROR

Students may confuse the meaning of the terms *experiment, outcome,* and *event.* Point out that for this situation, the action of spinning the spinner is an *experiment*, a specific spin, like a 5, is an *outcome*, and winning a $25 gift certificate is an *event.* As a second example, suggest that rolling a die is an *experiment,* the number showing on top is an *outcome,* and depending on the rules of the game being played, rolling an odd number might be a desired *event.*

TECHNOLOGY

For a related technology activity, see the *Technology Book.*

106

GOAL

LEARN HOW TO...
♦ find experimental probabilities

AS YOU...
♦ simulate the *Grand Giveaway*

KEY TERMS
♦ experiment
♦ outcome
♦ equally likely
♦ event
♦ probability
♦ experimental probability

3. d. The outcomes are equally likely because the measures of the 8 angles at the center of the spinner are equal.

Exploration 1

EXPERIMENTAL PROBABILITY

SET UP   *Work in a group of four. You will need:* • *Labsheets 3A and 3B* • *paper clip* • *pencil*

▶ You can use a spinner to estimate Nancy's chances of winning a gift certificate in the "Grand Giveaway." Spinning the spinner is an example of an **experiment**. The result of an experiment is an **outcome**.

3   "The spinner stops on 3" is one outcome of an experiment involving a spinner like the one shown on page 105.

   a. List the other possible outcomes.   1, 2, 4, 5, 6, 7, 8

   b. How many outcomes are there altogether?   **8 outcomes**

   c. Two outcomes are **equally likely** if they have the same chance of happening. What must be true about the spinner for the outcomes to be equally likely?   The number of degrees in each central angle must be the same.

   d. Is each of the eight numbers on the spinner equally likely to come up on each spin? How do you know?

▶ Winning a gift certificate on a spin is an example of an *event.* An **event** is a set of outcomes of an experiment.

4   Use the *Spin and Win $$$$$* table on page 105 to determine the outcomes that make up the following events.

   a   winning a gift certificate on a spin   1, 3, 4, 5, 7, and 8

   b. winning a gift certificate with a value of at least $25 on a spin   1, 3, and 7

Use Labsheets 3A and 3B for Questions 5–11.

5   Will moving to the back of the line improve Nancy's chances of winning a gift certificate? To find out, follow the directions for the *Grand Giveaway Experiment* on Labsheet 3A.   Students will investigate this question. Check students' work on Labsheet 3A.

6 Use the data in the *Trials Table* to complete the first three rows in the *Group Results Table* on Labsheet 3B. **Answers will vary. Check students' work.**

▶ **Experimental Probability** To decide whether she should move to the back of the line, Nancy can determine whether the *probability* of spinning a winning number is the same or different for each person in line. A **probability** is a number from 0 through 1 that tells how likely it is that an event will occur.

> You can use the following ratio to find the *experimental probability* of an event.
>
> $$\text{Experimental Probability} = \frac{\text{number of times an event occurs}}{\text{number of times the experiment is done}}$$

7 Use the data in the first three rows of the *Group Results Table* to find the experimental probabilities in the last three rows. **Answers will vary. Check students' work.**

8 Compare the experimental probabilities for winning a gift certificate on the second, third, and fourth spins. Do you think you are more likely to win on any particular spin? Explain.

9 **Try This as a Class** Complete the following to see how increasing the number of trials can affect experimental probabilities. **Answers will vary. Check students' work.**

  a. Combine your group results with those of the other groups in the class and record the totals in the first four rows of the *Class Results Table*.

  b. Find the experimental probability for each of the events in the last three rows and record them in the table.

10 a. Describe how the experimental probabilities of winning a gift certificate on the second, third, and fourth spins for your group compare with the probabilities for the whole class.

  b. Which set of probabilities, the ones for your group or the ones for the class, do you think give a better indication of an event occurring? Why? **The ones for the class because the more times you do the experiment the more accurate the results will be.**

11 **Try This as a Class** Look back at the *Setting the Stage*. Use the probabilities in the *Class Results Table* to answer these questions.

  a. Was Becky correct when she said moving to the back of the line would not make a difference? Why or why not?

  b. Was Nancy correct when she said the first contestant was lucky to win a $100 gift certificate on his spin? Explain. **Sample Response: Winning a $100 gift certificate is the least likely of all the possible outcomes, so it is lucky.**

8. There may be considerable variation in the probabilities. Ideally they will be about the same, which would indicate that there is no advantage to moving to the back of the line.

10. a. The probabilities for the group and the class will probably be close to one another, but there may be considerable variation because of the small number of trials for the group data. For the class data, the probability of winning a gift certificate should be about $\frac{3}{4}$ for each spin. The probability of winning at least $25 should be about $\frac{3}{8}$ for each spin, and the probability of winning a $100 gift certificate should be about $\frac{1}{8}$ for each spin. There will be less variability in the class data.

11. a. Yes; the probabilities of winning on the 3 spins are all about the same.

Question 8 It is likely that students will have results suggesting that one spin is more advantageous than others. Ask the groups to share their answers at this point so students will see that different groups found different spins to be better. This will lead into **Question 9**, where students combine the results of all groups.

Although there is not enough room in the tables on the labsheet, you might want to use the results to **Question 9** as an opportunity to introduce students to writing probability statements in the following format: P(winning on the first spin) = $\frac{3}{4}$. Students can then use this format in answering the **Checkpoint 12(b) and (c)**.

Question 10 If students have difficulty comparing the class results to the individual group results, suggest that they express the probabilities in decimal form or as equivalent fractions. Emphasize that the combined class results for each spin lie within the range of individual group results for that spin.

Exploration 1 continued

COMMON ERROR

Question 12(a) Students may list only those sums that appear in the trial table. Make sure students understand that the possible outcomes do not refer to the sums in the trial table and that the table does not contain all the possible sums. Instead students should make an organized list showing all the sums that could be made when the two number cubes are rolled.

Exploration 2

DEVELOPING MATH CONCEPTS

Having just seen in Question 12 that the results of an experiment do not always represent all possible outcomes, students will now investigate theoretical probability in which the probability is based on all the outcomes and the frequencies that should occur.

TEACHING NOTES

In **Question 13**, it is important to stress what *equally likely* means, that is, that each of the outcomes has the same chance of occurring. After students have answered the question, ask them to describe situations in which each of the five objects in the box might not be equally likely to be drawn. (If the spheres were not all the same size, or if the objects had different shapes.) Finally, point out that since each sphere is equally likely to be drawn, each of the five numbers 1–5 is also equally likely to be drawn. Ask students to describe how the spheres could be labeled so that each number would not be equally likely to be drawn. (Example: label the spheres 1, 1, 2, 3, 4. Drawing a 1 would be more likely than drawing a 2, a 3, or a 4.)

✔ **QUESTION 12**

...checks that you can find experimental probabilities.

12 ✔ **CHECKPOINT** A number cube has sides numbered 1 through 6. A pair of number cubes was rolled 20 times and the sum of the numbers was recorded in the *Trial Table*.

a. What are the possible outcomes of the experiment?
2, 3, 4, 5, 6, 7, 8, 9, 10, 11, and 12

b. Based on this experiment, what sum or sums seem to be most likely to occur? What is the experimental probability that they occur? $6; \frac{1}{4}$

TRIAL TABLE

Trial	1	2	3	4	5	6	7	8	9	10
Sum	12	5	8	7	6	9	5	6	7	6

Trial	11	12	13	14	15	16	17	18	19	20
Sum	3	7	10	6	6	2	8	2	5	7

c. What sum or sums seem to be least likely to occur? What is the experimental probability that they occur? 4 and 11 are possible outcomes that did not occur. Since they did not occur, they have a probability of 0. 3, 9, 10, and 12 only occurred once and each has a probability of $\frac{1}{20}$.

HOMEWORK EXERCISES ▶ See Exs. 1–16 on pp. 115–117.

GOAL

LEARN HOW TO...
- find theoretical probabilities
- recognize dependent and independent events

AS YOU...
- examine a promotional drawing

KEY TERMS
- theoretical probabilities
- dependent events
- independent events
- impossible event
- certain event

Exploration 2

THEORETICAL PROBABILITY

▶ A second promotion, *Select a Number*, also takes place at the store each day. Four shoppers are selected at random and given a chance to win a gift certificate by drawing a numbered sphere from a box. The box contains five spheres that are numbered 1 through 5. The spheres are not put back into the box after they are drawn. Nancy is also second in line for *Select a Number*.

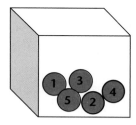

Select a Number and Win $$$$$	
Sphere number	Gift certificate value
1	$100
2	$25
3	$50
4	Sorry
5	Sorry

13. Yes; If the spheres are all identical except for the numbers written on them, each sphere would be equally likely.

13 On the first draw, is each of the five spheres equally likely to be drawn? Why or why not?

 Module 2 At the Mall

▶ **Theoretical Probability** Sometimes you can find the probability of an event without actually doing an experiment.

> If all of the outcomes of an experiment are equally likely, you can use this ratio to find the *theoretical probability* of an event.
>
> $$\text{Theoretical Probability} = \frac{\text{number of outcomes that make up the event}}{\text{total number of possible outcomes}}$$

14. b. Count the number of Sorrys and take the ratio to 5 or subtract the probability of winning from one, $1 - \frac{3}{5}$.

14 a. What is the theoretical probability that the first person in line wins a gift certificate? $\frac{3}{5}$

b. Discussion Explain two ways to find the probability that the first person in line does *not* win a gift certificate.

c. What is the probability that the first person in line does *not* win a gift certificate? $\frac{2}{5}$

▶ When it is Nancy's turn to draw, one number has already been drawn from the box.

15 Suppose the first person in line draws the sphere numbered 5.

a. What does the first person win? nothing

b. How many spheres are left in the box? Is each of the spheres equally likely to be drawn? 4; yes

c. What is the theoretical probability that Nancy will win a gift certificate if she draws next? $\frac{3}{4}$

d. In this case, is Nancy's chance of winning a gift certificate better than, the same as, or worse than if she had been the first person to draw? better than

16 Suppose the first person in line had won a gift certificate.

a. If Nancy draws next, what is the theoretical probability that she will win a gift certificate? $\frac{1}{2}$

b. Compare your answer in part (a) with your answer in Question 15(c). Does the outcome of the first draw affect the theoretical probability of winning a gift certificate on the second draw? Explain. Yes; Since the probabilities are different, the outcome of the first draw does affect the probability of winning on the second draw.

TIPS FROM TEACHERS
Tape five circles labeled with 1–5 and their correpsonding prizes to magnets that can be placed on a magnetic whiteboard. This way throughout the lesson you can model dependent and independent events by removing magnets from the board or by replacing them. A bulletin board and push pins can be used as an alternative to magnets.

TEACHING NOTES
You may want to use the following example to illustrate the definition of theoretical probability before students answer **Question 14**.

CLASSROOM EXAMPLES
Find the theoretical probablity of selecting a number between 0 and 9 that is divisible by 4.

Answer: Each of the 10 digits from 0 to 9 is equally likely to be selected. There are 2 numbers between 0 and 9 that are divisible by 4: 4 and 8. The theoretical probability is $\frac{2}{10} = \frac{1}{5}$.

DEVELOPING MATH CONCEPTS
Emphasize that the definition of theoretical probablity only applies when the outcomes are equally likely. For example, if five identical spheres numbered 1, 1, 2, 3, 4 are placed in a box, the possible outcomes of a draw are 1, 2, 3, 4, but drawing a 1 is more likely than the other outcomes. If you use the definition of theoretical probability in this case, you would get that the probability of drawing a 1 is $\frac{1}{4}$, but it is actually $\frac{2}{5}$, since 2 of the 5 equally likely spheres are labeled 1.

109

Exploration 2 *continued*

TEACHING NOTES

Question students as to the role replacement plays in deciding whether an outcome is dependent or independent of another. Ask students why not replacing the first item changes the probabilities for the second item drawn.

DEVELOPING MATH CONCEPTS

Question 19 addresses the range for all probabilities. Check that students understand 0 and 1 are the extremes, by asking them why a probability of 1.5 or $-\frac{1}{3}$ is not possible.

✔ QUESTION 18

...checks that you can find theoretical probabilities and identify dependent and independent events.

19. a. Sample Response: The first three draws were 1, 2, 3. The probability is 0.

b. Sample Response: The first three draws were 5, 4, 1. The probability is 1.

▶ **Dependent and Independent Events** In Questions 15 and 16, you discovered that the probability of winning a gift certificate on the second draw depends on the outcome of the first draw. If the probability that one event occurs is affected by whether or not another event occurs, the events are **dependent events**. If the probability of an event is not affected by whether or not another event occurs, the events are **independent events**.

17 Suppose you flip a nickel and get heads. Then you roll a number cube and get a five. Are these events *independent* or *dependent*? independent

18 ✔ CHECKPOINT There are five numbered spheres in a box.

a. An odd-numbered sphere is drawn and not replaced before the second draw. What is the theoretical probability of getting an odd-numbered sphere on the second draw? $\frac{1}{2}$

b. An odd-numbered sphere is drawn and replaced before the second draw. What is the probability of getting an odd-numbered sphere on the second draw? $\frac{3}{5}$

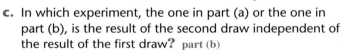

c. In which experiment, the one in part (a) or the one in part (b), is the result of the second draw independent of the result of the first draw? part (b)

19 Consider the original situation of three winning numbers and two losing numbers in the *Select a Number* promotion.

a. Describe a sequence of draws in which the last person to draw cannot win a gift certificate. In this case winning on the last draw is an **impossible event**. What is the theoretical probability of this impossible event?

b. Describe a sequence of draws in which the last person to draw is sure to win a gift certificate. In this case, winning on the last draw is a **certain event**. What is the theoretical probability of this certain event?

20 Nancy thought it was "unlucky" for the first contestant in the *Select a Number* promotion to draw a losing number. Do you agree with Nancy? Explain. Sample Response: Since the probability of winning on the first draw, $\frac{3}{5}$, is greater than the probability of losing, $\frac{2}{5}$, it was unlucky.

HOMEWORK EXERCISES ▶ See Exs. 17–27 on pp. 117–118.

Exploration 3

TR‹E E DIAGRAMS

SET UP *You will need Labsheet 3C.*

GOAL

LEARN HOW TO...
◆ use a tree diagram to model and find theoretical probabilities

AS YOU...
◆ analyze a promotional drawing

KEY TERM
◆ tree diagram

▶ The Game Store at the mall attracts customers by encouraging people to come in and play a different game each day. Today's game is *WORD DRAW*. The rules of the game are simple.

WORD DRAW

Each player is given a cup containing 4 letters.

Step 1 Without looking, each player removes one of the letters from his or her cup.

Step 2 The 3 remaining letters are then drawn out one at a time and placed in the order drawn to see if they make a three-letter word found in a dictionary.

Step 3 The 3 letters are returned to the cup and Step 2 is repeated 5 more times.

Players who make a word on at least two of their six tries win a prize.

▶ Finding the experimental probability of an event can require many trials and take a long time, so it may be more efficient to find the theoretical probability. Using a *tree diagram* may help you find the theoretical probability of an event. A **tree diagram** can by used to show all the possible outcomes of an experiment.

Exploration 3

CLASSROOM MANAGEMENT
Students may complete the work in Exploration 3 individually or with a partner.

GETTING STARTED
Go over the rules for *WORD DRAW* as a class. Make certain students understand that the letter they remove in Step 1 will not be used in the game.

Exploration 3 *continued*

TEACHING NOTES

Question 22 Provide a dictionary or confirm for students which 3-letter outcomes form words.

Likewise in **Question 23**, students may not be familiar with the word TARE or realize it is a word. In mathematics it refers to the weight of a container deducted from the total weight to determine the weight of the contents. Students may find it easier to understand as the net weight that is often printed on food items.

21. a. Nancy would have to draw the R on her first draw, the T on her second draw, and the E on her third draw.

c. Since the letter tiles are identical, on each draw, the tiles remaining in the cup are equally likely to be drawn, so each outcome is also equally likely.

EXAMPLE

Roulan and Nancy played *WORD DRAW*. They each received a cup containing the letters A, T, E, and R. Without looking, Nancy removed the A and Roulan removed the R. They decided to make *tree diagrams* to find all the possible outcomes of drawing three letters one at a time.

Nancy's tree diagram with the A removed			
1st Draw	2nd Draw	3rd Draw	Outcome
R	T — E		RTE
	E — T		RET
T	R — E		TRE
	E — R		TER
E	T — R		ETR
	R — T		ERT

Roulan's tree diagram with the R removed			
1st Draw	2nd Draw	3rd Draw	Outcome
A	T — E		ATE
	E — T		AET
T	A — E		TAE
	E — A		TEA
E	T — A		ETA
	A — T		EAT

Use the tree diagrams in the Example for Questions 21 and 22.

21 **a.** What must Nancy do to get the outcome RTE?

b. How many outcomes are shown in each tree diagram? 6

c. Are the outcomes equally likely? Why or why not?

22 What is the theoretical probability of each event?

a. Nancy forms a word when she draws her letters one at a time. 0

b. Roulan forms a word when he draws his letters one at a time.
Since ATE, TEA, and EAT are words, the probability is $\frac{3}{6}$ or $\frac{1}{2}$.

Use Labsheet 3C for Questions 23–26.

23 Roulan and Nancy are playing *WORD DRAW* for the Game Store's *Grand Prize Giveaway*. They win a $25 gift certificate if all four letters (A, E, T, and R), drawn one at a time, form the word TARE.

a. Complete the *Grand Prize Giveaway Tree Diagram* on Labsheet 3C. See margin.

b. How many possible outcomes are there? 24

c. What is the theoretical probability that A is drawn on the first draw? $\frac{1}{4}$

d. Circle the part of the tree diagram that describes drawing A on the first draw. See margin.

23. a., d. See Additional Answers beginning on page A1.

 Module 2 At the Mall

24 Use the *Grand Prize Giveaway Tree Diagram.*

  a. Suppose A is drawn on the first draw. What is the probability of drawing the T on the second draw? $\frac{1}{3}$

  b. If A and T are drawn on the first and second draws respectively, what is the probability of drawing the E on the third draw? $\frac{1}{2}$

  c. If A , T, and E are drawn on the first, second and third draws respectively, what is the probability of drawing the R on the fourth draw? 1

25 **a.** Three of the outcomes form words found in a dictionary. What are the three words? **TARE, TEAR, and RATE**

  b. What is the theoretical probability that a word will be formed? $\frac{1}{8}$

  c. What is the theoretical probability that either the word RATE or the word TEAR will be formed? $\frac{1}{12}$

26 To win the gift certificate, a player must form the word TARE. What is the theoretical probability that a player will win? $\frac{1}{24}$

27 **a.** Print the letters of the word RATIO on five identical slips of paper. **a–e. Check students' work.**

  b. Turn each slip face down and thoroughly mix the slips.

  c. Draw any three of the slips. Try to form a word with the three letters you picked.

  d. Repeat the experiment 10 times.

  e. What is the experimental probability that you can form a word when you draw any three letters from the pile?

  f. **Try This as a Class** How could you find the theoretical probability that you can form a word when you draw any three letters from the pile?

  g. Find the theoretical probability. How does it compare with the experimental probability in part (e)?

28  **CHECKPOINT** A number cube has sides numbered 1 through 6. Suppose you roll the number cube twice.

  a. Make a tree diagram that shows all the possible outcomes. **See margin.**

  b. Find the theoretical probability of rolling a 1 on the first roll and an odd number on the second roll. $\frac{1}{12}$

HOMEWORK EXERCISES ▶ See Exs. 28–33 on p. 119.

27. f. Make an organized list of all the outcomes OR Make a tree diagram, but remember that the order in which the letters are drawn is not important.

  g. $\frac{1}{2}$ (The 5 combinations of letters that give words are rat, rot, oat, air, and oar.)

 QUESTION 28

...checks that you can make and use tree diagrams.

TEACHING NOTES

In the **Try This as a Class Questions 27(f) and (g)**, work with students to make both an organized list and a tree diagram to compare the results. As you do, make sure students do not repeat letter combinations (*rat* is the same as *art*), since the order the letters are selected in is not important. Begin by choosing the letter R and having students determine the possible choices for the next letter after R and then for the 3rd letter, checking as the branches are drawn that they do not duplicate any groups of three letters. If the second branches are drawn to A, T, I, and O in that order, students will see that there are only 3 choices left for the letter after A, only 2 for the letter after T, 1 for the letter after I, and no choices left for the letter after O, so the O branch is not needed and can be eliminated. This gives all the combinations of 3 letters in which R is one of the letters. Next, repeat the process beginning with A, but not using R for any of the letters. Continue in this way until all of the combinations of 3 letters are found. In total there are 10 possible combinations; 5 will form words.

28. a. See Additional Answers beginning on page A1.

Key Concepts

ABSENT STUDENTS

For students who were absent for all or part of this section, the blackline Study Guide for Section 3 may be used to present the ideas, concepts and skills of Section 3.

CLOSURE QUESTIONS

Give an example of an event that is impossible.
One that is somewhat likely to occur.
One that is equally likely to occur or not occur.
One that is quite likely to occur.
One that is certain to occur.

Sample Response: Four identical spheres numbered 1, 2, 4, and 9 are placed in a box and one sphere is drawn at random.

The event, the sphere is labeled 5, is impossible.

The event, the sphere is numbered 2, is somewhat likely.

The event, the sphere is labeled with an odd number, is equally likely to occur or not occur.

The event, the number on the sphere is a perfect square, is quite likely.

The event, the number on the sphere is less than 10, is certain.

Define theoretical probability and explain how it is different from experimental probability. What is the range for all probabilities?

Sample Response: If all the possible outcomes are equally likely, theoretical probability is the ratio

number of successful outcomes
─────────────────────────────
total number of possible outcomes

and tells how likely it is that an event will happen. Theoretical probability is calculated probability, while experimental probability is probability based on performing an experiment. The range for all probabilities is from 0 through 1.

Key Terms

experiment

outcome

equally likely

event

probability

impossible event

certain event

experimental probability

theoretical probability

29. Experimental
probability = $\frac{5}{12}$;
Theoretical
probability = $\frac{1}{2}$

 Module 2   At the Mall

Section 3 Key Concepts

Outcomes and Events (p. 106)

An experiment is an activity whose results can be observed and recorded. The result of an experiment is an outcome. Outcomes are equally likely if they have the same chance of occurring. An event is a set of outcomes of an experiment.

Example   Suppose the experiment is to spin the spinner at the right once. The possible outcomes are A, B, C, and D. Spinning a B is an event. Spinning a consonant is also an event.

Experimental Probability (pp. 107–108)

A probability is a number from 0 through 1 that tells how likely something is to happen.

Probability

0	$\frac{1}{4}$	$\frac{1}{2}$	$\frac{3}{4}$	1
Impossible (cannot occur)	Somewhat likely to occur	Equally likely to occur or not occur	Quite likely to occur	Certain to occur

A probability that is found by repeating an experiment several times and recording the results is an experimental probability.

Example   The table shows the results of spinning the spinner above 12 times.

The experimental probability of A is $\frac{2}{12}$ or $\frac{1}{6}$, of B is $\frac{3}{12}$ or $\frac{1}{4}$, of C is $\frac{3}{12}$ or $\frac{1}{4}$, and of D is $\frac{4}{12}$ or $\frac{1}{3}$.

Trial	Letter	Trial	Letter
1	C	7	D
2	D	8	A
3	D	9	B
4	A	10	C
5	C	11	D
6	B	12	B

Theoretical Probability (pp. 108–110)

A theoretical probability is found without doing an experiment.

Example   Since the four outcomes (A, B, C, and D) on the spinner above are equally likely, the theoretical probability of spinning an A is $\frac{1}{4}$.

29   Key Concepts Question Based on the tables above, what is the experimental probability of spinning either an A or a C on the spinner above? What is the theoretical probability?

Section 3

Key Concepts

Key Terms

Dependent and Independent Events (p. 110)
When the occurrence of one event affects the probability of the occurrence of another event, the events are dependent. Otherwise, they are independent.

dependent events

Tree Diagrams (pp. 111–113)
A tree diagram can be used to show all the possible outcomes of an experiment.

independent events

Example
The tree diagram at the right shows the possible outcomes of two flips of a coin.

tree diagram

The probability of flipping at least one head is $\frac{3}{4}$.

First flip	Second flip	Outcome
H	H	H H
	T	H T
T	H	T H
	T	T T

30 **Key Concepts Question**

a. Make a tree diagram that shows all the possible outcomes of spinning the spinner on page 114 twice. **See margin.**

b. How many possible outcomes are shown on your diagram? **16**

c. What is the theoretical probability of spinning an A and then spinning a B? $\frac{1}{16}$

Section 3

Practice & Application Exercises

YOU WILL NEED

For Ex. 9:
♦ a paper clip

A number cube with sides numbered 1–6 is rolled once.

1. What are the outcomes of the experiment? **1, 2, 3, 4, 5, 6**

2. Are the outcomes equally likely? Why or why not?

3. What outcomes make up the following events?

   a. rolling an odd number **1, 3, 5**

   b. rolling an even number greater than 2 **4, 6**

2. Since the sides all have the same shape and size, the number cube is equally likely to come to rest on each side. So the outcomes are equally likely.

Use the tree diagram in the Example. How are the events flipping one head, flipping at most one head, and flipping at least one head different?

Sample Response:

There ar two ways to flip one head, HT or TH.

If you have 0 heads or 1 head, you have at most one head, so t here are three ways of flipping at most one head, TT, HT, and TH.

If you have1 head or 2 heads, you have at least one head, so t here are three ways of flipping at least one head, TH, HT, and HH.

Practice & Applications

Suggested Assignments

Core Course
Day 1: Exs. 1–7, 34–44
Day 2: Exs. 8–16
Day 3: Exs. 17–27
Day 4: Exs. 28–29, 31–33

Extended Course
Day 1: Exs. 4–7, 34–44
Day 2: Exs. 8–16
Day 3: Exs. 17–27
Day 4: Exs. 28–33

Note: Extended Course assignments can be used to differentiate within the regular classroom. In classrooms where students are grouped homogeneously, the material might be covered in fewer days. In this case assignments may be combined.

30. a. See Additional Answers beginning on page A1.

Practice & Applications

ADDITIONAL PRACTICE
See the *Teacher's Resource Book* for additional practice and application exercises for this section.

EXERCISE NOTES
Exercise 9 Students use a paper clip to create a spinner. Even though the circle for this spinner has a shorter radius, students should still open one end of the paper clip as they did on the labsheet in Exploration 1 to make it easier to decide in what sector the spinner stops.

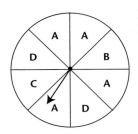

5. No; while landing on each sector is equally likely, the number of sectors for each outcome are not equal.

7. 4 sectors are labeled with vowels and 4 are labeled with consonants, so the spinner is just as likely to stop on a vowel as a consonant.

The spinner at the left is spun once.

4. What are the outcomes of the experiment? **A, B, C, D**

5. Are the outcomes equally likely? Why or why not?

6. What outcomes make up the event "the spinner stops on a consonant"? **B, C, D**

7. Is the spinner more likely to stop on a vowel or a consonant? Explain.

8. A penny is taped on the inside bottom of a bottle cap. The cap is then tossed in the air. The results for 12 tosses are shown in the Table. *Yes* means the cap landed with the penny up; *No* means the cap landed with the penny down.

Trial	1	2	3	4	5	6	7	8	9	10	11	12
Result	Yes	Yes	No	Yes	No	Yes	No	Yes	Yes	No	Yes	Yes

a. What is the experimental probability that the penny will land up? $\frac{2}{3}$

b. Find the experimental probability that the penny lands down in two different ways. $1 - \frac{2}{3} = \frac{1}{3}$ or $\frac{4}{12} = \frac{1}{3}$

9. An experiment consists of spinning the spinner at the right twice and finding the sum of the two numbers spun. **Results will vary. Check students' tables.**

Make a copy of the spinner. Use a paper clip for a pointer. Perform the experiment 12 times and record the results in a table like the one below.

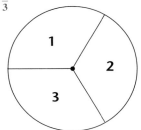

Trial	1	2	3	4	5	6	7	8	9	10	11	12
Sum	?	?	?	?	?	?	?	?	?	?	?	?

For Exercises 10–12, use the results in your table.

10. What is the experimental probability that the sum of the numbers spun is 3? **Answers will vary. Check students' work. (Theoretical is $\frac{2}{9}$ or about 22% of the time.)**

11. What sum(s) occurred most often? **Answers will vary. Check students' work. (Theoretically, 4 occurs most often, then 5 and 3.)**

12. What is the experimental probability of the sum(s) that occurred most often? **Answers will vary. Check students' work.**

Rock

Paper

Scissors

Games Use the information below for Exercises 13–16 and 28–30.

The game *Rock, Paper, Scissors* is played all over the world—not only as a form of recreation, but also as a way of settling disagreements.

The game uses the three different hand signs shown at the left. Two players pound the fist of one hand into the air three times. On the third beat each player displays one of the hand signs. Possible results are shown. If both players display the same symbol, the round is a tie.

Rock breaks scissors
Rock wins

Scissors cuts paper
Scissors wins

Paper covers rock
Paper wins

13. Play 20 rounds of *Rock, Paper, Scissors* with a partner. After each round, record each player's choice (using *R* for rock, *P* for paper, and *S* for scissors) and the result in a table like this one.

Round number	Player 1	Player 2	Result
1	R	P	Player 2 wins
2	S	S	Tie

14. Based on the results of your 20 rounds, what is the experimental probability of each result? Answers will vary. Check students' work.

   a. Player 1 wins.   b. Player 2 wins.   c. There is a tie.

15. Did Player 1 or Player 2 win more often? How can you tell using the experimental probabilities in Exercise 14?

16. **Writing** Do you think playing *Rock, Paper, Scissors* is a fair way to settle a disagreement? Explain.

Interpreting Data Nate traced a circle, cut out a cardboard strip as shown, and used a thumbtack to make a spinner.

17. What appears to be the theoretical probability that the pointer will stop in each region?

   a. A $\frac{1}{4}$ b. B $\frac{1}{8}$ c. C $\frac{1}{8}$ d. D $\frac{1}{2}$

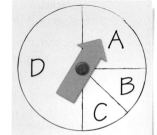

13. Results will vary. Check students' tables.

15. Answers will vary. Check students' work. You can tell which player won most often by comparing the probabilities. The player with the greater probability won most often.

16. Sample Response: I think it is a fair way to settle a disagreement because each player won about the same number of times.

HOME INVOLVEMENT
In order for students to complete **Exercises 13–16**, they will need someone at home to play 20 rounds of the game *Rock, Paper, Scissors* with them. Let students know that the other player does not necessarily need to be an adult, siblings as young as age 6 can often play after a brief demonstration.

EXERCISE NOTES
In **Exercise 17**, make sure students understand that, since the central angles of the sectors do not all have the same measure, the outcomes A, B, C, and D are not equally likely. One way to find the theoretical probability of each outcome is to divide the circle into 8 congruent sectors. Since Region A covers two sectors, the probability the pointer stops in region A is $\frac{2}{8}$ or $\frac{1}{4}$.

Section 3   Exploring Probability   117

Practice & Applications

EXERCISE NOTES

Exercise 26 If students have difficulty getting started, help them by brainstorming ideas about spinners, dice, etc.

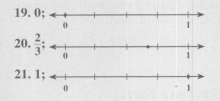

19. 0;

20. $\frac{2}{3}$;

21. 1;

Region	Frequency
A	9
B	5
C	5
D	21

26. Sample Response: Spin the spinner at the right once. The probability the spinner stops on A is $\frac{1}{2}$, the probability it stops on B is $\frac{1}{3}$, and the probability it stops on C is $\frac{1}{6}$.

18. Nate spun the pointer 40 times. The results are shown in the table. Use the data to calculate the experimental probability that the pointer will stop in each region.

a. A $\frac{9}{40}$ b. B $\frac{1}{8}$ c. C $\frac{1}{8}$ d. D $\frac{21}{40}$

For Exercises 19–21, a number cube with sides numbered 1 through 6 is rolled. Find each probability and plot it on a number line as on page 114. Label each point.

19. the theoretical probability of rolling a 7 See margin.

20. the theoretical probability of rolling a number less than 5 See margin.

21. the theoretical probability of rolling a number greater than 0
See margin.

22. a. Which of the events in Exercises 19–21 are certain?
rolling a number greater than 0

b. Which of the events in Exercises 19–21 are impossible?
rolling a 7

For Exercises 23–25, tell whether the events are equally likely.

23. "rolling an even number on a number cube with sides numbered 1 through 6" and "rolling an odd number using the same number cube" equally likely

24. "rolling a number less than 2 on a number cube with sides numbered 1 through 6" and "rolling a number greater than 3 using the same number cube" not equally likely

25. "getting 2 heads and a tail on 3 flips of a coin" and "getting 2 tails and a head on 3 flips of the same coin" equally likely

26. **Open-ended** Describe an experiment that has three outcomes whose probabilities are $\frac{1}{2}$, $\frac{1}{3}$, and $\frac{1}{6}$.

27. In a bag of 20 marbles, 4 marbles are blue.

a. One marble is drawn from the bag. What is the probability that it is a blue marble? That it is *not* a blue marble? $\frac{1}{5}$; $\frac{4}{5}$

b. Suppose a blue marble is drawn on the first draw and not replaced. What is the probability of drawing a blue marble on the second draw? $\frac{3}{19}$

c. Suppose another color (not blue) is drawn on the first draw and not replaced. What is the probability of drawing a blue marble on the second draw? $\frac{4}{19}$

d. Is drawing a blue marble on the second draw *dependent on* or *independent of* the first draw? Explain your answer. dependent on; The outcome of the first draw affects the probability of drawing a blue ball on the second draw.

28. a. Copy and complete the tree diagram shown at the right for the game *Rock, Paper, Scissors*. See margin.

b. How many outcomes are there? 9 outcomes

c. What outcomes make up the event "Player 1 does not win"?
RR, RP, PP, PS, SR, and SS

d. How is the event "Player 1 does not win" different from the event "Player 1 loses"? "Player 1 does not win" includes ties and "Player 1 loses" does not.

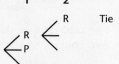

Player 1	Player 2	Result
	R	Tie
R		
P		

29. Writing In a fair game, each player has an equal chance of winning. Is *Rock, Paper, Scissors* a fair game? Explain. Rock, Paper, Scissors is a fair game. The probability of winning is $\frac{1}{3}$ for each player.

30. Challenge Suppose you notice that your partner never uses scissors.

a. Draw a tree diagram to show the possible outcomes if one player never uses scissors. See margin.

b. How would this affect your playing strategy? Sample Response: I would never use rock because I could only tie or lose if I did.

31. a. Draw a tree diagram to show all the possible outcomes when a coin is flipped three times. See margin.

b. How many outcomes are there? 8 outcomes

c. Do you think the outcomes are equally likely? Why or why not? Yes; The outcomes on each flip are equally likely.

32. Use your tree diagram from Exercise 31 to find the theoretical probability of each event.

a. no heads $\frac{1}{8}$ **b.** exactly one head $\frac{3}{8}$ **c.** a head on the first flip $\frac{1}{2}$

Reflecting ◀▷ on the Section

Write your response to Exercise 33 in your journal.

33. Describe two dependent events and two independent events. Answers will vary. Check students' work.

Spiral ◀▷ Review

Find each sum or difference. (Module 2, p. 100)

34. $-\frac{1}{5} + \left(-\frac{7}{15}\right)$ **35.** $\frac{5}{8} + \left(-4\frac{1}{2}\right)$ **36.** $4\frac{1}{3} - \left(-\frac{9}{10}\right)$ **37.** $-5\frac{11}{12} - \frac{3}{4}$

Combine like terms to simplify each expression. (Module 1, p. 43)

38. $12x - 10x + 1$ **39.** $n^2 - mn + mn$ **40.** $2s + 4st + 6s$
   $2x + 1$ n^2 $8s + 4st$

Classsify each angle as *acute*, *right*, *obtuse*, or *straight*. (Toolbox, p. 592)

41. 85° acute **42.** 140° obtuse **43.** 180° straight **44.** 95° obtuse

34. $-\frac{2}{3}$

35. $-3\frac{7}{8}$

36. $5\frac{7}{30}$

37. $-6\frac{2}{3}$

Journal

Exercise 33 checks that you can apply ideas about probability.

EXERCISE NOTES

Exercise 29 Students should use the results of their work from Exercise 28 to justify their work. Encourage them to cite the theoretical probabilities that can be found using their tree diagram.

28. a., 30. a., 31. a. See Additional Answers beginning on page A1.

120

Section ③
Extra Skill Practice

The table shows the results of sixty flips of two coins. Use the table for Exercises 1 and 2.

Two Heads	One Head/One Tail	Two Tails
14	28	18

1. What is the experimental probability of getting one head and one tail? $\frac{7}{15}$

2. What is the experimental probability of getting two tails? $\frac{3}{10}$

Suppose you roll the object shown. It has eight sides, numbered 1 through 8. All eight sides are equally likely. Find the theoretical probability of each of the events in Exercises 3–6.

3. rolling a 2 $\frac{1}{8}$

4. rolling a 7 or 8 $\frac{1}{4}$

5. rolling a number greater than 3 $\frac{5}{8}$

6. rolling a 2, 4, 6, or 8 $\frac{1}{2}$

7. In a sack of 25 apples, 8 are red, 10 are golden, and the rest are green.

   a. One apple is taken from the sack. What is the probability that it is golden? that it is green? that it is not green? golden: $\frac{2}{5}$; green: $\frac{7}{25}$; not green: $\frac{18}{25}$

   b. If 2 red apples have been taken from the sack, what is the probability that the next apple taken will be red? will be green? red: $\frac{6}{23}$, green: $\frac{7}{23}$

   c. Are the events below *dependent* or *independent*? Explain. See margin.
      Event 1: The first apple taken is golden.
      Event 2: The second apple taken is green.

8. José made a packing list for a weekend trip.

   a. Draw a tree diagram to show all the possible ways José could dress if he wears a pair of matching socks, a pair of pants, and a shirt. See margin.

   b. What is the theoretical probability that José wears the T-shirt with jeans and black socks? $\frac{1}{12}$

black socks
white socks
jeans
khaki pants
denim shirt
sweatshirt
T-shirt

Standardized Testing ▶ Free Response

1. A spinner is divided into 6 segments, each labeled with a different positive integer. The theoretical probability of spinning a number less than 8 is 1. The theoretical probability of spinning a multiple of 3 is $\frac{1}{3}$, a multiple of 4 is $\frac{1}{6}$, and an odd number is $\frac{2}{3}$. Draw the spinner. See margin.

2. What is the theoretical probability of getting all heads or all tails when a coin is flipped 3 times? 4 times? 5 times? 50 times? $\frac{1}{4}, \frac{1}{8}, \frac{1}{16}, \frac{1}{2^{49}}$

FOR ASSESSMENT AND PORTFOLIOS

Is it a Boy or a Girl?

The Situation See the *Teacher's Resource Book* for a sample solution for this Extended Exploration.

The Ten O'Neil Girls

Between September of 1930 and July of 1952, Julia O'Neil of Boston, Massachusetts, gave birth to 12 children. The first child was a boy. The next 10 were girls, and the last was a boy.

The Problem

It is somewhat unusual for a woman to have 12 children. It is even more unusual for a woman to give birth to 10 girls in a row, as it would be for a woman to give birth to 10 boys in a row. What was the probability that the O'Neils would have 10 girls or 10 boys in a row?

Something to Think About

♦ What is the probability that all of the children born to a family have the same gender if the family consists of one child? two children? three children? four children? five children?

♦ Is there a pattern in these probabilities?

Present Your Results

Explain how you solved this problem. Include any representations that may be needed to make your explanation clear.

After reading the E² situation together as a class, have students clarify that they understand what is meant by "pairs and sets" by showing how the number of children born is equal to 69.

Something to Think About suggests that students begin by breaking this problem into simpler ones with family sizes of 1 child, 2 children, 3 children, and so on until generalizing for *n* children. Encourage students to use various representations to look for a pattern, such as a diagram, a table, an organized list, etc. Students might relate the problem to that of flipping a coin where each side of the coin represents a boy or girl.

Using an E²: Suggestions for managing and evaluating an Extended Exploration are available in the *Teacher's Resource Book* for Modules 1 and 2. See also pages T44–T45 in the *Teacher's Edition*.

Alternate E²: See the *Teacher's Resource Book* for an alternate Extended Exploration that can be used after Module 2 Section 3.

121

Setting the Stage

ABOUT THE THEME

To incorporate the mall theme, this section begins with a teen survey about shopping malls, transportation, and types of stores they see as important in a mall.

GETTING STARTED

In Section 4, students will take a group survey and represent results in fraction, decimal, and percent form. Module 2 Section 4 *Warm-Up* assesses students' ability to write a number in fraction, decimal, and percent form, as well as solve proportions necessary for finding percent of a number in Exploration 2. Toolbox p. 588 can further help with fractions, decimals, and percents.

Section ④ Surveys, Proportions, and Percents

Your OPINION COUNTS!

Setting the Stage

According to a recent survey, average American teens spend more than $104 a week each, and about two-thirds of that money can be spent however they wish. Because of this buying power, store owners want to attract teens to malls. The store owners use surveys to answer questions like the ones at the left.

TEEN SURVEY

How often do you visit malls?

How do you get there?

What kinds of stores do you like?

Think About It

1 One survey asked teens what mall features they found most appealing. About 35% chose movie theaters. What does 35% mean? **Sample Response: 35 out of every 100, or a little more than one-third**

2 About how many dollars each per week can average American teens spend as they wish? **$69.33**

Exploration 1

Conducting a SURVEY

SET UP *Work in a group of four. You will need Labsheet 4A.*

▶ **To see how surveys can provide information, your group will conduct a survey.**

Use Labsheet 4A for Questions 3–5.

3 Answer the survey questions below. Record your group's results in the second column of each of the *Group Survey Results* tables.

Mall Survey

What kind of store do you think is most important at a mall? (Choose only one.)	**How often do you go to a mall?**
A. clothing	**A.** one or more times a week
B. shoes	**B.** once every 2 to 3 weeks
C. CD/DVD/video/music	**C.** once a month
D. sporting goods	**D.** less than once a month
E. department store	**E.** never
F. video arcade	

---

4 Suppose one out of four members of your group thinks a music store is most important at a mall. You can write this fact as a ratio in fraction form $\left(\frac{1}{4}\right)$, decimal form (0.25), or percent form (25%).

a. Use the *Group Survey Results* tables to record each of your group's ratios as a fraction, as a decimal, and as a percent. Answers will vary. Check students' work.

b. Explain how you changed from the fraction form of the ratios to the decimal form. **Divide the numerator by the denominator.**

c. How are the percent form and the decimal form of each ratio related? **Possible answers: The digits are the same or they are both parts of a hundred.**

d. Which form(s) of the ratio would you use to compare your group's results to those of another group? Why? **Sample Response: decimals or percents; They are easier to compare than fractions.**

LEARN HOW TO...
- use percents, fractions, and decimals to summarize the results of a survey
- identify and correct biased survey questions

AS YOU...
- conduct a survey

KEY TERM
- biased question

3. Answers will vary. Check students' work.

FOR ▶ HELP

with *fractions, decimals, and percents,* see
TOOLBOX, p. 588

Exploration 1

TEACHING NOTES
For students in geographic areas where there are no malls, you can replace the word "mall" with "shopping district", or identify a local shopping area to substitute for the word "mall" in the survey.

Question 4(a) Remind students to write each fraction in lowest terms.

Exploration 1 *continued*

TEACHING NOTES

Rewriting a biased question to show no bias may be an unfamiliar concept. In **Question 7** students may not recognize the subtle messages inherent in phrases such as "waste of time," "good," and "forced." Reviewing student work as a class may be necessary to build this concept.

You may want to have students work in *pair share* cooperative groups for **Question 8**. In *pair share* groups, pairs of 2 students can exchange the questions they wrote to check for bias, before sharing the questions with the class.

---

6. a. Sample Response: Kelly's; The question leads the listener to choose the fashion show.
   b. Sample Response: Sara's; The question leads the listener to agree.
   e. No. Sample Response: The questions don't ask a direct question, but are worded in a way that influences the listener.

7. a. The question prompts a negative attitude towards recycling; "Do you think recycling is of value?"
   b. The question favors a positive response; "Should we build a new high school?"
   c. The word forced favors a negative response; "Should all students take physical education?"

✔ **QUESTION 8**

...checks that you can write an unbiased survey question.

---

5 Based on your group's results, do you think you can make an accurate prediction of the percent of the students in your class who rank clothing stores as the most important? Explain. **Sample Response: No; The number of people in the group is too small.**

▶ **The way questions are asked can influence the results of a survey. For example, a group of students has been asked to plan an event to attract teenagers to a mall. A fashion show and a concert are possible events. The group will survey students to see which they prefer.**

6 Kelly and Sara suggest the survey questions shown.

  a. Which question is more likely to get responses favoring the fashion show? Explain.

  b. Which question is more likely to get responses favoring the concert? Explain.

  c. Which activity do you think Kelly would prefer? **a fashion show**

  d. Which do you think Sara would prefer? **a concert**

  e. Will either Kelly's or Sara's question produce responses that accurately reflect students' opinions? Why or why not?

Kelly: Wouldn't a fashion show be a better way to attract teen shoppers than a concert?

Sara: Do you agree that a concert would be more fun than a fashion show?

▶ **When a question produces responses that do not accurately reflect the opinions of the people surveyed, it is a biased question. A good survey asks questions that are not biased.**

7 Explain why each question below is biased. Then try rewriting each question so that it is not biased. **Sample responses are given.**

  a. "Is recycling a waste of time?"

  b. "Wouldn't building a new high school be a good idea?"

  c. "Should all students be forced to take physical education?"

8 ✔ **CHECKPOINT** Write an unbiased question that could be asked to find out whether a fashion show or a concert is a better way to attract students to the mall. **Sample Response: "Would you be more inclined to attend a fashion show or a concert at the mall?"**

HOMEWORK EXERCISES ▶ See Exs. 1–12 on p. 133.

Exploration 2

Proportions and PERCENTS

Some store owners at a mall think their sales will improve if more teenagers visit the mall. They know that about 40% of teenagers nationwide ride to malls with a parent or relative. They think a free shuttle service one Saturday each month might make it easier

for the 4000 teenagers in the area to get to their mall. They survey 250 local teenagers (students in grades 8–11) to see whether they would use a shuttle.

GOAL

LEARN HOW TO...
◆ use proportional reasoning to estimate the percent of a number
◆ identify representative samples

AS YOU...
◆ make predictions based on a sample

KEY TERMS
◆ population
◆ sample
◆ representative sample
◆ proportion
◆ cross product

▶ A survey is used to gather information about a group called a **population**. It may not be practical to contact every member of the population, so a smaller group called a **sample** is surveyed. The survey results are used to make predictions about the entire population.

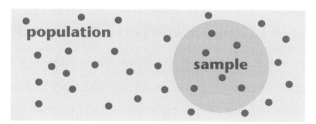

9 Discussion

a. What is the population that the store owners are trying to get information about? **4000 area teenagers**

b. What is the sample? **250 local teenagers**

▶ To make accurate predictions based on a sample, the sample must be representative of the whole population. A **representative sample** has the same characteristics as the population being studied.

Exploration 2

TEACHING NOTES
Question 9 Students should understand that the *population* is the entire group being studied, that is, the group we want information about. The *sample* is a small group taken from the population. It is the group about which information is actually collected. A sample may or may not be representative of the whole population. The idea of a representative sample will be developed in Questions 10 and 11 on page 126.

COMMON ERROR

As students answer **Question 10** encourage them to think about factors other than the size of the group (for example, geography, age, gender, political affiliation, and so on) that determine whether a sample is representative.

TEACHING NOTES

Question 12(a) Ask students for suggestions regarding ways to change the ratio 85 out of 250 to a percent. Any method that reuslts in an accurate percent is acceptable at this time. These answers will be used in the development of the estimation methods and proportion-solving method shown later in the Exploration.

The **Example on p. 127** shows two methods for estimating a percent of a number. If your students are not familiar with the percent bar model, you may need to introduce it to them. Show students how to model the "nice" fraction method using a percent bar as shown below.

Percent	Number
0	0
$\frac{1}{3}$ (33 $\frac{1}{3}$%)	1333 (4000 ÷ 3)
100	4000 students

11. b. library users; representative; A random selection of those people who use the library was made.
   c. all citizens of the area; not representative; It targets only those people who are listening to the news broadcast and are willing to make a phone call to voice an opinion.

10. a. No; Students who are not on the girls' softball team are not represented in the survey. It excludes boys.
   b. No; Students not in the band are not represented. Band members may have more interest in a concert.
   c. Yes; Students buying lunch are a more random sample, since choosing every 5th person allows for different genders, ages, and interest groups.

✔ QUESTION 11

...checks that you can tell whether a sample is representative.

10. d. No; Students who don't choose to take and complete the survey are not in the sample. Volunteers often complete surveys because they have already formed a strong opinion about the topic that they want heard.

---

10 **Try This as a Class** Tell whether each group of students would be a representative sample for the survey about which event, a fashion show or a concert, would be better for attracting teenagers to a mall. Explain your thinking.

a. members of a girls' softball team

b. members of the All-City Band

c. every fifth student in line for lunch in the cafeteria

d. every student who takes a survey and completes it

11 **✔ CHECKPOINT** Identify the intended population for each survey below. Also tell whether the sample from the population is representative. Explain your answers. **b–c. See margin.**

a. A pollster asks people attending a Democratic Party fundraiser whom they plan to vote for in a city council election. **registered voters; not representative; It is targeting only those who favor Democrats.**

b. A librarian asks every tenth person who enters the library what new books he or she would like the library to order.

c. A television news program asks viewers to phone in a vote for or against building a nuclear power plant.

12 **Discussion** Use the information about the mall given on page 125. Suppose 85 out of 250 teenagers surveyed by the store owners say they would use the shuttle.

a. Write the ratio of the number of teenagers who would ride the shuttle to the number of students in the sample as a percent. **34%**

b. Based on the results of the survey, do you think 2000 of the 4000 teenagers in the area will ride the shuttle? more than 2000 teenagers? fewer than 2000 teenagers? Explain. **No; No; Yes; Sample Response: 34% of the sample say they would use the shuttle. 2000 is half of the population and 34% is less than half.**

▶ **Estimating with Percents** You can use the percent you found in Question 12 to estimate the total number of teenagers in the area who might ride the shuttle.

EXAMPLE

To estimate 34% of 4000, you can use the following methods.

Method 1 You can estimate 34% of 4000 by using the nearest "nice" fraction. 34% is close to $33\frac{1}{3}$%, which equals the "nice" fraction $\frac{1}{3}$. So you can estimate $\frac{1}{3}$ of 4000.

Method 2 You can also estimate 34% of 4000 using multiples of 10%. A percent bar model shows how this method works.

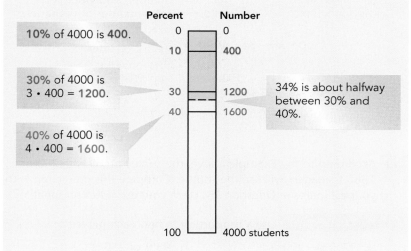

10% of 4000 is **400**.

30% of 4000 is 3 • 400 = 1200.

34% is about halfway between 30% and 40%.

40% of 4000 is 4 • 400 = 1600.

13 a. Refer to Method 1 in the Example. Estimate $\frac{1}{3}$ of 4000.
about 1300

b. Refer to Method 2. Use the fact that 34% is about halfway between 30% and 40% to estimate 34% of 4000. about 1400

c. Discussion Which of your estimates from parts (a) and (b) would you use to predict how many teenagers in the area might use a shuttle to get to the mall? Explain.

13. c. Sample Response: I would use both and say that between 1300 and 1400 teenagers would use the shuttle.

14 ✔ **CHECKPOINT** Estimate to find each percent.

a. 26% of 600 about 150 **b.** 68% of 50 about 35

c. 74% of 3000 about 2250 **d.** 21% of 150 about 30

✔ **QUESTION 14**

...checks that you can estimate a percent of a number.

Have students generate their own list of "nice" fractions to be used when applying Example Method 1.

TEACHING NOTES

After students have completed **Question 13**, you may want to go through another example with the class before they do the Checkpoint.

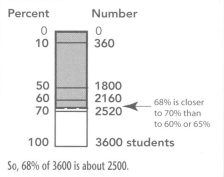

CLASSROOM EXAMPLE

Estimate 68% of 3600.

Sample Response:
Method 1
You can estimate 68% of 3600 by using the nearest "nice" fraction. 68% is close to $66\frac{2}{3}$%, which is equivalent to the "nice" fraction $\frac{2}{3}$. $\frac{2}{3}$ of 3600 is 2400.

Method 2
You can also estimate 68% of 3600 using multiples of 10%. A percent bar model shows how this method works.

So, 68% of 3600 is about 2500.

As students complete estimates in **Question 14**, encourage them to use both methods in the Example. Discuss how to decide which method is most suitable for each expression. (*If the percent is very close to a "nice fraction" use that approach. Otherwise multiples of 10% can be used.*)

127

Exploration 2 *continued*

TEACHING NOTES

After students have completed **Question 15**, you may want to go through another example with the class before they do the Checkpoint.

CLASSROOM EXAMPLE

Use a proportion to find 68% of 3600.

Answer: Let x = the part of 3600 we want to find. The proportion can be written:

$$\begin{array}{cc} \text{Percent} & \text{Number} \\ \text{part} \to \dfrac{68}{100} & = \dfrac{x}{3600} \begin{array}{l} \leftarrow \text{part} \\ \leftarrow \text{whole} \end{array} \end{array}$$

The cross products are equal.

$$100 \cdot x = 68 \cdot 3600$$
$$x = \frac{68 \cdot 3600}{100}$$
$$x = 2448$$

68% of 3600 is 2448.

Check to see that students are correctly setting up proportions for **Question 16** and that they are using equivalent fractions or the concept of equal cross products to solve the proportions.

---

15. Sample Response: Yes; 1360 is between the two estimates of 1300 and 1400.

▶ **Using a Proportion** Another way to predict the number of teenagers who would ride the shuttle is to write and solve a proportion. A **proportion** is a statement that two ratios are equal.

EXAMPLE

Use a proportion to find 34% of 4000.

SAMPLE RESPONSE

Percent means "out of 100," so 34% means "34 out of 100" or $\frac{34}{100}$.

Let x = the number of teenagers who would ride the shuttle. The proportion can be written:

$$\begin{array}{ccc} & \text{Percent} & \text{Number} \\ \text{part} \to & \dfrac{34}{100} = & \dfrac{x}{4000} \begin{array}{l} \leftarrow \text{number who would ride} \\ \leftarrow \text{total number of teenagers} \end{array} \end{array}$$

$$100 \cdot x = 34 \cdot 4000$$
$$x = \frac{34 \cdot 4000}{100}$$
$$x = 1360$$

In a proportion cross products are equal.

34% of 4000 is 1360.

15 According to the Example above, the survey predicts that about 1360 teenagers will use the shuttle. Compare this prediction with your estimates in Question 13. Were your estimates reasonable?

✔ **QUESTION 16**

...checks that you can find the percent of a number.

16 ✔ **CHECKPOINT** Use a proportion to find each percent.

   a. 37% of 1200 444   **b.** 93% of 250 232.5

17 **Try This as a Class** Suppose the survey convinced the store owners at the mall to run the shuttle. The first month 800 teenagers ride it.

   a. The second month the number of riders is 125% of the number of riders in the first month. How many riders are there in the second month? 1000 riders

   b. The third month the number of riders is 0.9% more than the number the second month. How many additional riders is this? 9 riders

   c. How many teenagers ride the shuttle the third month? 1009 students

HOMEWORK EXERCISES ▶ See Exs. 13–27 on pp. 133–135.

 Module 2 At the Mall

Samples and PERCENT

GOAL

LEARN HOW TO...
- write equations to solve percent problems
- find a representative sample

AS YOU...
- analyze the results of the Mall Survey

18 For your survey on page 123, the population was the entire class. What was the sample? **the four group members**

▶ **Finding a Part** You can use your group survey results to make predictions about the whole class.

EXAMPLE

Suppose 75% of the members of a group go to the mall once a month. There are 31 students in the class. You can use this information to predict how many students in the class go to the mall once a month.

First	Describe what you want to find.	75% of 31 is what number?
Next	Write your sentence as an equation.	$0.75 \cdot 31 = x$
Then	Solve the equation.	$23.25 = x$

Use the fraction or decimal equivalent of 75%.

About 23 students in the class go to the mall once a month.

19 **Use Labsheet 4A.** Count the students in your class. Then use your *Group Survey Results* data to predict each number below.
a–c. Answers will vary. Check students' work.
  a. the number of students in your class who visit the mall one or more times a week

  b. the number of students in your class who rank clothing stores as the most important stores at the mall

  c. the number of students in your class who rank video arcades as the most important

---

Exploration 3

CLASSROOM MANAGEMENT
Students can complete **Exploration 3** in the same groups they used for Exploration 1. When students reach **Question 21**, you may want them to rearrange their desks to form combined groups for the remainder of the Exploration.

TEACHING NOTES
If necessary, go through the following example with the class before students begin **Question 19**.

CLASSROOM EXAMPLE
Suppose 45% of the students in a group go to the mall once a month. There are 496 students in the school. Predict how many students in the school go to the mall once a month.

Answer:

First describe what you want to find.
45% of 496 is what number?

Next write your sentence as an equation.
$0.45 \cdot 496 = x$ $(45\% = 0.45)$

Then solve the equation.
$223.2 = x$

About 223 students go to the mall once a month.

DEVELOPING MATH CONCEPTS
Question 19 Make sure students are using the method shown in the Example. They should use the decimal form of their Labsheet data and a calculator for computation.

COMMON ERROR

As students answer **Question 21**, encourage them to recognize factors other than sample size that determine whether a sample is representative. Refer back to Question 10 in Exploration 2.

TEACHING NOTES

After students have completed **Question 22**, you may want to go through another example with the class before they do the Checkpoint.

CLASSROOM EXAMPLE

Suppose 10 out of 25 students in a group go to the mall once a month. To find what percent of the group goes to the mall once a month, you can write and solve an equation.

Answer:

First describe what you want to find.
10 is what percent of 25?

Next write your sentence as an equation.
$10 = \frac{x}{100} \cdot 25$
$10 = \frac{x}{4}$

Then solve the equation.

$4 \cdot 10 = 4 \cdot \frac{x}{4}$

$40 = x$

About 40% of the group go to the mall once a month.

---

20 **Try This as a Class** Think about the groups who answered the survey for the *Group Survey Results* tables on Labsheet 4A. Do you think your group is representative of the whole class? Why or why not? Answers will vary. Check students' work.

21 **Use Labsheets 4A and 4B.** Use the *Combined Group Survey Results* table to combine your group's survey data from Labsheet 4A with the data from two other groups. Try to choose two groups that will make the combined group as representative of the whole class as possible. Answers will vary. Check students' work.

▶ **Finding a Percent** You can use an equation to find the percent of students in your combined group who gave each response on the Mall Survey.

EXAMPLE

Suppose 4 out of 12 students in a group go to the mall once a month. To find what percent of the group goes to the mall once a month, you can write an equation.

First	Describe what you want to find.	4 is what percent of 12?
Then	Write your sentence as an equation.	$4 = \frac{x}{100} \cdot 12$
		$4 = \frac{12}{100}x$

---

22 **Try This as a Class**

    a. In the Example, why is *x* divided by 100? The missing number is represented as a percent and a percent is out of 100.

    b. Solve the equation in the Example.
    $33\frac{1}{3}$

Use completed Labsheet 4B for Questions 23–26.

✔ QUESTION 23

...checks that you can write and solve an equation to find a percent.

23 **✔ CHECKPOINT** In Question 21, you combined your group's data with the data from two other groups. Use an equation to find the percent of the students in your combined groups who gave each of the responses described in Question 19. Answers will vary. Check students' work.

24 Use the percents from Question 23 to predict the number of students in your class who gave each of the survey responses described in Question 19. Answers will vary. Check students' work.

25 Try This as a Class Find the actual number of students in your class who gave each of the responses described in Question 19.

    a. Compare your predictions in Questions 19 and 24 with the actual class results. Which predictions were more accurate?
       Question 24

    b. Do you think your *original group* or your *combined group* was more representative of the class? Explain. **Sample Response: combined group; The sample size was larger.**

26 Suppose each group below answered the mall survey questions on page 123. Explain whether you think your combined class results from Question 25 can be used to predict their responses.

    a. another class of students your age **Yes; the groups are similar.**

    b. a class of fifth grade students **No; the age difference may affect their responses.**

    c. the teachers at your school **No; the age difference may affect their responses.**

▶ **Finding the Total** You can use an equation to find the total when you know a part and the corresponding percent.

EXAMPLE

In one class, 2 students said they never went to a mall. These students made up 8% of the class. To find the total number of students in the class, you can write and solve an equation.

First	Describe what you want to find.	2 is 8% of what number?
Then	Write your sentence as an equation.	$2 = 0.08 \cdot x$
		$2 = 0.08x$

27 Solve the equation in the Example. How many students were in the class? **25 students**

28  **CHECKPOINT** Write and solve an equation to find each number.

    a. 36 is 45% of what number? $36 = 0.45x$; 80

    b. 7% of what number is 28? $0.07x = 28$; 400

✔ QUESTION 28

...checks that you can find a number when a percent of it is known.

HOMEWORK EXERCISES ▶ See Exs. 28–41 on pp. 135–136.

TEACHING NOTES
After students have completed **Question 27**, you may want to go through another example with the class before they do the Checkpoint.

CLASSROOM EXAMPLE

In one school, 42 students said they never went to the mall. These students made up 12% of the school. To find the total number of students in the school, you can write and solve an equation.

Answer:

First describe what you want to find.
42 is 12% of what number?

Next write your sentence as an equation.
$42 = 0.12 \cdot x$
$42 = 0.12x$

Then solve the equation.
$$\frac{42}{0.12} = \frac{0.12x}{0.12}$$
$350 = x$

There are 350 students in the school.

Key Concepts

ABSENT STUDENTS

For students who were absent for all or part of this section, the blackline Study Guide for Section 4 may be used to present the ideas, concepts, and skills of Section 4.

CLOSURE QUESTION

In one school 75 band members were surveyed. 12% said they never went to the mall. How many of those surveyed said they never went to the mall?

Sample Response:

The sample is the 75 band members who were surveyed.

12% of 75 = 0.12 · 75 = 9 band members.

Section 4

Key Concepts

Key Terms

population

biased question

sample

representative sample

proportion

cross products

Surveys (pp. 123–124)

You can conduct a survey to get information about a population. A survey should not contain any biased questions.

Example The question "Do you agree that football is more fun to watch than golf?" is biased because it encourages a response favoring football. A better question is "Do you prefer to watch football or golf?"

Representative Samples (pp. 125–126)

When making a prediction based on surveys, usually only a sample of the population is used. Care must be taken to choose a representative sample that has the same characteristics as the whole population.

Example A survey asks parents of school-age children if they favor a new state tax to help fund education. The sample is not representative because it does not include state residents without school-age children.

Estimating Percents (p. 127)

You learned two ways to estimate the percent of a number. You can use a "nice" fraction or you can use multiples of 10%.

Finding Percents (pp. 128–131)

To find the exact percent of a number, you can write and solve a proportion or an equation.

Examples

Use a proportion to find 26% of 80.

$$\text{part} \rightarrow \frac{26}{100} = \frac{x}{80} \leftarrow \text{part}$$
$$\text{whole} \rightarrow \qquad\qquad \leftarrow \text{whole}$$

$$26 \cdot 80 = 100x$$

cross products

$$20.8 = x$$

Use an equation to find 26% of 80.

26% of 80 is what number?

$$0.26 \cdot 80 = x$$

$$20.8 = x$$

---

29 **Key Concepts Question** In a 2003 survey, 120 of the 400 teens surveyed got their spending money from a regular job, 43% got money from odd jobs, and 48% got an allowance.

a. What percent of the teens had a regular job? 30%

b. How many of the teens got an allowance? 192

Section 4

Practice & Application Exercises

Write each percent as a fraction and as a decimal.

1. 40% $\frac{2}{5}$; 0.4

2. 74% $\frac{37}{50}$; 0.74

3. 115% $\frac{23}{20}$; 1.15

Write each decimal as a fraction and as a percent.

4. 0.67 $\frac{67}{100}$; 67%

5. 0.8 $\frac{4}{5}$; 80%

6. 0.005 $\frac{1}{200}$; 0.5%

Write each fraction as a decimal and as a percent.

7. $\frac{19}{100}$ 0.19; 19%

8. $\frac{3}{8}$ 0.375; 37.5%

9. $\frac{130}{200}$ 0.65; 65%

Tell whether each question in Exercises 10–12 is biased. Rewrite each biased question so that it is no longer biased.

10. "Wouldn't Smith make a much better governor than Jones?"

11. "Which kind of movie do you like better—dramas or comedies?"
    not biased

12. "Should teachers use video clips and movies to make their classes more interesting and effective?"

13. Suppose a middle school survey is given to find out if eighth graders should graduate a week before other students get out of school. The survey is given only to sixth graders.

    a. What is the population? middle school students

    b. What is the sample? sixth grade students

    c. Is this a representative sample? Why or why not?

Entertainment Some results from a survey of decision makers in the United States entertainment industry are shown below.

14. Explain whether you can conclude the following from this survey.

    A majority of people in the United States thinks that *viewers* and *ratings pressure* are most responsible for TV violence.

15. **Writing** How might the survey results differ if the question were asked to a representative sample of people in the United States?

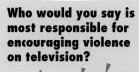

Who would you say is most responsible for encouraging violence on television?

Viewers	35%
Ratings pressure	33%
Network programmers	17%
Producers	5%
Writers	3%
Advertisers	2%
Program suppliers	1%
Directors	1%
Performers	2%
Outside media pressure	5%

Note: Due to rounding, percentages do not add up to 100%.

10. Biased; Sample Response: "Do you think Smith or Jones would make a better governor?"

12. Biased; Sample Response: "Should teachers use video clips and movies in classrooms?"

13. c. No; Sample Response: Sixth graders are not representative of the entire school.

14. No. Sample Response: The population for the survey was decision makers in the U.S. entertainment industry, not people in the United States.

15. Answers will vary. Sample Response: The percentage who held viewers responsible might be less.

Practice & Applications

SUGGESTED ASSIGNMENTS

Core Course
Day 1: Exs. 1–12
Day 2: Exs. 13–15, 42–49
Day 3: Exs. 16–26
Day 4: Exs. 28–37, 39–41

Extended Course
Day 1: Exs. 10–12
Day 2: Exs. 13–15, 42–49
Day 3: Exs. 16–20, 24–27
Day 4: Exs. 28–41, 50–51*

Note: Extended Course assignments can be used to differentiate within the regular classroom. In classrooms where students are grouped homgeneously, the material might be covered in fewer days. In this case assignments may be combined.
* denotes Extension Exercises

ADDITIONAL PRACTICE
See the *Teacher's Resource Book* for additional practice and application exercises for this section.

EXERCISE NOTES
Remind students to write all fractions in lowest terms.

DEVELOPING MATH CONCEPTS

In **Exercise 19**, encourage students to first consider the equivalent fraction method shown when solving percent problems. Once the proportion is set up, they should consider whether they can use mental math and equivalent fractions to solve the problem before proceeding to find cross products or multiplying by the least common denominator.

16. about 150, nice fraction or using multiples of 10%

17. about $66, nice fraction; about $64, using multiples of 10%

18. about 32, nice fraction; about 35 using multiples of 10%

Estimate each percent. Tell which method you used.

16. 76% of 200   17. 67% of $99   18. 55% of 64

Marketing Use the information at the left for Exercises 19 and 20. Round decimal answers to the nearest unit.

> **In a survey of 1200 teens:**
>
> **45.1%** thought women's clothing was the most important type of store at the mall;
>
> **15%** thought men's clothing was the most important;
>
> **30.9%** of the teens said they go to the mall once a month with their parents.

19. a. Estimate how many of the teens thought women's clothing was the most important type of store. Then find the actual number. Estimates will vary: about 540; 541

    b. Estimate how many of the teens thought men's clothing was the most important type of store. Then find the actual number. Estimates will vary: about 180; 180

20. a. Estimate how many of the 1200 teens said they go to the mall once a month with their parents. about 360

    b. **Alternative Method** Two methods for solving proportions are shown below. Use each method to find the number of teens surveyed who visit the mall once a month with their parents. Check students' work; about 371 teens

Undoing Method	**Equivalent Fraction Method**

Percent   Number   Percent   Number

part → $\frac{30.9}{100}$ = $\frac{x}{1200}$ ← part ← whole   part → $\frac{30.9}{100}$ = $\frac{x}{1200}$ ← part ← whole

What number times 100 is 1200?

$$1200 \cdot \frac{30.9}{100} = \frac{x}{1200} \cdot 1200$$

$$\frac{30.9}{100} \xrightarrow{\times 12} = \frac{x}{1200} \xleftarrow{\times 12}$$

Multiply both sides by the least common denominator.

$$\underline{?} = x \qquad\qquad \underline{?} = x$$

c. Based on your estimate in part (a), do your answers in part (b) seem reasonable? yes

d. Which method in part (b) do you like best? Why? Answers will vary.

Use a proportion to find each percent.

21. 16% of 210 33.6   22. 150% of 88 132   23. 42.2% of 500 211

24. 37.5% of 336 126 25. 105% of 20 21   26. 0.8% of 9000 72

27. In 1992, the Mall of America opened in Bloomington, Minnesota. Its area is about 4.2 million square feet. The table shows some of the largest malls in the United States. Use a percent to compare the area of each mall to the area of the Mall of America.

Mall	Area (square feet)
Woodfield Mall (Illinois)	2,700,000
The Galleria (Texas)	2,400,000
Tysons Corner Center (Virginia)	2,200,000

Use an equation to find each number or percent.

28. What is 40% of 80?
32

29. 0.5% of 90 is what number?
0.45

30. 30 is what percent of 125?
24%

31. 2 is what percent of 200?
1%

32. 65 is what percent of 50?
130%

33. 17% of what number is 34?
200

34. 7.2 is 12% of what number?
60

35. 30 is 150% of what number?
20

36. **Writing** Compare the three examples in Exploration 3. How are they alike? How are they different?

37. The Park at MOA, an indoor theme park, is inside the Mall of America. It offers several different types of attractions. Use the information shown in the graph. Tell what percent of the attractions are each type.

a. rides
about 46%

b. shops
about 10%

c. food venues
about 19%

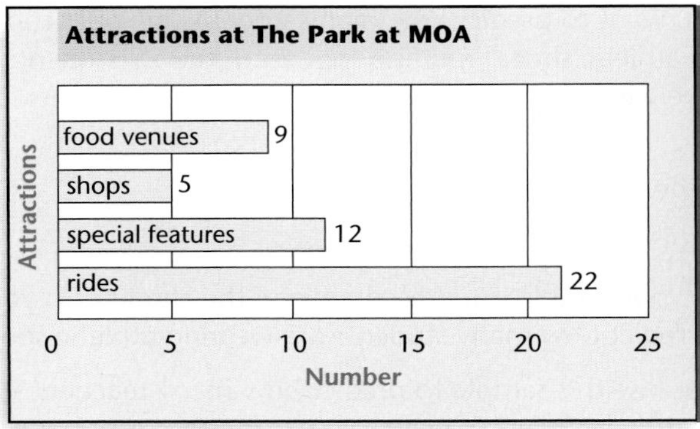

Attractions at The Park at MOA

Attractions (y-axis):
- food venues: 9
- shops: 5
- special features: 12
- rides: 22

Number (x-axis): 0, 5, 10, 15, 20, 25

27. Woodfield Mall: about 64%; The Galleria: about 57%; Tysons Corner Center: about 52%

36. Sample Response: They all involve writing equations to solve percent problems; Example 1 finds the percent of a number, Example 2 finds what percent one number is of another, and Example 3 finds a number when a percent of it is known.

COMMON ERROR
Each of the bars in the graph of **Exercise 37** represent the number of those types of shops at Camp Snoopy, not the percent. Students will have to use the graph to find the total number of shops and then calculate the percent of the total that each type represents.

Practice & Applications

EXERCISE NOTES

In Challenge Exercise 38, encourage students to rewrite the question using *x* to represent "a number." This will lead them to an equation with the variable on both sides. Remind students that they must apply any operations to both sides of the equation as they attempt to solve it.

39. a. Sample Response: Would you be more likely to eat at a new Italian or a new Chinese restaurant in the mall?

40. c. Sample Response: No. On an average night the theater takes in $420. After the cost of the posters, they only took in $360 on the night of the promotion.

38. Challenge 20% of a number is 24 less than the number. What is the number? 30

39. You are planning to open a restaurant at a mall. To obtain information on the type of restaurant that would be most successful, you conduct a survey.

  a. Give an example of a question you would ask on the survey.

  b. What is the population? **people who visit the mall**

  c. Describe a representative sample. **Sample Response: every 5th person entering the mall**

40. The typical Monday night attendance at a movie theater in a mall is about 70 people. To increase attendance, the manager advertises that the first 45 customers on Monday nights will receive a movie poster. On the next Monday night, the first 45 customers were 60 percent of the total audience.

  a. Use an equation to find the total audience size that night.
  $45 = 0.6x$, **75 people**

  b. Do you think the poster giveaway helped increase attendance? Why or why not?
  Sample Response: No; The increase was only 5 people.

  c. Suppose the posters cost the manager $2 each and the price of a ticket is $6. Was the promotion a good idea? Why?

Journal

Exercise 41 checks that you can use proportions and percents to analyze survey data.

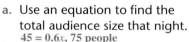 **Reflecting** ◀▶ **on the Section**

Write your response to Exercise 41 in your journal.

41. Suppose you want to predict how many students in your school are wearing athletic shoes. You find that 23 of the 29 students in your class are wearing athletic shoes. There are 583 students in your school.

  a. What is the population? **583 students in school**

  b. What is the sample? **29 students in class**

  c. Suppose your sample is representative of the students in your school. Predict how many students are wearing athletic shoes.
  about 462

  d. Could you use this sample to predict how many teachers are wearing athletic shoes? Explain. **No; The sample is only students.**

Spiral Review

42. What is the least possible perimeter of a rectangle whose area is 36 m²? (Module 1, p. 67) 24 m

Divide. Round each answer to the nearest tenth. (Toolbox, p. 582)

43. 50 ÷ 2.6 19.2   44. 680 ÷ 1.8 377.8   45. 9 ÷ 3.7 2.4

Find each product. (Toolbox, p. 580)

46. 0.18 • 10
    1.8
47. 6.2 • 0.01
    0.062
48. 0.3 • 100
    30
49. 0.15 • 1000
    150

Extension ▶ ▶

Sampling Methods

Several ways to take a sample from a population are described below.

With *self-selected sampling,* you let people volunteer.

With *systematic sampling,* you use a pattern to select people, such as choosing every other person.

With *convenience sampling,* you choose easy-to-reach people, such as those in the first row.

With *random sampling,* each person has an equally likely chance of being chosen.

50. Sample Response: Self-selected and convenience sampling are easy but are not likely to produce a representative sample of a population. Systematic and random sample are likely to produce a representative sample, but not all chosen may be willing or available to participate.

50. What are some advantages and disadvantages of each sampling method described above?

51. Which sampling method is most likely to produce a sample that is representative of the population? Explain. Random sampling; Each person in the population has an equally likely chance of being chosen and represented.

Students completing the **Extension Exercises** might want to write an unbiased question and then take a sample using each sampling method, compare the results, and present findings to the class or in a school newspaper article.

For each Exploration, the corresponding Extra Skill Practice Exercises are noted.

Exploration 1: Exs. 1–3
Exploration 2: Exs. 4–19
Exploration 3: Exs. 20–25

EXTRA HELP
Teacher's Resource Book
• Practice and Applications
• Study Guide

Technology Resources
• @Home Tutor
• Test Generator

ASSESSMENT
• Section 4 Quick Quiz
• Test Generator

Section 4
Extra Skill Practice

Tell whether each question is biased. Rewrite each biased question so that it is no longer biased.

1. "Do you really think this town needs another grocery store?" Sample Response: biased; "How do you feel about a grocery store being built in this town?"
2. "Wouldn't the city be a more exciting place to live than the country?" Sample Response: biased; "Would you prefer living in the city or the country?"
3. "Which football team do you like better—the Green Bay Packers or the Denver Broncos?" not biased

Estimate to find each percent.

4. 78% of 900
about 675
5. 86% of 1500
about 1275
6. 23% of 440
about 110
7. 48% of 37,000
about 18,500

8. 14% of 1500
about 225
9. 33% of $78
about $26
10. 11% of 82
about 8.2
11. 65% of 850
about 567

Use a proportion to find each percent.

12. 53% of 820
434.6
13. 12.5% of 48
6
14. 200% of 63
126
15. 86.9% of 10,000
8690

16. 62% of 3480
2157.6
17. 120% of 55
66
18. 28% of 470
131.6
19. 0.1% of 50,000
50

Use an equation to find each number or percent.

20. What is 80% of 165? 132

21. 15% of what number is 6? 40

22. 34 is what percent of 85? 40%

23. 50% of what number is 931? 1862

24. 190 is what percent of 304? 62.5%

25. What is 32% of 6350? 2032

Study Skills ◀▶ **Recalling Useful Facts**

Sometimes it is helpful to be able to quickly recall a mathematical fact without looking it up in a book or performing calculations. One technique that can help you memorize useful facts is to repeat them aloud until you can say them without hesitating.

1. Memorize the fraction equivalent of each common percent below by repeating it aloud. Check student recall.

$$50\% = \frac{1}{2} \qquad 25\% = \frac{1}{4} \qquad 20\% = \frac{1}{5}$$

2. For each percent in Exercise 1, describe a situation in which it would be useful to recall the fraction equivalent quickly. Answers will vary. Sample response: At a store with items on sale for 50%, 25%, or 20% off.
3. Name some other kinds of mathematical facts that you need to be able to recall quickly. Describe a situation in which quick recall of each fact can be helpful. Answers will vary. Check students' work.

Section ⑤ Working with Percents

IN THIS SECTION

EXPLORATION 1
- Estimating with Percents

EXPLORATION 2
- Percent of Change

The PRICE i$ RIGHT, Isn't It?

Setting the Stage

ABOUT THE THEME
More and more, consumers are encouraged to make purchases based on discounted prices and "good" buys. This section will deal with percents in a context familiar to many students--shopping. Bring in Sunday paper advertisements or have students collect ads to see if the buys they see advertised really are "good" deals.

GETTING STARTED
Module 2 Section 5 *Warm-Up* assesses prerequisite skills for calculating discounted prices of items on sale. In the *Warm-Up* students are asked to mentally find percents (in multiples of 5) of a number.

TEACHING NOTES
Question 2 Remind students that to find 10% of a number, they need only move the decimal point one place to the left. Also remind them that rounding to the nearest cent indicates the hundredths place.

Setting the Stage

For most people, shopping is the main attraction at the mall. Some people like to "shop 'til they drop," always looking for the best deals, while others buy on impulse. How about you? Do you compare prices to get the best deal?

One shopper tries to save money by comparing prices at two different stores.

Item	Higher Price	Lower Price
Top-selling CD	$18.99	$14.99
Brand-name jeans	$59.99	$54.99
Video game	$79.99	$49.48
Wristwatch	$29.99	$20.07
CD player	$179.99	$159.99

Think About It

1 Estimate the total amount of money the shopper can save by comparison shopping. **about $70**

2 **a.** Find 10% of the higher price of each item shown above. Round your answers to the nearest cent. **$1.90, $6, $8, $3, $18**

   b. For which items is the amount saved by comparison shopping greater than 10% of the higher price of the item? **on all items except the jeans**

   c. For which items can the shopper save more than 20% of the higher price? **CD, video game, wristwatch**

TEACHING NOTES

Because the *Bargain Basement Game* is timed, it is important after working **Questions 3 and 4** that students grasp the idea that a sale price can be found quickly by multiplying the original price by the percent to be paid. Students should also be able to use mental math with percents and fractions in order to effectively play the game. You may want to use one of the cards from the labsheet in a sample round, having groups demonstrate how they used mental math to make their decision.

Students should be assigned to teams of 4 or 5 to play the game. Assign students so teams are evenly matched with students of varying abilities.

TIPS FROM TEACHERS

Reuseable class sets of pre-cut and laminated cards from **Labsheet 5A** will expedite time needed for preparing to play the game.

GOAL

LEARN HOW TO...
◆ estimate percents
◆ use mental math to find percents
◆ use percents to solve problems

AS YOU...
◆ play *Bargain Basement*

Exploration 1
Estimating with PERCENTS

SET UP Work in a group of four. Your group will need: • one set of cards from Labsheet 5A • 4 index cards labeled A, B, C, and D

▶ **Mental math and estimation are important skills for comparison shopping. In *Bargain Basement*, your team will compete to find or to estimate sale prices using mental math.**

Wristwatch

Store A $7 off $30.99

Store B   25% off $40

Store C $\frac{1}{3}$ off $60.19

Store D   15% off $30

"15% off $30" means $30 – (15% of $30).

Bargain Basement Game

Each team receives a set of cards. Each card lists four prices for the same item at four different stores.

Your teacher will call out an item. Locate that card. Work as a group to decide which price is the lowest.

The teams have one minute to decide which price is the lowest. When time is called, hold up the index card indicating your group's choice, either A, B, C, or D.

All teams with the correct choice earns 20 points.

Your teacher may call on your group to justify your choice or to choose the next item for which the class will determine the best buy.

3 Discussion

   a. To find the amount of the discount at Store D, use mental math to find 15% of 30. Explain your thinking.

   b. Find the sale price of the watch at Store D. $25.50

   c. Find 85% of 30. $25.50

   d. Explain why 85% of 30 represents the sale price of a $30 item that is 15% off. Since you save 15%, you are paying 100% – 15%, or 85%.

3. a. $4.50; Sample Response: 15% of 30 = 10% of 30 plus 5% of 30 = 3 + $\frac{1}{2}$(3) = 3 + 1.5 = 4.5

4. b. $\frac{2}{3}$ ($60.19) = $40.13

4 Discussion

   a. Cheryl calculated the sale price for the watch at Store B by finding 75% of $40. Explain why Cheryl's method works.
75% of 40 is the same as 40 – (25% of 40).

   b. Use Cheryl's method to find the sale price of the watch at Store C.

   c. Which of the four stores offers the best buy? Store A ($23.99)

5 **Use Labsheet 5A.** Play a round of *Bargain Basement*. Be prepared to discuss the strategies your team used to determine the best buy.
Answers will vary. Check students' work.

| **HOMEWORK EXERCISES** | See Exs. 1–9 on pp. 144–145.

Exploration 2

PERCENT of CHANGE

SET UP Work in a group of 3 or more.

GOAL

LEARN HOW TO...
- estimate percents of change

AS YOU...
- analyze sale prices

KEY TERMS
- percent of decrease
- percent of increase
- percent of change

▶ In Exploration 1, you saw how a percent discount is sometimes taken off the price of an item. A percent discount is an example of a *percent of decrease*. If you know the original value and the amount of the decrease, you can find the *percent of decrease*.

$$\text{Percent of decrease} = \frac{\text{amount of decrease}}{\text{original amount}} \cdot 100$$

EXAMPLE

A store advertises that all items are on sale for 40% off. A shopper sees this price tag on a denim jacket. Is the price of the jacket 40% off?

SALE
~~$60~~
$38

SAMPLE RESPONSE

First   Find the amount of the decrease by subtracting the sale price from the original price.

Original price − sale price = amount of decrease

   $60   − $38   = $22

Then   Compare the amount of the decrease to the original amount.

$$x = \frac{22}{60} \cdot 100$$
$$x \approx 0.37 \cdot 100$$
$$x \approx 37$$

The denim jacket has been discounted by about 37%, not 40%.

Exploration 2

TEACHING NOTES

If needed, the following example can be used before students begin Question 6.

CLASSROOM EXAMPLE

A store advertises that all items are on sale for 60% off. A shopper sees a tag on a pair of pants that shows an original price of $27 and a sale price of $10.80. Is the price of the pants 60% off?

Answer:
First find the amount of the decrease by subtracting the sale price from the original price.

Original price	−	Sale price	=	Amount of decrease
$27	−	$10.80	=	$16.20

Next compare the amount of the decrease to the original amount.

$$x = \frac{16.20}{27}$$
$$x \cdot 27 = 16.20$$
$$x = 0.6$$

The pants have been discounted by 60%.

TEACHING NOTES

In **Question 6**, the focus is not to find the sale price, but to find the amount of discount for the following lesson on percent of decrease.

DEVELOPING MATH CONCEPTS

Point out the similarity between the formulas for percent of decrease and percent of increase. In both cases it is the amount of change over the original amount, multiplied by 100. To develop the formula you can use the **Example on page 141**. In the example, students can think of finding the percent of decrease as "The decrease is what percent of the original amount?" or in this case, "22 is what percent of 60?" Solving this equation to find the percent of decrease entails dividing the amount of decrease by the original amount as shown in the formula.

$22 = p \cdot 60$

$\dfrac{22}{60} = p$

$0.37 \approx p,$

so as a percent, p is 37%.

In **Question 9**, emphasize the difference between asking *what percent the marked-up price is of the original* and *what is the percent of increase*. You might give the example that an item that is originally $40 that is marked up to $120, is triple the original cost, so the new price is 300% of the original. Yet the increase is only 200% since you added twice the original cost to the original price. Do several more easy examples like this one so that students can see when asked the first question, that they are always adding the increase to 100% of the original number.

---

6 Try This as a Class

   a. Find the actual amount of decrease for a 40% discount on a $60 jacket. $\dfrac{40}{100} = \dfrac{x}{60}$ or $x = 0.40 \cdot 60$; $24

   b. What should be the sale price of the jacket? $36

▶ **Percent of decrease can be used to describe a variety of situations.**

✔ **QUESTION 7**

...checks that you can find a percent of decrease.

9. b. Sample Response: Solve the proportion $\dfrac{20}{12} = \dfrac{x}{100}$.

7 ✔ **CHECKPOINT** According to one survey, an average shopper visited 2.9 outlets per week in 2000. By 2002 the number of outlets visited per week had declined to 1.9.

   a. Estimate the percent of decrease in the number of outlets shoppers visited per week from 2000 to 2002. about 33%

   b. Find the percent of decrease. Round to the nearest tenth of a percent. How does your answer compare with your estimate? 34.5%; Sample Response: It was close to my estimate.

▶ **A** *percent of increase* **can be used to describe increases.**

$$\text{Percent of increase} = \frac{\text{amount of increase}}{\text{original amount}} \cdot 100$$

8 Discussion A store buys a book for $12 and marks up the price to sell for $20.

   a. What was the amount of the markup? $8

   b. Find the percent of increase after the markup. about 66.7%

9 a. In Question 8, the marked-up price of $20 is what percent of the original price of $12? 166.7%

   b. How did you get your answer?

10 Use estimation to determine which changes at the right represent the change described.

   a. an increase of less than 50%
      $91 to $118

   b. an increase of more than 100%
      24 hr to 56 hr, $0.49 to $1

$91 to $118

40 mi/hr to 70 mi/hr

24 hr to 56 hr

$0.49 to $1

▶ **Percent of increase and percent of decrease are examples of percents of change.**

11 From 1990 to 2004, the number of people aged 25–29 in the United States changed from about 21.3 million to 19.6 million. Find the percent of change. about 7.9%

12 ✔ **CHECKPOINT** The average hourly wage in the United States in 1979 was $6.33. In 1990, it was $10.19. In 2005, it was $16.11.

   a. To the nearest percent, what was the percent of change from 1979 to 1990? from 1990 to 2005? from 1979 to 2005?
   61%, 58%, 155%

   b. The 2005 hourly wage is what percent of the 1979 hourly wage? Round to the nearest percent. 255%

✔ **QUESTION 12**

...checks that you can estimate and find a percent of change.

HOMEWORK EXERCISES ▶ See Exs. 10–17 on pp. 146–147.

Section 5
Key Concepts

Estimating Percents (pp. 140–141)
You can use mental math to estimate the percent of a number.

Example Estimate the sale price of an $89 coat that is now on sale for 25% off.

> 25% off means you will pay 100% − 25% = 75% of the original cost.

$$75\% = \frac{3}{4}$$

$$\frac{3}{4} \text{ of } \$89 \approx \frac{3}{4} \text{ of } \$88$$

$$\frac{3}{4} \text{ of } \$88 = \$66$$

13 Key Concepts Question Suppose a store's sales decreased 19% from April to May and 19% from May to June.

   a. Sales were $9811 in April. Estimate the sales in May. about $8000

   b. Use your answer to part (a) to estimate the sales in June. about $6400

   c. Find the actual sales in May. Then use your answer to find the actual sales in June. Compare the answers with your estimates in parts (a) and (b). $7946.91; $6437.00; The actual sales and the estimates were close.

CLOSURE QUESTION
Explain two ways to estimate the sale price of a $92 item that is on sale for 20% off.

> Sample Responses:
>
> Method 1: Find $\frac{1}{5}$ of $90 and subtract that amount from $90.
>
> Method 2: Find $\frac{1}{5}$ of $90 and multiply by 4.
>
> Method 3: Find 10% of $90 and multiply that amount by 8 to find 80% of 90, which represents the sale price.
>
> Method 4: Find 10% of $90 and multiply that amount by 2 to find 20% of 90. Subtract the result to find 80% of 90.

ABSENT STUDENTS
For students who were absent for all or part of this section, the blackline Study Guide for Section 5 may be used to present the ideas, concepts, and skills of Section 5.

Key Concepts

CLOSURE QUESTION

Two items that are not the same price both increase by $2. Which item will have a greater percent of increase? Explain.

Sample Response: The lesser item will have a greater percent of increase because $2 represents a greater portion of the lesser item's original price. For example a $2 increase on a $5 item represents a 40% increase, while $2 on a $10 item only represents a 20% increase.

Practice & Applications

SUGGESTED ASSIGNMENTS

Core Course
Day 1: Exs. 1–9, 18–23
Day 2: Exs. 10–17, 24–30

Extended Course
Day 1: Exs. 1–9, 18–23
Day 2: Exs. 10–17, 24–30,
31–32*, 33–34

Note: Extended Course assignments can be used to differentiate within the regular classroom. In classrooms where students are grouped homogeneously, the material might be covered in fewer days. In this case assignments may be combined.
*denotes Extension Exercises

ADDITIONAL PRACTICE

See the *Teacher's Resource Book* for additional practice and application exercises for this section.

Key Terms

percent of change

percent of decrease

percent of increase

Section 5
Key Concepts

Percent of Change (pp. 141–143)

Percent of decrease and percent of increase are examples of percents of change.

Example
A shirt that normally sells for $50 is on sale for $40. What is the percent of decrease in the price?

$$\begin{array}{ccccc} \text{Original} & & \text{sale} & & \text{price} \\ \text{price} & - & \text{price} & = & \text{decrease} \\ \$50 & - & \$40 & = & \$10 \end{array}$$

Since 10 is $\frac{1}{5}$ of 50 and $\frac{1}{5} = 20\%$ the $10 discount is 20% of $50. The percent of decrease is 20%.

Example
The original price of a toy was $18. It is marked up to sell for $20. What is the percent of increase in the price?

$$\begin{array}{ccccc} \text{Increased} & & \text{original} & & \\ \text{price} & - & \text{price} & = & \text{markup} \\ \$20 & - & \$18 & = & \$2 \end{array}$$

Since $2 is $\frac{1}{9}$ of $18, the percent of increase is about 11%.

---

14 **Key Concepts Question** Suppose a store's sales decreased 19% from April to May and 19% from May to June as in Question 13.

14. a. No; The decrease in June was 19% of the sales in May, which were 19% less than the sales in April.

    a. Uma thinks that since sales decreased 19% in May and 19% in June, they decreased the same number of dollars each month. Is she correct? Explain why or why not.

    b. Did sales for the two months decrease by 38%? Explain.
      No; from $9811 in April to $6437.00 in June is about 34%, not 38%.

Section 5
Practice & Application Exercises

1. Sample Response: Change 69% to the "nice" fraction $\frac{2}{3}$, then find $\frac{2}{3}$ of 60. Find 10% of $60 and then multiply by 7.

1. Describe two different ways to estimate 69% of $59.98.

For Exercises 2–5, estimate the answer. Then find the exact answer.

2. 35% of 90
about 30; 31.5

3. 22% of 240
about 48; 52.8

4. 80% of 52
about 40; 41.6

5. 9% of 1195
about 120; 107.55

6. For each of the following discounts, determine what percent of the original price you will pay for the item.

   a. 60% off *40%*　　　b. 10% off *90%*　　　c. 30% off *70%*

7. Nathan has been shopping online. Two companies are having sales on the same bicycle helmet. Which company is selling the item for less? **Hard Hats USA**

Hard Hats USA
15% off the original price of $45.

Bike Safely, Inc.
Regularly $50, now 20% off.

8. A store advertises that all items are 30–40% off. The original price is crossed out on each price tag, and the sale price is written below it. Use estimation or mental math to check that each markdown is within the advertised range. Tell which tags are marked incorrectly and explain how you know.

8. a. incorrectly marked; The minimum markdown is $15.
   b. incorrectly marked; The minimum markdown is $39.
   c. correctly marked
   d. correctly marked
   e. correctly marked
   f. incorrectly marked; The minimum markdown is $72.

a. ~~$50~~ $37

b. ~~$130~~ $100

c. ~~$80~~ $55

d. ~~$29~~ $18

e. ~~$350~~ $240

f. ~~$240~~ $180

9. In a survey, 2051 teens in the United States were asked how they earned their spending money. Estimate the number of teens who made each of the responses below. Then find the actual number and compare it with your estimate. **about 1000, 964; about 650, 656; about 900, 923; about 500, 533; about 200, 226.**

About 47% said their parents gave them money when they needed it.

About 32% received a regular allowance.

About 45% did odd jobs.

About 26% worked part time.

About 11% worked full time.

EXERCISE NOTES

In **Exercises 1–9**, encourage students to use a variety of approaches. Their estimation strategies should include using multiples of 10% and using "nice" fractions. Their solving techniques should include proportions, equations, and equivalent fractions.

HOME INVOLVEMENT

Students can practice estimating and calculating discounts at grocery stores, on television shopping networks, or with mail and newspaper advertisements. While looking at newspaper advertisements, students might check whether discount prices at a particular store tend to be discounted the same each week. For example, after calculating the percent of discount on the club member prices of several items at a grocery store, the student might notice that club member prices generally reflect about a 10% savings.

Practice & Applications

EXERCISE NOTES

In **Exercise 14(a)–(b)**, students may be surprised to find that it doesn't matter which discount is applied first, 10% or 25%. The commutative and associative properties of multiplication can be used to show why this is so:

10% of (25% of 10) = 0.1(0.25 • 10)

$$= (0.1 \cdot 0.25)10$$
$$= (0.25 \cdot 0.10)10$$
$$= 0.25(0.1 \cdot 100)$$
$$= 25\% \text{ of } (10\% \text{ of } 10)$$

In **part(c)** students should recognize that combining the two gives a greater discount because both are being applied to the original price instead of the second percent being applied to the discounted price.

---

10. 9.234 million spectators attended the National Hockey League's regular season games in 1995. In 2004, 22.065 million attended.

   a. Estimate the percent of change in total spectators from 1995 to 2004. **about 150%**

   b. Find the actual percent of change in total spectators from 1995 to 2004. How does it compare with your estimate? **about 139%; Sample Response: Close, but a bit lower than my estimate.**

Use the double bar graph for Exercises 11–13.

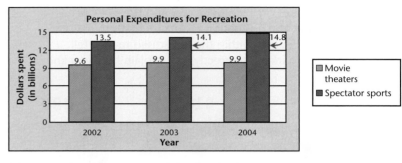

Personal Expenditures for Recreation

11. Describe the percent of change in the amount spent at movie theaters.

   a. from 2002 to 2003
   about a 3.1% increase

   b. from 2003 to 2004
   0% increase

12. Describe the percent of change in the amount spent on sports.

   a. from 2002 to 2003
   about a 4.4% increase

   b. from 2003 to 2004
   about a 5.0% increase

13. Based on your answers in Exercises 11 and 12, how much money do you think was spent at movie theaters and sports in 2005?
   Sample Response: Movies about 9.9 billion, sports about 15.5 billion.

14. a. The regular price of a necklace is $10 at two stores. At which store do you think the final sale price will be less? Why?
   Answers will vary. Check students' work.

   b. Find the final sale price of the necklace at each store. Was your prediction from part (a) correct? Explain. **$6.75 at both stores; Answers will vary.**

   c. Do you get the correct sale price if you add the two discounts together and then discount the price by that sum? Explain.
   No; Sample Response: You can multiply, not add, the discounts to get the correct sale price.

15. Find the percent of change. Be sure to tell whether it is a percent of increase or decrease. Round answers to the nearest percent.

a. \$9 to \$36
300% increase

b. 55 mi/hr to 25 mi/hr
55% decrease

c. 12 min/day to 25 min/day
108% increase

d. 2,654 people to 1,090 people
59% decrease

16. **Home Involvement** a–b. Answers will vary. Check students' work.

a. Interview an adult born before 1970 to find the prices of three items in the past.

b. Compare each price with its equivalent today. In each case, what is the percent of change?

Item	Price then	Price now	Percent of change
movie	?	?	?
house	?	?	?
car	?	?	?

Reflecting on the Section

17. Find three sale ads in a newspaper or magazine that use percent discounts. Use estimation or mental math to determine the items on which you would save the greatest amount and the least amount. Do you always save the most with the greatest percent discount? Explain. Answers will vary. Check students' work.

RESEARCH

Exercise 17 checks that you can apply percent of change.

Spiral Review

Use a proportion to find each percent. (Module 2, p. 132)

18. 28% of 5200
1456

19. 2% of 485
9.7

20. 77% of 830
639.1

21. 100% of 61
61

22. 3.8% of 7900
300.2

23. 95% of 350
332.5

Find the greatest common factor and the least common multiple for each pair of numbers. (Toolbox, p. 584)

24. 10, 15
GCF 5; LCM 30

25. 12, 16
GCF 4, LCM 48

26. 21, 49
GCF 7, LCM 147

Replace each ? with >, <, or =. (Toolbox, p. 585)

27. $\frac{1}{4}$? $\frac{1}{3}$ <

28. $\frac{3}{8}$? $\frac{1}{2}$ <

29. $\frac{2}{3}$? $\frac{12}{18}$ =

30. $\frac{7}{8}$? $\frac{5}{6}$ >

EXERCISE NOTES

Once students have completed **Exercise 16,** have them use the percent of change they calculated to predict what the prices of these items might be 40 years from now.

Practice & Applications

EXTENSION NOTES
Challenge students to explore what minimum percent of profit they think sellers need to make in order to still make a profit on items that must be sold at a discounted price at the end of a season. They may also want to take into account the fact that some of the items may not sell.

Extension ▶ ▶

Percent of Profit

Buyers are usually interested in the percent of decrease or increase in the cost of a product. Sellers are interested in how much the profit has changed. Profit is based on the selling price, s, of an item and the cost, c, of making an item. Two ways to calculate the percent of profit are shown at the right.

Percent of profit on cost $= \dfrac{s - c}{c}$

Percent of profit on selling price $= \dfrac{s - c}{s}$

31. Suppose a candy bar costs 35¢ to make, and sells for 50¢. What is the percent of profit on cost? What is the percent of profit on selling price? **about 43%; 30%**

32. Which percent of profit in Exercise 31 was greater? Do you think this will always be true? Explain your thinking. **on cost; Yes; Unless an item is sold at a loss, $s > c$, so $\dfrac{s-c}{c} > \dfrac{s-c}{s}$.**

Career ▪ Connection

Business Owner: Aricka Westbrooks

Aricka Westbrooks is the owner and manager of a company that sells fried turkeys.

33. Customers can purchase a fried turkey from Aricka Westbrooks's company at her store or by ordering online. Suppose that one year the company sold 450 Thanksgiving turkeys online. The next year, the number of Thanksgiving turkeys sold increased by 800. By what percent did the number of Thanksgiving turkeys sold online increase from the first year to the next? **about 178%**

34. Suppose that the number of turkeys the company sold online increased from 1347 last November to 1877 this November. The number of turkeys sold in the store increased from 2132 last November to 2500 this November. Which type of sales experienced greater growth? Explain. **Sample Response: online sales; online sales increased by about 39% while in-store sales increased by only about 17%.**

Section 5

Extra Skill Practice

For Exercises 1–6, estimate the answer. Then find the exact answer.

1. 55% of 340 *about 170; 187* 2. 65% of 44 *about 30; 28.6* 3. 7% of 48 *about 3.5; 3.36*

4. 12% of 75 *about 7.5; 9* 5. 38% of 160 *about 64; 60.8* 6. 30% of 45 *about 15; 13.5*

Use the bar graph for Exercises 7–9.

7. Find the percent of decrease in the price of unleaded gas from 2000 to 2002. *about 9%*

8. Find the percent of increase in the price of unleaded gas from 2002 to 2004. *about 30%*

9. Find the percent of increase in the price of unleaded gas from 2000 to 2004. *about 19%*

Average California Gasoline Prices

Year	Price
2000	$1.66
2002	$1.51
2004	$1.97

10. A bicycle shop buys a new bike for $350 and sells it for $455.

   a. What is the amount of the markup? *$105*

   b. What is the percent of increase after the markup? *30%*

Use the table for Exercises 11–13.

11. Find the percent of decrease in the number of bald eagles from 1800 to 1974. *about 99.4%*

12. Find the percent of increase in the number of bald eagles from 1974 to 2000. *about 718%*

13. Find the percent of change in the number of bald eagles from 1800 to 2000. *about 95% decrease*

Adult Bald Eagle Population in the Continental United States

Year	Number of adult eagles
1800	250,000
1974	1,582
2000	12,942

Standardized Testing ◀▶ Performance Task

For a Social Studies project, Diane and Rosa are ranking the 50 states based on the percent of increase in their populations from 2000 to 2005. Diane says New York's population increase was greater and should be ranked before North Carolina. Rosa disagrees. Who is right? Explain.

State	2000	2005
New York	18,998,889	19,254,630
North Carolina	8,078,429	8,683,242

Sample Response: Rosa is correct. New York only had a 1.3% increase in population while North Carolina had a 7.5% increase.

Extra Skill Practice

TEACHER NOTES
For each Exploration, the corresponding Extra Skill Practice Exercises are noted.

Exploration 1: Exs. 1–6
Exploration 2: Exs. 7–13

EXTRA HELP
Teacher's Resource Book
• Practice and Applications for Section 5
• Study Guide
• Practice and Applications for Sections 1–5

Technology Resources
• @Home Tutor
• Test Generator

ASSESSMENT
• Section 5 Quick Quiz
• Test Generator

Module Project

PROJECT NOTES

To help student groups begin thinking about the goal of their game and the possible rules, you may want to hold a discussion about board games students have played. Make a list of games, describe how a player wins each game, and list some of the more important rules for each game.

Labsheet: Each student needs a copy of Project Labsheets A and B, which are found in the *Teacher's Resource Book*.

Designing a Game

Many board games try to imitate what happens in real life. Working in a group, you will create a game that imitates shopping in a mall. You will play the completed game and refine it. Then your group will present the game to the class.

Getting Started You will start with a game board showing a map of a mall and an inventory list with prices. You will create rules, game pieces, game cards, and anything else needed to play the game. Your game will include math topics you learned about in this module, such as percents, proportions, and coordinate graphing.

Use Project Labsheets A and B. 1–4. Answers will vary.
Check students' work.

1. Your game must use the *Game Board* and the *Inventory List*. Describe a possible goal for your game. In other words, how can someone win?

2. With your group, discuss possible rules for your game.

3. In your game, you will move from grid intersection to grid intersection on the *Game Board*. For each player, construct game pieces small enough to fit easily on the board.

4. Think about what might happen as a player visits the various stores on the game board. Construct cards like the ones below. You may also want to create game money to spend at the stores.

SET UP

Work in a group.
You will need:
- Project Labsheets A and B
- items for game pieces
- markers
- cardstock
- scissors

You may want to have different types of cards for entering stores, rolling the number cubes, or landing on certain spaces.

Game cards can include information on prices, sales, and discounts.

Go to the music store

Quarter-note Sale! Everything $\frac{1}{4}$ off!

CD's regular price $15.99

Go to the video arcade. Stop to play games.

Lose one turn!

Writing Rules The rules of any game must be easy to understand and not leave room for arguments. Try to imagine playing your game and the situations you could encounter. **5–10. Answers will vary. Check students' work.**

5 As a group, discuss the rules of your game. Describe how pieces can move. For example, will players roll number cubes? Spin a spinner? You can use your knowledge of coordinate graphing to move pieces on your game board.

6 Write down the official rules of the game. Make sure that the rules explain all aspects of the game.

7 Playing the Game

   a. With your group, assemble the game and game pieces. Review the rules.

   b. Play the game.

8 After you have played the game, discuss each question below in your group.

   a. What math skills did you use while playing the game?

   b. What worked well in your game?

   c. What could you improve?

9 Revising the Game Make any changes necessary to improve your game. You may need to add or change rules.

10 As a group, prepare a presentation to give to the class. Each member of the group can present a part of the game. Include the following in your presentation.

the goal of the game	the rules
the mathematics used	the playing pieces
the cards	your own experience playing the game

PROJECT NOTES
Students may want to revise the rules and goals of their game as they progress through the stages of creating the game. Such revision should be encouraged as long as it is thoughtful and moves them toward completion of the project.

After groups have played and reviewed their own game, you may choose to have pairs of groups present their games to each other and then allow time for them to play each other's games. After playing the games, groups could provide constructive criticism to the group that created the game, allowing them to further improve their project. Games may then be played during a review session for the Module Test or be graded as part of the students' assessment for the module.

TEACHER NOTES

Students should complete the Review and Assessment independently in preparation for the Module Test.

Allow class time to discuss solutions and address any questions students may have. During this time, you may want to allow students to work in groups to share methods for solving the problems and to quiz each other on the concepts covered in this module.

14.
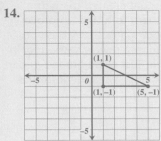

19. First Ball   Second Ball   Outcome

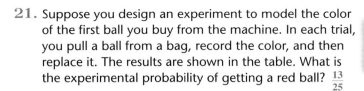

MODULE 2 — Review and Assessment

You will need: • *Review and Assessment Labsheet* (Ex. 14)

Evaluate each expression. (Sec. 1, Explors. 1, 2, and 3)

1. 123 + (–53)
  70

2. 3 + (–18)
  –15

3. 5 – (–12)
  17

4. –2 – 35
  –37

5. –6 • 15
  –90

6. (–24)(–8)
  192

7. –72 ÷ 8
  –9

8. –108 ÷ (–9)
  12

9. 6(–7)(–4) ÷ (–12)
  –14

10. –26 + 6 – (–20)
  0

11. –36 + (–6) + (–8)
  –50

12. What numbers have an absolute value of 5? (Sec. 1, Explor. 1) **–5 and 5**

13. Explain what is meant by the *opposite* of a number. Give three examples. (Sec. 1, Explor. 1) **Sample Response: The opposite of a number is the integer you add to that number to get a sum of 0; –2 and 2, –7 and 7, –0.34 and 0.34.**

14. **Use the Review and Assessment Labsheet.** In the game *Cyber Spaceship*, a player guides a spaceship around moving obstacles. Follow the directions on the labsheet to draw the triangular obstacle after a translation. (Sec. 1, Explor. 2) **See margin.**

Find each sum or difference. (Sec. 2, Explors. 1, 2, and 3)

15. $-\dfrac{5}{6} + \dfrac{3}{8}$
  $-\dfrac{11}{24}$

16. $-\dfrac{4}{5} - \dfrac{2}{3}$
  $-1\dfrac{7}{15}$

17. $-4\dfrac{3}{5} + 1\dfrac{2}{3}$
  $-2\dfrac{14}{15}$

18. $3\dfrac{9}{10} - \left(-2\dfrac{3}{5}\right)$
  $6\dfrac{1}{2}$

For Exercises 19–21, suppose a 25¢ toy machine is usually full of colored bouncing balls, but most of the balls have been sold and only 1 blue, 1 yellow, and 2 red balls are left. You have two quarters to spend on balls. (Sec. 3, Explors. 1, 2, and 3)

19. Draw a tree diagram showing all the possible outcomes. **See margin.**

20. What is the theoretical probability of getting two red balls when you buy two balls? $\dfrac{1}{6}$

21. Suppose you design an experiment to model the color of the first ball you buy from the machine. In each trial, you pull a ball from a bag, record the color, and then replace it. The results are shown in the table. What is the experimental probability of getting a red ball? $\dfrac{13}{25}$

50 Trials		
Blue	Yellow	Red
14	10	26

22. Is the following question biased? If so, rewrite the question so that it is no longer biased. (Sec. 4, Explor. 1)

"Do you agree that students should have access to the Internet in order to improve their education?" **Yes; Should students have access to the Internet?**

23. A middle school is conducting a survey to decide whether its spring dance should be open to students in grades 5–8 or just to students in grades 7 and 8. Tell whether each group of students would be a *representative sample* for the survey. Explain your thinking. (Sec. 4, Explor. 1)

a. all students whose last names begin with the letter "A" representative; This group should have the same characteristics as the rest of the population.

b. the students in Mr. Marshall's eighth grade English class not representative; Students in grades 5–7 are not represented.

24. In a survey of teens, 51% of the girls and 83% of the boys said athletic shoes were their favorite type of shoe. (Sec. 4, Explor. 2)

a. Suppose 1030 girls were surveyed. About how many of the girls said athletic shoes were their favorite type of shoe? about 525

b. Suppose 639 boys answered that athletic shoes were their favorite type of shoe. How many boys were surveyed? about 770

25. Of 500 New England youths surveyed, 90% said they visit a supermarket on a weekly basis. (Sec. 4, Explor. 3)

a. What was the sample? Do you think the sample was representative of all the young people in the United States? Explain. 500 New England youths; Sample Response: No; the sample is too small and only from one region of the country.

b. Use mental math to find how many of the 500 youths surveyed visit a supermarket on a weekly basis. 450 youths

Estimation For Exercises 26 and 27, estimate each answer. Explain how you found your estimate. (Sec. 5, Explor. 1)

26. An appliance store buys a television for $322 and marks up the price to $475 for resale. Estimate the percent of the markup.

27. A $66.50 item is discounted 30%. Estimate the sale price.
about $44.50; 30% ≈ $\frac{1}{3}$ and $\frac{1}{3}$ of $66 = $22, so $66.50 − $22 = $44.50.

28. The table shows the average weekly allowances for kids by age, based on one survey. Determine the percent increase in allowance for each of the following. Round your answers to the nearest whole percent. (Sec. 5, Explor. 2)

Age	Average Allowance
12	$9.58
13	$9.52
14	$13.47
15	$15.57
16	$17.84

a. age 13 to 14   b. age 13 to 15   c. age 12 to 16
41%   64%   86%

Reflecting ◀▶ on the Module

29. Writing Describe the mathematics you learned in this module. Discuss how you can use what you learned to be a better shopper.

26. about 50%: the markup is $153 and $\frac{153}{322} ≈ \frac{1}{2} = 50\%$.

29. Answers will vary. Check students' work.

Assessment Options

TEACHER'S RESOURCE BOOK
• Module 2 Tests A and B
• Module 2 Standardized Test
• Module 2 Performance Assessment
• Modules 1 and 2 Cumulative Test

TEST GENERATOR

The Mystery of Blacktail Canyon

Module 3 Overview

Mathematical models are used to interpret and solve problems related to a mystery story. Newly acquired skills and concepts allow students to unravel the mystery. In this module, students study length, area, and volume relationships, use scientific notation, solve equations, use equations and graphs to make predictions, and use indirect measurement to solve problems.

In the **Module Project**, students will solve *The Mystery of Blacktail Canyon* and identify the criminal. The complete mystery can be found in the *Teacher's Resource Book*. Although the project may be completed as a review at the end of the module, you may want students to complete parts of it as they work through the module. To successfully complete the project, students should read each chapter of the mystery before the section of the module shown in the table at the right. The module can also be completed without reading the entire mystery or doing the project.

Read	Before
Ch. 1	Sect. 1
Ch. 2	Sect. 2
Ch. 3	Sect. 3
Ch. 4	Sect. 4 Exp 1
Ch. 5	Sect. 4 Exp 2
Chs. 6 and 7	Sect. 5
Ch. 8	Sect. 6
Chs. 9 and 10	Module Project

Module 3 Planner

Day 1: Section 1	Day 2: Section 1	Day 3: Section 1	Day 4: Section 2	Day 5: Section 2
Setting the Stage, *pp. 156–157* Exploration 1 through Question 6, *pp. 158–159*	Exploration 1, *pp. 159–160*	Exploration 2, *pp. 161–162* Key Concepts, *p. 163*	Seting the Stage, *pp. 168–169* Exploration 1, *pp. 169–171*	Exploration 2 through Question 16, *pp. 172–174*

Day 6: Section 2	Day 7: Section 3	Day 8: Section 3	Day 9: Section 3	Day 10: E²
Exploration 2, *p. 174* Key Concepts, *p. 175*	Setting the Stage, *p. 180* Exploration 1 through Question 7, *pp. 181–182*	Exploration 1, *pp. 182–183*	Exploration 2, *pp. 184–185* Key Concepts, *p. 186*	Begin Extended Exploration, *p. 191*

Day 11: Review and Assessment	Day 12: Section 4	Day 13: Section 4	Day 14: Section 4	Day 15: Section 5
Mid-Module Quiz	Setting the Stage, *p. 192* Exploration 1 through Question 6, *pp. 193–194*	Exploration 1, *pp. 194–195*	Exploration 2, *pp. 196–197* Key Concepts, *p. 198*	Setting the Stage, *p. 204* Exploration 1, *pp. 205–207*

Day 16: Section 5	Day 17: Section 6	Day 18: Module Project	Day 19: Module Project	Day 20: Module Project
Exploration 2, *pp. 207–208* Key Concepts, *p. 209*	Setting the Stage, *p. 214* Exploration 1, *pp. 215–217* Key Concepts, *p. 217*	Begin Module Project *pp. 222–223*	Work on Module Project *pp. 224–225*	Finish Module Project *pp. 224–225*

Day 21: Review and Assessment	Day 22: Assessment			
Review and Assessment, *pp. 226–227*	Module 3 Test			

Materials List

Section	Materials
1	• calculator, 30 centimeter cubes
2	• Labsheets 2A, calculator, graph paper, graphing calculator (optional)
3	• Labsheet 3A, meter stick, masking tape, marker, graph paper,
4	• Labsheets 4A–4C, centimeter ruler, protractor, scissors, compass, graph paper
5	• Labsheet 5A, calculator
6	• Labsheet 6A, tape, compass, metric ruler
Rev & Assess	• Review and Assessment Labsheet, ruler, graph paper, compass
Project	• Project Labsheets A and B, detective notebook, text of *The Mystery of Blacktail Canyon*, clue cards and transcripts

Module 3 Objectives

Section	Objectives	NCTM Standards 2000*
1	• Find and estimate square roots. • Solve problems involving length, area, and volume relationships.	1, 2, 3, 4, 6, 7, 8, 9, 10
2	• Use the order of operations. • Graph equations and use the graphs to solve problems.	1, 2, 6, 7, 8, 9, 10
3	• Find positive slopes. • Use equations and graphs to model situations. • Use an equation of a fitted line to make predictions.	1, 2, 5, 6, 7, 8, 9, 10
4	• Understand and apply properties of similar figures, including similar triangles. • Solve indirect measurement problems. • Find a perpendicular bisector of a chord.	3, 4, 5, 6, 7, 8, 9, 10
5	• Write large numbers in decimal and scientific notation. • Solve equations involving decimals.	1, 2, 6, 7, 8, 9, 10
6	• Interpret statements with *and, or,* or *not.* • Organize information in a Venn diagram.	6, 7, 8, 9, 10

* See page T14.

154B

Section ① Square Roots and Measurement

Section 1 Planner

Section Objectives

Exploration 1
• Find and estimate square roots

Exploration 2
• Solve problems involving length, area, and volume relationships

Days for Section 1

First Day
Setting the Stage, *pp. 156–157*
Exploration 1 through Question 6, *pp. 158–159*

Second Day
Exploration 1, *pp. 159–160*

Third Day
Exploration 2, *pp. 161–162*
Key Concepts, *p. 163*

Teaching Resources

Teacher's Resource Book
• Warm-Up
• Practice and Applications
• Study Guide
• *The Mystery of Blacktail Canyon*, Ch. 1*
See page 155 for additional teaching resources.

* This module is based on a short mystery story. Each section uses excerpts from the story to introduce a mathematics concept. The complete story can be found in the *Teacher's Resource Book*. The portions of the story that go with each section are listed in the *Teaching Resources* for that section and in the table on page 154A. Note, however, that it is NOT essential that students read these portions of the story in order to complete the section. The excerpts in the *Setting the Stage* of each section are sufficient to complete the *Explorations*.

Materials List

Exploration 1
• calculator

Exploration 2
• 30 centimeter cubes

Assessment Options

EMBEDDED ASSESSMENT
• Find and estimate square roots
  Exercises 2, 4, 7, 12
• Solve problems involving length, area, and volume relationships
  Exercise 24

PERFORMANCE TASK/PORTFOLIO
• Exercise 16 on *p. 162*
• Exercise 24 on *p. 163 (writing)*
• Exercise 28 on *p. 164 (challenge)**
• Exercise 29 on *p. 164 (oral report)*

* indicates a problem-solving task that can be assessed using the Assessment Scales

QUIZZES/TESTS
• Section 1 Quick Quiz

TEST GENERATOR

Section 1 Overview

In this section, students are introduced to the cliff dwellings of the Anasazi people. As they examine the dwellings, they will learn about length, area, volume, and square roots.

Exploration 1
Students explore the concept of square root by estimating the length of the side of a square with a given area. Students learn about negative square roots and principal square roots. Both mental math and geometric models are used to find the square roots of perfect squares. Then, using the square roots of perfect squares as guides, students will estimate the square roots of other numbers that are not perfect squares. Calculators are also used to approximate the square roots of numbers.

Exploration 2
As students continue to explore the dimensions of some of the Anasazi dwellings, they use models to identify relationships between length, area, and volume. They will learn how altering the lengths of the edges of a cube affects the surface area and the volume of the cube and then describe this relationship.

154C

Guide for Assigning Homework

REGULAR SCHEDULING (45 MIN CLASS PERIOD)			EXERCISES TO NOTE		
Section/ P&A Pages	Core Assignment	Extended Assignment	Additional Practice/Review	Open-ended Problems	Extended Problems
1 pp. 164–167	**Day 1:** 1–6, SR 30–35 **Day 2:** 7–12,14–23 **Day 3:** 24–27, ROS 29	1–6, SR 30–35 7–8, 11–23 25–28, ROS 29	EP, p. 167	PA 16, 29	PA Challenge 13, 28

Key: PA = Practice & Application; ROS = Reflecting on the Section; SR = Spiral Review; TB = Toolbox; EP = Extra Skill Practice; Ext = Extension; ST = Standardized Testing

Math Background and Teaching Strategies

Classroom Notes

Bulletin Board display ideas for this section include:

- A desert scene or pictures of adobe structures or cliff dwellings

Visitors/field trips might include:

- An archaeologist
- Visit an archaeological dig site or natural history museum

Math Strands

Topic Spiraling and Integration

In this section, students build on their understanding of square roots and measurement relationships that were introduced in Books 1 and 2.

Exploration 1
As students explore the concept of square root, they learn to identify perfect squares and to use them to estimate square roots of other numbers. The logic involved is simple and, once students know a variety of perfect squares, it is readily applied. Students notice that the square root of any number other than a perfect square is a decimal. Recognizing that a number is between two consecutive perfect squares makes estimating its square root easy. For example, 54 is between the perfect squares 49 and 64, so the square root of 54 is between 7 and 8. Since 54 is closer to 49 than to 64, the square root of 54 will be closer to 7 than to 8. Try 7.3. Since $7.3^2 = 53.29$, the square root of 54 is greater than 7.3. Try 7.4. Since $7.4^2 = 54.76$, the square root of 54 is between 7.3 and 7.4 and is closer to 7.3. So to the nearest tenth, $\sqrt{54} = 7.3$. Using this process, students can quickly estimate square roots to the nearest tenth. Students will apply the concept of square root in Module 5 where they explore the Pythagorean theorem and in Module 7 as they simplify radicals.

Exploration 2
In Exploration 2, students learn that multiplying the linear dimensions of a geometric figure by a constant causes exponential changes in the area and volume. That is, if the lengths of the edges of a cube are multiplied by a constant c, then the surface area is multiplied by c^2, and the volume is multiplied by c^3. As students build larger and larger cubes, they will observe this exponential growth in a concrete way that strengthens their understanding of the relationship between one, two, and three dimensional figures. Most students will need more than one example to solidify this concept in order to apply it later in Modules 4 and 5, where they explore surface areas and volumes of other geometric figures.

Section ② Equations and Graphs

Section 2 Planner

Section Objectives

Exploration 1
• Use the order of operations

Exploration 2
• Graph equations and use the graphs to solve problems

Days for Section 2

First Day
Setting the Stage, *pp. 168–169*
Exploration 1, *pp. 169–171*

Second Day
Exploration 2 through Question 16, *pp. 172–174*

Third Day
Exploration 2, *p. 174*
Key Concepts, *p. 175*

Teaching Resources

Teacher's Resource Book
• Warm-Up
• Labsheet 2A
• Practice and Applications
• Study Guide
• *The Mystery of Blacktail Canyon*, Ch. 2
See page 155 for additional teaching resources.

Materials List

Setting the Stage
• Labsheet 2A

Exploration 1
• Labsheet 2A
• calculator

Exploration 2
• Labsheet 2A
• graph paper
• graphing calculator (optional)

Practice and Applications
• Labsheet 2A
• graph paper
• graphing calculator (optional)

Extra Skill Practice
• graph paper

Assessment Options

EMBEDDED ASSESSMENT
• Use the order of operations
  Exercises 10, 12, 18
• Graph equations and use the graphs to solve problems
  Exercises 21, 24

PERFORMANCE TASK/PORTFOLIO
• Exercise 20 on *p. 177 (challenge)*
• Exercise 21 on *p. 177 (history)*
• Exercise 34 on *p. 178 (journal)*

QUIZZES/TESTS
• Section 2 Quick Quiz

TEST GENERATOR

Section 2 Overview

In this section, students will explore different ways to estimate the speed of a car that has skidded to a stop. They will also estimate the appropriate distances to maintain between vehicles while driving.

Exploration 1
As students examine the skid marks left by a car, they apply a formula to determine the car's speed prior to stopping. This formula leads them to evaluate expressions involving square roots and a fraction bar. They will learn how to apply the order of operations when fraction bars and square roots are present. It is assumed that students are familiar with the order of operations; however, if review is necessary, refer them to the Toolbox exercises on page 589. In this exploration, students will also have an opportunity to explore simplifying expressions containing grouping symbols using a calculator.

Exploration 2
As students investigate the relationship between a car's speed and a recommended distance at which it should follow another car, they will learn how to graph both linear and nonlinear equations. Given an equation, students generate a table of values and plot the set of ordered pairs on a coordinate grid. As they do, they recognize that the resulting graph represents all the solutions of the equation.

Guide for Assigning Homework

REGULAR SCHEDULING (45 MIN CLASS PERIOD)			EXERCISES TO NOTE		
Section/ P&A Pages	Core Assignment	Extended Assignment	Additional Practice/Review	Open-ended Problems	Extended Problems
2 pp. 176–179	**Day 1:** 1–19 **Day 2:** 21–29 **Day 3:** 30–33, ROS 34, SR 35–42	1–20 21–29 30–33, ROS 34, SR 35–42	EP p. 179 TB, p. 589	PA 20	PA Challenge 20

Key: PA = Practice & Application; ROS = Reflecting on the Section; SR = Spiral Review; TB = Toolbox; EP = Extra Skill Practice; Ext = Extension; ST = Standardized Testing

Math Background and Teaching Strategies

Classroom Notes

Bulletin board display ideas for this section include:

• Newspaper photographs of vehicle accidents

Visitors might include:

• Highway patrol officer

Math Strands

Topic Spiraling and Integration
Since students have applied order of operations to evaluating expressions in Books 1 and 2, they should be familiar with the concept. If a review is required, refer them to the Toolbox on page 589 of Book 3. Ordered pairs were graphed in Modules 1 and 2 and will be developed further in Module 6.

Exploration 1
Students extend their understanding of the order of operations to include radicals and/or fraction bars. Since these are considered grouping symbols, the operations they contain are performed first. When more than one of these grouping symbols are present, there is a logical sequence that will make solving an equation more efficient. Recognizing that parentheses in a radical or in the numerator or denominator of a fraction should be evaluated first builds reasoning skills. In this exploration, students are encouraged to use a calculator to simplify expressions. Although a calculator may apply the order of operations, it will not recognize parentheses, radicals, or fraction bars unless they are keyed in. This fact will become evident as students explore simplifying expressions using a calculator. These skills will be especially useful as students work with quadratic functions in Module 6.

Exploration 2
Students should be familiar with graphing ordered pairs. Linear graphs and equations were explored in Section 1 of Module 2. This exploration extends students' understanding to include solutions of equations and nonlinear graphs. Linear and nonlinear graphs can be identified by their equations. Since the graph of a linear equation is a line, the relative rate of change of the variables, or slope, is constant. Linear equations involve just the first powers of the variables and addition, subtraction, multiplication, or division. The relative rate of change of the variables in a nonlinear equation is not constant. Nonlinear equations often involve radicals or exponents other than 1. Students will build on these ideas in the next section and in Module 6, where they analyze quadratic and exponential functions.

Section 3 Slope and Equations

Section 3 Planner

Section Objectives

Exploration 1
- Find positive slopes
- Use equations and graphs to model situations

Exploration 2
- Use an equation of a fitted line to make predictions

Days for Section 3

First Day
Setting the Stage, *p. 180*
Exploration 1 through Question 7,
pp. 181–182

Second Day
Exploration 1, *pp. 182–183*

Third Day
Exploration 2, *pp. 184–185*
Key Concepts, *p. 186*

Teaching Resources

Teacher's Resource Book
- Warm-Up
- Labsheet 3A
- Practice and Applications
- Study Guide
- *The Mystery of Blacktail Canyon,* Ch. 3
See page 155 for additional teaching resources.

Materials List

Exploration 2
- Labsheet 3A
- meter stick
- masking tape
- marker
- graph paper

Practice and Applications
- graph paper

Assessment Options

EMBEDDED ASSESSMENT
- Find positive slopes
  Exercises 2, 5
- Use equations and graphs to model situations
  Exercise 5
- Use an equation of a fitted line to make predictions
  Exercises 12, 13

PERFORMANCE TASK/PORTFOLIO
- Exercise 11–13 on *p. 188**
- Standardized Testing on *p. 190* *(open-ended)*
- Extended Exploration on *p. 191**

* indicates a problem-solving task that can be assessed using the Assessment Scales

QUIZZES/TESTS
- Section 3 Quick Quiz
- Mid-Module Quiz

TEST GENERATOR

Section 3 Overview

In this section, students will continue to explore linear equations and their graphs.

Exploration 1
Students will use graphs to explore rates while they examine how a person's stride affects the distance the person can cover in a given amount of time. They begin by investigating the relationship between a line's steepness and a rate of change. This leads into a study of slope. Students find the slope of a line by comparing its rise to its run. They learn how to use the slope to write an equation for a line passing through the origin.

Exploration 2
To make predictions using an equation, students gather data, make a scatter plot of the data, and draw a fitted line for the data. Students then use slope to estimate the equation of the fitted line and learn to adjust their equation by comparing values from the equation to values on the fitted line. This leads them to predict the height of a missing driver in the *The Mystery of Blacktail Canyon*.

Guide for Assigning Homework

REGULAR SCHEDULING (45 MIN CLASS PERIOD)			EXERCISES TO NOTE		
Section/ P&A Pages	Core Assignment	Extended Assignment	Additional Practice/Review	Open-ended Problems	Extended Problems
3 pp. 187–190	**Day 1:** 1–4, SR 15–22 **Day 2:** 5, 6, SR 23–26 **Day 3:** 8–13, ROS 14	1–4, SR 15–22 6, 7, SR 23–26 8–13, ROS 14	EP, p. 190	ST, p. 190	PA Challenge 7 E²

Key: PA = Practice & Application; ROS = Reflecting on the Section; SR = Spiral Review; TB = Toolbox; EP = Extra Skill Practice; Ext = Extension; ST = Standardized Testing

Math Background and Teaching Strategies

Classroom Notes

In Exploration 2, each group will need enough wall space to measure the heights of the group members.

Math Strands

Topic Spiraling and integration
This section builds on ideas about slope, lines, and equations introduced in Book 2. In Section 2 of this module, students graphed lines given their equation. In this section, they will learn to write an equation for a line from the points on the line. Only lines with positive slope are considered, and y-intercepts are not used. The ideas about slope and lines introduced here will be generalized and the slope-intercept form of a linear equation will be developed in Module 4.

Exploration 1
By comparing time and distance traveled, students discover that the slope of a line, *the ratio of its rise to its run*, is a rate, and that the steeper the line, the greater its slope. They also discover that in some cases the equation of a line can be written as $y = mx$, where m is the slope of the line. This idea will be used to find the equation of any line in Exploration 2. It is important for students to realize that when calculating slope, the order in which the y-coordinates are subtracted to find the rise and the x-coordinates are subtracted to find the run must be the same. It does not matter which pair of coordinates is subtracted from which as long as the coordinates from the same ordered pair are written first.

Exploration 2
To estimate the height of the missing driver, students collect height and foot length data and use it to construct a scatter plot. The objective is to fit a line to the data and use the fitted line to predict the driver's height. Using the ideas from Exploration 1, students guess that the equation of the fitted line is *height = slope • foot length*. However, they discover that points on the fitted line are not solutions to this equation, so the equation must be adjusted in some way. In Module 4, students will learn that this can be done by adding the y-intercept, but that idea is not introduced here because the y-intercept doesn't have a meaningful interpretation in this situation. Instead, students compare heights found using the equation and the fitted line to find a constant to add, thus obtaining the equation *height = slope • foot length + constant*. Students should understand that, because of the variability in real world data, a prediction made using this equation may not be exact, but it will give a reasonable approximation of the drivers height.

Section 4   Similar Figures and Constructions

Section 4 Planner

Section Objectives

Exploration 1
- Understand and apply properties of similar figures, including similar triangles
- Solve indirect measurement problems

Exploration 2
- Find a perpendicular bisector of a chord

Days for Section 4

First Day
Setting the Stage, *p. 192*
Exploration 1 through Question 6, *pp. 193–194*

Second Day
Exploration 1, *pp. 194–195*

Third Day
Exploration 2, *pp. 196–197*
Key Concepts, *p. 198*

Teaching Resources

Teacher's Resource Book
- Warm-Up
- Labsheets 4A, 4B, and 4C
- Practice and Applications
- Study Guide
- *The Mystery of Blacktail Canyon*, Chs. 4 and 5

See page 155 for additional teaching resources.

Materials List

Exploration 1
- Labsheet 4A
- centimeter ruler
- protractor

Exploration 2
- Labsheets 4B and 4C
- scissors
- compass
- ruler

Practice and Application Exercises
- ruler
- graph paper
- compass
- protractor

Assessment Options

EMBEDDED ASSESSMENT
- Understand and apply properties of similar figures, including similar triangles
  Exercises 3, 9, 10, 11
- Solve indirect measurement problems
  Exercise 14

PERFORMANCE TASK/PORTFOLIO
- Exercise 8 on *p. 199 (challenge)**
- Exercise 12 on *p. 200 (open-ended))*
- Exercise 15 on *p. 201 (visual thinking)*
- Exercise 19 on *p. 201 (visual thinking)**
- Extension on *p. 202*

* indicates a problem-solving task that can be assessed using the Assessment Scales

QUIZZES/TESTS
- Section 4 Quick Quiz

TEST GENERATOR

Section 4 Overview

In this section, students will see how similar figures can be used to make indirect measurements, and how the diameter of a circular object can be estimated using chords.

Exploration 1
Students explore similarity by measuring sides and angles of right triangles. In the process, they learn to identify *corresponding angles* and *corresponding sides* and how to name similar figures. They discover that two figures are similar if and only if the ratios of the corresponding sides are constant and the measures of corresponding angles are equal. Students apply their discoveries to generalize a test for similar triangles, and use what they know about similar triangles and solving proportions to find missing measures in similar triangles.

Exploration 2
Students use physical models to identify a chord of a circle and its perpendicular bisector. These models help students visualize the relationship between the perpendicular bisectors of any two chords of a circle. Applying this relationship, students will determine the diameter of a circular piece of pottery when only a piece of the pottery exists.

Guide for Assigning Homework

REGULAR SCHEDULING (45 MIN CLASS PERIOD)			EXERCISES TO NOTE		
Section/ P&A Pages	Core Assignment	Extended Assignment	Additional Practice/Review	Open-ended Problems	Extended Problems
4 pp. 199–203	**Day 1:** 1–7, SR 20–24 **Day 2:** 9–12, 14, SR 25–32 **Day 3:** 15–18, ROS 19	1–6, 8, SR 20–24 9–13, SR 25–32 15–18, ROS 19, 33–34	EP, p. 203	PA 12	Challenge PA 8, 13 Extension 33–34

Key: PA = Practice & Application; ROS = Reflecting on the Section; SR = Spiral Review; TB = Toolbox; EP = Extra Skill Practice; Ext = Extension; ST = Standardized Testing

Math Background and Teaching Strategies

Classroom Notes

Bulletin board display ideas for this section include:

• A display of varied sizes of triangles and circles as well as pictures of triangular and circular objects

Visitors might include:

• An archaeologist

Math Strands

Topic spiraling and Integration

Students explored triangles and circles in Module 3 of Book 2 and investigated similarity in Module 6 of Book 2. This section reviews similarity and introduces indirect measurement. These ideas will be revisited and extended in Module 5. Construction of perpendicular bisectors is also introduced in this section and will be used to explore the properties of quadrilaterals in Module 8.

Exploration 1

As students compare similar figures, they will discover that the ratio of the lengths of the corresponding sides of two similar figures is constant and their corresponding angles are congruent. Students may need to see multiple examples before accepting the fact that the corresponding angles of similar triangles always have the same measure. Using models such as tangrams or cutouts of similar triangles will allow students to physically move the pieces from angle to angle among the triangles therefore justifying the premise. Since the sum of the angle measures of any triangle is 180°, when two pairs of corresponding angles are congruent, the third pair must also be congruent. Use this logic to help students develop and accept the test for similar triangles described after Question 6 on page 194. Similarity will be revisited as students construct

triangles and identify congruent triangles in Module 6.

Exploration 2

In this exploration, students draw chords on cutouts of circles and construct the perpendicular bisectors of the chords. Initially, students use paper folding to construct the perpendicular bisectors. They discover that the perpendicular bisectors of the chords intersect in the center of the circle. Once the center has been determined, students can measure the length of the radius and use it to find the length of the diameter. Since it is not always possible to fold a circle, as students will see in the case of pottery fragments, students will also learn to construct perpendicular bisectors using a compass and straight edge.

154J

Section 5 Scientific Notation and Decimal Equations

Section 5 Planner

Section Objectives

Exploration 1
• Write large numbers in decimal and scientific notation

Exploration 2
• Solve equations involving decimals

Days for Section 5

First Day
Setting the Stage, *p. 204*
Exploration 1, *pp. 205–207*

Second Day
Exploration 2, *pp. 207–208*
Key Concepts, *p. 209*

Teaching Resources

Teacher's Resource Book
• Warm-Up
• Labsheet 5A
• Practice and Applications
• Study Guide
• *The Mystery of Blacktail Canyon,* Chs. 6 and 7
See page 155 for additional teaching resources.

Materials List

Setting the Stage
• Labsheet 5A

Exploration 1
• Labsheet 5A
• calculator

Practice and Applications
• calculator

Assessment Options

EMBEDDED ASSESSMENT
• Write large numbers in decimal and scientific notation
  Exercises 4, 10
• Solve equations involving decimals
  Exercises 15, 18, 22

PERFORMANCE TASK/PORTFOLIO
• Exercise 25 on *p. 210 (open-ended)*
• Exercise 26 on *p. 210 (research)*

QUIZZES/TESTS
• Section 5 Quick Quiz

TEST GENERATOR

Section 5 Overview

In this section, students will analyze data about the ages of bones, and use the length of a bone to estimate the height of an individual.

Exploration 1
Students analyze carbon-14 dating and the estimated ages of ancient bones written in scientific notation. Students compare numbers written in both decimal and scientific notation and practice writing numbers in both notations. They also convert from one to the other. Using a key sequence on the calculator, students will recognize how their calculator displays a number in scientific notation. They will find that on some calculators, a specific key can be used to enter a number in scientific notation. It is assumed that students have a working knowledge of powers of ten; however, those needing review can be referred to the Toolbox exercises on page 581.

Exploration 2
As students apply a formula to estimate the height of an individual based on the length of his or her femur, they will learn how to solve equations involving decimals. Students identify the inverse operations necessary for solving the equation and discuss how to eliminate decimals in an equation by multiplying by powers of ten.

Guide for Assigning Homework

REGULAR SCHEDULING (45 MIN CLASS PERIOD)			EXERCISES TO NOTE		
Section/ P&A Pages	**Core Assignment**	**Extended Assignment**	**Additional Practice/Review**	**Open-ended Problems**	**Extended Problems**
5 pp. 210–213	**Day 1:** 1–7, 9, 10, SR 27–37 **Day 2:** 11–25, ROS 26	1, 3, 5–10, SR 27–37 11–25, ROS 26	EP, p. 213 TB, p. 581	PA 25	PA Challenge 8

Key: PA = Practice & Application; ROS = Reflecting on the Section; SR = Spiral Review; TB = Toolbox; EP = Extra Skill Practice; Ext = Extension; ST = Standardized Testing

Math Background and Teaching Strategies

Classroom Notes

Visitors might include:

• A scientist who specializes in carbon dating

Math Strands

Topic Spiraling and Integration
Students explored scientific notation in Module 2 of Book 2. The concepts introduced and developed in this section will be extended when students learn the rules of exponents in Module 7. In this section, students use inverse operations, which were covered in Module 1, to solve equations with positive decimal coefficients. Negative, fractional, and decimal coefficients will be explored further in Module 4.

Exploration 1
The focus of this exploration is on identifying whether a number is written in scientific or in decimal notation and on converting numbers between decimal and scientific notation. It is important for students to recognize the value of writing very large numbers in scientific notation. Later in this book, students will compare populations and calculate distances to celestial bodies in the universe. They will find that comparing these very large numbers may be made easier by writing them in scientific notation. As students explore these ideas, they will recognize that a number is in scientific notation if it is written as the product of a power of ten and a number that is greater than or equal to 1 but less than 10. Moving decimal places is a strategy that helps students find the correct power of ten to use, but should not be taught at the expense of understanding what occurs when the decimal is moved to the right or left in a number. Since students will be using calculators to explore scientific notation, a knowledge of how their calculators display very large numbers and what keys are used to enter numbers in scientific notation will help the teacher offer appropriate assistance.

Exploration 2
The focus of this exploration is on using inverse operations to solve equations containing decimals. However, if students want to avoid working with decimals, they can also use powers of ten to move the decimals, just as they did in the first exploration. First, they decide what power of ten to multiply by to make all the numbers in the equation whole numbers and multiply both sides of the equation by it. Then, they use inverse operations to solve the equation. These skills will be applied throughout the book whenever students are required to solve equations.

154L

Section 6   Logical Thinking

Section 6 Planner

Section Objectives

Exploration 1
- Interpret statements with *and, or* and *not*
- Organize information in a Venn diagram

Days for Section 6

First Day
Setting the Stage, *p. 214*
Exploration 1, *pp. 215–217*
Key Concepts, *p. 217*

Teaching Resources

Teacher's Resource Book
- Warm-Up
- Labsheet 6A
- Practice and Applications
- Study Guide
- *The Mystery of Blacktail Canyon*, Chs. 8–10
See page 155 for additional teaching resources.

Materials List

Exploration 1
- Labsheet 6A
- tape

Practice and Application Exercises
- compass
- metric ruler

Assessment Options

EMBEDDED ASSESSMENT
- Interpret statements with *and, or* and *not*
  Exercises 3, 5, 6, 7–9
- Organize information in a Venn diagram
  Exercises 11, 14

PERFORMANCE TASK/PORTFOLIO
- Exercise 10 on *p. 219 (challenge)*
- Exercises 11–12 on *p. 219 (geography)*
- Exercise 14 on *p. 220 (research)*
- Standardized Testing on *p. 221*
- Module Project on *pp. 222–225**

* indicates a problem-solving task that can be assessed using the Assessment Scales

QUIZZES/TESTS
- Section 6 Quick Quiz
- Module Tests A and B
- Module Standardized Test
- Module Performance Assessment

TEST GENERATOR

Section 6 Overview

In this section, students will develop logical reasoning skills in preparation for solving *The Mystery of Blacktail Canyon* in the Module Project.

Exploration 1
As students examine each of the suspects from *The Mystery of Blacktail Canyon,* they learn to interpret statements containing logical connectives *and, or,* and *not*. A Venn diagram is used to organize the information collected and model relationships among groups of suspects. Although both the inclusive *or* and exclusive *or* are introduced, the exercises in this section will involve the inclusive *or*. Students will learn to draw and label a Venn diagram and interpret the information gleaned from the model.

Guide for Assigning Homework

REGULAR SCHEDULING (45 MIN CLASS PERIOD)			EXERCISES TO NOTE		
Section/ P&A Pages	Core Assignment	Extended Assignment	Additional Practice/Review	Open-ended Problems	Extended Problems
6 pp. 218–221	**Day 1:** 1–9, 11, ROS 14, SR 15–24	3–13, ROS 14, SR 15–24	EP, p. 221 Review & Assessment, pp. 226–227	PA 13, 14	Challenge PA 10 Mod Proj, pp. 222–225

Key: PA = Practice & Application; ROS = Reflecting on the Section; SR = Spiral Review; TB = Toolbox; EP = Extra Skill Practice; Ext = Extension; ST = Standardized Testing

Math Background and Teaching Strategies

Classroom Notes

Bulletin board displays for this section include:

- A large Venn diagram surrounded by clues to a mystery and/or a drawing of Sherlock Holmes or another notable detective.

Visitors might include:

- A police detective

Math Strands

Topic Spiraling and Integration
Students were introduced to the concept of Venn diagrams in Book 1 and the skill was developed in Module 8 of Book 2 where students classified quadrilaterals.

Exploration 1
The logic explored in this section may be confusing to some students. If marbles are being classified by their color, such as "red", and by clarity, such as "clear", students should recognize that the word *and* refers to those marbles that are both red and clear, therefore placing them in the center region. Marbles that are *not* red belong in regions other than the oval identified as red. Likewise, marbles that are *not* clear belong in regions other than the oval labeled clear. These are relatively obvious to most students. The word, *or*, however is interpreted in two ways. The exclusive meaning of the word is used in our everyday speech. When one speaks of going to a movie *or* going roller skating, one or the other of the activities will be done, but not both. In mathematics, however, the inclusive meaning of the word is applied. The Venn diagram clearly shows that a red marble *or* a clear marble refers to any marble that is red, clear, or both (that is, any marble included in either of the three interior regions of the Venn diagram). Possessing a firm understanding of the meaning of *and*, *or*, and *not* is essential for solving the mystery in the Module Project.

Differentiated Instruction

For students who are experiencing a Venn diagram for the first time, work with physical models may be necessary. Make two intersecting ovals using colored yarn. Attribute blocks work well for classification as they possess a variety of overlapping attributes. Write each specific attribute on an index card, then place an attribute card next to each string. Students can take turns placing a block in the region that best fits its attributes. This can continue until all the blocks have been properly placed. Students might enjoy making this into a game.

154N

Module 3

OVERVIEW

Mathematical models are used to interpret and solve problems related to a mystery.* In this module, students study length, area, and volume relationships, use scientific notation, solve equations, use equations and graphs to make predictions, and use indirect measurement to solve problems.

*See page 154A for more information about the mystery.

PREREQUISITE SKILLS

Warm-Up Exercises for each section are provided in the *Teacher's Resource Book*. You can use these exercises to review skills and concepts students will need for each section. In addition, the Spiral Review exercises at the end of each section in the student edition provide practice on prerequisite skills.

MODULE DIAGNOSTIC TEST

The Module Diagnostic Test in the *Teacher's Resource Book* can be used to assess students' prior knowledge of skills and concepts that will be taught in each section of this module. You can use test results to help structure your teaching to meet the diverse needs of your classroom.

MODULE 3

The Mystery of Blacktail Canyon

154

CONNECTING
MATHEMATICS
The & Theme

MODULE 3 · SECTION OVERVIEW

1 **Square Roots and Measurement**

As you learn about Anasazi ruins:

♦ Find and estimate square roots
♦ Describe patterns related to length, area, and volume

2 **Equations and Graphs**

As you investigate a car accident:

♦ Evaluate expressions with square roots and fraction bars
♦ Graph equations

3 **Slope and Equations**

As you search for a missing driver:

♦ Find the slope of a line
♦ Use an equation to make a prediction

4 **Similar Figures and Constructions**

As you estimate a cliff's height:

♦ Tell whether triangles are similar and make indirect measurements
♦ Find a perpendicular bisector of a chord

5 **Scientific Notation and Decimal Equations**

As you learn about carbon dating:

♦ Write very large numbers in scientific notation
♦ Solve equations involving decimals

6 **Logical Thinking**

As you solve the mystery:

♦ Use Venn diagrams to interpret statements with *and, or,* and *not.*

The Module Project ➤ Solving a Mystery

Do you like a good mystery story? You will read *The Mystery of Blacktail Canyon* and learn to use mathematics to solve mysteries. Then you will gather clues to identify a thief and write the conclusion to the mystery.

More on the Module Project
See pp. 222–225.

INTERNET
Resources and practice at
classzone.com

 155

Module Resources

TEACHER'S RESOURCE BOOK
Resources
• The *Math Gazette* (parent newsletter)
• Warm-Ups
• Labsheets
• Practice and Applications
• Study Guide

Assessment
• Section Quick Quizzes
• Mid-Module Quiz
• Module 3 Diagnostic Test
• Module 3 Tests A and B
• Module 3 Standardized Test
• Module 3 Performance Assessment

SPANISH RESOURCES
• The *Math Gazette* (parent newsletter)
• Practice and Applications
• Assessment
• Spanish Glossary

STUDENT WORKBOOK

TECHNOLOGY BOOK

TECHNOLOGY RESOURCES
• @Home Tutor
• Test Generator
• Activity Generator
• Professional Development DVD
• Online Activities

Section ① Square Roots and Measurement

IN THIS SECTION

EXPLORATION 1
♦ Finding Square Roots

EXPLORATION 2
♦ Length, Area, and Volume

Ancient Sites of Mystery

Setting the Stage

In *The Mystery of Blacktail Canyon*, a crime is committed. In this module you will read the story and solve the mystery. With the help of story characters who use their mathematical knowledge to solve mysteries, you will collect evidence that will help you identify the criminal who

THE FOUR CORNERS

has damaged an ancient site in Blacktail Canyon. Along the way, you will learn about the people who developed a culture in the North American desert.

The story takes place in the Four Corners region of the United States. Four Corners includes parts of Utah, Arizona, Colorado, and New Mexico.

Jim Cooper, one of the main characters, is an eighth grade student in Escavada, New Mexico. He is fascinated with mysteries, both ancient and modern. His new friend Nageela Ashilaka lives in Kenya, but travels everywhere with her father, Dr. B. B. Ashilaka, an expert on prehistoric dwellings. In spite of being confined to a wheelchair due to a disabling fall, Dr. Ashilaka continues his research with the help of his daughter.

◀ For centuries the Four Corners was inhabited by the *Anasazi* or *Ancestral Puebloans*. They often lived in villages, like Cliff Palace in Mesa Verde National Park in Colorado.

MAP OF BALCONY HOUSE
A Cliff Dwelling in Mesa Verde National Park, Colorado

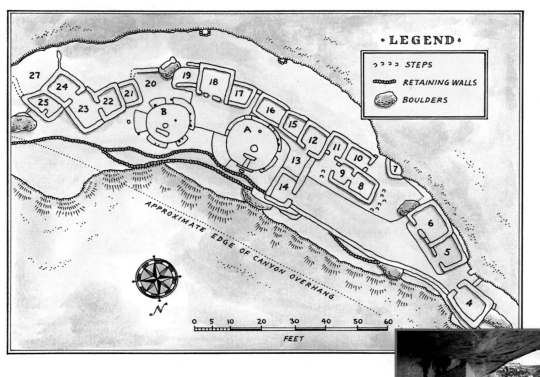

• LEGEND •

ɔɔɔɔ STEPS

RETAINING WALLS

BOULDERS

APPROXIMATE EDGE OF CANYON OVERHANG

0 5 10   20   30   40   50   60
FEET

Think About It ▸▸▸▸▸▸▸▸▸▸▸▸▸▸▸▸▸▸▸▸▸▸▸▸▸▸▸▸▸▸▸▸▸▸▸▸▸▸▸

Use the Map of Balcony House for Questions 1 and 2.

1 **a.** Copy the map scale onto the edge of a piece of paper.
   Check students' answers.

   b. Place your copy of the map scale on the map and use it to estimate the distance from the entrance of Room 4 to the northern-most corner of Room 25. about 140 ft

   c. About how long would it take you to walk from Room 4 to Room 25? Answers will vary. Sample Response: about 48 sec at 2 mi/hr

2 **a.** What is the approximate shape of Room 24? a square

   b. Estimate the area of Room 24. How does the area compare with the area of your classroom? 49 ft²; It is smaller.

▾
▲
Anasazi people began building Balcony House in the early 1200s. They lived there for less than 100 years.

GOAL

LEARN HOW TO...
- find and estimate square roots

AS YOU...
- find dimensions of a room at an archaeological site

KEY TERMS
- square root
- principal square root
- perfect square

3. b. a little more than 6 ft; Sample Response: The area of a square with sides 6 ft long is about 36 ft², which is a little less than 39 ft².

$$A = s \cdot s$$
$$A = s^2$$

s

s

Exploration 1

Finding $\sqrt{\text{Square Roots}}$

SET UP *Work with a partner. You will need a calculator.*

▶ In *The Mystery of Blacktail Canyon*, archaeologist Dr. B. B. Ashilaka and his daughter, Nageela, are studying ancient ruins. Their work involves finding the dimensions of archaeological sites.

3 Discussion The sketch shows a room at a site.

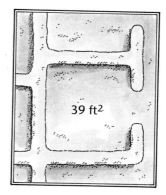

39 ft²

a. What is the approximate shape of the room? **a square**

b. Estimate the length of one side of the room. How did you make your estimate?

c. Let s = the length of one side of the room. Write an equation relating the area A of the room to s.
$A = s \cdot s$ or $A = s^2$

▶ The area of a square can be found by multiplying the length of one of the sides by itself, or by squaring the length of a side. The equation $A = s^2$ can also be used to find s, the length of a side of a square with area A.

EXAMPLE

If a side of a square is 4 cm long, then $A = 4^2$, or 16. The area is 16 cm².

If the area of a square is 25 cm², then $s^2 = 25$, so $s = 5$. The length of a side is 5 cm.

4 In the Example on the previous page, the number 5 is a solution of the equation $s^2 = 25$ and is a *square root* of 25. What is another square root of 25? –5

▶ If $A = s^2$, then s is a **square root** of A. Since $4^2 = 16$ and $(-4)^2 = 16$, both 4 and –4 are square roots of 16. The positive solution of $s^2 = 16$ is the **principal square root** of 16 and is indicated by $\sqrt{16}$.

$\sqrt{16} = 4$ The principal square root of 16 is 4.

The same symbol with a negative sign, $-\sqrt{16}$, indicates the negative square root.

$-\sqrt{16} = -4$ The negative square root of 16 is –4.

5 Use mental math to find each value.

a. $\sqrt{81}$ 9   b. $\sqrt{49}$ 7   c. $\sqrt{1}$ 1

d. $-\sqrt{9}$ –3   e. $-\sqrt{64}$ –8   f. $-\sqrt{144}$ –12

▶ The numbers 1, 4, 9, 16, and 25 are *perfect squares*. A **perfect square** is a number whose principal square root is a whole number.

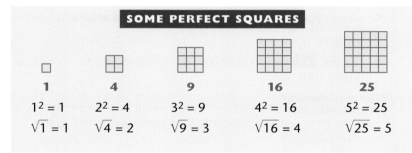

SOME PERFECT SQUARES

1	4	9	16	25
$1^2 = 1$	$2^2 = 4$	$3^2 = 9$	$4^2 = 16$	$5^2 = 25$
$\sqrt{1} = 1$	$\sqrt{4} = 2$	$\sqrt{9} = 3$	$\sqrt{16} = 4$	$\sqrt{25} = 5$

6 List the next five perfect squares after 25. Then list some numbers that are not perfect squares. 36, 49, 64, 81, 100; Sample Response: 3, 40, 65

▶ **Estimating Square Roots** In Question 3 you estimated $\sqrt{39}$. There are many situations in which you may need to estimate square roots.

7 Calculator Use the $\boxed{\sqrt{}}$ key to approximate $\sqrt{39}$. Compare this approximation with your estimate from Question 3.
about 6.24; Sample Response: 6.24 is a little more than 6 as estimated in Question 3.

TEACHING NOTES

In **Question 4**, students are led to recognize that every number has two square roots, a positive one and a negative one. Help them recognize that there are times, such as when finding a distance, when only the principal square root can be a solution to a problem. Use the examples below to lead them to the conclusion that the area of a square cannot have a negative square root, since length of a side of the square cannot be negative.

CLASSROOM EXAMPLES

Find the area of a square with sides 7 in. long.

7 in.

Answer: $A = 7 \cdot 7$ or 7^2
            $= 49$
The area is 49 in.²

Find the length of a side of a square whose area is 121 cm².

121 cm²

Answer: $s^2 = 121$
            $s = \sqrt{121}$
            $s = 11$
The length of a side is 11 cm.

Exploration 1 continued

TEACHING NOTES

Question 9(a) suggests a procedure for determining which of two consecutive integers the square root of a number is closer to. That is, (suppose) you want to know whether $\sqrt{a}$ is closer to integer b or integer $b + 1$. To find out, you can square $b + \frac{1}{2}$ and compare a to the value. If $a < \left(b + \frac{1}{2}\right)^2$, then $\sqrt{a}$ is closer to b. If $a > \left(b + \frac{1}{2}\right)^2$, then $\sqrt{a}$ is closer to $b + 1$.

DIFFERENTIATED INSTRUCTION

Visual learners may benefit from the use of a number line to find medians and estimate square roots.

8. a.

n	$\sqrt{n}$	n	$\sqrt{n}$
1	1	14	3.74
2	1.41	15	3.87
3	1.73	16	4
4	2	17	4.12
5	2.24	18	4.24
6	2.45	19	4.36
7	2.65	20	4.47
8	2.83	21	4.58
9	3	22	4.69
10	3.16	23	4.80
11	3.32	24	4.90
12	3.46	25	5
13	3.61		

9. a. 7; Sample Response: 45 is greater than 42.25, so $\sqrt{45}$ is greater than 6.5, and $\sqrt{45}$ is closer to 7.

d. Sample Response: about 6.71

8 Try this as a Class

a. Follow these steps to make a table. See margin.

Step 1 List the first 25 consecutive whole numbers in the first column.

Step 2 Find and record the principal square root of each perfect square.

Step 3 Use a calculator to approximate the principal square roots of the other numbers.

n	$\sqrt{n}$
1	1
2	1.41
3	1.73
4	2
5	?
6	?
7	?
8	?

b. Look at the whole numbers between 4 and 9. Compare their square roots with $\sqrt{4}$ and $\sqrt{9}$. The square roots are between $2 = \sqrt{4}$ and $3 = \sqrt{9}$.

c. Make some predictions about the square roots of the whole numbers between 25 and 36. Check your predictions. Sample Response: The square roots will be between 5 and 6.

9

a. Since 45 is not a perfect square, its principal square root is not a whole number. Is $\sqrt{45}$ closer to 6 or to 7? Explain how you know using the fact that $(6.5)^2 = 42.25$.

b. Estimate $\sqrt{45}$ to the nearest tenth. Do not use your calculator. Sample Response: about 6.7

c. Square your estimate in part (b) to check for accuracy. Sample Response: 44.89

d. Use your result in part (c) to improve your estimate.

e. Use the key on your calculator to find $\sqrt{45}$ to the nearest thousandth. 6.708

✔ QUESTION 10

...checks that you can estimate square roots.

10 ✔ CHECKPOINT

Estimate each square root to the nearest whole number. Then use a calculator to find each square root to the nearest tenth.

a. $\sqrt{55}$ about 7; 7.4

b. $\sqrt{37}$ about 6; 6.1

c. $\sqrt{62}$ about 8; 7.9

d. $\sqrt{103}$ about 10; 10.1

HOMEWORK EXERCISES ▶ See Exs. 1–23 on pp. 164–165.

Exploration 2

Length, AREA, and Volume

GOAL

LEARN HOW TO...
- describe patterns related to length, area, and volume

AS YOU...
- compare dimensions of rooms at an archaeological site

SET UP Work with a partner. You will need 30 centimeter cubes.

The Story So Far . . .

▶ Dr. Ashilaka and his group of amateur archaeologists take a field trip to Blacktail Canyon. While there, a sudden cloudburst forces everyone into the ruins of one of the dwellings. Jim asks about the size of a smaller room behind the room they are in, and Dr. Ashilaka asks him to estimate the size of the larger and smaller rooms.

"I know that my height and my arm span are about 5 feet. The big room is about twice my reach across the floor in both directions, and about twice my height. So, I guess it's about 10 by 10 by 10 feet. I can barely stand up in the center of the small room, and can just touch two walls. It must be about 5 by 5 by 5 feet." Jim looked puzzled. "I guess the big room is twice the size of the small one. But the funny thing is, it seems so much larger."

Dr. Ashilaka laughed and called Jim over. Nageela groaned and shook her head. She knew what was coming. She had heard the length, area, and volume lecture many times before.

11 **a.** Describe the shape of each room in the story.

  b. Why does Jim say the big room is twice the size of the smaller room? Do you agree? Explain. See margin.

11. a. Sample Response: Each room is a cube. The larger cube has edges 10 ft long, and the smaller cube has edges 5 ft long.

Exploration 2

COMMON ERROR

Jim's reasoning in **Question 11(b)** is common among students who have had limited experience comparing the lengths, areas, and volumes of geometric figures. Many students incorrectly assume that area and volume increase in the same proportions as the linear dimensions of a figure. The more concrete experiences students have, the more likely they are to intuitively understand that the area of a figure increases as square of the proportional increase in the side lengths. A square with a side 3 cm long has an area of 9 cm². If the lengths of sides are doubled (2 • 3 cm = 6 cm), the area increases to 2² or 4 times the original area (4 • 9 cm² = 36 cm²). If the side lengths are tripled (3 • 3 cm = 9 cm), the area of the new square increases to 3² or 9 times the original area (9 • 9 cm² = 81 cm²). This same pattern holds for the increase in volume except that the increase is the cube of the proportional increase. A cube with a side length of 2 cm has a volume of 8 cm³. If the side length is increased by a factor of 10 to 20 cm the volume increases to 10³ or 1000 times the original volume (1000 • 8 cm³ = 8000 cm³).

TEACHING NOTES

In Module 4, Section 1, students will explore the effect that increasing the length of a dimension has on the surface areas and volumes of cylinders and spheres.

11. b. See Additional Answers beginning on page A1.

TEACHING NOTES

In **Questions 12–14**, your class will generalize the relationships between length and area and length and volume. As you discuss **Question 14**, use an original figure with a side length other than 1 to help students learn how to see the patterns. For example, if an edge of one cube is 2 cm long and an edge of a second cube is 5 cm long, the edge length of the second cube is 2.5 times the edge length of the first cube. Thus, the area of a face of the second cube is 2.5^2 times the area of a face of the first cube and the volume of the second cube is 2.5^3 times the volume of the first cube.

CLASSROOM EXAMPLE

Suppose the length, width, and height of a prism are multiplied by 6. Describe what happens to the perimeter of the faces, the area of the faces, and the volume of the prism. Use the figure below to check.

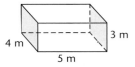

Answer: The perimeters of the faces of the new prism are 6 times those of the smaller prism. The areas of the faces of the new prism are $6^2 = 36$ times those of the smaller. The new prism's volume is $6^3 = 216$ times the smaller prism's.

Check:

perimeters of original faces: 16 m, 14 m, 18 m
perimeters of faces of new prism: 96 m, 84 m, 108 m
Perimeters are 6 × the original.

areas of original faces: 15 m², 12 m², 20 m²
areas of faces of new prism: 540 m², 432 m², 720 m²
Areas are 36 × the original.

volume of original prism: 60 m³
volume of new prism: 12,960 m³
Volume is 216 × the original.

12. See Additional Answers beginning on page A1.

162

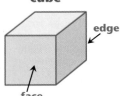

cube

edge

face

16. Jim only compared the lengths. If he had computed the volumes of the rooms, he would have found out that the volume of the larger room (10 ft · 10 ft · 10 ft = 1000 ft³) is 8 times the volume of the smaller room (5 ft · 5 ft · 5 ft = 125 ft³).

✔ **QUESTION 16**

...checks that you understand length, area, and volume relationships.

▶ Jim made a very rough estimate of the sizes of the rooms. You can use cubes to learn more about how the sizes of the rooms compare.

12 Build cubes with edges whose lengths are twice and three times those of a centimeter cube. Copy and complete the table.
See margin.

Cube Measurements			
Length of an edge	1 cm	2 cm	3 cm
Perimeter of a face	4 cm	?	?
Area of a face	1 cm²	?	?
Volume of the cube	1 cm³	?	?

13 Let s = the length of an edge of a cube. Write expressions for the perimeter of a face, the area of a face, and the volume of the cube.   perimeter of a face: $P = 4s$; area of a face: $A = s^2$; volume of the cube: $V = s^3$

▶ When you compare objects of different sizes, you need to know whether you are comparing lengths, areas, or volumes.

14 **Try This as a Class** Study your answers in Question 12. Look for patterns for how the length, the area, and the volume of the cubes are related.

a. What is the *perimeter of a face* of a cube multiplied by when the length of an edge is multiplied by 2? by 3? 2; 3

b. What is the *perimeter of a face* of a cube multiplied by if the length of an edge is multiplied by 4? by 5? by 10? by n? 4; 5; 10; n

c. Repeat parts (a) and (b) for the *area of a face*. What patterns do you notice? 4; 9; 16; 25; 100; n^2

d. Repeat parts (a) and (b) for the *volume of the cube*. What patterns do you notice? 8; 27; 64; 125; 1000; n^3

15 Without building a cube, predict the area of a single face and the volume of a cube whose dimensions are fourteen times those of a centimeter cube. area of a face = 196 cm²; volume of the cube = 2744 cm³

16 ✔ **CHECKPOINT** Jim Cooper made good estimates of the length, width, and height of each room, but he jumped to the wrong conclusion when comparing the volumes of the rooms. Explain Jim's mistake in the story on page 161. Use mathematics to support your answer.

HOMEWORK EXERCISES ▶ See Exs. 24–29 on pp. 165–166.

162 **Module 3** The Mystery of Blacktail Canyon

Section 1
Key Concepts

Squares and Square Roots (pp. 158–159)
Suppose $s^2 = n$. Then s is a square root of n. Every positive number has both a positive and a negative square root. The principal square root, indicated by $\sqrt{}$, is the positive square root.

Example $5^2 = 25$ and $(-5)^2 = 25$, so both 5 and -5 are square roots of 25. The principal square root of 25 is written $\sqrt{25}$, or 5. 25 is a perfect square since $\sqrt{25}$ is a whole number.

Estimating Square Roots (pp. 159–160)
You can use various methods to estimate a square root.

Example

Method 1 Use a calculator: $\sqrt{5} \approx 2.24$.

Method 2 Estimate between two integers by looking for the closest perfect squares less than and greater than a number: $\sqrt{4} < \sqrt{5} < \sqrt{9}$, so $2 < \sqrt{5} < 3$.
Note that $(2.5)^2 = 6.25$ and $5 < 6.25$. So, $\sqrt{5} < 2.5$ and $\sqrt{5}$ is closer to 2 than to 3.

Changing Dimensions (pp. 161–162)
When you compare sizes of objects, you need to know whether you are comparing lengths, areas, or volumes.

Example Suppose the length, width, and height of a prism are multiplied by 2 to create a larger prism. The areas of the faces of the larger prism are 2^2 or 4 times those of the smaller prism. The volume of the larger prism is 2^3 or 8 times the volume of the smaller prism.

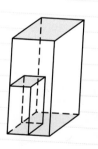

Key Terms

square root

principal square root

perfect square

Key Concepts

CLOSURE QUESTION
Suppose you know the area of one of the faces of a cube. Describe how you would find the dimensions of the cube and its volume.

Sample Response: Find the square root of the area of the face to determine the length of each edge of the cube. Calculate the volume by cubing the length of one edge of the cube.

ABSENT STUDENTS
For students who were absent for part or all of this section, the blackline Study Guide for Section 1 may be used to present the ideas, concepts and skills of Section 1.

17 Key Concepts Question

   a. Find the side length of a square whose area is 289 cm². **17 cm**

   b. Suppose each side of the square in part (a) is multiplied by 5. What is the effect on the area of the square? **The area of the square is multiplied by 5^2 or 25.**

Practice & Applications

SUGGESTED ASSIGNMENTS

Core Course

Day 1: Exs. 1–6, 30–35
Day 2: Exs. 7–12, 14–23
Day 3: Exs. 24–27, 29

Extended Course

Day 1: Exs. 1–6, 30–35
Day 2: Exs. 7–8, 11–23
Day 3: Exs. 25–29

Note: Extended Course assignments can be used to differentiate within the regular classroom. In classrooms where students are grouped homogeneously, the material might be covered in fewer days. In this case assignments may be combined.

ADDITIONAL PRACTICE

See the *Teacher's Resource Book* for additional practice and application exercises for this section.

EXERCISE NOTES

Exercises 1–6 Some students may find some of these mental calculations challenging because of the place values. Encourage them to make the problem simpler, or to look for perfect squares within the number and use them to calculate.

COMMON ERROR

Exercise 16 Some students may only think of using whole numbers as possible examples. Encourage them to consider fractions and decimals as well.

16. Sample Response:
$1 = \sqrt{1}, 3 > \sqrt{3}$
$\approx 1.73, 9 = \sqrt{9} = 3;$
counterexample:
$\frac{1}{4} < \sqrt{\frac{1}{4}} = \frac{1}{2}$

Copernicus, the crater nearest to the center in the photo, is an impact crater believed to be less than 1 billion years old.

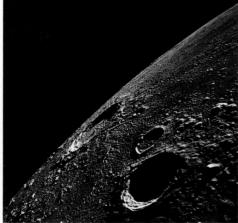

Section 1
Practice & Application Exercises

Mental Math Use mental math to find each value.

1. $\sqrt{100}$ 10
2. $-\sqrt{144}$ −12
3. $\sqrt{3600}$ 60
4. $\sqrt{0.49}$ 0.7
5. $\sqrt{\frac{16}{100}}$ $\frac{2}{5}$
6. $-\sqrt{9,000,000}$ −3000

7. The dimensions of a typical sheet of notebook paper are $8\frac{1}{2}$ in. by 11 in.

   a. What is the area of the paper? $93\frac{1}{2}$ in.²

   b. Suppose a square piece of paper has the same area. Estimate the dimensions of the square piece of paper to the nearest $\frac{1}{2}$ in. $9\frac{1}{2}$ in. × $9\frac{1}{2}$ in.

8. **Estimation** Use the sketch of a floor plan.

   a. Estimate the width of the bathroom.   about 2.3 m

   b. Estimate the perimeter of the living room.   about 18.4 m

   c. Estimate the area of the kitchen.   16.5 m²

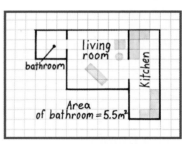

Estimation Estimate each square root to the nearest tenth.

9. $\sqrt{39}$ about 6.2
10. $\sqrt{55}$ about 7.4
11. $\sqrt{12}$ about 3.5
12. $\sqrt{125}$ about 11.2

13. **Challenge** The lunar crater Copernicus covers a circular area of about 6793 km². Estimate the diameter of the crater.   about 93 km

14. **Algebra Connection** What whole numbers can you substitute for *n* to make the statement $6 < \sqrt{n} < 7$ true?   37, 38, 39, 40, 41, 42, 43, 44, 45, 46, 47, 48

15. **Probability Connection** Suppose a spinner is equally likely to land on any integer from 1 through 100. Find the probability that it lands on a perfect square. $\frac{1}{10}$

16. Rae says that every positive number is greater than or equal to its square root. Find examples to support her statement. Can you find a counterexample?

Choosing a Method Find each value. Tell whether your answer is exact or an estimate.

17. $-\sqrt{810{,}000}$
−900; exact

18. $\sqrt{810}$
about 28.5; estimate

19. $-\sqrt{33}$
about −5.7; estimate

20. $\sqrt{0.25}$
0.5; exact

21. $\sqrt{1000}$
about 31.6; estimate

22. $\sqrt{0.0064}$
0.08; exact

23. **Estimation** The area of a square plot of land is about 9500 yd². Estimate the length of a side and the perimeter of the plot of land.
length of side ≈ 97.5 yd; perimeter of plot ≈ 390 yd

24. **Writing** A homeowner figures that the cost of carpet for the walk-in closet will be one-third the cost of carpet for the bedroom. The carpet chosen is sold by the square foot. Do you agree with the homeowner? Explain.

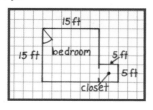

Air Conditioning For Exercises 25–27, use the ad below.

25. **Algebra Connection** Write an equation that you can use to estimate how much cooling capacity is needed for a room with a given floor area. $c = 10a + 3000$ where c represents the cooling capacity and a represents the floor area

26. A room in Bob Lang's house is 10 ft × 15 ft. Another room is 20 ft × 30 ft. Bob estimates that he needs an air conditioner with twice as much cooling capacity for the larger room as for the smaller room.

   a. Sketch each room. Label the dimensions. Then find the cooling capacity needed for each room. See margin.

   b. Do you think Bob is correct? Explain. Yes; Sample Response: 9000 is 2 · 4500

27. One room in Maria Franco's house is 18 ft × 12 ft. Another room is 18 ft × 24 ft. Maria estimates that she needs an air conditioner with twice as much cooling capacity for the larger room as for the smaller room.

   a. Sketch each room. Label the dimensions. See margin.

   b. Do you think Maria is correct? Explain. No; Sample Response: 7320 is only about 1.5 · 5160 so she needs about 1.5 times the cooling capacity for the larger room.

EXERCISE NOTES

Exercise 24 Remind students to use what they learned in Exploration 2 about the relationship between an increase in the length of the sides of a figure and the areas of the two figures.

Question 25 Students might recognize the cooling estimates as a "rule of thumb" similar to those studied in Module 3. Students could return to Section 3 of Module 1 to help them in writing an equation.

24. Sample Response: No; The area of the bedroom is 225 ft² and the area of the closet is 25 ft² so the cost of the closet carpet would be one-ninth the cost of the bedroom carpet.

26. a.

10 ft / 15 ft
cooling capacity: 4500 Btu/hr

20 ft / 30 ft
cooling capacity: 9000 Btu/hr

27. a.

18 ft / 24 ft
cooling capacity: 7320 Btu/hr

18 ft / 12 ft
cooling capacity: 5160 Btu/hr

Practice & Applications

EXERCISE NOTES

Challenge Exercise 28(c) After comparing the two boxes, students are asked to recommend a fair price for the large box based on the price of the small box. They will need to decide if the cost increase should be determined by the increase in the length of the sides, increase in the areas of the faces, or increase in volume. There is no single correct response for this exercise, but you may want to ask students to justify the choice they made.

28. Challenge A company makes and sells small and large boxes. The same materials are used to make each size.

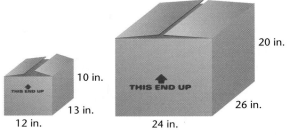

20 in.

10 in.

13 in.

12 in.

26 in.

24 in.

a. Compare the amount of cardboard needed to make each box. About how many times as much cardboard is needed for the large box? **4 times**

b. The volume of the large box is about how many times the volume of the small box? **8 times**

c. **Writing** The company plans to charge $1.50 for a small box. How much do you think the company should charge for a large box? **Sample Response: $1.50 · 4 = $6.00 if they charge by the amount of material used**

Oral Report

Exercise 29 checks that you can compare length, area, and volume relationships.

Reflecting ◀▶ on the Section

Be prepared to report on the following topic in class.

29. In *The Mystery of Blacktail Canyon*, Dr. Ashilaka asks Jim to estimate the size of two rooms in a dwelling. When Jim is done, Dr. Ashilaka gives him a lecture about the relationships among length, area, and volume. Pretend you are Dr. Ashilaka and write what you would say to Jim. Then present your lecture to the class. **Answers will vary. Check students' work.**

Spiral ◀▶ Review

30. Use the data to create a box-and-whisker plot. Identify any outliers. (Module 1, p. 23) **See margin.**

Amounts Raised by Students at a Charity Dance Marathon (dollars)
55, 60, 65, 70, 80, 80, 80, 90, 100, 110, 115, 150, 170, 175, 175, 450

Solve each equation. (Module 2, p. 86)

31. $|x| = 4$ **32.** $|n| = 11$ **33.** $-y = 19$ **34.** $-r = -6$

4 or –4   11 or –11   –19   6

35. a. $A(-2, -2)$,
$B(-2, 1)$,
$C(1, 1)$,
$D(2, -1)$
b. $A'(0, -2)$,
$B'(0, 1)$,
$C'(3, 1)$,
$D'(4, -1)$

Use the figure shown. (Module 2, p. 87)

35. a. Give the coordinates of points *A*, *B*, *C*, and *D*.

b. Give the coordinates of the image points *A'*, *B'*, *C'*, and *D'* after a translation of $(x + 2, y)$.

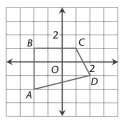

30. See Additional Answers beginning on page A1.

Mental Math Use mental math to find each value.

1. $\sqrt{490{,}000}$ 700   2. $-\sqrt{16}$ –4   3. $\sqrt{\dfrac{1}{100}}$ $\dfrac{1}{10}$ 4. $\sqrt{0.01}$ 0.1

5. $\sqrt{0.0036}$ 0.06   6. $-\sqrt{2500}$ –50   7. $\sqrt{0.0004}$ 0.02   8. $\sqrt{\dfrac{4}{25}}$ $\dfrac{2}{5}$

Estimation Estimate each square root to the nearest tenth.

9. $\sqrt{50}$ about 7.1   10. $\sqrt{22}$ about 4.7   11. $\sqrt{136}$ about 11.7   12. $\sqrt{67}$ about 8.2

13. $\sqrt{43}$ about 6.6   14. $\sqrt{94}$ about 9.7   15. $\sqrt{32}$ about 5.7   16. $\sqrt{85}$ about 9.2

Choosing a Method Find each square root. Tell whether your answer is exact or an estimate.

17. $\sqrt{28.4}$
about 5.3; estimate

18. $-\sqrt{63}$
about –7.9; estimate

19. $\sqrt{6.25}$
2.5; exact

20. $-\sqrt{9000}$
about –94.9; estimate

21. $\sqrt{4.81}$
about 2.2; estimate

22. $\sqrt{\dfrac{1}{36}}$
$\dfrac{1}{6}$; exact

23. $\sqrt{0.64}$
0.8; exact

24. $\sqrt{0.064}$
about 0.3; estimate

25. The volume of a cube is 64 cm³. What will be its volume if its edge length is halved? 8 cm³

Study Skills ◀▶ **Preparing for Assessment**

Planning ahead is important when you prepare for a test. Try to study every day instead of waiting until the night before a test. Also, be sure to practice what you have learned. Some people find it helpful to make review cards for important ideas, rules, and formulas.

Suppose you have 3 days to prepare for a test on this section.

1–4. Answers will vary. Check students' work.

1. Make a list of the important ideas in the section.

2. Develop a plan for dividing up the section so that you can study part of it each day.

3. Write and solve some practice problems for the topics you plan to study each day.

4. Make review cards of important ideas, rules, and formulas in the section.

TEACHER NOTES
For each Exploration, the corresponding Extra Skills Practice Exercises are noted.

Exploration 1: Exs. 1–24
Exploration 2: Ex. 25

EXTRA HELP
Teacher's Resource Book
• Practice and Applications
• Study Guide

Technology Resources
• @Home Tutor
• Test Generator

ASSESSMENT
• Section 1 Quick Quiz
• Test Generator

This section draws attention to the effect of friction on the ability of a car to stop quickly under varying road conditions. Although most of your students have had little or no experience driving a car, they should have some experience with the effects of friction on certain activities in which they have participated. Before reading the *Setting the Stage*, ask your students to brainstorm activities that require more or less than average friction. Possible activities may include skiing, ice skating or roller skating, sledding, water sliding, playing air hockey or playing a string instrument that used a bow (Rosin is rubbed on the bow to increase friction with the string, making a more vibrant tone). You might then ask students what role friction plays in their everyday life. (*Without the effects of friction between your shoe and the floor, you could not even take a single step.*)

GETTING STARTED

In Module 3 Section 2, students will be using order of operations to evaluate algebraic expressions and then using the solutions of equations to create graphs. The Section 2 *Warm-Up* refreshes students' skills in evaluating simple expressions in preparation for successful completion of the section.

Section ② Equations and Graphs

on the Road

Setting the Stage

SET UP You will need Labsheet 2A.

The Story So Far...

▶ On the drive back from Blacktail Canyon, Jim and Nageela find Highway Patrol Officer Ferrel Yellow Robe investigating a single-car accident. The officer explains how he knows that the missing driver of the car was going too fast on the wet curve.

"When I investigate an accident, I check the road conditions, the length of the skid, and the condition of the tire tread. There's a chart that we use to figure the speed the car was going when the driver hit the brakes, or we can plug the numbers into a formula. Just routine."

To estimate the car's speed, Ferrel needs to know the distance the car skidded and a number called the *coefficient of friction*. This number is a measure of the friction between the car's tires and the road surface.

Think About It

1 *Friction* is the force that resists the motion of objects in contact with each other. Try pushing a notebook quickly, then slowly, across two different surfaces, such as carpet and wood. Describe the amount of friction present in each instance.

2 Suppose you ride a bike across dirt, ice, dry asphalt, and wet asphalt. Which surface do you think is the least safe? the safest?
ice; dry asphalt

1. Sample Response:
There is more friction on a rough surface, like carpet, than on a smooth surface, like wood.

Module 3 The Mystery of Blacktail Canyon

▶ **Use Labsheet 2A for Questions 3–6.** In the story on page 168, Officer Yellow Robe mentions a chart. This chart is called a *Nomogram*.

3 Officer Yellow Robe measures the skid distance and estimates the coefficient of friction at the crash site. He then uses the data to draw a line as shown on the labsheet.

    a. Describe the road conditions. What is the coefficient of friction? wet concrete or wet asphalt; 0.6

    b. How long were the skid marks? 110 ft

    c. Estimate the car's speed when the driver hit the brakes. about 45 mi/hr

4 An officer measures 45 ft skid marks on wet asphalt at a crash site. Use the *Nomogram* to estimate the car's speed. about 29 mi/hr

5 A driver is traveling at 35 mi/hr on dry asphalt. Estimate how far the car will skid if the driver hits the brakes. about 51 ft

6 Can two cars traveling at the same speed leave different skid mark lengths? Explain.

Exploration 1

TIPS FROM TEACHERS
Help students practice using the formula at the beginning of **Exploration 1** by replacing each variable in the equation found on the note pad with the speed, distance, and coefficient of friction from Question 3.

Exploration 1

Order of Operations

SET UP | You will need: • Labsheet 2A • calculator

GOAL

LEARN HOW TO...
♦ evaluate expressions with square roots and fraction bars

AS YOU...
♦ estimate speeds of cars involved in accidents

Nomograms are only one way to estimate speed from skid marks. Most of the time, accident investigators use two formulas to find the speed.

The formula shown at the right is used first to find a coefficient of friction for the road where the accident happened. An officer drives a patrol car at a certain speed and then hits the brakes to find a skid distance.

Coefficient of friction →   Car's speed in miles per hour before braking →

$$f = \frac{s^2}{30d}$$

Distance in feet the car skidded before stopping →

6. Yes; Sample Response: Cars traveling at the same speed but under different road conditions can leave different length skid marks. For example, a car traveling 30 mi/hr on gravel skids about 60 ft, but a car traveling 30 mi/hr on dry concrete only skids about 37 ft.

TEACHING NOTES

Most students should be familiar with the order of operations. If not, you can use the mnemonic **P**lease **E**xcuse **M**y **D**ear **A**unt **S**ally to help them remember which operations should be performed first—evaluate expressions in **P**arentheses first, then **E**xponents, then **M**ultiplications and **D**ivisions in order from left to right, and finally, **A**dditions and **S**ubtractions in order from left to right.

The following example may be used prior to answering **Checkpoint Question 8** to ensure that students can use the formula properly, recognize the fraction bar as a grouping symbol, and apply order of operations.

CLASSROOM EXAMPLE

Officer Hayes conducts another skid test at a different accident site. The speed before the brakes were applied is 55 mph and the skid distance is 125 ft. Find the coefficient of friction.

Answer: $f = \dfrac{s^2}{30d}$

$= \dfrac{55^2}{30 \cdot 125}$

$= \dfrac{3025}{3750}$

≈ 0.81

The coefficient of friction is about 0.81.

7. **Step 1:** Copy the formula.
   Step 2: Substitute 32 for speed (*s*) and 50 for distance (*d*).
   Step 3: Evaluate the expression. She evaluated the numerator and the denominator separately before dividing the numerator by the denominator.

FOR ▶ HELP
with *the order of operations*, see
TOOLBOX, p. 589

EXAMPLE

Officer Patricia Hayes conducts a skid test at an accident site. She uses the formula $f = \dfrac{s^2}{30d}$ to find the coefficient of friction.

REPORTING OFFICER	LOCATION OF ACCIDENT
Hayes, Patricia	Mile 6, Adobe Road

DATE OF ACCIDENT			TIME OF ACCIDENT		AM	PM
Mo	Day	Yr	Hour	Min.		
05	19	07	3	41	☐	☒

Result of Skid Test

Speed before brakes were applied: 32 mi/hr

Skid distance: 50 ft

> The fraction bar is a grouping symbol. You may need to simplify the numerator and denominator before dividing.

$f = \dfrac{s^2}{30d}$

$f = \dfrac{32^2}{30 \cdot 50}$

$f = \dfrac{1024}{1500} \approx 0.68$

The coefficient of friction is about 0.68.

▶ For Questions 7 and 8, use the Example above.

7 **Try This as a Class** Explain each step of Officer Hayes's work. How did she use the order of operations? See margin.

✔ QUESTION 8

...checks that you understand how to evaluate an expression with a fraction bar.

8 **✔ CHECKPOINT** To make sure her results are accurate, Officer Hayes conducts two skid tests. She finds the coefficient of friction for each test, and then finds an average.

a. In her second skid test, Officer Hayes's speed is 34 mi/hr and her skid distance is 60 ft. Find the coefficient of friction. 0.64

b. Use your answer to part (a) and the coefficient of friction from the Example to find the mean coefficient of friction. 0.66

▶ **Another Grouping Symbol** When a patrol officer knows the coefficient of friction, he or she can use the formula shown at the left to estimate a car's speed when the brakes were applied. The $\sqrt{\ }$ symbol in the formula is a grouping symbol.

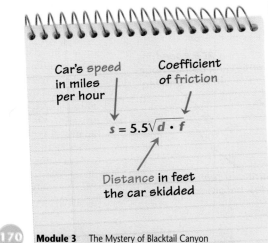

Car's speed in miles per hour

Coefficient of friction

$s = 5.5\sqrt{d \cdot f}$

Distance in feet the car skidded

EXAMPLE

A car skids 49 ft in an accident. The investigating officer finds that the coefficient of friction is 0.75. Estimate the car's speed.

SAMPLE RESPONSE

Evaluate the formula $s = 5.5\sqrt{d \cdot f}$ for $d = 49$ and $f = 0.75$.

$s = 5.5\sqrt{49(0.75)}$ ← Perform the operations under the $\sqrt{}$ symbol first.

$s = 5.5\sqrt{36.75}$

$s \approx 5.5(6.06)$ ← Then find the square root of 36.75.

$s \approx 33$ mi/hr

The car's speed was approximately 33 mi/hr.

9 ✔ CHECKPOINT Find each value.

a. $1.65\sqrt{32 \cdot 2}$ 13.2 **b.** $\dfrac{5 - 13}{2^3}$ −1 **c.** $\dfrac{3 - 21}{-2(3)}$ 3

d. $\sqrt{\dfrac{19 + 8}{3}}$ 3 **e.** $12\sqrt{\dfrac{12}{56 - 8}}$ 6 **f.** $8 + 2\sqrt{9 \cdot 4}$ 20

10

 Calculator You can use a calculator to simplify expressions with grouping symbols. For example, one way to simplify $5.5\sqrt{49(0.75)}$ is to enter a key sequence that uses parentheses to group operations under the $\sqrt{}$ symbol:

 (49 × 0.75) √ × 5.5 =

Does this key sequence work on your calculator? If not, describe another key sequence you could use.

11 Use Labsheet 2A. Suppose a car leaves 60 ft skid marks on dry gravel in a 30 mi/hr speed zone. Use the *Nomogram* and then the formula $s = 5.5\sqrt{d \cdot f}$ to estimate the car's speed. How do your answers compare? Was the driver speeding?

The results are about 30 mi/hr using the nomogram and about 30.1 mi/hr using the formula. The driver was not speeding

HOMEWORK EXERCISES See Exs. 1–20 on pp. 176–177.

---

10. Sample Response:
On a TI-73 Explorer graphing calculator, use the key sequence
$5.5 \times \sqrt{} (49 \times .75)$
ENTER.

✔ QUESTION 9

...checks that you can find the value of an expression with grouping symbols.

Exploration 2

12. b.

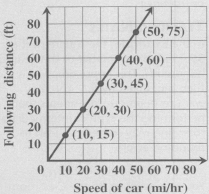

Exploration 2

GRAPHING EQUATIONS

SET UP You will need: • Labsheet 2A • graph paper • graphing calculator (optional)

▶ To prevent highway collisions, it is important to leave enough "following distance" between your car and the car ahead of you. The table models a relationship between speed and recommended following distance that drivers have used for years. Some new guidelines call for even greater following distances.

Use the table for Questions 12–14. You will use an equation and a graph to model the relationship between a car's speed and the recommended following distance.

Recommended Following Distances	
Speed of a car (mi/hr)	Following distance (ft)
10	15
20	30
30	45
40	60
50	75

12 a. Use the table to complete this equation:

Following distance = **?** • speed
following distance = 1.5 • speed

b. Follow these steps to graph the equation from part (a).
See margin.
First Make a coordinate grid. You want to show how following distance depends on speed, so put following distance on the vertical axis. In general, when one quantity depends on another, put the dependent quantity on the vertical axis.

Next Write the data in the table as ordered pairs: (Speed, Following distance).

Then Plot the ordered pairs. Draw a smooth curve through the points or connect the points in order with segments.

c. A driver is traveling at 45 mi/hr. Use your graph and the equation to recommend a following distance to the driver.
67.5 ft

d. Which model in part (c) did you find easier to use?
Answers may vary

e. Which model gave the more accurate answer?
the equation

13 Let s = the speed of a car in miles per hour. Let d = the recommended following distance in feet. Model the relationship in Question 12(a) with an equation using the variables s and d.
$d = 1.5s$

14 Discussion Some drivers estimate the distance between their car and the one ahead using a car length as a benchmark. At 50 mi/hr, how many car lengths would you recommend as a minimum following distance between two cars? Explain your thinking.

14. 5 car lengths;
   Sample Response:
   I used the equation
   $d = 1.5s$ to find the
   following distance
   of 75 ft
   ($d = 1.5 \cdot 50$
   $= 75$ ft). Then I
   divided 75 by 15 to
   get the number of
   car lengths.

Your Car

1 car length ≈ 15 ft

Car in Front

▶ The equation you wrote in Question 13 has two variables. An ordered pair of numbers that makes an equation with two variables true is a **solution of the equation**. The graph of an equation includes all possible solutions of the equation.

EXAMPLE

Follow these steps to graph the equation $y = 2x + 1$.

First Make a table of values. Include several values so you can see the pattern in the points you plot. Include both positive and negative values of x.

Then Plot the ordered pairs on a coordinate grid. Draw a curve or a line to show the pattern. Use arrowheads to show that the graph extends.

x	y	(x, y)
−2	−3	(−2, −3)
−1	−1	(−1, −1)
0	1	(0, 1)
1	3	(1, 3)
2	5	(2, 5)

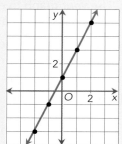

15 Try This as a Class Tell whether each ordered pair is a solution of the equation in the Example. Explain your thinking.

a. (−5, −9) yes **b.** (−4, 9) no **c.** (3, 1) no **d.** (9, 19) yes

15. Sample Response:
    I substituted the
    values for x and y
    into the equation to
    see if they made a
    true equation.

TEACHING NOTES

As students discuss **Question 14**, they should realize that they are writing a simple "rule of thumb" that they should be able to explain with no difficulty.

Question 15 can be discussed as a class or in pairs. Through their explanations, students will demonstrate that they understand that an ordered pair of numbers is a solution of the equation if and only if the point it represents lies on the graph. Ask questions such as: "Must all solutions be integers?" (*No, the ordered pair (0.5, 2) is a solution.*)
"How many solutions are there?" (*An infinite number. The graph extends forever.*)
"Which solutions make sense in the equation $d = 1.5s$ from Question 12, where s = speed of the car and d = the following distance in feet?" (*Only (0, 0) values in the first quadrant, since distance and speed can both only be positive or 0.*)

TEACHING NOTES

The following example may be used prior to answering **Checkpoint Question 16**.

CLASSROOM EXAMPLE

Graph the equation $y = -3x + 2$.

Answer: First make a table of values.

x	y	(x, y)
−1	5	(−1, 5)
0	2	(0, 2)
1	−1	(1, −1)
2	−4	(2, −4)

Then plot the ordered pairs on a coordinate grid. Draw a curve or a line to show the pattern. Use arrowheads to show that the graph extends.

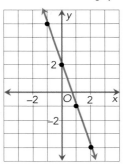

Checkpoint Question 16
Encourage students to first make a table, then plot the points on a coordinate grid, and finally draw the curve or line defined by the points. Remind them to plot three or more points before drawing a line.

Question 19 Students may need assistance using a graphing calculator (e.g. window settings, entering an equation).

16–18. a., 19. See Additional Answers beginning on page A1.

✔ QUESTION 16

...checks that you can graph an equation.

16 ✔ **CHECKPOINT** Graph each equation. a–c. See margin.

   a. $y = x$ **b.** $y = x - 4$ **c.** $y = -2x$

▶ **Linear and Nonlinear Graphs** When the graph of an equation is a straight line, the graph and the equation are **linear**. Now you will look at a relationship whose graph is **nonlinear**.

17 Copy and complete the table. Use the formula $s = 5.5\sqrt{d \cdot f}$ from page 170. (The coefficient of friction for dry concrete is 0.81.) Round all values to the nearest unit. See margin.

Skid Distance on a Dry, Concrete Road		
Skid distance d (ft)	Speed s (mi/hr)	(d, s)
1	5	(1, 5)
7	13	(7, 13)
33	28	(33, 28)
57	37	(57, 37)
95	?	?
129	?	?
154	?	?

18 a. Plot all the points in the table on a coordinate grid. Then draw a smooth curve through them to graph the equation $s = 5.5\sqrt{d \cdot f}$. See margin.

  b. Use your graph to estimate the speed of a car that leaves 19 ft skid marks on a road with a coefficient of friction of 0.81.
about 20 mi/hr

  c. Use your graph to estimate how far a car traveling at 55 mi/hr on a dry, concrete road will skid when the driver slams on the brakes. about 124 ft

  d. Use Labsheet 2A. Use the *Nomogram* to estimate how far a car traveling at 55 mi/hr on a dry, concrete road will skid. How does this estimate compare with your estimate from part (c)? About 125 ft; Sample Response: It is about the same.

19 Graphing Calculator Graph each equation. Tell whether the graph is *linear* or *nonlinear*. See margin.

   a. $y = x + 20$ **b.** $y = \sqrt{x}$ **c.** $y = 1 + \sqrt{x}$

HOMEWORK EXERCISES ▶ See Exs. 21–34 on pp. 177–178.

Section 2
Key Concepts

Order of Operations (pp. 169–171)

The order of operations is a set of rules for evaluating an expression so that the expression has only one value.

First Perform all calculations inside grouping symbols. Grouping symbols include parentheses, fraction bars, and square root symbols.

Next Evaluate any powers.

Next Perform multiplications and divisions in order from left to right.

Then Perform additions and subtractions in order from left to right.

Example $2\sqrt{6+3} = 2\sqrt{9} = 2(3) = 6$

> Do the addition inside the square root symbol first.

Graphing Equations (pp. 172–174)

The graph of an equation includes all possible solutions of the equation. Some graphs are linear. Some are nonlinear.

Examples

Linear graph

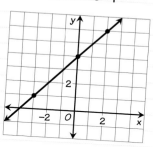

Nonlinear graph

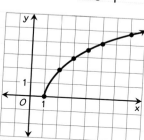

20 **Key Concepts Question** Use the equations graphed in the Examples above. For which equation is (10, 6) a solution? How do you know?

Key Terms

solution of the equation

linear

nonlinear

20. $y = 2\sqrt{x-1}$; Sample Response: Use the graph, or check by substituting 10 for x and 6 for y in the equation:
$6 \overset{?}{=} 2\sqrt{10-1}$
$6 \overset{?}{=} 2\sqrt{9}$
$6 \overset{?}{=} 2 \cdot 3$
$6 = 6$

Key Concepts

CLOSURE QUESTION

How might the order of operations be used in the process of graphing an equation?

> *Sample Response:* To graph the equation, you first find a table of values. The order of operations may be needed when evaluating the equation for different values of the first variable in the table.

ABSENT STUDENTS

For students who were absent for part or all of this section, the blackline Study Guide for Section 2 may be used to present the ideas, concepts and skills of Section 2.

Section ② Practice & Application Exercises

Evaluate each expression. Round decimals to the nearest hundredth.

1. $\dfrac{3 \cdot 10}{5 - 3}$ 15

2. $\dfrac{2(8 - 3)}{5}$ 2

3. $\dfrac{(-3)^2}{8 + 1 - 2(3)}$ 3

4. $9\sqrt{2 \cdot 3}$ 22.05

5. $-\sqrt{8 \cdot 2} + 7$ 3

6. $\dfrac{\sqrt{16 - 4}}{6}$ 0.58

Exercises 7–10 show the incorrect answers a student gave on a quiz. Describe the mistakes the student made. See margin.

7. $12 + 6 \div 3 = 6$

8. $3 \cdot 8 - 4 \cdot 5 = 100$

9. $\dfrac{3 + 5}{5} = 4$

10. $\sqrt{4 + 9} = 5$

Biology Scientists use the expression below to measure how circular a lake is. The closer the value of the expression is to 1, the more circular the lake. Use the expression for Exercises 11–13.

L = the length of the shoreline $\dfrac{L}{2\sqrt{\pi A}}$ *A* = the surface area of the lake

▲ Crater Lake lies in the "bowl" of an extinct volcano in Oregon.

13. b. Sample Response: No. The Lake of the Ozarks isn't even close to a circle. It is very long and skinny, so the ratio shouldn't be very close to 1.

11. The length of Crater Lake's shoreline is about 26 mi, and its surface area is about 21 mi². Evaluate the expression above for Crater Lake. about 1.6

12. a. Suppose a lake is perfectly circular and has a 2 mi diameter. Evaluate the expression for this lake. 1

b. Evaluate the expression for two other perfectly circular lakes. (You choose the diameters.) What pattern do you see? The value of the expression is always 1.

13. a. Evaluate the expression for the Lake of the Ozarks. The length of its shoreline is about 1350 mi, and its surface area is about 93 mi². about 39.5

b. You learned about the Lake of the Ozarks on page 63. Would you have expected a value close to 1 for this lake? Explain.

Evaluate each expression when *b* = 5 and *c* = –2. Round decimal answers to the nearest hundredth.

14. $3\sqrt{b + c}$ 5.20

15. $\dfrac{8b + 6}{c}$ –23

16. $\dfrac{c^3}{bc}$ 0.8

17. $\dfrac{b^2 + 8c}{9bc}$ –0.1

18. $\dfrac{30b}{5 \cdot 3} - c$ 12

19. $\dfrac{\sqrt{b^2 \cdot 36}}{c^2}$ 7.5

20. Challenge Write a numerical expression that equals 5. Your expression should include a fraction bar, a $\sqrt{}$ symbol, and at least three different numerical operations.

21. History The article below first appeared in a November 1896 issue of *Scientific American*.

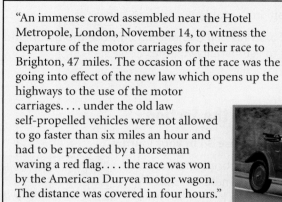

"An immense crowd assembled near the Hotel Metropole, London, November 14, to witness the departure of the motor carriages for their race to Brighton, 47 miles. The occasion of the race was the going into effect of the new law which opens up the highways to the use of the motor carriages. . . . under the old law self-propelled vehicles were not allowed to go faster than six miles an hour and had to be preceded by a horseman waving a red flag. . . . the race was won by the American Duryea motor wagon. The distance was covered in four hours."

◄ The annual race from London to Brighton is a test of endurance, not speed. Most of the cars were built before 1918.

a. Find the average speed of the winning car. Write an equation for the distance *d* it could travel in *h* hours at this speed.
   11.75 mi/hr; $d = 11.75h$
b. According to the article, what was the speed limit before the new law went into effect? Write an equation for the distance *d* a vehicle could travel in *h* hours at this speed.
   6 mi/hr; $d = 6h$
c. Graph the equations from parts (a) and (b) on the same pair of axes. Use the graph to estimate how long it would take to finish the race if you traveled at the old speed limit. **See margin.**

Graph each equation. 22–27. See margin.

22. $y = 2x - 3$　　**23.** $y = -3x$　　**24.** $y = -3x + 2$

25. $y = 4$　　**26.** $y = 90 + x$　　**27.** $y = 100 - x$

28. For which equations in Exercises 22–27 is (5, 95) a solution?
   $y = 90 + x$ and $y = 100 - x$

29. For which equation in Exercises 22–27 is (2.5, 4) a solution?
   $y = 4$

 Graphing Calculator **Graph each equation. Tell whether the graph is *linear* or *nonlinear*.** 30–32. See margin.

30. $y = x + \sqrt{5}$　　**31.** $y = 2\sqrt{x}$　　**32.** $y = 0.5x^2$

Section 2　Equations and Graphs　177

20. Sample Response:
$$\frac{\sqrt{100}}{6 - 4(-2 + 3)}$$

21. c.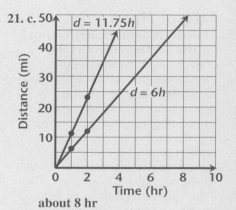

about 8 hr

22.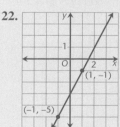

23.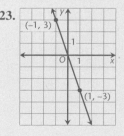

24–27. and 30–32. See Additional Answers beginning on page A1.

Practice & Applications

33. a.

Radius r (cm)	Volume V (cm³)
1	4
2	34
3	113
5	524
10	4189
20	33,510

33. b., 34. a. See Additional Answers beginning on page A1.

178

Radius r (cm)	Volume V (cm³)
1	?
2	?
3	?
5	?
10	?
20	?

Journal

Exercise 34 checks that you can use and interpret formulas and graphs.

34. c. Answers may vary. Sample Response: I would use the nomogram. You can quickly read the speed estimate.

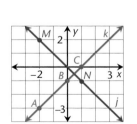

---

33. Geometry Connection A table, an equation, and a graph can all model the relationship between the radius r of a sphere and the volume V.

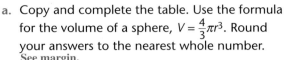

radius

sphere

a. Copy and complete the table. Use the formula for the volume of a sphere, $V = \frac{4}{3}\pi r^3$. Round your answers to the nearest whole number. See margin.

b. Graph the data in the table. Is the graph *linear* or *nonlinear*? See margin.

c. The radius of a tennis ball is about 6.5 cm. Use the graph and the equation to estimate its volume. **about 1150 cm³**

Reflecting on the Section

Write your response to Exercise 34 in your journal.

34. In this section, you used both a formula and a nomogram to estimate the speed of a car based on skid mark length. Another formula you can use is $s = 2\sqrt{5d}$. This formula does not include friction as a variable.

a. Copy and complete the table using the formula $s = 2\sqrt{5d}$ to estimate the speed s for each skid length d. See margin.

b. **Use Labsheet 2A.** For what road conditions does the formula $s = 2\sqrt{5d}$ give a good estimate of a car's speed? **dry brick or wet concrete**

c. If you want to quickly estimate a car's speed based on skid length, which of the methods would you use? Why?

Length of skid (ft)	Approximate speed of car (mi/hr)
1	$2\sqrt{5(1)} \approx 4.5$
5	?
15	?
35	?
55	?
75	?
100	?
150	?

Spiral Review

Estimate each value. (Module 3, p. 163)

35. $\sqrt{8}$
about 2.8

36. $\sqrt{11}$
about 3.3

37. $\sqrt{15}$
about 3.9

38. $\sqrt{0.144}$
about 0.4

39. Use the coordinate plane shown. List the ordered pairs for the points labeled on line j and line k. (Module 1, p. 51)
$A(-2, -3), B(0, -1), C(1, 0), M(-2, 2), N(1, -1)$

For each rate, write a unit rate (Module 1, p. 19)

40. $1.69 for 12 oz
$0.14/oz

41. 5.2 mi in 18 hr
0.29 mi/hr

42. $280 for 3.75 hr
$74.67/hr

Section 2

Extra Skill Practice

You will need: • *graph paper (Exs. 10–15 and 18–20)*

Evaluate each expression. Round decimal answers to the nearest hundredth.

1. $\dfrac{8 \cdot 3}{5 + 9 - 2(4)}$ 4

2. $8 + 6\sqrt{7 \cdot 4}$ 39.75

3. $\dfrac{\sqrt{13} + 5}{9}$ 0.47

4. $(5 + 3)\sqrt{4(12)}$ 55.43

5. $\dfrac{37 + 2(-5)}{3^3}$ 1

6. $\sqrt{\dfrac{7}{11 - 3}}$ 0.94

Evaluate each expression for $f = -3$ and $g = 4$. Round decimal answers to the nearest hundredth.

7. $\dfrac{2 - 6f}{g}$ 5

8. $\dfrac{\sqrt{f^2 - 2g}}{g - f}$ $\frac{1}{7}$ or 0.14

9. $\dfrac{8 + g}{-2f}$ −6

Graph each equation. 10–15. See margin.

10. $y = 4x$

11. $y = 2x + 6$

12. $y = -2x + 12$

13. $y = 3x - 8$

14. $y = x - 9$

15. $y = 0.5x + 2$

16. For which equations in Exercises 10–15 is (7, −2) a solution?
$y = -2x + 12;\ y = x - 9$

17. For which equations in Exercises 10–15 is (4, 4) a solution?
$y = -2x + 12;\ y = 3x - 8;\ y = 0.5x + 2$

Graph each equation. Tell whether the graph is *linear* or *nonlinear*. 18–20. See margin.

18. $y = \sqrt{4x}$

19. $y = x^3 - 1$

20. $y = 1.5x + 2.5$

Standardized Testing Multiple Choice

1. Evaluate $\dfrac{\sqrt{7 + 2 \cdot 3^2}}{3 + 6 \div 3}$. A

   Ⓐ 1   Ⓑ 3   Ⓒ 9   Ⓓ 2.6

2. Which point lies on the graph of $y = 3x - 2$? C

   Ⓐ (0, 2)   Ⓑ (5, 17)   Ⓒ (6, 16)   Ⓓ (4, 2)

3. Which ordered pair is *not* a solution of $y = 3 - 8x$? B

   Ⓐ (0, 3)   Ⓑ (3, 21)   Ⓒ (−1, 11)   Ⓓ (−3, 27)

Extra Skill Practice

TEACHER NOTES
For each Exploration, the corresponding Extra Skills Practice Exercises are noted.

Exploration 1: Exs. 1–9
Exploration 2: Exs. 10–20

EXTRA HELP
Teacher's Resource Book
• Practice and Applications
• Study Guide

Technology Resources
• @Home Tutor
• Test Generator

ASSESSMENT
• Section 2 Quick Quiz
• Test Generator

10.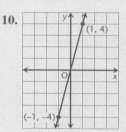

11.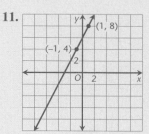

12–15. and 18–20. See Additional Answers beginning on page A1.

179

Section ③ Slope and Equations

BIG foot

Setting the Stage

The Story So Far…

Jim, Nageela, and Officers Ferrel Yellow Robe and Charlotte Lopez search for the missing driver of an abandoned car. When Jim finds some footprints, the officers think they can make some deductions about the person who left them.

"Do you think these are the driver's footprints?" Nageela asked.

"They must be," said Ferrel. "Otherwise, the rain would have washed them away. Now we can tell how tall the driver is."

"How will you do that?" asked Jim. "All I can tell is which way the tracks are going."

"It's all right here in the sand," said Charlotte. "All you have to do is look. By the looks of the stride, this person could cover quite a bit of ground if he or she was in a hurry. If he got to the top of the canyon, he'd be back to the main road easily by now."

Think About It

1 How do you think a person's height can be determined by examining his or her footprints?

2 What can you tell about the person who made the footprints in the photo on this page? Explain your thinking.

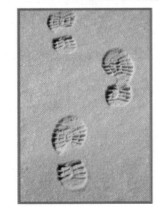

 180 **Module 3** The Mystery of Blacktail Canyon

Finding *SLOPE*

SET UP *Work with a partner.*

▶ In this exploration, you will use graphs to explore rates. The mathematics you will learn will help you find the height of the missing driver in Exploration 2.

3 Look back at the story on page 180. What does Charlotte mean by the word *stride*? How does your stride affect the distance you can cover in a given amount of time?

4 Discussion The red and blue lines on the coordinate plane below show distances two different people can walk over time. You and your partner should each choose one of the lines.

a. Work on your own. Choose four different travel times. For each time, find the distance traveled and calculate the walking rate. Record your results in a table like the one shown. **See margin.**

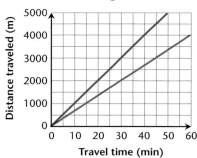

Walking Distances

Time (min)	Distance (m)	Rate (m/min)
?	?	?
?	?	?
?	?	?
?	?	?

b. Compare your tables. Which person is walking at a faster rate? **the person represented by the blue line**
c. How do the graphs show who is walking at a faster rate? **The graph of the faster rate is steeper.**
d. Suppose the missing driver in *The Mystery of Blacktail Canyon* has a faster walking rate than the rates you found. How would the graph of the driver's distance walked over time compare with the graphs shown? **It would be steeper. (It would start at the origin and be above the other graphs.)**

GOAL

LEARN HOW TO...
◆ find the slope of a line
◆ use equations and graphs to model situations

AS YOU...
◆ compare walking rates

KEY TERMS
◆ slope
◆ rise
◆ run

3. Sample Response: Stride is the distance between a person's footprints when he or she walks; It takes everyone about the same amount of time to complete one stride, but the length of the stride varies depending on the length of a person's legs and whether they are walking or running. The length of a stride determines how quickly a person can cover a distance.

Exploration 1

DIFFERENTIATED INSTRUCTION
For students who have difficulty remembering which coordinates are used to calculate the rise and which are used to calculate the run, you might demonstrate using a piece of yarn or string and a coordinate grid. Visual learners will benefit from seeing the yarn "run" along the horizontal axis (*x*-axis) as you stretch the yarn to form a line. Slowly rotate the line created by the yarn. They will see that the line will "rise" along the vertical axis (*y*-axis). Ask students what coordinate the first number in an ordered pair represents. (*the x-coordinate*) Is that used to find the rise or the run? (*the run*) Use several examples of ordered pairs to practice identifying which coordinates are used to find the rise and which are used to find the run.

If needed, the following example may be done before students complete **Checkpoint 6** on p. 182.

CLASSROOM EXAMPLE
Find the slope of the line in the graph below.

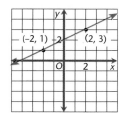

Answer: Slope $= \dfrac{\text{rise}}{\text{run}}$

$= \dfrac{3-1}{2-(-2)}$

$= \dfrac{2}{4} = \dfrac{1}{2}$

The slope is $\frac{1}{2}$ or 0.5.

4. a. See Additional Answers beginning on page A1.

181

Exploration 1 *continued*

DEVELOPING MATH CONCEPTS

Question 5 Students will notice that as long as the points chosen are on the line, it won't matter which ones you use to find the slope. For **part (c)**, ask students to use the coordinates in the example, subtract 4 from 1 and subtract 5 from 3. ($1 - 4 = -3; 3 - 5 = -2$)

Ask, "How does the fraction $\frac{-3}{-2}$ compare to the fraction $\frac{3}{2}$?" (*They are the same since they both equal 1.5.*) Ask students what the fraction would look like if you performed the subtraction of the rise in a different order than the subtraction of the run. (*either $\frac{-3}{2}$ or $\frac{3}{-2}$*) Ask how this fraction compares with either of the other slopes found. (*They are not equal since the slope is positive and the last fraction calculated is negative.*) Lead students to recognize the order in which the coordinates are subtracted is not important as long as the same order is used in calculating both the rise and the run.

DIFFERENTIATED INSTRUCTION

Visual learners might benefit from an illustration to model slope. A right triangle can be formed by using the line as the hypotenuse and two points on the line as vertices. The slope is identified by counting the intervals of the rise and run, writing the fraction, and simplifying.

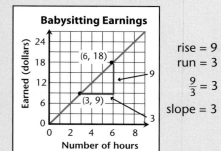

Babysitting Earnings

rise = 9
run = 3
$\frac{9}{3} = 3$
slope = 3

---

5. a., b. No; Sample Response: We tried several different pairs of points and always got the same answer.

c. Sample Response: If you don't always subtract the vertical and horizontal coordinates in the same order, it will change the sign of the slope.

✔ **QUESTION 6**

...checks that you can find the slope of a line.

7. slope of blue line = 100
slope of the red line = $66\frac{2}{3} \approx 66.7$
The slopes are the same as the walking rates.

▶ **Finding Slope** The **slope** of a line is a ratio that measures the line's steepness.

EXAMPLE

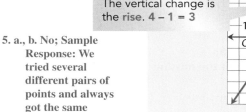

The horizontal change is the run. $5 - 3 = 2$

The vertical change is the rise. $4 - 1 = 3$

$\text{Slope} = \frac{\text{rise}}{\text{run}}$

$\text{Slope} = \frac{3}{2}$

The slope is $\frac{3}{2}$ or 1.5.

5 Try This as a Class

a. Use a different pair of points to find the slope of the line in the Example.

b. Does it matter which points you choose? Explain.

c. Why is the order in which you subtract one set of coordinates from the other set of coordinates important?

6 ✔ **CHECKPOINT** Find the slope of each line.

a. 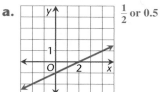 $\frac{1}{2}$ or 0.5

b. 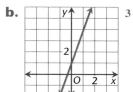 3

7 Look back at the graph in Question 4. Find the slope of each line. How does the slope compare with the person's walking rate?

▶ **Writing an Equation** You can use an equation to model the distance a person walking at a steady rate can cover in a given amount of time.

$$\text{Distance} = \text{rate} \cdot \text{time}$$
$$d = rt$$

8 Use the rates you found in Question 4. Write an equation that can be used to estimate the distance d each person can walk in t minutes. How is the slope you found in Question 7 related to your equation? $d = 100t; d = 66\frac{2}{3}t; \text{slope} = r$

▶ The slope of a line often gives you information about a situation. Sometimes you can use that information to write an equation.

EXAMPLE

Use the graph to find the daily rate Crownpoint Car Rental charges. Then write an equation for the total cost of renting a car for a given number of days.

SAMPLE RESPONSE

First Find the daily rate. To find the daily rate, find the slope of the line. The slope is 20, so the rate is $20 per day.

$$\text{Slope} = \frac{\text{rise}}{\text{run}}$$

$$= \frac{80 - 40}{4 - 2}$$

$$= 20$$

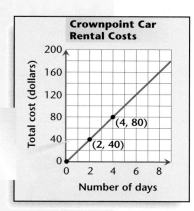

Crownpoint Car Rental Costs

y-axis: Total cost (dollars) 0, 40, 80, 120, 160, 200
x-axis: Number of days 0, 2, 4, 6, 8
Points: (4, 80), (2, 40)

Next Write an equation. Let C = total cost and d = the number of days.

$$\text{Total cost} = \text{daily rate} \cdot \text{number of days}$$

$$C = 20d$$

Then Check your work. Choose at least two points from the graph. Check that their coordinates are solutions of the equation $C = 20d$.

Choose (3, 60). $60 = 20(3)$ ✔

Choose (4, 80). $80 = 20(4)$ ✔

9 **Try This as a Class** How does the graph in the Example show what the units of the daily rate are?

10 **Try This as a Class** Suppose Crownpoint Car Rental's rate becomes $25 per day.

  a. How will the graph of rental costs be different? Since the slope will be greater, the line will be steeper.

  b. How will the equation be different? $C = 25d$

11 ✔ **CHECKPOINT** Write an equation for the graph shown at the right. Give an example of a problem you can use your equation to solve. $C = 3g$; Sample Response: What is the cost of 10 gal of gasoline at $3 per gallon?

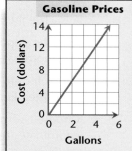

Gasoline Prices

y-axis: Cost (dollars) 0, 4, 8, 12, 14
x-axis: Gallons 0, 2, 4, 6

9. Sample Response: The rise is given in dollars and the run in days, so $\frac{\text{rise}}{\text{run}} = \frac{\text{dollars}}{\text{days}}$.

✔ **QUESTION 11**

...checks that you can apply the idea of slope to model a situation with an equation.

HOMEWORK EXERCISES ▶ See Exs. 1–7 on pp. 187–188

TEACHING NOTES

Exploration 1 introduces the concept of slope. During this exploration students use only basic concepts of slope in preparation for a more extensive study of slope and the y-intercept in Module 4.

If needed, the following example may be done before students complete **Checkpoint 11**.

CLASSROOM EXAMPLE

The graph below shows the charges for renting movies at Rent-a-Video. Use the graph to find the daily rate. Then write an equation for the cost of renting a video for a given number of days.

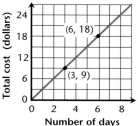

Rent-a-Video Costs

y-axis: Total cost (dollars) 0, 6, 12, 18, 24
x-axis: Number of days 0, 2, 4, 6, 8
Points: (6, 18), (3, 9)

Answer: First find the rate for renting a video one day. To find the rate for renting a video one day, find the slope of the line.

$$\text{Slope} = \frac{\text{rise}}{\text{run}}$$

$$= \frac{18 - 9}{6 - 3}$$

$$= \frac{9}{3}$$

$$= 3$$

The slope is 3, so the rate is $3 per day.

Next write an equation. Let C = cost and d = number of days.

$$\text{Cost} = \text{daily rate} \times \text{days}$$

$$C = 3d$$

Then check your work. Choose at least two points from the graph. Check that their coordinates are solutions of the equation $C = 3d$.

Choose (2, 6) $6 = 3(2)$ ✔

Choose (5, 15) $15 = 3(5)$ ✔

183

Exploration 2

COMMON ERROR

Question 12 Remind students that in drawing a fitted line, there should be approximately the same number of points on one side of the line as on the other. Check that they do not try to connect each point on the graph.

TEACHING NOTES

Question 14 Be aware that the equations most students write will not work. **This is intentional.** Students will learn how to make adjustments and write an equation for the fitted line in **Question 15**. Typically, the adjustment is made by adding the *y*-intercept. However, in this situation, the *y*-intercept does not have a meaningful interpretation—it does not make sense to say that the foot of a person 0 cm tall will be over 100 cm long. The *y*-intercept and the slope intercept form of a linear equation will be explored in Module 4 in contexts where the *y*-intercept has meaning. It is best not to introduce it here.

TECHNOLOGY NOTE

For a related technology activity, see the *Technology Book*.

12. See Additional Answers beginning on page A1.

14. Sample Responses:

a. slope $= \dfrac{180 - 170}{31 - 27}$

$= \dfrac{10}{4} = 2.5$

b. $h = 2.5f$

c. (27, 170); 2.5 · 27
$= 67.5 \neq 170$
(31, 180); 2.5 · 31
$= 77.5 \neq 180$
The equation is not correct.

184

Exploration 2

Using Equ+ati=ons

SET UP *Work in a group of four. You will need:* • *Labsheet 3A* • *meter stick* • *masking tape* • *marker* • *graph paper*

▶ In *The Mystery of Blacktail Canyon,* **Officer Yellow Robe says that he can use the footprints Jim found to estimate the height of the missing driver. In this Exploration, you will use an equation to estimate heights from foot lengths.** Answers for Questions 12–16 will vary. Check students' work. Sample responses from one group of students are provided. **Use Labsheet 3A for Questions 12–14.**

12 Follow the directions on the labsheet for collecting and recording data in the *Foot Length and Height Table.* You will use the data to make a scatter plot and a fitted line. See margin.

13 The footprint of the missing driver in *The Mystery of Blacktail Canyon* is 29 cm long. Use your fitted line to predict the person's height. Sample Response: 175 cm

14 Suppose you guess that an equation for your fitted line follows the pattern below.

Height = slope • foot length

a. Find the slope of your fitted line. (You may need to estimate the coordinates of the points you use to find the slope.)

b. Let *f* = foot length and let *h* = height. Write an equation for your fitted line, based on the pattern described above.

c. Choose two points on your fitted line to see whether their coordinates make the equation true. Do you think your equation is correct? Explain.

184

▶ In Question 14(c), you probably found that the equation in part (b) did not work for your fitted line. In Question 15, you will explore how to adjust the pattern to write an equation for your fitted line.

15 a. Copy and complete the table below. As shown, use two different methods to predict height. *See margin.*

Method 1: Use your fitted line to make a prediction.

Method 2: Use your equation from Question 14 to make a prediction.

Then Find the difference between the two predictions.

Foot length (cm)	Height (cm) (Fitted line prediction)	Height (cm) (Equation prediction)	Difference
24 cm	?	?	?
26 cm	?	?	?
28 cm	?	?	?
30 cm	?	?	?

b. How do your predictions compare?

c. Discussion How would you revise the equation you wrote in Question 14? Explain your thinking.

16 Use your revised equation from Question 15 to predict the height of the missing driver. Compare your prediction with the one you made in Question 13.

17 ✔ CHECKPOINT Use the scatter plot.

a. Which equation can you use to predict a person's height h if you know his or her lower arm length a: $h = 4.5a$ or $h = 4.5a - 35$? Explain your choice.

b. Use the equation you chose to predict the height of someone whose lower arm length is 45 cm.
Sample Response: 172.5 cm

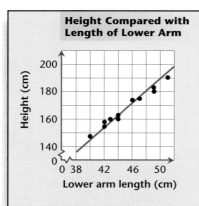

Height Compared with Length of Lower Arm

Height (cm) — vertical axis: 140, 160, 180, 200
Lower arm length (cm) — horizontal axis: 0, 38, 42, 46, 50

HOMEWORK EXERCISES ▶ See Exs. 8–14 on pp. 188–189.

15. b. The equation prediction is always about 102 less than the fitted line prediction.
c. Since the fitted line prediction is always about 102 more than the equation prediction, I would add 102 to the equation.
$h = 2.5f + 102$

16. Sample Response: $2.5 \cdot 29 + 102 = 174.5$; This is very close to the prediction I made in Question 13.

✔ QUESTION 17

...checks that you can use an equation of a fitted line to make predictions.

17. a. $h = 4.5a - 35$; Sample Response: I tested the coordinates of a point on the fitted line in both equations. I choose the point (50, 190). When the arm length is 50 cm, the equation $h = 4.5a - 35$ gives a height of 190 cm.

If needed, the following example may be done before students complete **Checkpoint 17**.

CLASSROOM EXAMPLE

The graph shows the number of free throws and the number of 3-point shots made by a school basketball team during 12 games. An equation of the fitted line shown is $s = 0.76f - 1.27$, where s = the number of 3-point shots made and f = the number of free throws made. Use the graph and the equation to predict how many 3-point shots will be made if 12 free throws are made.

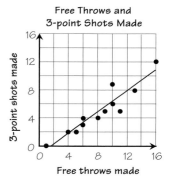

Free Throws and 3-point Shots Made

3-point shots made — vertical axis: 0, 4, 8, 12, 16
Free throws made — horizontal axis: O, 4, 8, 12, 16

Answer: Substitute 12 for f in the equation.

$s = 0.76(12) - 1.27$
$= 9.12 - 1.27$
$= 7.85$

About 8 3-point shots will be made if 12 free throws are made.

Checkpoint 17 The explanation students give for their choice is the most important part of their response as it demonstrates their understanding of the way in which an equation relates to a fitted line.

15. a. See Additional Answers beginning on page A1.

Key Concepts

CLOSURE QUESTION

Describe how to use a line to make predictions when given a set of data involving two variables.

Sample Response: Group the data in ordered pairs and graph them on a scatter plot. Draw a fitted line on the plot. You can then use the line to predict the value of one variable when given the other, or you can find an equation of the line and then use the equation to make predictions.

ABSENT STUDENTS

For students who were absent for part or all of this section, the blackline Study Guide for Section 3 may be used to present the ideas, concepts and skills of Section 3.

Section **3**

Key Terms

slope

rise

run

Key Concepts

Slope (pp. 181–183)

The slope of a line is the ratio of its rise to its run. Sometimes the slope of a line gives you information about an everyday situation.

Example Water is added to a tub at a steady rate. The graph shows the amount of water in the tub over time. The slope of the line is a rate.

$$\text{Slope} = \frac{\text{rise}}{\text{run}} = \frac{6-2}{3-1} = \frac{4}{2} = 2$$

Water is added to the tub at a rate of 2 gal/min.

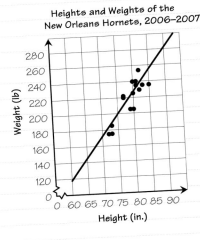

Filling a Tub

Equations for Predictions (pp. 184–185)

You can use an equation of a fitted line to make predictions.

Example An equation of the fitted line shown is

$$w = 5.5h - 213,$$

where w = weight in pounds, and h = height in inches. You can predict that a 78 in. tall player will weigh about 216 lb.

$$w = 5.5(78) - 213$$

$$w \approx 216$$

Heights and Weights of the New Orleans Hornets, 2006–2007

18 Key Concepts Question Explain how you can check to make sure that the equation for the fitted line in the second Example is the correct equation. **Sample Response: Choose points on the fitted line to get values to substitute into the equation to check it.**

 Module 3 The Mystery of Blacktail Canyon

Section ③

Practice & Application Exercises

YOU WILL NEED

For Exs. 6(d), 12:
♦ graph paper

Find the slope of each line.

1.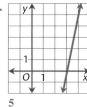

5

2.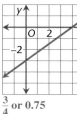

$\frac{3}{4}$ or 0.75

3.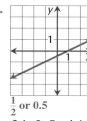

$\frac{1}{2}$ or 0.5

4. Darryl says that the slope of the line in Exercise 3 is 2. Explain what he did wrong. **Sample Response: He calculated the ratio of the run to rise instead of the rise to the run.**

5. Race Walking The first official world record in the 20 km race walk was set in 1918 by Niels Petersen of Denmark. In 1994, Bernardo Segura of Mexico set a new world record. The graph shows the average walking rates of these two athletes.

a. Which line shows Segura's walking rate? Explain.

b. Find each athlete's average rate.

c. Write equations you can use to find the average distance each athlete walks in a given amount of time. **See margin.**

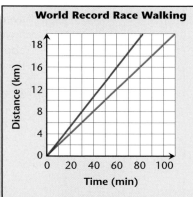

World Record Race Walking

6. The graph below models the relationship between the number of hours Sarah Kane works and the amount she gets paid.

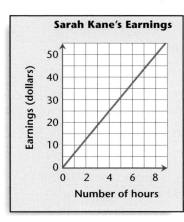

Sarah Kane's Earnings

a. How much does Sarah get paid per hour? **$6.25/hr**

b. Write an equation for the amount she makes based on the number of hours she works.

c. Suppose Sarah gets an 8% raise in her hourly wage. Write a new equation to model the amount she makes.

d. Graph the new equation. Find the slope of the graph. **See margin.**

5. a. the blue line; Sample Response: Since the blue line is steeper than the red line, it represents a faster walking rate.

5. b. Segura's walking rate = 16 km/hr or about 0.27 km/min; Petersen's walking rate = 12 km/hr or 0.2 km/min

6. b. $e = 6.25h$ where e = the amount earned and h = the hours worked

c. $e = 6.75h$ where e = the amount earned and h = the hours worked

---

Practice & Applications

SUGGESTED ASSIGNMENTS

Core Course
Day 1: Exs. 1–4, 15–22
Day 2: Exs. 5, 6, 23–26
Day 3: Exs. 8–14

Extended Course
Day 1: Exs. 1–4, 15–22
Day 2: Exs. 6, 7, 23–26
Day 3: Exs. 8–14

Note: Extended Course assignments can be used to differentiate within the regular classroom. In classrooms where students are grouped homogeneously, the material might be covered in fewer days. In this case assignments may be combined.

ADDITIONAL PRACTICE

See the *Teacher's Resource Book* for additional practice and application exercises for this section.

EXERCISE NOTES

Exercises 5 and 6 Remind students that the slope of a line can be interpreted as a rate. This concept may not be as obvious in **Exercise 6,** where a wage is the rate at which a person is paid, measured in dollars per hour.

5. c., 6. d. See Additional Answers beginning on page A1.

Practice & Applications

EXERCISE NOTES

Exercises 8–10 Lead students to recognize that the lines on the graph appear to be parallel. Although the equation $y = mx + b$ is not introduced until Module 4, you can ask students to find similarities in the equations and resulting parallel lines. You might challenge some of your students to try plotting the points of another similar equation. Ask, "What needs to remain the same as the other equations?" (*0.75*) "What can change?" (*+10, −10*) "Try writing and plotting an equation that makes a line parallel to lines *A, B,* and *C.*" Check to make sure the lines are parallel and that students have written an appropriate equation.

12. a.

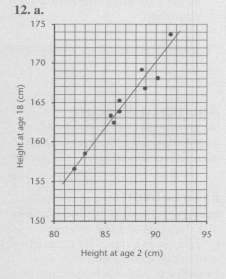

11. about 1.9; Sample Response: I divided the height of each woman at age 18 by her height at age 2. All of the answers rounded to 1.9, so the average is about 1.9.

12. b. See 12(a) for fitted line; slope
$$= \frac{172 - 155}{91 - 81} = \frac{17}{10}$$
or 1.7

c. $h = 1.7t$

e. $h = 1.7t + 17.3$; Since the fitted line prediction is always about 17.3 more than the equation prediction, I would revise the equation in part (c) by adding 17.3 to it.

7. Challenge Find the slope of a line that passes through the points (−2, 4) and (3, 4). 0

Match each equation with one of the lines. Explain your thinking.

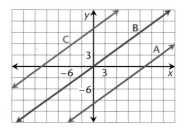

8. $y = 0.75x$ B; slope = 0.75, (0, 0) is on the line.

9. $y = 0.75x - 10$ A; slope = 0.75, (0, −10) is on the line.

10. $y = 0.75x + 10$ C; slope = 0.75, (0, 10) is on the line.

Human Development In Module 1, you used a rule of thumb that said your adult height will be twice your height at age 2. In Exercises 11–13, you will re-examine that claim. Use the data in the table for the exercises.

11. **Interpreting Data** On average, the height of a woman at age 18 is about how many times her height at age 2?

12. a. Use the data to make a scatter plot. Use the horizontal axis for *t*, the height at age 2, and the vertical axis for *h*, the height at age 18. **See margin.**

   b. Draw a fitted line. Then find its slope.

Heights of 10 Females (in centimeters)	
Height at age 2 (*t*)	Height at age 18 (*h*)
82.0	156.5
83.0	158.4
85.6	163.3
85.9	162.4
86.4	163.8
86.4	165.2
88.6	169.2
88.9	166.8
90.2	168.1
91.4	173.7

   c. Suppose you guess that an equation for your fitted line follows this pattern:

   height at age 18 = slope • height at age 2.

   Write an equation for your fitted line based on this pattern.

   d. As you did in Exploration 2, use two different methods to predict values for *h*. **See margin.**

   e. How would you revise the equation you wrote in part (c)? Explain your thinking.

13. Use your equation from Exercise 12(e) to predict the height of an 18-year-old woman who was 84 cm tall at age 2. 160.1 cm

12. d. See Additional Answers beginning on page A1.

Reflecting ◀▶ on the Section

Be prepared to discuss your response to Exercise 14 in class.

14. In Exploration 2 you predicted height from foot length using data collected from a sample of people. Do you think the sample will enable you to reasonably predict the height of anyone in the world from the person's foot length? Explain. No; Sample Response: The sample is too small and not representative. To get accurate results, data should be collected separately for adults and children. It should also be separated by gender and probably ethnicity. The sample size for each group should be greater.

Discussion

Exercise 14 checks that you understand how reasonable it is to make a prediction from a scatter plot.

Spiral ◀▶ Review

Evaluate each expression. (Module 3, p. 185)

15. $\dfrac{8(-4)}{-7+4}$ $10\frac{2}{3}$

16. $3\sqrt{8-(-8)}$ 12

17. $\dfrac{\sqrt{12\cdot 3}}{8}$ $\frac{3}{4}$

18. $\dfrac{(-12)^2}{11+1}$ 12

19. Tell what inverse operation you would use to solve $\frac{x}{8}=17$. Then solve the equation. (Module 1, p. 42) multiply by 8; $x=136$

Use a proportion to find each percent. (Module 2, p. 132)

20. 15% of 90 13.5

21. 22.5% of 118 26.55

22. 0.4% of 17 0.068

Use the 4-step problem solving approach for Exercises 23 and 24. (Module 1, p. 67)

23. To prepare for an upcoming sale, a grocery clerk plans to stack boxes for a display. The boxes will form a pyramid. The bottom row of boxes will hold 10 boxes. Each row will hold one box fewer than the row below. How many boxes will be in the pyramid? 55 boxes

24. You are helping to plan your school's sports banquet. There are two types of tables available. The rectangular tables seat 8 people and the round tables seat 6 people. Find a possible combination of tables to seat exactly 120 people given that you want to use some rectangular tables and some round tables.

24. Possible answers: 3 round and 16 rectangular, 6 round and 12 rectangular, 9 round and 8 rectangular, 12 round and 4 rectangular

Name the units in each rate. Then write a unit rate. (Module 1, p. 9)

25. $30 for 6 pairs of socks dollars and pairs of socks; $5/pair

26. $3.24 for 12 oranges dollars and oranges; $0.27/orange

Reflecting on the Section
Exercise 14 explores the question of whether the sample studied is representative of the population of interest. Make sure your students use what they know about samples and scatter plots during the class discussion. Ask, "What would we need to do to make this sample more representative of the world's population?" (*Sample responses may include adding data from other age groups or countries.*) "What factors might influence the result of your scatter plot?" (*Our feet and/or bodies may still be growing.*) For what population would your data be a good sample? (*Responses might include: middle school students or all eighth-graders.*)

Extra Skill Practice

Standardized Testing:

Answers will vary. Check students' work.

Sample Response: Two people hiked up a trail to a mountain lake, a distance of 8 km. They both left the trailhead at the same time, the more experienced hiker averaging 1.5 km/hr and the other averaging $\frac{1}{3}$ km/hr. The faster hiker reached the lake in $5\frac{1}{3}$ hr. However, after hiking 12 hr, the novice hiker was only half way to the lake and decided to pitch camp and continue on in the morning.

vertical axis: distance from trailhead in kilometers

horizontal axis: time in hours

The red line represents the faster hiker, so it is steeper than the green line which represents the slower hiker.

Section ③
Extra Skill Practice

Find the slope of each line.

1.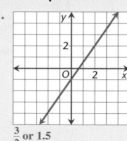
$\frac{3}{2}$ or 1.5

2.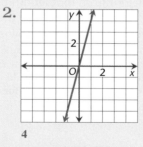
4

3.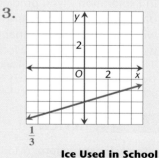
$\frac{1}{3}$

The scatter plot shows the number of pounds of ice used each day at a school lunch center based on the outdoor temperature. Use the scatter plot for Exercises 4–6.

Ice Used in School Lunch Center

4. Predict the amount of ice used if the temperature is 70°F. **about 128 lb**

5. Find the slope of the fitted line. **slope** $= \frac{160-110}{90-60} = \frac{5}{3}$

6. Let t = the temperature in degrees Fahrenheit. Let p = the number of pounds of ice used. Which equation can you use to predict the number of pounds of ice used if you know the outdoor temperature? **D**

  A. $p = \frac{5}{3}t$ B. $p = \frac{3}{5}t + 10$ C. $p = \frac{3}{5}t - 10$ D. $p = \frac{5}{3}t + 10$

Standardized Testing ◀▶ **Open-ended**

Make up a story that explains the graph below. Write a title and appropriate labels and scales on the graph. Be sure to explain how the situation shown by the red line is different from the situation shown by the green line. **See margin.**

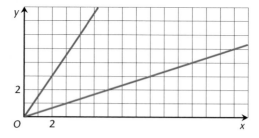

Mystery State

The Situation See the *Teacher's Resource Book* for a sample solution for this Extended Exploration.

Try the following puzzle. Is mystery or mathematics at work?

- ◆ Pick an integer between 1 and 10.
- ◆ Multiply your number by 6.
- ◆ Add 12.
- ◆ Divide by 3.
- ◆ Subtract 4.
- ◆ Divide by your original number.
- ◆ Add 4.
- ◆ Match the number with the corresponding letter of the alphabet (1 = A, 2 = B, *and so on*).
- ◆ Think of a state in the United States that begins with that letter.
- ◆ Look at the third letter of the name of the state. Think of a fruit that begins with that letter and grows in that state.
- ◆ Turn your book upside-down and look at the bottom of the page to complete the mystery.

The Problem

Explain why the mystery puzzle works. Then create a puzzle of your own and explain why it works.

Something to Think About

- ◆ How might examining a mystery puzzle with fewer steps help you?
- ◆ Does this puzzle work for any positive integer? Would it work for negative integers? decimals? fractions?

Present Your Results

Write your puzzle on a sheet of paper. Include the solution on the back. Explain why the puzzle above works, and why your mystery puzzle works.

You thought of oranges in Florida.

Extended Exploration

E² NOTES

Mathematical puzzles or "tricks" are engaging for students because they appear to be magical. It is the highly structured nature of mathematics that allows these tricks to work. If students feel intimidated by the complexity of the puzzle on this page as a model for creating their own puzzle, show them a simpler number trick. Remind them that theirs can be as complex or as simple as they wish to make it as long as it works. Also remind students that the puzzles they create don't have to involve states and fruits.

Using an E²: Suggestions for managing and evaluating an Extended Exploration are available in the *Teacher's Resource Book* for Modules 1 and 2. See also pages T44–T45 in the *Teacher's Edition*.

Section 4 Similar Figures and Constructions

ABOUT THE THEME

Before reading the *Setting the Stage*, ask your students to estimate the height of several things such as the classroom wall, the school, the flagpole, a tree, or a building that can be seen from the classroom. Ask how students made their estimates and what they could do to improve them. Then ask what they might do if accuracy was essential but there way no way of measuring the height directly. Allow students time to share some of their ideas before beginning this section. You can return to this question at the end of Exploration 1 to see if students have improved their strategies.

GETTING STARTED

Module 3 Section 4 *Warm-Up* assesses that students can solve proportions and identify perpendicular lines.

CLIFF DWELLERS

Setting the Stage

The Story So Far...

▶ The missing driver's tracks lead to a previously undiscovered cliff dwelling. Nageela wonders if her 40 m rope will reach the site. Charlotte Lopez has a method for estimating the cliff height.

She used her pocket knife to pry the ink cartridge out of the plastic body of the pen.

. . . Charlotte marked a spot on the ground, then paced off the distance to the foot of the cliff. Next, she had Jim stand between her marked spot and the cliff. Finally, she lay down with her head on the ground and sighted the top of Jim's head through the hollow pen.

"Take two steps back, Jim," she said.
"Good! Now, how tall are you?"

Drawing not to scale

Think About It

1 The diagram models the situation in the story selection. Which segment represents Jim**?** Which represents the cliff**?**
the shorter vertical segment; the longer vertical segment

2 What kind of triangles do you see in the diagram**?**
two right triangles

Exploration 1

Similar Figures
Similar Figures

Similar Figures

SET UP *You will need:* • *Labsheet 4A* • *centimeter ruler* • *protractor*

▶ As you will see in this exploration, Charlotte Lopez uses *similar* figures to estimate the cliff height. Two figures are **similar** if they have the same shape, but not necessarily the same size. The figures below are similar.

∠*P* and ∠*T* are *corresponding angles.*
Corresponding angles have the same measure.

$m\angle P = m\angle T$

> Read $m\angle T$ as "the measure of angle *T*."

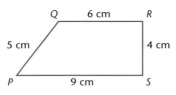

$\overline{PQ}$ and $\overline{TU}$ are *corresponding sides.* The lengths of **corresponding sides** are in proportion.

$$\frac{PQ}{TU} = \frac{QR}{UV}$$

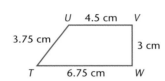

> Read $\overline{TU}$ as "segment *TU*." Read *TU* as "the length of segment *TU*."

3 a. Try This as a Class Name all pairs of corresponding angles and corresponding sides in the figures above.

b. Find the ratios $\frac{PQ}{TU}$, $\frac{QR}{UV}$, $\frac{RS}{VW}$, and $\frac{PS}{TW}$. What do you notice?

4 ✔ CHECKPOINT The figures below are similar. Copy and complete each statement.

a. $m\angle C = m\ \underline{\ ?\ }\ \angle G$

b. $\frac{BC}{FG} = \frac{?}{GH}\ CD$

c. $\frac{?}{AD} = \frac{EF}{?}\ \frac{AB}{AD} = \frac{EF}{EH}$

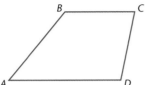

GOAL

LEARN HOW TO...
• tell whether triangles are similar
• make indirect measurements

AS YOU...
• estimate the height of a cliff

KEY TERMS
• similar
• corresponding angles
• corresponding sides

3. a. ∠*P*, ∠*T* $\overline{PQ}, \overline{TU}$
∠*Q*, ∠*U* $\overline{QR}, \overline{UV}$
∠*R*, ∠*V* $\overline{RS}, \overline{VW}$
∠*S*, ∠*W* $\overline{PS}, \overline{TW}$

b. $\frac{PQ}{TU} = \frac{5}{3.75} = \frac{4}{3}$,
$\frac{QR}{UV} = \frac{6}{4.5} = \frac{4}{3}$,
$\frac{RS}{VW} = \frac{4}{3}, \frac{PS}{TW}$
$= \frac{9}{6.75} = \frac{4}{3}$;
The ratios are all equal.

✔ QUESTION 4

...checks your understanding of the definition of similar figures.

Exploration 1

COMMON ERRORS
This exploration presents several new vocabulary terms to students. Some students may make errors simply due to insufficient attention to detail as they respond to questions. You may want your students to write in their journals the definitions of key terms and descriptions of the symbols used in this exploration.

TEACHING NOTES
Checkpoint Question 4
Students are asked to identify the corresponding elements of two similar figures. Make sure they understand that, for this question, they do not need to calculate the lengths of any sides or measures of any angles.

Exploration 1 *continued*

TEACHING NOTES

Question 7(d) Help students to use logical reasoning to explain why a protractor is not needed to determine similarity in these two triangles.

DIFFERENTIATED LEARNING

Question 7(d) Visual/tactile learners may benefit from using two of the similar triangles from a tangram set. By placing the smaller one over the larger one, they can identify a pair of congruent angles. Moving the smaller triangle from vertex to vertex on the larger triangle will reinforce the concept that all the corresponding angles are congruent. Students should recognize that, even though one triangle is smaller than the other, they are still similar. If tangrams are not available, similar triangles cut from tag board can be used.

DEVELOPING MATH CONCEPTS

Question 8 asks students to think about the test for similar triangles. Ask students why they can be certain that the third angles of any two triangles have the same measure if the two other pairs of angles are known to be congruent. (*The sum of the angle measures of all triangles is 180°.*) You might also ask what they know about the lengths of the sides of the triangles, if they know that two of the angles in each triangle have the same measure. (*The ratios of their corresponding side lengths are in proportion.*)

6., 8. See Additional Answers beginning on page A1.

194

---

5. B, C, and D; In each one, the corresponding angles are listed in the same order.

7. a. $m\angle ABC = m\angle ADE$
   b. $\angle BAC$ and $\angle DAE$ are the same angle, so $m\angle BAC = m\angle DAE$.
   c. $m\angle ACB = m\angle AED$; Sample Response: Since the sum of the measures of the angles of a triangle is 180°, if the measures of two angles of one triangle equal the measures of two angles of another triangle, then the third angles of the triangles must also have the same measures.
   d. $\triangle ABC \sim \triangle ADE$; Since two angles of $\triangle ABC$ have the same measures as two angles of $\triangle ADE$, the triangles are similar.

▶ **Naming Similar Figures** The symbol ~ means "is similar to." When you name similar figures, be sure to put their corresponding angles in the same order.

5 **Try this as a Class** The triangles at the right are similar. Which of the statements below are written correctly? Explain your thinking.

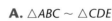

A. $\triangle ABC \sim \triangle CDE$

B. $\triangle ABC \sim \triangle EDC$

C. $\triangle BAC \sim \triangle DEC$

D. $\triangle ACB \sim \triangle ECD$

Symbols are used to show which angles have the same measure.

A vertex is a point where sides of a figure come together.

6 **Use Labsheet 4A.** You will use a protractor and a ruler to determine whether the *Two Triangles* are similar. See margin.

▶ **A Test for Similar Triangles** Two triangles are similar if two angles of one triangle have the same measures as two angles of the other triangle.

7 **Try This as a Class** The triangles from page 192 are shown below. The large triangle on the left can be divided into two smaller triangles as shown on the right.

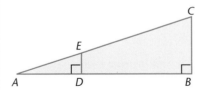 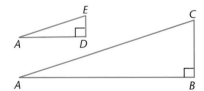

a. $\angle ABC$ and $\angle ADE$ are right angles. What does this tell you about their measures?

b. How do you know $\angle BAC$ and $\angle DAE$ have the same measure?

c. The sum of the measures of the angles of a triangle is 180°. Without using a protractor, what do you know about the measures of $\angle ACB$ and $\angle AED$? Explain.

d. Is $\triangle ABC \sim \triangle ADE$? How do you know?

8 **Discussion** Do you think the test for similar triangles would work for other figures? Explain. See margin.

▶

Indirect Measurement In *The Mystery of Blacktail Canyon*, Charlotte cannot directly measure the height of the cliff. She can use similar figures to make an indirect measurement.

EXAMPLE

To estimate the cliff height, Charlotte uses what she knows about similar triangles to write and solve a proportion.

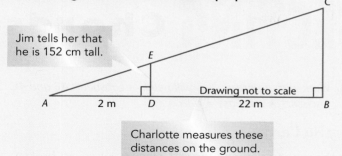

Jim tells her that he is 152 cm tall.

Drawing not to scale

A — 2 m — D — 22 m — B

Charlotte measures these distances on the ground.

Substitute known values. Let $h = BC$, the unknown cliff height.

$$\frac{AB}{AD} = \frac{BC}{DE}$$

$$\frac{24}{2} = \frac{h}{1.52}$$

Convert Jim's height from 152 cm to 1.52 m.

$$24(1.52) = 2h$$

Use cross products.

$$18.24 = h$$

The cliff dwellings are about 18 m above the canyon floor.

▶ **Try This as a Class** For Questions 9–11, use the Example.

9 Suppose you do not convert Jim's height to meters. What answer do you get? **1825 cm**

10 Can Charlotte use the proportion $\frac{DE}{BC} = \frac{DA}{BA}$ to find the cliff height? Explain.

11 In *The Mystery of Blacktail Canyon*, Nageela's climbing rope is 40 m long. She needs "as much going down as going up." Is her rope long enough to reach the cliff dwellings?

12 ✔ **CHECKPOINT** $\triangle RST \sim \triangle UVW.$
Tell which missing side length you can find. Then find it.
$UV;\ 6\frac{2}{3}$ in.

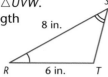

8 in.

R — 6 in. — T

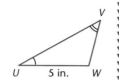

U — 5 in. — W

✔ **QUESTION 12**

...checks that you can use a proportion to find an unknown side length.

HOMEWORK EXERCISES ▶ See Exs. 1–14 on pp. 199–200.

10. Yes. As long as the numerators of the ratios are the lengths of corresponding sides and the denominators are the lengths of corresponding sides the ratios will be equal.

11. She needs about 36 m of rope, so her rope should be long enough.

TEACHING NOTES

Checkpoint Question 12 asks students to set up a proportion and solve for the unknown length. Before students complete the **Checkpoint**, you may want to review the use of equivalent fractions and cross products to solve for the unknown length using the classroom example below.

CLASSROOM EXAMPLE

Suppose a 100-m rope extends from the top of a cliff to the ground below and is supported by a tower part of the way down. If the cliff is 50 m high and the tower is 10 m high, use a proportion to find the length of the rope from the ground to the top of the tower.

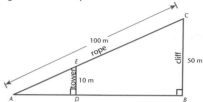

100 m rope

10 m

50 m cliff

Answer:

$$\frac{DE}{BC} = \frac{AE}{AC}$$

Substitute known values.
Let $l = AE$, the unknown length.

$$\frac{10}{50} = \frac{l}{100}$$

Equivalent Fractions	Cross Products
$\frac{10 \cdot 2}{50 \cdot 2} = \frac{l}{100}$	$10(100) = 50l$
$\frac{10 \cdot 2}{} = l$	$1000 = 50l$
$20 = l$	$\frac{1000}{50} = \frac{50l}{50}$
	$20 = l$

The length of the rope from the ground to the top of the tower is 20 m.

Exploration 2

TEACHING NOTES

Before beginning Exploration 2, give each student a "pottery" fragment (leftover or broken pottery pieces from the school's art teacher or a home gardening store, or pieces torn from disposable plates, jars, cups, etc.) and have them try to estimate the diameter of the platter or vessel opening from which it came. Explain that archaeologists may not have all the pieces of a broken pot or plate found at an ancient site. Instead, they may use a specially designed grid of concentric circles that they slide the fragment along until the arc of the pottery fragment's edge matches the curve of the circle. The length of the diameter can be read from the grid and recorded as the approximate size of a platter or of a vessel's opening. Tell students that they will learn another way to find a platter's size by using mathematical techniques.

After completing Exploration 2 students might want to trace their fragments, use perpendicular bisectors to find the center of the circle, and then compare the circle's diameter to their first estimate.

TECHNOLOGY NOTE

For a related technology activity, see the *Technology Book*.

BISECTING Chords

SET UP *Work with a partner. You will need:* • Labsheets 4B and 4C
• scissors • compass • ruler

The Story So Far...

▶ After using the rope to climb up the cliff, Nageela discovers broken pottery pieces in a dwelling. Jim is surprised that Nageela can estimate the original size of the pottery.

"You mean you can tell the diameter of a platter just by tracing a little broken part? How do you do it?"

".... It's easy, really." Nageela knelt and drew a circle with her finger. "But first you have to know a few things about circles."

13 Use Labsheet 4B.

a. Cut out *Circle 1*. Fold the circle in half and draw a segment on the crease. Then rotate the circle and repeat with a new crease. **Check students' work.**

b. What is another name for the segments you drew? Where do they intersect? Would other segments constructed in the same way intersect at the same point? **diameters; The diameters intersect at the center of the circle; Yes.**

c. Cut out *Circle 2* and fold it so points *K* and *L* meet. Draw a segment on the crease. Refold so points *M* and *N* meet. Draw a segment on the crease. Where do the segments intersect? **The segments intersect at the center of the circle.**

14 Try This as a Class $\overline{KL}$ and $\overline{MN}$ are chords. A **chord** is a segment that joins two points on a circle. The segment you drew through each chord is a **perpendicular bisector**. Why is this a good name for these segments?

14. Sample Response: The segments intersect the chords at right angles and divide the chords in half.

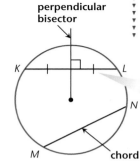

perpendicular bisector

K   *L*

N

M   chord

Symbols are used to show that the two halves of $\overline{KL}$ are equal in length.

Circles

A **circle** is the set of all points in a plane that are a given distance from a point called the center of the circle.

A **chord** is a segment that has both endpoints on the circle.

A **diameter** is a chord that passes through the center of the circle.

A **radius** is a segment that connects a point on the circle to the center.

center

Constructing a Circle

First Choose a radius.

Then Draw the circle.

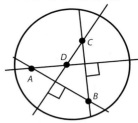

---

15 Discussion Use your compass to make a circle. Draw two chords. Then fold the circle to find the perpendicular bisector of each chord. What do you observe about the perpendicular bisectors of two chords drawn in the same circle? **The perpendicular bisectors intersect at the center of the circle.**

▶ Nageela found a pottery fragment that was originally part of a platter. Her first steps in estimating the platter's size are shown.

First Nageela traced the pottery fragment's outline in the sand.

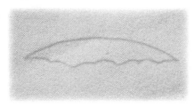

Then She drew two chords.

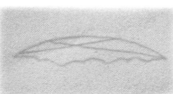

16 Discussion What do you think Nageela's next steps are?

17 ✔ **CHECKPOINT** Use Labsheet 4C. You will use perpendicular bisectors to estimate the original diameter of a *Circular Platter*.
Check students' constructions on Labsheet 4C.; about 16.6 cm

HOMEWORK EXERCISES ▶ See Exs. 15–19 on p. 201.

16. Sample Response: She will find the perpendicular bisectors of the chords, then measure the distance from the point where the perpendicular bisectors intersect to a point on the edge of the platter. This is the radius of the platter. If she doubles it, she will know the diameter of the platter.

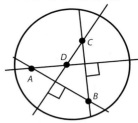

Key Concepts

CLOSURE QUESTION

How can you use perpendicular bisectors to find the center of a circle?

Sample Response: Draw two chords of the circle. Find the perpendicular bisector of each chord. The intersection of these two bisectors will be the center of the circle.

ABSENT STUDENTS

For students who were absent for part or all of this section, the blackline Study Guide for Section 4 may be used to present the ideas, concepts and skills of Section 4.

Section 4
Key Concepts

Key Terms

similar

corresponding angles

corresponding sides

Similar Figures (pp. 193–195)

Two figures are similar if they have the same shape, but not necessarily the same size. The measures of their corresponding angles are equal, and the ratios of their corresponding side lengths are in proportion.

Example $\triangle MNL \sim \triangle PQR$

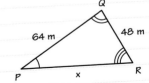

Similar Triangles and Indirect Measurement
(pp. 194–195)

Two triangles are similar if two angles of one triangle have the same measure as two angles of the other. You can use similar triangles to make indirect measurements and find missing side lengths.

Example Find the length of $\overline{PR}$ in the diagram above.

Let x = PR.
Solve for x.

$$\frac{ML}{PR} = \frac{NL}{QR}$$

$$\frac{60}{x} = \frac{36}{48}$$

$$x = 80$$

The length of $\overline{PR}$ is 80 m.

chord

perpendicular bisector

19. **Sample Response:** Label the endpoints of the segment and fold the paper so the endpoints meet. Label the midpoint of the segment, then fold the paper again so the midpoint meets the endpoints.

Circles and Chords (pp. 196–197)

The perpendicular bisectors of any two chords on a circle intersect at the center of the circle.

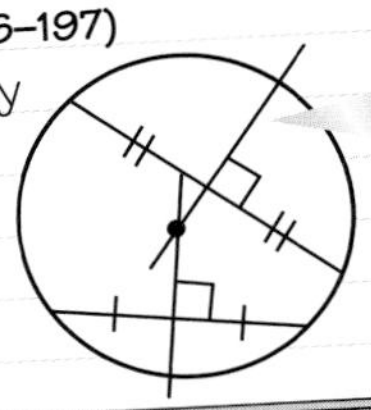

The perpendicular bisector forms a right angle with the chord. It divides the chord in half.

Key Concepts Questions

18 Use the triangles above. Find the length of $\overline{MN}$. **48 m**

19 Draw a line segment on a piece of paper. Describe a method for dividing the segment into four parts with equal lengths.

Section 4
Practice & Application Exercises

For Exercises 1–3, use similar figures *ABCD* **and** *MNQP.*

1. Find the ratio of the corresponding side lengths. $\frac{5}{3.3}$

2. Copy and complete each statement.

   a. $m\angle A = m\ \underline{\ ?\ }\ \angle M$

   b. $\frac{BA}{NM} = \frac{BC}{?}\ NQ$

   c. $\frac{QP}{CD} = \frac{?}{AD}\ MP$

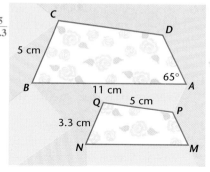

3. Find each measure.

   a. $m\angle M$ 65°

   b. *NM* 7.26 cm

   c. *CD* about 7.58 cm

For each pair of figures, write a mathematical statement saying the figures are similar.

4.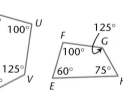

   STUV ~ HEFG

5.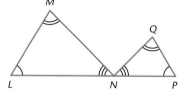

   △*LMN ~* △*PQN*

6.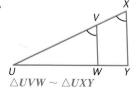

   △*UVW ~* △*UXY*

7.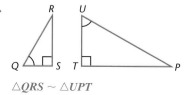

   △*QRS ~* △*UPT*

8. **Challenge** Suppose you push the triangles in Exercise 7 together, as shown. Name all the triangles you see. Without measuring, tell how you know that all the triangles are similar.

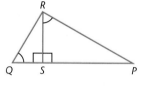

YOU WILL NEED

For Ex. 11:
♦ ruler

For Exs. 20–21:
♦ graph paper

For Exs. 18, 33:
♦ compass

For Ex. 34:
♦ protractor

8. △*QSR*, △*QRP*, △*RSP*;
$m\angle Q = m\angle PRS = m\angle Q$
and since $m\angle QRS = 90° - m\angle Q$,
$m\angle PRQ = m\angle PRS + m\angle QRS = m\angle Q + 90° - m\angle Q = 90°$.
Since two angles of each triangle have the same measures as two angles of each of the other triangles, the triangles are similar.

Practice & Applications

SUGGESTED ASSIGNMENTS

Core Course
Day 1: Exs. 1–7, 20–24
Day 2: Exs. 9–12, 14, 25–32
Day 3: Exs. 15–19

Extended Course
Day 1: Exs. 1–6, 8, 20–24
Day 2: Exs. 9–13, 25–32
Day 3: Exs. 15–19, 33–34*

Note: Extended Course assignments can be used to differentiate within the regular classroom. In classrooms where students are grouped homogeneously, the material might be covered in fewer days. In this case assignments may be combined.
*denotes Extension Exercises

ADDITIONAL PRACTICE
See the *Teacher's Resource Book* for additional practice and application exercises for this section.

EXERCISE NOTES
Exercises 4–7 If students have difficulty writing the mathematical statements, refer them to the description of naming similar figures at the top of page 194.

199

Practice & Applications

EXERCISE NOTES

Exercises 9–12 Students should recognize that when testing for similarity among figures other than triangles, knowing that the measures of the angles are congruent is not enough to determine similarity. This property only applies to triangles. For other figures they must also check the lengths of the sides to ensure that ratios of corresponding side lengths are proportional.

12. **Sample Response:** The corresponding angles may have the same measures, but the lengths of the corresponding sides may not be proportional. That is the case in each of the following sketches.

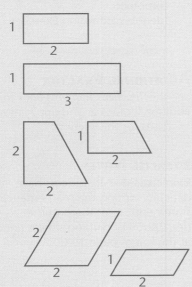

9. **Sample Response:** Because the corresponding angles of trapezoids MNQR and NLPQ have the same measures.

11. $\frac{PQ}{QR} = \frac{0.8}{1.4} \approx 0.57$ and $\frac{LP}{NQ} = \frac{2.5}{2.8} \approx 0.89$ Since the ratios are not equal, the trapezoids are not similar.

14. a. **Sample Response:** They are both right triangles and they each have an acute angle with the same measure.

b. 396 in. or 33 ft; **Sample Response:** Since the shadow of the monument is 6 times the length of Len's shadow, the height of the monument is 6 times Len's height. 6 · 66 in. = 396 in.

For Exercises 9–11, use the trapezoids MNQR and NLPQ.

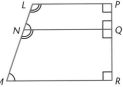

9. Byron assumes that the trapezoids are similar. Why do you think he might make that assumption?

10. Suppose the trapezoids are similar. Which of these statements would be true? **B**

A. $\frac{PQ}{QR} = \frac{MN}{NL}$

B. $\frac{PQ}{QR} = \frac{LP}{NQ}$

11. Use a ruler to check whether the statement you chose in Exercise 10 is true. Are the trapezoids similar? Why?

12. **Open-ended** Explain why you need to check more than the angle measures to tell whether the figures described below are similar. Sketch some examples to support your answers. **See margin.**

a. 2 rectangles   b. 2 trapezoids   c. 2 parallelograms

13. **Challenge** Kasey can see the top of a 788 ft tall skyscraper over the top of a 15 ft flag pole at her school. She estimates that she is about 300 ft away from the flagpole. About how many miles is she from the skyscraper? (*Note:* 1 mi = 5280 ft) **about 3 mi**

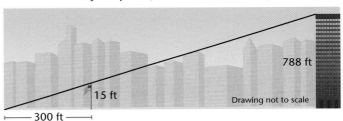

788 ft

15 ft

Drawing not to scale

— 300 ft —

14. As shown by the diagram, you can think of rays of light from the sun as hitting the ground at the same angle.

The monument's shadow is about 60 ft long.

Len is 66 in. tall. His shadow is about 10 ft long.

a. Explain how you know the triangles in the diagram are similar.

b. Estimate the height of the monument. Explain your method.

15. Visual Thinking Draw a large square on graph paper and cut it out. Use paperfolding to show that each of the four small triangles formed by the two diagonals is similar to each of the two larger triangles formed by just one diagonal.

16. a. Draw a rectangle and a diagonal. Then draw a smaller rectangle inside the first rectangle, as shown.

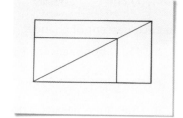

   b. Do the rectangles appear to be similar? What do you need to check to make sure?

   c. Repeat part (a) several times. Use different sizes of rectangles each time. Do all the rectangle pairs appear to be similar? **yes**

17. Use the method in Exercise 16 to make two parallelograms that are not rectangles. Does this method appear to produce similar parallelograms? Use examples to support your answer. **See margin.**

18. a. Draw a circle. Then draw two chords. The chords can be any length, but they should intersect. Connect the endpoints to form two triangles, as shown. **Answers will vary. Check students' drawings.**

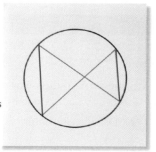

   b. Repeat part (a) at least three times, using different chords. **Answers will vary. Check students' drawings.**

   c. What do you notice about the triangles in each circle? **The triangles are similar.**

Reflecting on the Section

19. The design below uses similar figures and segments that are perpendicular bisectors. Create your own design. Explain which figures in your design are similar, and give the ratio of the corresponding sides. Which segments are perpendicular bisectors? **Answers will vary. Check students' work.**

---

15. Use the folded paper to show that the angles of each smaller triangle have the same measures as the angles of the larger triangles.

16. a.

   b. Yes; Measure the lengths of the sides to see if they are in proportion.

19. Answers will vary. Check students' work.

THINKING

Exercise 19 checks your understanding of similar figures and perpendicular bisectors of line segments.

EXERCISE NOTES

Exercise 16(b) Students may use the triangles resulting from drawing diagonals to determine whether the rectangles are similar. You might lead students to identify the similar triangles they see and ask how they might use them to determine the similarity of the rectangles. Students should label the vertex of each triangle identified.

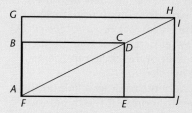

Ask, "Which triangles are similar? How do you know?
(△ABC ~ △AGH and △FDE ~ △FIJ; In the first set of similar triangles ∠A is shared by both triangles, and ∠B and ∠G are both right angles since they are the angles of a rectangle. When two corresponding angles have the same measure, the measures of the third angles of the triangles are equal making the triangles similar.
In the second set of triangles ∠F is the shared angle and ∠E and ∠J are right angles. Therefore, the two triangles are similar.)
Then ask, "By knowing that the triangles are similar, what do you know about the lengths of their corresponding sides? (They are proportional.) Ask students to identify corresponding sides. While doing this, they should recognize that they are also identifying the corresponding sides of the rectangles, therefore the rectangles are similar.

17. See Additional Answers beginning on page A1.

Practice & Applications

DEVELOPING MATH·CONCEPTS

Students who complete **Extension Exercises 33–34** can be challenged further to measure the distance from the right angle of each of the triangles they created to the center of the circle. Ask what they notice. (*They all have the same measure.*) Ask what that measure represents in the circle. (*the radius of the circle.*) Ask what part of the triangle the diameter of the circle represents. (*the hypotenuse*) Ask students to draw a line on their paper to represent the hypotenuse of a triangle. Mark the center of the hypotenuse and measure the length of one of the shorter segments formed. Use that length to mark a point from the center of the hypotenuse to anywhere on their paper. Connect the endpoints of the hypotenuse to the point made. What do they notice about the triangle they formed? (*It is a right triangle.*) Ask what kind of triangle would be formed if they repeated this procedure marking a point in a different location. (*Another right triangle will be formed.*) If they repeated this procedure several more times, what would the points they made represent? (*points on the arc of a circle with a diameter the length of the hypotenuse*)

20.

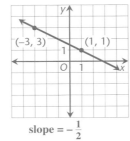

slope $= -\dfrac{1}{2}$

21.

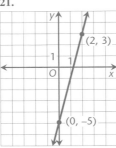

slope $= 4$

Spiral ◀▶ Review

Plot each pair of points on a coordinate plane and draw a line through them. Find the slope of the line. *(Module 3, p. 186)*

20. (1, 1) and (–3, 3)   **21.** (0, –5) and (2, 3)

Find each percent of change. *(Module 2, p. 144)*

22. A $45.00 book sells for $30.00. $33\frac{1}{3}\%$ decrease

23. A tree grows from 4 ft to 5 ft 6 in. 37.5% increase

24. In 1850, New Mexico's population was about 93,516. In 1860, it was about 61,547. about 34% decrease

Find each product. *(Toolbox, p. 589)*

25. $3.6 \cdot 10^2$ 360
26. $0.4 \cdot 10^1$ 4
27. $249 \cdot 10^3$ 249,000
28. $0.007 \cdot 10^2$ 0.7

29. $75.3 \cdot 10^4$ 753,000
30. $9.87 \cdot 10^5$ 987,000
31. $0.16 \cdot 10^2$ 16
32. $10.18 \cdot 10^6$ 10,180,000

Extension ▶ ▶

Making a Conjecture

33. Draw five circles with the same radius. For each circle, follow these steps: **Answers will vary. Check students' drawings.**

First) Draw a diameter.

Then) Choose a point on the circle and draw a triangle. The diameter should form one side of the triangle. Be sure to choose a different point for each circle.

Each vertex of the triangle should be on the circle.

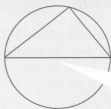

One side of the triangle should be the diameter of the circle.

34. Compare the angle measures of the triangles. Then make a conjecture about triangles drawn this way. Did the observations of other students support your conjecture? **They are all right triangles; Yes.**

Section 4
Extra Skill Practice

For Exercises 1–3, use the triangles shown. The triangles are similar.

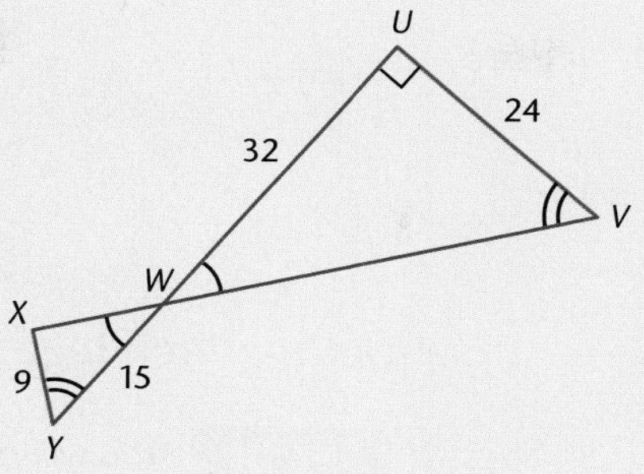

1. Find the ratio of the corresponding side lengths. $\frac{3}{8}$ or $\frac{8}{3}$

2. Copy and complete each statement.

   a. $\frac{WV}{WY} = \frac{?}{XY}$ $\frac{WV}{WY} = \frac{UV}{XY}$

   b. $\frac{UV}{?} = \frac{?}{YW}$ $\frac{UV}{XY} = \frac{VW}{YW}$

   c. $\triangle UVW \sim \underline{\ ?\ } \triangle XYW$

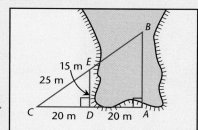

3. Find each measure.

   a. $m\angle X$ 90°   b. XW 12   c. VW 40

You are standing on shore at point A. A raft is anchored in a bay at point B. Your friends Cathy, Damien and Ellen are standing at points C, D, and E.

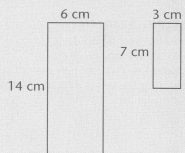

4. Which triangles are similar? How do you know? See margin.

5. Explain how your friends can help you find the distance from you to the raft by using similar triangles. Is there any information on the drawing that you will *not* need? See margin.

6. Find the distance from point A to point B.
   30 m

Standardized Testing ◀▶ **Free Response**

1. $\overline{AB}$ is the perpendicular bisector of $\overline{CD}$.

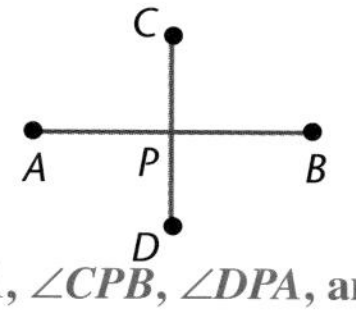

   a. Name two segments in the diagram that have the same measure. $\overline{PC}$ and $\overline{PD}$

   b. Name two angles in the diagram that have the same measure. any two of $\angle CPA$, $\angle CPB$, $\angle DPA$, and $\angle DPB$

2. Suppose the measures of the corresponding sides of two similar rectangles are in the ratio 2 : 1. Give possible dimensions of the rectangles. Include a sketch of the rectangles with their dimensions labeled. See margin.

Extra Skill Practice

TEACHER NOTES

For each Exploration, the corresponding Extra Skills Practice Exercises are noted.

Exploration 1: Exs. 1–6
Exploration 2: *Standardized Testing Free Response* Ex. 1

EXTRA HELP

Teacher's Resource Book
• Practice and Applications
• Study Guide

Technology Resources
• @Home Tutor
• Test Generator

ASSESSMENT
• Section 4 Quick Quiz
• Test Generator

4. $\triangle CDE \sim \triangle CAB$; $\angle C$ is in both triangles, and $m\angle CDE = m\angle CAB = 90°$, so two of the angles in $\triangle CDE$ have the same measures as two of the angles in $\triangle CAB$.

5. Use the proportion $\frac{BA}{ED} = \frac{AC}{DC}$. Substitute the known distances and solve for x: $\frac{x}{15} = \frac{40}{20}$; CE is not needed.

Standardized Testing

2. Check students' drawings. Sample Response:

6 cm   3 cm
7 cm
14 cm

203

Setting the Stage

ABOUT THE THEME

Detectives and forensic scientists have been trained to use a wide variety of means to solve a case. In Section 2, students explored how skid marks can be used to determine the speed of a car before braking. Section 3 showed how detectives can use a footprint to determine the height of the person making it. In this section students will see how scientists measure the relative age of bones. Before reading the *Setting the Stage,* show your students two running stop watches that were started at different times and two similar burning candles, one shorter than the other. Ask students what information they can learn about the two pair of objects based on observation. They can tell which candle has been burning longer; however, without knowing the rate at which the candles burn, there is no way to determine how much longer or how long it has been since the candles were lit. Students can, however, tell which watch was started first, how long it was running before the second one was started, and exactly when they were started. Ask students to brainstorm the evidence a scientist might look for that will reveal the age of very old objects. How can they tell that a bone is 100 years old? 1000 years old? 10,000 years old?

GETTING STARTED

Module 3 Section 5 *Warm-Up* assesses students' facility with multiplication when an exponent is present and assesses their ability to solve equations.

1. Sample Response: Because after this amount of time, only *half* of the carbon-14 remains.

2. one-fourth; one-eighth; $\frac{1}{2} \cdot \frac{1}{2} = \frac{1}{4}$ and $\frac{1}{2} \cdot \frac{1}{4} = \frac{1}{8}$

3. See Additional Answers beginning on page A1.

Section 5 Scientific Notation and Decimal Equations

IN THIS SECTION

EXPLORATION 1
♦ Using Scientific Notation

EXPLORATION 2
♦ Equations with Decimals

Forgotten BONES

Setting the Stage

SET UP You will need Labsheet 5A.

The Story So Far...

▶ Nageela visits Dr. Beatrice Leschensky, a scientist who is analyzing the bones found at the site. Dr. Leschensky explains how she uses *carbon dating* to estimate the age of the bones.

"Every living creature contains a certain amount of a radioactive substance known as *carbon-14.* After a plant or an animal dies, the carbon-14 decays, so that there is less and less carbon-14 over time. After about 5730 years, only half the carbon-14 remains. After another 5730 years or so, only one fourth the carbon-14 remains. After each additional 5730 years, only half the previous amount of carbon-14 remains. By measuring the amount of carbon-14 in these bones, I was able to estimate their age. That's all there is to it."

Think About It

1 Scientists say that carbon-14 has a half-life of 5730 years. Why is *half-life* a good term to use?

2 What fraction of carbon-14 is left in an 11,460-year-old bone? in a 17,190-year-old bone? How do you know?

3 **Use Labsheet 5A.** Use a table and a graph to model the *Half-Life of Carbon-14.* See margin.

▶ In this section, you will use mathematics to find out more about the bones found in the cliff dwelling in *The Mystery of Blacktail Canyon.*

 Module 3 The Mystery of Blacktail Canyon

Exploration 1

Using **Scientific** Notation

SET UP *You will need: • Labsheet 5A • calculator*

▶ Here is a summary of Dr. Leschensky's report on the bones found in the cliff dwelling. Use the report for Questions 4–6.

Carbon-14 Dating of Bone Samples					
Bone sample	Gender	Bone type	Diameter (cm)	Length (cm)	Estimated age (years)
1	male	femur	3.3	38.9	$1.7 \cdot 10^2$
2	female	femur	3.1	35.6	$1.18 \cdot 10^3$

$$10^3 = 10 \cdot 10 \cdot 10$$

4 **a.** About how many years old was each bone sample?

  b. To what year does each bone date back? (Assume *The Mystery of Blacktail Canyon* takes place in 2007.)

▶ **Writing Very Large Numbers** The ages in Dr. Leschensky's report are written in *scientific notation*. Scientists use this notation as shorthand for writing some numbers.

Decimal notation   **Scientific notation**

  5,900,000,000   = $5.9 \cdot 10^9$

  A number greater than or equal to 1 and less than 10   A power of 10

5 **Try This as a Class** Tell whether each number is in scientific notation. Explain your answers.

  a. $11.8 \cdot 10^7$ **b.** $6.9 \cdot 10^5$ **c.** $0.7 \cdot 10^{18}$ **d.** $1.2 \cdot 5^3$

6 Write each product as a number in decimal notation.

  a. $9.3 \cdot 10^4$ **b.** $4.5 \cdot 10^5$ **c.** $3.8 \cdot 10^6$ **d.** $2.3 \cdot 10^1$
    93,000   450,000   3,800,000   23

GOAL

LEARN HOW TO...
  ◆ write very large numbers in scientific notation

AS YOU...
  ◆ estimate ages of bones

KEY TERMS
  ◆ scientific notation
  ◆ decimal notation

4. a. Bone 1 was about 170 years old and bone 2 was about 1180 years old.
   b. Bone 1 dates to about 1837 and bone 2 to about 827.

FOR ▶ HELP
with *powers*, see
TOOLBOX, p. 589

5. a. No; 11.8 is greater than 10.
   b. Yes; 6.9 is greater than 1 and less than 10 and 6.9 is multiplied by a power of 10.
   c. No; 0.7 is less than 1.
   b. No; 5^3 is not a power of 10.

Exploration 1

DEVELOPING MATH CONCEPTS
Most students should recognize that it may be more convenient to write a very large number in scientific notation than to write it in standard notation. Ask students how many zeros are in one thousand. (*three*) "How many zeros are in a billion? a quadrillion?" (*9, 15*) "Is it easier to write a 1 followed by 15 zeros or 10^{15}?" Guide them to understand that it is also easier to compare the relative values of numbers by comparing the powers of ten than by comparing the numbers written in standard notation. You might write the numbers one billion (1,000,000,000) and 100 billion (100,000,000,000) on the board. Ask how many times as great one is as the other. Then write 10^9 and 10^{11} on the board and ask how many times as great one is as the other. "Which is easier to compare? Why?"

Section 5 Scientific Notation and Decimal Equations **205**

Exploration 1 continued

TEACHING NOTES

Checkpoint Question 10 asks students to write numbers in scientific notation. If they are having difficulty, you may either refer them to the illustration on page 203 or use the example below to review the process. Students who are having difficulty identifying the correct power of 10 may also be referred to the Toolbox on page 581.

CLASSROOM EXAMPLE

Energy is measured in BTUs (British thermal units). In the year 2000, the United States used 98,216,000,000,000,000 BTUs of energy. Write this number in scientific notation.

Answer:
First move the decimal point to get a number greater than or equal to one but less than 10.

98,216,000,000,000,000

Then count the number of places the decimal point moves to determine the power of 10 to use. The decimal point moved 16 places to the left.

The number written in scientific notation is $9.8216 \cdot 10^{16}$.

COMMON ERROR

Question 10 Students may forget the correct form for scientific notation and mistakenly write 9,200,000 as $0.92 \cdot 10^7$ instead of $9.2 \cdot 10^6$. Remind them that in scientific notation, a number greater than or equal to 1 but less than 10 is multiplied by a power of ten. The exponent indicates the number of places the decimal is moved when a number in decimal notation is rewritten in scientific notation.

---

7. Her answer is not in scientific notation since 35 is greater than 10.

8. Sample Response: Write the decimal with enough zeros to move the decimal right the number of places indicated by the power of 10.

9. a. The power of 10 is the number of times the = key is pressed.
   b. Check students' calculators. Sample Response: 5.88E12

✔ **QUESTION 10**

...checks that you can write very large numbers in scientific notation.

EXAMPLE

The age of the oldest fossils found on Earth is about 3,500,000,000. Write this age in scientific notation.

SAMPLE RESPONSE

First Move the decimal point to get a number greater than or equal to 1 and less than 10.

3,500,000,000

Then Count how many places the decimal point moves to decide on the power of 10.

$3.5 \cdot 10^9$

Decimal point moved 9 places to the left.

The fossils are about $3.5 \cdot 10^9$ years old.

---

7 **Try This as a Class** Jackie got a different answer for the Example above. Explain her mistake.

$$3,500,000,000 = 35 \cdot 10,000,000 = 35 \cdot 10^8$$

8 **Discussion** Describe how you can reverse the process in the Example to write $3.5 \cdot 10^9$ in decimal notation.

9 Calculator Many calculators use scientific notation to display very large numbers.

  a. Use the key sequence below.

  5.5 [×] 10 [=] [×] 10 [=] [×] 10 [=] [×] 10 [=] ···

  Continue multiplying each product by 10 until your calculator switches to scientific notation. How is the number of times you pressed the [=] key related to the power of 10 on the display?

  b. Your calculator may have a special key for entering numbers in scientific notation. For example, to enter $3.2 \cdot 10^{14}$, you might use one of these key sequences:

  3.2 [EXP] 14   3.2 [EE] 14

  Find out the key sequence that your calculator uses. Then practice by entering $5.88 \cdot 10^{12}$. How does the number appear on the display?

10 ✔ **CHECKPOINT** Write each number in scientific notation.

  a. 2390
  $2.39 \cdot 10^3$

  b. 4,500,000
  $4.5 \cdot 10^6$

  c. 365,000,000,000
  $3.65 \cdot 10^{11}$

11 Use Labsheet 5A. Look back at Dr. Leschensky's report on page 205. Bone sample 2 contains about $\frac{7}{8}$ of the original amount of carbon-14. Use your graph from Question 3 to estimate its age. How does this estimate compare with Dr. Leschensky's? **about 1000 yr; Sample Response: The age estimated by Dr. Leschensky is 180 yr older.**

HOMEWORK EXERCISES ▶ See Exs. 1–10 on pp. 210–211.

Exploration 2

Equations with D.e.c.i.m.a.l.s

The Story So Far...

▶ Dr. Leschensky believes that the bones found in the cliff dwelling came from two skeletons, one male and one female. She explains how she can use the bones to learn more about these skeletons.

"We have a number of equations that help us predict the heights of people based on different bones of the body. . . . Since we have the measurements of two femurs, we will use these equations." She erased the chalkboard and wrote two formulas on it.

Male height from femur length	Female height from femur length
$h = 61.41 + 2.38f$	$h = 49.74 + 2.59f$

"You see, h represents height and f is femur length in centimeters.... When we use the formulas, we get close to the real height, but the answer may not be exact."

12 Look back at Dr. Leschensky's data from page 205 to estimate the height of each skeleton to the nearest centimeter. Explain why it may not be reasonable to make a closer estimate.

13 Dr. Leschensky is 172 cm tall. Write an equation you could use to estimate her femur length. **$172 = 49.74 + 2.59f$ where f is the length of her femur.**

12. Bone 1:
    $h = 61.41 + 2.38 \cdot 38.9 \approx 154$ cm
    Bone 2: $h = 49.74 + 2.59 \cdot 35.6 \approx 142$ cm;
    Sample Response: The length of the bone may have changed due to drying and wear.

DIFFERENTIATED INSTRUCTION

Some students may benefit from using fraction bars or another tactile model as they complete the labsheet. Scientists have found that the carbon-14 found in bones deteriorates by half every 5,730 years. Each new bar they place on the model indicates the passage of 5,730 years. In the first model all the carbon is present. The second model shows how much is left after 5,730 years. This time span is referred to as a half life because it takes that long for the bone to lose half of its carbon-14. Ask students to divide in half the remaining half of the model. Then ask how many groups of 5,730 years have passed for that much carbon to be remaining. (*two groups representing 2 half lives*) Encourage students to continue to divide the remaining carbon in half using their fraction bars as they complete the table.

Exploration 2

TEACHING NOTES

Ask students if they know where on the body the femur is located. (*the thigh bone that extends from the base of the hip to the knee joint*) They may be interested to know that the femur is the bone most likely to be found intact or in the best condition because it is the largest, most dense bone in the human body.

Section 5 Scientific Notation and Decimal Equations **207**

TEACHING NOTES

If needed, you may want to present the following example before students complete **Checkpoint Question 17**.

CLASSROOM EXAMPLE

Suppose Jim and Nageela find a skeleton that is 104 cm long. Use the formula $h = 61.41 + 2.38f$ to estimate the length of the femur of the skeleton to the nearest centimeter.

Answer: Substitute 104 for h in the formula. Then solve using inverse operations.

$$104 = 61.41 + 2.38f$$
$$104 - 61.41 = 61.41 + 2.38f - 61.41$$
$$42.59 = 2.38f$$
$$\frac{42.59}{2.38} = \frac{2.38f}{2.38}$$
$$17.89 = f$$

The length of the femur of the skeleton is about 18 cm long.

COMMON ERROR

Questions 16 and 17 If students are using paper and pencil to solve, they may misplace the decimal point when performing calculations. Emphasize the method demonstrated in Question 16 and encourage them to use it.

14., 16. See Additional Answers beginning on page A1.

208

---

15. She was correct. The answers are different because the length of the femur was rounded to the nearest hundredth.

EXAMPLE

Jim's height is 152 cm. Nageela uses the formula $h = 61.41 + 2.38f$ to estimate his femur length to the nearest centimeter.

Substitute 152 for h. Then solve using inverse operations.

$$152 = 61.41 + 2.38f$$
$$152 - 61.41 = 61.41 + 2.38f - 61.41$$
$$90.59 = 61.41 - 61.41 + 2.38f$$
$$90.59 = 2.38f$$
$$\frac{90.59}{2.38} = \frac{2.38f}{2.38}$$
$$38.06 \approx f$$

Jim's femur is about 38 cm long.

14 **Try This as a Class** Describe the steps in the Example above. Tell which inverse operations were used. **See margin.**

15 **Discussion** As shown at the left, Nageela checks her solution from the Example. She wonders if she is wrong. What do you think? Explain.

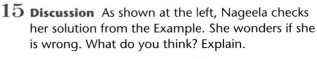

$$152 \overset{?}{=} 61.41 + 2.38(38.06)$$
$$152 \neq 151.99$$

16 **Discussion** You can first multiply both sides of the equation shown in the Example by a power of ten to avoid working with decimals.

$$100(152) = 100(61.41 + 2.38f)$$

a. Copy this first step. Then finish solving the equation. **See margin.**

b. Show how you would use this method to solve $9.7 = 3 + 2.7x$. What power of ten did you use? Why? **See margin.**

✔ **QUESTION 17**

...checks that you can solve an equation involving decimals.

17 ✔ **CHECKPOINT** Solve each equation. Round decimal solutions to the nearest hundredth and check your solutions.

a. $28.6 = 3.7x + 5.3$ b. $4.1 + 0.5n = 4.1$ c. $\frac{x}{9.8} + 1 = 10$
   6.30   0   88.2

d. $0.57r - 3 = 8.2$ e. $\frac{m}{5.5} - 120 = 2.5$ f. $\frac{t}{4.5} - 13 = -12$
   19.65   673.75   4.5

18 Estimate Dr. Leschensky's femur to the nearest centimeter by solving the equation you wrote in Question 13. **47 cm**

HOMEWORK EXERCISES ▶ See Exs. 11–26 on pp. 211–212.

Section 5
Key Concepts

Key Terms

Scientific Notation (pp. 205–207)

Scientific notation is a useful way to write large numbers. You can change between decimal notation and scientific notation.

Example

decimal notation $\longrightarrow$ scientific notation

$320,000 = 3.2 \cdot 100,000 = 3.2 \cdot 10^5$

A number greater than or equal to 1 and less than 10

A power of ten

Example

scientific notation $\longrightarrow$ decimal notation

$9.4 \cdot 10^3 = 9.4 \cdot 1000 = 9400$

Solving Equations with Decimals (pp. 207–208)

You can use inverse operations to solve equations with decimals.

Example

Solve $\dfrac{x}{3.3} + 1.6 = 4.8$.

$\dfrac{x}{3.3} + 1.6 - 1.6 = 4.8 - 1.6$ Subtract **1.6** to both sides to undo the addition.

$\dfrac{x}{3.3} = 3.2$

$3.3\left(\dfrac{x}{3.3}\right) = 3.3(3.2)$ Multiply both sides by **3.3** to undo the division.

$x = 10.56$

Key Terms

decimal notation

scientific notation

Key Concepts Questions

19 **a.** Which number is greater, $5.9 \cdot 10^8$ or $6.8 \cdot 10^7$? $5.9 \cdot 10^8$

b. Do you need to rewrite the numbers in decimal notation to be able to tell which is greater? Explain.

20 Show how to check the solution in the last Example.

19. b. No; Since the numbers are in scientific notation, the one with the greater power of 10 is the greater number.

20. $\dfrac{21.12}{3.3} - 1.6 \overset{?}{=} 4.8$;

$6.4 - 1.6 \overset{?}{=} 4.8$

$4.8 = 4.8$

Key Concepts

CLOSURE QUESTION

Using examples, show how to convert a number in decimal notation to scientific notation and a number in scientific notation to decimal notation.

Check student examples.
Sample Response: To convert a number in decimal notation to scientific notation, move the decimal point so that the number is greater than or equal to 1 and less than 10. Then multiply it by a power of ten. The exponent for this power of ten is equal to the number of places the decimal point had to be moved. To convert from scientific notation to decimal notation, move the decimal point to the right the number of places indicated by the exponent.

ABSENT STUDENTS

For students who were absent for part or all of this section, the blackline Study Guide for Section 5 may be used to present the ideas, concepts and skills of Section 5.

210

Section 5
Practice & Application Exercises

For Exercises 1–4, write each number in decimal notation.

1. Approximate age of Earth: at least $4.5 \cdot 10^9$ years **4,500,000,000 yr**

2. The distance from Earth to the sun: about $9.3 \cdot 10^7$ mi **93,000,000 mi**

3. Speed of light: about $1.86 \cdot 10^5$ mi/sec **186,000 mi/sec**

4. Distance light travels in a year: about $5.88 \cdot 10^{12}$ mi **5,880,000,000,000 mi**

5. Which numbers below are written in scientific notation? Explain. **See margin.**
   A. $7.987 \cdot 10^2$ B. $3.57 \cdot 10^{99}$ C. $82.1 \cdot 10^3$ D. $5.13 \cdot 2^{10}$

Astronomy A *light-year* is the distance that light travels in a vacuum in one year. One light-year $\approx 5.88 \cdot 10^{12}$ miles. Use this fact and the bar graph below for Exercises 6–8.

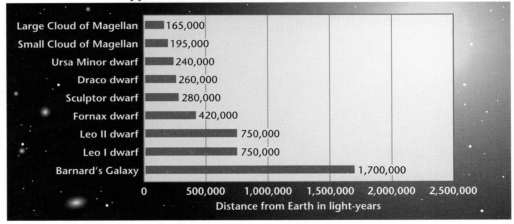

Approximate Distances to Galaxies Near Earth

Galaxy	Distance from Earth in light-years
Large Cloud of Magellan	165,000
Small Cloud of Magellan	195,000
Ursa Minor dwarf	240,000
Draco dwarf	260,000
Sculptor dwarf	280,000
Fornax dwarf	420,000
Leo II dwarf	750,000
Leo I dwarf	750,000
Barnard's Galaxy	1,700,000

6. Which galaxy is a little more than 10 times as far from Earth as the Large Cloud of Magellan? **Barnard's Galaxy**

7. Calculator Find the distance to each galaxy in miles. Write your answers in scientific notation. Round the decimal part of each number to the nearest tenth. **See margin.**

8. **Challenge** Suppose a fictional space ship travels from Earth to the Large Cloud of Magellan in 3 weeks. Estimate its speed in miles per hour. **about $1.925 \cdot 10^{15}$ mi/hr**

9. **Oceanography** On average, the ocean is about $3.795 \cdot 10^3$ m deep. Its deepest point is $11.033 \cdot 10^3$ m.

    a. Which of these measurements is in scientific notation? $3.795 \cdot 10^3$

    b. Give each measurement in kilometers. Use decimal notation.
       3.795 km and 11.033 km

10. **Population Growth** In 1650, the world population was about 470 million. In 2006, it was about 6.528 billion.

    a. Write each population in scientific notation and in decimal notation.

    b. **Estimation** Compare the 1650 and 1990 populations. About how many times greater is the 1990 world population?
       about 14 times greater

FOR ▶ HELP

with *the metric system*, see
TOOLBOX, p. 581

10. a. $470,000,000 = 4.7 \cdot 10^8$
      $6,528,000,000 = 6.528 \cdot 10^9$

Solve each equation. Round decimal answers to the nearest hundredth and check your solutions.

11. $12.5 = 2.5x$ 5   12. $0.7x - 2 = 19$ 30   13. $\dfrac{m}{0.3} = 8$ 2.4

14. $12 = 0.5p + 2.5$ 19   15. $12.4 = \dfrac{w}{2.4} + 2.4$ 24   16. $\dfrac{n}{0.33} - 9 = 12.99$ 7.26

17. $8.3 + 0.7n = 8.3$ 0   18. $0.15p + 12.95 = 13.15$ 1.33

19. $4.1x + 5.8 = 10$ 1.02   20. $0.36 + 1.05x = 9.92$ 9.10

Shoe Sizes The formulas below relate United States shoe size *s* to foot length *f* in inches. Use the formulas for Exercises 21–24.

Men's shoes	Women's shoes
$s = 3f - 22$	$s = 3f - 20.7$

21. Barry wears men's shoe size 10. Estimate his foot length to the nearest inch.   11 in.

22. Tia wears women's shoe size 8. Estimate her foot length to the nearest inch.   10 in.

23. Edie usually wears a women's size 10 shoe. She wants to try on a pair of men's running shoes. Running shoes come in whole and half sizes. What size should she try on?
size $8\frac{1}{2}$ or 9

24. According to these formulas and your foot length measurement in inches, what size shoe should you wear?   Answers will vary. Check students' work.

COMMON ERROR
In **Exercises 11–20**, students use inverse operations to solve equations with decimals. Some students may have difficulty finding the correct place for the decimal point after multiplying or dividing. You may want to refer them to **Question 16** on page 208 for an example of how to use powers of ten to avoid working with decimals.

EXERCISE NOTES
Exercise 23 Students will use a two-step process to solve this problem. They must first use inverse operations with the formula for *f*. Next they use that value for *f* in the formula to solve for the size of men's shoes.

Practice & Applications

EXERCISE NOTES

Open-ended Exercise 25 You may want to ask students to exchange word problems and then solve the problems written by each other. Poorly worded problems or those that cannot be solved should be returned and rewritten.

Help students efficiently find large numbers for **Exercise 26** by asking under what headings or topics examples of large numbers can be found. (*science, industry, business*)

25. **Sample Response:** In United States sizes, Ismail wears a men's size $9\frac{1}{2}$ and Tracy wears a women's size $7\frac{1}{2}$. Find their European shoe sizes. (43 and 38)

RESEARCH

Exercise 26 checks that you know how scientific notation is applied.

25. **Open-ended** If you buy shoes from another country, you may need to know your European shoe size. The formulas below relate European size e to United States size u. Write a word problem that can be solved by using one or both of the formulas.

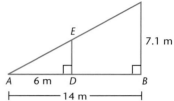

Men's shoes	Women's shoes
$e = 1.29u + 30.8$	$e = 1.24u + 28.7$

Reflecting ◀▶ **on the Section**

26. Find three large numbers in a newspaper or encyclopedia. Write them in scientific notation and add labels that explain what the numbers mean. Answers will vary. Check students' work.

Spiral ◀▶ **Review**

27. $\triangle ABC \sim \triangle ADE$. Find the length of $\overline{DE}$. about 3.0 m
(Module 3, p. 198)

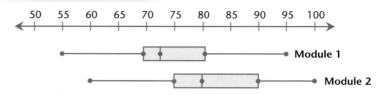

Find each sum or difference. (Module 2, p. 86)

28. $-8 + 7$
    -1

29. $6 - (-11)$
    17

30. $92 + (-2)$
    90

31. $-15 - (-21)$
    6

32. $-50 + 50$
    0

33. $0 - (-12)$
    12

34. $-18 - (-5)$
    -13

35. $3 - 5 + 8$
    6

Use the box-and-whisker plots. (Module 1, p. 23)

36. Estimate the median score on the Module 2 test. about 80

37. Estimate the high score on the Module 1 test. about 95

Section 5

Extra Skill Practice

Write each number in scientific notation.

1. $5{,}180{,}000$ $5.18 \cdot 10^6$
2. 870 $8.7 \cdot 10^2$
3. $28{,}900{,}000$ $2.89 \cdot 10^7$
4. $3{,}120$ $3.12 \cdot 10^3$
5. $362{,}900{,}000{,}000$ $3.629 \cdot 10^{11}$
6. $15{,}000$ $1.5 \cdot 10^4$

Write each number in decimal notation.

7. $3.5 \cdot 10^8$ $350{,}000{,}000$
8. $5.23 \cdot 10^3$ 5230
9. $8.1 \cdot 10^5$ $810{,}000$
10. $6.91 \cdot 10^1$ 69.1
11. $4.8 \cdot 10^{14}$ $480{,}000{,}000{,}000{,}000$
12. $2.25 \cdot 10^2$ 225
13. $4.76 \cdot 10^4$ $47{,}600$
14. $1.853 \cdot 10^7$ $18{,}530{,}000$
15. $6 \cdot 10^{10}$ $60{,}000{,}000{,}000$

Solve each equation. Round decimal answers to the nearest hundredth and check your solutions.

16. $18.1 = 2.2k + 6.4$ 5.32
17. $\dfrac{t}{8.1} + 13.5 = 29.9$ 132.84

18. $0.39w + 4.5 = 8.4$ 10
19. $24.6 + \dfrac{q}{0.2} = 30.1$ 1.1

20. $5.08z + 6.17 = 16.47$ 2.03
21. $32.91 = \dfrac{m}{3.34} + 12.83$ 67.07

22. $15.6 = 1.6v + 7.36$ 5.15
23. $38.62 = \dfrac{r}{6.49} + 27.53$ 71.97

24. $1.2g + 110.9 = 121.7$ 9
25. $0.02x + 0.13 = 6.16$ 301.5

26. $\dfrac{c}{0.17} + 6.9 = 11.3$ 0.75
27. $3.62n + 0.23 = 9.43$ 1.33

28. $76.8y + 5.31 = 12.99$ 0.1
29. $6.387 + 2.8p = 15.349$ 3.20

Standardized Testing ◀▶ Multiple Choice

1. The area of the Pacific Ocean is about $166{,}000{,}000$ km^2. How is this measure expressed in scientific notation? **D**

   Ⓐ 1.66 million km^2
   Ⓑ $16.6 \cdot 10^7$ km^2
   Ⓒ 1.668 km^2
   Ⓓ $1.66 \cdot 10^8$ km^2

2. What is the value of y in the equation $16.8 = \dfrac{y}{1.2} + 4.8$? **B**

   Ⓐ 144 Ⓑ 14.4 Ⓒ 1.44 Ⓓ 0.144

TEACHER NOTES

For each Exploration, the corresponding Extra Skills Practice Exercises are noted.

Exploration 1: Exs. 1–15
Exploration 2: Exs. 16–29

EXTRA HELP

Teacher's Resource Book
• Practice and Applications
• Study Guide

Technology Resources
• @Home Tutor
• Test Generator

ASSESSMENT
• Section 5 Quick Quiz
• Test Generator

Setting the Stage

ABOUT THE THEME

Throughout this module students have been exposed to ways in which evidence is collected and analyzed in order to solve a case. Once all the evidence is presented, detectives must use deductive reasoning to narrow down the suspects and finally solve the crime. Before reading the *Setting the Stage*, you can prepare students to use the logical connectives *and*, *or*, and *not* by playing a simple game called "Did You See That Person Who…" You will need to set up a circle of chairs containing one less chair than the number of players. All the players take a seat with one person, the caller, standing in the center of the circle. The caller constructs a sentence that describes any number of people in the circle. The first part of the sentence must begin with "Did you see that (girl, boy, person) who…" The second half of the sentence uses two descriptors joined by *and*, *or*, or *not*. For example, "Did you see that girl who has dark hair and is wearing sneakers?" or "Did you see that person who is wearing a T-shirt or an earring?" or "Did you see that guy who has red hair but is not wearing jeans?" Once the person in the center of the circle calls out the sentence, all those fitting the description must stand up and move to a different seat. The caller also tries to take an empty seat. The person left standing is now the caller and constructs the next sentence.

GETTING STARTED

Module 3 Section 6 *Warm-Up* assesses whether students can use logical reasoning to find the percent of a group of objects.

Section 6 Logical Thinking

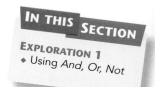

Whodunit?

Setting the Stage

The Story So Far…

▶ The police know that the thief has blood type A. They also know that he or she did not go on Dr. Ashilaka's field trip. Jim and Nageela use a computer database at the police station to see which of the 22 suspects match up with these clues. But Jim thinks they have made a mistake.

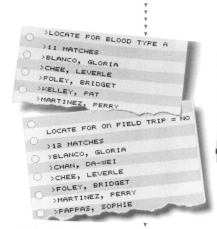

>LOCATE FOR BLOOD TYPE A
>11 MATCHES
>BLANCO, GLORIA
>CHEE, LEVERLE
>FOLEY, BRIDGET
>KELLEY, PAT
>MARTINEZ, PERRY

LOCATE FOR ON FIELD TRIP = NO
>12 MATCHES
>BLANCO, GLORIA
>CHAN, DA-WEI
>CHEE, LEVERLE
>FOLEY, BRIDGET
>MARTINEZ, PERRY
>PAPPAS, SOPHIE

"My first step was to search for suspects with blood type A. The computer found 11 people who match up. But then I ran a new search to find suspects who did not go on the field trip. Now look! Twelve people! That makes a total of 23 suspects, but there are only 22 suspects in the database! And I haven't even searched for suspects with the right height or hair color yet."

"Oh no," moaned Nageela. "You're right! We've done something wrong!"

1. Jim had the computer search for suspects with blood type A and then suspects who did not go on the field trip.

Think About It

1 What did Jim tell the computer to search for?

2 Do you think Jim and Nageela did something wrong? Use the printout from Jim's computer search to help explain your thinking. No; Sample Response: The suspects who have blood type A and who did not go on the field trip, like Gloria Blanco, are on both search lists.

Exploration 1

Using AND, OR, NOT

SET UP *Work as a class. You will need: • Labsheet 6A • tape*

GOAL

LEARN HOW TO...
◆ interpret statements with *and, or,* and *not*
◆ organize information in a Venn diagram

AS YOU...
◆ analyze clues in a mystery

KEY TERMS
◆ Venn diagram
◆ and
◆ or
◆ not

▶ You will use a diagram to search for suspects who have blood type A and were absent from the field trip to Blacktail Canyon.

3 **Use Labsheet 6A.** The *Suspect List* gives information about each of the 22 suspects in *The Mystery of Blacktail Canyon.* Your class should follow these steps: **See margin.**

◆ Your teacher will assign a suspect name to each student in the class. Write your suspect's name on a small slip of paper.

◆ Your teacher will draw a large diagram on the board. Tape your suspect's name in the correct part of the diagram.

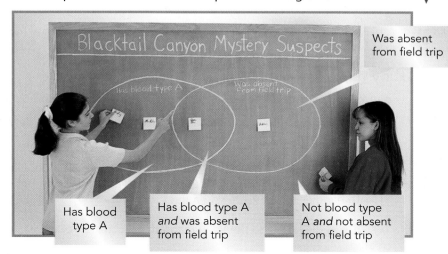

Was absent from field trip

Has blood type A

Has blood type A *and* was absent from field trip

Not blood type A *and* not absent from field trip

4 Look back at the story on page 214. How could your class diagram help Nageela and Jim understand their mistake?

▶ The diagram your class made is a *Venn diagram.* **Venn diagrams** are used to model relationships between groups. They can help you interpret statements that use the words *and, or,* and *not.*

Exploration 1

TEACHING NOTES
Before students begin Exploration 1, review what they observed from the game they played. Some students may have erroneously thought that the word *and* is more inclusive, selecting a larger sample, while expecting that *or* is more exclusive, selecting a smaller sample. But just the opposite is true. The word *or* selects a sample that meets either criterion, while the word *and* selects only those elements that meet both criteria.

DEVELOPING MATH CONCEPTS
Question 3 The words *and, or,* and *not* are sometimes called Boolean operators. They are powerful tools for sorting large amounts of complex data stored in computer databases. Long before they became so commonly used with computers, they were represented graphically through Venn diagrams.
Elements of the set that are *not* included in either of the criteria are outside of both circles of the Venn diagram. The other elements belong in one circle or the other. Those meeting the first criterion *and* the second criterion are placed in the intersection of the two circles. The word *or,* in contrast, selects every element in either of the circles, including those placed in the intersection.

4. Sample Response: It shows that suspects who have blood type A and who did not go on the field trip are on both search lists.

3. See Additional Answers beginning on page A1.

215

Exploration 1 *continued*

DIFFERENTIATED INSTRUCTION

Some students may benefit from concrete experiences using Venn diagrams. Make large loops of colored yarn by tying the ends together to form a circle. Place these loops overlapping each other on a desk. Give students a group of similar objects such as buttons, attribute blocks, colored geometric shapes, or seeds. Allow them to describe the attributes of the objects in their set and write one attribute on a note card or small piece of paper. Repeat this process until all the attributes have been recorded on separate cards. They should then randomly choose two cards, place one by each of the circles and sort the objects into the appropriate regions. On a piece of paper they can then record the number of objects selected by the words *and*, *or*, and *not*.

TEACHING NOTES

The following example may be used before discussing Question 6.

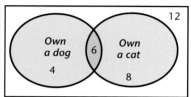
216

---

5. d. No; Sample Response: After you add the number of small pots and the number of pots with handles, you must subtract the number that are both small and have handles, otherwise some pots will be counted twice—once in each group.

EXAMPLE

This Venn diagram organizes information about eight pieces of pottery Nageela found on one shelf of a cliff dwelling. She used the letters A–H to label the pieces.

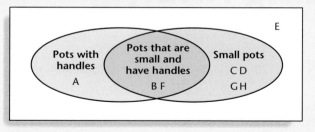

▶ The diagrams below show groupings that use the words *and, or,* and *not.* Notice that the word *or* has special meaning in mathematics. It means *one or the other or both.*

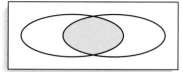

2 pots are small **and** have handles.

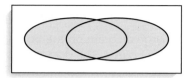

7 pots are small **or** have handles (or both).

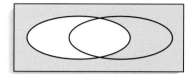

5 pots do **not** have handles.

5 Try This as a Class Use the Venn diagram from the Example.

   a. How many pots are small? How many are *not* small? **6 pots; 2 pots**

   b. How many pots have handles? How many do *not* have handles? **3 pots; 5 pots**

   c. How many pots are *not* small *and* do *not* have handles? **1 pot**

   d. To count the number of small pots or pots with handles, Angela says you should add the number of small pots and the number with handles to get 9. Do you agree? Explain.

6 Try This as a Class Use the Venn diagram of suspects your class created.

   a. How many suspects do *not* have blood type A? **11 suspects**

   b. How many have blood type A *or* were absent from the field trip? **14 suspects**

   c. How many do *not* have blood type A *and* were not absent from the field trip? **8 suspects**

   d. In what group will Jim and Nageela find the thief? **In the group of people who have blood type A and who were absent from the field trip.**

7 ✓ **CHECKPOINT** Six friends were talking about whether they had been to Canada and Mexico. Paolo, Maria, Dan, and Jim have been to Mexico. Paolo, Maria, and Stacey have been to Canada. Rob has never visited either country. Use this information to make a Venn diagram. Shade the diagram to show which friends have been to Canada or Mexico. **See margin.**

HOMEWORK EXERCISES ▶ See Exs. 1–14 on pp. 218–220.

✓ **QUESTION 7**

...checks that you can use a Venn diagram to interpret statements with *and*, *or*, and *not*.

Section 6
Key Concepts

Key Terms

Venn Diagram (pp. 215–217)
A Venn diagram models relationships among groups. It can help you interpret statements that use the words *and*, *or*, and *not*.

Venn diagram

Example Joshua kept track of how many days in August were sunny and how many days were over 90°. He made the Venn diagram below.

and

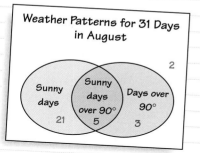

Weather Patterns for 31 Days in August

or

Number of sunny days:
$21 + 5 = 26$

not

Number of days that were sunny or over 90°: $21 + 5 + 3 = 29$

Number of days that were not sunny and not over 90°: **2**

8 **Key Concepts Question** Use the Venn diagram above.

a. How many days in August were not over 90°? **23 days**

b. About what percent of the days in August were not over 90°? Give your answer to the nearest percent. Show how you got your answer. **about 74%; Sample Response: Solve the proportion**
$\frac{23}{31} = \frac{x}{100}$ **for** x.

TIPS FROM TEACHERS
Checkpoint Question 7 requires students to make a Venn diagram to represent the information given. Some students may find it helpful to write each name on a small piece of paper, moving it around to determine where it belongs. Once all the names have been placed, write the names (or first letters of names) in the Venn diagram and complete the task.

Key Concepts

CLOSURE QUESTION
Think of three different school sports. How would you make a Venn diagram to show the number of people in your class who play each sport?

Sample Response: Make three overlapping ovals. Label each oval with one of the sports. Place the names of people who play all three sports in the center overlap, then put the names of the people who play two of the sports in the overlap of just those two ovals. Place the names of the people who play one of the sports in its oval, but not in any overlapping region. Finally, place the names of those people who play none of the sports outside all of the ovals.

ABSENT STUDENTS
For students who were absent for part or all of this section, the blackline Study Guide for Section 6 may be used to present the ideas, concepts and skills of Section 6.

7. See Additional Answers beginning on page A1.

217

Practice & Applications

SUGGESTED ASSIGNMENTS

Core Course
Day 1: Exs. 1–9, 11, 14–24

Extended Course
Day 1: Exs. 3–24

Note: Extended Course assignments can be used to differentiate within the regular classroom. In classrooms where students are grouped homogeneously, the material might be covered in fewer days. In this case assignments may be combined.

ADDITIONAL PRACTICE

See the *Teacher's Resource Book* for additional practice and application exercises for this section.

COMMON ERROR

Exercise 5 Some students may neglect to include the three runners who have won both races among those who have won one or the other. You may want to refer students to the example in the *Key Concepts* on page 217 for assistance.

YOU WILL NEED

For Exs. 22–24:
- compass
- metric ruler

Section 6
Practice & Application Exercises

Language Arts In everyday English, the word *or* can be *exclusive* or *inclusive*, as shown below.

Exclusive *Or*
Nao drives or takes a bus to work. Nao either drives or takes a bus, not both. She cannot do both at the same time.

Inclusive *Or*
Nao eats lunch or reads at noon. Nao can eat lunch, read, or do both activities at once.

For Exercises 1 and 2, tell whether the *or* used is *inclusive* or *exclusive*. (*Note*: All other exercises in this book use the inclusive *or*.)

1. Brad has saved enough money to buy either a touring bike *or* a mountain bike. He can afford only one bike. **exclusive or**

2. On cold days, Maria wears a sweater *or* a jacket or both. **inclusive or**

Track For Exercises 3–6, use the Venn diagram below.

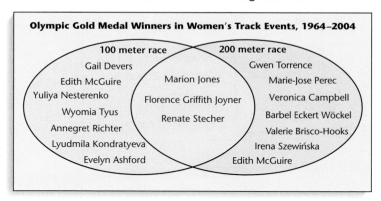

Olympic Gold Medal Winners in Women's Track Events, 1964–2004

100 meter race		200 meter race
Gail Devers		Gwen Torrence
Edith McGuire	Marion Jones	Marie-Jose Perec
Yuliya Nesterenko	Florence Griffith Joyner	Veronica Campbell
Wyomia Tyus	Renate Stecher	Barbel Eckert Wöckel
Annegret Richter		Valerie Brisco-Hooks
Lyudmila Kondratyeva		Irena Szewińska
Evelyn Ashford		Edith McGuire

3. Which runners have won the 100 m race and the 200 m race?
   Marion Jones, Florence Griffith Joyner, and Renate Stecher

4. How many runners have won the 100 m race? **10**

5. How many runners have won the 100 m race or the 200 m race? **17**

6. In the 1996 Olympics, Svetlana Masterkova won the gold medal in the 800 m race, but she has not won the gold medal in an Olympic 100 m or 200 m race. Describe where to put her name in the diagram on page 216. **inside the rectangle, but outside both ovals**

For Exercises 7–10, use the Venn diagram at the right.

7. How many students acted in *Hello Dolly* or in *A Midsummer Night's Dream?* **42 students**

8. a. How many drama students acted in both plays?
9 students
b. How many drama students did not act in both plays?
38 students

Drama Students Acting in Student Productions

Hello Dolly
A Midsummer Night's Dream
9
20
13
5

9. The drama teacher estimates that about 60% of the students acted in *Hello Dolly.* How close is this estimate?
About 62% of the students acted in *Hello Dolly*, so she was only off by 2%.

10. Challenge Suppose some students act in *The Marriage Proposal,* a short play with only three characters. Two of these students also act in both *Hello Dolly* and *A Midsummer Night's Dream.* The third student does not appear in either of these plays. Revise the Venn diagram to include this information. **See margin.**

Geography For Exercises 11 and 12, use the map below.

11. Make a Venn diagram that includes all 50 states. Use these categories: **See margin.**

- States that border another country or a Great Lake
- States that border an ocean

12. Use your Venn diagram to answer each question.

a. How many states border another country or a Great Lake? **20 states**

b. How many states border an ocean? **23 states**

c. How many states border an ocean or a country or a Great Lake? **36 states**

d. How many states do not border an ocean? **27 states**

e. What percent of the states border an ocean and border a country or a Great Lake? **14%**

EXERCISE NOTES
Exercise 10 Students are expected to add a third set to their Venn diagram. This set has two elements which intersect both of the previous sets, and one which does not intersect either. You may want to discuss with your students where they would place a student who acted in *The Marriage Proposal* and *Hello Dolly,* but not in *A Midsummer Night's Dream.*

10–11. See Additional Answers beginning on page A1.

Practice & Applications

Exercise Notes

Reflecting on the Section
Exercise 14 Students are asked to gather responses from two questions, chosen by each student, and to organize the results using a Venn diagram. If possible, display students' Venn diagrams and discuss the relationship between the two questions students asked. Some will probably have most of the responses either in the intersection of the two circles or outside of both. Others might have two distinct groups in the circles with none in the intersection. Discuss how the questions chosen affect the Venn diagram. Encourage them to look for possible correlations in the results.

18. a.

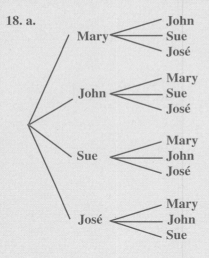

13. **Open-ended** Write a word problem that can be solved using a Venn diagram. Then solve the problem. Explain your solution using the words *and, or,* and *not.* Answers will vary. Check students' work.

RESEARCH

Exercise 14 checks that you can create and interpret a Venn diagram.

Reflecting on the Section

14. Collect data from friends and family members and use the data to make a Venn diagram. For example, you may want to ask people two questions, such as, "Do you like to watch soccer?" and "Do you like to watch figure skating?" Share your Venn diagram with your class. Explain how you collected your data. Answers will vary. Check students' work.

Spiral Review

Solve each equation. Round decimal answers to the nearest hundredth. (Module 3, p. 209)

15. $30.9 = 0.3x + 6$
83

16. $\dfrac{p}{0.12} = 5$ 0.6

17. $24 = 13.2 + 0.7n$
15.43

18. The eighth grade class is asked to choose two students to help plan an event for the school's field day. Mary, John, Sue, and José all volunteer. The class decides to choose names out of a hat to decide who will help. (Module 2, p. 118)

    a. Copy and complete the tree diagram showing the possible pairs of students who can be chosen. See margin.

    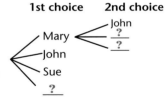

    1st choice   2nd choice

    b. Find the probability that José and Sue will help plan the trip. $\dfrac{1}{6}$

Tell whether each triangle is *isosceles, equilateral,* or *scalene.*
(Toolbox, p. 593)

19.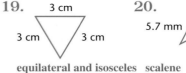
3 cm
3 cm   3 cm

equilateral and isosceles

20. 6.1 mm
5.7 mm
10.2 m

scalene

21. 2.5 in.
2.5 in.   1.9 in.

isosceles

Use a compass to draw a circle with the given radius or diameter.
(Module 3, p. 197) 22–24. Check students' drawings.

22. $r = 1.5$ cm

23. $d = 5$ cm

24. $r = 6$ cm

Section 6

Extra Skill Practice

For Exercises 1–5, use the Venn diagram below. It shows the animals that a class chose for their research reports.

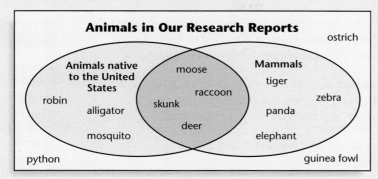

Animals in Our Research Reports

ostrich

Animals native to the United States
robin, alligator, mosquito

moose, raccoon, skunk, deer

Mammals
tiger, zebra, panda, elephant

python

guinea fowl

1. Which animals native to the United States are mammals? **moose, raccoon, skunk, deer**

2. Which animals are not mammals and not native to the United States? **ostrich, python, guinea fowl**

3. How many animals are native to the United States? **7 animals**

4. The mosquito belongs to which category or categories? **animals native to the United States**

5. A llama is a mammal that is native to South America. Describe where you would put a llama in the Venn diagram. **in the blue part of the oval labeled "Mammals"**

6. Make a Venn diagram of the days of the week. In one category put all the days you are at school. In another category put all the days that contain the letter *n*. **See margin.**

Standardized Testing ▶ Performance Task

Many letters of the alphabet show line symmetry. Some have a vertical line of symmetry, some have a horizontal line of symmetry, and some have both. Make a Venn diagram that organizes all 26 capital letters by the types of line symmetry they show. **See margin.**

A
vertical line of symmetry

D
horizontal line of symmetry

H
vertical and horizontal lines of symmetry

Module Project

PROJECT NOTES

Although the entire Module Project may be completed as a review after completing the Module, you may want to have your students complete parts of it as they work through the Module. The chart below can be used as an assignment guide.

After completing this section...	students can answer these project questions.
2	1–4
3	5–6
5	7–12
6	13–19

To complete the Module Project, students should read *The Mystery of Blacktail Canyon*, which is provided in the *Teacher's Resource Book* for Module 3. (See page 154A of the Teacher's Edition for a section-by-section breakdown of reading assignments.) Also note the reading references referred to in the project questions. It is important for students to have read these chapters for successful completion of the project.

Labsheets and other materials:
In addition to *The Mystery of Blacktail Canyon*, students will need Project Labsheet A to answer **Question 15** and Project Labsheet B to answer **Question 17**. You will also need to choose clues and transcripts for the class to use in **Questions 16–19**. (For instructions, see the Project Notes on pages 224–225 of the Teacher's Edition.) Labsheets, clues, and transcripts are provided in the *Teacher's Resource Book*.

1., 3. See Additional Answers beginning on page A1.

222

Solving a Mystery

For this project, you will solve the mystery and identify the criminal in *The Mystery of Blacktail Canyon*. You may find it helpful to keep track of ideas, clues, and important developments in a "detective's notebook."

Understanding the Problem Solving a mystery is like solving any other problem. Your first step is to understand the situation. The questions below will help get you started with your notebook. Sample responses are given for Questions 1–4.

Project Questions 1–4 are based on Chapters 1 and 2 of *The Mystery of Blacktail Canyon*.

1 Why have Dr. Ashilaka and Nageela come to the Four Corners region? What do they hope to find? **See margin.**

2 What crime is Dr. Ashilaka afraid someone might commit? **theft of Anasazi treasures**

3 Whom does Jim Cooper see at Dr. Ashilaka's lecture? What observations, if any, does Jim make about each person? **See margin.**

4 Why does Officer Yellow Robe think there is something strange about the rental car that had skidded to a stop at the edge of the washout? **The car was going pretty fast, there was blood on the glass and dashboard, and there was no driver in sight.**

Making Predictions In Chapter 3 of *The Mystery of Blacktail Canyon*, Officer Charlotte Lopez examines the footprints and the length of the stride of the person they are tracking. You used Charlotte's measurement of foot length to predict the missing driver's height in Section 3 on pages 184–185. You can also use her clue about the missing driver's stride length to get more information.

5 The scatter plot is based on stride length and height data collected from 10 adults. Which equation best matches the fitted line? $y = 0.6x + 84$

    A. $y = 0.6x - 84$

    B. $y = 0.6x$

    C. $y = 0.6x + 84$

SET UP

Work individually or with a partner.
You will need:
- *The Mystery of Blacktail Canyon*
- *Project Labsheet A (Question 15)*

CLUE Measurements taken by Officer Lopez:
- **foot length: 29 cm**
- **stride length: 155 cm**

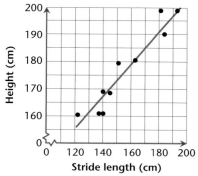

Stride Length and Height

6 a. Use the equation you chose in Question 5 to predict the height of the driver from the stride length measurement. **177 cm**

b. Use this prediction and the one from Exploration 2 of Section 3 to give a reasonable range of heights for the driver.
Sample Response: 174 cm to 177 cm

Gathering and Reviewing Evidence To answer the questions below, you need to read Chapter 7 of *The Mystery of Blacktail Canyon*. You will use some of the skills you have learned to estimate the heights of two suspects, Ms. Weatherwax and Mr. Martinez.

 7 How can knowing the heights of Ms. Weatherwax and Mr. Martinez help Jim and Nageela find the thief?

In Chapter 7 Jim measures Ms. Weatherwax's stride length. Her stride is about 22 hand-widths long. After leaving the school, Jim and Nageela find that Jim's hand is 7 cm wide.

 8 How many centimeters long is Ms. Weatherwax's stride? **154 cm**

 9 Look back at Questions 5 and 6. Use the information to estimate Ms. Weatherwax's height. Describe your method.

In the story, Jim measures Mr. Martinez's shadow length. At the same time, he also measures Nageela's height and shadow length. Use the diagrams below for Questions 10 and 11.

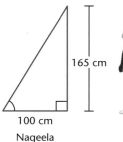

165 cm

100 cm
Nageela

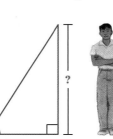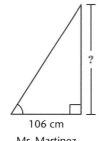

?

106 cm
Mr. Martinez

10 Are the triangles in the diagram similar? How do you know?

11 Find Mr. Martinez's height. Describe your method.

$$\frac{165 \text{ cm}}{100 \text{ cm}} = \frac{h}{106 \text{ cm}} \quad \text{where } h \text{ represents Mr. Martinez's height}$$
$$100h = 106(165)$$
$$h = 174.9 \text{ cm}$$

7. Jim and Nageela already know Ms. Weatherwax's and Mr. Martinez's blood types and that both people have bumps on their heads, so knowing their heights and comparing the heights to the range in Question 6(b) may help Jim and Nageela determine if either of the two can be eliminated as suspects.

9. about 175 cm using the fitted line on the scatter plot about 176.4 cm using the equation for the fitted line

10. Since two angles in the triangle for Nageela have the same measures as two of the angles in the triangle for Mr. Martinez, the triangles are similar.

PROJECT NOTES
The Mystery of Blacktail Canyon like most mysteries, is filled with characters and clues. Some clues purposely lead in the wrong direction, but others are essential to solving the mystery. Students will be more effective if they record observations, clues, and thoughts in a specific place. You may also want to prompt the class by asking questions such as, "What have you learned?" "What new questions do you have?" "Who are your prime suspects?" following each reading.

Module 3   Module Project   **223**

PROJECT NOTES

Instructions to the Teacher for using Clues Handout Sets and Interview Transcripts: The final result of the mystery depends on the clue set (and corresponding transcripts) distributed. You may choose for everyone in class to receive the same materials and get the same result, or you may want to give different materials to different groups or to different classes.

Choose a Clues Set (Set 1, 2, or 3) and cut the clues apart. Divide the separated clues among the group members. In **Question 16**, the group members will discuss the clues and narrow the possible suspect list from three to two people. (See *Project Notes* on page 225.)

 Summarize the clues you have gathered. Make sure you list everything you know or suspect about the thief. Below are some questions to consider.

♦ What do you know about the person's appearance?

♦ Do you know the person's height and foot size?

♦ How does knowing that the thief was injured help you?

♦ Did the suspect attend Dr. Ashilaka's lecture? the field trip? How do you know?

♦ Is the thief a stranger or someone who knows the area? Explain your reasoning.

Using a Venn diagram In Section 6, you narrowed down the list of suspects in *The Mystery of Blacktail Canyon.* You can narrow down the list further by identifying suspects whose height is the same as the height of the person who left the footprints in Blacktail Canyon.

Questions 13–15 are based on Chapter 8 of *The Mystery of Blacktail Canyon.*

 Look back at your notes from Questions 5 and 6. About how tall do you think the person who left the footprints is? **174 cm to 177 cm**

 Sketch the diagram shown. Shade your sketch to show where you would put suspects who fit the description of the thief. **See margin.**

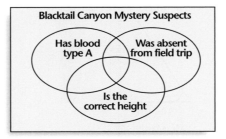

Blacktail Canyon Mystery Suspects

Has blood type A — Was absent from field trip — Is the correct height

 Use Project Labsheet A. Make a list of the people on the *Suspect List* who fit the description of the thief. **Perry Martinez, Teresa Seowtewa, Alice Weatherwax**

12. Answers will vary. Sample responses: The thief has an injury on his or her forehead. The thief is 174 cm to 177 cm tall and has a footprint 29 cm long. Knowing the thief was injured lets us eliminate suspects that don't have a recent injury to the forehead, and from the blood, we may be able to get his or her blood type and DNA.
Since the suspect had a pamphlet from the lecture, he or she had attended the lecture, but drove to the Blacktail site, so he or she was not on the field trip.
The thief knows the area since he or she was able to drive directly from the lecture to the site without studying maps.

14. See Additional Answers beginning on page A1.

Drawing Conclusions Throughout this project, you have used mathematics to help identify a thief. You have discovered some characteristics of the guilty person, and you have narrowed a list of 22 possible suspects to three. Now you will receive more information from your teacher that will help you narrow the list even further.

 SET UP

 16 Some information gathered during an investigation is useful. Some is not. Review the clue cards. Discuss the clues with your group. Write down the names of people you believe may have committed the crime. Explain why you feel these people and no others are guilty. **See margin.**

 17 **Use Project Labsheet B** Complete the labsheet and review the interview transcripts from the police investigation. Who do you now believe committed the crime? Is your final suspect one of the people you chose in Question 16? Explain why you feel this person and no one else is guilty. **See margin.**

18 Have your teacher check your answers to Questions 16 and 17. If you made an error, review your evidence and revise your solution. Record your new conclusion, explaining your errors as well as your new answer. **Answers will vary. Check students' work.**

Like you, Nageela and Jim think they know the identity of the thief. Ferrel, Jack, and Charlotte agree with their conclusion. At the end of Chapter 10, the five sleuths leave the station to catch the suspect.

 19 What happens after the police, Nageela, and Jim leave the station? Write an ending to *The Mystery of Blacktail Canyon* in your journal.
Answers will vary. Check students' work.

Work in a group of four.
You will need:
- *Project Labsheet B*
- *Your "detective's notebook" or journal*
- *Clues and transcripts chosen by your teacher*

PROJECT NOTES
Distribute the Interview Transcripts to the groups for **Question 17**. There are interviews for seven people: Cooper, Martinez (two), Pappas, Seowtewa (two), Suarez, Sullivan, and Weatherwax (two). For Martinez, Seowtewa, and Weatherwax, one of the two interviews <u>implicates</u> the suspect while the other one exonerates the suspect. (Note: The other interviews are provided in case a group still suspects the wrong person after **Question 16**; if so, the interview transcript will exonerate that person.) The interviews have file numbers listed. Distribute the interviews to a group according to which clue set the group received, as shown below. The group members will discuss the interviews and narrow the possible suspect list from two to one. (see below)

For **Question 16:** Distribute *Clues Handout* sets to result in the given possible suspects:
Set #1: Martinez or Weatherwax
Set #2: Martinez or Seowtewa
Set #3: Seowtewa or Weatherwax

For **Question 17**: Distribute transcript sets to accompany a given clue set, resulting in the final suspect listed:

After Clues Set #1, distribute transcripts 123–1, 113–2, 123–3, 112–4, 123–5, 123–6, and <u>111–7</u>; Weatherwax

After Clues Set #2, distribute transcripts 123–1, <u>222–2</u>, 123–3, 112–4, 123–5, 123–6, and 223–7; Martinez

After Clues Set #3, distribute transcripts 123–1, 113–2, 123–3, <u>333–4</u>, 123–5, 123–6, and 223–7; Seowtewa

Underlined transcripts are those that implicate the suspect.

16–17. See Additional Answers beginning on page A1.

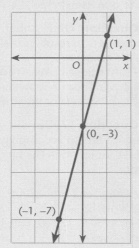

226

You will need • *graph paper* (Exs. 9–12) • *compass, ruler, and Review and Assessment Labsheet* (Ex. 18)

Find each value. Describe your method. Tell whether your answer is exact or an estimate. (Sec. 1, Explor. 1)

1. $\sqrt{0.09}$
0.3; mental math; exact

2. $\sqrt{16,000}$
about 126.5; calculator; estimate

3. $-\sqrt{96}$
about −9.8; calculator; estimate

4. $\sqrt{\frac{4}{81}}$ $\frac{2}{9}$; mental math; exact

5. Keith claims that the large can will hold twice as much as the small can. Is he correct? Explain. (Sec. 1, Explor. 2)
See margin.

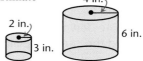

Find each value. (Sec. 2, Explor. 1)

6. $\dfrac{3(4) + 21}{\sqrt{102 + 19}}$ 3

7. $\sqrt{\dfrac{8(3) + 2(-4)}{36}}$ $\frac{2}{3}$

8. $\dfrac{5^2}{4(-3) + 87}$ $\frac{2}{9}$

Graph each equation. Tell whether the graph is *linear* or *nonlinear*.
(Sec. 2, Explor. 2) 9–12 See margin.

9. $y = 4x - 3$

10. $y = -2x + 1$

11. $y = x^2 + 1$

12. $y = 3x - 6$

Find the slope of each line. (Sec. 3, Explor. 1)

13.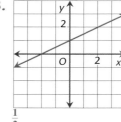
$\frac{1}{2}$

14.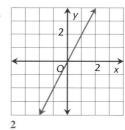
2

15.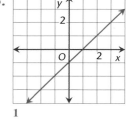
1

16. The scatter plot compares the populations of a number of counties in Texas in 2000 with the populations in 1990. The 1990 population is on the horizontal axis and the 2000 population is on the vertical axis. (Sec. 3, Explor. 2)

a. Which equation best fits the fitted line on the scatter plot?
 I. $y = 1.2x - 660$ **I**
 II. $y = 1.2x$
 III. $y = x + 800$

b. Use the equation you chose in part (a) to predict the 2000 population for a county that had a population of 6200 in 1990. 6780

County Populations

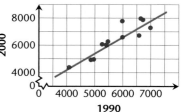

17. Estimate the height of the building if the person shown is about 6 ft tall. **about 30 ft** (Sec. 4, Explor. 1)

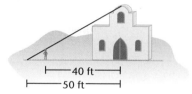

| 40 ft |
| 50 ft |

18. **Use the Review and Assessment Labsheet.** Follow the directions to find the diameter of the tree trunk. Mark a radius and a chord. (Sec. 4, Explor. 2)

Write each number in scientific notation. (Sec. 5, Explor. 1)

19. About 52,500,000 pet dogs lived in the United States in 1991. $5.25 \cdot 10^7$

20. The area of Mexico is about 762 thousand square miles. $7.62 \cdot 10^5$

For Exercises 21 and 22, write each product in decimal notation. (Sec. 5, Explor. 1)

21. The entrance to Mesa Verde Park is $6.95 \cdot 10^3$ ft above sea level. **6950 ft**

22. The mesa dwellings were abandoned about $7 \cdot 10^2$ years ago. **700 yr**

23. **Writing** Jill Wu is an anthropologist. She finds the incomplete skeleton of a 180 cm tall male at a site. She thinks another bone (a tibia) found nearby is part of the same skeleton. Explain how she can use the formula $h = 78.62 + 2.52t$, where h = the height of the skeleton and t = the length of the tibia in centimeters, to see whether she is correct. (Sec. 5, Explor. 2)

For Exercises 24–27, use the table. (Sec. 6, Explor. 1)

24. Make a Venn diagram that includes the means of transportation listed. Use the categories *Has Engine* and *Travels Only On Ground.* **See margin.**

25. Which means of transportation have an engine? **airplane, helicopter, speedboat, bus, car, train, truck**

26. Which means of transportation have an engine and travel only on the ground? **bus, car, train, truck**

27. Add two more means of transportation to the Venn diagram. **Sample Response: raft (neither), motorcycle (both)**

Reflecting ▸on the Module

28. **Writing** Explain how mathematics is important to the work of a police officer. What kinds of mathematics are used in investigations? **Answers will vary. Check students' work.**

Means of Transportation
airplane
bicycle
bus
car
helicopter
skateboard
skis
speedboat
train
truck

18. about 22 cm or $8\frac{5}{8}$ in.; Check students' drawings.

23. Sample Response: Substitute 180 for h in the formula and solve for t to get $t \approx 40$ cm. If the bone is from the same skeleton, it should be about 40 cm long.

24. See Additional Answers beginning on page A1.

Inventions

Module 4 Overview

Students analyze different inventions and test the effects of design variations. Students see how surface area, volume, slopes of lines, rational numbers, and combinations and permutations are related to inventions, such as the tin can, television, and Braille.

Module 4 Planner

Day 1: Section 1	Day 2: Section 1	Day 3: Section 1	Day 4: Section 2	Day 5: Section 2
Setting the Stage, p. 230 Exploration 1, pp. 231–233	Exploration 2, *through* *Question 18 pp. 234–236*	Exploration 2, *from* *Question 19 pp. 236–237* Key Concepts, pp. 238–239	Setting the Stage, p. 245 Exploration 1, pp. 246–247	Exploration 2, through *Question 11 pp. 248–249*
Day 6: Section 2	**Day 7: E²**	**Day 8: Section 3**	**Day 9: Section 3**	**Day 10: Section 3**
Exploration 2, *from* *Question 12 pp. 249–250* Key Concepts, p. 251	Work on Extended Exploration, p. 257	Setting the Stage, p. 258 Exploration 1, pp. 259–260	Exploration 2, *through* *Question 19 pp. 261–263*	Exploration 2, *from* *Question 20 p. 263* Key Concepts, pp. 264–265
Day 11: Review and Assessment	**Day 12: Section 4**	**Day 13: Section 4**	**Day 14: Section 4**	**Day 15: Section 4**
Mid-Module Quiz	Setting the Stage, pp. 270–271 Exploration 1, *through* *Question 7 pp. 271–272*	Exploration 1, *from* *Question 8 p. 273*	Exploration 2, *through* *Question 17 pp. 274–276*	Exploration 2, *from* *Question 18 p. 276* Key Concepts, p. 277
Day 16: Section 5	**Day 17: Section 5**	**Day 18: Section 5**	**Day 19: Section 6**	**Day 20: Section 6**
Setting the Stage, pp. 283–284 Exploration 1, *through* *Question 6 pp. 285–287*	Exploration 1, *from* *Question 7 p. 287*	Exploration 2, pp. 288–290 Key Concepts, pp. 291–292	Setting the Stage, p. 297 Exploration 1, *through* *Question 5 p. 298*	Exploration 1, *from* *Question 6 pp. 299–300* Key Concepts, p. 300
Day 21: Module Project	**Day 22: Review and Assessment**	**Day 23: Review and Assessment**	**Day 24: Assessment**	
Begin Module Project, pp. 304–305	Review and Assessment pp. 306–307	Discuss Review and Assessment pp. 306–307 Finish Module Project, pp. 304–305	Module 4 Test	

Materials List

Section	Materials
1	• Labsheet 1A, modeling clay, plastic knife, metric ruler, calculator
2	• Labsheet 2A, compass, metric ruler, scissors, tape, 8.5 in. x 11 in. sheet of paper, five cans of different sizes and shapes, calculator
3	• Labsheet 3A, graph paper
4	• calculator
5	• Labsheets 5A–5C, colored markers or pencils
6	• calculator
Project	• Project Labsheet A, metric ruler, material for building ramps and cylinders, small object (to be moved)

Module 4 Objectives

Section	Objectives	NCTM Standards 2000*
1	• Find the circumference and area of a circle. • Find volumes of rectangular prisms and cylinders. • Find the volume of a sphere. • Recognize the effects of linear dimension changes on area or volume.	1, 2, 3, 4, 6, 7, 8, 9, 10
2	• Find the surface area of a cylinder. • Find and interpret surface area to volume ratios.	1, 2, 3, 4, 6, 7, 8, 9, 10
3	• Find and interpret positive and negative slopes. • Identify slopes of horizontal and vertical lines and the y-intercept of a line. • Write equations in slope-intercept form. • Use equations in slope-intercept form and their graphs to model real-world situations.	1, 2, 3, 6, 7, 8, 9, 10
4	• Recognize the characteristics of rational numbers. • Use notation for repeating decimals. • Solve equations containing rational numbers.	1, 2, 6, 7, 8, 9, 10
5	• Use a tree diagram or the counting principle to count the number of ways a sequence of choices can be made. • Use the counting principle to find the number of permutations of a group of items. • Use a tree diagram to find the number of combinations of items chosen from a group of items.	1, 2, 6, 7, 8, 9, 10
6	• Use the counting principle to determine the probability of an event.	1, 2, 5, 6, 7, 8, 9, 10

* See page T14.

Section 1 Circumference, Area, and Volume

Section 1 Planner

Section Objectives

Exploration 1
- Find the circumference of a circle
- Find the area of a circle

Exploration 2
- Find volumes of rectangular prisms and cylinders
- Find the volume of a sphere
- Recognize the effects of linear dimension changes on area or volume

Days for Section 1

First Day
Setting the Stage, p. 230
Exploration 1, pp. 231–233

Second Day
Exploration 2 through Question 18, pp. 234–236

Third Day
Exploration 2 from Question 19, pp. 236–237
Key Concepts, pp. 238–239

Materials List

Exploration 1
- calculator

Exploration 2
- Labsheet 1A
- calculator
- modeling clay
- plastic knife
- metric ruler

Teaching Resources

Teacher's Resource Book
- Warm-Up
- Labsheet 1A
- Practice and Applications
- Study Guide
See page 229 for additional teaching resources.

Assessment Options

EMBEDDED ASSESSMENT
- Find the circumference of a circle
  Exercises 1, 3
- Find the area of a circle
  Exercise 5
- Find volumes of rectangular prisms and cylinders
  Exercises 10, 11, 13, 16
- Find the volume of a sphere
  Exercises 22a, 23
- Recognize the effects of linear dimension changes on area or volume
  Exercises 20b, 24, 25

PERFORMANCE TASK/PORTFOLIO
- Exercise 4 on *p. 240 (challenge)*
- Exercise 9 on *p. 241 (open-ended)*
- Exercise 24 on *p. 242 (open-ended)*
- Exercise 25 on *p. 243 (challenge)**
- Exercise 26 on *p. 243 (journal)*
- Standardized Testing on *p. 244 (open-ended)*

* indicates a problem-solving task that can be assessed using the Assessment Scales

QUIZZES/TESTS
- Section 1 Quick Quiz

TEST GENERATOR

Section 1 Overview

In this section, students will review the concepts of circumference and area while looking at inventions that have made pancakes a popular breakfast food for Americans.

Exploration 1
Scatter plots are used to represent the relationship between a circles's diameter or radius and its circumference and area. Students will interpret the plots and discuss their relationship to the formulas for circumference and area of a circle.

Exploration 2
Students will envision a stack of pancakes and use the stack to develop the formula for the volume of a cylinder. In an activity with clay and spheres, students explore how changing the diameter, a linear dimension, changes the volume, a 3-dimensional change. Through several practice and application problems students continue to explore how changing a linear dimension of a figure affects its circumference, area, or volume.

Guide for Assigning Homework

REGULAR SCHEDULING (45 MIN CLASS PERIOD)			EXERCISES TO NOTE		
Section/ P&A Pages	**Core Assignment**	**Extended Assignment**	**Additional Practice/Review**	**Open-ended Problems**	**Extended Problems**
1 pp. 239–243	**Day 1:** 1–3, 5–7 **Day 2:** 10–18, 21 **Day 3:** 22–24, ROS 26, SR 27–35	1–9 10–18 even, 19–21, SR 27 22–25, ROS 26, SR 32–35	EP, p. 244 TB, p. 589	PA 9, 24 ST 1, 2	PA Challenge 4, 19, 25

Key: PA = Practice & Application; ROS = Reflecting on the Section; SR = Spiral Review; TB = Toolbox; EP = Extra Skill Practice; Ext = Extension; ST = Standardized Testing

Math Background and Teaching Strategies

Classroom Ideas

Bulletin Board display ideas for this section include:

- pictorial history of inventions with a time line
- student work display of pancake designs from Question 11 p. 233

Visitors/field trips might include:

- inventors

Math Strands

Topic Spiraling and Integration

Measurement concepts, area and circumference of circles, and volume of cylinders and spheres are reviewed in this section. Since the circumference is the distance around a circle, the formula πd calculates a linear measure. Area is the amount of surface covered by a figure. The formula πr^2 calculates the number of square units of surface covered by a circular region. Volume is the amount of space, measured in cubic units, enclosed by a three-dimensional figure. Students should label answers with the correct units, for example, ft for circumference, ft^2 for area, or ft^3 for volume. Exact answers for circumference and area of circles and volume of cylinders and spheres should be written with the symbol π. Estimates can be made using an approximate value for π such as 3.14.

Exploration 1

Students used scatter plots and the equations of fitted lines to model relationships in Module 1. In this exploration, the formulas for the circumference and area of a circle are reintroduced by examining data displayed in scatter plots. The fitted line on the scatter plot for diameter and circumference approximates the graph of the formula $C = \pi d$. By examining the coordinates of points on the line, students discover that the circumference is a little more than 3 times the diameter. On the scatter plot for radius and area, the data points follow a curve since in the formula $A = \pi r^2$ the radius is squared. In Module 6 students will explore other situations that model linear and non-linear change.

Exploration 2

The formula for the volume of a cylinder is developed as an extension of the formula for the volume of a prism. Substituting πr^2 for the area of the base in the formula $V = Bh$ produces $V = \pi r^2 h$. This formula is applied in Section 2 of this module where students compare surface area to volume ratios in order to determine the efficiency ratings of various cylindrical containers. The formula for the volume of a sphere is not developed in this section, but is used in application problems. Volumes of pyramids and cones are developed in Module 5.

Section 2 Working with Cylinders

Section 2 Planner

Section Objectives

Exploration 1
- Find the surface area of a cylinder

Exploration 2
- Find and interpret surface area to volume ratios

Days for Section 2

First Day
Setting the Stage, *p. 245*
Exploration 1, *pp. 246–247*

Second Day
Exploration 2 through Question 11, *pp. 248–249*

Third Day
Exploration 2 from Question 12, *pp. 249–250*
Key Concepts, *p. 251*

Teaching Resources

Teacher's Resource Book
- Warm-Up
- Labsheet 2A
- Practice and Applications
- Study Guide
See page 229 for additional teaching resources.

Materials List

Exploration 1
- compass
- metric ruler
- scissors
- tape
- $8\frac{1}{2}$ in. by 11 in. sheet of paper

Exploration 2
- Labsheet 2A
- metric ruler
- five cans with different sizes and shapes
- calculator

Extented Exploration
- compass
- ruler
- scissors
- tape
- $8\frac{1}{2}$ in. by 11 in. sheet of paper

Assessment Options

EMBEDDED ASSESSMENT
- Find the surface area of a cylinder
  Exercises 2, 8
- Find and interpret surface area to volume ratios
  Exercises 10, 12, 14a–b

PERFORMANCE TASK/PORTFOLIO
- Exercise 15 on *p. 253 (research)*
- Exercise 17 on *p. 254 (challenge)*
- Exercise 19 on *p. 254 (visual thinking)*
- Extended Exploration on *p. 257**

* *indicates a problem solving task that can be assessed using the Assessment Scales*

QUIZZES/TESTS
- Section 2 Quick Quiz

TEST GENERATOR

Section 2 Overview

In this section, students will study the invention of the tin can, learning how they can use the surface area and volume of a can to compare the efficiency of different cans. Students can construct their own cans from a net so they will have a physical model of a cylinder.

Exploration 1
Students begin this exploration by creating their own can from a single sheet of paper. They then build on this experience, working as a class to develop the formula for finding the surface area of a cylinder.

Exploration 2
Students discuss the advantages of an *efficient* can (one that uses a small amount of metal compared to the amount of food or drink it holds). Then they measure various sizes of cylindrical containers and calculate the ratio of each container's surface area to its volume in order to determine the container's efficiency rating.

Guide for Assigning Homework

REGULAR SCHEDULING (45 MIN CLASS PERIOD)			EXERCISES TO NOTE		
Section/ P&A Pages	Core Assignment	Extended Assignment	Additional Practice/Review	Open-ended Problems	Extended Problems
2 pp. 252–256	**Day 1:** 1–9 **Day 2:** 10–14 **Day 3:** 15, 16, ROS 19, SR 20–27	1–9 10–14 15–18, ROS 19, Ext 28–30	EP, p. 256	PA 15	PA Challenge 17 Ext 28–30 E², p. 257

Key: PA = Practice & Application; ROS = Reflecting on the Section; SR = Spiral Review; TB = Toolbox; EP = Extra Skill Practice; Ext = Extension; ST = Standardized Testing

Math Background and Teaching Strategies

Classroom Notes

Student work displays for this section might include:

• paper cans from the E²

• cans with their efficiency ratings (from Question 10 of Exploration 2)

Math Strands

Topic Spiraling and Integration

Exploration 1

In Section 1 of this module, students learned to use the formulas for the circumference and area of a circle. Now, in Exploration 1 of Section 2, these formulas serve as the basis for developing the formula for surface area of a cylinder. The 3-dimensional cylinder is laid out in 2-dimensional shapes on a piece of paper. In Module 5, students will design nets for various 3-dimensional shapes. Though the circles and rectangle of this layout do not form one connected net, they can be taped or glued together to form a cylinder and could be easily attached to create a net.

Exploration 2

As they write ratios to represent the efficiencies of cans, students apply the formula for the volume of a cylinder learned in Section 1 of this module and the formula for the surface area of a cylinder from Exploration 1. For ease of comparison, students represent the ratio of the surface area of a cylinder to its volume in decimal form.

In Section 1 of this module, students represented the exact area and circumference of circles by using the π symbol. An approximation for π is also used in the application exercises of this section. By combining like terms, students can represent the formula for the surface area of a cylinder in terms of π.

Practice and Applications Exercise 1 could be completed as:

$$2\pi r^2 + 2\pi rh = 2\pi(2)^2 + 2\pi(2)(7)$$
$$= 8\pi + 28\pi$$
$$= 36\pi \text{ cm}^2$$

As an approximation, $36\pi \approx 36(3.14)$ or 113.04 cm^2

The ratios for efficiency could also be written using exact surface areas and volumes, however, students would need to understand how to simplify each fraction by recognizing $\frac{\pi}{\pi}$ as a form of 1, or by substituting the approximation 3.14 for π in the numerator and denominator prior to converting the ratio to a decimal, as in the following examples:

$$\frac{S.A.}{V} = \frac{36\pi \text{ cm}^2}{28\pi \text{ cm}^3} = \frac{36}{28} \approx 1.29$$

or $\dfrac{36\pi \text{ cm}^2}{28\pi \text{ cm}^3} \approx \dfrac{36(3.14)}{28(3.14)} = \dfrac{113.04}{87.92} \approx 1.29$

Section 3 Planner

Section Objectives

Exploration 1
- Find and interpret positive and negative slopes
- Identify slopes of horizontal and vertical lines

Exploration 2
- Identify the *y*-intercept of a line
- Write an equation in slope-intercept form
- Use equations in slope-intercept form and their graphs to model real-world situations

Days for Section 3

First Day
Setting the Stage, *p. 258*
Exploration 1, *pp. 259–260*

Second Day
Exploration 2 through Question 19, *pp. 261–263*

Third Day
Exploration 2 from Question 20, *p. 263*
Key Concepts, *pp. 264–265*

Materials List

Exploration 1
- Labsheet 3A
- graph paper

Exploration 2
- graph paper

Practice and Applications
- graph paper
- graphing calculator (optional)

Teaching Resources

Teacher's Resource Book
- Warm-Up
- Labsheet 3A
- Practice and Applications
- Study Guide
See page 229 for additional teaching resources.

Assessment Options

EMBEDDED ASSESSMENT
- Find and interpret positive and negative slopes
  Exercises 1, 8
- Identify slopes of horizontal and vertical lines
  Exercises 5, 8
- Identify the *y*-intercept of a line
  Exercises 12, 14
- Write an equation in slope-intercept form
  Exercises 18, 21
- Use equations in slope-intercept form and their graphs to model real-world situations
  Exercises 16, 17

PERFORMANCE TASK/PORTFOLIO
- Exercise 9 on *p. 266 (estimation)*
- Exercise 11 on *p. 266 (writing)*
- Exercise 24 on *p. 268 (challenge)*
- Standardized Testing on *p. 269 (open-ended)*

QUIZZES/TESTS
- Section 3 Quick Quiz
- Mid-Module Quiz

TEST GENERATOR

Section 3 Overview

In this section, students will explore slope and linear equations as they examine the electronics market.

Exploration 1
By studying a graph of black-and-white TV sales, students investigate how rates relate to slope. Using the graph, students learn to distinguish between lines with negative and positive slopes. Students also explore horizontal and vertical lines, determining slope and making generalizations regarding the slopes of these lines.

Exploration 2
As they compare market trends for VCR and DVD players, students are lead to discover the slope-intercept form of the equation of a line. Using the data, students learn to identify and interpret the *y*-intercept. They then explore the slope-intercept forms of horizontal, vertical, and parallel lines and make generalizations concerning them.

Guide for Assigning Homework

REGULAR SCHEDULING (45 MIN CLASS PERIOD)			EXERCISES TO NOTE		
Section/ P&A Pages	Core Assignment	Extended Assignment	Additional Practice/Review	Open-ended Problems	Extended Problems
3 pp. 265–269	**Day 1:** 1–8, 10, 11 **Day 2:** 12–17, SR 30–35 **Day 3:** 18–23, 25–28, ROS 29	1–7 odd, 8–11 12–17, SR 30–35 18, 21–25, 28, ROS 29	EP, p. 269	ST, p. 269 PA Challenge 24(d)	PA Challenge 24

Key: PA = Practice & Application; ROS = Reflecting on the Section; SR = Spiral Review; TB = Toolbox; EP = Extra Skill Practice; Ext = Extension; ST = Standardized Testing

Math Background and Teaching Strategies

Classroom Notes

Bulletin Board display ideas for this section include:

- an "estimate the slope of this line" interactive display with answers hidden under a flap where students can then check how close their estimate is

- student researched and graphed data displays for sales of modern style TVs (plasma, LCD, flat panel screen, high definition) with use of slope to predict future sales

- line graphs from magazines and newspapers

Small groups might be assigned one of the line graphs from the bulletin board and asked to write a summary of what the graph reports and what the slopes of the segments indicate.

Math Strands

Topic Spiraling and Integration

Exploration 1
Exploration 1 connects ideas about rates from Module 1 with slopes from Module 3. Students should be familiar with the concepts presented in this exploration since slope of a line is a review from Module 3. Previously the graphs focused on situations modeled by lines with positive slopes graphed in the first quadrant. Now students extend these concepts to include negative slope and graphs in all four quadrants of the coordinate plane. Slopes for horizontal and vertical lines are also introduced.

Exploration 2
With mastery of the concept of slope, students learn to use the slope and y-intercept to write an equation from a graph. The focus during the exploration is upon writing the equation of a graphed line in slope-intercept form, however in Practice and Application Exercise 23 students are shown how using the information from the slope-intercept form of a line can be used to graph a linear equation. They are then asked to apply this method instead of making a table of points.

In Module 6, students will study other graphs and functions that model changes in data. Their experience with studying a linear equation in a specific form will assist them in recognizing patterns in exponential and quadratic equations.

228H

Section 4 Rational Numbers

Section 4 Planner

Section Objectives

Exploration 1
- Recognize the characteristics of rational numbers
- Use notation for repeating decimals

Exploration 2
- Solve equations containing rational numbers

Days for Section 4

First Day
Setting the Stage, *pp. 270–271*
Exploration 1 through Question 7, *pp. 271–272*

Second Day
Exploration 1, *p. 273*

Third Day
Exploration 2 through Question 17, *pp. 274–276*

Fourth Day
Exploration 2 from Question 18, *p. 276*
Key Concepts. *p. 277*

Teaching Resources

Teacher's Resource Book
- Warm-Up
- Practice and Applications
- Study Guide
See page 229 for additional teaching resources.

Materials List

Exploration 1
- calculator

Assessment Options

EMBEDDED ASSESSMENT
- Recognize the characteristics of rational numbers
  Exercises 3, 5
- Use notation for repeating decimals
  Exercises 4(b)–(c)
- Solve equations containing rational numbers
  Exercises 10, 11, 23, 25

PERFORMANCE TASK/PORTFOLIO
- Exercise 5 on *p. 278 (writing)*
- Exercise 23 on *p. 279 (geometry connection)*
- Exercise 25 on *p. 279 (challenge)*
- Exercises 42–45 on *p. 281 (extension)*
- Standardized Testing on *p. 282 (open-ended)*

QUIZZES/TESTS
- Section 4 Quick Quiz

TEST GENERATOR

Section 4 Overview

In this section, students will explore the invention of numbers through a famous Egyptian papyrus. Students learn about the symbols used to write Egyptian numbers and how these symbols were used to represent rational numbers.

Exploration 1
Although they had symbols for a few special fractions, the ancient Egyptians wrote most fractions as sums of unit fractions. To imitate the Egyptian system, students are challenged to write modern fractions as the sum of unit fractions for which the Egyptians had symbols. Students recognize that the Egyptian fraction system made it possible for Egyptians to represent all the positive rational numbers. *Rational number* is defined and many examples of rational numbers such as fractions, mixed numbers, integers, terminating decimals, and repeating decimals are given.

Exploration 2
Students read part of an Egyptian papyrus relating to a problem about the surface area of a basket. Students use the formula for the surface area of a hemisphere to solve the problem and in the process discover that they must multiply or divide rational numbers to solve equations. *Reciprocal* is defined and students apply it in solving equations with fractional coefficients.

Guide for Assigning Homework

REGULAR SCHEDULING (45 MIN CLASS PERIOD)			EXERCISES TO NOTE		
Section/ P&A Pages	Core Assignment	Extended Assignment	Additional Practice/Review	Open-ended Problems	Extended Problems
4 pp. 278–281	**Day 1:** 1–2, SR 31–37 **Day 2:** 3–7 **Day 3:** 8–13, SR 38–41 **Day 4:** 14–29, 26–29, ROS 30	1–2, SR 31–37 3–7 8–13, SR 38–41, Ext 42–45 14, 15, 19, 23–29, ROS 30	TB, p. 585 EP, p. 282	ST, p. 282	Ext 42–45 PA Challenge 25

Key: PA = Practice & Application; ROS = Reflecting on the Section; SR = Spiral Review; TB = Toolbox; EP = Extra Skill Practice; Ext = Extension; ST = Standardized Testing

Math Background and Teaching Strategies

Classroom Notes

Bulletin board display ideas for this section include:

- student developed board that shows fractions written as the sum of unit fractions with Egyptian notation

Student interest centers for this section might include:

- activity sheets for other number systems (Mayan, Babylonian, binary)

Math Strands

Topic Spiraling and Integration

Exploration 1

By now students should be familiar with fraction and decimal operations and be prepared to use them throughout Book 3. A connection to rational numbers is made through the Egyptian numeration system and by examples in our common numeration system. The vocabulary of rational, terminating decimal, finite, and repeating decimal is emphasized. In Module 7, when students learn to simplify radicals, their vocabulary will be extended to include irrational number.

Exploration 2

Students began solving equations in Module 1. In this Module, they review reciprocals and apply multiplication and division of fractions in the context of solving equations. Students will continue to use formulas and equations that involve fractions and decimals as they study geometry topics in Module 5, graphs and functions in Module 6, and inequalities in Module 7. Spiral Review Exercises in the succeeding modules will also include practice with rational numbers and solving of equations containing them.

The context of the Moscow Papyrus and Egyptian symbols motivate the development of the formula for surface area of a hemisphere. Students should be able to apply the formulas for the surface area and volume of a sphere, since volume was reviewed in Sections 1 and 2 of this module.

Section 5 Counting Techniques

Section 5 Planner

Section Objectives

Exploration 1
- Use the counting principle to count the number of choices
- Find the number of permutations of a group of objects

Exploration 2
- Find numbers of combinations

Days for Section 2

First Day
Setting the Stage, *pp. 283–284*
Exploration 1 through Question 6,
pp. 285–287

Second Day
Exploration 1 from Question 7, *p. 287*

Third Day
Exploration 2, *pp. 288–290*
Key Concepts, *pp. 291–292*

Teaching Resources

Teacher's Resource Book
- Warm-Up
- Labsheets 5A, 5B, and 5C
- Practice and Applications
- Study Guide
See page 229 for additional teaching resources.

Materials List

Setting the Stage
- Labsheet 5A

Exploration 1
- colored markers or pencils

Exploration 2
- Labsheet 5B

Practice and Applications
- Labsheet 5C

Assessment Options

EMBEDDED ASSESSMENT
- Use the counting principle
  Exercises 2, 3
- Find numbers of permutations
  Exercises 9, 12
- Find numbers of combinations
  Exercises 14, 15

PERFORMANCE TASK/PORTFOLIO
- Exercise 17 on *p. 294 (writing)**
- Exercise 18 on *p. 294 (challenge)*
- Exercise 19 on *p. 295 (oral report)*
- Exercises 25–27 on *p. 295 (extension)*
- Standardized Testing on *p. 296 (performance task)*

* *indicates a problem solving task that can be assessed using the Assessment Scales*

QUIZZES/TESTS
- Section 5 Quick Quiz

TEST GENERATOR

Section 5 Overview

In this section, students will explore the invention of the Braille alphabet. The goal is to allow students to explore the counting principle, permutations, and combinations in situations other than probability and to recognize the way in which mathematics is linked to combinatorics. This is a difficult section for many students. Unless the content is required in your state or district curriculum framework, you may consider skipping this section.

Exploration 1
This exploration shows students how the counting principle is related to the development the Braille alphabet. This concept is then extended to permutations, allowing students to discover ways to find the number of arrangements when the order is important.

Exploration 2
In Exploration 2 students use the arrangements of dots in the top four positions of Braille symbols to determine how many symbols can be made using just these positions. The second exploration builds on the concepts in the first exploration as students recognize how a situation changes when the order in which items are selected is not an issue. Students will use the counting principle and permutations to build the concept of combinations. Working as a class, students will develop strategies for finding combinations using factorials.

228K

Guide for Assigning Homework

Math Background and Teaching Strategies

Classroom Notes

Bulletin board display ideas for this section include:

• the Braille system with messages written in Braille

Interest centers might include:

• activity cards students can manipulate in order to find the number of pizzas with 3 toppings that can be made from 5 topping choices, or the number of ways a radio station can play four of their five favorite songs in a row

• a Braille children's book and a pair of sunglasses with blackened lenses

Visitors/field trips might include:

• a speaker who uses Braille to read

• a person or company who uses optimization/combinatorics to do scheduling/routing of 911 calls, bus routes, or tournaments.

Math Strands

Topic Spiraling and Integration

The use of combinatorics is ever increasing as computer software designers attempt to create programs to model various choices that could be made in routing calls, locating fire stations, or determining efficient ways to design bus routes. This section introduces students to both permutations and combinations with the goal that students will be able to determine the difference between the two. The Extra Skill and Practice exercises are of mixed type so that students will get the opportunity to practice determining whether permutations or combinations are applicable to the situation.

Exploration 1

Students begin by using tree diagrams to represent the number of choices for a situation. This model is then connected to the counting principle that shows how the number of choices at each branching of the tree diagram can be represented numerically and then multiplied to find the total number of ways the choices can be made. The counting principle allows students to progress from a concrete model (tree diagram) to a more abstract representation (the product of choices). Through the counting principle and permutation activities, the concept of factorials begins to be developed and applied.

Exploration 2

Combinations are approached from the perspective of eliminating duplicate responses since order is not important. In the last few exercises of this exploration, students begin to informally develop the formula

$$C_{n,r} = \frac{n!}{(n-r)!r!}$$

for the number of combinations of n things taken r at a time. Factorials are formally defined at this point.

Section 6 — Working with Probability

Section 6 Planner

Section Objectives

Exploration 1
• Use the counting principle to determine the probability of an event

Days for Section 6

First Day
Setting the Stage, *p. 297*
Exploration 1 through Question 5, *p. 298*

Second Day
Exploration 1, *pp. 299–300*
Key Concepts, *p. 300*

Teaching Resources

Teacher's Resource Book
• Warm-Up
• Practice and Applications
• Study Guide
See page 229 for additional teaching resources.

Materials List

Exploration 1
• calculator

Assessment Options

EMBEDDED ASSESSMENT
• Use the counting principle to determine the probability of an event
  Exercises 4, 6, 7

PERFORMANCE TASK/PORTFOLIO
• Exercise 8 on *p. 302 (writing)*
• Exercise 9 on *p. 302 (open-ended)*
• Exercise 10 on *p. 302 (challenge)*
• Exercise 11 on *p. 302 (visual thinking)*
• Module Project on *pp. 304–305*

QUIZZES/TESTS
• Section 6 Quick Quiz
• Module Tests A and B
• Module Standardized Test
• Module Performance Assessment

TEST GENERATOR

Section 6 Overview

In this section, students will continue their study of counting as they explore how to use the counting principle to determine the probability of an event. In the Setting the Stage activity, students create a key for a 3-digit combination lock.

Exploration 1
Using their 3-digit keys from the Setting the Stage, students explore the probability that all students chose a different 3-digit key. They begin their exploration of this problem by looking at a simpler situation. A chart helps them model the possible combinations. Using the chart to count the ways to choose a different key and to count the total ways to choose keys, students determine the probability that two people choose different keys. Then students use a formula involving the counting principle to find the probability. Finally, students apply the formula to find the probability that each person in the class chose a different 3-digit key.

Guide for Assigning Homework

REGULAR SCHEDULING (45 MIN CLASS PERIOD)			**EXERCISES TO NOTE**		
Section/ P&A Pages	**Core Assignment**	**Extended Assignment**	**Additional Practice/Review**	**Open-ended Problems**	**Extended Problems**
6 pp. 301–302	**Day 1:** 1–3, SR 12–13 **Day 2:** 4–8, ROS 11	1–3, SR 12–13 4–10, ROS 11	EP, p. 303 Review & Assessment, pp. 306–307	PA 9	PA Challenge 10 Mod Proj, pp. 304–305

Key: PA = Practice & Application; ROS = Reflecting on the Section; SR = Spiral Review; TB = Toolbox; EP = Extra Skill Practice; Ext = Extension; ST = Standardized Testing

Math Background and Teaching Strategies

Classroom Notes

Bulletin Board display ideas for this section might include:

- a combination lock that shows how the counting principle can be used to determine the probability of entering the correct key; students can try their luck at finding the "key".

- real world problems whose solutions involve using the counting principle to find a probability (include students' examples from PA Question 10)

- a display of the probabilities determined for the key problem in Exploration 1 and the actual results of Question 9 for each math class.

Math Strands

Topic Spiraling and Integration

Exploration 1

In this section students bring together their knowledge of probability, studied in Module 2, with the counting principle, covered in the previous section of this module. Students see how the counting principle can be applied in more complex problem-solving situations as they find probabilities of events occurring within their classroom. The problem is approached using the *solve a simpler problem* strategy, one of the problem-solving strategies students have seen throughout Books 1, 2, and 3.

In working with probability concepts, students also review the basic skills of writing fractions in simplest form and writing fractions as decimals. When using the counting principal to find the probability of an event, it is best if students leave the numerator and/or the denominator written as a product of factors (instead of finding the products) before simplifying the fraction. Students should see the value in simplifying fractions before multiplying especially in problems where there are several choices and the product is large. You can remind them of this through the example on page 299, by showing how in $\frac{6 \cdot 5}{6 \cdot 6}$, $\frac{6}{6}$ is a form of 1 and therefore the fraction is easily simplified to $\frac{5}{6}$.

Module 4

OVERVIEW

Students analyze different inventions and test the effects of design variations. Students see how surface area, volume, slopes of lines, rational numbers, and combinations and permutations are related to inventions, such as the tin can, television, and Braille.

PREREQUISITE SKILLS

Warm-Up Exercises for each section are provided in the *Teacher's Resource Book*. You can use these exercises to review skills and concepts students will need for each section. In addition, the Spiral Review exercises at the end of each section in the student edition provide practice on prerequisite skills.

MODULE DIAGNOSTIC TEST

The Module Diagnostic Test in the *Teacher's Resource Book* can be used to assess students' prior knowledge of skills and concepts that will be taught in each section of this module. You can use test results to help structure your teaching to meet the diverse needs of your classroom.

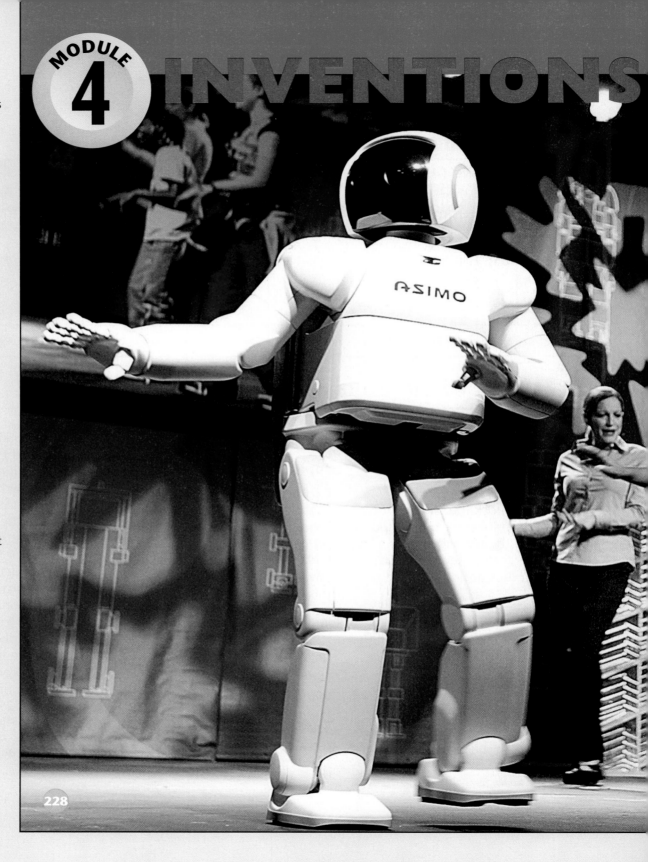

MODULE 4 INVENTIONS

228

CONNECTING
MATHEMATICS
The & Theme

MODULE 4 — SECTION OVERVIEW

① Circumference, Area, and Volume

As you study the invention of pancakes:
- ◆ Find the circumference and area of a circle
- ◆ Find volumes of prisms, cylinders, and spheres

② Working with Cylinders

As you read about tin cans:
- ◆ Find the surface area of a cylinder
- ◆ Find and interpret the ratio of surface area to volume

③ Slopes and Equations of Lines

As you explore TV sales:
- ◆ Identify positive, negative, zero, and undefined slopes
- ◆ Write equations of lines in slope-intercept form

④ Rational Numbers

As you learn to write fractions using the Egyptian number system:
- ◆ Recognize characteristics of rational numbers
- ◆ Solve equations containing rational numbers

⑤ Counting Techniques

As you learn about Braille:
- ◆ Find numbers of permutations
- ◆ Find numbers of combinations

⑥ Working with Probability

As you examine keys for locks:
- ◆ Find probabilities of events

The Module Project

Building a Ramp

The ancient Egyptians may have used ramps and cylinders to move the stone blocks that form the Pyramids of Giza. You will use mathematics to design and build your own model ramp and cylinders that you can use to move small objects.

More on the Module Project
See pp. 304–305.

INTERNET
Resources and practice at
classzone.com

Module Resources

TEACHER'S RESOURCE BOOK
Resources
- The *Math Gazette* (parent newsletter)
- Warm-Ups
- Labsheets
- Practice and Applications
- Study Guide

Assessment
- Section Quick Quizzes
- Mid-Module Quiz
- Module 4 Diagnostic Test
- Module 4 Tests A and B
- Module 4 Standardized Test
- Module 4 Performance Assessment
- Modules 3 and 4 Cumulative Test
- Mid-Year Test

SPANISH RESOURCES
- The *Math Gazette* (parent newsletter)
- Practice and Applications
- Assessment
- Spanish Glossary

STUDENT WORKBOOK

TECHNOLOGY BOOK

TECHNOLOGY RESOURCES
- @Home Tutor
- Test Generator
- Activity Generator
- Professional Development DVD
- Online Activities

Setting the Stage

ABOUT THE THEME

Students will learn some fun facts about the invention of the pancake and different devices invented for creating "the perfect" pancake. They will explore how the formulas for the circumference and area of a circle are developed and use these formulas to perform calculations. Pancakes are used again in Exploration 2, providing a context for developing formulas for the volumes of cylinders (stacks of pancakes) and spheres (round donut-hole type pancakes called Aebelskivers).

GETTING STARTED

In preparation for the lessons on circumference, area, and volume, Module 4 Section 1 *Warm–Up* asks students to identify the radius and diameter of a circle and the dimensions of a figure.

Section ① Circumference, Area, and Volume

Perfect Pancakes

Setting the Stage

Ask people to describe a typical American breakfast and many will mention pancakes, but pancakes are popular all over the world. There are French *crêpes,* Russian *blini,* and German *Pfannkuchen,* to name just a few. Pancakes may be thick or thin, fried or baked, sweet, salty, or even spicy. But the typical American pancake is sweet and fluffy and served with syrup.

Today one pancake restaurant chain alone serves a total of nearly 2 million pancakes each day in the United States and Canada. The popularity of pancakes has led to inventions such as the pancake ring for making multiple pancakes at once, specialty pans that allow you to flip a pancake without removing it from the pan, and even griddles that allow you to cook special designs or lettering into your pancakes.

This pancake ring makes four perfectly round $3\frac{1}{2}$ in. diameter pancakes.

1. a. **Sample Response: An 8 in. diameter pan is needed. Two pancake rings together are 7 in. across, but on the diagonal, I added some extra space for the center hole where the handle is.**

Think About It

1 a. Estimate the minimum size skillet needed to use the pancake ring shown at the left.

   b. Suppose an average pancake is $6\frac{1}{2}$ in. in diameter. How many pancakes laid side-by-side would fit across your classroom? **Answers will vary by class. Check students' work.**

2 A catering service claims it has sold 30,000,000 pancakes that, if laid end-to-end, would stretch from Los Angeles to Springfield, Illinois, a distance of 1857 mi. About what diameter pancakes does the catering service sell? **about 4 in.**

▶ **In this module, you will learn about the history of certain inventions and see how these inventions relate to mathematics.**

Exploration 1

Exploration 1

TEACHING NOTES

In **Question 3(a)** tell students that the value of π given by the calculator is an approximation of π.

Question 4 reviews the concept of circumference developed in Books 1 and 2. If students' work with circumference has been limited, you may choose to have them use string to measure the circumference and diameter of circular objects and then have the class create their own scatter plot of the data obtained. In answering **part (b)**, suggest that students examine the coordinates of points on the graph, or choose a diameter, calculate the corresponding circumference using the formula, and then compare it to the points with the same diameters that are plotted on the graph.

Finding Circumference and AREA

GOAL

LEARN HOW TO...
◆ find the circumference and area of a circle

AS YOU...
◆ interpret scatter plots

KEY TERMS
◆ circumference
◆ area

▶ The **circumference** of a circle is the distance around it. The exact relationship between the circumference and the diameter of a circle is given by the formula $\frac{C}{d} = \pi$, or $C = \pi d$.

3 a. [calculator] Calculator Press the [π] key on a calculator. What number appears? **3.141592654 (number of digits displayed may vary)**

b. π is actually a letter from the Greek alphabet. Does this mean that it is a variable? Explain.

c. Which is a closer approximation for π, 3.14 or $\frac{22}{7}$? Explain.

4 Try This as a Class Some students measured the diameter and the circumference of several circular objects. Then they made a scatter plot and drew a fitted line.

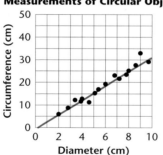

Measurements of Circular Objects

Circumference (cm) vs. Diameter (cm)

a. Does the scatter plot show a positive or negative correlation between the diameter and the circumference of a circle? Explain. **positive; the data points are moving upward and to the right.**

b. How do the data support the formula for the circumference of a circle?

c. Why is only Quadrant I used for the graph? **The other quadrants would only be used for negative diameters or negative circumferences which are not possible.**

3. b. No; A variable is a symbol used to represent a quantity that is unknown or that can change and is known and does not change.

c. Sample Response: $\frac{22}{7}$; The difference between $\frac{22}{7}$ and π is about 0.00126 and the difference between π and 3.14 is about 0.00159.

4. b. The fitted line shows that for each diameter, the circumference is about 3 times the diameter. The formula uses π • the diameter for the circumference, which calculates to be a little more than 3 times the diameter.

TECHNOLOGY NOTE
For a related technology activity, see the *Technology Book*.

231

✔ QUESTION 6

...checks that you can find the circumference of a circle.

5. Since π represents a non-repeating and non-terminating number, any number we use for π is only an approximation for the actual value. Thus to show the actual value of 20 times pi you must use the symbol.

9. The graph in the middle best represents the relationship of πr². Sample Response: I tested a few different radius lengths by using the formula and then locating those coordinate pairs on each graph to see which ones were closest to the fitted line or curve of the scatter plots.

EXAMPLE

To find the circumference of a circle with a diameter of 20 cm, evaluate the expression πd when d = 20.

To approximate the circumference, use 3.14 for π.

$C = \pi d$
$= \pi(20)$
$\approx (3.14)(20)$
≈ 62.8

To find the exact circumference, substitute 20 for d. Use parentheses to show multiplication.

The circumference is about 62.8 cm.

5 Discussion You can also give the circumference in the Example in terms of π. Explain why the circumference is exactly 20π cm.

6 ✔ CHECKPOINT

  a. Find the exact circumference of a circle with r = 6 cm. **12π cm**

  b. Approximate the circumference of a circle with d = 15 cm. Use 3.14 for π. **47.1 cm**

7 What length strip of metal is needed to make one of the four circular parts of the pancake ring shown on page 230? **about 11 in.**

▶ The **area** of a circle is the number of square units of surface the figure covers. You can use the equation $A = \pi r^2$ to find the area of a circle when you know its radius.

8 a. Name a circular object used in daily life. Describe the circumference of the object. **Answers will vary. Sample Response: pair of eyeglasses; the wire around one lens**

  b. Describe the area of the object. **Sample Response: the glass lens**

9 Discussion Which of the following best represents the relationship between a circle's area and its radius? How do you know?

Area Measurements of Circular Objects

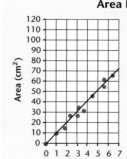
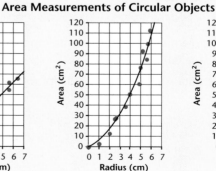
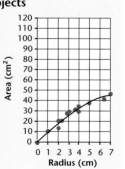

▶ When you know a circle's radius, you can find both the exact area and an approximate area of the circle.

FOR▶HELP
with *exponents*, see
TOOLBOX, p. 589

EXAMPLE

Find the area of a circle with a radius of 2.4 cm. Use 3.14 for π to find an approximate area.

2.4 cm

SAMPLE RESPONSE

Exact Area

$A = \pi r^2$

$= \pi(2.4)^2$

$= \pi(5.76)$

$= 5.76\pi$

Approximate Area

$A = \pi r^2$

$= \pi(2.4)^2$

$\approx (3.14)(5.76)$

≈ 18.0864

This is an approximation because 3.14 is an approximation for π.

The exact area is 5.76π cm².

An approximate area is 18.0864 cm².

▶ Unless otherwise instructed, when you are asked to approximate the value of an expression involving π, use 3.14 for π and round to the nearest hundredth, if necessary.

10 ✔ **CHECKPOINT** Find the exact area and an approximate area of each circle.

   a. circle with $r = 6$ cm 36π cm²; 113.04 cm²

   b. circle with $d = 15.2$ cm 57.76π cm²; 181.37 cm²

✔ **QUESTION 10**

...checks that you can find the area of a circle.

11 You have been assigned to reinvent the pancake shape so that it will no longer be circular. The marketing department wants the new design to produce a pancake that has about the same area as a standard 5.5 in. diameter circular ring.

   a. Sketch your design and label its dimensions.
   Check students' sketches.
   b. Show how the area is equal to that of a 5.5 in. diameter circular ring.
   Check students' work. (area of 5.5 in. diameter ring ≈ 23.75 in.²)
   c. How will the length of the metal strip needed for your design differ from the length needed for a 5.5 in. diameter ring?
   Check students' work. (circumference of a 5.5 diameter ring ≈ 17.27 in.)

HOMEWORK EXERCISES ▶ See Exs. 1–9 on pp. 239–241.

Exploration 1 *continued*

TEACHING NOTES
Question 11 Encourage students to be creative in their designs, and to use a combination of shapes. Display designs on a class bulletin board or have students send their designs with letters to a local diner or business that sells pancakes.

HOME INVOLVEMENT
Question 11 At home students might use their designs to create a mold out of cardboard covered with aluminum foil. Then under supervision of an adult, they could try cooking a pancake using their mold.

Exploration 2

Finding VOLUME

SET UP *Work in a group of four. You will need • Labsheet 1A • metric ruler • 2 5-oz cans of modeling clay • plastic knife*

▶ **DO NOT TRY THESE AT HOME!** Have you ever watched old movies where actors try to set a record swallowing goldfish? or eating pies? Setting eating records is dangerous to your health, but studying eating records can help you understand volume.

- ◆ Paul Hughes ate 39 jelly sandwiches in 60 min.

- ◆ Peter Dowdeswell ate 62 pancakes with butter and syrup in 6 min 58.5 sec.

12 On average, what fraction of a sandwich did Paul Hughes consume per minute? Do you think this is an amazing feat?

▶ Another way to decide whether Hughes's feat was amazing is to estimate the volume of what he ate. A stack of 39 jelly sandwiches would be shaped like a right *prism*. A **prism** is a **polyhedron** in which two of the faces, the **bases**, are congruent and parallel. The other faces are parallelograms. In a right prism, the other faces are rectangles.

> A **polyhedron** is a 3-dimensional object made up of flat surfaces, or **faces**, that are polygons.

Volume of a Prism
Volume = Area of the base × height
$V = Bh$

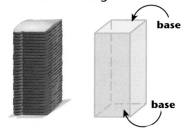

base

base

13 The shape of the bases of a prism determine the type of prism.

  a. Why does it make sense to call the prism shown above a *rectangular* prism? **The bases are rectangles.**

  b. If the bases of a rectangular prism have length *l* and width *w*, what is another way to write the formula $V = Bh$ using *l* and *w*? $V = lwh$

 Module 4 Inventions

14 Each sandwich Paul Hughes ate measured 5 in. by 3 in. and was $\frac{1}{2}$ in. thick. Assume each sandwich is a rectangular prism.

    a. Estimate the height of a stack of 39 sandwiches. **about 20 in.**

    b. Find the actual height. **19.5 in.**

    c. Find the area of the base of the stack of sandwiches. **15 in.²**

    d. Find the volume of the sandwiches Paul Hughes ate. **292.5 in.³**

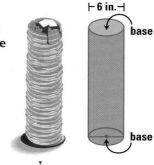

▶ How does Peter Dowdeswell's record compare with Paul Hughes's record? To see, imagine a stack of 62 pancakes. The stack would be shaped like a *circular cylinder*. A **cylinder** is a 3-dimensional figure that has a curved surface and two flat, parallel, congruent bases. A circular cylinder has two circular bases.

15 Each pancake was $\frac{3}{8}$ in. thick and had a 6 in. diameter.

    a. Show with your hands the approximate height of the stack of 62 pancakes. Compare your estimate with others in your class. **Answers will vary. Check students' work.**

    b. Find the actual height of the stack of 62 pancakes. **23.25 in.**

▶ You can use the formula for the volume of a prism to find the volume of a cylinder: **Volume = area of base • height** or **$V = Bh$.** In this book, all the cylinders are circular cylinders, so you can use the formula for the area of a circle to find *B*.

EXAMPLE

Approximate the volume of a cylinder with a height of 10 in. and a diameter of 8 in.

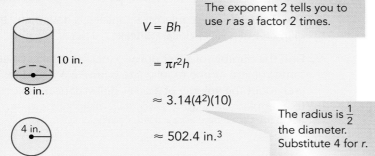

The exponent 2 tells you to use *r* as a factor 2 times.

$$V = Bh$$

$$= \pi r^2 h$$

$$\approx 3.14(4^2)(10)$$

The radius is $\frac{1}{2}$ the diameter. Substitute 4 for *r*.

$$\approx 502.4 \text{ in.}^3$$

The volume of the cylinder is about 502.4 in.³

Exploration 2 *continued*

TEACHING NOTES

Question 16 With the class, work through the Example again, finding the exact volume so students can see where the 160 comes from. Remind students that the commutative property allows them to change the order of multiplication so π160 is the same as 160π.

DEVELOPING MATH CONCEPTS

Question 19 After completing **part (e)**, ask students, "The diameter of a regular pancake is 3 times the diameter of a silver dollar pancake, so why is the volume of one regular pancake 9 times the volume of one silver dollar pancake and not 3 times?" (*The height of $\frac{1}{4}$ in. is constant, so students are only comparing the areas of the circles created by the pancakes. Diameter is a linear measurement, but the area of a circle is 2-dimensional and uses the factor r twice in the formula $A = \pi r^2$.*) Refer students back to the scatter plots in Exploration 1. The circumference plot is a linear graph, so the circumference increases at a constant rate relative to the diameter. However, the area plot shows a non-linear graph, with area increasing as the square of the radius. To check for understanding of this concept, ask students, "If the diameter of a regular pancake had been 4 times the diameter of a silver dollar pancake, how would the volume be affected?" (*The volume would be 16 times as great since $4^2 = 16$.*)

✔ **QUESTION 18**

...checks that you can find the volumes of rectangular prisms and cylinders.

16. a. 3.14 is an approximation of π, so the volume calculated with 3.14 for π is an approximate value.

b. The exact value of π cannot be expressed as a decimal or fraction, so the exact answer must be expressed in terms of π and $\pi(4^2)(10) = 160\pi$.

---

16 a. Discussion In the Example, why is the volume of the cylinder *about* 502.4 in.³ and not *exactly* 502.4 in.³?

b. The volume of the cylinder in the Example is *exactly* 160π in.³ Explain why this is true.

17 a. Use the information in Question 15 to find the volume of the stack of pancakes eaten by Peter Dowdeswell. **about 657.05 in.³**

b. Who ate a greater volume of food, Dowdeswell or Hughes? **Peter Dowdeswell**

18 ✔ **CHECKPOINT** Find the volume of each figure.

a. rectangular prism: *l* = 5 ft, *w* = 8 ft, *h* = 9 ft **360 ft³**

b. cylinder: *r* = 5 cm, *h* = 3 cm **75π cm³ or 235.5 cm³**

▶ Silver dollar pancakes are so named because they are similar in size to silver dollars.

19 Try This as a Class

a. Suppose you normally eat four regular 6 in. diameter pancakes before you feel full. If each pancake is about $\frac{1}{4}$ in. thick, find the volume of pancakes you normally eat. **V = 9π in.³ or about 28.26 in.³**

b. Suppose you decide to try the new silver dollar size pancakes. Each one is 2 in. in diameter and about $\frac{1}{4}$ in. thick. Find the volume of one pancake. **$V = \frac{1}{4}\pi$ in.³ or about 0.79 in.³**

c. How many silver dollar pancakes must you eat to consume the same volume as the regular pancakes you normally eat? **36**

d. The diameter of a regular size pancake is how many times the diameter of a silver dollar pancake? **3 times**

e. Find the number of silver dollar pancakes it takes to equal the same volume as one regular size pancake. What does this tell you about the volume of a silver dollar pancake in comparison to a regular pancake? **9 silver dollar pancakes; A silver dollar has one-ninth the volume of one regular pancake.**

▶ In American folklore, the fictional lumberjack Paul Bunyan was a man of enormous size, strength, and appetite. One legend involves his circular pancake griddle. It had a diameter of 236 ft, or 2832 in.!

20 Suppose Paul Bunyan made a giant pancake that covered the entire circular pancake griddle and had a thickness of $\frac{3}{8}$ in.

    a. Find the volume of the pancake in cubic inches.
    751,896 in.³ ≈ 2,360,953.44 in.³
    b. How would the volume of the pancake compare with the volume of the 62 pancakes Peter Dowdeswell ate? (See Question 17(a). The volume would be about 3593 times that of the pancakes Peter Dowdeswell ate.

▶ A **sphere** is a 3-dimensional figure made up of a set of points that are an equal distance from a given point, called the center.

21 An *Aebleskiver* is a traditional Scandinavian spherical shaped pancake. The seven molds of the pan are each the shape of a hemisphere (half-sphere), usually with a radius of 2 in. The pancake is flipped to create a sphere.

    a. Suppose you wanted to make an *Aebleskiver* pan with molds one-half the diameter of the regular size holes. How might this affect the amount of pancake batter needed for each hole?

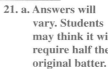

    b. **Use Labsheet 1A.** Complete the activity and table. See margin.

    c. Does a sphere with one-half the volume of a larger sphere have a diameter equal to one-half the diameter of the larger sphere? Explain. No; Sample Response: When our group laid the hemisphere with one half the volume on top of the original hemisphere, its diameter covered more than half the diameter of the larger.

▶ The formula for the volume *V* of a sphere is $V = \frac{4}{3}\pi r^3$ where *r* = radius.

22 **a.** Find the exact volume of a sphere with a radius of 1 in. $\frac{4}{3}\pi$ in.³

    b. Find the exact volume of a sphere with a radius of $\frac{1}{2}$ in.

    c. Compare the volumes. If one sphere's radius is one-half that of a second sphere, how do the diameters compare?

    d. **Discussion** If you were to increase the radius of a sphere to 5 times its original size, how would this affect the volume of the sphere? Why? The volume would be 125 times the volume of the original sphere. The increase in volume is the cube of the increase in the radius, or 5³.

21. a. Answers will vary. Students may think it will require half the original batter.

22. b. $\frac{1}{6}\pi$ in.³

    c. Its volume is $\frac{1}{8}$ the volume of the original sphere.

| HOMEWORK EXERCISES | ▶ See Exs. 10–26 on pp. 241–243.

The formula for the volume of a sphere is given here and used in the applications. The formula will be developed in Module 5 while studying cones.

In **Question 21**, remind students to use the commutative and associative properties of multiplication to simplify the exact volumes in **parts (a) and (b)**.
In **part (c)**, students may find it easier to compare the volumes if they leave their answer to **part (b)** as $\frac{4}{24}\pi$ instead of reducing it to $\frac{1}{6}\pi$.
Part (d) can be related back to the discussion on area and how altering the radius of a circle affected its area. The formula for area used r^2. Now that the formula for volume uses r^3—how do they think this will affect the volume when *r* is changed? A cube serves as another example since the length, width, and height are the same measure. Doubling the length of an edge makes the length twice as long, the width twice as long, and the height twice as long, so when they are multiplied to find the volume, the volume is increased by 2 · 2 · 2 or 8 times the original volume. (Students explored this idea in *The Mystery of Blacktail Canyon* Module 3, Section 4.) Similarly, *r* · *r* · *r* in the formula for the volume of a sphere produces the same effect on volume. Students will explore more of this concept in the Practice and Applications exercises for this section.

21. b. See Additional Answers beginning on page A1.

Key Concepts

ABSENT STUDENTS

For students who were absent for all or part of this section, the blackline Study Guide for Section 1 may be used to present the ideas, concepts, and skills of Section 1.

CLOSURE QUESTION

Write the formulas for the circumference of a circle, the volume of a prism, the volume of a cylinder, and the volume of a sphere. Then name the variables in each and what they represent.

Sample Response:

$C = \pi d$: C = circumference, d = diameter

$V = Bh$: V = volume, B = area of the base, h = height of prism,

$V = \pi r^2 h$ V = volume, r = radius, h = cylinder height,

$V = \frac{4}{3}\pi r^3$, V = volume, r = radius

Key Terms

circumference

area

polyhedron

face

prism

base

cylinder

Section 1
Key Concepts

Circumference (pp. 231–232)

π is the ratio of the circumference of a circle to its diameter.
π is approximately equal to 3.14.

$$\frac{C}{d} = \pi$$

$$C = \pi d$$

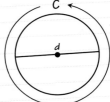

The circumference C of a circle is the distance around the circle.

Area (pp. 232–233)

The area A of a circle with radius r is equal to πr^2.
$A = 16\pi$ in.^{2} is the exact area of a circle with radius 4 in.
$A \approx 50.24$ in.^{2} is an approximation, since 3.14 is substituted for π.

Prisms and Cylinders (pp. 234–236)

A polyhedron is a 3-dimensional figure made up of flat surfaces, or faces, that are polygons. A prism is a polyhedron in which two faces, the bases, are congruent and parallel. The other faces are parallelograms.

A cylinder has a curved surface and two flat, parallel, congruent bases. In this book, all the cylinders have circular bases.

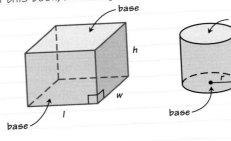

Use the formula $V = Bh$ to find the volume of a rectangular prism and a cylinder.

Key Concepts Questions

23 The formula for the circumference of a circle is sometimes written as $C = 2\pi r$, where r = the radius of the circle. Explain how this formula is related to the formula $C = \pi d$. Then find the circumference of a circle with radius 5 cm. **Sample Response: $2r$ is equivalent to d; about 34 cm**

24 The height of a circular cylinder is 5 in. The diameter of a base is 4 in. Find its volume. **exactly 20π in.^{3} or approximately 62.8 in.^{3}**

Section 1

Key Concepts

Key Term

Spheres (p. 237)

A sphere is a 3-dimensional figure made up of a set of points that are an equal distance from a given point, called the center.

The formula $V = \frac{4}{3}\pi r^3$ can be used to find the volume V of a sphere when the radius r is known.

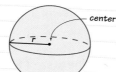

center

sphere

25 Key Concepts Question Find the volume of a sphere with a radius of 4 cm. **exactly $85\frac{1}{3}\pi$ cm³ or approximately 267.95 cm³**

Section 1

Practice & Application Exercises

1. Find the exact circumference of a circle with the given radius or diameter.

   a. $r = 12$ m **24π m**   b. $d = 10$ ft **10π ft**   c. $d = 1.1$ cm **1.1π cm**

2. Approximate the circumference of each circle in Exercise 1.
   a. 75.36 m; b. 31.4 ft; c. 3.45 cm

3. The smallest bicycle ever ridden had wheels with a diameter of 0.76 in. The largest bicycle ever ridden had wheels with a diameter of 10 ft.

   a. Find the circumference of a wheel on each bicycle.
      smallest bicycle: about 2.39 in.; largest bicycle: about 31.4 ft
   b. How far would each bicycle travel in one complete turn of its wheels? **smallest bicycle: about 2.39 in.; largest bicycle: about 31.4 ft**

   c. The world's smallest bicycle was ridden a distance of 13 ft 5 in. About how many turns did the wheels make? **about 68**

   d. Suppose the wheels on the world's largest bicycle made as many turns as your answer to part (c). How far would it travel? **about 2135.2 ft**

Practice & Applications

SUGGESTED ASSIGNMENTS

Core Course
Day 1: Exs. 1–3, 5–7
Day 2: Exs. 10–18, 21
Day 3: Exs. 22–24, 26–35

Extended Course
Day 1: Exs. 1–9
Day 2: Exs. 10–18 even, 19–21, 27
Day 3: Exs. 22–26, 32–35

Note: Extended Course assignments can be used to differentiate within the regular classroom. In classrooms where students are grouped homogeneously, the material might be covered in fewer days. In this case assignments may be combined.

ADDITIONAL PRACTICE

See the *Teacher's Resource Book* for additional practice and application exercises for this section.

COMMON ERRORS

Exercise 3 relates distances to turns of wheels. For **part (c)**, be sure students convert the distance ridden to inches before determining the number of turns.

Practice & Applications

EXERCISE NOTES

Exercise 8 If students do not recognize the connection between the radii and the side lengths of the square, you might suggest they try "pulling" the circles apart and making a sketch with the dimensions labeled. This may also help them see that the area of the shaded region is the area of the square minus the area of one circle with radius 5 cm (the four quarter-circles form a full circle). This exercise could also be completed as a class, with the teacher modeling how to visually break the problem into parts.

4. **Challenge** Suppose two identical circles just touch each other. Then a rectangle is drawn as shown. The distance d is the diameter of each circle.

   a. Write an expression for the perimeter of the rectangle. $4d$

   b. Evaluate your expression when $d = 2$. 8

5. Find the exact area of a circle with the given radius or diameter.

   a. $r = 8$ ft 64π ft²   b. $r = 30$ cm 900π cm² c. $d = 1.4$ m 1.96π m²

6. Approximate the area of each circle in Exercise 5.
   a. 200.96 ft²; b. 2826 cm²; c. 6.154 m²

7. **Costume Design** The Goodspeed Opera House in East Haddam, Connecticut, was a difficult place to perform the play *Bloomer Girl*. The hoop skirts in the women's 1860s costumes were too large for the narrow halls, stairways, and doors. Hoop skirts have a hoop around the hem of the skirt. This hoop can be made of steel.

   a. The wardrobe master of the play said, "The real super hoops were about 11 ft in diameter, but if we had one in the show, it would cover about half the stage." Approximate the area the super hoop would cover. about 95 ft²

   b. According to the wardrobe master's comment, about what size (in square feet) is the opera house stage? about 190 ft²

   c. Find the length of steel needed to make a super hoop.
   about 34.54 ft

   d. The women acting in *Bloomer Girl* ended up wearing hoop skirts that were 6 ft in diameter. Determine the length of steel needed to make each hoop. about 18.84 ft

   e. About what fraction of the stage did a 6 ft diameter hoop cover? about $\frac{1}{6}$

8. Each vertex of square *ABCD* is at the center of a circle with radius 5 cm. The circles just touch each other. Find the area of the shaded region. about 21.5 cm²

9. Open-ended One of the most unusual aircraft ever designed for the U.S. Navy was the Vought–Sikorsky V-173, also known as the "Flying Pancake." It was 26 ft 8 in. long and had a wingspan of 23 ft 4 in.

a. The Flying Pancake is round and flat. How do you know from just its measurements that its shape is not a circle?

b. Approximate the distance around the edge of the aircraft. Explain your method.

c. Approximate the area of the top of the Flying Pancake. Explain your method.

Find the volume of each figure.

10.

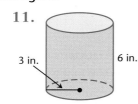

8 cm

6 cm

5 cm

rectangular prism
240 cm³

11.

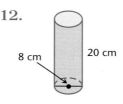

3 in.

6 in.

right cylinder
54π in.³ or about 169.56 in.³

12.

8 cm

20 cm

right cylinder

Find the volume of a cylinder with the given dimensions.

13. $r = 2$ cm
$h = 10$ cm

14. $r = 6.3$ cm
$h = 6.3$ cm

15. $r = 13$ cm
$h = 10$ cm

Find the volume of a rectangular prism with the given dimensions.

16. $l = 26$ cm
$w = 26$ cm
$h = 10$ cm
6760 cm³

17. $l = 13$ cm
$w = 14$ cm
$h = 7$ cm
1274 cm³

18. $l = 4$ cm
$w = 5$ cm
$h = 12$ cm
240 cm³

19. Challenge

a. The cylinder in Exercise 14 can fit into two of the rectangular prisms in Exercises 16–18. Which two prisms can it fit into?
16 and 17

b. The prism in Exercise 17 can fit into one of the cylinders in Exercises 13–15. Which cylinder can it fit into? 15

13. 40π cm³ or about 125.6 cm³

14. 250.047π cm³ or about 785.15 cm³

15. 1690π cm³ or about 5306.6 cm³

9. a. The length and width have different measures. In a circle the length and width refer to the diameter and all the diameters of a circle are the same length.

b. Answers may vary. Sample Response: I found the average of the two lengths and then calculated the circumference of a circle using that average as the diameter.
$C = 25$ ft · 3.14 = 78.5 ft

c. Answers may vary. Sample Response: I used the longer measure of 26 ft 8 in. for the diameter, to account for the area of the two tail fins as well as the circular part and came up with
$A = (13.33$ ft$)^2$ · 3.14 ≈ 557.94 ft²
or about 558 ft².

12. 320π cm³ or about 1004.8 cm³

EXERCISE NOTES

For **Exercise 21** students will probably find the volume of the large popcorn box in cubic feet and the volume of the regular box in cubic inches. They will need the fact that 1 ft³ = 1728 in.³ (12 · 12 · 12) to compare the volumes.

20. Music Sarah Hopkins, an Australian composer and performer, has experimented with the musical sounds of cylindrical instruments called "whirlies." Whirlies are played by whirling them through the air at different speeds. Differences in length and diameter affect the pitch and sound of each instrument.

Whirlies are flexible ▶ cylindrical hoses of various lengths and diameters.

	High Voiced Whirly	Deep Voiced Whirly
Diameter (mm)	25	32
Length (m)	1	1.75
Length (mm)	?	?
Volume (mm³)	?	?

a. Copy and complete the table.
$$\begin{array}{lcc} \text{length (mm)} & 1000 & 1750 \\ \text{volume (mm}^3\text{)} & 490{,}625 & 1{,}406{,}720 \end{array}$$

b. Sarah Hopkins also made a whirly that is exactly twice as long as a Deep Whirly. Its diameter is the same as the Deep Whirly's. How does doubling the length of a Deep Whirly affect its volume? It doubles the volume.

Beauclerc Elementary School in Jacksonville, Florida, made the largest popcorn box on record. The box was a rectangular prism 39 ft 11$\frac{1}{2}$ in. long, 20 ft 8$\frac{1}{2}$ in. wide, and 8 ft high.

21. a. Estimate the volume of the popcorn box. Calculate the actual volume of the popcorn box to the nearest cubic foot.
about 6400 ft³, about 6620 ft³

b. Suppose a regular-sized popcorn box is shaped like a rectangular prism 3$\frac{1}{2}$ in. wide, 7$\frac{1}{2}$ in. long, and 10$\frac{1}{2}$ in. high. What is the volume of the box? 275.625 in.³

c. About how many regular-sized boxes of popped popcorn would be needed to fill the large popcorn box? Explain.

21. c. about 41,503; Multiply the volume of the large popcorn box by 12³ = 1728 to convert it to in.³. Then divide that volume by the volume of the regular size box to get an estimate.

22. a. $\dfrac{256{,}0000}{3}\pi$ in.³

22. Find the exact volume of a sphere with the given dimension.

a. $r = 40$ in.   **b.** $r = 5.1$ m   **c.** $d = 2$ ft $\frac{4}{3}\pi$ ft³
                    176.868π m³

23. Approximate the volume of each sphere in Exercise 22.
a. 267,946.67 in.³; b. 555.37 m³; c. 4.19 ft³

24. Open-ended Explore how doubling a circle's radius affects each of the following. Check students' work.

a. the circumference of the circle doubles the circumference

b. the area of the circle quadruples the area

25. Challenge Two students have been exploring the effects of changing the base radius and height of a cylinder on its volume. Below are their conclusions. Decide whether each conclusion is *true* or *false* and explain why. **See margin.**

Tripling the height will triple the volume.

Tripling the radius will triple the volume.

Tripling both the height and the radius will triple the volume.

R e f l e c t i n g ◀▶on the Section

Write your response to Exercise 26 in your journal.

26. Rosa takes a carton of milk out of the refrigerator and empties it into the glass shown. Amazingly, the milk fills the glass so it is perfectly even with the rim. Was the milk carton full when Rosa began filling her glass? Explain your reasoning.

7 cm
19 cm
7 cm
$d = 7$ cm
$h = 14$ cm

S p i r a l ◀▶Review

27. The table shows sales of CDs at a record store. Make a scatter plot using the data. Put hours of operation on the horizontal axis. If it makes sense to draw a fitted line, do so. (Module 1, p. 56)
See margin.

Hours of Operation	54	48	60	65	40	60	48	56
CDs Sold	710	530	850	940	520	740	630	750

Find each quotient. (Toolbox, p. 582)

28. $0.141 \div 12$
0.01175

29. $6.2 \div 3.1$
2

30. $12.4 \div 12$
1.03

31. $150.62 \div 18$
8.367

Find each answer. (Toolbox, p. 589)

32. $4(2 + 3^2)$
44

33. $5 \cdot 6 - 3$
27

34. $11(6) \div 2$
33

35. $16 - 8 + \dfrac{42}{6}$
15

Section 1 Circumference, Area, and Volume **243**

EXERCISE NOTES
Reflecting on the Section
Exercise 26 Students should assume that when the carton is full of milk, the indented section beyond the 19 cm height does not hold any milk.

Journal

Exercise 26 checks that you can find and compare the volumes of two different containers.

26. No; The volume of the carton is $7 \cdot 7 \cdot 19 = 931$ cm³ and the volume of the glass is $3.5^2 \cdot 3.14 \cdot 14 = 538.51$ cm³. The milk carton holds almost 2 glasses of milk when full, so it was not full when Rosa began filling the glass.

25. The first statement is true because you have only tripled one factor, the height. So for example, a cylinder with radius 10 cm and height 1 cm has a volume of 100π cm³, and a cylinder with radius 10 cm and height 3 cm has a volume of 300π cm³, which is 3 times as great.

The second statement is false. You are only tripling the radius, but in the formula for the volume of a cylinder, $V = \pi r^2 h$, the radius is squared, so the volume is multiplied by 3 twice. Thus the new volume will be 9 times the original volume.

The third statement is also false. Tripling the height multiplies the volume by 3 and tripling the radius multiplies the volume by 9. Thus, tripling both the height and the radius will multiply the volume by 3 and 9, or 27.

27.

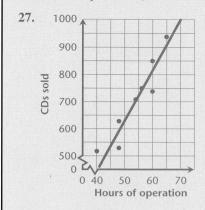

CDs sold / Hours of operation

243

TEACHER NOTES
For each Exploration, the corresponding Extra Skill Practice Exercises are noted.

Exploration 1: Exs. 1–6
Exploration 2: Exs. 7–12

EXTRA HELP
Teacher's Resource Book
• Practice and Applications
• Study Guide

Technology Resources
• @Home Tutor
• Test Generator

ASSESSMENT
• Section 1 Quick Quiz
• Test Generator

Section 1
Extra Skill Practice

Find the exact circumference of each circle.

1.

30 cm

30π cm

2.

8 in.

16π in.

3.

12 ft

12π ft

Find the exact area of each circle.

4.

13 cm

42.25π cm²

5.

4 in.

16π in.²

6.

16 ft

64π ft²

Approximate the volume of each prism, cylinder, or sphere.

7.

12 mm
18.2 mm
3120.28 mm³

8.
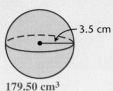
3.5 cm
179.50 cm³

9.
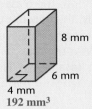
8 mm
6 mm
4 mm
192 mm³

10. rectangular prisms:

   a. $l = 4$ ft, $w = 2\frac{1}{2}$ ft, $h = 5\frac{1}{2}$ ft
     55 ft³

   b. $l = 6.3$ m, $w = 2.5$ m, $h = 5.9$ m
     92.93 m³

11. cylinders:

   a. $d = 10\frac{1}{2}$ in., $h = 17$ in.
     1471.29 in.³

   b. $d = 0.5$ mm, $h = 1.2$ mm
     0.24 mm³

12. spheres:

   a. $r = 10$ in.
     4186.67 in.³

   b. $d = 6.4$ m
     137.19 m³

Standardized Testing ◀▶ Open-Ended

1. How are the formulas for finding the volume of a prism and a cylinder alike? How are they different?

2. Write a word problem that involves finding the volume of a prism or a cylinder found in your home. **Sample Response: A cereal box has a length of 10 in., a width of 3 in., and a height of 14 in. What is the volume of the cereal box? Answer: 420 in.³**

1. **Sample Response: Both use the formula $V = Bh$. The base of a prism is a polygon, so the area of its base, B, will always be exact. The base of a cylinder is a circle, so the formula for the area of its base is $B = \pi r^2$ and will only be exact when left in terms of π.**

Section ② Working with Cylinders

IN THIS SECTION

EXPLORATION 1
♦ Surface Areas of Cylinders

EXPLORATION 2
♦ Surface Area and Volume

Setting the Stage

The French general Napoleon Bonaparte once said, "An army marches on its stomach." He was not exaggerating. Hunger and poor nutrition caused more casualties in Napoleon's armies than actual combat. In 1795, the French government offered a prize of 12,000 francs to anyone who could invent a way to preserve food for the military.

Nicolas Appert, a candy maker from Paris, won the prize in 1809. Appert found that food could be preserved for months by sealing it in glass jars and heating the jars in boiling water. Glass jars break easily, however, and soldiers needed stronger containers.

Peter Durand, an English inventor, solved this problem. Durand patented the use of metal cans for storing food. These cans were made of tin plate (iron coated with tin to prevent rusting) and came to be known as "tin cans." Tin cans were first used in 1813 to supply food to the British military.

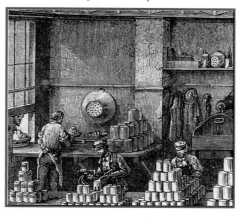

Think About It

1 What two-dimensional shapes could you cut from a sheet of tin plate to make a tin can? **two circles and a rectangle**

2 What factors might a manufacturer consider before designing a can? **Sample Response: the cost of the material, the capacity of the container.**

Setting the Stage

ABOUT THE THEME
With the various packaging options available for food in today's world, students may not think of the tin can as an incredible invention. Ask them to imagine what it would be like if everything carried in their lunch bag, or snacks taken with them in the car or to activities, etc. were in glass jars. Reading the *Setting the Stage* will provide some historical background on this invention. Through the explorations students will study different aspects of the tin can while investigating relationships between a can's surface area and its volume.

GETTING STARTED
Module 4 Section 2 *Warm-Up* provides a review of skills used in Section 1 that are necessary for completing Section 2.

TEACHING NOTES
Question 2 Promote discussion by showing students several different sizes of cans of food. Have them consider why the manufacturers chose the can sizes that they did.

Students should work individually for this exploration. Shorten the set-up time by organizing materials in sets ahead of time. If you run a strip of tape down the length of each ruler, each student can receive a piece without it becoming tangled.

TEACHING NOTES

Question 3 Wrapping a sheet of paper around a can helps students gain an intuitive feeling about a realistic radius and height for **part (a)**. The rectangle used for the lateral surface of the paper can should fit around the top and bottom exactly. Any overlap indicates that the length is too great and therefore will result in a calculated surface area greater than the actual one.

GOAL

LEARN HOW TO...
◆ find the surface area of a cylinder

AS YOU...
◆ make a paper can

KEY TERM
◆ surface area

Exploration 1

Surface Areas of Cylinders

SET UP *You will need: • compass • metric ruler • scissors • tape • $8\frac{1}{2}$ in. by 11 in. sheet of paper*

▶ A tin can is made by cutting two circles and a rectangle from a sheet of tin plate. The rectangle is rolled into a tube. The circles are added to the ends of the tube to form a cylinder.

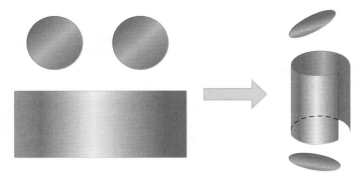

3 Think about the dimensions of cans you see in the supermarket. You can create your own can from a single sheet of paper.

   a. Choose a realistic radius and height for your paper can. Give the radius and the height in centimeters. Answers will vary. Check students' work.

   b. Use a compass to draw two circles having the radius you chose in part (a). Label the radius of each circle *r* as shown.
Answers will vary. Check students' work.

   c. **Discussion** In order for the tube and the circles to form a can, how should the length, *l*, of the rectangle pictured on the paper be related to the radius, *r*, of each circle? $l = 2\pi r$

d. Using the radius from part (a), calculate the length *l* of the rectangle to the nearest tenth of a centimeter.
    Answers will vary. Check students' work.
e. How should the width, *w*, of the rectangle pictured on the paper be related to the height you chose in part (a)?
    It should be the same.
f. Draw a rectangle with the length and the width you found in parts (d) and (e). When drawing the rectangle, measure *l* and *w* to the nearest tenth of a centimeter. *Answers will vary. Check to make sure that students are measuring carefully (to the nearest 0.1 cm).*
g. Cut out the circles and the rectangle you drew. Tape the edges of the rectangle together with no overlap to form a tube. Tape the circles to the ends of the tubes to complete your can.
    Check students' work.

▶ A cylinder's *surface area* is the sum of the areas of the circles and the rectangle that form the cylinder. In general, the **surface area** of a 3-dimensional figure is the combined area of the figure's outer surfaces.

4 **Try This as a Class** Use the paper can you made in Question 3.

a. How is the area of each circle related to the can's radius?
    $Area = \pi \cdot (radius)^2$
b. How can you use the length and width of the rectangle to find its area? $Area = length \cdot width$

c. How can you use the can's radius and height to find the area of the rectangle? $Area = 2\pi \cdot radius \cdot height$

d. Use your answers from parts (a) and (c) to write a formula for the surface area, *S.A.*, of a cylinder in terms of its radius, *r*, and height, *h*. $S.A. = 2\pi r^2 + 2\pi rh$

e. Find the surface area of your paper can. *Answers will vary. Check students' work.*

5 ✔ **CHECKPOINT** Approximate the surface area of each can.

a. 3.4 cm 286.12 cm^2

10 cm

b. 3.9 cm 303.70 cm^2

8.5 cm

✔ **QUESTION 5**

...checks that you can find a cylinder's surface area given its radius and height.

6 Which of the cans in Question 5 uses more metal? Explain.
    can (b); its surface area is greater.

HOMEWORK EXERCISES ▶ See Exs. 1–9 on p. 252.

DEVELOPING MATH CONCEPTS
Questions 3 and 4 ask students to express the relationship between the radius of the base of a cylinder and the length of the rectangle that makes the cylinder's side, and the relationship between the radius and the area of the base. You may want to review the formulas for the area and circumference of a circle before asking your students to work these questions.

The surface area of a cylinder is given by the formula *S.A.* = $2\pi r^2$ + $2\pi rh$. **Question 4** is designated as a *Try This as a Class* so that the teacher can help students use their answers to **parts (a)–(c)** to develop the formula for surface area in **part (d)**.

Break the problem into parts, first figuring out how to represent the area of each circle (πr^2 and πr^2), then combining them into one expression ($2\pi r^2$).

For the rectangle, begin with the basic formula for area of a rectangle, *l* · *w*, and help students work towards substituting the parts of the can in place of *l* and *w*. *l* is the same as the circumferences of the circles, so students should use the formula for circumference—either πd or $\pi(2r)$ to find *l*. *w* is the same as the height of the can which is represented by *h*.

Write the formula *l* · *w* on the board and ask students to help replace the variables with the expressions just discussed. Using the commutative and associative properties of multiplication, show how this becomes $2\pi rh$.

Although the question asks for the formula in terms of the radius, it may be easier for some students to leave part of it in terms of the diameter. Make sure students understand that $2\pi r^2 + 2\pi rh$ is the same as $2\pi r^2 + (2r)\pi h$ and $2\pi r^2 + \pi dh$.

247

Exploration 2

TEACHING NOTES

Question 7 Lead the discussion by asking students, "How might efficient cans compare to non-efficient cans in cost to produce? in weight? in costs to ship?" (*They cost less to produce, require less packaging by the case, and weigh less, so they may be easier to carry and to ship.*) Students may want to approach the question from the perspective of the consumer as well, discussing how less packaging might be a selling point to environmentally conscience consumers concerned about materials waste or to consumers interested in the savings manufacturers might pass on to customers.

You may want to lead a brief discussion of **Question 8** with the class. After that, students should work in groups. For ease of comparison, students should record the decimal form of the ratio $\frac{S.A.}{V}$ throughout the exploration.

TECHNOLOGY NOTE

For a related technology activity, see the *Technology Book*.

248

GOAL

LEARN HOW TO...
- ◆ find and interpret the ratio of a cylinder's surface area to its volume

AS YOU...
- ◆ compare the efficiency of different cans

Exploration 2

Surface Area and Volume

SET UP *Work in a group. You will need: • Labsheet 2A • metric ruler • five cans with different sizes and shapes • calculator*

▶ An *efficient* can is one that uses a small amount of metal compared to the amount of food or drink it holds.

7 Discussion What are some advantages of efficient cans? Possible answers: They cost less to produce, require less packaging, and weigh less, so they are easier to carry and cost less.

▶ A small juice can uses about 300 cm² of metal and holds about 400 cm³ of juice. A large juice can uses about 400 cm² of metal and holds about 600 cm³ of juice.

8 Mental Math

    a. How much metal is used per cubic centimeter of juice for the small can? 0.75 cm²

    b. How much metal is used per cubic centimeter for the large can? 0.67 cm²

    c. How did you get your answers? Sample Response: I divided the amount of metal used in each can by the amount of juice it can hold.

    d. Which can is more efficient? Explain. The larger can is more efficient because it used less metal per cubic centimeter.

▶ **Using Ratios** In Question 8 parts (a) and (b), you calculated the ratio of a can's surface area, *S.A.*, to its volume, *V*. The ratio $\frac{S.A.}{V}$ is one measure of the efficiency of the can. Your group will use this ratio to compare the efficiency of your cans.

9 If the ratio $\frac{S.A.}{V}$ is greater for can A than for can B, what can you say about the efficiency of the cans? Explain. Can B is more efficient than can A because it uses less material per unit of volume.

10 a. Make a table like the one shown. Include rows for cans A–E.
Check students' tables.

Can	Diameter	Height	Radius	S.A.	V	$\frac{S.A.}{V}$
A	?	?	?	?	?	?
B	?	?	?	?	?	?

FOR ◄ HELP
with *the volume of a cylinder*, see
MODULE 4, p. 235

b. Measure the diameter and height of each of your cans to the nearest tenth of a centimeter. Record the measures in your table.
Answers will vary. Check students' work.

c. Complete the rest of the table.
Answers will vary. Check students' work.

d. Rank your cans from most efficient to least efficient.
Answers will vary. Check students' work.

11 ✔ CHECKPOINT Rank the cans shown from most efficient to least efficient. Explain your thinking. tomato can, tuna can, milk can;

I ranked the cans from least to greatest value of $\frac{S.A.}{V}$.

5.2 cm
5.2

3.2 cm
MILK
6.3 cm

5 cm
TOMATOES
11.8 cm

✔ QUESTION 11

...checks that you can find and interpret the ratio of a cylinder's surface area to its volume.

► Of all cans having a given volume, which one uses the least metal? Canning companies often want to solve this problem, since using less metal reduces costs. You will explore this problem below.

Use Labsheet 2A for Questions 12 and 13.

12 Labsheet 2A shows four cylinders.

   a. Find each cylinder's surface area and volume.

   b. What do you notice about the volumes? They are the same.

13 a. What are the height and the radius of the cylinder with the least surface area? height 4, radius 2

   b. What is the ratio of the cylinder's height to its radius? 2 to 1

12. a. **cylinder A:**
S.A. = 106.76,
V = 50.24;
cylinder B:
S.A. = 75.36,
V = 50.24;
cylinder C:
S.A. = 125.6,
V = 50.24;
cylinder D:
S.A. = 414.48,
V = 50.24

TEACHING NOTES
Question 10 Small errors in measuring the radius of a can will result in large errors in the surface area and volume. Encourage your students to measure carefully.

For **Question 11**, you may want to remind students that efficiency is determined by finding the ratio of surface area to volume.

For **Question 13**, all four cylinders on **Labsheet 2A** are found to have the same volume. The cylinder with the least surface area is the one where the radius is half the height. You might choose to discuss with your students how they could show whether that is true for other groups of cylinders having the same volume. Do this before the students go on to **Question 14**.

249

Exploration 2 continued

TEACHING NOTES

Question 14(a) First have students identify which parts of the equation change in each step. (*πr²h is substituted for V; then 2r for h.*) Next ask what *πr²h* represents (*volume of a cylinder*) and why *2r* replaces *h* (*It states that a cylinder with height equal to twice its radius or h = 2r has the least surface area, so this substitution is made.*) In **Question 14(b)**, work through the problem with students showing how to use the commutative and associative properties of multiplication to rewrite *πr²(2r)* as *2πr²r = 2πr³*. They can then substitute 3.14 for *π* and solve for *r³* in the equation to get 2(3.14)*r³* ≈ 800; so, 6.28*r³* ≈ 800; *r³* ≈ 127. Allow students to try **parts (d) and (e)** on their own or with a partner and then summarize their findings as a class.

14. a. Sample
   Response: First
   the engineer set
   up the equation
   V = 800. Then
   V was replaced
   with the formula
   for the volume
   of a cylinder,
   πr²h. Finally, the
   height, *h*, was
   replaced with
   2*r* since it was
   stated that the
   height is twice
   the radius.
   e. 10.06 cm. When
   the height is
   twice the radius,
   you have the
   cylinder that has
   the least surface
   area for its
   volume.

15. a. *V* = 274, so
   πr²h = 274.
   Because *r* = *h*,
   πr² · *r* = 274
   and *πr³* = 274.
   Then *r³* = $\frac{274}{\pi}$
   ≈ $\frac{274}{3.14}$ ≈ 87.

16. Sample Response:
   The manufacturer
   may want to use
   a can that is a
   standard size for
   the product. For
   example, a juice
   can needs to be
   easy to hold while
   drinking and still
   hold a standard
   amount of juice.

14 **Try This as a Class** Of all cylinders having a given volume, the cylinder whose height is equal to its diameter (twice its radius) has the least surface area.

a. A snack food company plans to sell peanuts in cans with a volume of 800 cm³. An engineer at the company found the dimensions of the can that has this volume and uses the least amount of metal. The engineer's solution starts like this:

$$V = 800$$
$$\pi r^2 h = 800$$
$$\pi r^2 (2r) = 800$$

Explain each step of the solution so far.

b. Show that $\pi r^2(2r) = 800$ can be written as $r^3 \approx 127$.
   2(3.14)*r³* = 800; so, 6.28*r³* = 800; *r³* ≈ 127.

c. Explain why the solution of $r^3 \approx 127$ must satisfy $5 < r < 6$.
   5³ = 125 and 6³ = 216; since 5³ < *r³* < 6³, the value of *r* must be between 5 and 6.

d. ▣ Calculator Use a calculator and a guess-and-check strategy to find *r* to the nearest hundredth. What is the radius of the peanut can that uses the least amount of metal? *r* = 5.03; about 5.03 cm

e. Find the height of the peanut can that uses the least amount of metal. How did you get your answer?

15 A company is producing cylindrical metal containers that are open at the top and that will hold 274 in.³ of flour. The containers will have plastic lids. To find the dimensions of the container that uses the least metal, you can find the value of *r* for which $\pi r^3 = 274$, or $r^3 \approx 87$.

a. Of all open cylinders (cylinders with no tops) having a given volume, the cylinder whose height is equal to its radius has the least surface area. Explain how you can use this information and the formula for the volume of a cylinder to obtain $r^3 \approx 87$.

b. Use a calculator and a guess-and-check strategy to find *r* to the nearest hundredth. *r* ≈ 4.43 in.

c. What are the dimensions of the open cylindrical container that holds 274 in.³ of flour and uses the least amount of metal? *r* = *h* ≈ 4.43 in.

16 **Discussion** Why might a food or drink manufacturer use a can that does not have the least surface area for its volume?

▌ HOMEWORK EXERCISES ▶ See Exs. 10–19 on pp. 253–254.

Section 2
Key Concepts

Key Term

Surface Area of a Cylinder (pp. 246–247)

The surface area, S.A., of a cylinder with radius r and height h is given by the formula $S.A. = 2\pi r^2 + 2\pi rh$.

surface area

Example You can use the radius and height of the cylinder shown to find its surface area.

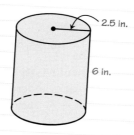

2.5 in.

6 in.

$S.A. = 2\pi r^2 + 2\pi rh$

$\approx 2(3.14)(2.5)^2 + 2(3.14)(2.5)(6)$

≈ 133.45

The cylinder's surface area is about 133.45 in.^{2}

Comparing Surface Area to Volume (pp. 248–250)

For a container (such as a can) with surface area S.A. and volume V, the ratio $\frac{S.A.}{V}$ is a measure of the container's efficiency. The smaller this ratio, the more efficient the container.

Example

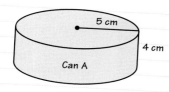

5 cm

4 cm

Can A

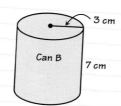

3 cm

Can B

7 cm

$\frac{S.A.}{V} \approx \frac{282.6}{314}$

≈ 0.90

$\frac{S.A.}{V} \approx \frac{188.4}{197.82}$

≈ 0.95

The ratio $\frac{S.A.}{V}$ is less for Can A than for Can B, so Can A is more efficient than Can B.

17 Key Concepts Question A coffee can has a radius of 8 cm and a height of 16 cm. A tomato sauce can has a radius of 3 cm and a height of 8 cm. Which can is more efficient? Explain.

the coffee can; The ratio of surface area to volume for the coffee can is less than the same ratio for the tomato can.

Key Concepts

CLOSURE QUESTION

Explain how you can use the ratio $\frac{Surface\ Area}{Volume}$ or $\frac{S.A.}{V}$ to find the most efficient use of materials to make a can or cylinder.

Sample Response: The lower the ratio, the more efficient the can or cylinder.

ABSENT STUDENTS

For students who were absent for all or part of this section, the blackline Study Guide for Section 2 may be used to present the ideas, concepts, and skills of Section 2.

Practice & Applications

SUGGESTED ASSIGNMENTS

Core Course
Day 1: Exs. 1–9
Day 2: Exs. 10–14
Day 3: Exs. 15, 16, 19–27

Extended Course
Day 1: Exs. 1–9
Day 2: Exs. 10–14
Day 3: Exs. 15–19, 28–30*

Note: Extended Course assignments can be used to differentiate within the regular classroom. In classrooms where students are grouped homogeneously, the material might be covered in fewer days. In this case assignments may be combined.

*denotes Extension Exercises

ADDITIONAL PRACTICE
See the *Teacher's Resource Book* for additional practice and application exercises for this section.

EXERCISE NOTES
Unless otherwise stated, it is assumed that students will use 3.14 for π when calculating surface area of a cylinder. If students use the π key on their calculator, please note that their answers will vary slightly from those printed in the answer key. Most answers in the key are rounded to the nearest hundredth. No exact answers (leaving the symbol π in the answer) are given for surface area.

Section ②
Practice & Application Exercises

For Exercises 1–6, find the surface area of a cylinder with the given radius r and height h.

1. $r = 2$ cm, $h = 7$ cm
   113.04 cm²

2. $r = 1$ m, $h = 3$ m
   25.12 cm²

3. $r = 6$ in., $h = 6$ in.
   452.16 in.²

4. $r = 8$ ft, $h = 4$ ft
   602.88 ft²

5. $r = 1.7$ m, $h = 8$ m
   103.56 m²

6. $r = 2.4$ in., $h = 9.6$ in.
   180.63 in.²

7. **Mental Math** Use mental math to estimate the surface area of a circular cylinder with a radius of 1 in. and a height of 4 in. Use $\pi \approx 3$. about 30 in.²

Science Sometimes stars explode, releasing tiny particles called neutrinos that may eventually reach Earth. The sun is also a source of neutrinos. To detect neutrinos, scientists built the "Super Kamiokande," a huge cylindrical tank of water located in a mine near Toyama, Japan.

◀ The top, bottom, and side of the tank are completely covered with light detectors. The tank has a radius of about 20 m and a height of about 40 m.

8. Estimate the surface area of the tank. about 7536 m²

9. The light detectors are mounted on rectangular frames like the one shown. Each frame is about 210 cm by 280 cm and holds 12 detectors.

   a. About how many frames were needed to cover the inside of the tank? about 1282 frames

   b. About how many light detectors were needed?
   about 15,384 light detectors

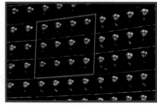

Find the ratio of surface area to volume for each can.

10.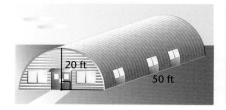
3.8 cm
6 cm

about 0.86

11.
4.3 cm
5.4 cm

about 0.84

12.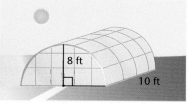
3.3 cm
5 cm

about 1.01

13. Use your answers for Exercises 10–12 to rank the cans shown above from most efficient to least efficient.

water chestnuts, olives, chili peppers

14. Architecture A *Quonset hut* is a building shaped like a half cylinder and made of corrugated steel. Examples of a Quonset hut and of a greenhouse also shaped like a half cylinder are shown.

20 ft
50 ft

8 ft
10 ft

a. Find the ratio of surface area to volume for each building. Include the floors of the buildings when calculating surface area. **Quonset hut: 0.20; greenhouse: 0.61.**

b. Which building encloses space more efficiently? Explain.
the Quonset hut; It encloses a greater volume per square foot of surface area.

c. **Writing** Would the more efficient of the two buildings be the better building in all situations? Why or why not?

Look back at your answers to Questions 12–14 on pages 249–250 in Exploration 2. Use what you learned to complete Exercises 15 and 16.

15. Research Go to a supermarket and look at some of the canned foods sold. Find a can that uses (approximately) the least amount of metal possible for its volume. Also find a can that uses a large amount of metal for its volume. Explain how you chose your cans.
Answers will vary. Check students' work.

16. Agriculture A farmer decides to roll hay into large cylindrical bales, each with a volume of 100 ft³. (A bale this size will feed 2 horses for about a month.) To keep the bales dry, the farmer plans to seal them in plastic wrap. What should the dimensions of each bale be if the farmer wants to use the least amount of plastic wrap possible?
radius: about $2\frac{1}{2}$ ft; height: about 5 ft

14. c. Sample Response: No; Which building is better depends on the situation. For example, the greenhouse's greater ratio of surface area to volume allows more light in, which is beneficial to the plants grown inside.

Practice & Applications

EXERCISE NOTES

Students completing **Challenge Exercise 17** may enjoy exploring how the total surface area is related to the number of equal-sized pieces produced. Suggest students look at 2, 3, 4, 5, and 6 pieces and summarize their findings about how the number of pieces affects the surface area. They might also determine if cutting the wood vertically as shown is better than cutting it into the same number of pieces horizontally to create full cylinders.

Students should recognize that as the log is cut vertically into equal-sized pieces, the original surface area of the cylinder is retained and the area of two 12 in. x 18 in. (or 432 in.²) rectangles are added for each piece cut. Therefore, the total surface area is $720\pi + 432n$ where n represents the number of equal-sized pieces greater than or equal to 2. After writing this expression for this particular size wood piece, students could then generalize it for a cylinder of wood with radius r and height h.

For the log in Question 17, the surface is greater for horizontal cuts, because each time an additional cut is made, the surface area increases by the area of two circles or 904.32 in.² This option may not be practical for cutting with an ax or for stacking pieces so that they fit into a small fireplace.

23.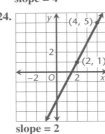

slope = 4

24.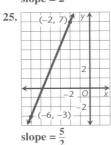

slope = 2

25.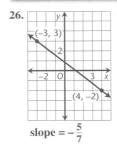

slope = $\frac{5}{2}$

Visual THINKING

Exercise 19 checks your understanding of the surface area of a cylinder.

26.

slope = $-\frac{5}{7}$

---

17. Challenge A log of firewood burns faster if you chop it into pieces before throwing it in a fireplace. This is because chopping a log increases the total area of wood exposed to the flames. For example, suppose you chop a log into four equal-sized pieces as shown.

12 in.

18 in.

a. Find the surface area of the log before it was chopped up. 2260.8 in.²

b. Find the combined surface area of the four chopped-up pieces. 3988.8 in.²

c. Compare your answers from parts (a) and (b). By what percent does chopping up the log in four pieces increase the surface area? about 76%

18. Algebra Connection The surface area of a cylinder is 850 cm². Find a radius and a height that this cylinder could have. (Hint: First choose a radius. Then use the formula S.A. = $2\pi r^2 + 2\pi rh$ to solve for the height.) **Answers will vary. Sample Response: radius = 5 cm, height = 22.07 cm**

Reflecting ◀▶ on the Section

19. Describe how you can find a cylinder's surface area either by using a formula or by thinking about the shapes that form the cylinder. **Sample Response: Use the formula $2\pi r^2 + 2\pi rh$ or find the area of the top and bottom of the cylinder (two circles) and add the area of the rectangle that makes up the side of the cylinder.**

Spiral ◀▶ Review

Estimation Estimate each percent. (Module 2, p. 132)

20. 11% of 200
about 20

21. 19% of 3500
about 700

22. 79% of 660
about 560

Plot each pair of points on a coordinate plane and draw a line through them. Find the slope of the line. (Module 3, p. 186)

23. (0, 0) and (1, 4)

24. (4, 5) and (2, 1)

25. (–6, –3) and (–2, 7)

26. (4, –2) and (–3, 3)

27. The equation for finding the area of a triangle is $A = \frac{1}{2}bh$, where A is the area of a triangle, b is the length of the base of the triangle, and h is the height of the triangle. Find the area of each triangle below. (Toolbox, p. 595)

a. $A = 24$ in.^{2}

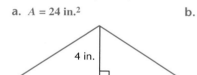

b. $A = 26$ m^2

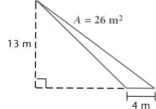

13 m

4 m

TEACHER NOTES

Below is the derivation of the equation in **Exercise 28**.

$$\frac{S.A.}{V} = \frac{2\pi r^2 + 2\pi rh}{\pi r^2 h}$$
$$= \frac{2\pi r(r + h)}{\pi r^2 h}$$
$$= \frac{2(r + h)}{rh}$$

Let $h = 2r$.

$$= \frac{2(r + 2r)}{r(2r)}$$
$$= \frac{(3r)}{r^2}$$

$$\frac{S.A.}{V} = \frac{3}{r}$$

Extension ▶ ▶

Maximum Efficiency

28. Cylindrical containers have the maximum efficiency when the height is twice the radius ($h = 2r$). For these special cylinders, the efficiency ratio simplifies to $\frac{S.A.}{V} = \frac{3}{r}$.

a. Use the formula to complete the table below. **See margin.**

The Efficiency of Cylindrical Containers Whose Height is Twice the Radius			
Container Name	Height h	Radius r	Efficiency $\frac{3}{r}$
A	2	1	3
B	6	3	?
C	?	6	?
D	?	9	?
E	24	?	?

$$\frac{3}{r} = \frac{3}{1} = 3$$

b. From the results of your table, what do you think is happening to the ratio of surface area to volume when the radius increases? **The ratio of surface area to volume decreases as the radius increases.**

c. Which container has the lowest efficiency ratio? **Container E**

29. Find a radius and height in centimeters of a cylinder with maximum efficiency of 5. **Sample Response: radius: 0.6 cm; height: 1.2 cm**

30. Find a radius and height in centimeters of a cylinder with maximum efficiency of 0.1. **Sample Response: radius: 30 cm; height: 60 cm**

28. a. See Additional Answers beginning on page A1.

Extra Skill Practice

TEACHER NOTES

For each Exploration, the corresponding Extra Skill Practice Exercises are noted.

Exploration 1: Exs. 1–6
Exploration 2: Exs. 7–13

EXTRA HELP

Teacher's Resource Book
• Practice and Applications
• Study Guide

Technology Resources
• @Home Tutor
• Test Generator

ASSESSMENT
• Section 2 Quick Quiz
• Test Generator

2. **Sample Response:** The lines both intersect the *y*-axis at 2 and appear to be equally steep, although the first line slopes up to the right while the second slopes down to the right.

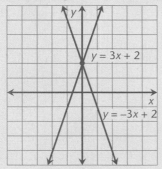

$y = 3x + 2$
$y = -3x + 2$

Section ② Extra Skill Practice

Find the surface area of the cylinder with the given radius *r* and height *h*.

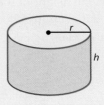

1. *r* = 5 in., *h* = 3 in.
   251.2 in.²
2. *r* = 3 in., *h* = 5 in.
   150.72 in.²
3. *r* = 11 cm, *h* = 40 cm
   3523.08 cm²
4. *r* = 9.5 cm, *h* = 9.5 cm
   1133.54 cm²
5. *r* = 1.8 m, *h* = 6.2 m
   90.432 m²
6. *r* = 33 ft, *h* = 100 ft
   27,562.92 ft²

Find the ratio of surface area to volume for each cylinder.

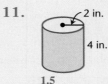 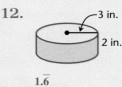

7. 1 in. 2.3̄   6 in.

8. 2.5 in. 1.46̄   3 in.

9. 1.5 in. 1.73̄   5 in.

10. 3.5 in.   1 in.
    about 2.6

11. 2 in.   4 in.
    1.5

12. 3 in.   2 in.
    1.6̄

13. Suppose you have six plastic storage containers with the same dimensions as the cylinders in Exercises 7–12. Which container was made most efficiently? Explain. **The cylinder with a radius of 2.5 in. and a height of 3 in.; The ratio of surface area to volume is lowest.**

Study Skills ▶ Comparing and Contrasting

When you compare and contrast objects or ideas, you consider how they are alike and how they are different. Comparing and contrasting can help you see how things are related and extend your understanding of what you have learned.

1. Compare and contrast the formulas for the surface area and volume of a cylinder.

2. Graph *y* = 3*x* + 2 and *y* = −3*x* + 2. Compare and contrast the lines that you graphed. **See margin.**

3. Give an example of when comparing and contrasting helped you make a decision.
   Answers will vary. Check students' work.

1. **Sample Response:** The two formulas are alike in that they both use π, *r*, and *h*. They are different in that the formula for surface area ($2\pi r^2 + 2\pi rh$) uses both multiplication and addition and has an answer in square units, while the formula for volume ($\pi r^2 h$) uses only multiplication and has an answer in cubic units.

FOR ASSESSMENT AND PORTFOLIOS

Getting the Most Out of a Can

SET UP *You will need:* • *compass* • *ruler* • *scissors* • *tape*
• $8\frac{1}{2}$ *in. by 11 in. sheet of paper*

The Situation See the *Teacher's Resource Book* for a sample solution for this Extended Exploration.

Most cans you find in a supermarket are designed to have a specific volume. However, a package manufacturer sometimes needs to design a can or other cylindrical container that uses a fixed amount of material and has the greatest volume possible.

The Problem

Make a "paper can" with the greatest volume possible by cutting and taping together two circles and a rectangle from an $8\frac{1}{2}$ in. by 11 in. sheet of paper. (The circles and the rectangle should all be from a single piece of paper and should not be a combination of several smaller pieces.)

Something to Think About

◆ How must the length of one side of the rectangle for your can be related to each circle's radius?

◆ Which dimension–the *radius* or the *height*– has a greater effect on the can's volume?

◆ Is it possible for you to make your can without wasting any paper?

Present Your Results

Give the radius and the height of the can you made, and explain how you chose those dimensions. Explain why you think it is not possible to make a can that has a greater volume. Show any diagrams, tables, or equations you used to solve the problem.

Extended Exploration

E² NOTES

Introduce the E² by reminding students of how they created a cylinder from an $8\frac{1}{2}$ in. x 11 in. sheet of paper in Exploration 1. Now their task is to make a can that has the greatest volume. Students may be interested to know that packaging is a multi-billion dollar industry and many universities such as Michigan State and Clemson University offer a degree in packaging science. In their jobs, package design engineers might research, develop, test, market, or even sell package designs. A web search of packaging design degrees can lead students to sites where they can find out more about what a student in this field will study and the jobs they might obtain with a degree in packaging science.

Using an E²: Suggestions for managing and evaluating an Extended Exploration are available in the *Teacher's Resource Book* for Modules 1 and 2. See also pages T44–T45 in the *Teacher's Edition*.

Alternate E²: See the *Teacher's Resource Book* for an alternate Extended Exploration that can be used after Module 4, Section 2.

ABOUT THE THEME

The invention of the television has had a great impact on the students of today. Students will see how increases and decreases in the sales of black-and-white TVs are represented by the slopes of lines on a graph. After completing this section students might want to research sales data for LCD, high definition, flat panel, or plasma TVs and make a graph of the data to display in the classroom, along with predictions for future sales.

GETTING STARTED

In preparation for using the slope and y-intercept to graph lines, the *Warm-Up* for Module 4 Section 3 assesses student ability to graph a line by plotting points and to identify where that line intersects the *x-axis* or *y-axis*.

DEVELOPING MATH CONCEPTS

Question 3 Students should recognize that the steeper the segment joining two points is, the greater the change in sales over that interval is. They should also recognize that segments that go down from left to right represent a decrease in sales. If this is not evident, use an overhead transparency of the graph and write the approximate change in sales above each segment of the graph, using negative numbers to represent decreases in sales and positive numbers to represent increases. Ask students to explain how the steepness of a line is related to the amount of decrease/increase.

Section ③ Slopes and Equations of Lines

Color My World

Setting the Stage

If you try to buy a black-and-white TV today, you may have trouble finding one. Demand for black-and-white TVs has almost disappeared. In 1995, more than 98% of all TVs sold were color TVs.

Although the first color telecast was in 1953, it was not until 1970 that color TVs began outselling black-and-white TVs.

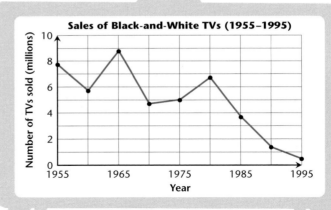

Sales of Black-and-White TVs (1955–1995)

Think About It

1 About how many black-and-white TVs were sold in 1980?
about 6.7 million.

2 In what year did sales of black-and-white TVs begin making a steady decline? 1980

3 **Discussion** During which periods did sales of black-and-white TVs increase? decrease? How can you tell? Sales increased between 1960 and 1965 and between 1970 and 1980. The line of the graph extends upward from left to right. Sales decreased between 1955 and 1960, between 1965 and 1970, and between 1980 and 1995. The line of the graph extends downward from left to right.

Exploring Slope

Exploration 1

TEACHING NOTES
Prior to beginning **Question 4** a brief review of the procedure used to determine the slope from two points might be necessary. A classroom example is provided.

GOAL

LEARN HOW TO...
- find and interpret positive and negative slopes
- identify slopes of horizontal and vertical lines

AS YOU...
- investigate TV sales

CLASSROOM EXAMPLE
Use the points $(4,-2)$ and $(-5, 7)$ to find the slope of the line.

Answer: slope $= \dfrac{\text{rise}}{\text{run}}$

$= \dfrac{\text{vertical change}}{\text{horizontal change}}$

$= \dfrac{7 - (-2)}{-5 - 4}$

$= \dfrac{9}{-9}$

$= -1$

SET UP You will need: • Labsheet 3A • graph paper

▶ In Module 3, you learned that the *slope* of a line is a ratio that measures the steepness of the line.

$$\text{slope} = \frac{\text{rise}}{\text{run}} = \frac{\text{vertical change}}{\text{horizontal change}}$$

In this exploration, you will see how slope can give you other information about a line.

FOR ◄HELP
with *slope*, see
MODULE 3, p. 186

Use Labsheet 3A for Questions 4–9.

4 **Try This as a Class** Labsheet 3A shows the *Graph of Black-and-White TV Sales* that you saw in the *Setting the Stage*. Ordered pairs for certain points are included on the graph.

  a. The first row of the table below has been completed for you. Explain how the rise, run, and slope were found.

  b. Why is the slope negative? The rise is negative and the run is positive, so the ratio is negative.

5 Complete the table on the labsheet. For each five-year period:
See margin.
- Find the slope of the graph for each period.
- Tell whether the graph slants *up* or *down* from left to right.
- Tell whether TV sales were *increasing* or *decreasing*.

6 Look at the periods in the table where the graph's slope is positive.

  a. For these periods, does the graph slant *up* or *down* from left to right? up

  b. Were sales of black-and-white TVs *increasing* or *decreasing*? increasing

7 Repeat Question 6 for the periods where the graph's slope is negative. a. down; b. decreasing

4. a. The rise was found by subtracting the *y*-coordinate for 1955 (7.7) from the *y*-coordinate for 1960 (5.7). The run was found by subtracting the *x*-coordinate for 1955 (1955) from the *x*-coordinate for 1960 (1960). The slope is the ratio of the rise to the run: $-\dfrac{2}{5}$ or -0.4.

COMMON ERROR
Question 5 Students may concentrate on determining the difference between points, ignoring whether the rise or run is negative. After completing **Question 5**, students should realize any errors. Tell students that in future problems it might help to first identify whether a graph is increasing or decreasing (from left to right) and then determine whether the slope will be positive or negative before calculating the actual slope.

5. See Additional Answers beginning on page A1.

Exploration 1 continued

TEACHING NOTES

As students discuss **Question 9**, help them recognize the relationship between slope and rate. Slope not only indicates whether something is increasing or decreasing, but also how quickly it is doing so. In **part (b)**, ensure that students realize the rate is described as an *annual* rate of decrease as well as a decrease over the entire *5-year* period.

DEVELOPING MATH CONCEPTS

Questions 11–12 For many students, identifying the rise and run for horizontal lines can be difficult. Ask students, "How far do you have to go up/down to get to the next point?" It may take a while for students to realize that not having to move up or down indicates a rise of zero. It often confuses students that there are several points they could use to determine the run. Show them that it does not matter which points they choose, since the result is always 0. For vertical lines, utilize students' knowledge of divisibility by zero. Relate the concept that divisibility by zero is undefined to the slope of a vertical line being undefined. For students who still have difficulty with which slopes equal zero and which are undefined, let them enter a slope such as $\frac{5}{0}$ (5 ÷ 0) on their calculator and see that it will give them an error message, whereas $\frac{0}{5}$ will display a zero.

---

8 a. Based on your observations from Questions 6 and 7, what can you say about the slope of a line that slants *up* from left to right? **It is positive.**
  b. What can you say about the slope of a line that slants *down* from left to right? **It is negative.**

9 Discussion Look at the graph and the table on the labsheet.

  a. By looking at the slopes in the table, how can you tell when sales were increasing most rapidly? decreasing most rapidly?

  b. The graph's slope for the period 1955–1960 represents a decrease of TV sales at a rate of 0.4 million per year or 26% over a 5-year period. Describe the rate and the percent of decrease for the period 1985–1990.

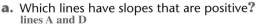

FOR HELP
with *rates*, see
MODULE 1, p. 9

✔ QUESTION 10

...checks that you understand the relationship between a line's appearance and its slope.

9. a. Sample Response: The sales were increasing most rapidly when the positive slope is the greatest; Sales were decreasing most rapidly when the absolute value of the negative slope is the greatest.

10 ✔ CHECKPOINT Use the lines shown.

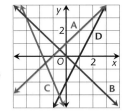

  a. Which lines have slopes that are positive? **lines A and D**
  b. Which lines have slopes that are negative? **lines B and C**

▶ **Horizontal and Vertical Lines** You have seen that some lines have positive slopes and some have negative slopes. In Questions 11 and 12, you will explore the slopes of horizontal and vertical lines.

11 a. Draw several horizontal lines on a coordinate plane. **Answers will vary.**
  b. Find the slope of each line. **Slope is 0.**
  c. What do you notice about the slopes? **They are all 0.**

12 a. Draw several vertical lines on a coordinate plane. Then try to find the slope of each line. What do you notice? **The run is always 0 so the division can't be performed.**
  b. The slope of a vertical line is said to be *undefined*. Why do you think this is so?

✔ QUESTION 13

...checks that you can identify slopes of horizontal and vertical lines.

9. b. It decreased at a rate of 0.46 million per year or 62% over the 5-year period.

13 ✔ CHECKPOINT Identify the slope of each line or tell if the slope is undefined.

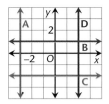

  a. line A **undefined**
  b. line B **0**
  c. line C **0**
  d. line D **undefined**

HOMEWORK EXERCISES ▶ See Exs. 1–11 on pp. 265–266.

12. b. Since division by zero is undefined and in order to identify the slope of a vertical line division by zero is necessary, then the slope of a vertical line must also be undefined.

 Module 4 Inventions

260

Slope-Intercept Form

GOAL

LEARN HOW TO...
- identify the y-intercept of a line
- write an equation of a line in slope-intercept form

AS YOU...
- model sales of DVD players and VCRs

KEY TERMS
- y-intercept
- slope-intercept form

SET UP *Work with a partner. You will need graph paper.*

▶ The sale of VCRs was nearing its peak in 1997 when DVD players hit the market. Soon after the introduction of the DVD player, VCR sales began to decrease. In this exploration, you and your partner will look for relationships between lines and their equations as they relate to the sale of VCRs and DVD players.

14 An electronics store sold 800 DVD players and 600 VCRs this year. Based on market trends, the store manager expects DVD sales to increase by about 160 DVD players per year and VCR sales to decrease by about 120 VCRs per year over the next five years.

   a. You and your partner should each choose one of the tables below. Copy and complete your table. **See margin.**

Expected DVD Player Sales	
x = years from now	y = DVD players sold
0	800
1	$800 + 160(1) = 960$
2	$800 + 160(2) = 1120$
3	?
4	?
5	?

Expected VCR Sales	
x = years from now	y = VCRs sold
0	600
1	$600 - 120(1) = 480$
2	$600 - 120(2) = 360$
3	?
4	?
5	?

   b. Make a scatter plot of the ordered pairs (x, y) in your table. What do you notice about the points in the scatter plot? **See margin.**

   c. Draw a line through the points in your scatter plot. Find the slope of the line. **DVD sales: 160; VCR sales: –120**

   d. Look for a pattern in your table. Use the pattern to write an equation relating y and x. **DVD sales: $y = 160x + 800$; VCR sales: $y = -120x + 600$**

Exploration 2

CLASSROOM MANAGEMENT
Students should work in pairs for **Questions 14 and 15**, however each student will need a sheet of graph paper for **Question 14**. You may want them to continue in pairs for the entire exploration, or you may have students work independently until **Try This as a Class Question 19**.

DEVELOPING MATH CONCEPTS
Question 14 In Module 1 and Module 3 students were instructed to find a fitted line instead of connecting all the points of their scatter plot, yet in **Question 14(c)** students are instructed to draw a line through the points of their scatter plot. Ask, "Why does the line in this plot pass through each point?" (*The points lie on a straight line.*) Follow-up with, "How does the data for this plot differ from the other plots in which you had to fit a line that did not go through all the points? (*This data was generated by using a formula, so all the x- and y-values are solutions to the equation used to generate them. Therefore since the equation is linear, the solutions all lie on the line represented by the equation. In previous scatter plots, the points represent data collected from experiments or trials, not from an equation.*)

14. a–b. See Additional Answers beginning on page A1.

TEACHING NOTES

Question 16 After students learn to identify the *y*-intercept on the graph and in an equation, ask them how the coordinates of the *y*-intercept identify a point on the *y*-axis. (*The x-coordinate always has a value of 0 which indicates that the point will always lie on the y-axis.*)

If needed, discuss the following example before students complete **Checkpoint Question 17**.

CLASSROOM EXAMPLE

Find the *y*-intercepts of each line.

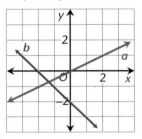

Answer: The *y*-intercept of line *a* is 0. The *y*-intercept of line *b* is –2.

Point out to students that in slope-intercept form, the equation of a line is written as $y = mx$ "plus *b*", so if they see an equation with "minus *b*", they must remember that this is equivalent to "plus the opposite of *b*" and therefore the *y*-intercept is negative *b*. The text **Example** illustrates this situation and should be reviewed as a class. Some students may not think $y = 0.5x$ is in slope-intercept form since there appears to be no *b*. To demonstrate that it is in slope-intercept form (in this case $b = 0$), refer to line *a* in the classroom example above where they found the *y*-intercept to be 0, and remind them that $y = 0.5x + 0$ is equivalent to $y = 0.5x$.

---

15 Discussion Compare the equations that you and your partner wrote in Question 14(d) with the lines you drew in part (c).

   a. How is the slope of each line related to the equation of the line? **The slope is the coefficient of *x*.**

   b. Is there any other way in which the lines and the equations are related? Explain. **The number being added (the constant) is the *y*-coordinate of the point where the line crosses the *y*-axis.**

▶ The **y-intercept** of a line is the *y*-coordinate of the point where the line crosses the *y*-axis.

16 a. Look back at the lines you drew in Question 14. Give the *y*-intercept of each line. **DVD sales: 800, VCR sales: 600**

   b. How is the *y*-intercept of each line related to the line's equation? **It is the number being added (the constant).**

   c. What information do the *y*-intercepts give you about the sales of VCRs and DVD players? **The number of players sold this year.**

✔ **QUESTION 17**

...checks that you can identify the *y*-intercept of a line.

17 ✔ **CHECKPOINT** Give the *y*-intercept of each line.

a.
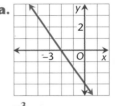

b.
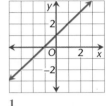

c.

▶ Suppose a line has slope *m* and *y*-intercept *b*. An equation of this line is $y = mx + b$. When an equation is in this form it is in **slope-intercept form**.

EXAMPLE

To write an equation in slope-intercept form for the line shown, first find the line's slope and *y*-intercept.

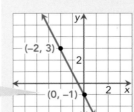

The *y*-intercept is –1.

$$\text{slope} = \frac{-1-3}{0-(-2)} = \frac{-4}{2} = -2$$

Then substitute the values for the slope *m* and the *y*-intercept *b* into $y = mx + b$.

$$y = -2x + (-1)$$

$$y = -2x - 1$$

18 a. Identify the slope and the y-intercept of the line with equation $y = -\frac{2}{3}x + 7$. **Slope:** $-\frac{2}{3}$; **y-intercept: 7**

b. Suppose the slope of a line is 5 and its y-intercept is $\frac{1}{2}$. Write an equation of the line. $y = 5x + \frac{1}{2}$

c. Is the equation $5x + y = 20$ in slope-intercept form? Explain.
No; In slope-intercept form, the equation has y isolated on one side.

19 **Try This as a Class** Use the coordinate plane shown.

a. Find the slope of line k. Write an equation in slope-intercept form for the line. $\frac{3}{2}$; $y = \frac{3}{2}x$

b. Find the slope of line m. Write an equation in slope-intercept form for line m. $\frac{3}{2}$; $y = \frac{3}{2}x - 10.5$

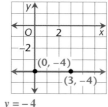

c. What do you notice about the two lines?
They have the same slope and they are parallel.

d. What do you notice about the two equations?
The equations have the same slope but a different y-intercept.

e. Suppose line l has the same slope as lines k and m. What does that tell you about line l?
It is parallel to lines k and m.

f. Write an equation for line l in slope-intercept form. $y = \frac{3}{2}x + 9$

g. Write an equation in slope-intercept form for a line that is parallel to lines m, k, and l. **Sample Response:** $y = \frac{3}{2}x + 3$

20 a. Write an equation in slope-intercept form for the horizontal line. How is this equation different from the other linear equations you have seen?
$y = 3$; There is no x term.

b. Can you write an equation in slope-intercept form for the vertical line? Explain. No; The slope of the line is undefined.

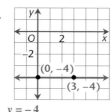

c. What is true about the x-coordinate of each point on the vertical line? Use your answer to write an equation of the line.
The x-coordinate is -2; $x = -2$

d. How can you find an equation of a horizontal or vertical line just by looking at the coordinates of one point on the line?
See margin.

21 **✔ CHECKPOINT** For each line, write an equation in slope-intercept form.

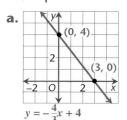 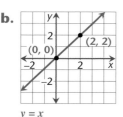 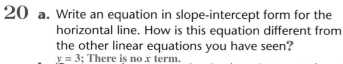

a. (0, 4) (3, 0) $y = -\frac{4}{3}x + 4$

b. (0, 0) (2, 2) $y = x$

c. (0, -4) (3, -4) $y = -4$

HOMEWORK EXERCISES ▶ See Exs. 12–29 on pp. 266–268.

TEACHING NOTES
Try This as a Class Question 19
Students might assume that the y-intercept of line m is the point halfway between –9 and –12. Instruct students that although it may "appear" to be halfway there is no way to be certain without using the slope of the line and a known point that falls on the grid lines. Show the class how they can use the slope-intercept form of an equation to find the y-intercept.

$$y = 1.5x + b$$

Using the point (9, 3), which is on the line, substitute the coordinates for x and y.

$$3 = 1.5(9) + b$$

Solve for b.

$$3 = 13.5 + b$$
$$-10.5 = b$$

Have students try it on their own with a different point on the line such as (3, –6). They will discover that they get the same y-intercept using any point on the line.

DEVELOPING MATH CONCEPTS
Question 19(c)–(g) develops the concept that lines parallel to each other all have the same slope.

20. d. The equation of a horizontal line has the form $y = k$ where k is the y-coordinate of any point on the line. The equation of a vertical line has the form $x = k$ where k is the x-coordinate of any point.

263

Key Concepts

ABSENT STUDENTS

For students who were absent for all or part of this section, the blackline Study Guide for Section 3 may be used to present the ideas, concepts, and skills of Section 3.

Key Term

Section 3
Key Concepts

Slope (pp. 259–260)

The slope of a line can be positive, negative, zero, or undefined.

Positive slope

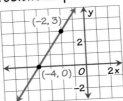

$$\frac{\text{vertical change}}{\text{horizontal change}} = \frac{3-0}{-2-(-4)}$$

$$= \frac{3}{2}$$

Negative slope

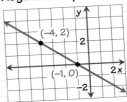

$$\frac{\text{vertical change}}{\text{horizontal change}} = \frac{0-2}{-1-(-4)}$$

$$= -\frac{2}{3}$$

Zero slope

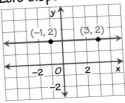

$$\frac{\text{vertical change}}{\text{horizontal change}} = \frac{2-2}{3-(-1)}$$

$$= \frac{0}{4}$$

$$= 0$$

Undefined slope

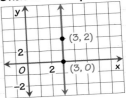

$$\frac{\text{vertical change}}{\text{horizontal change}} = \frac{2-0}{3-3}$$

$$= \frac{2}{0} \leftarrow \text{undefined}$$

y-intercept

y-intercept (p. 262)

The y-intercept of a line is the y-coordinate of the point where the line crosses the y-axis.

---

22. a. Answers will vary. The line must extend downward from left to right and pass through point (0, 5).

22 Key Concepts Question For each part, draw a line that satisfies the given condition(s).

a. The line has a negative slope and a *y*-intercept of 5.

b. The line has a slope that is undefined. **Answers will vary. The line can be any vertical line.**

Section 3
Key Concepts

Key Term

Slope-Intercept Form (pp. 261–263)

If a line has slope m and y-intercept b, then an equation of the line is $y = mx + b$. This equation is in slope-intercept form.

slope-intercept form

Example Since the slope of the line shown is $\frac{1}{2}$ and the y-intercept is -3, an equation of the line is $y = \frac{1}{2}x + (-3)$, or $y = \frac{1}{2}x - 3$.

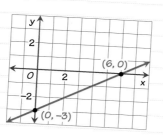

CLOSURE QUESTION

Why is $y = mx + b$ called the slope-intercept form of the equation of a line?

Sample Response: Because the slope, m, and the y-intercept, b, are easily read from the equation $y = mx + b$.

---

23 Key Concepts Question A line passes through the points $(0, 5)$ and $(2, 0)$. Is this enough information for you to write an equation of the line? If so, write an equation of the line in slope-intercept form. If not, explain why not. **Yes;** $y = -\frac{5}{2}x + 5$

Section 3
Practice & Application Exercises

Find the slope of each line.

1.
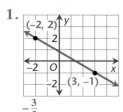

$-\frac{3}{5}$

2.
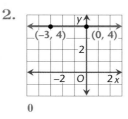

0

3.
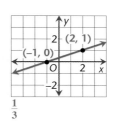

$\frac{1}{3}$

Find the slope of the line through the given points. You may find it helpful to plot the points and draw a line through them first.

4. $(2, 7)$ and $(4, 1)$ -3

5. $(3, 8)$ and $(6, 8)$ 0

6. $(-9, -4)$ and $(5, 0)$ $\frac{2}{7}$

7. $(-4, 4)$ and $(3, -5)$ $-\frac{9}{7}$

YOU WILL NEED

For Ex. 22:
- graphing calculator or graph paper

For Exs. 23-28:
- graph paper

Practice & Applications

SUGGESTED ASSIGNMENTS

Core Course
Day 1: Exs. 1–8, 10, 11
Day 2: Exs. 12–17, 30–35
Day 3: Exs. 18–23, 25–29

Extended Course
Day 1: Exs. 1–7 odd, 8–11
Day 2: Exs. 12–17, 30–35
Day 3: Exs. 18, 21–25, 28–29

Note: Extended Course assignments can be used to differentiate within the regular classroom. In classrooms where students are grouped homogeneously, the material might be covered in fewer days. In this case assignments may be combined.

ADDITIONAL PRACTICE

See the *Teacher's Resource Book* for additional practice and application exercises for this section.

EXERCISE NOTES

Exercise 9 Students will need to find the approximate change in the number of nests over a 5-year period and divide that number by 5 to find the average annual number of nests. This is to be done for each 5-year period. The results for **Exercise 9** can be used to support answers to **Exercises 10 and 11**, but **Exercises 10 and 11** can also be completed by studying the graph and comparing the slopes visually.

8. Use the lines shown.

   a. Which line has a positive slope?
      line A
   b. Which line has a negative slope?
      line C
   c. Which line has a slope of zero?
      line B
   d. Which line has a slope that is undefined?
      line D

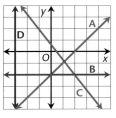

Endangered Species The Kemp's ridley sea turtle was listed as endangered by the United States government in 1970. While the species is now recovering, it is still endangered. Most Kemp's ridley turtles nest on a single beach in Mexico. The graph shows how the number of nests on the beach changed from 1970 to 1995.

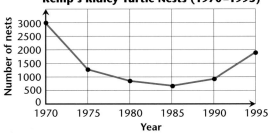

Kemp's Ridley Turtle Nests (1970–1995)

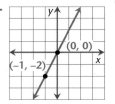

9. **Estimation** For each five-year period shown on the graph's horizontal axis, estimate the average annual rate of change in the number of turtle nests. Start with 1970–1975. Organize your results in a table. See margin.

10. During which five-year period from Exercise 9 did the number of turtle nests increase most rapidly? decrease most rapidly?
    1990–1995; 1970–1975

11. **Writing** Mexico and the United States decided to work together to protect the beach where the Kemp's ridley turtles nest. About when do you think they made this decision? Explain.
    Sample Response: 1985; The number of nests began to increase in 1985.

For each line, find the slope and the y-intercept.

12.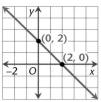

13.

14.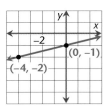

slope: −1; y-intercept: 2   slope: 2; y-intercept: 0   slope: $\frac{1}{4}$; y-intercept: −1

9. See Additional Answers beginning on page A1.

Environment Air pollution causes acid rain, which can damage the environment. From 1975 to 1978, scientists measured the acidity of rain and snow in a Colorado forest. The graph shows a fitted line that the scientists found for their data. Use the graph for Exercises 15–17.

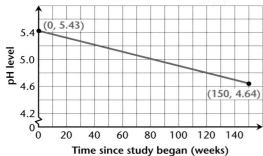

Acidity of Rain and Snow

(0, 5.43)

(150, 4.64)

pH level

Time since study began (weeks)

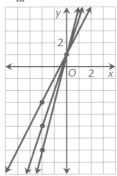

▲
The acidity of rain or snow is given by a pH level. A decreasing pH level means that acidity is increasing.

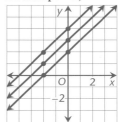

15. It got worse; The line shows a decrease in pH which means that the acidity of the rain increased.

22. a. slope = 1;

The lines are parallel; Lines with the same slope are parallel to each other.

b.

They all have the same y-intercept; they have different slopes.

15. **Interpreting Data** Did the environmental situation in the forest get better or worse during the years 1975–1978? Explain.

16. a. Identify the line's slope and y-intercept.
    slope: about –0.005, y-intercept: 5.43
    b. What information does the slope give about the situation?
    The slopes indicate the rate at which the pH is decreasing per week.
    c. What information does the y-intercept give about the situation? The y-intercept shows pH level at the time the study began.

17. The scientists' study ended after 150 weeks. Estimate the acidity of rain and snow in the forest 20 weeks after the study ended. Explain your thinking. about 4.58; Sample Response: I assumed the trend would continue, so I solved the equation $y = -0.005x + 5.43$ for $x = 170$.

Write an equation in slope-intercept form for the line through the given points. You may find it helpful to plot the points and draw a line through them first.

18. (0, 7) and (1, 2) $y = -5x + 7$ 19. (0, 4) and (2, 8) $y = 2x + 4$

20. (–5, 5) and (3, –1) $y = -\frac{3}{5}x + 2$ 21. (–3, –5) and (4, –5) $y = -5$

22. Graphing Calculator Use a graphing calculator or graph paper to complete parts (a) and (b).

    a. Give the slope of the lines $y = x + 2$, $y = x + 3$, and $y = x + 4$. Then graph all three lines on the same coordinate plane. What do you notice about the lines? Write a statement about lines with the same slope.

    b. Graph $y = 2x + 1$, $y = 3x + 1$, and $y = 4x + 1$ on the same coordinate plane. How are the lines alike? How are they different?

ALTERNATIVE APPROACHES
Exercises 18–21 Instead of graphing the points to find the slope and y-intercept students might choose to use the formula for slope and then the slope-intercept form of a line with one of the given points and solve to find *b*. This latter method was introduced in the teaching notes for Question 19 of Exploration 2.

Exercises 18–28 Some students may benefit from using a computer with graphing software that graphs the points and lines for them so that they can concentrate on writing the equations, finding relationships between lines, and identifying slopes and y-intercepts.

Practice & Applications

EXERCISE NOTES

Exercise 24 If students happen to be using a graphing calculator for this challenge exercise, they may need to set the window of their calculator to a square screen for the lines to appear perpendicular. The rectangular screens of many graphing calculators do not always accurately portray this relationship.

24. b.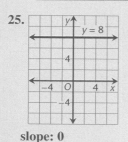

c.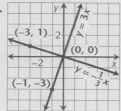

25.

slope: 0

23. a.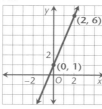

b.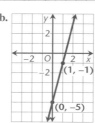

c.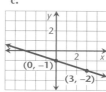

Discussion

Exercise 29 checks that you understand slopes and equations of lines.

24.a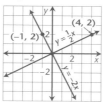

23. Maria uses what she knows about slope-intercept form to graph the equation $y = \frac{3}{4}x + 2$.

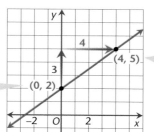

The slope is $\frac{3}{4}$. Count 3 units up and 4 units right. Plot a second point, then draw the line.

The y-intercept is 2. Plot the point (0, 2).

Use Maria's method to graph each equation.

a. $y = \frac{5}{2}x + 1$ b. $y = 4x - 5$ c. $y = \frac{1}{3}x - 1$

24. Challenge Graph each pair of lines on a coordinate plane.

a. $y = -2x$, $y = \frac{1}{2}x$ b. $y = 3x$, $y = -\frac{1}{3}x$ c. $y = \frac{2}{3}x$, $-\frac{3}{2}x$
    See margin.   See margin.

d. Describe the relationship between the lines in each pair. Write equations for two other lines that have this relationship.
    The lines in each pair are perpendicular; Sample Response: $y = \frac{2}{5}x$, $y = -\frac{5}{2}x$

Graph each equation. Give the slope of each line. 25.–28. See margin.

25. $y = 8$ **26.** $y = -4$ **27.** $x = 3$ **28.** $x = -1$

Reflecting ◀▶ on the Section

Be prepared to discuss your response to Exercise 29 in class.

29. Given a graph of a line, what can you tell about its slope, even before you do any calculations? How can you find an equation of the line? Possible Responses: It is possible to tell if the slope is positive, negative, 0, or undefined; Identify two points on the line to find the slope and determine where the line crosses the y-axis to determine the y-intercept.

Spiral ◀▶ Review

30. Find the surface area of a cylinder that has a radius of 4 in. and a height of 10 in. (Module 4, p. 251) 351.68 in.²

Use an equation to find each percent or number. (Module 2, p. 132)

31. 33 is what percent of 60?   **32.** What is 15% of 30?
    55%   4.5

Write each number in scientific notation. (Module 3, p. 209)

33. 700   **34.** 2593   **35.** 101,000
    $7 \cdot 10^2$ $2.593 \cdot 10^3$ $1.01 \cdot 10^5$

26., 27., and 28. See Additional Answers beginning on page A1.

268

Section 3

Extra Skill Practice

Find the slope of the line through the given points. You may find it helpful to plot the points and draw a line through them first.

1. (0, 1) and (1, 4) 3
2. (4, –3) and (2, 5) –4
3. (–1, –1) and (8, –4) $-\frac{1}{3}$
4. (3, –5) and (7, 5) $\frac{5}{2}$
5. (5, –3) and (1, –3) 0
6. (6, –2) and (6, 6) undefined

Use the lines shown for Exercises 7–10.

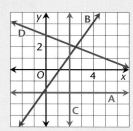

7. Which line has a positive slope? line B

8. Which line has a negative slope? line D

9. Which line has a slope of zero? line A

10. Which line has a slope that is undefined? line C

For each line, write an equation in slope-intercept form.

11.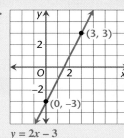

$y = 2x - 3$

12.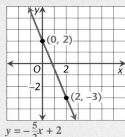

$y = -\frac{5}{2}x + 2$

13.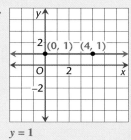

$y = 1$

Write an equation in slope-intercept form for the line through the given points. You may find it helpful to plot the points and draw a line through them first.

14. (3, 7) and (5, 7)
$y = 7$

15. (0, 5) and (5, 0)
$y = -x + 5$

16. (3, 4) and (–2, –2)
$y = 3x - 2$

Standardized Testing ◀▶ Open-ended

Write an equation in slope-intercept form for a line that satisfies the given condition(s). Sample responses are given.

1. The line has a negative slope and a y-intercept of 4. $y = -5x + 4$

2. The line has a slope of 3 and a negative y-intercept. $y = 3x - 2$

3. The line has a slope of zero and a positive y-intercept. $y = 2$

4. The line is steeper than the line with equation $y = -2x + 7$. $y = -3x + 7$

Extra Skill Practice

TEACHER NOTES

For each Exploration, the corresponding Extra Skill Practice Exercises are noted.

Exploration 1: Exs. 1–10
Exploration 2: Exs. 11–16

EXTRA HELP

Teacher's Resource Book
• Practice and Applications
• Study Guide

Technology Resources
• @Home Tutor
• Test Generator

ASSESSMENT
• Section 3 Quick Quiz
• Mid-Module Quiz
• Test Generator

In this section students are introduced to the number system used by the ancient Egyptians. As they study of the Egyptian numeration system, students are challenged to apply their skills and understanding of fractions to write common fractions as the sum of unit fractions, the method the Egyptians used to represent fractions. Both our current numeration system and the Egyptian numeration system are built on a base 10 number system. For exposure to other base number systems you may want to show students examples of the Mayan number system (base 5) or the binary system (base 2). The history of Egyptian hieroglyphs and other early writing systems could be combined with a social studies or English lesson.

GETTING STARTED

Module 4 Section 4 *Warm-Up* assesses student facility with multiplying and dividing fractions and with solving equations containing integers. In this section, students will apply these skills in a new context as they solve equations containing rational numbers.

Section 4 Rational Numbers

Writing Numbers

Setting the Stage

Throughout the ages, many systems have been invented for recording numbers. As early as 3400 B.C., the Egyptians had developed a system for using hieroglyphs to write numbers. They used tally marks for the first nine numerals and wrote symbols for the first few powers of ten.

Egyptian Symbols for One Through Nine								
Symbol	|	||	|||	||||	||| ||	||| |||	|||| |||	|||| ||||	||||| ||||
Value	1	2	3	4	5	6	7	8	9

Egyptian Symbols for Powers of Ten		
Symbol	**Description**	**Value**
|	a vertical staff	1
∩	a heel bone or a yoke	10
၄	a scroll or a coil of rope	100
⌇	a lotus flower	1000
⌐	a pointing finger	10,000
⌐	a fish or a tadpole	100,000
👨	an astonished man	1,000,000

▲
How do we know how the Egyptians wrote numbers? Much of our knowledge of Egyptian mathematics comes from the Rhind Papyrus. The papyrus contains information from sources dating back to about 1850 B.C.

Sometimes the Egyptians wrote the numerals from left to right or down the page, but most of the time they wrote them from right to left as in ‖‖∩999ᒉᒉᒉᒉ⌐. From the tables, you can see that

⌐	represents	100,000
ᒉᒉᒉᒉ	represents	4,000
999	represents	300
∩	represents	10
and ‖‖	represents	4
which all adds up to		104,314.

So the Egyptian numeral ‖‖999ᒉᒉᒉᒉ⌐ represents 104,314.

Think About It

1 What number does the Egyptian numeral ∩∩∩999𝕷9𝕷𝕷𝕷𝕷ᴊᴊ represent? **26,230**

2 Write 2396 as an Egyptian numeral.

Exploration 1

Rational Numbers

SET UP Work with a partner. You will need a calculator.

GOAL

LEARN HOW TO...
- recognize the characteristics of rational numbers
- use notation for repeating decimals

AS YOU...
- explore ratios and Egyptian fractions

KEY TERMS
- rational number
- terminating decimal
- repeating decimal

▶ To record measurements such as the length of a side of a field or the amount of grain in a sack, the Egyptians had to invent a way to write fractions.

For some common fractions they used special symbols such as ⏢ for $\frac{1}{2}$, ⏚ for $\frac{2}{3}$, and ✕ for $\frac{1}{4}$.

The symbol ⬯, which meant "part of," was used with a numeral to write fractions that have a numerator of 1. Here are a few examples with their modern equivalents:

 ↔ $\frac{1}{3}$ ⬯∩ ↔ $\frac{1}{10}$ |||⬯ ||∩∩9 ↔ $\frac{1}{125}$ ⏢ || ↔ $2\frac{1}{2}$

All other fractions were written as sums of fractions with numerators of 1 and distinct denominators.

read from right to left, $\frac{1}{2} + \frac{1}{4}$

 ⏢ ↔ $\frac{3}{4}$

$\frac{1}{3} + \frac{1}{15}$

 ↔ $\frac{2}{5}$

FOR◀HELP

with *adding fractions*, see **MODULE 2, p. 100**

3 What is the modern equivalent of each fraction?

a.
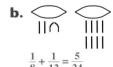
$\frac{1}{9}$

b.
$\frac{1}{8} + \frac{1}{12} = \frac{5}{24}$

c.
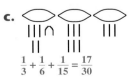
$\frac{1}{3} + \frac{1}{6} + \frac{1}{15} = \frac{17}{30}$

Section 4 Rational Numbers **271**

Exploration 1

TEACHING NOTES

Discuss with students the different fraction symbols. Make sure students understand that the symbol for $\frac{2}{3}$ ⏚ is different from the "part of" symbol with two staffs placed underneath. This latter combination ⬯|| should not be used since it represents a fraction $\left(\frac{1}{2}\right)$ for which there is a unique symbol, ⏢ .

Exploration 1

TEACHING NOTES

In **Question 4(c)**, students need to write $\frac{7}{8}$ as the sum of fractions that have numerators of 1 and *distinct* denominators. Explain that $\frac{1}{8} + \frac{1}{8} + \frac{1}{8}$ ... seven times does not have *distinct* denominators. It may take several trials before students realize that $\frac{7}{8} = \frac{4}{8} + \frac{2}{8} + \frac{1}{8} = \frac{1}{2} + \frac{1}{4} + \frac{1}{8}$. If students are not making progress, suggest they try breaking $\frac{7}{8}$ into different groups of eighths and then checking to see if those fractions can be reduced to unit fractions.

Rational number and irrational number are defined separately. Irrational number is defined in Module 7 Section 2 during a lesson on simplifying radicals. If students seem to have the impression that all numbers are rational, you could introduce a few numbers that do not fit the definition of rational, such as pi or 0.04004000400004...

When defining *terminating decimal*, make sure students understand the meaning of *finite*.

COMMON ERRORS

Question 6 Since our decimal system is based on powers of 10, in order to develop the concept of a terminating decimal, students will write equivalent fractions with denominators that are powers of 10. You may need to clarify that powers of 10 refers to the decimal place values students are accustomed to: 10ths, 100th, 1000ths, etc. Emphasize that the equivalent fractions they write must have integer numerators, not decimals. Some students will think $\frac{3}{8}$ cannot be written with a power of 10 as a denominator. Encourage them to try denominators beyond 10 or 100.

---

4. a.

b.

c. Sample Response:

$\frac{1}{2} + \frac{1}{4} + \frac{1}{8} \leftrightarrow$

---

4 Use Egyptian symbols to represent each fraction.

   a. $\frac{1}{25}$ **b.** $\frac{1}{100}$ **c.** $\frac{7}{8}$

▶ The Egyptians' numeration system made it possible for them to write all the positive *rational numbers*. A **rational number** is a number that can be written in the form $\frac{a}{b}$ where a and b are integers and $b \neq 0$. In our system, we have many different ways of writing rational numbers.

> **EXAMPLE**
>
> 0.3 is a rational number because it can be written as $\frac{3}{10}$.
>
> 3.8 is a rational number because it can be written as $\frac{38}{10}$.
>
> 9 is a rational number because it can be written as $\frac{9}{1}$.
>
> $-2\frac{1}{3}$ is a rational number because it can be written as $\frac{-7}{3}$.

5 Use your calculator to write each rational number as a decimal. Give the decimal displayed on the calculator. Do not round. *Answers will vary depending on the calculator used.*

  a. $\frac{1}{2}$ **b.** $\frac{1}{3}$ **c.** $\frac{4}{25}$ **d.** $\frac{3}{8}$ **e.** $\frac{5}{11}$

  0.5   0.3333333   0.16   0.375   0.4545454

FOR ▶ HELP

with *equivalent fractions*, see

TOOLBOX, p. 585

6 For each fraction, try to write an equivalent fraction that has a power of 10 as its denominator.

  a. $\frac{1}{2}$ **b.** $\frac{1}{3}$ **c.** $\frac{4}{25}$ **d.** $\frac{3}{8}$ **e.** $\frac{5}{11}$

  $\frac{5}{10}$ not possible $\frac{16}{100}$ $\frac{375}{1000}$ not possible

7 **Discussion** In Question 6, were you able to write $\frac{1}{3}$ and $\frac{5}{11}$ as fractions with denominators that are powers of 10? Why or why not? **No; there is no multiple of 3 that is a power of 10 and no multiple of 11 that is a power of 10.**

▶ The rational numbers $\frac{1}{2}$, $\frac{2}{5}$, and $\frac{3}{8}$ can be written as *terminating decimals*. A **terminating decimal** contains a finite number of digits. Some rational numbers, such as $\frac{1}{3}$ and $\frac{5}{11}$, can be written as *repeating decimals*. A **repeating decimal** contains a digit or group of digits that repeats forever.

272 **Module 4** Inventions

8 **Try This as a Class** Any rational number can be written as a terminating or a repeating decimal. Explain how you can tell whether a particular fraction will be a *terminating* or a *repeating* decimal.

9 **a.** Without using your calculator, divide 7 by 11 and find the answer to five decimal places. 0.63636

   b. Explain how you know the decimal will continue to repeat beyond the place where you stopped dividing. Since the remainders begin repeating, the digits in the quotient will also repeat.

▶ You can use a bar to show which digits in a decimal repeat.

EXAMPLE

$$\frac{16}{33} = 0.484848... = 0.\overline{48}, \text{ so}$$

$\frac{16}{33}$ is exactly equal to $0.\overline{48}$ and $-\frac{16}{33}$ is exactly equal to $-0.\overline{48}$.

10 Write your answer to Question 9(a) using a bar to show which digits repeat. $0.\overline{63}$

11 In the decimal $0.6\overline{3}$, only the digit 3 repeats, $0.6\overline{3} = 0.633333...$. Write each decimal below using six decimal places, as shown in the Example. Then write the decimals in order from least to greatest.

   a. $0.8\overline{2}$ $0.\overline{828}$ $0.\overline{82}$ 0.822

   b. $-0.8\overline{28}$ $-0.\overline{8}$ -0.8 $-0.82\overline{8}$

12  Write each rational number as a terminating or a repeating decimal. Then write the numbers in order from least to greatest. $-3\frac{1}{4}, -\frac{14}{16}, \frac{5}{37}, 6$

   a. $\frac{5}{37}$ $0.\overline{135}$ **b.** $-3\frac{1}{4}$ -3.25 **c.** 6 6 **d.** $-\frac{14}{16}$ -0.875

HOMEWORK EXERCISES ▶ See Exs. 1–7 on p. 278.

---

8. If the denominator of the fraction can be multiplied by some whole number to make it a power of 10, the fraction will be a terminating decimal. Otherwise it will be a repeating decimal.

11. a. 0.822222,
0.828828,
0.828282,
0.822000; 0.82,
$0.\overline{82}, 0.\overline{82}, 0.\overline{828}$
b. −0.828282,
−0.888888,
−0.800000,
−0.828888;
$-0.\overline{8}, -0.\overline{828},$
$-0.82\overline{8}, -0.8$

✓ QUESTION 12

...checks that you can write a rational number as a terminating or a repeating decimal.

Section 4   Rational Numbers   273

DEVELOPING MATH CONCEPTS
In answering **Question 8**, students may just say that 3 and 11 (the denominators of $\frac{1}{3}$ and $\frac{5}{11}$ from the definition of repeating decimal on page 272) do not divide any power of 10 exactly, so if a denominator is not a factor of 10, 100, 1000... it will be a repeating decimal. This reasoning is correct, but ask how they can be certain that a number won't eventually divide a power of 10 such as 1,000,000 or 100,000,000,000 exactly. Ask students which factors other than 1 and 10 do divide 10. (*2 and 5*) Then have them look at the factors of the denominators for each of the fractions in Question 5 that represent terminating decimals. They are all multiples of 2 and/or 5. That is, their only prime factors are 2 and/or 5. Based on this information, ask students how they would classify the fraction $\frac{9}{40}$. (*Terminating since* $40 = 2 \cdot 2 \cdot 2 \cdot 5$)

COMMON ERROR
In **Question 8**, when describing how they can tell whether a fraction will be a terminating or repeating decimal, students often forget that they must write the fraction in simplest form before checking the factors of the denominator. For example, some students will say $\frac{9}{60}$ is a repeating decimal because 3 is a factor of the denominator. However, $\frac{9}{60} = \frac{3}{20}$ and $\frac{3}{20}$ is a terminating decimal since the only prime factors of 20 are 2 and 5.

TEACHING NOTES
Question 11 Students should carry out terminating decimals to 6 places by writing zeroes after the last digit shown. Once the given numbers are carried out to 6 places the process of comparing decimals is the same as they learned with terminating decimals.

Exploration 2

TEACHING NOTES

In **Question 13**, the class should work together to develop the formula for the exterior surface of a *hollow* hemisphere ($2\pi r^2$) by taking half the formula for volume of a sphere. Later in the exploration students will return to this Egyptian basket problem and see how rational numbers can be used in solving equations. In the Practice and Applications, students will find the surface area of a *solid* hemisphere that includes the exterior surface ($2\pi r^2$) plus the area of the exposed circle (πr^2) where the sphere was sliced in half. Students should be aware of the difference between the two.

Exploration 2

Equations With Rational Numbers

▶ The Egyptians also invented ways to approximate surface areas and volumes. For example, one of the problems in the Moscow Papyrus explains how to find the surface area of a "basket". The third line of the basket problem shows that the diameter of the basket is $4\frac{1}{2}$ units long. Can you find this numeral in the hieroglyphics below?

Scholars disagree ▶ about the shape of the basket referred to in the Moscow Papyrus (written in about 1850 B.C.). We will assume the basket was a hemisphere.

13 **Try This as a Class** The formula for the surface area of a sphere is $S.A. = 4\pi r^2$, where r is the radius of the sphere.

a. The surface area of the basket is similar to the surface area of the curved surface of a hemisphere. Write a formula for finding the area of the curved surface of a hemisphere. $S.A. = 2\pi r^2$

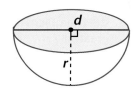

▲ a hemisphere with radius r and diameter d

b. The basket has a diameter of $4\frac{1}{2}$ units. What is the radius? Write your answer as a fraction. $\frac{9}{4}$ units

c. Use the radius you found in part (b) to write an equation representing the exact surface area of the basket. Simplify the equation. $S.A. = 2\pi\left(\frac{9}{4}\right)^2;\ \frac{81}{8}\pi$

▶ To approximate the surface area of the basket you would need to substitute a value such as 3.14 or $\frac{22}{7}$ for π in the equation you wrote. The Egyptians did not use these values for π. What value did they use and how does it compare to the approximations we often use today? Answer Questions 14 and 15 to find out.

14 The next to last line of the basket problem is given below. It reads, "You get 32. Behold this is its surface!"

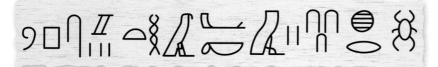

a. Use your equation from Question 13(c). Replace *S.A.* with 32 and choose a variable to represent the Egyptians' value for π. Replace π with the variable you chose. $32 = \frac{81}{8}p$

b. To solve for the variable, you can undo the multiplication by dividing by the fraction. What fraction will you need to divide by to solve your equation? $\frac{81}{8}$

▶ The Egyptians invented ways to calculate with positive rational numbers, but methods for calculating with negative rationals were not invented until centuries later. The sign rules for multiplying and dividing negative rational numbers are the same as those for integers.

EXAMPLE

Solve $8 = -\frac{4}{5}n$.

SAMPLE RESPONSE

$$8 = -\frac{4}{5}n$$

Undo multiplication by dividing both sides of the equation by $-\frac{4}{5}$.

$$8 \div \left(-\frac{4}{5}\right) = -\frac{4}{5}n \div \left(-\frac{4}{5}\right)$$

$$8 \cdot \left(-\frac{5}{4}\right) = -\frac{4}{5}n \cdot \left(-\frac{5}{4}\right)$$

To divide by $-\frac{4}{5}$, multiply by its reciprocal, $-\frac{5}{4}$.

$$-\frac{40}{4} = n$$

$$-10 = n$$

15 a. Use the Example as a guide to help solve your equation from Question 14(a) to find what fraction the Egyptians used for π.

b. What fraction did the Egyptians use for π? To what decimal is this close? $\frac{256}{81}$; 3.16

16 **Discussion** Describe the steps you would use to solve each equation.

a. $\frac{1}{8} = -\frac{9}{2}x$ b. $-4\frac{1}{2}x = 180$ c. $-\frac{2}{3}x + 5 = 11$

TEACHING NOTES
Question 16 On the board, solve each problem using the steps that the students describe. Then have students check the results in the original equations to be sure they are the correct solutions. If necessary, revise any steps.

15. a. $32 = \frac{81}{8}p$; $32 \div \frac{81}{8}$

$= p$; $32 \cdot \frac{8}{81} = p$;

$p = \frac{256}{81}$

16. a. Divide both sides of the equation by $-\frac{9}{2}$ (or multiply both sides by its reciprocal, $-\frac{2}{9}$).

b. Write $-4\frac{1}{2}$ as a fraction. Then divide both sides of the equation by the fraction (or multiply both sides by the reciprocal of the fraction.)

c. Subtract 5 from both sides of the equation. Then divide both sides by $-\frac{2}{3}$ (or multiply both sides by the reciprocal).

Section 4   Rational Numbers   **275**

TEACHING NOTES

Question 19 Allow students to use either method developed in Questions 17 and 18 to solve each equation.

17. b. $\dfrac{3\left(\frac{50}{3}\right)}{5} = \dfrac{50}{5} = 10$

▶ Sometimes equations are written so that the variable is part of a fraction. In Questions 17–19 you will develop methods for solving equations like $\dfrac{3x}{5} = 10$.

17 One way to solve the equation $\dfrac{3x}{5} = 10$ is to rewrite it as $\dfrac{3}{5}x = 10$.

   a. Solve $\dfrac{3}{5}x = 10$. $\dfrac{50}{3}$ or $16\frac{2}{3}$

   b. Check that your answer is a solution of the equation $\dfrac{3x}{5} = 10$.

18 Another way to solve $\dfrac{3x}{5} = 10$ is to first multiply both sides of the equation by 5.

   a. Discussion Why is it helpful to use this as a first step?
   Multiplying by 5 eliminates the fraction.
   b. Finish solving the equation. $3x = 50;\ x = \dfrac{50}{3}$ or $16\frac{2}{3}$

19 Solve each equation.

   a. $\dfrac{5y}{6} = 18$ $\dfrac{108}{5}$ or $21\frac{3}{5}$ **b.** $21 = \dfrac{-3n}{10}$ 70   **c.** $\dfrac{-p}{8} + 10 = 20$ 80

20 Consider the equation $-\dfrac{3}{4}x + \dfrac{1}{6} = \dfrac{11}{12}$.

   a. What is the least common denominator of the fractions? 12

   b. Multiply both sides of the equation by the LCD of the fractions and solve the resulting equation. $-9x + 2 = 11;\ -1$

   c. Check that your solution in part (b) is a solution of the original equation. $-\dfrac{3}{4}(-1) + \dfrac{1}{6} = \dfrac{3}{4} + \dfrac{1}{6} = \dfrac{11}{12}$

   d. Discussion Could you solve the original equation by multiplying both sides by 48? What is the advantage of using the LCD instead? Yes; Sample Response: The arithmetic is easier when the LCD is used.

21 Discussion

   a. What would be your first step in solving $2n + 0.5 = -0.7$?
   Subtract 0.5 from both sides of the equation.
   b. What would be your second step? Divide the answer, –1.2, by 2.

   c. Solve $2n + 0.5 = -0.7$. What is the value of n? -0.6

✔ **QUESTION 22**

...checks that you can solve equations containing rational numbers.

22 ✔ **CHECKPOINT** Solve each equation and check your solution.

   a. $-\dfrac{2}{3}y - \dfrac{1}{2} = 4$ **b.** $2.9 - 0.2x = 1.2$ **c.** $-1.1 = -0.5a - 1.2$

    $-\dfrac{27}{4}$ or $-6\frac{3}{4}$ 8.5 -0.2

HOMEWORK EXERCISES ▶ See Exs. 8–30 on pp. 278–280.

Key Concepts

Rational Numbers (pp. 271–273)

A rational number can be written in the form $\frac{a}{b}$, where a and b are integers and $b \neq 0$. When written as a decimal, a rational number either terminates or repeats.

rational numbers

$$\frac{13}{50} = 0.26$$
terminating decimal

$$\frac{8}{11} = 0.727272... = 0.\overline{72}$$
repeating decimal

Equations with Rational Numbers (pp. 274–276)

You can solve equations that contain rational numbers. Recall that the sign rules for multiplying and dividing negative rational numbers are the same as those for multiplying and dividing integers.

Example

$$-\frac{3}{4}x + 5 = 10$$

$$-\frac{3}{4}x + 5 - 5 = 10 - 5$$

Subtract 5 from both sides.

$$-\frac{3}{4}x = 5$$

$$-\frac{3}{4}x \div \left(-\frac{3}{4}\right) = 5 \div \left(-\frac{3}{4}\right)$$

Divide both sides by $-\frac{3}{4}$.

$$-\frac{3}{4}x \cdot \left(-\frac{4}{3}\right) = 5 \cdot \left(-\frac{4}{3}\right)$$

To divide by $-\frac{3}{4}$ multiply by its reciprocal, $-\frac{4}{3}$.

$$x = -\frac{20}{3} = -6\frac{2}{3}$$

Key Terms

rational number

terminating decimal

repeating decimal

Key Concepts Questions

23 Check that $-6\frac{2}{3}$ is a solution of the equation $-\frac{3}{4}x + 5 = 10$.

24 Solve the equation $20 = -1.5y - 7$. Explain the steps you use.
–18; Add 7 to both sides of the equation. Then divide both sides of the resulting equation by –1.5.

23. $-\frac{3}{4}\left(-6\frac{2}{3}\right) + 5 =$

$-\frac{3}{4}\left(-\frac{20}{3}\right) + 5 =$

$5 + 5 = 10$

Key Concepts

CLOSURE QUESTION

Explain two ways to solve an equation that has a fractional coefficient.

Sample Response: After isolating the variable term, divide both sides of the equation by the fraction. Or multiply both sides by the denominator of the fraction and then afterwards, divide each side by the numerator.

ABSENT STUDENTS

For students who were absent for all or part of this section, the blackline Study Guide for Section 4 may be used to present the ideas, concepts, and skills of Section 4.

1. What is the modern equivalent of each fraction?

a. $\frac{1}{5}$ b. c.

2. Use Egyptian symbols to represent each fraction.

a. $\frac{1}{125}$ b. $\frac{1}{1000}$ c. $\frac{4}{5}$

3. Write each rational number as a quotient of two integers.

a. -4 $\frac{-4}{1}$ b. $\sqrt{16}$ $\frac{4}{1}$ c. 0.25 $\frac{1}{4}$ d. $2\frac{3}{7}$ $\frac{17}{7}$

4. Write each rational number as a terminating or repeating decimal.

a. $2\frac{3}{5}$ 2.6 b. $\frac{9}{11}$ $0.\overline{81}$ c. $\frac{8}{27}$ $0.\overline{296}$ d. $\frac{7}{20}$ 0.35

5. **Writing** Explain why 0.666667 is not exactly equal to $\frac{2}{3}$.

6. Write the repeating decimals below in order from least to greatest. Explain your thinking.

$0.1\overline{25}$ $\qquad$ $0.12\overline{5}$ $\qquad$ $0.1\overline{2}$ $\qquad$ $0.\overline{125}$

7. Write the numbers $\frac{16}{3}$, $-14.\overline{14}$, -1, $5\frac{4}{9}$, 14.1, 5.33, and $-\sqrt{4}$ in order from least to greatest. $-14.\overline{14}, -\sqrt{4}, -1, 5.33, \frac{16}{3}, 5\frac{4}{9}, 14.1$

Solve each equation.

8. $\frac{3}{5}n = 15$ $\quad$ 25

9. $10 = -1.25x$ $\quad$ -8

10. $1\frac{2}{3}r = 120$ $\quad$ 72

11. $\frac{5}{6}b + 15 = 14$

12. $9 = \frac{3}{4}h + 12$ $\quad$ -4

13. $-2.25s - 7 = 20$ $\quad$ -12

14. $\frac{2x}{3} = -7$ $\quad$ $-\frac{21}{2}$ or $-10\frac{1}{2}$

15. $15 = \frac{-5x}{3}$ $\quad$ -9

16. $\frac{x}{5} - 2 = -3$ $\quad$ -5

17. $3x + 6 = 4.5$ $\quad$ -0.5

18. $-\frac{3}{4}x = \frac{11}{12}$

19. $-0.5x - 1.25 = 6.75$

20. $-\frac{4}{5}x + \frac{3}{5} = \frac{13}{25}$ $\quad$ $\frac{1}{10}$

21. $\frac{2}{3}x + 6 = \frac{4}{9}$

22. $6.25x + 3 = -4.5$ $\quad$ -1.2

23. Geometry Connection The area of the triangle is 209 ft². Find the length of the base of the triangle. **22 ft**

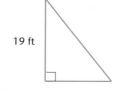

19 ft

24. Music The City Youth Orchestra has four sections. The circle graph shows what fraction of the orchestra play in three of the sections.

a. Let n be the fraction of the orchestra members that play brass instruments. Write an equation that shows that the sum of the fractional parts of the orchestra is 1. $n + \frac{1}{24} + \frac{5}{9} + \frac{1}{6} = 1$

b. What fraction of the orchestra members play brass instruments? How did you find your answer?

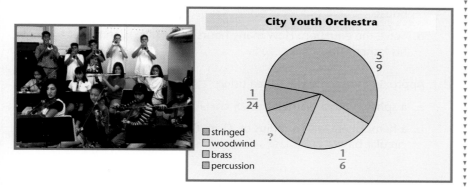

City Youth Orchestra

$\frac{5}{9}$

$\frac{1}{24}$

?

$\frac{1}{6}$

☐ stringed
☐ woodwind
☐ brass
☐ percussion

25. Challenge Soft drinks come in four sizes at a local convenience store: small, medium, large, and jumbo. The small is $\frac{1}{9}$ the size of the jumbo. The jumbo is 2 times the size of the large, and the medium is $\frac{1}{3}$ the size of the large. If the medium is 12 ounces, find the size of the jumbo, the large, and the small.
Jumbo = 72 oz, large = 36 oz, and small = 8 oz.

26. Jill was planning a hiking trip through Europe. To get a feel for metric distances, she converted miles to kilometers. To do this, she multiplied the number of miles by 1.6.

a. Write an equation Jill could have used to estimate distances in kilometers given distances in miles.

b. About how many kilometers is 55 mi? **88 km**

c. About how many miles is 120 km? **75 mi**

d. How would she convert kilometers to miles? **divide the number of kilometers by 1.6.**

Baker   37 mi | 60 km
Barstow 99 mi | 159 km

EXERCISE NOTES

In **Challenge Exercise 25**, students can use a variable to represent the large drink. Using this variable they can write expressions that describe the jumbo, medium, and small drinks. Then by setting the medium drink expression equal to 12 ounces and solving for the variable, the number of ounces for each size drink can be found.

24. b $\frac{17}{22}$; Sample Response: I simplified the equation in part (a) and solved for n.

26. a. $k = 1.6m$ where k = the number of kilometers and m = the number of miles

Practice & Applications

EXERCISE NOTES

For **Exercise 27(c)**, students might be able to show that 0° Celsius substituted in the first formula gives the value of 32° for F and that when 32° is substituted for F in the second formula the result is 0° Celsius. For those students who were able to show the equivalence using values for C and F, challenge them to show that the formulas are equivalent without substituting numbers for C and F. They may try replacing C in the first formula with the expression $\frac{5}{9}F - 17\frac{7}{9}$ or try solving one of the formulas for the other given variable.

27. c.
$$F = \frac{9}{5}C + 32$$
$$F - 32 = \frac{9}{5}C$$
$$\frac{5}{9}(F - 32) = C$$
$$\frac{5}{9}F - \frac{5}{9} \cdot 32 = C$$
$$\frac{5}{9}F - \frac{160}{9} = C$$
$$\frac{5}{9}F - 17\frac{7}{9} = C$$

28. a. Let t be the time in hours that he has driven. Then in t hours he has driven 57.5 mi, so his original distance from the campground, 345 mi, is decreased by 57.5t mi. He will be at his father's when this distance is 161 mi.

Discussion

Exercise 30 checks that you understand terminating and repeating decimals.

30. a. $\frac{7}{40}$ terminates because the only prime factors of 40 are 2 and 5. $\frac{5}{14}$ repeats because $\frac{5}{14}$ is in lowest terms and 7 is a factor of 14. $\frac{6}{15}$ terminates because $\frac{6}{15} = \frac{2}{5}$.

27. The equation $C = \frac{5}{9}F - 17\frac{7}{9}$ can be used to convert degrees Fahrenheit (F) to degrees Celsius (C).

   a. What is the Celsius temperature for 212°F? 100°C

   b. What is the Fahrenheit temperature for –20°C? –4°F

   c. Show that the formula $F = \frac{9}{5}C + 32$ is equivalent to $C = \frac{5}{9}F - 17\frac{7}{9}$. See margin.

28. a. Elian drives 345 mi from his home to a campground. He travels at an average rate of 57.5 mi/hr. He plans to stop on the way at his father's house, which is 161 miles from the campground. Explain why you can use the equation $345 - 57.5t = 161$ to find the time in hours it will take Elian to get to his father's house.

   b. Solve the equation. How many hours will it take Elian to get to his father's house? 3.2; 3.2 hr

29. Approximate each surface area using $\frac{22}{7}$ for π.

   a. a sphere with a diameter of 28 cm about 2464 cm²

   b. a hemisphere with a radius of 21 in. (Include the area of the circular base.) about 4158 cm²

Reflecting ◀▶ **on the Section**

Be prepared to discuss your response to Exercise 30 in class.

30. a. Without dividing, determine whether each fraction is equivalent to a repeating decimal or to a terminating decimal. Explain your decision in each case.

$$\frac{7}{40} \qquad \frac{5}{14} \qquad \frac{6}{15}$$

   b. Check your answers by dividing.
   $\frac{7}{40} = 0.175$; $\frac{5}{14} = 0.3\overline{571428}$; $\frac{6}{15} = 0.4$

Spiral ◀▶ **Review**

Evaluate each expression. Round decimal answers to the nearest hundredth. (Module 3, p. 175)

31. $\frac{12 + 13}{7}$ 3.57

32. $\frac{9}{2}\sqrt{6 + 5}$ 14.92

33. $\frac{8}{12 - 3}$ 0.89

Tell whether each ordered pair is a solution of the equation $y = -x + 2$.
(Module 3, p. 175)

34. (0, 2) yes   **35.** (–1, –1) no   **36.** (–2, 0) no   **37.** (2, 4) no

Solve each equation. Round decimal solutions to the nearest hundredth. (Module 3, p. 220)

38. $19 = 2.5x - 3.1$ 8.84

39. $\frac{n}{4.4} + 39 = 52.6$ 59.84

40. $3.7 + 0.06z = 11$ 121.67

41. $\frac{r}{2} + 21 = 31.1$ 20.2

Extension ▶ ▶

Repeating Decimals

The decimal 0.25 can be written as the fraction $\frac{25}{100}$, or $\frac{1}{4}$. A repeating decimal such as $0.\overline{36}$ can also be written as a fraction.

Step 1	Write an equation.	$x = 0.\overline{36}$
Step 2	Multiply both sides by 100 since $0.\overline{36}$ has two digits that repeat.	$100x = 100(0.\overline{36})$
Step 3	Subtract $x = 0.\overline{36}$ from the resulting equation.	$100x = 36.\overline{36}$ $-x = -0.\overline{36}$ $99x = 36$
Step 4	Solve for x and write the fraction in lowest terms.	$x = \frac{36}{99} = \frac{4}{11}$
Step 5	Check that $\frac{4}{11} = 0.\overline{36}$.	$4 \div 11 = 0.36363636...$

Write each repeating decimal as a fraction in lowest terms. Check your solutions.

42. $0.\overline{48}$ $\frac{16}{33}$ **43.** $0.\overline{2}$ $\frac{2}{9}$ **44.** $0.\overline{123}$ $\frac{41}{333}$ **45.** $0.5\overline{8}$ $\frac{53}{90}$ (multiply by 10)

TEACHING NOTES

Extension Exercise 45 requires that students carry out the decimal places to $5.8\overline{8}$ after multiplying x by 10. This way when $x = 0.5\overline{8}$ is subtracted from $10x = 5.8\overline{8}$, the repeating portions will be subtracted to result in $9x = 5.3$. After solving for x, students will need to clear out the decimal in the fraction $\frac{5.3}{9}$ (by multiplying by $\frac{10}{10}$) to obtain $\frac{53}{90}$, the fraction for $0.5\overline{8}$.

Extra Skill Practice

TEACHER NOTES
For each Exploration, the corresponding Extra Skill Practice Exercises are noted.

Exploration 1: Exs. 1–13
Exploration 2: Exs. 14–28

EXTRA HELP
Teacher's Resource Book
• Practice and Applications
• Study Guide

Technology Resources
• @Home Tutor
• Test Generator

ASSESSMENT
• Section 4 Quick Quiz
• Test Generator

Section ④
Extra Skill Practice

Write each rational number as a quotient of two integers.

1. 1.37 $\frac{137}{100}$

2. $-\sqrt{25}$ $\frac{-5}{1}$

3. 0.125 $\frac{1}{8}$

4. $5\frac{3}{8}$ $\frac{43}{8}$

Write each rational number as a terminating or repeating decimal.

5. $1\frac{3}{4}$ 1.75

6. $\frac{7}{13}$ $0.\overline{538461}$

7. $\frac{8}{15}$ $0.5\overline{3}$

8. $\frac{9}{25}$ 0.36

9. Order the numbers 0.35, $-\frac{3}{10}$, $-0.\overline{3}$, $\frac{2}{5}$, and $\frac{1}{3}$ from least to greatest. $-0.\overline{3}, -\frac{3}{10}, \frac{1}{3}, 0.35, \frac{2}{5}$

Replace each ? with >, <, or =.

10. $-2.5\overline{8}$? -2.6 $>$

11. $-8.\overline{42}$? $-8.\overline{4}$ $>$

12. $-\frac{2}{3}$? $-\frac{5}{8}$ $<$

13. $-9\frac{5}{6}$? $-9.8\overline{3}$ $=$

Solve each equation.

14. $3.2x - 2.7 = -8.4$ -1.78125

15. $-2.5x + 3 = 5.75$ -1.1

16. $2.6 = 2.7 + 2.5x$ -0.04

17. $\frac{2}{3}x + 1 = \frac{1}{6}$ $-\frac{5}{4}$

18. $\frac{3}{5} - \frac{2}{5}x = \frac{21}{25}$ $-\frac{3}{5}$

19. $6\frac{1}{4} = -\frac{5}{12}x$ -15

20. $\frac{1}{8}x = -3$ -24

21. $3 = 5 + \frac{2}{3}y$ -3

22. $4 = \frac{7}{3}m$ $\frac{12}{7}$ or $1\frac{5}{7}$

23. $0.5 = 0.75x + 1.25$ -1.5

24. $-\frac{2}{5}m - \frac{1}{10} = \frac{3}{10}$ -1

25. $3.2 + 0.4x = 1.2$ -5

26. $\frac{3}{2}t + 30 = 15$ -10

27. $2 = 4 - \frac{1}{4}s$ 8

28. $6 - \frac{4}{9}x = \frac{1}{9}$ $-\frac{53}{4}$ or $-13\frac{1}{4}$

Standardized Testing ▶ Open-ended

Write a real-world problem that can be modeled by each equation.
Answers will vary. Sample responses are given.

1. $\frac{3}{5}y = 30$ Kelly saves $\frac{3}{5}$ of all the money she earns. How much must she earn to save $30?

2. $\frac{1}{2}n + 12 = 40$ Moses purchased a $12 single CD and a half-priced boxed set. The total cost was $40. What was the regular price of the boxed set?

Section 5 Counting Techniques

IN THIS SECTION

EXPLORATION 1
♦ Counting and Permutations

EXPLORATION 2
♦ Combinations

Reading is Believing

Setting the Stage ▸▸▸▸▸▸▸▸▸▸▸▸▸▸▸▸▸▸▸▸▸▸▸▸▸▸▸▸▸

SET UP *You will need Labsheet 5A.*

Louis Braille (1809–1852) was blinded in an accident when he was only three years old. As a young boy, he anxiously awaited the day when he could go to school and learn to read. In her book *Seeing Fingers: The Story of Louis Braille*, Etta DeGering describes Louis's first year in school.

> **Seeing Fingers** by Etta DeGering
>
> Since Monsieur Becheret, the teacher, lectured one day and questioned the next, Louis did not find it too difficult to compete with his sighted classmates. After a few weeks he stood at the top of most of his classes.
>
> In arithmetic he could often work a problem in his head as quickly as the other pupils on paper. But when it came to the reading and writing periods there was nothing for him to do. There were no books for blind boys to read and no way for them to write. This he learned the first day of school. When the primers were passed out, he held out his hand and was given one. He touched [his cousin] Jean to see how the reading was done. He held his book in the same way, but the pages told him no magic words.
>
> "Are there no books for blind boys to read?" he asked the teacher.
>
> When Monsieur Becheret said "None that I know of," Louis put his head down on his desk and wept.

Section 5   Counting Techniques   **283**

Setting the Stage

ABOUT THE THEME
The invention of the Braille system made an incredible impact on the education of those with limited sight. Equally impressive is that Louis Braille invented this code when he was the age of most middle school students. Through this system of dots, students explore permutations and combinations and learn why Louis had to use at least 6 dots to form all the letters of the alphabet.

GETTING STARTED
In preparation for learning the counting principle, Module 4 Section 5 *Warm-Up* reviews possible outcomes of an event.

Most students would be interested to see and feel a book that is written in Braille. Consult your public library or local chapter for the blind about borrowing a Braille typed book. As students examine the book, discuss with them places they may have seen Braille used. Ask them to look for signs in Braille next time they visit a public building, often room numbers, rest rooms, museums, and interpretive sites have signs in Braille. The 2003 Alabama state quarter design features an image of Helen Keller with her name in block letters and Braille.

TIPS FROM TEACHERS
Make a set of six overhead transparencies of an enlarged diagram of the six-position Braille symbol. Fill in a different dot on each one so that when all six are overlaid it shows all the circles filled. This way you can use them throughout the lesson, overlaying the transparencies to represent the different Braille symbols.

Students will need the labsheet and a soft surface such as a pad of paper for **Question 1**. It is essential that students complete the activity for students to understand the Braille alphabet since it is used in both explorations of this section.

Louis did not give up, however. Between the ages of 12 and 15, he created a code that he hoped would allow blind students to read. His code used groups of raised dots to represent letters of the alphabet. Today the code Louis created is called Braille in his honor. The Braille alphabet is shown below.

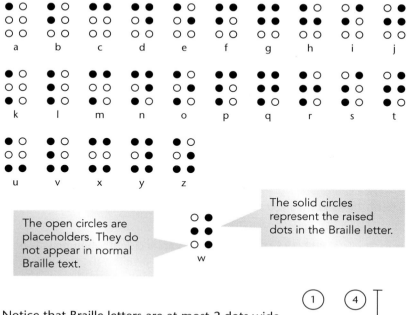

The open circles are placeholders. They do not appear in normal Braille text.

The solid circles represent the raised dots in the Braille letter.

Notice that Braille letters are at most 2 dots wide and at most 3 dots high. The 6 possible dot positions form a Braille *cell*. The cell at the right shows how the dot positions are numbered.

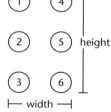

Think About It

1 **Use Labsheet 5A.** One day at school, Louis showed the Braille alphabet to some of his classmates. As his classmates discussed what the new alphabet would allow them to do, his friend Gabriel interrupted them excitedly. "Already I know the alphabet. I have written a sentence." Follow the directions on the labsheet to read *Gabriel's Sentence*. I can write; I: 2, 4; C: 1, 4; A: 1; N: 1, 3, 4, 5; W: 2, 4, 5, 6; R: 1, 2, 3, 5; I: 2, 4; T: 2, 3, 4, 5; E: 1, 5.

▶ In this section, you will discover why Louis Braille's decision to use 6 dot positions in a Braille cell was a very important one. You will also explore how he constructed the Braille alphabet.

Exploration 1

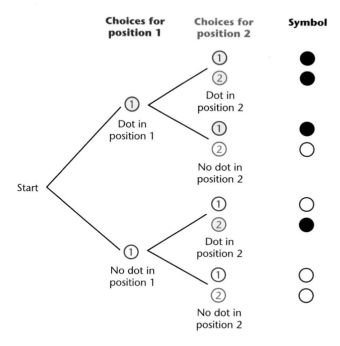

Counting and Permutations

SET UP *You will need colored markers or pencils.*

GOAL

LEARN HOW TO...
- use the counting principle to count numbers of choices
- find the number of permutations of a group of objects

AS YOU...
- work with Braille symbols

KEY TERMS
- counting principle
- permutation

▶ **In this exploration, you will answer this question: What would have happened if Louis Braille had chosen fewer than 6 dot positions for his Braille cell?**

2 How many different symbols could Louis Braille have made if he had used only 1 dot position for the Braille cell? **2 symbols**

▶ **You can use a tree diagram to find the number of different symbols you can make with a Braille cell that has 2 dot positions.**

Choices for position 1   **Choices for position 2**   **Symbol**

Dot in position 1 — ① ② Dot in position 2 → ● ●

Dot in position 1 — ① ② No dot in position 2 → ● ○

Start

No dot in position 1 — ① ② Dot in position 2 → ○ ●

No dot in position 1 — ① ② No dot in position 2 → ○ ○

Section 5   Counting Techniques   **285**

Exploration 1

TEACHING NOTES

You may want to have students approach this exploration from the view point that they are Louis Braille, attempting to devise a code for reading by using dots. To keep the system from getting too complicated, Louis had to try to use as few dots as possible. The students will try to create a code with only 1 dot, with only 2 dots, with only 3 dots, etc. to see how many symbols they could represent with each system.

If you ask students how many Braille symbols they can create with only 2 positions for dots, most would be able to draw the first 3 symbols listed next to the tree diagram. However, many would forget that having both dots "unraised" on the paper (shown as not shaded) should also be represented. Help students understand how the tree diagram was created, observing that the *Choices for position 2* branches include what was already chosen from the branch in position 1, plus the raised or not raised dot for the 2nd position.

As an alternative visual you can simplify the tree diagram to

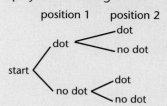

and show 2 vertical dots with the positions labeled.

○ position 1
○ position 2

Students follow a branch until it ends and then color the result, (dot, dot) or (dot, no dot) etc.

285

Exploration 1 *continued*

TEACHING NOTES

You may want to review the concept of choices as it relates to probability, such as: the two choices for flipping a coin are head or tails. In **Question 3**, the 2 choices are a raised dot in a position or no raised dot in that same position.

For **Question 4**, ensure that the students have accounted for all 3 positions in their tree diagram.

USING MANIPULATIVES

Sets of two different colored disks can be used to make the tree diagrams in **Questions 3 and 4**. A colored disk in a position represents a raised dot while a white disk represents no dot. Straws or pipe cleaners can be used as branches.

DIFFERENTIATED INSTRUCTION

In place of making a tree diagram, provide the student with a sheet of several sets of the 2-position cells. The student is to cover each 2-position cell differently using the colored disks system described above in *Using Manipulatives*. Repeat this activity for the 3-position cell from **Question 4**. A student using this method can then count the number of different ways they were able to cover the cells.

4. a. See Additional Answers beginning on page A1.

3 Use the tree diagram on the previous page for a 2-position Braille cell.

    a. How many choices are there for position 1 of the cell? **2 choices**

    b. For each choice for position 1, how many choices are there for position 2? **2 choices**

    c. How many different symbols can you make with a 2-position Braille cell? **4 choices**

4 **a.** Draw a tree diagram that lists the number of different symbols you can make with a 3-position Braille cell like the one shown. Use color to indicate the choices in your tree diagram, as was done in the diagram on the previous page. **See margin.**

    b. How many choices are there for position 1? for position 2? for position 3? **2 choices; 2 choices; 2 choices**

    c. How many different symbols can you make with a 3-position Braille cell? **8 different symbols**

    d. How are your answers to parts (b) and (c) related? **Multiply the number of choices for each position to get the number of different symbols, 2 · 2 · 2.**
    e. Is this relationship also true for parts (a) and (b) of Question 3? **Yes**

▶ The relationship you described in Question 4(d) is called the **counting principle**. This principle says that the total number of ways a sequence of decisions can be made is the product of the number of choices for each decision.

EXAMPLE

To find the number of different symbols you can make with a Braille cell that has only 4 dot positions, use the counting principle.

$$\begin{matrix} \text{number of} \\ \text{symbols} \end{matrix} = \begin{matrix} \text{choices for} \\ \text{position 1} \end{matrix} \times \begin{matrix} \text{choices for} \\ \text{position 2} \end{matrix} \times \begin{matrix} \text{choices for} \\ \text{position 3} \end{matrix} \times \begin{matrix} \text{choices for} \\ \text{position 4} \end{matrix}$$

$$= \quad 2 \quad \times \quad 2 \quad \times \quad 2 \quad \times \quad 2$$

$$= \quad 16$$

> There are 2 choices for each position: have a raised dot, or do not have a raised dot.

You can make 16 different symbols with a Braille cell that has 4 dot positions.

5 ✔ **CHECKPOINT** How many different symbols can you make with each type of Braille cell? Explain.

    a. a 5-position Braille cell **32 symbols; multiply 2 · 2 · 2 · 2 · 2 or find 2^5.**

    b. a 6-position Braille cell **64 symbols; multiply 2 · 2 · 2 · 2 · 2 · 2 or find 2^6.**

6 **Discussion** Could Louis Braille have used a Braille cell with fewer than 6 positions for his code? Explain.

▶ **Today new technologies make it easier for blind people to go to school or hold a job. Braille keyboards and Braille printers enable the blind to communicate in written form. Electronic Braille displays are used to convert text on a computer screen into Braille text.**

7 Max Jones uses a Braille keyboard and a Braille display at his job. He needs to choose a password for his company's e-mail system. He decides to use an arrangement of the letters in his first name. You can find the number of passwords from which Max can choose by using the counting principle.

    a. How many choices are there for the first letter in an arrangement of the letters in *Max*? **3 choices**

    b. After the first letter of the arrangement is chosen, how many choices are there for the second letter? **2 choices**

    c. After the first and second letters of the arrangement are chosen, how many choices are there for the third letter? **1 choice**

    d. **Discussion** Use the counting principle to find the number of different arrangements of the letters in *Max*. How many of these arrangements can Max use as a password? Explain your reasoning. **There are 6 possible arrangements; He can only use 5 of the arrangements because he wants to use a rearrangement of the letters.**

▶ **An arrangement of a group of items in a definite order is a** **permutation** **of the items. For example, AMX and MAX are permutations of the letters M, A, and X.**

8 ✔ **CHECKPOINT** Find the number of permutations of the letters in each word.

    a. HAT **6**   **b.** DEAL **24**   **c.** SIGNAL **720**

HOMEWORK EXERCISES ▶ See Exs. 1–12 on p. 293–295.

✔ **QUESTION 5**

...checks that you can use the counting principle to count numbers of choices.

▲ This student is using a small computerized device with a Braille keyboard. He is able to write in Braille and hear back what he has written by means of synthetic speech.

6. Sample Response: No; While 5 positions can be used for the 26 letters of the alphabet, more than 6 extra symbols are needed for punctuation marks and digits.

✔ **QUESTION 8**

...checks that you can find the number of permutations of a group of items.

TEACHING NOTES
Checkpoint Question 5 Ask students what benefits using the counting principle has over using a tree diagram to answer **Question 5**. (*As more position options are added the tree diagram will become crowded with branches and more difficult to draw. The counting principle allows you to account for all the choices you would have at the end of the tree by simply multiplying the number of choices at each new position.*)

Discussion Question 6
If during the discussion students are satisfied that fewer than 6 positions is reasonable, ask, "How do you suppose Louis Braille indicated numerals in his text, or question marks?" Students will realize that our written language is comprised of more than just the 26 letters of the alphabet.

Discussion Question 7(d)
During the discussion, students should observe that in this situation each position has more than 2 choices. There are 3 choices for the first position. Once that position is filled there are only 2 choices left for the second position and 1 choice left for the third position. The resulting expression for the total number of permutations is 3 · 2 · 1.

Exploration 2

COMMON ERRORS

Question 10 In reading the results from the tree diagram on **Labsheet 5B**, students may not immediately recognize that 1, 2 and 2,1 represent the same symbol. You may want them to work together to draw each symbol for the positions chosen.

TIPS FROM TEACHERS

Seat 4 students in chairs to represent the dot positions. Those who are standing represent raised dots and those sitting represent blanks. Ask students to model each combination by standing and sitting.

10. b. No; Sample Response: The order in which a dot is chosen does not change its position, therefore, 1, 4 and 4, 1 represent the same letter or symbol.

c. 6 symbols

10. a. See Additional Answers beginning on page A1.

GOAL

LEARN HOW TO...
◆ find numbers of combinations

AS YOU...
◆ investigate the first ten letters of the Braille alphabet

KEY TERM
◆ combination

Exploration 2

Combinations

SET UP   You will need Labsheet 5B.

▶ In *Seeing Fingers: The Story of Louis Braille,* Etta DeGering describes how Louis created the first ten letters of the Braille alphabet.

> The first ten letters had been the most difficult. [Louis] made them from different arrangements of the top four dots of the [Braille cell]. **A** was dot 1, **B** dots 1 and 2, **C** dots 1 and 4....

▶ The first ten Braille letters (a-j) occupy the first row of the Braille alphabet on page 284. As the passage above states, each letter is formed using only dots in the top 4 positions of a Braille cell.

9 Draw all possible Braille symbols (including symbols that are not letters of the Braille alphabet) that have exactly 1 dot in the top 4 positions and no dots in the bottom 2 positions. How many symbols did you get? **4 symbols**

Use Labsheet 5B for Questions 10 and 11.

10 You can use the unfinished *Tree Diagram* on the labsheet to find the Braille symbols with exactly 2 dots in the top 4 positions and no dots in the bottom 2 positions.

a. Finish drawing the tree diagram. How many paths through the tree diagram are there? **See margin.**

b. Does each path through the tree diagram represent a *different* Braille symbol? Explain.

c. How many Braille symbols are there with exactly 2 dots in the top 4 positions and no dots in the bottom 2 positions? Draw each symbol.

▶ In Question 10, you formed Braille symbols by choosing 2 of the top 4 positions in a Braille cell. The order in which you chose the positions did not matter. An arrangement or selection of a group of items in which the order is not important is a **combination** of the items.

11 **a.** Write a multiplication expression for the number of permutations you found in Question 10(a). $4 \cdot 3$

b. What fraction of the total number of permutations does the number of symbols you found in Question 10(c) represent? $\frac{1}{2}$

12 **Try This as a Class** Use the counting principle.

a. Write a multiplication expression for the number of permutations of 3 dots selected from the 4 dot positions.
$4 \cdot 3 \cdot 2$

b. Try drawing all possible Braille symbols that have exactly 3 dots in the top 4 positions and no dots in the bottom 2 positions. How many symbols did you make?

c. What fraction of the total number of permutations does the actual number of symbols you found in part (b) represent? $\frac{1}{6}$

13 **a.** Find the number of permutations of 4 dots selected from the dots in the top 4 positions of a Braille cell. Explain what you did.

b. How many Braille symbols have exactly 4 dots in the top 4 positions and no dots in the bottom 2 positions? Check by drawing the symbol(s).

c. What fraction of the total number of permutations does the number of symbols you drew represent? $\frac{1}{24}$

14 **Try This as a Class** Use your results from Questions 9–13.

a. Copy and complete the table. $4, 4, \frac{1}{1};\ 12, 6, \frac{1}{2};\ 24, 4, \frac{1}{6};\ 24, 1, \frac{1}{24}$

Number of dots in top 4 positions	Number of permutations	Number of Braille symbols	Fraction of permutations represented by the Braille symbol
1	?	?	?
2	?	?	?
3	?	?	?
4	?	?	?

b. The value of 5!, read "five factorial," is the product $5 \cdot 4 \cdot 3 \cdot 2 \cdot 1 = 120$. How does the factorial of the number of dots in the top 4 positions relate to its fraction of permutations?

12. b. 4 symbols

13. a. 24; Sample Responses: I multiplied $4 \cdot 3 \cdot 2 \cdot 1$; or I created a tree diagram to show the number of paths through the diagram.

b. 1 symbol

14. b. Sample Response: The fraction of permutations that represents the symbol is the reciprocal of the factorial of the number of dots used. When the number of dots is 3, the fraction of permutations is $\frac{1}{3 \cdot 2 \cdot 1}$ or $\frac{1}{6}$.

TEACHING NOTES

In **Questions 11(b) and 12(c)** students are asked to make a connection between the number of permutations and actual number of symbols created. This connection will be covered in more depth later during the Exploration. For now emphasize that the number of symbols created are *combinations* of the items.

In **Question 12(a)**, help students recognize that the expression $4 \cdot 3 \cdot 2$ is used since there are 4 possibilities for the first position, 3 possibilities remaining for the dot in the second position, and 2 possibilities remaining for the dot in the third position. You may ask what the equation would be if 3 dots were used from 5 dot positions. Student should observe that the expression for this permutation is $5 \cdot 4 \cdot 3$. There are only 3 factors since there are only 3 positions. A tree diagram may help students to visualize what is occurring.

Exploration 2 *continued*

TEACHING NOTES

Students may want to compare answers to **Question 15** with a partner and then share results as a class to be sure they found all the possible arrangements. Remind students that they might try organizing their results using a tree diagram. Invite students up to the board or overhead to sketch the symbols they formed. Continue until the class is convinced that all possibilities are represented. In addition to a tree diagram and organized list, students could write the expression (6 · 5) ÷ 2 to represent the number of permutations (6 choices for first location, 5 for next) divided by 2 (since each combination is counted twice).

In **Question 16**, students should discover that factorials are used both in the permutation and in the fraction used to determine the number of symbols (combinations). Some students may also conclude that dividing the number of permutations by the factorial of the number of dots results in the number of Braille symbols. This conclusion supports the informal development for the formula for finding the number of combinations for *n* objects taken *r* at a time:

$$C_{n,\,r} = \frac{n!}{(n-r)!\; r!}$$

---

15. b. Sample Response: Determine the number of permutations by multiplying 6 · 5. Multiply the product by $\frac{1}{2 \cdot 1}$, or divide the product by 2 to get 15. This is the same result as in part (a).

16. c. Sample Response: There are 4 symbols that can be made using the top 3 positions and if I combine each of those with each of the 2 ways to place 1 dot in the bottom 2 positions the result will be 2 · 4 or 8 symbols.

✔ **QUESTION 17**

...checks that you can find numbers of combinations.

---

15 a. How many Braille symbols can be formed that use exactly 2 dots when the dots occupy any of the 6 positions in a Braille cell? 15

b. Discussion Use what you discovered in Question 14(b) to describe a method you might use to find the number of combinations using exactly 2 dots when the dots occupy any of the 6 positions of a Braille cell. Compare your answer to your answer in part (a).

16 a. Look at the top 4 positions of the two Braille symbols shown below. How can you determine the 3-dot symbol from the 1-dot symbol?

16. a. Sample Response: Reverse the pattern of the 1 dot symbol so that the other 3 dots are used in place of the 1 dot.

b. Explain why the number of symbols with 3 dots in the top 4 positions must equal the number of symbols with 1 dot in the top 4 positions. Use this fact and your results from Question 9 to check your answer to Question 12(b). Sample Response: The pattern can be reversed for all 4 positions.

c. Discussion How would you use the results from part (b) to determine the number of symbols that can be made from placing exactly 3 dots in the top 4 positions and 1 dot in the bottom 2 positions? How many did you find?

17 ✔ CHECKPOINT

a. Suppose 2 of the letters in the word SWIFT are selected randomly. How many combinations of letters are possible? 10

b. In how many ways can a 3-person committee be selected from the 5 people in the Math Club? 10

HOMEWORK EXERCISES ▶ See Exs. 13–19 on pp. 294–295.

Section 5
Key Concepts

Using a Tree Diagram to Count Choices (pp. 285–286)

You can use a tree diagram to count choices in a given situation.

Example Brian has a pair of **blue pants** and a pair of **gray pants**. He also has a **white shirt**, a **blue-striped shirt**, a **gray-striped shirt**, and a **plaid shirt**. The tree diagram shows that there are 8 different outfits Brian can wear.

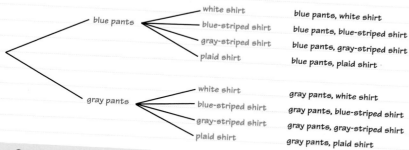

The Counting Principle (p. 286)

The total number of ways that a sequence of decisions can be made is the product of the number of choices for each decision.

Example In the Example above, Brian can choose his pants in 2 ways and his shirts in 4 ways. So Brian can choose $2 \cdot 4 = 8$ outfits.

Example Suppose a license plate can have any three letters followed by any three digits from 0 to 9 and that the letters and digits can repeat. Since there are 26 possible letters and 10 possible digits, the number of possible license plates is:

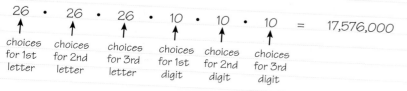

18 **Key Concepts Question** In the license plate Example above, suppose a letter or digit can be used only once. How many plates are possible? **11,232,000 plates**

Key Concepts

ABSENT STUDENTS

For students who were absent for all or part of this section, the blackline Study Guide for Section 5 may be used to present the ideas, concepts, and skills of Section 5.

Key Concepts continued

CLOSURE QUESTION

Explain how combinations and permutations are similar and how they are different from each other.

Sample Response: Both combinations and permutations use the counting principle. In combinations the order in which the items are chosen does not matter. In permutations order does matter.

Section 5

Key Concepts

Key Terms

permutation

Permutations (p. 287)

A permutation of a group of items is an arrangement of the items in a definite order.

Example A pizzeria offers 3 specialty pizzas: the Meat Combo (M), the Vegetarian (V), and the Supreme (S). Each way of arranging the pizzas on the menu is a permutation. You can find the number of permutations using the counting principle:

$$3 \quad \cdot \quad 2 \quad \cdot \quad 1 \quad = \quad 6$$

choices for 1st pizza   choices for 2nd pizza   choices for 3rd pizza

combination

Combinations (pp. 288–290)

A combination is a selection of items from a group where order is not important.

Example The Shaw family wants to buy 2 of the 3 specialty pizzas listed in the Example above. Since the order in which the pizzas are chosen is not important, each possible selection is a combination. You can use a tree diagram to find the number of combinations.

1st Pizza	2nd Pizza	Selection
M	V	M, V
	S	M, S
V	M	V, M
	S	V, S
S	M	S, M
	V	S, V

The selections with the same color are the same combination. There are 3 possible solutions.

19 Key Concepts Question Does counting the ways to choose 3 of 8 possible toppings for a pizza involve permutations or combinations? Explain. **Combinations; The order in which the toppings is chosen doesn't matter.**

Section 5

Practice & Application Exercises

For Ex. 26:
- Labsheet 5C

1. A certain model of car is available in 6 exterior colors: white, red, navy blue, forest green, tan, and maroon. The car is also available in 2 interior colors: black and gray.

   a. Draw a tree diagram showing the different color choices available for the exterior and interior of the car. See margin.

   b. In how many ways can you choose an exterior color and an interior color for the car? 12 ways

2. **Consumer Electronics** Rosa Hernandez wants to buy a new TV and a new DVD player. A consumer magazine she reads rates 3 TVs and 5 DVD players as "best buys." If Rosa limits her choices to the "best buys," in how many ways can she choose a TV and a DVD player? 15 ways

3. At a certain restaurant, dinners include one entrée, one vegetable, and one dessert from the menu shown.

   a. Draw a tree diagram showing the different dinners that a customer at the restaurant can order. See margin.

   b. How many different dinners can a customer order? 18 dinners

   Entrée
   spaghetti, chicken, roast beef

   Vegetable
   corn, squash

   Dessert
   apple pie, cherry pie, pecan pie

4. **Forensics** One method police can use to produce composite drawings of crime suspects is a kit containing clear plastic sheets that show facial features and can be combined to create likeness. One kit contains 195 hairlines, 99 eyes and eyebrows, 89 noses, 105 mouths, and 74 lower faces. How many different faces can be created? 13,349,986,650

Find the number of permutations of the letters in each word.

5. HI 2   6. TEA 6   7. MULE 24

8. BAKERY   9. SPINACH   10. CENTRIFUGAL
   720   5040   39,916,800

11. **Sports** In the Olympics, 8 swimmers participate in the final race of the women's 100-meter freestyle event. In how many different orders can the swimmers finish the race? 40,320 orders

Section 5   Counting Techniques   293

Practice & Applications

SUGGESTED ASSIGNMENTS

Core Course
Day 1: Exs. 1–4, 20–24
Day 2: Exs. 5–12
Day 3: Exs. 13–17, 19

Extended Course
Day 1: Exs. 1–4, 20–24
Day 2: Exs. 5–12
Day 3: Exs. 13–19, 25–27*

Note: Extended Course assignments can be used to differentiate within the regular classroom. In classrooms where students are grouped homogeneously, the material might be covered in fewer days. In this case assignments may be combined.

*denotes Extension Exercises

ADDITIONAL PRACTICE

See the *Teacher's Resource Book* for additional practice and application exercises for this section.

EXERCISE NOTES

In **Exercises 1 and 3**, students are asked to draw a tree diagram to represent the different possibilities. Students should understand that the counting principle will tell them the number of possible outcomes, but a tree diagram also shows what each of those outcomes is. Make sure students are aware that in the menu shown for **Exercise 3**, the different choices within a category are separated by commas.

In **Exercise 4** students should realize that a tree diagram is inappropriate for situations with so many choices. In this case the counting principle should be used.

1. a. and 3. a. See Additional Answers beginning on page A1.

12. The keypad for the Allen's garage door opener has the 10 digits, 0–9. They must choose a code using 4 digits, none of which can be used more than once, to open the door. How many possible codes could they choose? **5040 codes**

13. Mrs. McLeish requires her students to answer 2 of the 4 essay questions on a history test. How many combinations of 2 questions can Mrs. McLeish's students answer? **6 combinations**

14. **Personal Finance** Ian finds 6 books in a bookstore that he would like to read, but he only has enough money to buy 4 of them. How many combinations of 4 books can Ian buy? (*Hint*: Choosing 4 books to buy is the same as choosing 2 books *not* to buy.)
15 combinations

15. Kaya has roses, lilies, tulips, daisies, and poppies growing in her flower garden. She wants to make a bouquet for a friend. How many combinations of types of flowers can Kaya have in the bouquet if she uses each of the following?

    a. exactly 1 type of flower **5**   b. exactly 2 types of flowers **10**

    c. exactly 3 types of flowers **10**   d. at least 3 types of flowers **16**

Geometry Connection A *complete graph* is a collection of points, called *vertices*, and segments, called *edges*, such that every pair of vertices is joined by an edge. One complete graph is shown below.

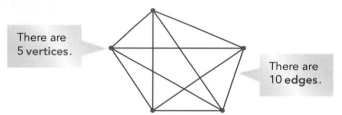

There are 5 **vertices**.

There are 10 **edges**.

16. Copy the table. For each number of vertices in the table, draw a complete graph with that many vertices. In the table, record the number of edges each complete graph has. **See margin.**

Number of vertices	Number of edges
2	?
3	?
4	?
5	?
6	?

17. **Writing** Look at the table. Explain how you can use the number of vertices as well as the concepts you explored for combinations to determine the number of edges.

17. Sample Response: Multiply the number of vertices by one less than the number and divide the product by the factorial of 2.

18. **Challenge** Write a formula for the number of edges, e, in a complete graph with v vertices. $e = \dfrac{v(v-1)}{2}$

16. See Additional Answers beginning on page A1.

Reflecting ◀▶ on the Section

Be prepared to report on the following topic in class.

19. Describe how a combination differs from a permutation. Use at least two real-world examples to help illustrate the difference.

Order is important in a permutation but not in a combination; Sample Response: Choosing a president and a vice president of a club involves permutations. Choosing a two-person committee involves combinations.

Oral Report

Exercise 19 checks that you know the difference between a combination and a permutation.

Spiral ◀▶ Review

Find the slope of a line that passes through each pair of points.
(Module 3, p. 186)

20. (3, 2) and (7, 5) $\frac{3}{4}$ 21. (5, 1) and (7, 4) $\frac{3}{2}$ 22. (3, 4) and (4, 6) 2

Find the theoretical probability of each outcome when you roll a six-sided number cube. (Module 2, p. 114)

23. rolling an even number $\frac{1}{2}$ 24. rolling a number less than 5 $\frac{2}{3}$

Extension ▶ ▶

Pascal's Triangle

The triangle of numbers shown below is part of *Pascal's triangle*. You can use Pascal's triangle to solve problems involving combinations. To find the number of combinations of *r* objects taken from a group of *n* objects, locate the (*r* + 1)st entry in row *n*.

26.
```
    1  6  15 20 15  6  1
  1  7  21 35 35 21  7  1
1  8  28 56 70 56 28  8  1
```

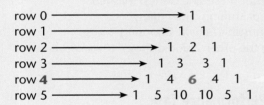

row 0 ———————→ 1
row 1 ———————→ 1 1
row 2 ———————→ 1 2 1
row 3 ———————→ 1 3 3 1
row 4 ———————→ 1 4 6 4 1
row 5 ———————→ 1 5 10 10 5 1

> The number of combinations of 2 objects taken from a group of 4 objects is the 3rd entry in row 4. There are 6 combinations.

25. **Writing** Look at the numbers in Pascal's triangle that are not equal to 1. Explain how each of these numbers is related to the two numbers directly above it. It is the sum of the two numbers directly above it.

26. **Use Labsheet 5C.** The labsheet shows the part of *Pascal's Triangle* given above. Use the pattern you found in Exercise 25 to complete rows 6–8 of Pascal's triangle.

27. Suppose you have 8 short-sleeved shirts and want to pack 4 of these shirts to take on a vacation to Florida. Use Pascal's triangle to find the number of ways you can choose the 4 shirts. 70 ways

DIFFERENTIATED INSTRUCTION

For advanced students, assign the **Extension Exercises 25–27.** The Extension begins to use more formal terminology associated with combinatorics. Students completing these exercises may also be interested in exploring the formula

$$C_{n,\,r} = \frac{n!}{(n-r)!\,r!}$$

for the number of ways *r* objects can be selected from a group of *n* objects, using it when applicable with the Extra Skills Practice Exercises.

Extra Skill Practice

Section 5

Extra Skill Practice

1. At a video rental store, there are 6 comedies, 8 dramas, and 3 science fiction films that Maureen wants to see. In how many ways can she choose one of each type of movie to rent? **144 ways**

2. How many permutations are there of the letters in the word FLOWERS? **5040 permutations**

3. A president and a vice president are to be selected from a 6-member student council committee. In how many ways can the selection be made? **30 ways**

4. Two of the 5 players on a basketball team are to be selected as co-captains. In how many ways can the selection be made? **10 ways**

5. In how many ways can 4 people line up for a photograph? **24 ways**

6. In a group of 4 people, each person shakes hands with everyone else once. How many handshakes are there? **6 handshakes**

7. In how many ways can you complete a 10-question true-false test if every question must be answered? 2^{10} **or 1024 ways**

8. In how many ways can you complete a 10-question multiple-choice test if there are 4 choices for each question and every question must be answered? 4^{10} **or 1,048,576 ways**

9. In how many ways can 8 books be arranged on a shelf? **40,320 ways**

10. A chicken dinner comes with any 3 of these side dishes: mashed potatoes, baked beans, corn, rice, or stuffing. How many combinations of 3 side dishes are possible? (*Hint*: Choosing 3 side dishes is the same as *not* choosing the other 2 side dishes.) **10 combinations**

Standardized Testing ◀▶ Performance Task

Tonya makes 3 sketches of different classmates for her art class.

1. In how many ways can Tonya select 2 of the 3 sketches to include in her final portfolio? Is this a *permutation* problem or a *combination* problem? Explain. **3 ways; combinations problem; The order in which she selects her sketches is not important.**

2. After her art class is over, Tonya decides to hang all 3 of the sketches she made in a row on her bedroom wall. In how many ways can she arrange the sketches? Is this a *permutation* problem or a *combination* problem? Explain. **6 ways; permutations problem; The order in which she hangs her sketches is important.**

Section 6 Working with Probability

IN THIS SECTION

EXPLORATION 1
◆ Probability and Counting

Lock It Up!

Setting the Stage ▶▶▶▶▶▶▶▶▶▶▶▶▶▶▶▶▶▶▶▶▶▶▶▶▶▶▶

Have you ever misplaced your keys? You would not be as likely to lose special keys made in ancient Rome. Occasionally large bronze keys were made as long as your arm and weighed over 10 lb! It was a great relief in 1862 when Linus Yale, Jr. invented the modern combination lock. The only "key" needed to open a combination lock is a special sequence of numbers or letters.

Think About It

1 Suppose that the key for a combination lock is a 3-digit sequence using the numbers 1, 2, 3, 4, or 5, and that each number is used only once. Use the counting principle to find the number of possible 3-digit keys. **60 keys**

2 Create your own 3-digit key. Use any of the numbers 1, 2, 3, 4, or 5, but do not use any number more than once. Keep your key a secret for now. **Answers will vary. Check students' work.**

3 For each group described below, do you think the probability that everyone chose a different key is closer to 0, 0.25, 0.50, 0.75, or 1? **Answers will vary.**
  a. a group of 4 students
  b. your entire class

Setting the Stage

ABOUT THE THEME
Students begin this section by learning about the invention and evolution of keys. The idea of a *key* as a code to undo a lock sets the stage for finding the number of possible keys. In today's world where privacy of information is a focus, students should be familiar with different types of keys. Students may use combination locks for their school lockers or bicycles. In addition, a key might refer to a personal identification code for a bank account, or a password for a computer. Students apply what they have learned about the counting principle to find the probability of duplicate keys appearing within their classroom.

GETTING STARTED
Module 4 Section 6 *Warm-Up* assesses students' mastery of the counting principle that is used when finding probabilities in this section. Since probabilities can be represented in both fraction and decimal form, the *Warm-Up* also assesses students' abilities to represent a fraction as a decimal.

Before reading the Setting the Stage, ask your students if they have ever heard of someone accidentally going to a car in a parking lot which looks like theirs, but isn't. Before noticing their error, they put their key in the door and unlock it! Does that mean that all keys for the same kind of car are the same? Of course not, but they are not all different either. Car manufacturers must decide how many duplicate ke ys can be made and still maintain an acceptably low probability of someone opening the wrong door. Ask your students what they think. Are 2 matching keys out of every 100 acceptable? 2 out of every 1000? 2 out of every 10,000?

COMMON ERROR

For **Questions 5–8**, remind students that as they solve for probabilities involving different numbers of people they have to find a new denominator (total ways to choose keys), as well as a new numerator (ways to choose different keys).

DIFFERENTIATED INSTRUCTION

Some learners may benefit from not having to copy the chart from the book. Providing a larger copy of the chart from **Question 4(c)** with all the choices completed along the outside edge will allow the student to focus on identifying which choices are the same and which are different. Be sure the boxes are void of question marks. You may want to provide two different colored markers or highlighters for the student to distinguish between same and different keys. **Questions 5(a–c)** could then be color coded for the student, using both colors for **part (a)**, one for **part (b)** and the other for **part (c)**.

4. c.

	1-2-3	1-3-2	2-1-3	2-3-1	3-1-2	3-2-1
1-2-3	S	D	D	D	D	D
1-3-2	D	S	D	D	D	D
2-1-3	D	D	S	D	D	D
2-3-1	D	D	D	S	D	D
3-1-2	D	D	D	D	S	D
3-2-1	D	D	D	D	D	S

GOAL

LEARN HOW TO...
- use the counting principle to determine the probability of an event

AS YOU...
- solve the duplicate key problem

Exploration 1

Probability and Counting

▶ **How likely is it that everyone in your class chose a different 3-digit key in Question 2? You can find out by looking at a simpler situation and thinking about probability.**

4 Suppose a 3-digit key can be made with only the numbers 1, 2, and 3, and each number cannot be used more than once in a key.

  a. How many different keys are possible? **6 keys**

  b. Use the numbers 1, 2, and 3 to list all the possible keys.
  123, 132, 213, 231, 312, 321

  c. Suppose two people each choose one of the keys from part (b). The model at the left can be used to show all the ways they can choose two keys. Copy and complete the model. Mark each box with a **D** if the people choose different keys or with an **S** if they chose the same key.
  See margin.

1st person's choice

2nd person's choice	1-2-3	1-3-2	2-1-3	?	?	?
1-2-3	S	?	?	?	?	?
1-3-2	D	?	?	?	?	?
2-1-3	?	?	?	?	?	?
?	?	?	?	?	?	?
?	?	?	?	?	?	?
?	?	?	?	?	?	?

◀ The **S** shows that the 1st and 2nd persons both choose 1-2-3. The **D** shows that the 1st person chooses 1-2-3 but the 2nd person chooses 1-3-2.

5 Use your completed model from Question 4.

  a. How many ways are there for two people to choose the keys? How does the model show this? **36 ways; Sample Response: Each box in the table represents one way that two people can choose a key.**

  b. What is the probability that both people choose the same key? $\frac{1}{6}$

  c. What is the probability that both people choose different keys? $\frac{5}{6}$

▶ You can also use the counting principle to find the probability that the two people in Question 4 choose *different* keys.

EXAMPLE

Two people each choose one of the six 3-digit keys. The probability that they choose *different* keys is given by this ratio:

Probability that two people choose different keys $= \dfrac{\text{Ways to choose different keys}}{\text{Total ways to choose keys}}$

Use the counting principle.

Probability that two people choose different keys $= \dfrac{6 \cdot 5}{6 \cdot 6}$

> If each person chooses a *different* key, the first person has **6** choices and the second person has **5** choices.

> If each person can choose *any* key, the first person has **6** choices and the second person also has **6** choices.

$= \dfrac{5}{6},$

or about 0.83

6 Discussion In the Example, why does the second person have 5 choices rather than 6? **One of the 6 choices has already been taken by the first person.**

7 Try This as a Class Suppose three people each choose one of the keys you listed in Question 4(b).

  a. Find the total number of ways for three people to choose the keys. **216 ways**

  b. How many ways can the three people all choose different keys? **120 ways**

  c. What is the probability that everyone chooses a different key? $\dfrac{5}{9} \approx 0.56$

8 ✔ **CHECKPOINT**

  a. Suppose four people each choose one of the keys you listed in Question 4(b). What is the probability that everyone will choose a different key? $\dfrac{5}{18} \approx 0.28$

  b. What is the probability that everyone will choose a different key if there are 5 people choosing keys? $\dfrac{5}{54} \approx 0.09$

9 Try This as a Class In Question 2, each person in your class chose a 3-digit key that uses the numbers 1, 2, 3, 4, or 5.

  a. Find the probability that everyone in a group of four would choose a different 3-digit key. **See margin.**

  b. Based on your answer to part (a), what percent of the time would you expect at least two members of a group to have the same key? **About 10% of the time, since 90% of the time they should have different keys.**

✔ **QUESTION 8**

...checks that you can use the counting principle to find probabilities.

DEVELOPING MATH CONCEPTS
Make sure your students understand the difference between *all* of the people having the same key and *any* of the people having the same key. The more people involved, the lower the probability that they will all have the same key, but the more likely that any two of them will have the same key.

TEACHING NOTES
If needed, the following example may be used before students complete **Checkpoint Question 8**.

CLASSROOM EXAMPLE

Suppose 3 digits are picked randomly from 0–9. Find the probability that the first and third are the same.

Answer: If the first and third digits must be the same, there are 10 possibilities for the first digit, 10 possibilities for the second one, and 1 possibility for the third.

Probability $= \dfrac{\text{ways to pick the first and third digits the same}}{\text{total ways to pick the digits}}$

$= \dfrac{10 \cdot 10 \cdot 1}{10 \cdot 10 \cdot 10}$

$= \dfrac{1}{10} = 0.1$

The probability is 0.1.

Checkpoint Question 8 Before students begin this question, ask them to estimate the answers based on the Example and their answers to **Question 7**.

9. a. See Additional Answers beginning on page A1.

TEACHING NOTES

To help students answer **Question 9(e)**, suggest they calculate the probabilities for groups of 5, 6, 7... to see the change occurring. Then have students use their observations to estimate the probability for their class size.

Key Concepts

CLOSURE QUESTION

Define what is meant by probability. Then explain how the counting principle can be used to help solve some probability problems.

Answer:

$$\text{Probability} = \frac{\text{number of successful choices}}{\text{total number of choices}}$$

Sample Response: The counting principle can be used to find both the number of successful choices in the numerator and the total number of choices in the denominator. Then the probability can be found.

ABSENT STUDENTS

For students who were absent for all or part of this section, the blackline Study Guide for Section 6 may be used to present the ideas, concepts, and skills of Section 6.

Practice & Applications

SUGGESTED ASSIGNMENTS

Core Course
Day 1: Exs. 1–3, 12–13
Day 2: Exs. 4–8, 11

Extended Course
Day 1: Exs. 1–3, 12–13
Day 2: Exs. 4–11

---

9. e. less than; Sample Response: There are only 30 possibilities for choosing different 3-digit keys. If there are 25 students in a class there is a greater chance that some will have chosen the same key than if only 4 people are choosing keys. The probability that everyone in a class of 25 chooses a different key is 0.003.

---

10. b. less than; The probability for three 6-sided number cubes is $\frac{5}{9} \approx 0.56$

---

c. Form a group of four students. Check to see if any two people chose the same key. **Results will vary. About 0.003 chance for a class of 25 students.**

d. How does the probability in part (a) compare to your answer to Question 3 on page 297? **Answers will vary.**

e. Would you expect the probability that everyone in your class chose a different 3-digit key to be greater than or less than that for a group of four students? Explain.

f. Check to see if any two people in your class chose the same key. **Answers will vary.**

HOMEWORK EXERCISES ▶ See Exs. 1–11 on pp. 301–302.

Section 6

Key Concepts

Probability and Counting (pp. 298–300)

You can use the counting principle to find some probabilities.

Example Suppose three 6-sided number cubes are rolled. The probability that the cubes show different numbers is given by this ratio:

$$\text{Probability the cubes show different numbers} = \frac{\text{Ways to roll different numbers}}{\text{Total ways to roll cubes}}$$

If different numbers must be rolled, there are 6 possibilities for the 1st cube, 5 possibilities for the 2nd cube, and 4 possibilities for the 3rd cube. If any numbers can be rolled, there are 6 possibilities for each cube.

$$\text{Probability} = \frac{6 \cdot 5 \cdot 4}{6 \cdot 6 \cdot 6}$$
$$= \frac{5}{9}, \text{ or about } 0.56$$

10 **Key Concepts Question** Suppose you roll three 4-sided number pyramids. The sides of each pyramid are numbered 1, 2, 3, and 4.

a. What is the probability that all the pyramids show different numbers on the bottom? $\frac{3}{8} = 0.375$

b. Is this probability *greater than, less than,* or *equal to* the probability for three 6-sided number cubes? Explain.

Section 6

Practice & Application Exercises

For Exercises 1–3, suppose three coins are tossed and the number of heads is recorded.

1. List all the possible outcomes when three coins are tossed.
   HHH, HHT, HTH, HTT, THH, THT, TTH, TTT

2. What is the probability of getting 3 heads? 2 heads? 1 head? 0 heads? $\frac{1}{8} = 0.125$; $\frac{3}{8} = 0.375$; $\frac{3}{8} = 0.375$; $\frac{1}{8} = 0.125$

3. What is the probability of getting at least one head? $\frac{7}{8} = 0.875$

4. **Government** Your Social Security number is a 9-digit number. Suppose the last four digits are chosen randomly from the numbers 0–9.

   a. How many sequences are possible for the last four digits?
   10,000 sequences

   b. What is the probability of getting a 5 or 0 in the last digit?

   c. What is the probability of getting two 5s in the last two digits?

   4. b. $\frac{1}{5} = 0.2$

   c. $\frac{1}{100} = 0.01$

5. Suppose a license plate has 4 letters followed by a 1-digit number and then 3 more letters. The letters and number are chosen randomly.

   a. How many license plates are possible if the letters cannot repeat? $3.315312 \cdot 10^{10}$

   b. Compare the probability that a license plate spells MATH4YOU with the probability that the first four letters spell MATH.
   See margin.

   c. Repeat parts (a) and (b) if the letters can be repeated.
   See margin.

6. **History** In a game popular in France during the seventeenth century, a player tried to roll a six-sided number cube four times without getting a 6. What is the probability that a player wins this game? $\frac{625}{1296} \approx 0.48$

7. A student finds a combination lock in the hallway that uses a 3-number key based on the numbers from 0 to 24.

   a. How many possible keys are there for this type of lock?
   15,625 keys

   b. What is the probability the student will open the lock on the first try? $\frac{1}{15,625}$

ADDITIONAL PRACTICE

See the *Teacher's Resource Book* for additional practice and application exercises for this section.

TEACHING NOTES

The following questions can be asked to check for student understanding before assigning the Practice and Application Exercises.

What are the chances that a player will roll two ones with fair dice? $\left(\frac{1}{6} \cdot \frac{1}{6} = \frac{1}{36}\right)$

If a player throws a pair of fair dice and gets two ones, what are the chances that he will roll two ones the next time? $\left(\frac{1}{36}\right)$

If the chances are always the same, why are we surprised to see the same pair rolled twice in a row? (Because there are 35 equally likely ways to roll something else.)

What is the probability of rolling a pair of ones twice? $\left(\frac{1}{36} \cdot \frac{1}{36} = \frac{1}{1206}\right)$

COMMON ERROR

For **Exercise 1**, students should make an organized list or a tree diagram rather than simply trying to think of all of the possible options.

DEVELOPING MATH CONCEPTS

Exercise 6 You may want to ask your students, "If you always bet against the player, and play a thousand times, can you expect to win more often, lose more often, or to be even? (*Sample Response: about even since the probability of the player winning is 0.48*)

5. b–c. See Additional Answers beginning on page A1.

301

Practice & Applications

EXERCISE NOTES

For **Exercise 9**, students can exchange problems with a partner and then try to solve each others problem. Following this, students can offer constructive criticism and revise any necessary parts of their problems. Students' problems could then be displayed in the classroom or printed in a school paper.

13. a.

Science Test Scores

Stem	Leaf
4	1 8
5	2 3 9
6	1 4 6 8
7	0 2 5 5 7 8
8	1 1 1 5 6 7
9	3 4 6 8 9

7 | 2 = 72

13. d. Either the stem-and-leaf plot or the box-and-whisker plot could be used to find the median, but only the stem-and-leaf plot could be used to find the mode.

8. a. $\frac{511}{512} = 0.998$

b. high; It means that the probability that your neighbors' opener will get them into your house is low.

Visual THINKING

Exercise 11 checks that you can find probabilities using a visual model.

11. a. Sample Response: The color in the top triangle in each square is the color the first person chose, and the color in the bottom triangle is what the second person chose. The table shows that there are 9 possible ways.

---

 302 **Module 4** Inventions

---

8. Electronics A certain model of automatic garage door opener can be assigned one of 512 possible codes. If the openers for two garage doors have the same code, then the transmitter for one door will also open the other door.

  a. Find the probability that two neighbors who each buy this brand of garage door opener get openers with different codes.

  b. Writing If you are one of the neighbors in part (a), do you want the probability you found to be high or low? Explain.

9. Open-ended Describe a real-world problem whose solution involves using the counting principle to find a probability. Check students' work.

10. Challenge Suppose a group of n people is randomly selected. For each value of n, find the probability that everyone in the group has a different birthday. (Assume no one is born on February 29 of a leap year, so that there are 365 equally likely birthdays possible.)

  a. $n = 5$ about 0.97   **b.** $n = 10$ about 0.88   **c.** $n = 20$ about 0.59

Reflecting ◀▶ on the Section

11. a. Suppose two people each choose 1 of 3 colors: red (R), yellow (Y), or blue (B). Explain how the model shows all the ways the people can choose their colors.

  b. What is the probability that the two people choose different colors? the same color? $\frac{2}{3} \approx 0.67$; $\frac{1}{3} \approx 0.33$

Spiral ◀▶ Review

12. Michael Kiefer needs to choose 2 of his 4 suits to take on a business trip. How many combinations of 2 suits can Michael choose? (Module 4, p. 292) 6 combinations

13. Choosing a Data Display Some test scores for a science class are listed below. (Module 1, p. 23)

78, 61, 94, 68, 52, 81, 70, 64, 53, 86, 99, 72, 87, 59, 81, 75, 93, 81, 66, 75, 48, 96, 85, 77, 98, 41

  a. Display the scores using a stem-and-leaf plot. See margin.

  b. Display the scores using a box-and-whisker plot. See margin.

  c. Find the median and the mode of the test scores. median: 76, mode: 81

  d. Which display did you use to find each average in part (c)? Why? See margin.

1st person's choice

2nd person's choice

The 1st person chooses yellow and the 2nd person chooses blue.

13. b. See Additional Answers beginning on page A1.

302

One model of a briefcase has a lock with three dials. Each dial can show a digit from 0 to 9. The lock opens when the dials are turned to a certain three-digit key, such as 2-0-7. Suppose Jamal, Lisa, and Kim each randomly choose a key for this model of briefcase. Find the probability of each outcome.

1. The last two digits in Jamal's key are both 8. $\frac{1}{100} = 0.01$

2. Each digit in Lisa's key is less than 7. $\frac{343}{1000} = 0.343$

3. None of the digits in Kim's key are 0 or 5.

4. Each digit in Kim's key is either 0 or 5.

5. Jamal and Lisa have different keys. $\frac{999}{1000} = 0.999$

6. Jamal, Lisa, and Kim have different keys. $\frac{498,501}{500,000} \approx 0.997$

3. $\frac{64}{125} = 0.512$

4. $\frac{1}{125} = 0.008$

One popular game involves rolling five 6-sided number cubes. Find the probability of each outcome when rolling the number cubes.

7. all ones $\frac{1}{7776} \approx 0.00013$

8. all even numbers $\frac{1}{32} = 0.03125$

9. all different numbers $\frac{5}{54} \approx 0.093$

10. all numbers greater than 2 $\frac{32}{243} \approx 0.13$

11. no fours $\frac{3125}{7776} \approx 0.40$

12. all perfect squares $\frac{1}{243} \approx 0.0041$

Standardized Testing ◀▶ Free Response

1. Suppose you flip a coin 4 times. What is the probability that you get all heads? $\frac{1}{16} = 0.0625$

2. A certain two-person game is played with pegs that have 6 possible colors: black, blue, green, red, white, and yellow. Player 1 forms a sequence of 4 pegs that is not shown to Player 2, such as green-black-yellow-green. (The same color may be used more than once.) Player 2 tries to guess Player 1's sequence.

   a. What is the probability that Player 2 correctly guesses Player 1's sequence on the first try? $\frac{1}{1296} \approx 0.00077$

   b. What is the probability that Player 2 guesses the wrong color for every position in Player 1's sequence on the first try? $\frac{625}{1296} \approx 0.48$

Extra Skill Practice

EXTRA HELP
Teacher's Resource Book
- Practice and Applications for Section 6
- Study Guide
- Practice and Applications for Sections 1–6

Technology Resources
- @Home Tutor
- Test Generator

ASSESSMENT
- Section 6 Quick Quiz
- Test Generator

Module Project

This project could be completed in conjunction with a physics lesson in science class.

Introducing the Project

The Pyramids of Giza would be noteworthy no matter when they were built, but knowing the primitive technology available to the builders makes them even more remarkable. Most of the tools known as simple machines had not yet been invented. They had no pulleys with which to lift the heavy blocks of stone. They did not even have a wheel and axle to build a cart for hauling the stones. All they had was a ramp, probably made of packed dirt, and the knowledge that it was easier to roll a round log up the ramp than to push and drag a flat block of stone.

While the Egyptians were primitive, they were also excellent problem solvers. They had to find efficient cylinders on which to roll the stones. As your students work on the module project, you may want to have them think of their work as a scale model. What are some of the real problems they would have to solve if they built a full-sized version? Would these considerations change their solution?

1. See Additional Answers beginning on page A1.

304

Building a Ramp

The ancient Egyptians built the Pyramids of Giza using thousands of stone blocks. The Egyptians may have used ramps and logs to roll the blocks into place. The diagrams show how you can model this process using a miniature ramp, several cylinders, and a small block.

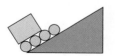 

Step 1 Use one more cylinder than is needed to support the block.

Step 2 Roll the block up the ramp to the edge of the highest cylinder. The cylinders will roll some as the block rolls.

Step 3 Move the lowest cylinder to the front of the block.

Step 4 Repeat Steps 2 and 3 until the block reaches the top of the ramp.

For your module project, you will design and build a model ramp with cylinders that you can use to move small objects.

Working with Cylinders One step in building your model is choosing the diameter of the cylinders. The diameter may affect how much the cylinders cost and how easy they are to use.

Use Project Labsheet A for Questions 1–4.

1 The labsheet shows four diagrams of a *Ramp and Cylinders*. Use the diagrams to complete the table at the bottom of the labsheet. See margin.

2 As the diameter of the cylinders decreases, what happens to:

a. the number of cylinders you need to move the block?
  More cylinders are needed to move the block.

b. the volume of material needed for all the cylinders? The combined volume decreases.

3 How does the diameter of the cylinders affect the number of times you must move a cylinder from the lowest position to the highest position on the ramp? The number of times you must move a cylinder increases as the diameter decreases.

4 What are some advantages of using cylinders with a small diameter? What are some disadvantages? Be sure to discuss how the diameter affects the cost and ease of use of the cylinders.

4. Sample Response: Cylinders with smaller diameters weigh less so they would be easier to maneuver, but more of them are required so they would cost more to produce.

SET UP

You will need:
- *Project Labsheet A*
- *ruler*
- *material for ramp*
- *material for cylinders*
- *small object (to be moved)*

 Module 4   Inventions

Choosing a Ramp's Slope Like the slope of a line, a ramp's slope is the ratio of its rise to its run. Suppose you want to design a ramp that is 6 ft wide and reaches 8 ft above the ground. The diagrams show four ramps with different slopes that you could design.

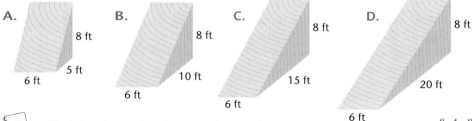

A. 8 ft   5 ft   6 ft

B. 8 ft   10 ft   6 ft

C. 8 ft   15 ft   6 ft

D. 8 ft   20 ft   6 ft

 5 a. Find the slope of each ramp shown above.

b. How does a ramp's slope affect how much effort it takes to move an object a fixed distance (say, 4 ft) up the ramp?

c. For ramps of the same height, how does the slope of the ramp seem to affect the ramp's length?
The greater the slope, the shorter the ramp.

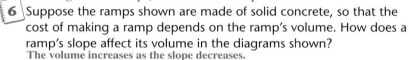 5. a. $\frac{8}{5}; \frac{4}{5}; \frac{8}{15}; \frac{2}{5}$

b. As the slope decreases, the effort required to move an object up the ramp decreases.

6 Suppose the ramps shown are made of solid concrete, so that the cost of making a ramp depends on the ramp's volume. How does a ramp's slope affect its volume in the diagrams shown?
The volume increases as the slope decreases.

Building Your Ramp and Cylinders Before designing and building your own model ramp and cylinders, think about these factors:

- the size of the object you want to move up your ramp
- the number of cylinders you want to use, as well as each cylinder's diameter d and length l
- the height h and width w you want your ramp to have
- the desired steepness of your ramp as measured by the ramp's slope $\frac{h}{b}$, where b is the length of the ramp's base
- the advantages of certain ramp slopes and cylinder sizes

7 a. Make a sketch of the ramp and cylinders you plan to build. Label all dimensions with their measures. **Check students' work.**

b. Choose the materials you will use. The cylinders can be wooden dowels, markers, paper towel rolls, or other household items. Your ramp might be made from cardboard or wood.

c. Construct your ramp and cylinders. Then test how well your model works by trying to move a small object up the ramp using the procedure described on page 304.

PROJECT NOTES

In designing a ramp, the actual choice of length depends on the materials available, their cost, and how the ramp will be used—what is being moved up the ramp and how it is to be moved. For example, one person could roll a 50-gal barrel up a long ramp with a small slope, but not up a short ramp with a steep slope.

If you know the length and height of a ramp and the weight of the object to be moved, you can set up a proportion to calculate the effort it will take to move the object. (This ignores friction which was a very important consideration for the Egyptians.)

$$\frac{\text{Effort}}{\text{Weight of Object}} = \frac{\text{Height of Ramp}}{\text{Length of Ramp}}$$

Ask your students to answer these questions: How much force would be required to push or roll a 300-lb barrel up a 6-ft ramp to a 2-ft high loading dock? How much force would be required if the ramp was 4 ft long? (*100 lb; 150 lb*)

If working with a science teacher, students may want to use a spring scale to compare how much easier it is to move an object up a ramp than to lift it the same height. Students can gather data from their ramps by tying a string around the object and suspending it from a spring scale and taking a reading. Then read the scale while dragging the object up the ramp at a slow, steady rate, once with the cylinders and then again without the cylinders. Then they can compare the results.

305

MODULE 4 Review and Assessment

1. The Ferris wheel at the 1893 World's Columbian Exposition in Chicago had a diameter of 250 ft. Its 36 passenger cabs could hold a total of 2160 people. Suppose the cabs were evenly spaced. About how far apart would they have been? (Sec. 1 Explor. 1) 21.81 ft

2. Which has greater volume: a box shaped like a rectangular prism 12 in. long, 11 in. wide, and 9 in. high or 6 jars shaped like circular cylinders that are 14 in. tall and 4 in. in diameter? (Sec. 1 Explor. 2) the box

3. Suppose the length of each edge of a cube is tripled. (Sec. 1, Explor. 2)

   a. How does the surface area of the new cube compare to the surface area of the original cube? 9 times greater

   b. How do the volumes of the two cubes compare? 27 times greater

Find the surface area of the cylinder with the given radius r and height h. Use $\pi = 3.14$. (Sec. 2, Explor. 1)

4. $r = 3$ cm, $h = 4$ cm
   131.88 cm^2

5. $r = 2$ in., $h = 6$ in.
   100.48 in.^{2}

6. $r = 1.5$ ft, $h = 12$ ft
   127.17 ft^2

Find the ratio of surface area to volume for each cylinder. Use $\pi = 3.14$. (Sec. 2, Explor. 2)

7.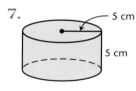
   5 cm
   5 cm

8.
   4 cm
   10 cm

9. 3 cm
   12 cm

   0.8   0.7   0.83

10. Suppose three cans have the same dimensions as the cylinders above. Which can is most efficient? Explain. (Sec. 2, Explor. 2)
    The can in Ex. 8; It has the lowest ratio of surface area to volume.

For each line, find the slope and the y-intercept. Then write an equation of the line in slope-intercept form. (Sec. 3, Explors. 1 and 2)

11.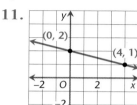
    (0, 2)
    (4, 1)

12.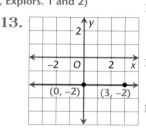
    (1, 2)
    (0, −1)

13. (0, −2) (3, −2)

11. slope: $-\frac{1}{4}$;
    y-intercept: 2;
    $y = -\frac{1}{4}x + 2$

12. slope: 3;
    y-intercept: −1;
    $y = 3x - 1$

13. slope: 0;
    y-intercept: −2;
    $y = -2$

14. Explain why the slope of a vertical line is undefined. (Sec. 3, Explor. 1)

15. Write equations in slope-intercept form for 2 lines that are parallel. Explain why they are parallel. (Sec. 3, Explor. 2)

16. Write each rational number as a terminating or a repeating decimal. (Sec. 4, Explor. 1)

a. $\frac{5}{11}$ $0.\overline{45}$ b. $-3\frac{1}{4}$ -3.25 c. $\frac{14}{16}$ 0.875

17. Write the numbers in order from least to greatest. (Sec. 4, Explor. 1)

$0.\overline{72}, \frac{5}{7}, 0.7\overline{2}, 0.72, \frac{3}{4}, -0.7, -\frac{8}{11}, -0.72, -\frac{3}{4}$

Solve each equation. (Sec. 4, Explor. 2)

18. $5 = -2.5x$ -2 19. $12 + \frac{2}{3}t = 4$ -12 20. $\frac{2}{3}b + 11 = 5$ -9

21. At a local pizza parlor, 5 employees work on Saturday nights: Armand, Cathy, Ishana, Jim, and Susan. Employees must wear uniforms consisting of tan or black pants and red, green, or black shirts. (Sec. 5, Explors. 1 and 2)

  a. How many different uniforms are possible? **6 uniforms**

  b. On one Saturday night, all 5 employees decide to line up and sing "Happy Birthday" to a customer. In how many different ways can they line up? **120 ways**

  c. Usually, 2 employees are needed to take telephone orders on Saturday nights. List all possible combinations of 2 employees who can be assigned to answer telephones.

22. A bank customer who uses an automatic teller machine (ATM) chooses a 4-digit password. (Sec. 6, Explor. 1)

  a. How many different passwords are possible? **10^4 or 10,000 passwords**

  b. What is the probability that the first and last digits in a customer's password are both greater than 6? $\frac{9}{100} = 0.09$

Reflecting ◀▶ on the Module

23. **Writing** Make a list of what you think are the ten most important mathematical concepts in this module. Write and solve a problem that illustrates each concept. **Answers will vary. Check students' work.**

14. Sample Response: The run of a vertical line is always 0. To calculate the slope division by zero is necessary. Since division by zero is undefined, the slope must also be undefined.

15. Sample Response: $y = mx$ and $y = mx + b$. (Students may substitute any numbers for m and b in the equations as long as the slope (m) is the same in both equations.) They are parallel because the slope is the same in both equations.

17. $-\frac{3}{4}, -\frac{8}{11}, -0.72,$ $-0.7, \frac{5}{7}, 0.72, 0.7\overline{2},$ $0.\overline{72}, \frac{3}{4}$

21. c. Armand and Cathy, Armand and Ishana, Armand and Jim, Armand and Susan, Cathy and Ishana, Cathy and Jim, Cathy and Susan, Ishana and Jim, Ishana and Susan, Jim and Susan.

TEACHER'S RESOURCE BOOK
• Module 4 Tests A and B
• Module 4 Standardized Test
• Module 4 Performance Assessment
• Modules 3 and 4 Cumulative Test
• Mid-Year Test

TEST GENERATOR

MODULE 5 — Architects and Engineers

Module 5 Overview

Exploring the work of architects and engineers emphasizes the importance of mathematics. Students create two- and three-dimensional models, find surface areas and volumes of three-dimensional figures, explore properties of transversals, make scale drawings, and explore perimeters and areas of similar figures while examining architecture from around the world.

Module 5 Planner

Day 1: Section 1	Day 2: Section 1	Day 3: Section 1	Day 4: Section 2	Day 5: Section 2
Setting the Stage, *p. 310* Exploration 1, *pp. 311–313*	Exploration 2 *through* Question 15, *pp. 313–314*	Exploration 2, *p. 315* Key Concepts, *p. 316*	Setting the Stage, *p. 321* Exploration 1, *pp. 322–324*	Exploration 2, *pp. 324–326*
Day 6: Section 2	**Day 7: Section 3**	**Day 8: Section 3**	**Day 9: Section 3**	**Day 10: Section 3**
Exploration 3, *pp. 327–329* Key Concepts, *pp. 330–331*	Setting the Stage, *pp. 337–338* Exploration 1 *through* Question 4, *p. 338*	Exploration 1, *p. 339*	Exploration 2 *through* Question 15, *pp. 340–341*	Exploration 2, *p. 342* Key Concepts, *p. 343*
Day 11: Review and Assessment	**Day 12: Section 4**	**Day 13: Section 4**	**Day 14: Section 4**	**Day 15: Section 4**
Mid-Module Quiz	Setting the Stage, *pp. 348–349* Exploration 1 *through* Question 6, *pp. 349–350*	Exploration 1 *from* Question 7, *pp. 350–352*	Exploration 2 *through* Question 16, *pp. 352–353*	Exploration 2, *p. 354* Key Concepts, *pp. 355–356*
Day 16: E²	**Day 17: Section 5**	**Day 18: Section 5**	**Day 19: Section 5**	**Day 20: Section 6**
Work on Extended Exploration, *p. 362*	Setting the Stage, *pp. 363–364*	Exploration 1 *through* Question 7, *pp. 365–366*	Exploration 1 *from* Question 8, *pp. 366–367* Key Concepts, *pp. 368–369*	Setting the Stage, *p. 374* Exploration 1 *through* Question 6, *pp. 375–377*
Day 21: Section 6	**Day 22: Section 6**	**Day 23: Module Project**	**Day 24: Module Project**	**Day 25: Review and Assessment**
Exploration 1 *from* Question 7, *p. 377*	Exploration 2, *pp. 378–380* Key Concepts, *p. 381*	Begin Module Project, *pp. 386–387*	Complete Module Project, *pp. 386–387*	Review and Assessment, *pp. 388–389*
Day 26: Review and Assessment				
Module Test				

308A

Materials List

Section	Materials
1	• Labsheets 1A–1D, centimeter cubes, ruler
2	• Labsheets 2A–2B, compass, protractor, ruler, plain white paper, scissors, tape, package for commercial product
3	• Labsheets 3A–3B, centimeter grid paper, tape or glue, construction paper, scissors, protractor
4	• Labsheets 4A–4D, metric ruler, scissors, paper clip
5	• Labsheets 5A–5B, metric ruler, protractor
6	• Labsheet 6A, tape measure, ruler, plain or graph paper
Project	• graph paper (optional), ruler, large sheets of sturdy paper, colored pencils or markers, scissors, tape
Rev & Assess	• ruler

Module 5 Objectives

Section	Objectives	NCTM Standards 2000*
1	• Use isometric dot paper to draw figures made with cubes • Explore volumes and surface areas of figures made with cubes • Draw three-dimensional and flat views of figures	3, 4, 6, 7, 8, 9, 10
2	• Name congruent figures • Apply the triangle inequality • Create and explore nets for three-dimensional figures • Identify and count faces, edges, and vertices of three-dimensional figures • Construct angle bisectors • Determine whether two triangles are congruent by comparing two sides and the included angle	2, 3, 4, 6, 7, 8, 9, 10
3	• Identify triangles by their side lengths • Use the Pythagorean theorem to find an unknown side length of a right triangle	1, 2, 3, 4, 6, 7, 8, 9, 10
4	• Find surface areas of prisms and pyramids • Find volumes of prisms, pyramids, cones, and composite figures	1, 2, 3, 4, 6, 7, 8, 9, 10
5	• Identify pairs of angles formed by intersecting lines • Determine measures of angles formed by parallel lines cut by a transversal • Identify complementary and supplementary angles	1, 2, 3, 4, 6, 7, 8, 9, 10
6	• Make a scale drawing • Find perimeters and areas of similar figures	1, 2, 3, 4, 6, 7, 8, 9, 10

* See page T14.

Section 1 Planner

Section Objectives

Exploration 1
• Draw rectangular prisms and figures made with cubes
• Find volumes and surface areas of figures made with cubes

Exploration 2
• Draw three-dimensional figures
• Draw flat views

Days for Section 1

First Day
Setting the Stage, *p. 310*
Exploration 1, *pp. 311–313*

Second Day
Exploration 2 through Question 15, *pp. 313–314*

Third Day
Exploration 2, *p. 315*
Key Concepts, *p. 316*

Teaching Resources

Teacher's Resource Book
• Warm-Up
• Labsheets 1A, 1B, 1C, and 1D
• Practice and Applications
• Study Guide
See page 309 for additional teaching resources.

Materials List

Exploration 1
• Labsheets 1A–1C
• centimeter cubes
• ruler

Exploration 2
• Labsheets 1A and 1D
• centimeter cubes
• ruler

Key Concepts
• Labsheet 1A

Practice and Applications
• Labsheets 1A and 1D
• metric ruler

Extra Skill Practice
• Labsheet 1A
• ruler

Assessment Options

EMBEDDED ASSESSMENT
• Draw rectangular prisms and figures made with cubes
  Exercises 1, 2
• Find volumes and surface areas of figures made with cubes
  Exercises 2, 6
• Draw three-dimensional figures
  Exercises 6, 7
• Draw flat views
  Exercise 11

PERFORMANCE TASK/PORTFOLIO
• Exercise 2(d) on *p. 317 (writing)*
• Exercise 14 on *p. 319 (challenge)*
• Exercise 15 on *p. 319 (visual thinking)*

QUIZZES/TESTS
• Section 1 Quick Quiz

TEST GENERATOR

Section 1 Overview

In this section, students will explore three-dimensional geometry through the eyes of an architect.

Exploration 1
As students construct and draw prisms, they learn how surface area and volume are affected by the addition or removal of one or more cubes. The development of spatial reasoning builds an understanding of the physical world in which we live and provides the basis for abstract thought used in geometry.

Exploration 2
The focus of this exploration is on perspective. Students examine figures from varied sides and angles and complete drawings of three-dimensional figures from different perspectives. The concept of flat views is presented as students identify the shape of a structure based on two-dimensional views. Construction and drawing are inherent in the activities which strengthen spatial reasoning skills, thus preparing students for the higher order skill of segmenting a space figure and identifying the faces that result.

Guide for Assigning Homework

REGULAR SCHEDULING (45 MIN CLASS PERIOD)			EXERCISES TO NOTE		
Section/ P&A Pages	Core Assignment	Extended Assignment	Additional Practice/Review	Open-ended Problems	Extended Problems
1 pp. 317–319	**Day 1:** 1–7 **Day 2:** 8–13 **Day 3:** ROS 15, SR 16–25	1–7 11–14 ROS 15, SR 16–25	EP, p. 320	PA 7(b)	Challenge PA 14

Key: PA = Practice & Application; ROS = Reflecting on the Section; SR = Spiral Review; TB = Toolbox; EP = Extra Skill Practice; Ext = Extension; ST = Standardized Testing

Math Background and Teaching Strategies

Classroom Notes

Bulletin board display ideas for this section include:

• Pictures of buildings from varied views

Visitors might include:

• An architect or city planner

• An artist or school art teacher

Math Strands

Topic Spiraling and Integration
Students experienced drawing three-dimensional figures in Module 7 of Book 2. Surface area and volume were explored in Module 4. The spatial reasoning and problem-solving developed in this section prepares students for the study of polyhedra and their nets in Section 3.

Exploration 1
Spatial visualization and reasoning are developed in this exploration through visualizing and drawing structures with depth. Students may notice that, when using isometric dot paper, each side of a cube is represented with a rhombus. This occurs because the view is not from directly in front, but from an angle that allows the viewer to see three faces of the cube. By observing a cube from such an angle, students should recognize that the shape of each visible face is a rhombus. An art teacher may be asked to reinforce the concept of perspective for students. Once they have had the opportunity to draw figures, students look for relationships between surface area and volume. They study the effect that removing a cube has on both volume and surface area. Since total volume is determined by the number of cubes used, the volume always decreases 1 cm^3. Surface area, however, is affected by the location of the cube and the number of exposed faces of the cube removed.

Exploration 2
Students build on the spatial skills developed in Exploration 1 by viewing structures from various perspectives. They notice that the orientation of a structure may block the view of a cube. Therefore several different views may be necessary to visualize the entire structure. Students then compare the perspective views to straight-on or flat views of the structure. Flat views are void of depth and only allow students to see the exposed faces of the cubes visible from the side they are viewing. Although this section is designed for individual exploration, students may benefit from teaming with another student as they build and sketch the different views of the structures. The skills developed in this exploration prepare students for the study of polyhedra in Section 3.

Section 2 Planner

Section Objectives

Exploration 1
• Name congruent figures
• Apply the triangle inequality

Exploration 2
• Identify and count parts of 3-dimensional figures
• Create nets for pyramids and prisms

Exploration 3
• Bisect an angle using a compass
• Compare triangles using two sides and the included angle

Days for Section 2

First Day
Setting the Stage, *p. 321*
Exploration 1, *pp. 322–324*

Second Day
Exploration 2, *pp. 324–326*

Third Day
Exploration 3, *pp. 327–329*
Key Concepts, *pp. 330–331*

Materials List

Exploration 1
• compass and protractor
• ruler
• plain white paper

Exploration 2
• Labsheets 2A and 2B
• compass and ruler
• scissors and tape

Exploration 3
• plain white paper
• compass and protractor
• ruler, scissors, and tape

Practice and Applications
• compass and ruler
• package for a real product

Extra Skill Practice
• compass and straightedge
• scissors and tape

Teaching Resources

Teacher's Resource Book
• Warm-Up
• Labsheets 2A and 2B
• Practice and Applications
• Study Guide
See page 309 for additional teaching resources.

Assessment Options

EMBEDDED ASSESSMENT
• Name congruent figures
  Exercise 11
• Apply the triangle inequality
  Exercises 3, 4, 6, 8
• Identify and count parts of 3-D figures
  Exercises 12, 17, 19(c)
• Create nets for pyramids and prisms
  Exercises 14, 19(b)
• Bisect an angle using a compass
  Exercise 20
• Compare triangles using two sides and the included angle
  Exercise 26

PERFORMANCE TASK/PORTFOLIO
• Exercise 1 on *p. 332 (visual thinking)*
• Exercise 4 on *p. 332 (algebra connection)*
• Exercises 13–14 on *p. 333 (open-ended)*
• Exercise 19(d) on *p. 334 (challenge)*
• Exercise 29 on *p. 335 (oral report)*
• Standardized Testing on *p. 336*

QUIZZES/TESTS
• Section 2 Quick Quiz

TEST GENERATOR

Section 2 Overview

In this section, students will learn how to build 3-dimensional figures from 2-dimensional patterns.

Exploration 1
Students construct triangles using a ruler and compass. Through their explorations, students will discover and apply the triangle inequality and be able to identify congruent triangles by the side-side-side rule for congruent triangles.

Exploration 2
Students use a compass and ruler to construct nets for pyramids and prisms. The term tetrahedron is introduced to identify a specific pyramid. As students explore the faces of other polyhedra, they see how nets are used by architects to construct models.

Exploration 3
In order to draw the triangular faces for a net of a pyramid, students will learn how to bisect an angle using a compass and ruler. Having drawn the triangular faces of the pyramid net, students identify the included angle for any two given sides of a face. By constructing models of congruent triangles, students will be able to visualize the side-angle-side rule for identifying congruent triangles.

Guide for Assigning Homework

REGULAR SCHEDULING (45 MIN CLASS PERIOD)			EXERCISES TO NOTE		
Section/ P&A Pages	Core Assignment	Extended Assignment	Additional Practice/Review	Open-ended Problems	Extended Problems
2 pp. 332–335	**Day 1:** 1–11 **Day 2:** 12–19(c), SR 30–39 **Day 3:** 20–28, ROS 29	1–11 12–19, SR 30–39 20–28, ROS 29	EP, p. 336	PA 13, 14, 19(d)	Challenge PA 19(d)

Key: PA = Practice & Application; ROS = Reflecting on the Section; SR = Spiral Review; TB = Toolbox; EP = Extra Skill Practice; Ext = Extension; ST = Standardized Testing

Math Background and Teaching Strategies

Classroom Notes

Bulletin board display ideas for this section include:

• Movable items that incorporate triangles, such as an umbrella

• Nets of various shapes interspersed among the 3-dimensional figures they form

Math Strands

Topic Spiraling and Integration

In Module 4, students constructed a net for a cylinder. In this section they use nets to explore pyramids and composite 3-dimensional figures. Students also bisect angles using a compass and straightedge, continuing work with constructions introduced in Module 3. Introduction of the SAS rule for congruent triangles also extends the work with triangles done in Module 3.

Exploration 1

By constructing triangles using a ruler and compass, students discover that two triangles whose sides have the same measures are congruent. The conditions sufficient for two triangles to be congruent are extended in Exploration 3 where students discover the SAS rule for congruent triangles. Congruence is applied in Module 6 as students transform figures and in Module 8 when they explore rotational symmetry. Students will also learn that for three segments to form a triangle, the sum of the length of any two sides must be greater than the length of the third side. This concept will be developed further in Section 3 in classifying triangles.

Exploration 2

The idea of a net that was introduced in Module 4 is developed further as students construct nets for polyhedra. Using the nets, students recognize the relationship among the numbers of faces, vertices and edges of a polyhedron and express this relationship using the formula $(F + V) - 2 = E$. Students continue to build on their ability to express relationships using an equation in Module 6 when they use equations to model functions, and in Module 8 as they describe sequences using equations.

Exploration 3

Students develop concepts of congruence as they bisect an angle and identify the congruent angles and triangles that result. This leads to the discovery of the SAS rule for congruent triangles. Angle and angle measurement concepts are applied to the find the sum of the measures of the interior angles of a polygon and rotational symmetry in Module 8.

Section 3 Working with Triangles

Section 3 Planner

Section Objectives

Exploration 1
- Identify different types of triangles by looking at their side lengths

Exploration 2
- Use the Pythagorean theorem to find an unknown side length of a right triangle

Days for Section 3

First Day
Setting the Stage, *pp. 337–338*
Exploration 1 through Question 4, *p. 338*

Second Day
Exploration 1, *p. 339*

Third Day
Exploration 2 through Question 15, *pp. 340–341*

Fourth Day
Exploration 2, *p. 342*
Key Concepts, *p. 343*

Teaching Resources

Teacher's Resource Book
- Warm-Up
- Labsheets 3A and 3B
- Practice and Applications
- Study Guide
See page 309 for additional teaching resources.

Materials List

Setting the Stage
- centimeter grid paper
- scissors
- tape or glue
- construction paper

Exploration 1
- Labsheet 3A
- centimeter grid paper
- scissors
- construction paper
- tape or glue
- protractor

Practice and Applications
- graph paper
- Labsheet 3B

Assessment Options

EMBEDDED ASSESSMENT
- Identify different types of triangles by looking at their side lengths
  Exercises 1–3
- Use the Pythagorean theorem to find an unknown side length of a right triangle
  Exercises 8–10

PERFORMANCE TASK/PORTFOLIO
- Exercise 14 on *p. 344 (visual thinking)*
- Exercise 17(c) on *p. 345 (research)*
- Exercise 19 on *p. 345 (challenge)*
- Exercise 21 on *p. 346 (oral report)*
- Exercise 28 on *p. 346 (extension)*
- Standardized Testing on *p. 347*

QUIZZES/TESTS
- Section 3 Quick Quiz
- Mid-Module Quiz

TEST GENERATOR

Section 3 Overview

In this section, students explore relationships among the side lengths of triangles. The *Setting the Stage* activity introduces students to a method used by the ancient Egyptians to construct right angles. The activity serves as an introduction to the Pythagorean theorem.

Exploration 1
Students investigate a method for classifying a triangle as acute, obtuse, or right by examining the lengths of the sides of the triangle. The concepts developed in this exploration reinforce classification of triangles and their properties.

Exploration 2
Students are introduced to the Pythagorean theorem and use the equation to find an unknown side length in a right triangle. Students apply what they learned about the Pythagorean theorem to determine the height of a face of a square pyramid. Spatial skills are used as students visually bisect a pyramid. They then identify the triangle formed from a cross section of the pyramid and use the Pythagorean theorem to find the length of its hypotenuse. Students see that this length is also the height of a face of the pyramid.

Guide for Assigning Homework

Math Background and Teaching Strategies

Classroom Notes

Bulletin board display ideas for this section include:

- Pictures of objects in the shape of a triangle

- Displays of student work

Visitors may include:

- An architect, surveyor, geologist or astronomer

Math Strands

Topic Spiraling and Integration

Students apply what they have learned about square roots and build on the triangle concepts studied in Module 3 as they explore the attributes of right triangles and learn to use the Pythagorean theorem. Students will apply the Pythagorean theorem as they find surface areas and volumes of pyramids in the next section and in Module 8 as they explore the tangent, sine, and cosine ratios.

Exploration 1

Students explore the relationship between the sides of acute, obtuse and right triangles. They discover how to determine the type of triangle by comparing the sum of the squares of the lengths of the two shorter sides of a triangle to the square of the length of the longer side. This discovery leads them to recognize the unique nature of a right triangle. The Pythagorean theorem is introduced informally during this exploration and used to identify right triangles. In Exploration 2, students will expand on this concept and use the theorem to solve problems involving right triangles.

Exploration 2

The Pythagorean theorem is formally introduced in this exploration. Students begin by using the theorem to find unknown side lengths of triangles. Some students may need to replace the variables in the equation with known side lengths of a triangle in the order given in the equation $a^2 + b^2 = c^2$ regardless of which side is unknown. Others may be confident enough to try solving for a side such as b using the equation $b^2 = c^2 - a^2$. Students apply what they have learned about square roots to solve the equations. These concepts are developed further in Module 7 where students use the product property to simplify square roots and simplify radical expressions. Once students have developed facility with using the Pythagorean theorem, they learn how it can be applied to find the height and area of a face of a pyramid. Having the ability to visualize the right triangles imbedded in a pyramid is essential in Section 4 where students find surface areas of pyramids.

308H

Section 4 Surface Area and Volume

Section 4 Planner

Section Objectives

Exploration 1
- Find the surface area of prisms and pyramids

Exploration 2
- Find volumes of prisms, pyramids, cones, and composite 3-dimensional figures

Days for Section 4

First Day
Setting the Stage, *pp. 348–349*
Exploration 1 through Question 6, *pp. 349–350*

Second Day
Exploration 1 from Question 7, *pp. 350–352*

Third Day
Exploration 2 through Question 16, *pp. 352–353*

Fourth Day
Exploration 2, *p. 354*
Key Concepts, *pp. 355–356*

Teaching Resources

Teacher's Resource Book
- Warm-Up
- Labsheets 4A, 4B, 4C, and 4D
- Practice and Applications
- Study Guide
See page 309 for additional teaching resources.

Materials List

Exploration 1
- Labsheet 4A
- metric ruler
- scissors

Exploration 2
- Labsheet 4B

Extension
- Labsheet 4C–4D
- scissors
- paper clip

Extended Exploration
- compass and ruler
- 8.5 in. by 11 in. plain paper
- colored pencils or markers

Assessment Options

EMBEDDED ASSESSMENT
- Find the surface area of prisms and pyramids
  Exercises 2, 5, 6, 8
- Find volumes of prisms, pyramids, cones, and composite 3-dimensional figures
  Exercises 12, 15, 16

PERFORMANCE TASK/PORTFOLIO
- Exercise 7 on *p. 357 (challenge)*
- Exercise 20 on *p. 359 (open-ended)*
- Exercise 21 on *p. 359 (journal)*
- Exercises 27–28 on *p. 360 (extension)*
- Standardized Testing on *p. 361**
- Extended Exploration on *p. 362**

* indicates a problem-solving task that can be assessed using the Assessment Scales

QUIZZES/TESTS
- Section 4 Quick Quiz

TEST GENERATOR

Section 4 Overview

In this section, students discuss the surface area and volume of an igloo in preparation for finding surface areas and volumes of other three-dimensional figures.

Exploration 1
Students use nets to find the surface area of rectangular, trapezoidal, and triangular prisms. In doing so, they evaluate formulas for the areas of rectangles, trapezoids, and triangles. Finding the surface area of a regular pyramid requires that students apply the Pythagorean theorem to find the height of one of the triangular faces of the pyramid.

Exploration 2
Students investigate block pyramids and block prisms to discover the relationship between the volume of a pyramid and the volume of a prism with the same bases and heights. Students are then introduced to the relationship between the volume of a cylinder and the volume of a cone with the same radius and height and use a formula to find the volumes of cones and composite figures.

Guide for Assigning Homework

REGULAR SCHEDULING (45 MIN CLASS PERIOD)			EXERCISES TO NOTE		
Section/ P&A Pages	Core Assignment	Extended Assignment	Additional Practice/Review	Open-ended Problems	Extended Problems
4 pp. 357–360	**Day 1:** 1–3, SR 22–26 **Day 2:** 4–6, 8 **Day 3:** 9–11, 17–18 **Day 4:** 12–16, 20, ROS 21	1–3, SR 22–26 4–8 9–11, 18–19 12–15, 20, ROS 21, 27–28	EP, p. 361	PA 20 ST 1–2	PA Challenge 7, 19 Ext 27–28 E², p. 362

Key: PA = Practice & Application; ROS = Reflecting on the Section; SR = Spiral Review; TB = Toolbox; EP = Extra Skill Practice; Ext = Extension; ST = Standardized Testing

Math Background and Teaching Strategies

Classroom Notes

Bulletin board display ideas for this section include:

- Pictures of many different architectural styles of dwellings, from ancient to modern

Math Strands

Topic Spiraling and Integration

The concepts students explored in Module 4 will be extended in this section as students find the surface areas and volumes of prisms and pyramids, and the volumes of cones. Students will utilize the skills developed earlier in this module when they constructed nets for three-dimensional figures and used the Pythagorean theorem to find an unknown length of a side of a right triangle. The spatial awareness developed in this section will be utilized in the next two sections of this module, in Module 6 as students explore parabolas, and in Module 8 as they work with polygons, rotational symmetry, properties of quadrilaterals and geometric probabilities.

Exploration 1

Students use spatial visualization to construct nets for right prisms and regular pyramids and use the nets to find the surface areas. In finding the surface area of a pyramid, students apply the Pythagorean theorem to find the height of a *triangular face* of the pyramid. Students should understand that the height of the *pyramid* is the perpendicular distance from the base to the apex, the common vertex of the faces, and is not the same measure as the height of a *triangular face*. By constructing a net and measuring the heights of both the pyramid and a triangular face, students grasp this concept.

Exploration 2

Students apply the formula for finding the volume of a cube from Module 4 and explore the relationship between the volume of a cube and a pyramid with the same base and height. They find that the volume of a pyramid is about one third the volume of a cube with the same base and height. This discovery is applied to cones and cylinders where they find the same relationship exists when the base and height of the two figures are the same. In applying formulas for surface area and volume to composite figures, students will notice that the surface area where the figures interface is not considered in the total surface area of the figure, but is used for the calculation of volume.

Section 5 Planner

Section Objectives

Exploration 1
- Identify pairs of angles formed by intersecting lines
- Determine measures of angles formed by parallel lines cut by a transversal
- Determine the measures of complementary and supplementary angles

Days for Section 5

First Day
Setting the Stage, *pp. 363–364*

Second Day
Exploration 1 through Question 7, *pp. 365–366*

Third Day
Exploration 1 from Question 8, *pp. 366–367*
Key Concepts, *pp. 368–369*

Teaching Resources

Teacher's Resource Book
- Warm-Up
- Labsheets 5A and 5B
- Practice and Applications
- Study Guide
See page 309 for additional teaching resources.

Materials List

Setting the Stage
- Labsheets 5A and 5B
- metric ruler
- protractor

Exploration 1
- ruler
- protractor

Assessment Options

EMBEDDED ASSESSMENT
- Identify pairs of angles formed by intersecting lines
  Exercises 20–23
- Determine measures of angles formed by parallel lines cut by a transversal
  Exercises 24–28, 29
- Determine the measures of complementary and supplementary angles
  Exercises 1–3, 9–11, 35

PERFORMANCE TASK/PORTFOLIO
- Exercise 32 on *p. 370 (writing)*
- Exercise 34 on *p. 371 (algebra connection)*
- Exercise 36 on *p. 371 (challenge)*
- Exercise 37 on *p. 371 (discussion)*

QUIZZES/TESTS
- Section 5 Quick Quiz

TEST GENERATOR

Section 5 Overview

In this section, students investigate vertical, complementary, and supplementary angles and the pairs of angles formed when two lines are intersected by a transversal. Students see how the language of mathematics models the relationships between the pairs of angles formed by the three lines.

Exploration 1
Students discuss how the names for alternate interior angles and alternate exterior angles help describe the location of the angles. After measuring pairs of alternate interior angles formed when parallel lines are cut by a transversal, students formulate a rule for the measures of these angles. After examining diagrams of these kinds of angles, students formulate definitions for vertical, corresponding, complementary, and supplementary angles. The relationship between supplementary angles will help students determine the measures of vertical angles and corresponding angles.

Guide for Assigning Homework

REGULAR SCHEDULING (45 MIN CLASS PERIOD)			EXERCISES TO NOTE		
Section/ P&A Pages	**Core Assignment**	**Extended Assignment**	**Additional Practice/Review**	**Open-ended Problems**	**Extended Problems**
5 pp. 369–372	**Day 1:** SR 38–46 **Day 2:** 1–16 **Day 3:** 17–35, ROS 37	SR 38–46 1–16 17–27 odd, 29–36, ROS 37, 47	EP, p. 373		Challenge PA 36 Career Connection 47

Key: PA = Practice & Application; ROS = Reflecting on the Section; SR = Spiral Review; TB = Toolbox; EP = Extra Skill Practice; Ext = Extension; ST = Standardized Testing

Math Background and Teaching Strategies

Classroom Notes

Visitors may include:

• Surveyor or map maker

Math Strands

Topic Spiraling and Integration
Students were introduced to parallel lines and transversals in Module 6 of Book 2 and worked with angle measures and corresponding angles as they identified similar figures in Module 3 of Book 3. Students will apply the angle pair relationships in Module 8 where they use the properties of parallel lines and transversals to justify angle properties of quadrilaterals.

Exploration 1
Continuing the exploration of geometry and spatial reasoning, students engage in activities that require them to identify alternate interior, alternate exterior, corresponding, vertical, complementary, and supplementary angles. The amount of vocabulary reviewed in this section may inhibit some students from developing an understanding of the relationships between the angles formed when parallel lines are intersected by a transversal. Relating each term to a more common meaning can help students make connections that will allow them to distinguish among the angles. As students master this language, they should learn to identify the relationships between angles and visually recognize angles that appear to be congruent.

Students used the notation for the measure of an angle, $m\angle$, in Module 3 when they studied similar figures and the symbol for congruent, $\cong$, in Section 2 when they studied congruent figures. In this section, they learn to correctly apply the notation in new contexts. When comparing angles, the focus is on their measures and the notation for the measure of an angle is used, e.g. $m\angle 3 = 52°$, or $m\angle 4 = m\angle 6$. When the focus is on angles with equal measures, the notation for congruence should be used, e.g. $\angle 4 \cong \angle 6$. Students should be encouraged to use this notation properly throughout the section.

Section 6 Scale Drawing and Similar Figures

Section 6 Planner

Section Objectives

Exploration 1
• Make a scale drawing

Exploration 2
• Apply relationships between perimeters and areas of similar figures

Days for Section 6

First Day
Setting the Stage, *p. 374*
Exploration 1 through Question 6,
pp. 375–377

Second Day
Exploration 1 from Question 7, *p. 377*

Third Day
Exploration 2, *pp. 378–380*
Key Concepts, *p. 381*

Teaching Resources

Teacher's Resource Book
• Warm-Up
• Labsheet 6A
• Practice and Applications
• Study Guide
See page 309 for additional teaching resources.

Materials List

Exploration 1
• Labsheet 6A
• tape measure and ruler
• plain or graph paper

Exploration 2
• ruler

Practice and Applications
• ruler
• plain or graph paper

Assessment Options

EMBEDDED ASSESSMENT
• Make a scale drawing
  Exercises 1, 2
• Apply relationships between perimeters and areas of similar figures
  Exercises 13, 14, 18, 20

PERFORMANCE TASK/PORTFOLIO
• Exercise 6 on *p. 382 (writing)*
• Exercise 7 on *p. 382 (open-ended)*
• Exercise 8 on *p. 382 (create your own)*
• Exercise 12 on *p. 383 (writing)*
• Exercise 17 on *p. 383 (challenge)**
• Exercise 22 on *p. 384 (research)*

* indicates a problem-solving task that can be assessed using the Assessment Scales

QUIZZES/TESTS
• Section 6 Quick Quiz
• Module Tests A and B
• Module Standardized Test
• Module Performance Assessment

TEST GENERATOR

Section 6 Overview

In this section, students will see how architects use floor plans to show the rooms of a building in proportion to each other. Scale drawings and the relationships between perimeters and areas of similar figures will be explored as students study floor plans.

Exploration 1
Students study the meaning of a scale and practice choosing an appropriate scale to make a drawing. They convert actual measurements to scale measurements by making scale drawings of their classroom. As they make their drawings, students use estimation, solve proportions, and learn to label sketches with actual measurements.

Exploration 2
Students will learn how to use the scale on a drawing to find the perimeter and area of the actual figure. To do this, they will first investigate the relationship between the perimeters and the areas of various parts of their classroom and the perimeters and areas of the scale drawings they made of the classroom. These discoveries are applied to another floor plan and finally to other geometric figures.

Guide for Assigning Homework

Math Background and Teaching Strategies

Classroom Notes

Visitors might include:

• An architect or interior designer

Math Strands

Topic Spiraling and Integration
Students apply many skills throughout this section that have been developed in previous modules. In Module 1, students used ratios to solve simple problems involving rates. Proportions and cross products were used to find percents in Section 4 of Module 2. Similar figures were explored in Module 3 where students used ratios to compare the corresponding sides of figures for determining similarity. In this section, students use ratios and proportions to create a scale drawing of a figure. As they compare areas and perimeters of similar figures, they will revisit the concepts developed in Module 3 where they found relationships among perimeters, areas and volumes of similar figures, and in Module 4 where they applied these discoveries to volumes of prisms, cylinders, and cones. The concept of ratio is used as students explore the tangent, sine, and cosine ratios in Module 8 and similarity and scale are applied as students explore size transformations in Section 4 of Module 6.

Exploration 1
This exploration reviews two methods for solving a proportion, using equivalent fractions and using cross products. Students should notice that when using equivalent fractions, they must find the factor that one of the known numerators or denominators can be multiplied by to get the other numerator or denominator and then multiply by that factor to find the unknown numerator or denominator. Using cross products is a variation of the general method students learned for solving equations. In the proportion $\frac{x}{12} = \frac{3}{4}$, both sides of the equation are multiplied by 12 to isolate the variable, $x = \frac{3 \cdot 12}{4}$. This is the solution of the equation $4x = 3 \cdot 12$ formed when using cross products.

Exploration 2
As students review the relationships between the areas and perimeters of similar figures that they discovered in Module 3, they write proportions to find the area or perimeter of a figure given the area or perimeter of a similar figure. Students should know the relationships between the units of measure used for perimeter and those used for area, such as: 1 ft = 12 in., but 1 ft^2 = 144 in.^{2}; 1 m = 100 cm, but 1 m^2 = 10,000 cm^2. Graph paper can be used to model these relationships to help students grasp the concepts.

Module 5

OVERVIEW

Exploring the work of architects and engineers emphasizes the importance of mathematics. Students create two- and three-dimensional models, find surface areas and volumes of three-dimensional figures, explore properties of transversals, make scale drawings, and explore perimeters and areas of similar figures while examining architecture from around the world.

PREREQUISITE SKILLS

Warm-Up Exercises for each section are provided in the *Teacher's Resource Book*. You can use these exercises to review skills and concepts students will need for each section. In addition, the Spiral Review exercises at the end of each section in the student edition provide practice on prerequisite skills.

MODULE DIAGNOSTIC TEST

The Module Diagnostic Test in the *Teacher's Resource Book* can be used to assess students' prior knowledge of skills and concepts that will be taught in each section of this module. You can use test results to help structure your teaching to meet the diverse needs of your classroom.

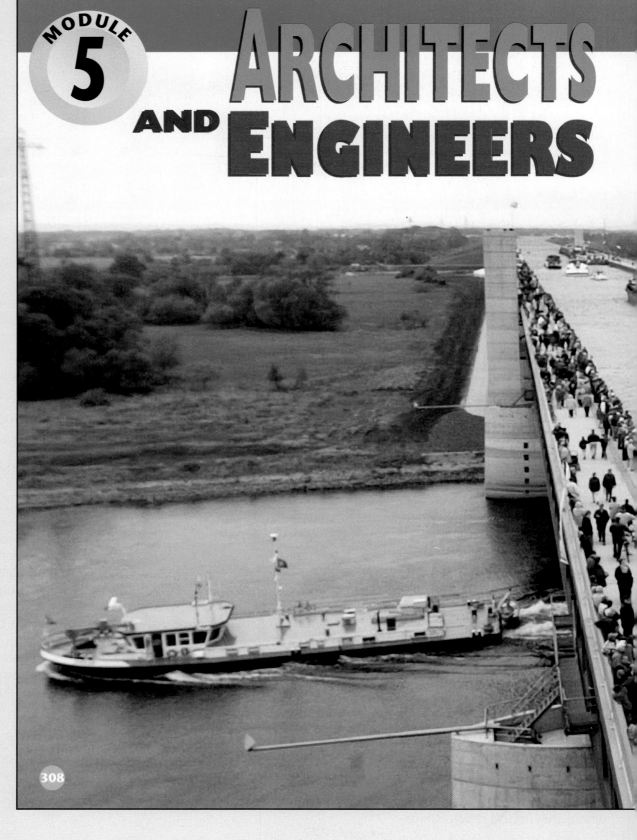

MODULE 5

ARCHITECTS AND ENGINEERS

308

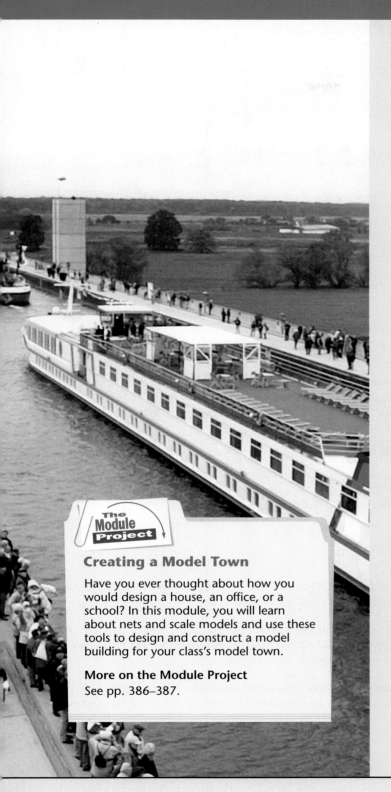

The Module Project

Creating a Model Town

Have you ever thought about how you would design a house, an office, or a school? In this module, you will learn about nets and scale models and use these tools to design and construct a model building for your class's model town.

More on the Module Project
See pp. 386–387.

INTERNET
Resources and practice at
classzone.com

Module Resources

TEACHER'S RESOURCE BOOK
Resources
- The *Math Gazette* (parent newsletter)
- Warm-Ups
- Labsheets
- Practice and Applications
- Study Guide

Assessment
- Section Quick Quizzes
- Mid-Module Quiz
- Module 5 Diagnostic Test
- Module 5 Tests A and B
- Module 5 Standardized Test
- Module 5 Performance Assessment

SPANISH RESOURCES
- The *Math Gazette* (parent newsletter)
- Practice and Applications
- Assessment
- Spanish Glossary

STUDENT WORKBOOK

TECHNOLOGY BOOK

TECHNOLOGY RESOURCES
- @Home Tutor
- Test Generator
- Activity Generator
- Professional Development DVD
- Online Activities

310

Where *do you* Stand?

Setting the Stage

This picture shows the Sears Tower in Chicago. At the time of its completion in 1974, it was the world's tallest building, with 110 stories and a height of 1454 ft.

When architects design buildings, they must be able to visualize the geometric figures within them and draw many different views.

The Sears Tower is actually a group of nine towers of various heights, so the tower's appearance changes when it is viewed from different sides.

Think About It

1 The cross sections below are drawn as if the viewer were looking down on the Sears Tower from above. Match the cross sections to the lettered areas in the diagram. **A, D, B, C**

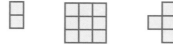

2 Would the cross sections look the same if the viewer could look up at the building from below? Explain.

3 In the photo you can see two sides of the Sears Tower. Will it look the same when viewed from the corner formed by the two sides you cannot see? Explain. **No. The building is not symmetrical.**

▶ **In this module you will see how architects and engineers use mathematics to design and construct buildings and other structures.**

Exploration 1

CUBES & PRISMS

TIPS FROM TEACHERS
Labsheet 1A is used multiple times throughout this exploration. It is helpful to have multiple double-sided copies available.

Students should work in pencil rather than in pen to enable them to experiment and erase when necessary.

GOAL

LEARN HOW TO...
- ◆ draw rectangular prisms and figures made with cubes
- ◆ find volumes and surface areas of figures made with cubes

AS YOU...
- ◆ use isometric dot paper

SET UP You will need: • Labsheets 1A–1C • ruler • centimeter cubes

▶ When presenting project ideas, architects and engineers often show their clients drawings of the structures they are to build. These drawings give the viewer a sense of how the finished structures will look in three dimensions.

Here are steps you can use to sketch a rectangular prism.

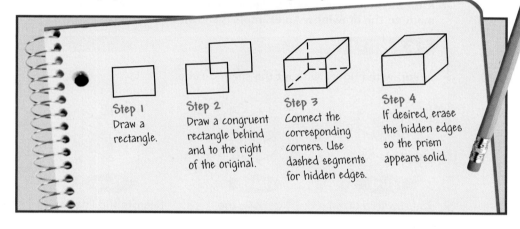

Step 1
Draw a rectangle.

Step 2
Draw a congruent rectangle behind and to the right of the original.

Step 3
Connect the corresponding corners. Use dashed segments for hidden edges.

Step 4
If desired, erase the hidden edges so the prism appears solid.

DEVELOPING MATH CONCEPTS
Building spatial skills is critical for the development of geometric thinking and reasoning. Geometry, as the study of our physical world, requires that an individual visualize, construct, and reproduce or draw figures in both two and three dimensions. Once these skills are established, students will make the algebraic connections required to solve geometric problems and use logical reasoning for geometric "proof."

TEACHING NOTES
Some students may need to make several attempts before successfully drawing a figure in **Question 4**. It is important to allow them this opportunity so they build the confidence necessary for drawing the more complex structures that follow.

4 a. Follow the steps above to sketch your own rectangular prism.
a–c. See margin.
b. Repeat part (a), but place the second rectangle behind and to the left instead of behind and to the right. How is this view of the prism different from the view you drew in part (a)?

c. Sketch a prism that is wider than your original prism. Then sketch another prism that is shorter than your original prism.

▶ You can also use special paper called *isometric dot paper* to help draw three-dimensional figures. The prefix *iso-* means "equal" and *metric* means "measure," so *isometric* means "equal measure."

isometric dot paper

5 Discussion Look at the isometric dot paper. Why do you think it was given the name *isometric dot paper*? All segments drawn by connecting two dots next to each other (either above or below or diagonally) are equal in measure.

4. See Additional Answers beginning on page A1.

Exploration 1 *continued*

COMMON ERROR

Question 6 Some students may connect the wrong dots on the isometric dot paper. Remind them to follow the directions carefully to insure that they are drawing a cube.

TIPS FROM TEACHERS

Prepare an overhead transparency of Labsheet 1A. Guide students step-by-step through the drawings until they are able to do them independently.

DIFFERENTIATED INSTRUCTION

For students who struggle seeing the figures on **Labsheet 1B** in three dimensions, shade the rhombus that makes up the top of each of the visible cubes. An overhead transparency can be made to help students visualize each cube in the structure.

To complete **Question 8**, visual and/or kinesthetic learners may need to physically manipulate the cube models rather than using a diagram or watching a demonstration. Each student will need at least four centimeter cubes.

If students fail to count the surface under the base blocks in **part (b)**, advise them to physically turn the structure over to see the bottom surfaces of the base blocks.

TEACHING NOTES

For **Question 9**, have centimeter cubes available for those who need them. Each student pair will need at least 10 cubes to complete Labsheet 1C.

312

▶ **Drawing Figures Made with Cubes** Here are steps you can use to draw on isometric dot paper.

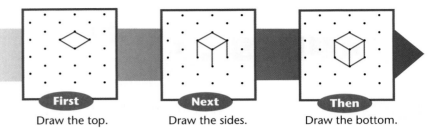

First	Next	Then
Draw the top.	Draw the sides.	Draw the bottom.

6 **Use Labsheet 1A.** Draw a cube on the *Isometric Dot Paper.*
   Check students' work.

7 **Use Labsheet 1B.** Follow the directions on the labsheet to make *Isometric Drawings.* **Check students' work.**

▶ After architects meet with a client, there are often adjustments to be made to the drawings. An example is shown below.

> **EXAMPLE**
>
> **Redraw the figure without the shaded cube.**
>
>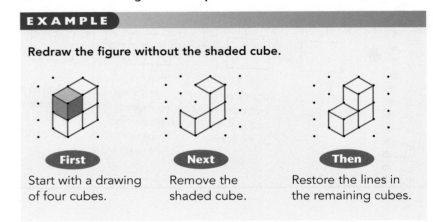
>
> | First | Next | Then |
> |---|---|---|
> | Start with a drawing of four cubes. | Remove the shaded cube. | Restore the lines in the remaining cubes. |

8 **Try This As a Class** Use centimeter cubes to build the two figures shown in the Example.

   a. Compare the volumes of the figures. The first figure has a volume of 4 cm³, the second has a volume of 3 cm³.
   b. Compare the surface areas of the figures. The first figure has a surface area of 16 cm² and the second has a surface area of 14 cm².

Use Labsheet 1C for Questions 9 and 10.

9 Follow the directions on the labsheet to redraw each of the *Cube Figures.* You will find the volume and the surface area, including the base, before and after the change.

9. a.

Before:
V = 4 unit³,
S.A. = 18 unit²;
After: 3 unit³,
S.A. = 14 unit²

b.

Before:
V = 8 unit³,
S.A. = 32 unit²;
After: 7 unit³,
S.A. = 30 unit²

10 a. How did removing one block affect the volume of each of the *Cube Figures?* It decreased the volume by one cubic unit.

b. How did it affect the surface area of the figures? It decreased the surface area.

c. Discussion Were the volume and surface area affected in the same way for both figures? Explain.

11 ✔ **CHECKPOINT** **Use Labsheet 1A.** Draw a rectangular prism that is not a cube. Find its surface area and volume. Check students' work.

▌ **HOMEWORK EXERCISES** ▶ See Exs. 1–7 on pp. 317–318.

See Exs. 1–7 on pp. 317–318.

Exploration 2

Points of View

SET UP You will need: • Labsheets 1A and 1D • centimeter cubes • ruler

▲ front view

▲ back view

▲ side view

◀ Construction of the White House began in 1792. President and Mrs. John Adams became its first residents in 1800.

▶ In Exploration 1 you used isometric dot paper to draw figures made with cubes. This type of drawing can be used to help show how a real building will appear. But, as you will see, one viewpoint does not always show you the whole building.

12 The picture at the right shows the front and left sides of a building. Use centimeter cubes to build a model of the building. How many cubes did you use? 4

left   front

Section 1 Geometry and Perspective **313**

QUESTION 11
...checks that you can draw a rectangular prism and find its surface area and volume.

GOAL
LEARN HOW TO...
◆ draw 3-dimensional figures and flat views

AS YOU...
◆ model simple buildings with cubes

10. c. No. The volume always changed by one cubic unit. The change in surface area was determined by the number of faces that were adjacent to the cube that was removed.

TEACHING NOTE
If students need more guidance in drawing figures with a block removed, discuss the following example before students begin **Question 9** on page 312.

CLASSROOM EXAMPLE
Redraw the figure without the shaded cube.

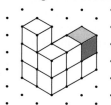

Answer:

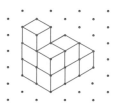

DEVELOPING MATH CONCEPTS
As they discuss **Question 10(c)**, students should notice that if a shaded cube is adjacent to only one other cube, all but one of its faces are exposed. When it is removed, five exposed faces are removed, leaving one exposed face in its place. If a cube is adjacent to two other blocks, all but two of its faces are exposed. When it is removed, four exposed faces are removed leaving two exposed faces in its place. Ask students to use this knowledge to determine how many faces are exposed when a cube is adjacent to three other cubes. (*three*) Ask: How do you think the surface area is affected when that cube is removed? (*It is not affected at all. Three exposed faces are removed leaving three exposed faces in their place.*)

313

Question 13 Discuss with the students the difference between two-dimensional and three-dimensional figures as they relate to views. We need only take one look at a two-dimensional figure to know its shape. Since three-dimensional figures have depth, it often takes several different views to attain an accurate visual picture of the entire structure.

COMMON ERROR

Question 15(a) Students may try to build this structure using 5 blocks as in the structure in Question 12. Help them see that even though the two structures appear to be the same, the one in Question 15 has been rotated 180° and the 2 block tower cannot conceal a fifth block as it did in Question 12. Allow skeptics to build the structure and try to add the fifth block. They will see that from this view a fifth block would be visible and not hidden as in the building in Question 12.

TIPS FROM TEACHERS

Provide students with a sheet of construction paper on which to build their structures. It not only reduces the noise, but also makes it easier for students to rotate a figure. Simply turn the paper to obtain the different views.

13. c.

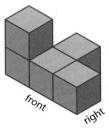

right   back

14. **Sample Response: Parts of buildings can be hidden from view behind larger or taller parts of a building.**

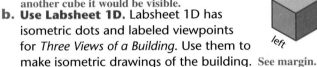

✔ **QUESTION 15**

...checks that you can draw three-dimensional figures from different points of view.

13 Two other views of the building in Question 12 are shown below.

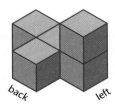
front   right

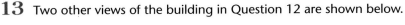
back   left

a. Add cubes to the model you built in Question 12 so the buildings will have the views shown above. How many cubes did you add? **1**

b. What can be seen in these two views that was not visible in the first view? **the fifth cube on the back**

c. **Use Labsheet 1A.** Sketch the building from the right-back view.

14 Why is it important to show different views of a building?

15 ✔ **CHECKPOINT**

a. Suppose each cube in this building shares at least one face with another cube. Can there be more than four cubes in the building? Explain. **No. If there were another cube it would be visible.**

b. **Use Labsheet 1D.** Labsheet 1D has isometric dots and labeled viewpoints for *Three Views of a Building*. Use them to make isometric drawings of the building. **See margin.**

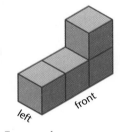
left   front

▶ **Flat Views** The views of the buildings you have seen so far give them a three-dimensional appearance. Suppose you were to view the buildings straight on from any side. What you would see would appear flat and could be called a *flat view*.

 Module 5   Architects and Engineers

15. b. See Additional Answers beginning on page A1.

16 Use centimeter cubes to build the four-cube building shown in Question 15. Position it so that the flat view from the front of the building is as shown at the right. **Check students' work.**

front view

17 Flat views of two other sides of the building in Question 15 are shown. Sketch the right-side view of the building. **right-side view:**

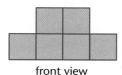

left-side view

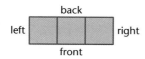

back view

18 a. How are the front and back views of the building in Question 15 related? **They are congruent, but they are mirror images of each other.**
b. How are the left- and right-side views related? **They are the same.**

▶ A flat view of the top of the building in Question 15 is shown at the right. This top view shows what the building looks like from directly above and also identifies each of the sides.

back

left   right

front

19 a. The building in Question 15 is not the only cube building that could have the flat view of the top shown above. Explain why.

b. Use flat views to draw the four side views of another building that has the same top view as shown above.

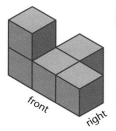

front

right

20 ✔ **CHECKPOINT** The building at the left contains only five cubes. Draw flat views of the building from each of the following viewpoints: front, back, left, right, and top. **See margin.**

21 What is the maximum number of cubes that could be used to build a cube building with the following front and side views? **20**

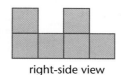

front view   right-side view

22 What is the minimum number of cubes that could be used to build the cube building in Question 21?

HOMEWORK EXERCISES ▶ See Exs. 8–15 on pp. 318–319.

19. a. Sample Response: The top view shows only the cubes in the base. It does not show height.

b. Sample Response:

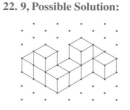

left   right   front   back

✔ **QUESTION 20**

...checks that you can draw flat views from different viewpoints.

22. 9, Possible Solution:

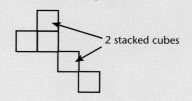

TEACHING NOTES

Questions 16 and 17 Flat views can be deceiving as they do not show depth. The front and back views of the structure shown are straightforward and should need no explanation. Ask students what they notice when they compare the left-side view to a right-side view. Ask: "Would it be possible to build this structure from the left-side view?" (*No; It is impossible to tell how many blocks are behind either of the visible faces.*) Students may want to create several structures that would give this same view. Then ask: "What cubes are not visible in the top view?" (*The cube that is under the stacked cubes on the right side of the building.*) This will lead students into **Question 19**.

After completing **Questions 16–18** you may want students to create their own structures and draw flat views of them for additional practice.

Checkpoint Question 20 Most students will benefit from using centimeter cubes to build this structure, rotating it and viewing it from different angles as they draw the flat views.

Question 22 Inform students that each cube in this structure must be adjacent to another cube on a complete side. If that is not the restriction, the minimum possible is 7 cubes. You might challenge students to try to create this structure using only 7 cubes (all must touch each other on a side or corner). A possible arrangement is shown below. (top view)

2 stacked cubes

20.

front   back   left   right

back
left   right
front
top

315

Key Concepts

CLOSURE QUESTION

Is it possible to accurately construct a three-dimensional building using only one isometric drawing or one flat view drawing? Explain.

Sample Response: Not necessarily. One isometric drawing does not show all the possible views of a structure, but it is possible that all the cubes used in the structure are visible from that one view. The same is true of a flat view. However, with a flat view, there is no way of knowing the number of cubes that may be hidden behind a visible cube.

ABSENT STUDENTS

For students who were absent for part or all of this section, the blackline Study Guide for Section 1 may be used to present the ideas, concepts, and skills of Section 1.

Section 1
Key Concepts

Isometric Drawings (pp. 311–313)

Isometric dot paper can be helpful in drawing three-dimensional figures.

Example Four different views of the same figure are shown on isometric dot paper.

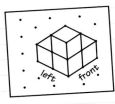
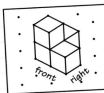
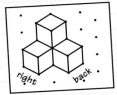
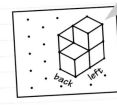

The volume is 4 cubic units. The surface area is 18 square units, including the base.

Flat Views (pp. 314–315)

Flat views of a building can be used to show what the building will look like when viewed directly from the front, back, left side, or right side, or from the top (directly above).

Example These are flat views of the building modeled above.

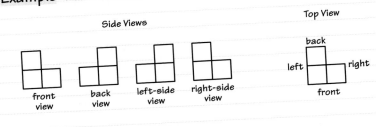

Side Views

Top View

front view — back view — left-side view — right-side view

back — left — right — front

Key Concepts Question

23 **Use Labsheet 1A.** Imagine removing the top cube from the figure above. On the *Isometric Dot Paper*, draw four different views of the new figure. Then draw five different flat views.
See margin.

23. See Additional Answers beginning on page A1.

Section 1

Practice & Application Exercises

YOU WILL NEED

For Exs. 2, 3, 5–7, and 12–14:
◆ Labsheet 1A (2 copies)

For Ex. 11:
◆ ruler

For Ex. 15:
◆ Labsheet 1D

1. Sketch a cube using the steps on page 311 for drawing a rectangular prism.

Use the *Isometric Dot Paper* on Labsheet 1A for Exercises 2 and 3.

2. a. Draw a rectangular prism.

   b. Draw a rectangular prism that has the same height and width but is twice as long as the prism in part (a).

   c. Draw a rectangular prism that has the same height and length but is three times as wide as the prism in part (a).

   d. **Writing** Record the number of cubes, the surface area, and the volume of each rectangular prism you drew in parts (a)–(c). What relationships do you notice among these measurements? See margin.

3. How many different rectangular prisms can you draw that are made up of 12 cubes? 4 prisms: 1 · 1 · 12; 1 · 2 · 6; 1 · 3 · 4; 2 · 2 · 3

4. Prisms are named for their bases. Steps similar to those for drawing a rectangular prism can be used to sketch other prisms.

   a. Sketch a triangle.

   b. Sketch a congruent triangle that is placed behind and to the right of the triangle in part (a).

   c. Connect corresponding vertices to form a triangular prism.

   d. Sketch a prism as in parts (a)–(c) with a trapezoid (instead of a triangle) for a base.

Use Labsheet 1A. On the *Isometric Dot Paper*, draw the figure that results from removing the shaded cube(s). Then give the volume and the surface area of the figure before and after removing the cube(s). Assume that there are no gaps on the bottom layer. Also assume that the only hidden cubes are directly beneath the cubes on the top layer.
5–6. See margin.

5.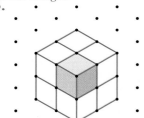

6.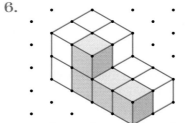

---

1. Sample Response:

2. Sample responses are given.

   a.

   b.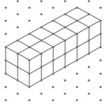

   c.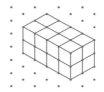

4. a–c.

   d.

Practice & Applications

SUGGESTED ASSIGNMENTS

Core Course
Day 1: Exs. 1–7
Day 2: Exs. 8–13
Day 3: Exs. 15–25

Extended Course
Day 1: Exs. 1–7
Day 2: Exs. 11–14
Day 3: Exs. 15–25

Note: Extended Course assignments can be used to differentiate within the regular classroom. In classrooms where students are grouped homogeneously, the material might be covered in fewer days. In this case assignments may be combined.

ADDITIONAL PRACTICE
See the *Teacher's Resource Book* for additional practice and application exercises for this section.

CLASSROOM MANAGEMENT
Have additional copies of **Labsheet 1A** available for students. Making double-sided copies reduces the amount of paper used. Encourage students to conserve paper by making their initial drawing near the top left of the paper.

COMMON ERROR
Exercise 3 Remind students that not every structure that can be made with 12 cubes is a rectangular prism. For this exercise they are to limit their structures to rectangular prisms only.

2. d., 5–6. See Additional Answers beginning on page A1.

Practice & Applications

EXERCISE NOTES
Exercises 11–13 Students may benefit from using centimeter cubes to build the structure before attempting to draw the views.

11.

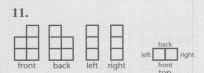
front   back   left   right

back
left □ right
front
top

13.

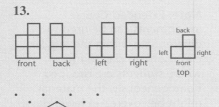
front   back   left   right

back
left □ right
front
top

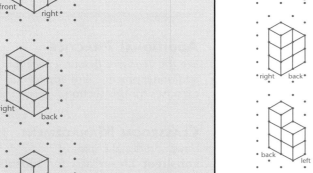
front   right

right   back

back   left

7. a.

b. Check students' work. Sample Responses:

12.

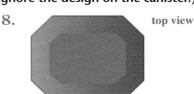
front   right

right   back

back   left

7. **Use Labsheet 1A.** A client has hired you to build an addition on the office building shown at the right.

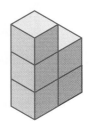

a. The pink face represents the place where the client might like to have the addition attached. On the *Isometric Dot Paper*, redraw the building with the addition in place. (Add only one cube.)

b. **Open-ended** Select another location where you might ask the client to consider adding the additional office space. Redraw the building with the addition in place.

For Exercises 8–10, tell whether each view shows the *front view*, the *left-side view*, or the *top view* of the canister at the right. (Ignore the design on the canister.)

front

8.   top view

9.   10.

front view   left-side view

11. Assume the building at the right contains five cubes. Draw flat views of the building from each of the following viewpoints: front, back, left, right, and top. See margin.

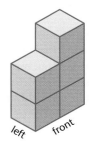
left   front

Use the *Isometric Dot Paper* on Labsheet 1A for Exercises 12–14.

12. Draw and label front-right, right-back, and back-left views of the building in Exercise 11.

13. Suppose that the view shown in Exercise 11 is for a building containing six cubes. Think about where the hidden cube must be located if it shares at least one face with another cube. Then carry out the steps in Exercises 11 and 12 for the six-cube building. See margin.

14. Challenge Five flat views of a figure made with cubes are shown. On *Isometric Dot Paper*, draw a view of the figure from the front-right corner.

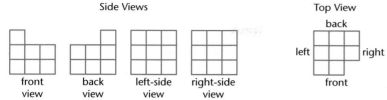

Side Views

front view | back view | left-side view | right-side view

Top View

back

left | right

front

Reflecting ◀▶ on the Section

15. Use Labsheet 1D. A blue 3-dimensional figure and a green three-dimensional figure were put together to form the building shown below at the right. The two colors help you see how the figures fit together. Use shading to show how the blue and green figures below fit together to form each of the *Three Buildings* shown on the labsheet. **See margin.**

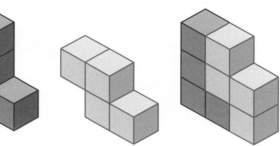

VISUAL THINKING

Exercise 15 checks that you can visualize figures made with cubes.

14. There are several possible responses. Check students' work. Sample Response:

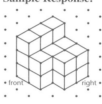

• front   right •

Spiral ◀▶ Review

16. Evetta, Luisa, and Yoko are auditioning for a part in a play. The order of their auditions will be determined by a random drawing. What is the probability of each event? (Module 4, p. 300)

a. Evetta auditions first.
$\frac{1}{3}$ or about 0.33

b. Yoko does not audition last.
$\frac{2}{3}$ or about 0.67

Use mental math to find each value. (Module 3, p. 163)

17. $\sqrt{36}$ 6

18. $\sqrt{9}$ 3

19. $\sqrt{144}$ 12

Estimate each square root to the nearest tenth. (Module 3, p. 163)

20. $\sqrt{56}$ 7.5

21. $\sqrt{10}$ 3.2

22. $\sqrt{31}$ 5.6

Find each sum or difference and write it in lowest terms.
(Module 2, p. 100)

23. $\frac{3}{8} + \frac{1}{6}$ $\frac{13}{24}$

24. $\frac{2}{5} + \left(-\frac{3}{4}\right)$ $-\frac{7}{20}$

25. $-\frac{13}{15} - \frac{41}{45}$ $-1\frac{7}{9}$

EXERCISE NOTES
Exercise 14 Challenge students to use centimeter cubes to construct the figure as shown by the flat views before drawing it on isometric dot paper.

15.

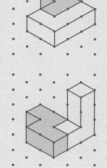

Extra Skill Practice

4.

5–9. See Additional Answers beginning on page A1.

320

Section ① Extra Skill Practice

You will need: • *Labsheet 1A* (Exs. 3–5, 8, and 9) • *ruler* (Exs. 3–5 and 7–9)

Follow the steps on page 311 for drawing a rectangular prism.

1. Sketch a rectangular prism whose height is twice its width.

2. Sketch a rectangular prism whose height is one-third its width.

Use the *Isometric Dot Paper* on Labsheet 1A. Draw all the different rectangular prisms that can be made from each number of cubes. 4–7. See margin.

3. three cubes   4. four cubes   5. eight cubes

6. **Writing** Record the number of cubes, the surface area, and the volume of each rectangular prism you drew in Exercises 3–5. What relationships do you notice among these measurements?

7. Assume the building at the right contains five cubes. Draw flat views of the building from each of the following viewpoints: front, back, left, right, and top.

Use the *Isometric Dot Paper* on Labsheet 1A for Exercises 8 and 9. 8–9. See margin.

8. Draw and label left-front, right-back, and back-left views of the building at the right.

9. Suppose that the view shown in Exercise 7 is for a building containing six cubes. Think about where the hidden cube must be located if it shares at least one face with another cube. Then carry out the steps in Exercises 7 and 8 for the six-cube building.

1. Sample Response: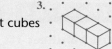

2. Sample Response:

3.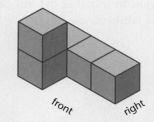

Study Skills ▷ **Identifying Weaknesses**

When you complete a module or a section of a textbook, it can be helpful to identify anything that you do not fully understand. By writing out a list of questions to discuss with your teacher or other students, you can fill in any gaps in your understanding before moving on.

Describe a topic in this section about which you have questions. Write down your questions and try to obtain answers. Write the answers in your own words to be sure you understand them fully.
Check students' work.

Section ② Geometry and Constructions

Building BLOCKS

Setting the Stage

Setting the Stage ▶▶▶▶▶▶▶▶▶▶▶▶▶▶▶▶▶▶▶▶▶▶▶▶▶▶▶▶▶

KEY TERM
♦ congruent

Paul Spooner is a mechanical engineer of sorts. He designs and constructs moving sculptures made from paper and other simple materials. With scissors, glue, paper folding, and craftsmanship, Spooner's 2-dimensional patterns can be turned into playful 3-dimensional animals that you animate with the turn of a handle.

Over 45 separate pieces were put together to create the anteater sculpture. ▶

Think About It

1 What is the mathematical term for the general shape of the 3-dimensional figure the anteater is standing on in the photograph?
rectangular prism

2 **a.** Describe the general shape of the anthill in the photograph.
pyramid
b. What 2-dimensional shape is formed between two adjacent dashed lines on the anthill? **triangle**

3 Two figures are **congruent** if they are the same shape and size. Do any of the figures in Spooner's sculpture appear to be congruent? Explain. **Yes; The triangles that form the pyramid are congruent, the front and back of the anteater appear to be congruent. So do the opposite sides of the platform he is standing on.**

Section 2 Geometry and Constructions (321)

Setting the Stage

ABOUT THE THEME
Mechanical engineers are not limited to designing structures such as draw-bridges and windmills. Some prefer a more whimsical application of their talents. Students might be interested to know that the sculpture constructed by Paul Spooner has moveable parts. When the handle is turned the circle rotates and the ant disappears into the anthill.

GETTING STARTED
Students will be utilizing what they know about geometric figures to identify faces and draw nets. Module 5, Section 2 *Warm-Up* assesses student facility with drawing geometric shapes from a description.

TEACHING NOTES
Students may notice that the anthill appears to be a cone. If this is true, the shapes formed by the dotted lines would not be exact triangles since the bases would be slightly curved. Make sure students know they are to identify the *general shape* of each of the figures in the sculpture, including the shapes formed between the dotted lines.

Exploration 1

TEACHING NOTES

You may want to model **Constructing a Triangle** on the overhead for students to follow. Make sure they understand that the arcs they construct must be long enough to intersect.

TECHNOLOGY NOTE

For a related technology activity, see the *Technology Book*.

GOAL

LEARN HOW TO...
- name congruent figures
- apply the triangle inequality

AS YOU...
- construct triangles

KEY TERMS
- side-side-side rule
- triangle inequality

Exploration 1

Constructing TRIANGLES

SET UP *Work in a group of three. You will need:* • *compass* • *ruler* • *plain white paper* • *protractor*

▶ In this exploration, you will learn about congruent triangles. You will also learn how to construct a triangle using a compass and a ruler.

Student Resource

Constructing a Triangle

You can construct a triangle if you know its side lengths. The figures below show the steps for constructing a triangle that has side lengths of 4 in., $3\frac{1}{2}$ in., and 3 in.

Step 1 Draw a line segment 4 in. long. Label the endpoints *A* and *B*.

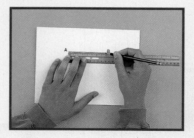

Step 2 Adjust the compass to a radius of $3\frac{1}{2}$ in. Put the compass point on *A* and draw an arc.

An arc is part of a circle.

Step 3 Adjust the compass to a radius of 3 in. Put the compass point on *B*. Draw another arc that intersects the first arc.

Step 4 Label the point where the arcs intersect *C*. Draw segments from *A* to *C* and from *B* to *C*.

4 a. Each member of your group will construct a triangle with side lengths of 5 in., 4 in., and 3 in., starting with a different side length. (Use the *Student Resource* on the previous page.)

Person 1: Draw the 5 in. line segment first.

Person 2: Draw the 4 in. line segment first.

Person 3: Draw the 3 in. line segment first.
Check students' work.

b. How do the three triangles compare? The triangles are the same, just rotated.

▶ **If two figures are congruent, it is possible to fit one figure onto the other so that all the corresponding parts match. In the diagram at the left, △ABC is congruent to △DEF. This is written △ABC ≅ △DEF. Corresponding angles of congruent triangles have the same measure, and corresponding sides are the same length.**

5 Are your triangles from Question 4 congruent? Explain.

6 **Discussion** Suppose you are given the statement △ABC ≅ △DEF.

a. How can you tell which angles are corresponding angles?

b. How can you tell which sides are corresponding sides?

▶ **One way to determine if triangles are congruent is to measure the lengths of their sides. If the sides of one triangle have the same lengths as the sides of another triangle, the triangles are congruent. This is called the side-side-side rule.**

7 a. Label the vertices of each of the triangles your group made in Question 4. (Use different letters for each triangle.)
Check students' work.

b. Write statements like the one in Question 6 telling that the triangles are congruent. Be sure to list the corresponding vertices in the same order. Sample Response: △LMN ≅ △TUV

8 ✔ **CHECKPOINT** Construct and label two congruent triangles. Explain how you know the triangles are congruent.
Check students' work.

9 Try to construct triangles with the given side lengths.

a. 2 in., 3 in., 2 in.
Check students' triangles.

c. 1 in., 1 in., 1 in.
Check students' triangles

b. 1 in., 2 in., 3 in. impossible

d. 1½ in., 1½ in., 4 in. impossible

10 **Try This as a Class** Look at your work in Question 9.

a. How can you predict whether three side lengths can be used to construct a triangle? Explain. The sum of the lengths of the two shorter sides must be greater than the length of the longest side.

b. Test your answer to part (a) by making up 3 side lengths that can be used to construct a triangle and 3 that cannot. Then try to construct each triangle. Sample Response: 4 cm, 5 cm, 7 cm; 2 cm, 5 cm, 7 cm; With 7 cm used for the base of the triangle, the side lengths 2 cm, and 5 cm, will not meet unless they lay flat directly on top of the base, therefore not forming a triangle.

Section 2 Geometry and Constructions **323**

---

5. Yes; The corresponding sides have the same length and the corresponding angles are congruent.

∠A corresponds to ∠D.
$\overline{BC}$ corresponds to $\overline{EF}$.

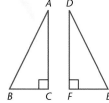

6. a. Corresponding angles are named in the same order, so ∠A ≅ ∠D, ∠B ≅ ∠E, and ∠C ≅ ∠F.

b. Corresponding sides are listed in the same order as the vertices that correspond, so $\overline{AB} ≅ \overline{DE}$, $\overline{BC} ≅ \overline{EF}$, and $\overline{CA} ≅ \overline{FD}$.

✔ **QUESTION 8**

...checks that you can identify congruent triangles.

Exploration 2

DEVELOPING MATH CONCEPTS

Prior to working **Question 12**, discuss with your students the difference between two- and three-dimensional figures. Ask them to name some three-dimensional figures with which they are already familiar. Encourage students to use correct mathematical terms such as rectangular prism, cylinder, and cube. Show students a three-dimensional model and ask how two-dimensional figures are related to the three-dimensional figure. Students should relate that a face of the three-dimensional figure is a two-dimensional figure.

COMMON ERROR

After drawing the net in **Question 12**, make sure students cut only the outer lines. They should not cut the four triangles apart from each other. Folding and creasing all the inner lines with a thumbnail or ruler before folding the figure together will make it easier to form the three-dimensional figure.

▶ The relationship among the side lengths of a triangle that you described in Question 10 is the **triangle inequality**.

✔ QUESTION 11

...checks that you understand the relationship among the side lengths of any triangle.

11 ✔ CHECKPOINT Tell whether it is possible to construct a triangle with the given side lengths.

a. 2 cm, 4 cm, 6 cm No   **b.** 3 cm, 9 cm, 8 cm Yes

c. $\frac{1}{2}$ in., $\frac{1}{4}$ in., $\frac{3}{8}$ in. Yes   **d.** 1.5 m, 4.9 m, 3.4 m No

HOMEWORK EXERCISES ▶ See Exs. 1–11 on p. 332.

GOAL

LEARN HOW TO...
♦ identify and count parts of 3-dimensional figures
♦ create nets for pyramids and prisms

AS YOU...
♦ build a house with a modified mansard roof

KEY TERMS
♦ net
♦ pyramid
♦ tetrahedron
♦ base
♦ face
♦ edge
♦ vertex (plural: vertices)

Exploration 2

Constructing N E T S

SET UP *You will need: • Labsheets 2A and 2B • compass • ruler • scissors • tape*

▶ You can use a compass and the straight edge of a ruler to create two-dimensional patterns for some of the 3-dimensional figures that Paul Spooner uses in his moving sculptures. A two-dimensional pattern that can be folded into a 3-dimensional figure is a **net**.

12 The anthill in the *Setting the Stage* is a *pyramid*. Follow the steps below to construct a net to make a simple pyramid.
Check students' work.

First	**Next**	**Then**
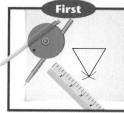	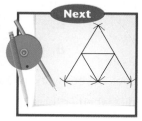	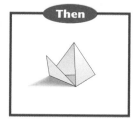
Use a compass and a straightedge to construct any equilateral triangle.	Construct another equilateral triangle on each side of the original triangle.	Cut out the net and fold it along the sides of the original triangle.

▶ A **pyramid** is a polyhedron with one base that is a polygon. The other faces are triangles and meet at a common vertex. A pyramid with four triangular faces, including the base, is a **tetrahedron**.

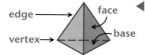
edge → face
vertex → base

◀ A pyramid is named for the shape of its base. This tetrahedron may also be called a triangular pyramid.

13 Refer to the tetrahedron you made in Question 12.

   a. How many edges does the tetrahedron have? **6 edges**

   b. How many vertices? **4 vertices**

   c. How many faces, including the base? **4 faces**

   d. How are the faces related? How can you tell?

13. d. They are congruent. Sample Response: Each triangle in my tetrahedron is an equilateral triangle with the same edge length.

14 ✔ **CHECKPOINT**

   a. How many edges does a cube have? **12 edges**

   b. How many vertices? **8 vertices**

   c. How many faces, including the base? **6 faces**

   d. How are the faces related? How can you tell?

✔ **QUESTION 14**

...checks that you can identify and count parts of a 3-dimensional figure.

14. d. The faces are congruent. Sample response: All the faces are squares with the same edge length.

▶ **Nets for Buildings** Architects sometimes make nets to build cardboard models of the buildings they design. A model of a building allows an architect to see what the real building will look like and make changes before it is actually built.

15 The roof of the house in the sketch below is a modified mansard roof. This type of roof creates extra space for living quarters in an attic.

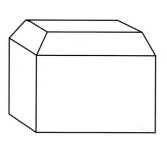

◀ The four-sided roof of this house is a mansard roof. Each side of the roof has two slopes, with the lower slope steeper than the upper slope.

15. a. a rectangle and 4 trapezoids;

or

   a. What polygons are used to create the modified mansard roof? Sketch one face of the roof.

   b. What polygons are used to create the vertical walls of the building? Sketch one wall. **rectangles;**

Exploration 2 *continued*

TEACHING NOTES

In preparation for creating their own nets in **Question 16**, and to develop spatial visualization skills, have students mark the edges of the net that they think will fold together when the three-dimensional figure is formed. For example, the two vertical edges at the ends of the net could both be marked with the letter *a*. Then as students fold the figure, they can check their prediction.

Checkpoint Question 19 Instruct students to use a full sheet of paper for their net. If drawn too small, students will not notice discrepancies in the lengths of matching edges on the folded figure. Have students use rulers to draw their nets and then check the result by cutting out the nets and folding them into a prism. Students can then identify any errors and modify their nets.

DIFFERENTIATED INSTRUCTION

For students with limited fine motor dexterity, cut and fold the net on **Labsheet 2A** prior to class. The student can then fold and tape it together. For **Question 19**, students can match nets to corresponding solid figures rather than drawing.

Students with highly developed spatial skills can be challenged to draw complex nets and then ask a partner to predict the solid figure that will result.

HOME INVOLVEMENT

Ask students to find empty containers, such as cereal boxes, that can be cut apart (with parental permission). When they are laid out flat, students will see the nets of the solid figures.

20. a. See Additional Answers beginning on page A1.

326

---

18. Sample Response: Remove the trapezoids and the smallest rectangle. Replace the two removed polygons from the lower right corner with a rectangle congruent to the one in the lower left corner.

✔ QUESTION 19

...checks that you can sketch a net for a prism.

19. Sample Response: Check students' nets. Be sure corresponding edges are the same length. 12 edges, 8 vertices, 6 faces

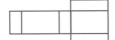

Use the *Net for a House* on Labsheet 2A for Questions 16–18.

16 Follow the directions on the labsheet to make a model of a house with a modified mansard roof. **Check students' work.**

17 **a.** How many edges does the model have? **20 edges**

   b. How many vertices does the model have? **12 vertices**

   c. How many faces, including the top and the bottom, does the model have? **10 faces**

18 **Discussion** How could you modify the *Net for a House* on Labsheet 2A to create a net for a rectangular prism?

19 ✔ **CHECKPOINT** Sketch a net for a rectangular prism. Then find the number of edges, the number of vertices, and the number of faces, including the bases.

20 **Use Labsheet 2B.** In the mid 1700s, a Swiss mathematician named Leonhard Euler observed a relationship among the numbers of faces, edges, and vertices of a polyhedron.

   a. Complete the *Three-Dimensional Figures* chart on the labsheet. **See margin.**

   b. Look for a relationship among the number of faces, edges, and vertices. If you only know the number of faces and vertices, how can you determine the number of edges? **Add the number of faces and vertices, then subtract 2 from the sum.**

   c. Write an equation that shows the relationship among the number of faces, vertices, and edges. $F + V - 2 = E$

21 If a polyhedron has 7 faces and 10 vertices, how many edges will it have? **15 edges**

22 The 3-dimensional figure shown is an *icosahedron*. An icosahedron has 20 faces (all triangles) that are joined by 30 edges. How many vertices does an icosahedron have? **12 vertices**

HOMEWORK EXERCISES ▶ See Exs. 12–19 on pp. 332–334.

 Module 5 Architects and Engineers

Exploration 3

Angles and *Triangles*

SET UP Work with a partner. You will need: • *plain paper* • *compass* • *ruler* • *scissors* • *protractor* • *tape*

GOAL

LEARN HOW TO...
- bisect an angle using a compass
- compare triangles using two sides and the included angle

AS YOU...
- construct a net for a pyramid

KEY TERMS
- angle bisector
- included angle

▶ At the right is a net for the anthill in Paul Spooner's paper anteater shown in the *Setting the Stage*. You need a protractor to draw this net, but some nets like it can be constructed by bisecting angles.

The steps below show how to bisect an angle using a compass and a straightedge, such as the straight edge of a ruler.

Bisecting an Angle

Student Resource

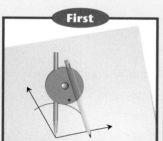

First

Place the compass point on the vertex of the angle. Draw an arc that intersects both sides of the angle.

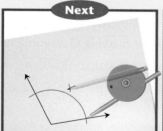

Next

Place the compass point at one of the points where the original arc intersects the sides of the angle. Draw an arc inside the angle. Use the same compass setting to draw an arc from the other intersection point as shown.

Then

Use a straightedge to draw a ray from the vertex of the angle through the point where the two arcs intersect.

This ray is the **angle bisector**. It divides the original angle into two congruent angles.

Exploration 3

TIPS FROM TEACHERS

Model the process of bisecting an angle on the overhead projector as students work on paper.

Begin by having students use a straightedge to draw an angle. Advise them to make the angle 90° or greater for ease in bisecting.

For each step of the process, lay the compass on its side with the center point at the appropriate place (the vertex of the angle, the point where an arc intersects a side of the angle, etc.) and the pencil at an appropriate starting point. Then draw the arc. This way students can actually see from the image how to place their compasses.

Numbering each step as it is completed and asking students to do the same allows for easy reference as students complete constructions on their own.

Have extra paper available to allow for students' errors.

TECHNOLOGY NOTE

For a related technology activity, see the *Technology Book*.

COMMON ERROR

Before students cut out the net they created in **Question 23**, make sure they understand that they are to cut along the segments they drew between each ray and not along the curve of the arc.

TEACHING NOTES

Before completing **part (c)** of **Question 24**, have students label each point on their nets to match the diagram. The labels should be written inside the triangles so that when the nets are folded, the labels will be visible, making it easier to identify each triangle and segment.

24. a. They are radii of the same circle.
b. They were constructed by bisecting two congruent angles.

23 Use a compass and a ruler. Follow the instructions below. The diagrams will help you and your partner draw nets for the triangular faces of two simple pyramids.

Check students' work.

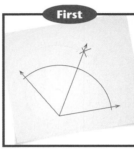
First

Draw an obtuse angle. Then follow the steps on page 327 to bisect the angle, using a large radius for the intial arc.

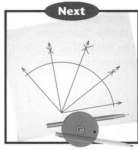
Next

Bisect each of the two new angles that you just formed. You do not have to draw the first arc again, just use the one already drawn.

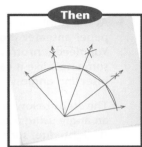
Then

Use a straightedge to connect the points where the arc intersects each ray. Cut out the net formed by the four triangles.

24 **Discussion** Suppose the diagram below represents the nets you and your partner made in Question 23.

    a. How do you know that $\overline{AB}$, $\overline{AC}$, $\overline{AD}$, $\overline{AE}$, and $\overline{AF}$ are congruent?

    b. How do you know that $\angle BAC$, $\angle CAD$, $\angle DAE$, and $\angle EAF$ are congruent?

    c. Fold the two outer triangles of your net on top of the two inner triangles. Then fold again, so that all four triangles overlap. How are $\triangle BAC$, $\triangle CAD$, $\triangle DAE$, and $\triangle EAF$ related?
    They are congruent triangles.

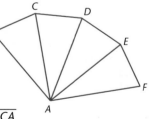

25 **a.** Identify the angle between sides $\overline{BA}$ and $\overline{CA}$ in $\triangle BAC$ above. This angle is referred to as the **included angle** between sides $\overline{BA}$ and $\overline{CA}$. $\angle BAC$

    b. Identify the included angle between sides $\overline{AC}$ and $\overline{CB}$. $\angle ACB$

26 Use a ruler and a protractor to complete parts (a)–(e). You and your partner should each make a triangle.

   a. Draw a triangle and label the vertices *A*, *B*, and *C*.

   b. Draw a segment that is congruent to $\overline{AB}$. Label the endpoints of the new segment *P* and *Q*.

   c. Draw an angle with the same measure as ∠*ABC* that has *Q* as its vertex and $\overrightarrow{QP}$ as a side.

   d. On the side of ∠*Q* that does not contain point *P*, draw a segment with the same length as $\overline{BC}$ that has one endpoint at *Q*. Label the other endpoint *R*.

   e. Connect points *P* and *R* to form another triangle.

   f. Discussion How are △*ABC* and △*PQR* related? Explain.

27 Try This as a Class Suppose two sides and the included angle of one triangle are congruent to two sides and the included angle of another triangle. Based on the results of Questions 25 and 26, what do you think is the relationship between the two triangles? **They are congruent.**

28 ✔ **CHECKPOINT**

   a. How are △*ABC* and △*DEF* related? Explain your reasoning.

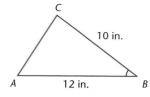

10 in.   10 in.   12 in.   12 in.

   b. The diagram does *not* indicate that △*ABC* ≅ △*EDF*. Why?

29 a. The net you made in Question 23 is made up of four congruent triangles. Tape two edges of the net together to form the sides of a pyramid. **Check students' work.**

   b. What shape needs to be added to the net to form the base of the pyramid? **a square**

   c. Make a sketch to show how you could change the net to include a base.

   d. Discussion Compare the net you sketched in part (c) with the net that your partner sketched. **Answers will vary.**

   29. c. Sample response:

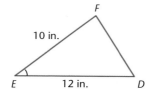

HOMEWORK EXERCISES ▶ See Exs. 19–28 on pp. 334–335.

---

26. a–e. Sample Response:

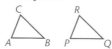

f. They are congruent. Sample Response: The sides of △*ABC* are congruent to the sides of △*PQR*, so △*ABC* ≅ △*PQR*.

✔ **QUESTION 28**

...checks that you can compare triangles based on two sides and the included angle.

28. a. △*ABC* ≅ △*DEF*; $\overline{AB} ≅ \overline{DE}$, $\overline{CB} ≅ \overline{FE}$, and the included angles ∠*ABC* and ∠*DEF* are congruent, so △*ABC* ≅ △*DEF* since two sides and the included angle of △*ABC* are congruent to two sides and the included angle of △*DEF*.

   b. The vertices are not written in an order that pairs congruent angles and congruent sides.

TEACHING NOTES

Question 27 Emphasize to students that they are now generalizing from the specific experience in **Question 26**. Ask several partner pairs to share their observations so the class can articulate the SAS (side-angle-side) rule for congruent triangles.

After completing **Checkpoint Question 28**, if students need additional guidance in applying the SAS rule, you may want to discuss the following Classroom Example.

CLASSROOM EXAMPLE

State the corresponding sides and angles that are shown to be congruent in the triangles below. Then tell if you can say the triangles are congruent.

Answer: $\overline{BC} ≅ \overline{FD}$, $\overline{AC} ≅ \overline{ED}$, and ∠*C* ≅ ∠*D*; You can say that △*ABC* ≅ △*EFD* since two sides and the included angle of one triangle are shown to be congruent to two sides and the included angle of the other triangle.

TEACHING NOTES

Discussion Question 29(d)

Ask, "For the net to work, what is important about the side lengths of the base?" (*They must be the same length as the base of each triangle.*) "Where must the base be attached to the net? Is there more than one possibility?" (*Have students sketch designs on the board until all the possibilities are shown.*)

329

Key Concepts

CLOSURE QUESTION

State the SAS (side-angle-side) rule for congruent triangles.

Sample Response: The SAS rule states that if two pairs of corresponding sides and the included angles of two triangles are congruent then the triangles are congruent.

Key Terms

congruent

side-side-side rule (SSS)

included angle

Section ②
Key Concepts

Congruent Figures (pp. 321–322)

Figures are congruent if they have the same size and shape.

Congruent Triangles (pp. 323-324 and pp. 328–329)

If the three sides of one triangle are congruent to the sides of another triangle, then the triangles are congruent. This is known as the side-side-side rule (SSS).

Example △RST ≅ △WXY

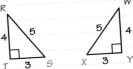

If two figures are congruent, then their corresponding parts are congruent. In the example above,

$\overline{ST}$ and $\overline{XY}$ are corresponding sides.
$\overline{ST} \cong \overline{XY}$

△RST ≅ △WXY

∠T and ∠Y are corresponding angles.
∠T ≅ ∠Y

If two sides and the included angle of one triangle are congruent to two sides and the included angle of another triangle, then the triangles are congruent. This is known as the side-angle-side rule (SAS).

Example △LMN ≅ △XYZ

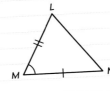
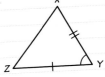

30 Key Concepts Question △CMD ≅ △TSQ. List the corresponding sides and the corresponding angles of the triangles. $\overline{CM} \cong \overline{TS}$, $\overline{MD} \cong \overline{SQ}$, $\overline{DC} \cong \overline{QT}$, ∠C ≅ ∠T, ∠M ≅ ∠S, ∠D ≅ ∠Q

Section 2
Key Concepts

Triangle Inequality (pp. 323–324)
The triangle inequality states that the sum of the lengths of any two sides of a triangle is greater than the length of the third side.

Nets for Pyramids and Prisms (pp. 324–326)
A pyramid is a polyhedron with one base that is a polygon. The other faces are triangles and meet at a common vertex. Pyramids and other 3-dimensional figures can be built from 2-dimensional nets.

Examples This pyramid is a tetrahedron because it has four faces. All the faces, including the base, are triangles. Pairs of faces meet in segments called edges. A tetrahedron has 4 faces, 6 edges, and 4 vertices.

pyramid

pyramid net

edge → face

base ← vertex

A rectangular prism has 6 faces, 12 edges, and 8 vertices.

prism

prism net

Bisecting Angles (pp. 327–328)
You can use a compass and a straightedge to bisect an angle.

Key Terms

triangle inequality

angle bisector

pyramid

net

tetrahedron

base

face

edge

vertex

CLOSURE QUESTIONS
Explain how prisms and pyramids are alike and how they are different.

Sample Response: Both are named for their bases, but pyramids have only one base. All other faces of a prism are parallelograms while all other faces of a pyramid are triangles.

ABSENT STUDENTS
For students who were absent for part or all of this section, the blackline Study Guide for Section 2 may be used to present the ideas, concepts, and skills of Section 2.

Key Concepts Questions

31 Give three side lengths that could be used to construct a triangle and three side lengths that could not. **Sample Response: triangle 5 cm, 6 cm, 9 cm; not a triangle 5 cm, 6 cm, 12 cm**

32 **a.** Sketch a net for a square pyramid. Draw the base in the center as in the pyramid net above.

b. How many edges does the square pyramid have? How many vertices? How many faces, including the base? **8 edges, 5 vertices, 5 faces**

32. a.

SUGGESTED ASSIGNMENTS

Core Course
Day 1: Exs. 1–11
Day 2: Exs. 12–19(a–c), 30–39
Day 3: Exs. 20–29

Extended Course
Day 1: Exs. 1–11
Day 2: Exs. 12–19, 30–39
Day 3: Exs. 20–29

Note: Extended Course assignments can be used to differentiate within the regular classroom. In classrooms where students are grouped homogeneously, the material might be covered in fewer days. In this case assignments may be combined.

ADDITIONAL PRACTICE

See the *Teacher's Resource Book* for additional practice and application exercises for this section.

COMMON ERROR

In **Exercises 12–14**, some students might mistakenly count both sides of a net which join to form a single edge of the 3-dimensional figure. Refer students to the nets they made or have one available to help them visualize that some of the sides of a net join to form a single edge in the 3-dimensional figure.

3. Yes; The sum of the lengths of segments *x* and *w* is greater than the length of segment *y*, so these three segments will form a triangle.

11. See Additional Answers beginning on page A1.

YOU WILL NEED

For Exs. 5–10:
♦ compass
♦ ruler

For Ex. 15:
♦ package for a real product
♦ ruler

For Exs. 16, 18, and 19:
♦ compass
♦ straightedge

1. No; The sum of the lengths of segments *k* and *m* is less than the length of segment *n*, so the segments will not form a triangle.

FOR ◄ HELP
with *similar triangles*, see
MODULE 3, p. 198

2. Yes; The sum of the lengths of segments *r* and *s* is greater than the length of segment *t*, so these three segments will form a triangle.

Section ② Practice & Application Exercises

Visual Thinking Without measuring or making any drawings, decide whether each set of line segments could form the sides of a triangle. Explain your thinking.

1. 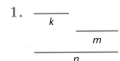 2. 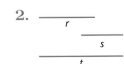 3.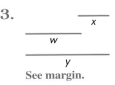

See margin.

4. **Algebra Connection** A triangle has side lengths 3, 8, and *x*. Use inequalities to describe all the possible values of *x*.
x is greater than 5, but less than 11; $5 < x < 11$

Tell whether it is possible to construct a triangle with the given side lengths. If it is possible, construct the triangle.

5. 3 in., 2 in., 2 in. Yes; Check students' constructions.

6. 4 in., 1 in., 2 in. No

7. 3 in., 3 in., 3 in. Yes; Check students' constructions.

8. 5 in., 2 in., 3 in. No

9. 3 in., 2 in., $2\frac{1}{2}$ in. Yes; Check students' constructions.

10. $1\frac{3}{4}$ in., $1\frac{5}{8}$ in., $3\frac{3}{4}$ in. No

11. Compare the triangles below. Which appear to be similar? Which appear to be congruent? Explain how you can check. Then write mathematical statements like the ones in the Examples on page 330 telling which triangles are congruent. See margin.

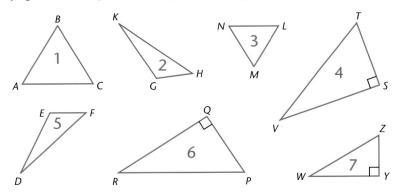

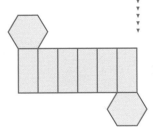

12. A net for a hexagonal prism is shown at the left. How many faces, edges, and vertices will the prism have? 8 faces, 18 edges, and 12 vertices

13. Open-ended Sketch a net for a pentagonal prism. How many faces, edges, and vertices will the prism have?

14. Open-ended Sketch a net for a hexagonal pyramid. How many faces, edges, and vertices will the pyramid have?

15. Home Involvement a–c. Answers will vary. Check students' work.

a. Find a real product whose package is a prism.

b. Estimate the area of each face and the total surface area of the package.

c. Carefully unfold the package and sketch its net.

16. The base of a building does not have to be a rectangle. For example, a hexagon can form the base of a tower, a carousel, a ticket office, or a circus tent.

a. Follow the steps below to construct a regular hexagon.
Check students' work.

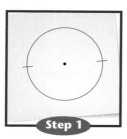

Step 1

Draw a circle with a compass. Leave the compass set to the circle's radius. Use a straightedge to mark the endpoints of a diameter.

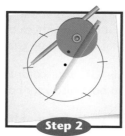

Step 2

Set the compass point on one endpoint of the diameter and mark two arcs that intersect the circle. Do the same for the other endpoint.

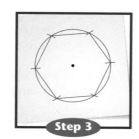

Step 3

Connect the six points to form a regular hexagon.

b. In Step 3, what other polygon can you form by connecting the six points and drawing a diameter? **a trapezoid**

c. What other polygon can you form by connecting every other point you drew on the circle in Step 2? **an equilateral triangle**

17. If a polyhedron has 9 faces and 9 vertices, how many edges will it have? **16 edges**

18. A *dodecahedron* is a 3-dimensional figure with 12 faces and 30 edges. How many vertices does a dodecahedron have?
20 vertices

---

13. Sample net: 7 faces, 15 edges, 10 vertices

14. Sample net: 7 faces, 12 edges, 7 vertices

FOR ▶ HELP

with *regular polygons*, see
TOOLBOX, p. 594

DEVELOPING MATH CONCEPTS

In **Exercises 13–14**, it is important that students see there is more than one solution to each of these problems. You might display students' nets on a bulletin board to reveal varied solutions. An alternative is to demonstrate by using two packages, such as cereal boxes, cutting them apart in different ways and displaying them so students can see the two different nets for the same three-dimensional figure.

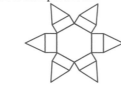

Exercise 19(d) Students may realize that if the triangles are too short, they will not meet to form the roof as shown. Ask students to formalize this in a statement about the triangles' heights in relation to the dimensions of its hexagonal base. (*The triangle height must be greater than the perpendicular distance from one edge of the hexagon to its center, or greater than half the perpendicular distance between two opposite edges of the hexagon.*) At half the length, all the triangles will meet together at the center of the hexagon, but the roof will be flat.

19. **a.** The base of the tent pictured below is a regular hexagon. What shapes are the other faces of the tent? **triangles and rectangles**

19. b. Sample sketch:

b. Make a rough sketch of a net for the tent, including the base.

c. How many faces, edges, and vertices does the tent have?
13 faces, 24 edges, 13 vertices

d. **Challenge** Use a compass and a straightedge to create a net for the tent. Cut it out and check that your design works. If it does not, tell what needs to be changed. **Check students' work.**

20. Sample response:

20. Draw an acute angle. Use your compass and straightedge to bisect the angle. Do not erase your compass marks.

For Exercises 21–24, choose the letter of the polyhedron that matches each net.

| A. triangular pyramid | B. triangular prism | C. octagonal pyramid | D. octagonal prism |

21. D

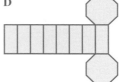

22. B

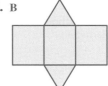

23. C

24. A

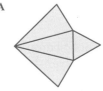

25. Writing Which net for a pyramid in Exercises 21–24 can be constructed using angle bisectors as on page 328? Which net for a pyramid cannot be constructed that way? Explain.

Tell whether the triangles in each pair are congruent. Explain.

26. △ABC, △DEF

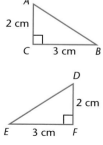

Congruent; SAS

27. △PQS, △RSQ

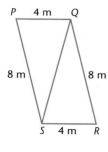

Congruent; SSS

28. △ABC, △WXY

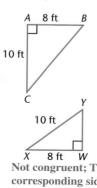

Not congruent; The corresponding sides are not congruent.

Reflecting ◀▶ on the Section

Be prepared to report on the following topic in class.

29. Describe how you can draw a right angle by constructing an angle bisector. Then describe how to use this construction to draw a net for a cube using a compass and a straightedge.

Spiral ◀▶ Review

30. Assume the building at the right contains seven cubes. Think about where the hidden cubes must be located if they each share at least one face with another cube. Draw flat views of the building from each of the following viewpoints: front, back, left, right, and top. See margin. (Module 5, p. 316)

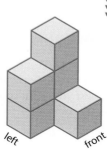

left   front

Solve each equation. (Module 4, p. 277)

31. $-2.4x = 72$ –30

32. $-0.9y + 1.8 = 0.9$ 1

33. $32 = -2.5z - 18$ –20

34. $-2.7 = 5.4m$ –0.5

35. $1.5n - 3.5 = -0.5$ 2

36. $4 + 9.6k = 0.8$ $-0.\overline{3}$

37. $\frac{3}{5}a = 27$ 45

38. $\frac{2}{3}b - 5 = 5$ 15

39. $\frac{4}{3}c + 9 = 49$ 30

---

25. Octagonal pyramid; An even number of congruent angles is required to construct nets using the angle bisecting method. The triangular pyramid has an odd number of congruent angles and cannot be constructed using angle bisectors.

Oral Report

Exercise 29 checks that you can use constructions to draw nets.

29. Sample Response: Draw and bisect a segment to construct a right angle with vertex A. Use the compass to construct congruent segments $\overline{AB}$ and $\overline{AD}$ on the side of the right angle. With the same compass setting and centers A and D, draw intersecting arcs. Label the intersection C. Draw $\overline{BC}$ and $\overline{DC}$ to complete the square $ABCD$. Repeat to construct 6 squares in this pattern.

EXERCISE NOTES

You may want to review or have students review, in groups, the conditions for congruency before assigning **Exercises 26–28**.

In preparing an oral report for **Exercise 29**, remind students that their description should be clear enough that anyone could follow along and accurately perform the constructions.

30.

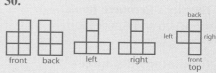

front   back   left   right   back left right front top

335

4. a. 10 faces, 24 edges, 16 vertices

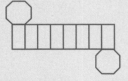

b. 6 faces, 10 edges, 6 vertices

Standardized Testing. See Additional Answers beginning on page A1.

336

Section ② Extra Skill Practice

You will need: • *compass, straightedge* (Exs. 5–6) • *scissors, tape* (Ex. 5)

Tell whether it is possible to construct a triangle with the given side lengths.

1. 5 cm, 4 cm, 10 cm No   2. $2\frac{5}{16}$ in., 4 in., $1\frac{5}{8}$ in. No   3. 8 m, 24 m, 24 m Yes

4. Sketch a net for each polyhedron. Then tell how many faces, edges, and vertices it will have. a–b. See margin.

   a. octagonal prism   b. pentagonal pyramid

5. a. Make a rough sketch of a net for a hexagonal pyramid. Then use a compass and straightedge to create the net.

   b. Build the pyramid. If your net does not work, explain how to fix it.
      Check students' work.

5. a. Sample Response:

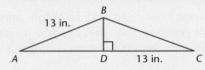

6. Draw an obtuse angle. Use your compass and straightedge to bisect the angle. Do not erase your compass marks. Sample Response:

Tell whether the triangles in each pair are congruent. Explain.

7. △PQR, △NML

8. △ABD, △CBD Not congruent; *BC > BA*

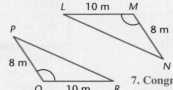

7. Congruent; Two sides and the included angle of △PQR are congruent to two sides and the included angle of △NML.

Standardized Testing ▶ Performance Task

Two identical pyramids can be put together with the bases attached to form a new polyhedron. Copy and complete the table below. Explain the reasoning you used to complete the table. See margin.

Number of sides on the base of each pyramid	Number of faces on the new polyhedron	Number of edges on the new polyhedron	Number of vertices on the new polyhedron
3	?	?	?
4	?	?	?
5	?	?	?
100	?	?	?

Section ③ Working with Triangles

Right ON!

IN THIS SECTION

EXPLORATION 1
♦ Triangle Side Length Relationships

EXPLORATION 2
♦ The Pythagorean Theorem

Setting the Stage ▸▸▸▸▸▸▸▸▸▸▸▸▸▸▸▸▸▸▸▸▸▸▸▸▸▸▸▸▸▸▸▸▸▸

> **SET UP** Work in a group of three or four. You will need: • scissors • centimeter grid paper • tape or glue • construction paper

The pyramids at Giza in Egypt were built as tombs for Egyptian kings, their families, and their servants. King Khufu's pyramid, shown in the center at the right, is the largest pyramid ever built. Many skilled craftspeople and laborers worked together to build the pyramids at Giza. There were stonecutters and polishers, crews who transported the giant stones, and laborers called *rope stretchers*.

The rope stretchers tied equally spaced knots in a piece of rope. They knew they could form a right triangle with side lengths of 3, 4, and 5 units by arranging the rope as shown. The rope triangle was then used at a construction site to measure distances and to form 90° angles at the corners of a pyramid.

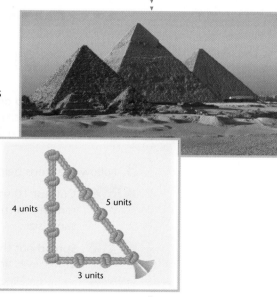

Think About It

1 a. Cut three squares from centimeter grid paper. One square should have sides 3 units long, one should have sides 4 units long, and one should have sides 5 units long. **Check students' work.**

b. Label each square with its area and the length of one side. **Check students' work.**

Section 3   Working with Triangles   **337**

Setting the Stage

ABOUT THE THEME
The Egyptians were the master architects and builders for their time. Although their technique of rope stretching seems rudimentary to us, it was very effective way of forming 90° angles. You might provide groups of students with pieces of lightweight rope (or clothesline) or heavy twine and allow them to perform a demonstration of rope stretching.

GETTING STARTED
Module 5 Section 3 *Warm-Up* assesses that students can identify triangles and evaluate square roots. These skills are fundamental to the application of the Pythagorean theorem.

Setting the Stage, *cont.*

TEACHING NOTES

In **Question 2(d)**, students are asked to think about whether the area of the square constructed on the longest side of any triangle (the square of the length of the side) is always equal to the sum of the areas of the squares on the other two sides (the sum of the squares of the lengths of the sides). If students check an equilateral triangle, they will quickly discover that the areas of the squares constructed on the sides do not have this relationship.

Make sure students keep the squares they have cut out for use in the *Triangle Table* In **Question 5** of Exploration 1.

Exploration 1

COMMON ERROR

In **Question 3**, some combinations of squares may appear to form right triangles when actually they do not. For example, squares with side lengths of 7 cm, 14 cm, and 15 cm may appear to form a right triangle, especially if they have not been cut out carefully. Emphasize that the sides of the triangle forming the right angle must be perpendicular. Students can use a protractor or a corner of a piece of paper to check.

After completing Exploration 1, students can check these triangles using the equation $a^2 + b^2 = c^2$.

DEVELOPING MATH CONCEPTS

Question 4 If a group has not tried a set of squares that do not form a triangle, encourage them to explore that possibility. This will provide a concrete experience for better understanding of the basic principle behind the triangle inequality.

---

2. b. Yes. Sample Response: Measure the angle that appears to be a right angle with a protractor.

2 **a.** Use your three squares to form a triangle. Tape the arrangement into place on construction paper. Label the two shorter sides *a* and *b* and the longest side *c*. **Check students' work.**

 b. Is the triangle a right triangle? Explain how you can check.

 c. What is the relationship between the areas of the two smaller squares and the area of the largest square? **They are equal.**

 d. Do you think this relationship is the same for all triangles? How can you find out? **Answers will vary. Sample Response: No; Try it with a triangle that is not a right triangle.**

▶ **Your discovery about the 3-4-5 triangle is part of a larger pattern. In this section, you will learn more about the relationship among side lengths of triangles.**

Exploration 1

TRI▲NGLE Side Length Relationships

SET UP Work in a group of three or four. You will need: • Labsheet 3A • centimeter grid paper • scissors • construction paper • tape or glue • protractor

3 Follow the steps below with your group. **Check students' work.**

First Cut out 10 squares from the grid paper with side lengths ranging from 6 cm to 15 cm. No two squares should be the same size.

Next Spread out the squares. Have one group member close his or her eyes and choose a square. Set this square aside.

Then Work together to try to form 3 triangles with the remaining 9 squares. (The triangles do not have to be right triangles.)

4. a. Sample Response: Yes; If the sum of the lengths of any 2 sides is not greater than the length of the third side, a triangle cannot be formed.

4 **a.** Are there some sets of squares that will not form a triangle? If so, explain why.

 b. Tape or glue each triangle to construction paper. **Check students' work.**

Use Labsheet 3A for Questions 5 and 6.

5 Follow the directions on the labsheet to complete the *Triangle Table* for the triangles made by your group. **Answers will vary. Check students' work.**

6 **Try This as a Class** Share your group's data from the *Triangle Table* with the other groups in your class. **a–b. Answers will vary. Check students' work.**

    a. Use the extra spaces in the *Triangle Table* to record the data from other groups for any triangles that your group did not make.

    b. How many different triangles did your class find altogether? Do you think that these are all the possible arrangements? How could you find out?

    c. Look at the last two columns in the *Triangle Table*. What do you notice about the relationship between the sum of the areas of the smaller squares and the area of the largest square for an acute triangle? a right triangle? an obtuse triangle?

▶ A triangle may appear to be a right triangle even if it is not. If you know the side lengths of a triangle, you can tell what type of triangle it is.

EXAMPLE

Tell whether a triangle with side lengths of 12 in., 16 in. and 21 in. is a right triangle.

SAMPLE RESPONSE

$(12)^2 + (16)^2 \overset{?}{=} (21)^2$

$144 + 256 \neq 441$

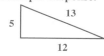 For a right triangle, if you square the lengths of the two shorter sides and add the results, the sum must equal the length of the longest side squared.

This triangle is not a right triangle.

---

7 Is the triangle in the Example *obtuse* or *acute*? Explain.
    Sample Response: obtuse; $12^2 + 16^2 < 21^2$

8 ✔ **CHECKPOINT** Tell whether a triangle with the given side lengths is *acute*, *right*, or *obtuse*.

    a. 11 cm, 13 cm, 20 cm obtuse   **b.** 16 mm, 18 mm, 10 mm acute

    c. 17 in., 15 in., 8 in. right   **d.** 6.5 cm, 4.2 cm, 7.9 cm obtuse

9 Give the side lengths of a triangle (other than a 3-4-5 triangle) that the Egyptian rope stretchers could have used to form a right angle. Sketch a picture of a rope triangle with these new side lengths.

HOMEWORK EXERCISES ▶ See Exs. 1–7 on p. 344.

FOR▶HELP

with *classifying triangles*, see **TOOLBOX, p. 593**

6. c. The sum of the areas of the smaller squares is greater than the area of the largest square; The sum of the areas of the smaller squares is equal to the area of the largest square; The sum of the areas of the smaller squares is less than the area of the largest square.

9. Sample Response:

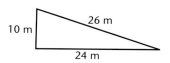

✔ **QUESTION 8**

...checks that you can use the lengths of the sides of a triangle to determine what type of triangle it is.

CLASSROOM MANAGEMENT

For **Question 5**, students should assign each member of the group specific roles as they fill in the *Triangle Table* on **Labsheet 3A**. Roles may include:
- label sides
- give length of each triangle side
- record results in table
- calculate area of squares in column 2
- identify types of triangles for column 5

TEACHING NOTES

Question 6 You may want to make an overhead of the Triangle Table from Labsheet 3A to display results for class discussion. For part (b) it is not necessary to find ALL arrangements of sides, however students should describe a process such as an organized list that would enable them to do so.

Use the following Classroom Example to support the Example on this page and prior to completing **Checkpoint Question 8**.

CLASSROOM EXAMPLE

Is the triangle a right triangle? Justify.

```
        26 m
10 m  /|
     / |
    /__|
    24 m
```

Answer:

$(10)^2 + (24)^2 \overset{?}{=} (26)^2$

$100 + 576 \overset{?}{=} 676$

$676 = 676$

The triangle is a right triangle.

339

I. M. Pei is a Chinese American architect who has designed many famous modern buildings around the world, including the East Building of the National Gallery in Washington, D.C. which makes use of a cluster of glass pyramids. You may want students to research this building for photos.

TEACHING NOTES

Encourage students to identify some of the many right triangles in the photo of the Louvre Museum on this page.

Question 10 If students are having trouble writing an equation to restate the theorem, refer them back to the *Triangle Table* from Exploration 1.

GOAL

LEARN HOW TO...
◆ use the Pythagorean theorem to find an unknown side length of a right triangle

AS YOU...
◆ explore the dimensions of the I.M. Pei Pyramid

KEY TERMS
◆ Pythagorean theorem
◆ hypotenuse
◆ leg

Exploration 2

The PYTHAGOREAN Theorem

Architect I.M. Pei designed a pyramid as part of the Louvre Museum in Paris, France. The pyramid, shown below, utilizes many right triangles in its structure. In his design, the architect relied on the work of Pythagoras, a Greek mathematician who made an important discovery about right triangles.

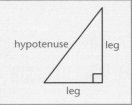

The **Pythagorean theorem** says that in a right triangle the square of the length of the *hypotenuse* is equal to the sum of the squares of the lengths of the *legs*. The **hypotenuse** is the side opposite the right angle. The **legs** are the sides adjacent to the right angle.

10 **Try This as a Class** Use the diagram above.

    a. Let *a* and *b* represent the lengths of the legs of the right triangle. Let *c* represent the length of the hypotenuse. Restate the Pythagorean theorem as an equation relating *a*, *b*, and *c*.
$a^2 + b^2 = c^2$

    b. Suppose you know the length of each leg in a right triangle. How can you use the equation you wrote in part (a) to find the length of the hypotenuse? **Square the length of each leg, add them, and then find the square root of the sum.**

11 ✔ **CHECKPOINT** A skateboard ramp has a height of 3 ft on one side and extends 13 ft along the ground. What is the approximate distance a skateboarder will travel from the top to the bottom of the ramp? *about 13.34 ft*

▶ You can use the Pythagorean theorem to find the length of one side of a right triangle if you know the lengths of the other two sides.

EXAMPLE

Use the Pythagorean theorem to find the unknown side length of the triangle below.

SAMPLE RESPONSE

The hypotenuse is given, so you need to find the length of one leg.

Let a = the unknown side length.

$$a^2 + b^2 = c^2$$
$$a^2 + 9^2 = 17^2$$
$$a^2 + 81 = 289$$
$$a^2 + 81 - 81 = 289 - 81$$
$$a^2 = 208$$
$$a \approx 14.42$$

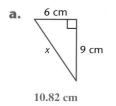

The length of the unknown side is about 14.42 cm.

Use the Example to answer Questions 12–14.

12 How can you tell from looking at the triangle that the unknown side length is a leg of the triangle, and not the hypotenuse? *Sample Response: It is adjacent to the right angle, not opposite it.*

13 In the equations in the Example, why was 81 subtracted from both sides before solving for a? *Sample Response: To isolate the variable on one side of the equation.*

14 Why is the length of the third side not an exact measurement? *The sum 208 is not a perfect square.*

15 ✔ **CHECKPOINT** For each triangle, find the unknown side length. Round to the nearest hundredth.

a.
6 cm
x 9 cm
10.82 cm

b.
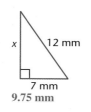
141 m
x
100 m
99.40 m

c.
x 12 mm
7 mm
9.75 mm

FOR◄HELP
with *square roots*, see
MODULE 3, p. 163

✔ **QUESTION 11**

...checks that you can use the Pythagorean theorem to find the length of the hypotenuse of a right triangle.

✔ **QUESTION 15**

...checks that you can use the Pythagorean theorem to find an unknown side length.

COMMON ERROR

Question 13 addresses a common error students make in solving equations involving square roots. Some students may think they can find the square root of each term in the equation before they isolate the variable. This faulty reasoning is based on the misconception that the square root of a number is equivalent to the sum of the square roots of two numbers whose sum equals the original number.

Use a simpler problem to clarify this concept. For example, $25 = 9 + 16$, but $\sqrt{25} \neq \sqrt{9} + \sqrt{16}$.

TEACHING NOTES

Checkpoint Question 15 Make sure students show all their work to help you more precisely identify errors in applying the Pythagorean theorem.

Before completing the **Checkpoint**, you may want students to work the following example.

CLASSROOM EXAMPLE

Use the Pythagorean theorem to find the unknown side length in the triangle below.

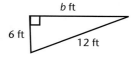

Answer: The hypotenuse is given, so the length of one leg needs to be found. Let b = the unknown side length.

$$6^2 + b^2 = 12^2$$
$$36 + b^2 = 144$$
$$36 - 36 + b^2 = 144 - 36$$
$$b^2 = 108$$
$$\sqrt{b^2} = \sqrt{108}$$
$$b \approx 10.39$$

The length of the unknown side is about 10.39 ft.

DEVELOPING MATH CONCEPTS

If your students are comfortable solving problems using the equation $a^2 + b^2 = c^2$, you might want to discuss using the other equations in the same "family" of equations.

$$a^2 = c^2 - b^2$$
$$b^2 = c^2 - a^2$$

Students who are ready may want to try applying one of these equations to the *Classroom Example* problem found on the previous page.

DIFFERENTIATED INSTRUCTION

Visual and tactile learners may need a concrete model to see that the height of a face of a pyramid is the hypotenuse of another right triangle as shown in the diagram in the **Example**. Cut two congruent isosceles triangles from index cards as shown, saving one of the gray sections.

Fold each triangle in half by folding the endpoints of the base together. In one of the triangles, start on the base and cut halfway up along the fold. In the other triangle, start at the vertex and cut about halfway down along the fold. Connect the triangles by sliding one between the other as shown below, forming two perpendicular triangles resembling the square pyramid in the example.

Show where a face of the pyramid is by placing a sheet of colored acetate across two edges or by cutting a triangle to form the face of the pyramid. Finally, trim the reserved section of note card and slide it into place as in the example so that students see that the hypotenuse of this triangle is the height of a triangular face of the pyramid.

342

---

16 Suppose the length of the hypotenuse of a right triangle is $\sqrt{90}$, and the lengths of the legs are equal. Find the length of the legs. Round your answer to the nearest hundredth. **6.71**

▶ The Louvre pyramid is a square pyramid. The height of the pyramid is 71 ft and each side of the base is 116 ft long. The *slant height* of the pyramid is the height of each of the faces. You can use the Pythagorean theorem to find the slant height.

EXAMPLE

To find the slant height of the Louvre pyramid:

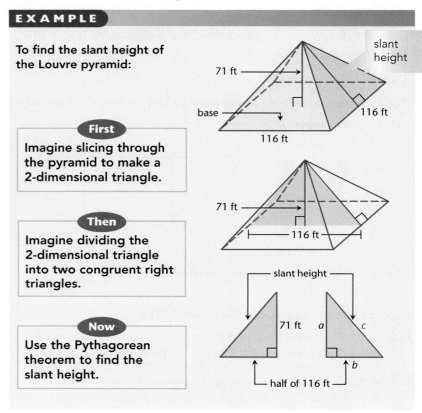

First
Imagine slicing through the pyramid to make a 2-dimensional triangle.

Then
Imagine dividing the 2-dimensional triangle into two congruent right triangles.

Now
Use the Pythagorean theorem to find the slant height.

17 **Try This as a Class** Use the Example above.

  a. Use the Pythagorean theorem to find the length of the hypotenuse of one of the congruent right triangles. $\sqrt{8405}$ ft

  b. Find the slant height of the Louvre pyramid to the nearest foot.
  About 92 ft

  c. Now that you know the slant height of the pyramid, explain how you can find the area of one triangular face of the pyramid. Find $\frac{1}{2}bh$ where $b = 116$ ft and $h = 92$ ft.

HOMEWORK EXERCISES ▶ See Exs. 8–21 on pp. 344–346.

Key Concepts

Side Lengths of Triangles (pp. 338–339)

If you know the side lengths of a triangle, you can identify it as acute, right, or obtuse. Let c equal the length of the longest side of the triangle and a and b equal the lengths of the two shorter sides.

If $a^2 + b^2 > c^2$, then the triangle is acute.

If $a^2 + b^2 = c^2$, then the triangle is right.

If $a^2 + b^2 < c^2$, then the triangle is obtuse.

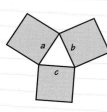 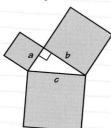 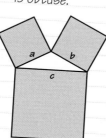

The Pythagorean Theorem (pp. 340–342)

In a right triangle, the sum of the squares of the lengths of the **legs** is equal to the square of the length of the **hypotenuse**, the longest side of the triangle. This relationship is known as the Pythagorean theorem.

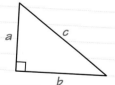

$$a^2 + b^2 = c^2$$

Key Terms

Pythagorean theorem

leg

hypotenuse

Key Concepts Question

18 Yuka drew a right triangle and labeled the side lengths as shown. Assume the legs are labeled correctly. Explain why the hypotenuse must be labeled incorrectly. Then use the lengths of the legs to find the correct length of the hypotenuse.

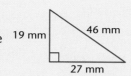

19 Is a triangle with side lengths of 5.4 cm, 9.2 cm, and 7.8 cm *acute*, *right*, or *obtuse*? acute

Key Concepts

CLOSURE QUESTIONS

How can you use the lengths of the sides of a triangle to determine whether the triangle is acute, obtuse or right?

When can you use the Pythagorean theorem and what does it tell you?

Sample Response: Find the sum of the squares of the lengths of the shorter sides of the triangle. If this sum is *less than* the square of the length of the longest side, the triangle is obtuse. If the sum is *greater than* the square of the length of the longest side, the triangle is acute. If the sum is to *equal* the square of the length of the longest side, the triangle is a right triangle.

If a triangle is a right triangle, you can use the Pythagorean theorem to find the length of one of the sides given the lengths of the other two sides.

ABSENT STUDENTS

For students who were absent for part or all of this section, the blackline Study Guide for Section 3 may be used to present the ideas, concepts, and skills of Section 3.

18. In a triangle, the sum of the lengths of the shorter sides must be greater than the length of the longest side, but $19^2 + 27^2 = 1090$ and $46^2 = 2116$ so the hypotenuse must be labeled incorrectly.; $\sqrt{1090} \approx 33.02$ mm

Practice & Applications

ADDITIONAL PRACTICE

See the *Teacher's Resource Book* for additional practice and application exercises for this section.

EXERCISE NOTES

Exercise 14 Some students may need to draw a diagram showing compass directions on their graph paper to help them visualize the directions, north, south, east, and west.

COMMON ERROR

Exercise 15 Some students may think the solution is related to the area or circumference of the trampoline rather than to its diameter. You might suggest that they sketch the door first and then have them show how they would tilt a trampoline to make it fit.

344

---

7. Sample Response: Yes; the square root of the sum of the squares of the legs is about 20.81, which is close to 21. Allowing for measurement errors, the angle is probably a right angle.

14.

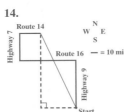

About 121 mi

Section 3
Practice & Application Exercises

Tell whether a triangle with the given side lengths is *acute*, *right*, or *obtuse*.

1. 5 cm, 12 cm, 13 cm right
2. 5 mm, 9 mm, 7 mm obtuse
3. 8 in., 10 in., 9 in. acute
4. 11.5 m, 6.2 m, 7 m obtuse
5. 16 cm, 20 cm, 17 cm acute
6. 15 mm, 12 mm, 9 mm right

7. **Carpentry** Carpenters can use a method like the one used by the rope stretchers of ancient Egypt to check whether a corner is "square." For example, a carpenter took the measurements shown to check a right angle on a table. Is the angle opposite the 21 in. diagonal a right angle? Explain your thinking.

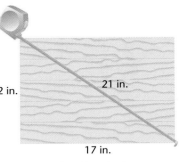

For each right triangle, find the unknown side length. Give each answer to the nearest hundredth if necessary.

8. 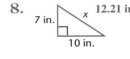 12.21 in.

9. 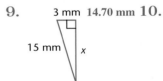 14.70 mm

10. 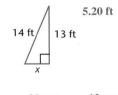 5.20 ft

11.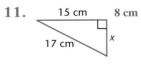

12.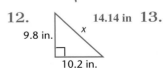

13.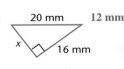

14. **Visual Thinking** Sharon Ramirez receives directions for a party. Use graph paper to sketch Sharon's route. Draw a single segment connecting Sharon's house and her friend's house. Find the distance represented by the segment.

Hey Sharon!
Here are the directions to the party!
Hope you can make it!
First drive 70 mi north on Highway 9.
Then drive 80 mi west on Route 16.
Then drive 40 mi north on Highway 7.
Then drive 30 mi east on Route 14.

15. Can a circular trampoline with a diameter of 16 ft fit through a doorway that is 10 ft high and 8 ft wide? (Assume that the legs of the trampoline can be removed.) Explain your answer. No; the diagonal of the door opening is only about 12.81 ft.

344

16. The size of a television set is indicated by the length (to the nearest inch) of a diagonal of the screen.

a. Which of the following would be considered a 30 in. TV?

b. A store advertises a 25 in. TV with an aspect ratio of 4:3. That means that the ratio of the width of the screen to its length is 4:3. Find the length and width of the screen. Explain your method.

17. Architecture Many building codes specify that the ratio of the rise of a stair to its tread cannot exceed the ratio 3:4.

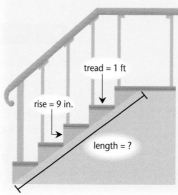

a. Find the ratio of the rise to the tread on the staircase shown. Does the staircase shown follow the building code described above?
Yes; 9 in.:12 in. = 3:4

b. What is the length of the line along the staircase shown? 75 in.

c. **Research** Measure the rise and the tread of a stair in your home or school. Find the ratio of the rise to the tread. Does the staircase follow the building code described above? Answers will vary.

18. The Transamerica Pyramid, located in San Francisco, California, has a shape that approximates a square pyramid with wing-like structures on two of the triangular faces. The pyramid has a height of 853 ft and a base length of 175 ft. Suppose a spider crawls up one of the two faces of the pyramid that have no wings. The spider starts at the bottom and crawls to the top along the slant height of the pyramid. How far does the spider crawl? About 857.48 ft

19. Challenge Find the next 3 terms in the sequence 3, 4, 5, 6, 8, 10, 9, 12, 15, ... Explain how you got your answer.
12, 16, 20; The pattern is 1 × 3, 1 × 4, 1 × 5, 2 × 3, 2 × 4, 2 × 5, 3 × 3, 3 × 4, 3 × 5, 4 × 3, 4 × 4, 4 × 5, ...

16. a. The 26 in. by 15 in. television

16. b. Sample Response: 15 × 20 in.; I considered reasonable widths for a television screen, then multiplied by $\frac{4}{3}$ to find the length. I tried 18 in. but a 24 in. by 18 in. screen would have a diagonal of 30 in. So I tried a length of 15 in., which resulted in a 15 in. × 20 in. screen, which has a 25 in. diagonal.

EXERCISE NOTES
Exercise 17(b) The line in the diagram represents the distance along the staircase and is the sum of the lengths of the hypotenuses of the right triangles formed by each stair.

Exercise 19 can be solved in many different ways including using right triangles, finding patterns in the differences between terms, or by using trial and error. You may want to have students compare the methods they used.

Practice & Applications

EXERCISE NOTES

In the **Reflecting on the Section Exercise 21**, students write a speech explaining the usefulness of the Pythagorean theorem. Those having trouble getting started can be referred back to **Exercise 14** and asked to think about finding the distance between two points that cannot actually be measured. They should be encouraged to think of the work done by a surveyor, geologist, astronomer, or architect and the applications of the Pythagorean theorem to their work.

Extension Exercise 28(c) Suggest that students do a web search for the "Pythagorean theorem." There are numerous informative sites available written in "kid friendly" language.

28. b. Sample Response: The square of the length of a side of a triangle is equal to the area of the square constructed on that side. So the fact that the combined area of the two smaller squares is equal to the area of the largest square shows that the sum of the squares of the legs of the right triangle is equal to the square of the hypotenuse. This is the Pythagorean theorem.

---

20. A maintenance worker needs to repair a light fixture mounted on a building. She leans a 20 ft ladder against the building with the foot of the ladder 5 ft from the building. How far up the building does the ladder reach? Round your answer to the nearest hundredth. **19.36 ft**

Oral Report

Exercise 21 checks that you can explain how to use the Pythagorean theorem.

Reflecting ◀▶ on the Section

21. Imagine you just discovered the relationship among the side lengths of a right triangle. Unfortunately, no one believes your discovery is very important. Write a persuasive speech explaining how useful your discovery is. Make visual aids to use with your speech. **Answers will vary.**

Spiral ◀▶ Review

Estimate the square root to the nearest tenth. (Module 3, p. 163)

22. $\sqrt{57}$ **7.5**   23. $\sqrt{148}$ **12.2**   24. $\sqrt{12}$ **3.5**

25. Find the surface area of a can with a diameter of 7 cm and height of 13 cm. (Module 4, p. 251) **362.67 cm²**

There are 7 red apples and 5 green apples in a paper bag.
(Module 2, p. 114)

26. What is the probability of drawing a red apple at random? $\frac{7}{12}$

27. Suppose a green apple is drawn first and not replaced. What is the probability of getting a green apple on a second draw? $\frac{4}{11}$

Extension ▶ ▶

A Pythagorean Puzzle

28. **Use Labsheet 3B.** Hundreds of proofs have been written for the Pythagorean theorem. Many are in the form of diagrams that illustrate the theorem. Follow the directions on the labsheet to complete a *Pythagorean Puzzle*.

   a. What do you notice about the relationship between the two smaller squares and the large one you built? **The combined area of the two smaller squares is equal to the area of the largest square.**

   b. How might this puzzle be used to justify the Pythagorean theorem? **See margin.**

   c. Through research, see if you can find other ways to "prove" the Pythagorean theorem. **Answers will vary.**

Section ③

Extra Skill Practice

For Exercises 1–4, tell whether a triangle with the given side lengths is *acute,* *right,* **or** *obtuse.*

1. 6 in., 12 in., 14 in. obtuse

2. 7.5 m, 18 m, 19.5 m right

3. 8 mm, 10 mm, 12.8 mm acute

4. 21 ft, 25 ft, 33 ft obtuse

For each triangle, find the unknown side length. Round each answer to the nearest hundredth if necessary.

5.
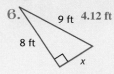
8.31 in.
13 in.
x
10 in.

6.
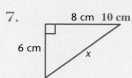
9 ft   4.12 ft
8 ft
x

7.
8 cm   10 cm
6 cm
x

Tell whether the given side lengths could be the side lengths of a right triangle. Explain why or why not.

8. 4.5 cm, 6 cm, 7.5 cm Yes; $4.5^2 + 6^2 = 7.5^2$

9. 3 in., 3 in., 5 in. No; $3^2 + 3^2 \neq 5^2$

10. 2.5 m, 6 m, 6.5 m Yes; $2.5^2 + 6^2 = 6.5^2$

11. 6 m, 6 m, 10 m No; $6^2 + 6^2 \neq 10^2$

12. a. Find the exact length of the hypotenuse of each right triangle in the spiral at the right. $\sqrt{5}, \sqrt{6}, \sqrt{7}, \sqrt{8}, \sqrt{9} = 3$

   b. What pattern do you notice? **The radicand increases by 1 each time.**

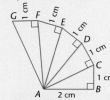

G   F   E   D   C   B
1 cm   1 cm   1 cm   1 cm
A   2 cm

Standardized Testing ◀▶ Performance Task

1. The lengths of the two shortest sides of a triangle are given. What is a possible length of the third side if the triangle is acute? right? obtuse? **Possible answers are given.**

   a. 6 cm, 4.5 cm

   b. 2 in., $5\frac{1}{2}$ in.

   1. a. acute: $6 < x < 7.5$
      right: $x = 7.5$
      obtuse: $7.5 < x < 10.5$
      b. acute: $5.5 < x < \sqrt{34.25}$
      right: $x = \sqrt{34.25}$
      obtuse: $\sqrt{34.25} < x < 7.5$

2. Find the combined area of all four triangular faces of the pyramid. Assume the triangular faces are congruent. **48 ft²**

   5 ft
   3 ft
   3 ft

Extra Skill Practice

TEACHER NOTES
For each Exploration, the corresponding Extra Skills Practice Exercises are noted.

Exploration 1: Exs. 1–4
Exploration 2: Exs. 5–12

Note: Although students may be able to work Exercises 5–11 following Exploration 1, it is recommended that they wait until the completion of Exploration 2.

EXTRA HELP
Teacher's Resource Book
• Practice and Applications
• Study Guide

Technology Resources
• @Home Tutor
• Test Generator

ASSESSMENT
• Section 3 Quick Quiz
• Mid-Module Quiz
• Test Generator

Setting the Stage

ABOUT THE THEME

Some of the earliest "architects" were the indigenous people who built homes using the materials that were readily available to them. These structures were designed to easily incorporate the available materials as well as to fit the needs of the people. Ask students to think of homes they have studied such as the tepee, grass hut, adobe dwelling, etc. In our modern times of manufactured materials, homes take on varied sizes and shapes. A goal of many home designs is to obtain the most living space using the least amount of material possible. In this section, students will find surface areas and volumes of prisms and pyramids and explore the relationships between them.

GETTING STARTED

This section applies concepts of three-dimensional figures and nets. Module 5, Section 4 *Warm-Up* assess that students have a grasp of these basic concepts.

Section 4 Surface Area and Volume

IN THIS SECTION

EXPLORATION 1
♦ Surface Areas of Prisms and Pyramids

EXPLORATION 2
♦ Volumes of Prisms, Pyramids, and Cones

Where You Live

Setting the Stage

People around the world build homes to keep them safe and comfortable in their environments. The design of the buildings and the materials used for construction depend on local conditions. In the passage below from *Black Star, Bright Dawn* by Scott O'Dell, Bright Dawn describes how she and her friends Katy and Oteg made an igloo.

Black Star, Bright Dawn
by Scott O'Dell

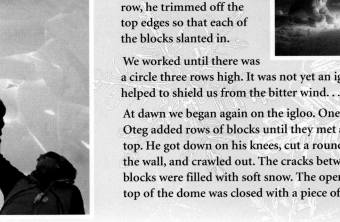

I had helped to make an igloo at school, so I showed her how to cut the blocks. I handed them to Oteg and he put them side by side in a circle. When he had one row, he trimmed off the top edges so that each of the blocks slanted in.

We worked until there was a circle three rows high. It was not yet an igloo, but it helped to shield us from the bitter wind. . .

At dawn we began again on the igloo. One by one Oteg added rows of blocks until they met above the top. He got down on his knees, cut a round hole in the wall, and crawled out. The cracks between the blocks were filled with soft snow. The opening at the top of the dome was closed with a piece of clear ice.

Think About It

1 Igloos have a dome shape that encloses a large volume for a given surface area.

    a. What does *volume* mean?   **b.** What does *surface area* mean?

    c. What do volume and surface area tell you about a structure?

2 Why would it be desirable to have a large volume compared to the surface area? **to provide maximum space with minimum amount and cost of materials, or the minimum exposure to the outside**

Exploration 1 ·····························►►►►►►►►►►►

SURFACE AREAS of PRISMS and PYRAMIDS

SET UP   *You will need: • Labsheet 4A • metric ruler • scissors*

Long ago, people did not always have a choice of building materials. In the Southwest, *adobe houses* were built from baked mud bricks because mud was usually available. Rooms of an adobe house were built roughly in the shape of a rectangular prism.

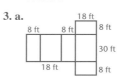

30 ft · 8 ft · 18 ft

3 **a.** Sketch a net for the rectangular prism shown above. Use the dimensions shown to label the length of each edge of the net.

   b. The surface area of the prism is the total area of all six faces, including the bases. Find the area of each face of the prism. Then find the surface area of the prism. **240 + 540 + 240 + 540 +144 +144; *S.A.* = 1848 ft²**

1. a. Volume is the number of cubic units required to fill a 3-dimensional figure.

   b. Surface area is the total area of all faces of a 3-dimensional figure.

   c. They tell you the capacity of the structure and the amount of material required to cover the outside.

3. a.

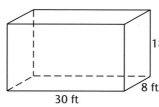

8 ft · 8 ft · 18 ft · 8 ft · 30 ft · 18 ft · 8 ft

Section 4   Surface Area and Volume

Exploration 1

TEACHING NOTES
Question 3 It helps to have students write the area of each rectangular face on their net. This way students can easily check their work with other students and identify any errors in calculating the surface areas.

DEVELOPING MATH CONCEPTS
Help students recognize that the photo on this page shows a figure in perspective. The diagram shows the actual shape of the structure. Refer them to Section 1 where they explored different views of buildings to help them connect the diagram to the photo.

Exploration 1 *continued*

TEACHING NOTES
Following **Question 4,** you may want to present the following Classroom Example to your class.

CLASSROOM EXAMPLE

Find the surface area of the trapezoidal prism shown.

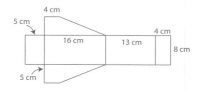

Answer:

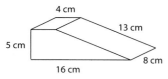

S.A. = areas of trapezoids + areas of rectangles

$$= 2\left[\frac{1}{2}(16+4)5\right] + (5 \cdot 8) +$$
$$(13 \cdot 8) + (4 \cdot 8) + (16 \cdot 8)$$

$$= 100 + 40 + 104 + 32 + 128$$

$$= 404$$

The surface area of the trapezoidal prism is 404 cm².

TEACHING NOTES

Question 7 Have students measure to the nearest centimeter. Again, it is helpful for students to make a habit of writing the area of each face on the net when finding surface areas.

5. a.

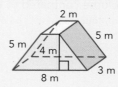

b.

▶ You can find the surface area (*S.A.*) of any prism by adding the areas of all the faces.

EXAMPLE

To find the surface area of the trapezoidal prism shown, you need to use the formula $A = \frac{1}{2}(b_1 + b_2)h$ for the area A of a trapezoid with height h and base lengths b_1 and b_2.

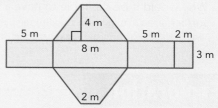

S.A. = areas of trapezoids + areas of rectangles

$$= 2\left[\frac{1}{2}(8+2)4\right] + (5 \cdot 3) + (8 \cdot 3) + (5 \cdot 3) + (2 \cdot 3)$$

$$= 40 + 15 + 24 + 15 + 6$$

$$= 100$$

The surface area of the trapezoidal prism is 100 m².

4 Discussion

a. In the example, why is the figure called a trapezoidal prism?
The bases are trapezoids and all other faces are rectangles.

b. How is sketching the net of a figure helpful in finding its surface area? Sample Response: It helps you to see the shape of each face whose area you need to find. It can also be helpful for labeling the dimensions.

5 Sketch a net for each prism. Label the length of each edge.

a.   **b.**

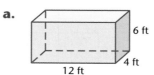   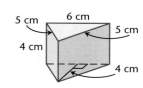

✔ QUESTION 6

...checks that you can find the surface area of a prism.

6 ✔ CHECKPOINT Find the surface area of each prism in Question 5. **a.** 288 ft² **b.** 88 cm²

▶ Surface Area of a Pyramid You can use a method similar to the one in the Example to find the surface area of a pyramid.

7 Use Labsheet 4A. Follow the directions to make a square pyramid.
Check students' work. The base edge is 6 cm, and the triangle height is 5 cm. *SA* = 96 cm²

▶ The pyramid in Question 7 is a **regular pyramid**, because the base is a regular polygon and its other faces are congruent isosceles triangles. The **slant height** of a regular pyramid is the height of a triangular face.

8 Try This as a Class

a. How is the slant height of the pyramid different from the height of the pyramid?

b. Explain how to use the slant height of the pyramid, the length of an edge of the base, and the Pythagorean theorem to find the height of the pyramid. Then find the height.

c. Measure the height of your pyramid. How does the height you calculated in part (b) compare with your measurement?
$h = 4$ cm; They are the same.

d. Did you need the height of the pyramid to find its surface area? Explain. No, for the surface area you only need the length of the base and the slant height.

▶ The surface area of a regular pyramid can be found using the height of one of the triangular faces.

8. a. Sample Response: The height of the pyramid is perpendicular to the base of the pyramid, the slant height is not. The slant height is the length of the hypotenuse of a right triangle that has the height of the pyramid as one leg.

b. The pyramid's height, the slant height, and a segment equal in length to half the edge of the base form a right triangle. Use the Pythagorean theorem and solve for the length of the missing leg, which is the pyramid's height; $h = 4$ cm.

EXAMPLE

Find the surface area of the square pyramid.

SAMPLE RESPONSE

Use the Pythagorean theorem to find the slant height, c.

$$5^2 + 12^2 = c^2$$
$$169 = c^2$$
$$13 = c$$

$$S.A. = \left(\begin{array}{c}\text{area of}\\\text{base}\end{array}\right) + 4 \times \left(\begin{array}{c}\text{area of one}\\\text{triangular face}\end{array}\right)$$

$$= 10 \cdot 10 + 4\left(\frac{1}{2} \cdot 10 \cdot 13\right)$$

$$= 100 + 260$$

$$= 360$$

The surface area of the square pyramid is 360 m².

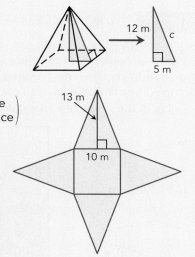

DEVELOPING MATH CONCEPTS

As students complete **Question 8** they should see the difference between the height of the pyramid and the height of one of the triangular faces. In **part (b)** students may need to refer back to Section 3 where they used the Pythagorean theorem to find the missing height of one face on a pyramid. Help them see that they can use the Pythagorean theorem to find the height of the pyramid when the height of a face and the length of the base of the imbedded triangle are known. Students learn that the pyramid's height is not needed to calculate the surface area, but it will be important in Exploration 2 when they find the volumes of pyramids and cones.

TEACHING NOTES

In **Question 8(c)**, students are asked to measure the height of the pyramid they constructed. Since they will not be able to measure the height through the center as shown in the Example, students will need to devise another method. They might choose to stand a ruler perpendicular to their desk while laying another across the apex of the pyramid to read the height of the pyramid.

CLASSROOM EXAMPLE

Find the surface area of the tetrahedron shown where all edges are 6 ft long.

Answer: Use the Pythagorean theorem to find the height of one of the triangles.

$3^2 + h^2 = 6^2$

$9 + h^2 = 36$

$9 - 9 + h^2 = 36 - 9$

$h^2 = 27$

$\sqrt{h^2} = \sqrt{27}$

$h \approx 5.2$

S.A. = 4(area of one of the triangles)

$\approx 4\left[\frac{1}{2}(6)(5.2)\right]$

≈ 62.4

The surface area of the tetrahedron is about 62.4 ft².

Exploration 2

DEVELOPING MATH CONCEPTS

Before beginning **Exploration 2**, review the difference between area and volume, and discuss a method for finding the volume of a rectangular prism and a cylinder.

---

9 **Discussion**

a. Why is it necessary to find the slant height of the pyramid in the Example on page 351 in order to calculate the surface area of the pyramid? **So you can find the area of each triangle using the formula $A = bh$.**

b. In the Example, a right triangle is used to find the slant height of the pyramid. The length of one leg of this triangle is the height of the pyramid. Explain why the length of the other leg is 5 m. **The other leg is half the length of the base. So half of 10 m = 5 m.**

✔ **QUESTION 10**

...checks that you can find the surface area of a pyramid.

10 ✔ **CHECKPOINT** Find the surface area of each square pyramid.

a.
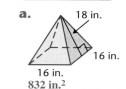
18 in.

16 in.

16 in.

832 in.²

b.
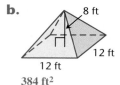
8 ft

12 ft

12 ft

384 ft²

c.

20 cm

17.5 cm

17.5 cm

1006.25 cm²

HOMEWORK EXERCISES ▶ See Exs. 1–8 on p. 357.

GOAL

LEARN HOW TO...
◆ find volumes of prisms, pyramids, and cones

AS YOU...
◆ look at models of block pyramids and prisms

KEY TERM
◆ circular cone

Exploration 2

VOLUMES of PRISMS, PYRAMIDS, and CONES

SET UP You will need Labsheet 4B.

Winter *mat houses* were once used by people living in the Plateau region of the northwestern United States. These homes were usually occupied from mid-October to mid-March. A mat house was built roughly in the shape of a triangular prism.

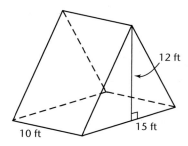
12 ft

10 ft

15 ft

11 In Module 4 you learned how to use the formula

Volume = area of base × height, or $V = Bh$

to find the volume of a cylinder or a rectangular prism. This formula can also be used to find volumes of prisms with other bases.

a. Discussion How can you use this formula to find the volume of the triangular prism on page 352?

b. Calculate the volume of the triangular prism. **900 ft³**

11. a. Find the area of the triangular base using $A = \frac{1}{2}bh$. Then multiply by the height of the prism, which is 10 ft.

▶ **Volume of a Pyramid** The Great Pyramid of Giza is made from blocks of stone. The sides are jagged, but they look smooth when viewed from afar, as if the block pyramid had straight edges and flat faces. Now you will look at block pyramids and block prisms to discover the relationship between the volume of a pyramid and the volume of a prism with the same base and height.

Use Labsheet 4B for Questions 12–14.

12 Follow the directions on the labsheet to complete the *Table of Volumes*. **See margin.**

13 Look at the Volume Ratio column of the table. What patterns do you notice in the values? **As the height increases, the ratio decreases.**

14 **Discussion** If the last column of the table were continued, the ratio for the 50th entry would be 0.343 and the ratio for the 100th entry would be 0.338. What "nice" fraction do the ratios appear to be approaching? $\frac{1}{3}$

15 **Try This as a Class** Use your answer to Question 14.

a. The volume of a prism is about how many times the volume of a pyramid that has the same base and height? **about 3 times**

b. Using V for the volume, B for the area of the base, and h for the height, write a formula for the volume of a pyramid. $V = \frac{1}{3}Bh$

c. Use your formula from part (b) to find the volume of a pyramid that has the same base and height as the triangular prism on page 352. **300 ft³** (Be sure the students use the triangular base of the prism as the base of the pyramid.)

16 ✔ **CHECKPOINT** Find the volume of each 3-dimensional figure.

a. triangular prism **60 cm³**

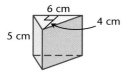

b. square pyramid **243 ft³**

✔ **QUESTION 16**

...checks that you can find volumes of prisms and pyramids.

ALTERNATIVE APPROACH
Question 14 As students discuss the patterns they notice in the labsheet table, they are to predict what "nice" fraction the ratio is approaching. The data in the table on **Labsheet 4B** can be converted to a spreadsheet allowing students to easily view ratios up to the 100th entry. This enables students to see that the ratios are approaching 0.33333 or $\frac{1}{3}$.

TIPS FROM TEACHERS
Question 16 Encourage students to write down the formula they will use for finding the volume of each figure before they begin solving the problems.

12. See Additional Answers beginning on page A1.

353

▶ **Volume of a Cone** The relationship between the volume of a cone and the volume of a cylinder with the same base and height is the same as the relationship between the volume of a pyramid and the volume of a prism with the same base and height.

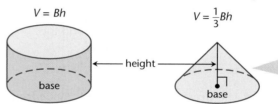

$V = Bh$ $V = \frac{1}{3}Bh$

height

base   base

> A **circular cone** is a 3-dimensional figure with a circular base and a vertex that are not in the same plane.

▶ **All the cones in this book have circular bases. You can refer to them as cones rather than as *circular cones*.**

17 Try This as a Class

a. How would you find the area of the base of a cone?
   Square its radius and multiply by π.

b. Write a formula for the volume of a cone in terms of the radius of the base *r* and the height *h*. $V = \frac{1}{3}\pi r^2 h$

c. The radius of the base of a cone is 5 ft, and the height of the cone is 10 ft. Use the formula you wrote in part (b) to find the volume of the cone. 261.67 ft³

---

18 ✔ **CHECKPOINT** The shape of tepees used by Native American peoples on the Great Plains resembles a cone. A typical tepee might have stood 18 ft high and had a diameter of 15 ft at its base. Estimate the volume of such a tepee. about 1059.75 ft³

▶ **Most buildings are made up of a variety of 3-dimensional figures. The shape below is an alternate representation of a mat house. It is a triangular prism with half of a cone at either end.**

19. a. Find the sum of the volume of the cone (since the two halves make a whole cone) and the volume of the triangular prism.

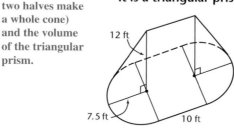

12 ft

7.5 ft   10 ft

19 a. Discussion Describe how you would find the volume of a mat house shaped like the figure above.

b. Find the volume. 1606.5 ft³

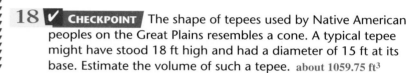

HOMEWORK EXERCISES ▶ See Exs. 9–21 on pp. 358–359.

Section 4 Key Concepts

Surface Areas of Prisms and Pyramids (pp. 349–352)

The surface area of a pyramid or a prism is the sum of the areas of the faces of the figure, including the base or bases. You can use a net to help you find the surface area.

Example

right square prism

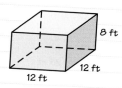

8 ft
12 ft
12 ft

net for the prism

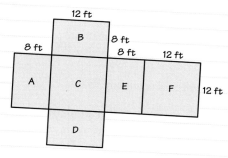

12 ft

B

8 ft
8 ft
8 ft
12 ft

A   C   E   F

12 ft

D

S.A. = area A + area B + area C + area D + area E + area F
    = (8 • 12) + (8 • 12) + (12 • 12) + (8 • 12) + (8 • 12) + (12 • 12)
    = 96 + 96 + 144 + 96 + 96 + 144
    = 672

The surface area of the prism is 672 ft².

The base of a regular pyramid is a regular polygon, and its other faces are congruent isosceles triangles. You use the slant height of a pyramid rather than the height of the pyramid to find its surface area.

regular pyramid

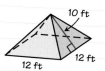

10 ft
12 ft
12 ft

Key Terms

regular pyramid

slant height

20 Key Concepts Question

a. Find the surface area of the pyramid above. 384 ft²

b. If you stack the pyramid directly on top of the prism above, what will be the surface area of the new figure? Explain.
768 ft²; The resulting figure has one 12 × 12 square face, four 12 × 8 rectangular faces and four triangular faces with base 12 and height 10.

Key Concepts

CLOSURE QUESTION

Explain how a net can be used to find the surface area of a prism or a pyramid.

Sample Response: Draw the faces and base(s) of the prism or pyramid. Find the area of each face and the base(s), then add the areas to find the total surface area.

Key Concepts

CLOSURE QUESTION
Explain the relationship between the volume of a cone and the volume of a cylinder.

Sample Response: The volume of a cone is $\frac{1}{3}$ the volume of a cylinder with the same base and height.

ABSENT STUDENTS
For students who were absent for part or all of this section, the blackline Study Guide for Section 4 may be used to present the ideas, concepts, and skills of Section 4.

Key Term

circular cone

Section 4
Key Concepts

Volumes of Prisms (p. 353)

You can use the formula Volume = area of base × height, or $V = Bh$, to find the volume of any prism. Many buildings consist of two or more 3-dimensional figures. To find the volume, you add the volumes of the parts.

Example
Volume of rectangular prism
$$V = Bh = (12 \cdot 25)18 = 5400$$

Volume of triangular prism
$$V = Bh = \left(\frac{1}{2} \cdot 12 \cdot 8\right)25 = 1200$$

The total volume is 6600 m³.

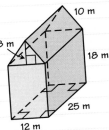

Volumes of Pyramids and Cones (pp. 353–354)

The volume of a pyramid is one-third the volume of a prism with the same base and height. The volume of a cone is one-third the volume of a cylinder with the same base and height.

The formula Volume = $\frac{1}{3}$ × area of base × height, or $V = \frac{1}{3}Bh$, can be used to find the volume of a pyramid or a cone.

Example
$$V = \frac{1}{3}Bh$$
$$= \frac{1}{3} \cdot \pi r^2 \cdot h$$
$$\approx \frac{1}{3} \cdot (3.14) \cdot 3^2 \cdot 5$$
$$\approx 47.1$$

The volume of the cone is about 47.1 m³.

21 Key Concepts Question

a. Find the volume of the prism and the volume of the pyramid on page 355. prism: 1152 ft³; pyramid: 384 ft³

b. If you stack the pyramid directly on top of the prism, what will be the volume of the new figure? 1536 ft³

Section 4

Practice & Application Exercises

YOU WILL NEED

For Exs. 27–28:
- ◆ Labsheets 4C and 4D
- ◆ scissors
- ◆ paper clip

Find the surface area of each rectangular or triangular prism. Round answers to the nearest hundredth if necessary.

1. 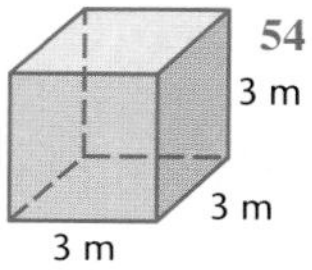 54 m² 3 m / 3 m / 3 m

2. 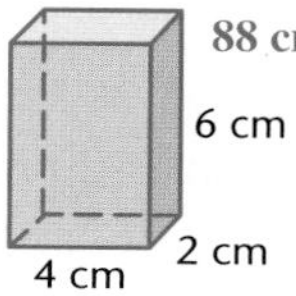 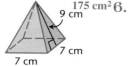 88 cm² 6 cm / 4 cm / 2 cm

3. 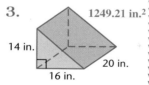 1249.21 in.² 14 in. / 16 in. / 20 in.

Find the surface area of each square pyramid. Round answers to the nearest hundredth if necessary.

4. 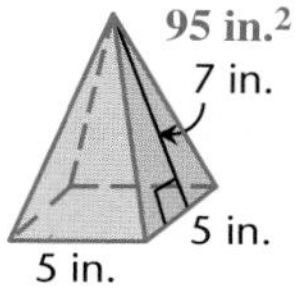 95 in.² 7 in. / 5 in. / 5 in.

5. 175 cm² 9 cm / 7 cm / 7 cm

6. 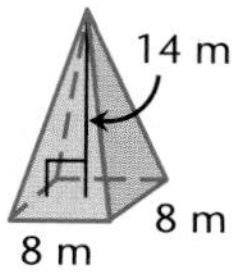 296.96 m² 14 m / 8 m / 8 m

7. **Challenge** Many products are packaged in boxes that are the shape of a rectangular prism. In some cases more unusual shapes are used. A net for a box designed to hold a desk lamp is shown.

   a. Find the surface area of the box. **576 in.²**

   b. Sketch a view of the box that looks three-dimensional.
   See margin.

   c. Find the volume of the box. **768 in.³**

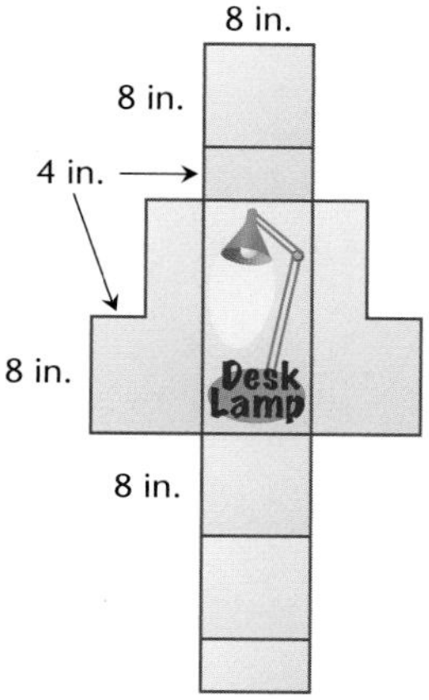

8. The figure below represents a Navajo *hogan* like the one shown in the photograph. The base is a square and the edges that form the peak of the roof are each 8 ft long.

   a What two 3-dimensional figures combine to form the figure shown? **a rectangular prism and a square pyramid**

   b. Sketch a net of the figure. Label the edges with their lengths.
   See margin.

   c. Find the surface area of the figure to the nearest hundredth.

8 in. / 8 in. / 4 in. / 8 in. / **Desk Lamp** / 8 in.

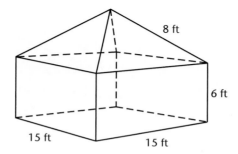

8 ft / 6 ft / 15 ft / 15 ft

8. c. about 668.52 ft²

Practice & Applications

SUGGESTED ASSIGNMENTS

Core Course
Day 1: Exs. 1–3, 22–26
Day 2: Exs. 4–6, 8
Day 3: Exs. 9–11, 17–18
Day 4: Exs. 12–16, 20–21

Extended Course
Day 1: Exs. 1–3, 22–26
Day 2: Exs. 4–8
Day 3: Exs. 9–11, 18–19
Day 4: Exs. 12–15, 20–21, 27–28*

Note: Extended Course assignments can be used to differentiate within the regular classroom. In classrooms where students are grouped homogeneously, the material might be covered in fewer days. In this case assignments may be combined.

* Extension Exercises

ADDITIONAL PRACTICE

See the *Teacher's Resource Book* for additional practice and application exercises for this section.

EXERCISE NOTES

Exercise 8(c) Students may get a surface area of 669 ft² if the height of the triangle is rounded to the nearest tenth (2.8) before calculating the areas of the triangular faces.

7. b. and 8. b. See Additional Answers beginning on page A1.

357

Practice & Applications

EXERCISE NOTES

If answers to **Exercises 12–14 and 15(b)** are based on 3.14 for π they will be slightly less than if the π key on the calculator is used. You may want to direct your students to calculate using the same method.

Exercise 16(b) Answers may vary if the slant height measure is rounded to the nearest tenth *prior to* calculating areas of the triangular faces.

Find the volume of each pyramid or cone with the given height and base. Round answers to the nearest hundredth if necessary.

9. height = 3 in.
4 in.³

2 in.
2 in.

10. height = 4 cm
5.33 cm³

2 cm
4 cm

11. height = 2 m
4.67 m³

2 m
2 m
5 m

The base is a trapezoid.

12. height = 23.5 ft
2559.04 ft³
10.2 ft

13. height = 20 mm
3014.4 mm³
12 mm

14. height = 14 yd
1186.92 yd³
18 yd

15. The diagram represents a *yurt*, which is a dwelling used by nomadic tribes. The walls of a yurt fold up, making it easy to put up and take down. It is also very weather resistant.

   a. What two 3-dimensional figures combine to form the yurt?
a cylinder and a cone

   b. Find the volume of the yurt in the diagram. 339.88 ft³

2.7 ft

4 ft

4.7 ft

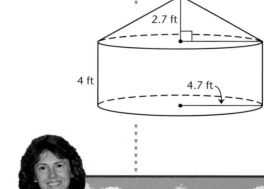

16. The Christa McAuliffe Planetarium in Concord, New Hampshire, incorporates a square pyramid in its design. Each side of the pyramid's base is 724 in. long. The height of the pyramid is 360 in.

   a. Find the volume of the pyramid.
62,901,120 in.³

   b. Find the total area of the triangular faces of the pyramid. Round your answer to the nearest hundredth.
about 739,251.86 in.²

Find the surface area and the volume of each composite figure.

17.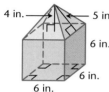
4 in. — 5 in.
6 in.
6 in.
6 in.

S.A. = 240 in.², *V* = 264 in.³

18.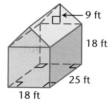
9 ft
18 ft
25 ft
18 ft

S.A. is about 2796 ft², *V* = 10,125 ft³

19. **Challenge** Find the surface area and the volume of the figure at the right. (*Hint*: The heights of the triangles are different.)
S.A. is about 443 in.², *V* = 640 in.³

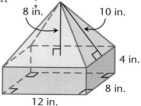
8 in. — 10 in.
4 in.
8 in.
12 in.

20. **Open-ended** Sketch a 3-dimensional figure made up of two or more 3-dimensional figures. Then sketch a net of the figure. Find its surface area and volume. Answers will vary. Check students' work.

Reflecting on the Section

Write your response to Exercise 21 in your journal.

21. Draw a sketch of a house that you have seen. Describe how you can estimate its surface area and volume. Explain why the surface area and volume might be useful information about the house.

Journal

Exercise 21 checks that you understand surface area and volume.

21. Answers will vary. Check students' work. Surface area may be helpful in siding or painting the exterior and wallpapering or painting the interior. Volume might be used to determine size of air conditioning or heating unit that needs to be installed to heat or cool a house of that size.

22. not congruent; Corresponding sides $\overline{PR}$ and $\overline{DF}$ are not congruent.

Spiral Review

Tell whether the triangles in each pair are congruent. Explain your reasoning. (Module 5, p. 330)

22. △FED, △RQP

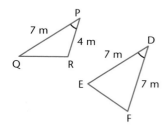
P
7 m
4 m
D
Q
R
7 m
E
7 m
F

23. △WZX, △YZX congruent; SAS

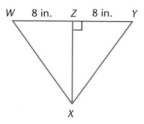
W   8 in.   Z   8 in.   Y
X

Write an equation in slope-intercept form of a line that has the given slope and y-intercept. (Module 4, p. 265)

24. slope = 3, y-intercept = 2
$y = 3x + 2$

25. slope = −4, y-intercept = 5
$y = -4x + 5$

Practice & Applications

27. Labsheet 4D answers are given.
  - a. $2\pi r$
  - b. the circumference of the partial circle
  - c. the radius of the partial circle

The box-and-whisker plot below models 51 T-shirt prices from 18 different Internet sites. All prices are rounded to the nearest dollar. (Module 1, p. 23)

T-Shirt Prices on the Internet

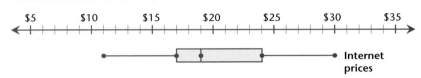

Internet prices

26. a. About what percent of the T-shirt prices are greater than or equal to $17? *75%*

  b. About what percent of the T-shirt prices are between the lower quartile and the upper quartile? *50%*

  c. About what percent of the prices are less than or equal to $19? *50%*

Extension ▶ ▶

Surface Areas of Cones

Use Labsheets 4C and 4D for Exercises 27 and 28.

27. Follow the *Pattern for a Cone* directions on Labsheet 4C to form a cone. Then find the *Dimensions of a Cone* as you complete Labsheet 4D.

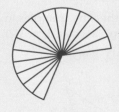

28. Suppose the partial circle from Labsheet 4C is divided into sections and they are rearranged to form a figure like a parallelogram.

  a. What is a good approximation of the height of the "parallelogram"? Why? *s; Each section is a sector of a circle with radius s.*

  b. What is a good approximation of the length of a base of the "parallelogram"? How can you tell?

  c. Use your answers from parts (a) and (b) to find an expression for the area of the "parallelogram." This expression represents the surface area of the cone, not including the circular base of the cone. $A = \pi rs$

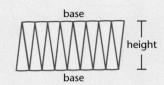

base

height

base

28. b. πr; Each base has length equal to one-half the circumference of the partial circle.

Section 4
Extra Skill Practice

Find the surface area of each prism or pyramid. Round to the nearest hundredth if necessary.

1. 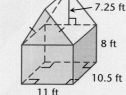 520 m²
   10 m
   8 m
   10 m

2. 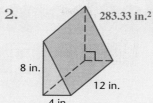 283.33 in.²
   8 in.
   12 in.
   4 in.

3. 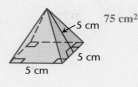 75 cm²
   5 cm
   5 cm
   5 cm

For Exercises 4 and 5, round answers to the nearest hundredth if necessary.

4. The height of a cone is 2 m and the radius of the base is 4 m. Find the volume. **33.49 m³**

5. The height of a square pyramid is 9 ft and the length of each side of the base is 0.5 ft. Find the volume. **0.75 ft³**

6. The volume of a cone is $64y^3$. Find the volume of a cylinder with the same base area and height as the cone. **$192y^3$**

Find the surface area and the volume of each figure. Round answers to the nearest hundredth if necessary.

7. 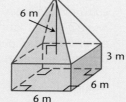 7.25 ft
   8 ft
   10.5 ft
   11 ft
   S.A. is about 730.35 ft², V = 1342.69 ft³

8. 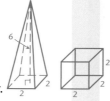 6 m
   3 m
   6 m
   6 m
   S.A. is about 188.52 m², V = 180 m³

Standardized Testing ◀▶ Open-ended

1. Sketch a square pyramid and a square prism that have the same volume. Label the heights and the dimensions of the bases.

2. For each situation, sketch two rectangular prisms that fit the description. Label the length of each edge. **a–c. See margin.**

   a. The volume of one prism is three times the volume of the other.

   b. The volume of one prism is eight times the volume of the other.

   c. The surface area of one prism is twice the surface area of the other.

 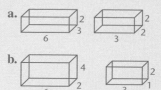

EXTENDED **E²** EXPLORATION

FOR ASSESSMENT AND PORTFOLIOS

Mathematical

SET UP   *You will need:* • *compass* • *ruler* • $8\frac{1}{2}$ *in. by 11 in. plain paper* • *colored pencils or markers*

The Situation   See the *Teacher's Resource Book* for a sample solution for this Extended Exploration.

Some very beautiful artwork is based on geometric designs. The design shown was created using a compass and the straight edge of a ruler.

The Problem

Create your own design using two or three of the following constructions: *constructing a circle, a triangle or equilateral triangle, a hexagon, or an angle bisector.* Your design should almost cover a sheet of paper, and you should use only a compass and a straightedge.

Something to Think About

◆ Do you want your design to be symmetrical?

◆ How can you make variations on the constructions you have already learned to make your designs more interesting?

◆ How else can you add to your design?

Present Your Results

Create a poster displaying your design. Add color if you wish. On a separate sheet of paper, describe how you used constructions to make your design. Also note anything special you used in your design that was not one of the constructions mentioned above.

Section ⑤ Angles Formed by Intersecting Lines

IN THIS SECTION

EXPLORATION 1
♦ Parallel Lines and Transversals

Meet Me in the MIDDLE

Setting the Stage ‣‣‣‣‣‣‣‣‣‣‣‣‣‣‣‣‣‣‣‣‣‣‣‣‣‣‣‣‣‣‣‣‣

SET UP Work with a partner. You will need: • Labsheets 5A and 5B
• protractor • metric ruler

In 1750, as part of a competition to improve trade links between France and England, an engineer proposed that a tunnel be built under the English Channel. Over 230 years later, engineering companies were bidding for the job.

The tunnel was to be built by two teams of workers: one digging from England and one digging from France. The idea was for each team to build one half of the *Chunnel*, as the English Channel Tunnel has become known. The two halves would meet in the middle.

According to Derek Wilson in his book *Breakthrough, Tunnelling the Channel,* one company submitted a very low bid to construct the Chunnel. The company was asked if it had carefully planned for the meeting of the two halves. The reply was, "Oh well, if we miss you'll get two tunnels for the price of one."

Setting the Stage

ABOUT THE THEME
The English Channel tunnel (*Chunnel*) is an engineering feat that required accurate calculations to become a reality. This section shows students how transversals and the angles formed by them could be used to ensure that the two halves of the *Chunnel* would meet to form one tunnel through the channel.

GETTING STARTED
Module 5, Section 5 *Warm-Up* assesses student understanding of the vocabulary used in this section.

Prior to reading the **Setting the Stage**, you may want students to play the game *Bridges*.

SET UP: Work with a partner. You will need:
• an $8\frac{1}{2}$ in. × $8\frac{1}{2}$ in. square of graph paper

• two different colored markers

Each player's goal is to be the first to build one continuous line from one edge of the paper to the other. The players take turns drawing a line connecting the diagonal corners of a single square on the graph paper. They can draw anywhere on the paper, either to continue their own line, or to block their opponent's. Once a segment has been drawn in a square the square cannot be used again. One player tries to connect the left side to the right, while the other tries to connect the top to the bottom. The first player to complete one continuous path of his or her color from edge to edge wins.

After playing the game, ask students to describe real-world situations where it is necessary to construct a path between points and describe problems that may occur.

Setting the Stage, cont.

TEACHING NOTES

Question 2(c) Remind students that 1 mi = 5280 ft.

As students prepare to move on to **Exploration 1**, they should be aware of the notation that is used in describing angles. You might refer to the **Section 5 Key Concepts** where the notation for congruence, equality, angle, and angle measure are used. Throughout this section, help students use proper notation. The congruence notation, ≅, is used to describe angles that have the same size, whereas the equal sign, =, is used to compare angle measures. If angles are congruent, their measures are equal and if the measures of two angles are equal, the angles are congruent. Students should also recognize and use the notation for angle measure. Angle measure notation is used to denote the measures of angles in statements like "$m\angle 1 + m\angle 3 = 180°$", whereas angle notation is used to name angles as in "$\angle 1$ and $\angle 3$ are supplementary."

TECHNOLOGY NOTE

For a related technology activity, see the *Technology Book*.

Think About It

Use Labsheets 5A and 5B for Questions 1 and 2.

1 **a.** Work with a partner. One of you should complete the *Chunnel Dig from England* while the other completes the *Chunnel Dig from France*. Follow the directions on each labsheet to dig a portion of a mock Chunnel. **a–c. Answers will vary. Check students' work.**

   b. Fold Labsheet 5A along the right edge of the box and line up the right edge of the box with the left edge of the box on Labsheet 5B.

   c. Do your two halves of the tunnel line up? If not, measure to the nearest millimeter the gap between the two ends.

2 The distance from Folkestone to Coquelles along a straight line is about 29 mi.

   a. Estimate the actual distance represented by the value you found in Question 1(c). **Answers will vary.**

   b. In the drawings on your labsheets, 1 cm represents 1 mi. How many miles does 1 mm on the drawing represent? **0.1 mi**

   c. Use the result from part (b) and your measurement from Question 1(c). Find the size, in miles, of the gap between the ends of your two tunnels. How big is the gap in feet?

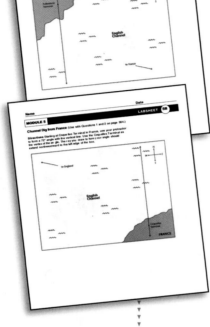

FOR ▶ HELP

with *measurements and conversions*, see

TABLE OF MEASURES, p. 601

TOOLBOX, p. 581

2. c. Let x = the number of millimeters from Question 1(c). distance in miles = $0.1x$; distance in feet = $528x$

Exploration 1

Parallel Lines AND Transversals

SET UP Work in a group. You will need: • ruler • protractor

▶ In the Chunnel Dig activity you completed, you did not have precision equipment to line up the two tunnels. The following questions will help you see why the tunnels would meet if precise measurements could be made.

3 The angle that the tunnel makes with the north-south line drawn at the Folkestone Terminal can be described as 72° *east of south*.

   a. How many degrees east of north is the tunnel? Answer this question by measuring the angle on Labsheet 5A. **108°**

   b. Explain how you can obtain the measure of the angle in part (a) *without* using a protractor by recognizing that the north-south line creates a straight angle.

   c. Using the phrases *west of north* and *west of south*, give two ways to describe the angle that the tunnel makes with the north-south line drawn at the Coquelles Terminal in France. **72° west of north; 108° west of south**

▶ In Question 3, you found pairs of supplementary angles. Two angles whose measures have a sum of 180° are **supplementary angles**. Each angle is a **supplement** of the other angle.

4. Two of the angles below are supplementary. Name these angles.
∠ABC and ∠DEF

5 ✔ **CHECKPOINT** Suppose ∠P and ∠R are supplementary. If m∠P = 82°, what is m∠R? **98°**

GOAL

LEARN HOW TO...
◆ identify and find the measures of pairs of angles formed by intersecting lines

AS YOU...
◆ learn about the construction of the Chunnel

KEY TERMS
◆ supplementary, complementary angles
◆ supplement, complement
◆ transversal
◆ alternate interior, alternate exterior, vertical, corresponding angles

3. b. The sum of the measures of the angle that the tunnel makes with the north-south line and the angle in part (a) is 180°. So, the measure of the angle in part (a) is 108°.

✔ **QUESTION 5**

...checks that you can find the supplement of an angle.

Exploration 1

CLASSROOM MANAGEMENT
This exploration is best done in groups of 3 or 4 to allow for active discussion of concepts and answers to questions.

TEACHING NOTES
Question 3 To help students become comfortable with the angle terms, ask them the everyday meanings of "alternate," "interior," and "exterior." Identify responses that can be used to help explain the meanings of the terms. Use the following example to help students distinguish between interior and exterior angles.

CLASSROOM EXAMPLE
Draw two parallel lines intersected by a transversal. Then label the interior angles with the numbers 1 through 4 and label the exterior angles with the numbers 5 through 8.

Sample Answer: In the figure, *l* ‖ *m*.

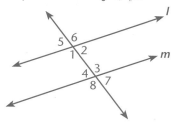

Exploration 1 *continued*

TEACHING NOTES

Following **Question 6**, you may want to ask students how the engineers might have known to begin digging at a 72° angle. Students may notice that if you draw a transversal from the Folkestone Terminal to the Coquelles Terminal, the alternate interior angles between the two parallel lines measure 72°. Make sure students understand that engineers used survey equipment and maps to determine the direction in which they should begin digging.

COMMON ERRORS

Question 9 Students may incorrectly infer that alternate interior and alternate exterior angles are formed only when two parallel lines are cut by a transversal. Alternate interior and alternate exterior angles are all formed when any two lines are cut by a transversal, however they are congruent *only* when those lines are parallel.

6 In the Chunnel Dig activity, suppose that east-west lines were also drawn at the terminals in England and France.

   a. Measure the angle that the tunnel makes with an east-west line drawn at Folkestone Terminal in England. Describe the angle using the phrase *south of east*. **18° south of east**

   b. How is the angle in part (a) related to the angle 72° east of south? **Sample Response: The two angles together form a right angle. The sum of the measures of the two angles is 90°.**

   c. *Without* using a protractor, determine the measure of the angle that the tunnel makes with an east-west line drawn at Coquelles Terminal in France. Then describe the angle using the phrase *north of west*. **18° north of west**

▶ **In Question 6, you found pairs of *complementary angles*. Two angles whose measures have a sum of 90° are complementary angles. Each angle is a complement of the other angle.**

✔ **QUESTION 7**

...checks that you can find the complement of an angle.

8. b. Sample Response: The angles are alternate because they are on opposite sides of the transversal. They are exterior because they are outside the parallel lines.

7 ✔ **CHECKPOINT** Find the complement of each angle.

   a. 22° **68°**   **b.** 50° **40°**   **c.** 18° **72°**   **d.** 84° **6°**

8. A **transversal** is a line that intersects two or more lines in a plane at separate points. In the diagram, line *t* is a transversal of lines *m* and *n*.

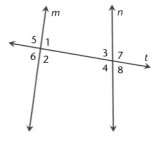

   a. Angles 1 and 4 are **alternate interior angles**. Angles 6 and 7 are *not* alternate interior angles. Identify another pair of alternate interior angles. **∠2 and ∠3**

   b. Angles 6 and 7 are **alternate exterior angles**. How does this name describe the location of the angles?

   c. Identify another pair of alternate exterior angles. **∠5 and ∠8**

9 **Discussion** Use a ruler and a protractor.

   a. Draw a pair of parallel lines cut by a transversal. Measure the angles formed. **Check students' work.**

   b. What do you notice about pairs of alternate interior angles? **The angles have the same measure so they are congruent.**

   c. What do you notice about pairs of alternate exterior angles? **The angles have the same measure so they are congruent.**

   d. Compare your results with those of other group members. **The results should be the same.**

   e. Repeat parts (a)–(d) with nonparallel lines. What do you notice? **The angles do not have the same measure so they are not congruent.**

10 **Try This as a Class** Suppose two lines are cut by a transversal. *a–b. See margin.*

 a. What can you conclude about the measures of the alternate interior angles?

 b. What seems to be true about the measures of the alternate exterior angles?

11 **Discussion** Lines *p* and *q* in the diagram are parallel.

 a. Describe what vertical angles are.

 b. Give three examples of vertical angles. ∠1 and ∠7, ∠2 and ∠8, ∠3 and ∠5

 c. Describe what corresponding angles are.

 d. Give three examples of corresponding angles. ∠1 and ∠3, ∠2 and ∠4, ∠6 and ∠8

> Arrowheads indicate parallel lines.

> ∠4 and ∠6 are **vertical angles**.

> ∠5 and ∠7 are **corresponding angles**.

12 **Try This as a Class** Use the diagram in Question 11.

 a. What relationship do you think exists between vertical angles formed by intersecting lines? Vertical angles have the same measure so they are congruent.

 b. What relationship do you think exists between corresponding angles formed when parallel lines are cut by a transversal?

▶ **Angle Measures** You can use the relationships between pairs of angles, including supplementary angles, to find measures of angles formed when parallel lines are cut by a transversal.

13 **Discussion** Use the diagram in Question 11. Suppose *m*∠6 is 56°. Explain how to find each angle measure. *a–c. See margin.*

 a. *m*∠5 **b.** *m*∠2 **c.** *m*∠8

14 ✔ **CHECKPOINT** Use the diagram at the right.

 a. Name all the pairs of alternate interior angles, alternate exterior angles, vertical angles, and corresponding angles. See margin.

 b. Suppose lines *p* and *n* are parallel and *m*∠1 is 60°. Find *m*∠8, *m*∠5, and *m*∠4. *m*∠8 = 120°; *m*∠5 = 60°; *m*∠4 = 120°

HOMEWORK EXERCISES ▶ See Exs. 1–37 on pp. 369–371.

---

11. a. Sample Response: Two angles that have the same vertex and whose sides are opposite rays are vertical angles.

11. c. Sample Response: Corresponding angles are angles that are in the same position with respect to two lines and a transversal that intersects the lines.

12. b. When two parallel lines are cut by a transversal, the corresponding angles are congruent.

✔ **QUESTION 14**

...checks that you can identify and find the measures of pairs of angles formed by intersecting lines.

TEACHING NOTES
You may want to use the following Classroom Example as a review before students begin **Checkpoint Question 14**.

CLASSROOM EXAMPLE

In the diagram, *p* ∥ *q*. List the pairs of congruent angles, identifying each pair as vertical angles, alternate interior angles, alternate exterior angles, or corresponding angles.

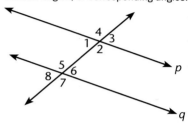

Answer:
∠1 ≅ ∠3, ∠2 ≅ ∠4, ∠5 ≅ ∠7, ∠8 ≅ ∠6; vertical angles

∠1 ≅ ∠6, ∠2 ≅ ∠5; alternate interior angles

∠3 ≅ ∠8, ∠4 ≅ ∠7; alternate exterior angles

∠1 ≅ ∠8, ∠2 ≅ ∠7, ∠4 ≅ ∠5, ∠3 ≅ ∠6; corresponding angles

10. a. Sample Response: If the lines are parallel, the alternate interior angles are congruent. If the lines are not parallel, the alternate interior angles are not congruent.

 b. Sample Response: If the lines are parallel, the alternate exterior angles are congruent. If the lines are not parallel, the alternate exterior angles are not congruent.

13. a–c. and 14. a. See Additional Answers beginning on page A1.

367

Key Concepts

CLOSURE QUESTION

Describe the relationship between the two acute angles that form a right triangle.

Sample Response: The angles are complementary.

When two nonparallel lines are intersected by a transversal, what types of angles are always congruent?

Sample Response: only vertical angles

ABSENT STUDENTS

For students who were absent for part or all of this section, the blackline Study Guide for Section 5 may be used to present the ideas, concepts, and skills of Section 5.

Section 5
Key Concepts

Key Terms

supplementary angles

complementary angles

supplement

complement

vertical angles

transversal

alternate interior angles

alternate exterior angles

corresponding angles

Supplementary and Complementary Angles (pp. 365–366)

Two angles whose measures have a sum of 180° are supplementary angles. Two angles whose measures have a sum of 90° are complementary angles.

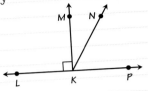

Examples

∠LKN is a supplement of ∠NKP.

∠MKN is a complement of ∠NKP.

Intersecting Lines and Transversals (pp. 366–367)

When two lines intersect they form four angles. Angles that have the same vertex and whose sides are opposite rays are vertical angles, and they are always congruent.

∠1 ≅ ∠3, so m∠1 = m∠3.   ∠2 ≅ ∠4, so m∠2 = m∠4.

A transversal is a line that intersects two or more lines in a plane at separate points. When two lines are cut by a transversal, various angles are formed.

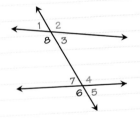

- **Alternate interior angles** are between the two lines and are on opposite sides of the transversal.

- **Alternate exterior angles** are outside of the two lines and are on opposite sides of the transversal.

- **Corresponding angles** are in the same position with respect to two lines and a transversal.

15 Key Concepts Question

a. Which two angles in △ABC are complements? ∠A and ∠B are complements.

b. What is the measure of ∠B? 54°

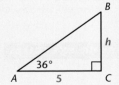

Section 5

Key Concepts

Parallel Lines and Transversals (pp. 366–367)

When parallel lines are cut by a transversal, there are special relationships among the angles formed.

- Alternate interior angles are congruent.

  $m\angle 3 = m\angle 7$ 　　　 $m\angle 4 = m\angle 8$

- Alternate exterior angles are congruent.

  $m\angle 1 = m\angle 5$ 　　　 $m\angle 2 = m\angle 6$

- Corresponding angles are congruent.

  $m\angle 2 = m\angle 4$ 　　　 $m\angle 3 = m\angle 5$

  $m\angle 1 = m\angle 7$ 　　　 $m\angle 6 = m\angle 8$

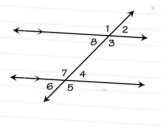

16　Key Concepts Question Use the parallel lines diagram above. Suppose the measure of ∠8 is 50°. What is the measure of ∠2? of ∠6? of ∠4? Explain.

16. Since ∠2 and ∠8 are vertical angles, $m\angle 2 = m\angle 8 = 50°$. Since the lines are parallel and ∠6 and ∠8 are corresponding angles, $m\angle 6 = m\angle 8 = 50°$. Since the lines are parallel and ∠4 and ∠8 are alternate interior angles, $m\angle 4 = m\angle 8 = 50°$.

Section 5

Practice & Application Exercises

Mental Math Use mental math to find the supplement of each angle.

1. 60° 120°　　2. 132° 48°　　3. 90° 90°　　4. 18° 162°

5. 45° 135°　　6. 24° 156°　　7. 120° 60°　　8. 98° 82°

Mental Math Use mental math to find the complement of each angle.

9. 63° 27°　　10. 19° 71°　　11. 48° 42°　　12. 81° 9°

13. 12° 78°　　14. 22° 68°　　15. 36° 54°　　16. 74° 16°

CLOSURE QUESTION

When two parallel lines are intersected by a transversal, what types of angles are always congruent?

Sample Response: alternate interior angles, alternate exterior angles, corresponding angles, and vertical angles

Practice & Applications

SUGGESTED ASSIGNMENTS

Core Course

Day 1: Exs. 38–46

Day 2: Exs. 1–16

Day 3: Exs. 17–35, 37

Extended Course

Day 1: Exs. 38–46

Day 2: Exs. 1–16

Day 3: Exs. 17–27 odd, 29–37, 47

Note: Extended Course assignments can be used to differentiate within the regular classroom. In classrooms where students are grouped homogeneously, the material might be covered in fewer days. In this case assignments may be combined.

ADDITIONAL PRACTICE

See the *Teacher's Resource Book* for additional practice and application exercises for this section.

EXERCISE NOTES

Exercises 17–19 require that students know the sum of the measures of the angles of a triangle.

Exercise 32 asks students to develop a logical sequence of relationships between angles to prove that two exterior angles are congruent. Some students may be tempted to base conclusions on informal observations, such as "they look like it." You may want to provide the hint that there is more than one solution and each solution requires at least three steps to conclude that the measures of the angles are equal.

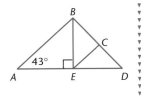

Use the diagram at the left for Exercises 17–19.

17. Name an angle that is a supplement of ∠AEC. ∠CED

18. Name an angle that is a complement of ∠BEC. ∠CED

19. Name an angle that is a supplement of ∠BCE. ∠DCE

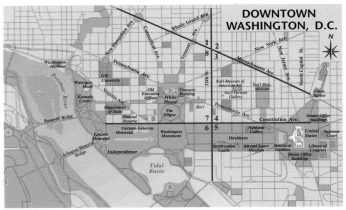

The map shows part of the street layout of Washington, D.C. In the diagram, 12th St. is a transversal of Massachusetts Ave. and Constitution Ave. Replace each ? with the correct angle.

20. ∠2 and ? are vertical angles. ∠8

21. ∠6 and ? are corresponding angles. ∠8

22. ∠3 and ? are alternate interior angles. ∠7

23. ∠5 and ? are alternate exterior angles. ∠1

29. m∠1 = 110°;
m∠2 = 70°;
m∠3 = 110°;
m∠4 = 70°;
m∠5 = 110°;
m∠6 = 70°

32. ∠4 and ∠5 are supplementary, so m∠4 = 180° − m∠5. ∠5 and ∠6 are also supplementary, so m∠6 = 180° − m∠5. Thus m∠4 = m∠6. ∠6 and ∠8 are corresponding angles and since lines p and q are parallel, m∠8 = m∠6. Therefore, m∠4 = m∠8.

In the diagram, line p is parallel to line q and line r is parallel to line s. Find each angle measure.

24. m∠7 30°

25. m∠5 150°

26. m∠4 30°

27. m∠6 30°

28. m∠1 30°

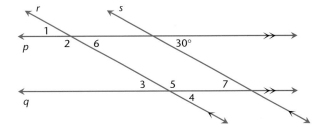

For Exercises 29–31, use the diagram below. Lines m and n are parallel.

29. Find the measures of angles 1–6.

30. What is the sum of the measures of angles 1 and 2? 180°

31. What is the sum of the measures of angles 5 and 6? 180°

32. Writing Lines p and q are parallel. Use the relationships between supplementary angles and between corresponding angles to explain why m∠4 = m∠8.

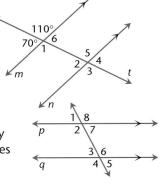

33. Algebra Connection Line m and line n are parallel. What is the value of x? What is the value of y? Explain your reasoning.

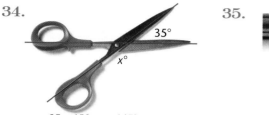

Algebra Connection For Exercises 34 and 35, write and solve an equation to find the value of each variable.

34.

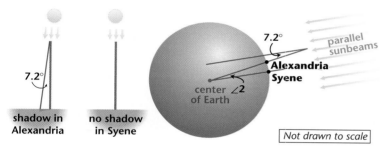

35°

$x°$

$x + 35 = 180; x = 145°$

35.

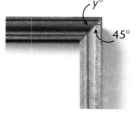

$y°$

45°

$y + 45 = 90; y = 45°$

36. Challenge In the 3rd century B.C., Eratosthenes used the fact that sunbeams are parallel to estimate Earth's circumference. At noon on the summer solstice, Eratosthenes measured the shadow cast by a pole in Alexandria. He knew that at noon the sun would be directly over Syene and would cast no shadow there.

7.2°

parallel sunbeams

Alexandria
Syene

7.2°

center ∠2 of Earth

shadow in Alexandria   **no shadow in Syene**

Not drawn to scale

a. What is the measure of ∠2 in the diagram? Explain.

b. Eratosthenes believed the distance between Alexandria and Syene was 5000 *stades*, or about 575 mi. Use this distance to estimate Earth's circumference in miles. Explain your method. See margin.

Reflecting ◀▶**on the Section**

Be prepared to discuss your response to Exercise 37 in class.

37. A highway is to be built to join Town A and Town B. If road r is parallel to road s, are the measures of the angles correctly labeled? Explain why or why not. See margin.

t

Town A

60° r

highway

60°

Town B s

33. $x = 125$; $y = 125$; $(3x - 250)$ and x are the measures of alternate exterior angles, and since lines m and n are parallel, the measures of alternate exterior angles are equal. Thus, $3x - 250 = x$. Solving $3x - 250 = x$ for x gives $x = 125$. y and x are the measures of corresponding angles, and since the measures of corresponding angles are equal, $y = x = 125$.

36. a. 7.2°; The rays of light from the sun are parallel, and the line through the center of the Earth and Alexandria is a transversal. Furthermore, ∠2 and the angle whose measure is 7.2° are alternate interior angles, and since alternate interior angles are congruent, $m∠2 = 7.2°$.

Discussion

Exercise 37 checks that you understand the relationships between pairs of angles formed by a transversal.

EXERCISE NOTES
Reflecting on the Section
Exercise 37 If students are confused as to how to proceed with this problem, ask them to use the angle measures given and fill in the missing angle measures using what they know about supplementary angles as shown.

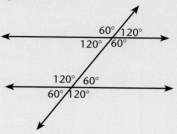

60° 120°
120° 60°

120° 60°
60° 120°

They should notice that the original measures were labeled incorrectly since alternate interior angles, alternate exterior angles, and corresponding angles are not equal. You can also help them use spatial skills to notice that two of the angles labeled 60° are obviously greater than a 90° right angle, making a measure of 60° impossible.

36. b. about 28,750 mi; Let $C =$ the circumference of Earth and $d =$ the distance between Alexandria and Syene. Then $\frac{7.2°}{360°} = \frac{d}{C} \approx \frac{575 \text{ mi}}{C}$. Solving the proportion gives $C \approx 28,750$ mi.

37. The angles are not labeled correctly. They are same-side interior angles and should be supplementary, not congruent. 60° and 120° would be acceptable measures for the two angles.

EXERCISE NOTES

The answers for **Exercises 38–39** use 3.14 for π. If students use the π key on their calculators their answers will vary slightly.

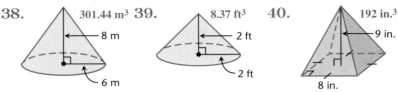

Spiral ◀▶ Review

Find the volume of each circular cone or regular pyramid. Round answers to the nearest hundredth if necessary. (Module 5, p. 356)

38. 301.44 m³

← 8 m

6 m

39. 8.37 ft³

← 2 ft

2 ft

40. 192 in.³

← 9 in.

8 in.

Copy and complete each equation. (Table of Measures, p. 601; Toolbox, p. 581)

41. 28 in. = _?_ ft
28 in. = $2\frac{1}{3}$ ft

42. 1.5 mi = _?_ ft
1.5 mi = 7920 ft

43. 3 yd = _?_ in.
3 yd = 108 in.

44. 36 mm = _?_ cm
36 mm = 3.6 cm

45. 248 cm = _?_ m
248 cm = 2.48 m

46. 2.6 km = _?_ m
2.6 km = 2600 m

Career ▮ Connection

Surveyor: Wendy Lathrop

You have learned that if two parallel lines are cut by a transversal, then alternate interior angles are congruent. It is also true that if two lines are cut by a transversal and alternate interior angles are congruent, then the two lines are parallel. Surveyor Wendy Lathrop has used this second fact while surveying boundary lines.

47. The diagram shows how Wendy Lathrop would construct angles to survey around several objects.

a. What is the relationship between line *AB* and line *CD*? Explain your reasoning. Since the alternate interior angles formed by the transversal *CB* are congruent, the lines are parallel.

b. In order to project line *AB* beyond the tree through point *E*, what must the measure of ∠*DEF* be? 60°

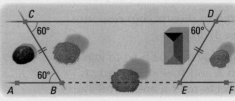

Section 5

Extra Skill Practice

Find the supplement of each angle.

1. 102° 78°   2. 81° 99°   3. 152° 28°   4. 13° 167°

Find the complement of each angle.

5. 8° 82°   6. 27° 63°   7. 58° 32°   8. 89° 1°

For Exercises 9–13, use the diagram.

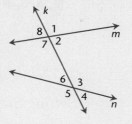

9. Is line *k* a transversal? Explain. Yes, it intersects lines *m* and *n* at different points.
10. Identify each pair of vertical angles.
   ∠1 and ∠7, ∠2 and ∠8, ∠3 and ∠5, ∠4 and ∠6
11. Identify each pair of corresponding angles.
   ∠1 and ∠3, ∠2 and ∠4, ∠5 and ∠7, ∠6 and ∠8
12. Identify each pair of alternate interior angles.
   ∠2 and ∠6, ∠3 and ∠7
13. Identify each pair of alternate exterior angles. ∠1 and ∠5, ∠4 and ∠8

In the diagram, line *k* is parallel to line *p*.
Find each measure.

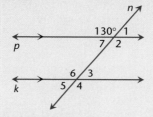

14. m∠1 50°   15. m∠7 50°

16. m∠6 130°   17. m∠5 50°

18. m∠3 180°

1. Line *n* is parallel to line *k*. Lines *p* and *q* are transversals that intersect at a point on line *n*. Which of the following statements is not true? C

   A m∠2 = m∠4

   B m∠1 = 180° – m∠2

   C m∠6 = m∠7

   D m∠1 = m∠5 + m∠6

2. Line *n* is parallel to line *k* and line *q* is a transversal. If m∠1 = 40° and m∠2 = 75°, what is m∠3? B

   A 65°   B 115°

   C 140°   D 75°

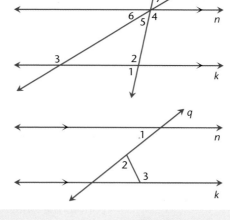

Extra Skill Practice

373

Setting the Stage

About the Theme

Students study the floor plan of an elementary school in preparation for the study of scale drawings where they will make a scale drawing of their classroom.

Getting Started

Module 5, Section 6 *Warm-Up* assesses student facility with ratios, areas, and perimeters as these skills will be used extensively throughout this section.

Teaching Notes

Question 2 Students do not need to set up a proportion to determine the answer to the question. Pose a question, such as "If $\frac{1}{16}$ in. = 5 ft, how many sixteenths equal 10 ft? 25 ft? etc."

Section 6 — Scale Drawing and Similar Figures

BUILDING MODELS

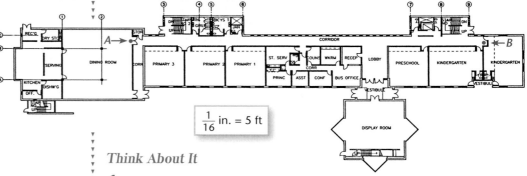

Setting the Stage

An architect designing a building will draw a floor plan to show the rooms of the building in proportion to one another. You may have used such a floor plan to help locate an exhibit in a museum, a store in a mall, or even a classroom in your school. The floor plan below is for the first floor of the Cesar Chavez Elementary School in Chicago, Illinois.

$$\frac{1}{16} \text{ in.} = 5 \text{ ft}$$

Think About It

1 How does the plan designate a doorway? **by an arc**

2 How many feet are represented by 1 in. on the drawing? **80 ft**

3 Estimate the length of the long corridor from the dining room to the kindergarten at the other end of the building, that is from *A* to *B*. **about 295 ft**

SCALE DRAWINGS

GOAL

LEARN HOW TO...
- make a scale drawing

AS YOU...
- measure and draw your classroom

KEY TERM
- scale

SET UP *Work in a group. You will need: • Labsheet 6A • ruler • tape measure • plain or graph paper*

▶ The floor plan on page 374 is an example of a *scale drawing* with a *scale* of 1 in. to 80 ft. The **scale** is the ratio of a length in the drawing to the corresponding length in the actual school.

To make a scale drawing, you need to choose a scale and convert the actual measurements to those for the drawing. You will practice these skills by making scale drawings of your desktop and your classroom.

EXAMPLE

Students in Rosa's class were asked to measure the length and width of their rectangular desktops and make scale drawings that would fit on a 4 in. by 6 in. card.

Step 1 Rosa measured the length and width of her desktop and labeled a sketch of the desktop with the actual measurements. Rosa's school desktop measured 24 in. by 18 in.

Step 2 She used the scale of $\frac{1}{2}$ in. to 3 in. for her scale drawing.

Step 3 Rosa set up proportions to find the length x in inches and width y in inches for the scale drawing of her desktop.

$$\text{length in drawing} \longrightarrow \frac{x}{24} = \frac{\left(\frac{1}{2}\right)}{3} \text{ and } \frac{y}{18} = \frac{\left(\frac{1}{2}\right)}{3} \longleftarrow \text{length in drawing}$$
$$\text{actual length} \longrightarrow \phantom{\frac{x}{24}} \phantom{\frac{(\frac{1}{2})}{3}} \phantom{\frac{y}{18}} \phantom{\frac{(\frac{1}{2})}{3}} \longleftarrow \text{actual length}$$

4 Discussion Use the information in the Example.

a. What do the measures $\frac{1}{2}$ in. and 3 in. in the scale represent?

b. Why do you think Rosa chose a scale of $\frac{1}{2}$ in. to 3 in. for her scale? Answers will vary. Sample response: She divided the width of the desk (24 in.) by the width of the card (4 in.) and got 6 in. So 1 in. on the scale drawing equals an actual length of 6 in. or $\frac{1}{2}$ in. equals 3 in.

4. a. $\frac{1}{2}$ in. is a length on the scale drawing. 3 in. is an actual length.

Exploration 1

DEVELOPING MATH CONCEPTS

A proportion is set up for students in the **Example**. Remind students that a proportion is an equation stating that two ratios are equal. Then review the reasoning used to set up the proportion. Ask, "What measures are being compared in the problem?" (*lengths on the drawing and actual lengths*) "How are these measures used to help set up the proportion? (*One of the measures will be used in the numerator of each ratio and the other measure will be used in the denominators.*) "How do you know that the 24 goes in the denominator of the first ratio?" (*24 in. is the actual length of the desk.*) How do you know that the $\frac{1}{2}$ goes in the numerators of the ratios?" (*In the scale, the $\frac{1}{2}$ is a measure on the drawing.*)

TEACHING NOTES

Question 4 Discussion Students should recognize that there are many ways to express a scale. Ask the questions, "How is the scale 1 in. = 6 in. related to the scale in part (b)?" "What other ways are there to represent this scale?" (*Sample Responses: $\frac{1}{4}$ in. = $1\frac{1}{2}$ in.; 2 in. = 12 in., etc.*)

Exploration 1 *continued*

TEACHING NOTES

In the **Example**, students may need to be reminded that the arrows show that since the denominator 3 is multiplied by 8 to obtain the denominator 24, for the fractions to be equivalent, the numerator $\frac{1}{2}$ must be multiplied by 8 to obtain the value of x.

Question 5(c) Students should have access to a 4 × 6 card or they should draw a 4 × 6 rectangle on their paper to provide a frame of reference.

The following Classroom Example may be used after **Question 5** if students need additional practice setting up and solving proportions.

CLASSROOM EXAMPLE

The dimensions of a room in a scale drawing are 8.4 cm by 13.6 cm. The scale in the drawing is 2 cm to 3 m. Find the actual dimensions of the room.

Answer: Let x = the length of the room (m) and y = the width of the room (m).

Cross Products	Equivalent Fractions

$\begin{array}{l} \text{drawing} \rightarrow \frac{2}{3} = \frac{8.4}{x} \\ \text{actual} \rightarrow \end{array}$ $\dfrac{2}{3}\overset{\times 4.2}{\underset{\times 4.2}{=}}\dfrac{8.4}{x}$

$\quad 2x = (8.4)(3) \qquad 3 \cdot 4.2 = x$

$\quad 2x = 25.2 \qquad\quad 12.6 = x$

$\quad\ x = 12.6$

$\begin{array}{l} \text{drawing} \rightarrow \frac{2}{3} = \frac{13.6}{y} \\ \text{actual} \rightarrow \end{array}$ $\dfrac{2}{3}\overset{\times 6.8}{\underset{\times 6.8}{=}}\dfrac{13.6}{y}$

$\quad 2y = (13.6)(3) \qquad 3 \cdot 6.8 = y$

$\quad 2y = 40.8 \qquad\quad 20.4 = y$

$\quad\ y = 20.4$

The dimensions of the room are 12.6 m by 20.4 m.

---

5. a. Since the denominator 3 was multiplied by 8 to get 24, the numerator $\frac{1}{2}$ must also be multiplied by 8 to get an equivalent fraction.

▶ Rosa could have used equivalent fractions or cross products to solve the proportions for the length and width of the desktop in her scale drawing.

EXAMPLE

Rosa's desktop is 24 in. long and 18 in. wide. The scale she selected for the scale drawing of her desktop was $\frac{1}{2}$ in. to 3 in. Solve the proportion to find the length of the desktop in her scale drawing.

$$\begin{array}{l}\text{length in drawing} \longrightarrow \\ \text{actual length} \longrightarrow\end{array} \frac{x}{24} = \frac{\left(\frac{1}{2}\right)}{3}$$

Use Equivalent Fractions or **Use Cross Products**

$$\overset{\times 8}{\frac{x}{24}} = \underset{\times 8}{\frac{\left(\frac{1}{2}\right)}{3}}$$

$$x = \frac{1}{2} \cdot 8$$

$$x = 4 \text{ in.}$$

$$\frac{x}{24} = \frac{\left(\frac{1}{2}\right)}{3}$$

$$3x = \frac{1}{2} \cdot 24$$

$$3x = 12$$

$$x = 4 \text{ in.}$$

In the scale drawing, the length of her desktop was 4 in.

---

5 **a.** In the equivalent fractions example above, why is $\frac{1}{2}$ multiplied by 8?

 b. Use one of the methods in the Example to find the width of the desktop in Rosa's scale drawing. **3 in.**

 c. Did her drawing fit on the card? **Yes**

▶ Before making a scale drawing of her classroom, Rosa made a sketch of the floor plan. She included the door, her desk, and a table on the sketch since she wanted to show them on her scale drawing.

Next she measured the length and width of the classroom and the locations of the door, her desk, and the table and recorded the measurements. Her partially completed measurements table is shown on Labsheet 6A.

Then she chose an appropriate scale and used it to find the measurements for the scale drawing and recorded them in the measurements table. Finally, using the measurements in her table, she drew the scale drawing shown on Labsheet 6A.

6 Use Labsheet 6A.

   a. Complete Rosa's table of measurements for her scale drawing. *See margin.*

   b. Based on Rosa's scale drawing, about how far is the actual distance from the center of the doorway to the center of the front edge of the table? *about 420 in.*

▶ Before you make a scale drawing that includes any of the features of your classroom, make a sketch and label it with the actual measurements.

7 **Try This as a Class** You will be making a scale drawing of your classroom on an $8\frac{1}{2}$ in. by 11 in. piece of paper. Think about the size of your classroom and what it contains. *a–c. Answers will vary. Check students' work.*

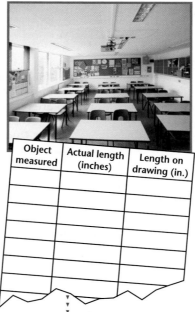

   a. Copy the table. To the nearest inch, measure the length of each wall of your classroom, the dimensions and location of your desk, any doors, and one other feature. Record the actual measurements in the table.

Object measured	Actual length (inches)	Length on drawing (in.)

   b. Select an appropriate scale and use it to find the measurements for the scale drawing. Record your answers in the table.

   c. Make a scale drawing of your classroom using the measurements you found in part (b).

8 **Discussion** Compare your scale drawing with those of your classmates.

   a. Do all the drawings use the same scale?

   b. Do they all look the same? Why or why not? *See margin.*

8. a. If the class selected the scale in Question 7(a), all of the drawings should use the same scale. Otherwise, the scales may be different.

9 Pick a feature in your classroom such as a tabletop, a door, or a window.

   a. What would be the dimensions of the feature in a scale drawing with a scale of 2 in. to 1 ft? *Answers will vary. Check students' work.*

   b. Is this a good scale to use? Why or why not? *See margin.*

10 ✔ **CHECKPOINT** Make a scale drawing of one wall of your classroom. Include at least one feature and the scale. *Answers will vary. Check students' work.*

 ✔ **QUESTION 10**

...checks that you can make a scale drawing.

HOMEWORK EXERCISES ▶ See Exs. 1–8 on p 382.

Question 6 Students will be measuring in fractions of an inch. They may need to review the increments on a ruler and the process of measuring with fractions.

CLASSROOM MANAGEMENT

Question 7 You may want to divide the class into groups, assigning each group a wall or door to measure.

TEACHING NOTES

Question 7(c) Students might find that their measurements are not on a standard ruler. Help them decide how they will measure $\frac{5}{6}$ of an inch by employing methods such as rounding to the nearest eighth of an inch. Then pose a question such as: "Why is $\frac{1}{3}$ inch = 1 ft not a good scale to use?" (*Standard rulers are divided into eighths of an inch increments. Eighths do not divide evenly into thirds.*)

Question 10 Point out that students are not making a floor plan, but a drawing of the entire wall area of their classroom.

8. b. If all the scales were the same, the drawings should have the same overall shape and size. If the scales were different, the overall shape should be the same but the sizes will vary. Since students could choose different features, the features shown on the drawings will be different.

9. b. Sample Response: No; A drawing of an average classroom would not fit on an $8\frac{1}{2}$ in. × 11 in. sheet of paper.

6. a. See Additional Answers beginning on page A1.

Exploration 2

COMMON ERROR

Question 13(b) Students may assume that the area doubles when the length of the sides are doubled. If necessary, have students draw two similar rectangles on graph paper, one with dimensions that are double the other. Then ask them to count the squares in each figure. They should notice that the area is the square of the scale or 4 times the area of the original figure.

TEACHING NOTES

Question 14 Encourage students to discover ways of determining the perimeter and area of a similar figure when the perimeter and area of the original figure are known. Students may discover that they can find the perimeter of a similar figure by multiplying the known perimeter by the scale, and find the area by multiplying the known area by the square of the scale. You may ask students how to find the *volume* of a three-dimensional figure that is similar to one with a known volume. (This relationship was explored in Modules 3 and 4.)

378

Exploration 2

PERIMETERS and AREAS of SIMILAR FIGURES

SET UP *Work with a partner. You will need: • scale drawings and classroom measurements from Exploration 1 • ruler*

▶ You can use the scale on a drawing to find the perimeter and the area of the actual figure if you know how the perimeters of similar objects are related and how the areas are related.

For Questions 11–13, use the table below.

	Measurement on scale drawing (in inches or square inches)	Actual measurement (in inches or square inches)	Ratio of measurement on scale drawing to actual measurement
length of front wall	?	?	?
length of back wall	?	?	?
length of right wall	?	?	?
length of left wall	?	?	?
perimeter of classroom floor	?	?	?
area of classroom floor	?	?	?

11 Copy the table. Use the measurements of your classroom and your scale drawing from Question 7 on page 377 to complete the first four rows of the table. Answers will vary. Check students' work.

12 **a.** Find the perimeter of your scale drawing and the perimeter of your actual classroom floor. Answers will vary. Check students' work.

b. Find the ratio of the perimeters. What do you notice? It is the same as the ratio of the lengths.

13 **a.** Find the area of your scale drawing and the area of your actual classroom floor. Answers will vary. Check students' work.

b. Find the ratio of the areas. What do you notice? It is the square of the ratio of the lengths.

14 **Try This as a Class** Use your answers to Questions 12 and 13.

a. How is the perimeter of a scale drawing related to the actual perimeter? The ratio of the perimeters is equal to the scale of the drawing.

b. How is the drawing's area related to the actual area? The ratio of the areas is equal to the square of the scale of the drawing.

▶ You can use what you have learned about the relationship between perimeters and areas of similar figures to find unknown measurements.

EXAMPLE

△**ABC is similar to** △**DEF. Use the information in the diagram to find the perimeter of** △**DEF.**

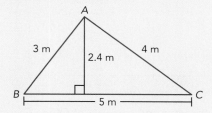
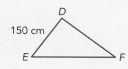

SAMPLE RESPONSE

> Recall that *AB* is read as "the length of segment *AB*."

First Find the scale. It is the ratio of *DE* to *AB*.

$$\text{scale} = \frac{DE}{AB} = \frac{150 \text{ cm}}{3 \text{ m}} = \frac{50 \text{ cm}}{1 \text{ m}}$$

Next Use the fact that the ratio of the perimeters is the same as the scale to write a proportion.

$$\frac{\text{Perimeter of } \triangle DEF}{\text{Perimeter of } \triangle ABC} = \frac{50 \text{ cm}}{1 \text{ m}}$$

Then Solve the proportion. Let *P* = the perimeter of △DEF.

$$\frac{P}{3 \text{ m} + 4 \text{ m} + 5 \text{ m}} = \frac{50 \text{ cm}}{1 \text{ m}}$$

$$\frac{P}{12 \text{ m}} = \frac{50 \text{ cm}}{1 \text{ m}}$$

$$12 \text{ m} \cdot \frac{P}{12 \text{ m}} = 12 \text{ m} \cdot \frac{50 \text{ cm}}{1 \text{ m}}$$

$$P = 600 \text{ cm}$$

The perimeter of △DEF is 600 cm or 6 m.

15 **Try This as a Class** Use the triangles in the Example.

   a. What is the ratio of the area of △DEF to the area of △ABC? How do you know? **See margin.**

   b. Find the area of △ABC. Use it and your answer to part (a) to find the area of △DEF. **6 m²; 1.5 m² or 15,000 cm²**

Example Students should be aware that the scale can be determined by finding the ratio of corresponding side lengths of similar figures.

The following Classroom Example may be used to reinforce this concept.

CLASSROOM EXAMPLE

In the figure shown, △*JKL* is similar to △*PQR*. Use the information in the diagram to find the perimeter of △*PQR*.

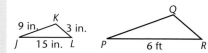

Answer:

First Find the scale (the ratio of *JL* to *PR*).

$$\text{scale} = \frac{JL}{PR} = \frac{15 \text{ in.}}{6 \text{ ft}} = \frac{5 \text{ in.}}{2 \text{ ft}}$$

Next Use the fact that the ratio of the perimeters is the same as the scale to write a proportion.

$$\frac{\text{perimeter of } \triangle JKL}{\text{perimeter of } \triangle PQR} = \frac{5 \text{ in.}}{2 \text{ ft}}$$

Then Solve the proportion. Let *p* = perimeter of △*PQR*.

$$\frac{27 \text{ in.}}{p} = \frac{5 \text{ in.}}{2 \text{ ft}}$$

$$p \cdot 5 \text{ in.} = 27 \text{ in.} \cdot 2 \text{ ft}$$

$$\frac{p \cdot 5 \text{ in.}}{5 \text{ in.}} = \frac{27 \text{ in.} \cdot 2 \text{ ft}}{5 \text{ in.}}$$

$$p = \frac{27 \text{ in.}}{5 \text{ in.}} \cdot 2 \text{ ft}$$

$$p = 10.8 \text{ ft}$$

The perimeter of △*PQR* is 10.8 ft.

COMMON ERROR

Question 15 Some students may assume 1 m² = 100 cm². Remind them that 1 m = 100 cm, so 1 m² = 100² or 10,000 cm².

15. a. See Additional Answers beginning on page A1.

379

COMMON ERROR

Question 16(a) Some students may fail to measure the doorway as part of the perimeter. Remind them that the perimeter is the complete distance around the room, not just the wall space.

16 The scale drawing below is for the offices of a small business.

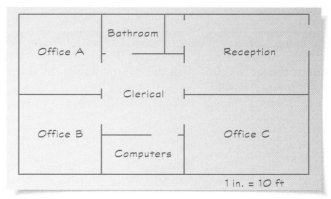

1 in. = 10 ft

a. Measure to find the perimeter and the area of Office C in the scale drawing. perimeter = 5 in., area = 1.5 in.²

b. Use your answer to part (a) and the scale to find the perimeter and the area of the actual Office C.
perimeter = 50 ft, area = 150 ft²

c. The area of the actual computer room is 50 ft². Without measuring, find the area of that room in the scale drawing.
0.5 in.²

✔ **QUESTION 17**

...checks that you can use a scale to find perimeters and areas.

17 ✔ **CHECKPOINT** Each pair of figures is similar. Find each missing perimeter or area.

a. Perimeter of △ACD = 72 in.
Perimeter of △ABE = __?__

Area of △ACD = 216 in.²
Area of △ABE = __?__
24 in.; 24 in.²

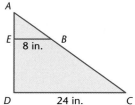

b. Perimeter of WXYZ = 30 yd
Perimeter of PQRS = __?__

Area of WXYZ = 50 yd²
Area of PQRS = __?__
135 ft; 1012.5 ft²

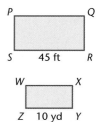

HOMEWORK EXERCISES ▶ See Exs. 9–22 on pp. 383–384.

Key Concepts

Scale Drawings (pp. 375–377)

The scale of a drawing is the ratio of a length on the drawing to the length of the corresponding part of the actual object. To find out how long to make a segment in a scale drawing, you can use a proportion.

Key Term

scale

Example A building is 30 ft high. Find the height h of the building in a scale drawing if the scale is 1 in. to 10 ft.

height in drawing $\longrightarrow$ $\dfrac{h}{30 \text{ ft}} = \dfrac{1 \text{ in.}}{10 \text{ ft}}$
actual height $\longrightarrow$

$$10h = 30$$
$$h = 3$$

The height of the building in the scale drawing is 3 in.

Perimeters and Areas of Similar Figures (pp. 378-380)

If the ratio of corresponding sides of similar figures is $\dfrac{a}{b}$, then the

ratio of their perimeters is $\dfrac{a}{b}$, and the ratio of their areas is $\dfrac{a^2}{b^2}$.

Example Parallelogram ABCD is similar to parallelogram PQRS.

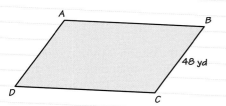

> The scale is 36 ft to 48 yd, or 3 ft to 4 yd.

48 yd

36 ft

$$\frac{\text{Perimeter of } PQRS}{\text{Perimeter of } ABCD} = \frac{3 \text{ ft}}{4 \text{ yd}}$$

$$\frac{\text{Area of } PQRS}{\text{Area of } ABCD} = \left(\frac{3 \text{ ft}}{4 \text{ yd}}\right)^2 = \frac{9 \text{ ft}^2}{16 \text{ yd}^2}$$

18 Key Concepts Question Use the parallelograms in the Example.

a. The perimeter of *ABCD* is 256 yd. Find the perimeter of *PQRS*.
192 ft

b. The area of *PQRS* is 1800 ft². Find the area of *ABCD*. 3200 yd²

Key Concepts

CLOSURE QUESTIONS

How is the scale of similar figures related to the perimeter of the figures? to the area of the figures?

> *Sample Response:* The ratio of the perimeters of the figures is the same as the scale (or ratio of the lengths of the corresponding sides). The ratio of the areas of the figures is the square of the scale.

ABSENT STUDENTS

For students who were absent for part or all of this section, the blackline Study Guide for Section 6 may be used to present the ideas, concepts, and skills of Section 6.

382

Practice & Applications

ADDITIONAL PRACTICE

See the *Teacher's Resource Book* for additional practice and application exercises for this section.

EXERCISE NOTES

Exercises 2–4 You may want to help students decide on an appropriate scale by giving them possible situations that would cause them to make a scale drawing of each item. Possibilities include: a bookstore poster displaying the dictionary, an enlarged postcard advertising a credit card, a CD cover using the pyramid as its artwork.

3–4. See Additional Answers beginning on page A1.

YOU WILL NEED

For Exs. 1–5, 7, and 8:
- ruler
- plain or graph paper

For Exs. 17–19 and 22:
- ruler

2. Sample Response:
Scale: $\frac{1}{16}$ in. = 1 in.

6. Sample Response:
I decided about how big I wanted the drawing to be, then chose one measurement and decided what scale would work. Then I checked the others to be sure my drawing would be a reasonable size.

Section 6

Practice & Application Exercises

1. The scale drawing below uses the scale $\frac{1}{16}$ in. to 5 ft. Make a scale drawing of the gymnasium using the scale $\frac{1}{8}$ in. to 5 ft.

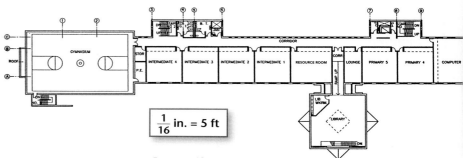

$\frac{1}{16}$ in. = 5 ft

Based on measurements of $1\frac{5}{16}$ in. by $\frac{13}{16}$ in., the new scale drawing should be a $2\frac{5}{8}$ in. by $1\frac{5}{8}$ in. rectangle.

In Exercises 2–4, the dimensions of several objects are given. Make a scale drawing of the top view, the front view, and the right-side view of each object. Include the scale. 2–4. Scales and views may vary. Check students' work.   3–4. See margin.

2. A dictionary is 12 in. long, 9 in. wide, and 3 in. thick.

3. A credit card is 85 mm long, 55 mm wide, and 1 mm thick.

4. The base of a rectangular prism is 24 ft long and 18 ft wide. The height is 36 ft.

5. **Estimation** Estimate and then find the dimensions of a room in your home. Make a scale drawing of the floor and of one of the four walls. Include the scale(s). Answers will vary. Check students' work.

6. **Writing** Describe the process you went through to choose the scale for one of the scale drawings you made in Exercises 2–5.

7. **Open-ended** Choose an object that is more complex than a single rectangular prism and make detailed scale drawings of the top view, the front view, and the right-side view. Answers will vary. Check students' work.

8. **Create Your Own** Make a scale drawing of the floor and all four walls of your ideal bedroom. Include the doors, windows, closets, and furniture in your drawing, and identify the scale. Answers will vary. Check students' work.

The perimeter of a room is 16 yd and the area of the room is 16 yd². What would be the perimeter and the area of the room in a scale drawing with each of the following scales?

9. 1 in. to 36 in.
16 in.; 16 in.²

10. 1 ft to 4 yd
4 ft; 1 ft²

11. 3 in. to 4 yd
12 in.; 9 in.²

12. Writing Describe the process you went through to find the answer in Exercise 11.

The two figures in each diagram are similar. Use the given information to replace each __?__ with the correct measurement. Round answers to the nearest hundredth if necessary.

13. Area of $\triangle ABC$ = 5.25 cm²
Area of $\triangle XYZ \approx$ __?__
58.3 mm²

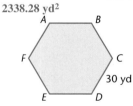

14. Perimeter of $STUV$ = 58 ft
Perimeter of $DEFG$ = __?__
348 in.

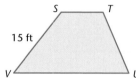

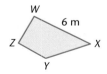

15. Area of $PQRSTU \approx$ 9353.1 ft²
Area of $ABCDEF \approx$ __?__
2338.28 yd²

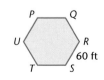

16. Perimeter of $WXYZ$ = 16.5 m
Perimeter of $KLMN \approx$ __?__
2200 cm

17. Challenge Use a ruler and the trapezoids in Exercise 14.

a. Find all the unknown side lengths of the trapezoids.

b. Find the height of each trapezoid.

12. Sample Response: To find perimeter, I used the proportion $\frac{3}{4} = \frac{x}{16}$. To find area, I used the proportion $\frac{9}{16} = \frac{x}{16}$ since the ratio of areas is the square of the ratio of perimeters.

17. Answers have been rounded to the nearest foot. Students' answers may vary slightly.
a. ST = 8 ft, TU = 13 ft, UV = 22 ft; DE = 48 in., EF = 78 in., FG = 132 in.
b. height of $STUV$ = 12 ft, height of $DEFG$ = 72 in.

COMMON ERROR
Exercises 13 and 15 ask students to calculate the areas of similar figures based on a scale. Some students may not remember to square the scale to do this. Refer them to **Question 13** on page 378 for review.

EXERCISE NOTES
Exercise 17 Students should explain how they used a ruler and the scale to solve the problem.

Practice & Applications

EXERCISE NOTES

Exercise 22 asks students to find a floor plan of an actual building. This may be difficult for some students. You may want to have available home decorating/architecture magazines, brochures of museums or other public buildings, or newspapers containing floor plans. If resources are limited, make copies of several floor plans for student use.

Scale: 3 in. = 10 mi

The scale on the map of Minneapolis is 3 in. to 10 mi.

18. **Estimation** Estimate the perimeter of the city on the map. Then use your answer to estimate the actual perimeter of the city. **Sample Response: about 10 in.; about 33 mi**

19. **Estimation** Estimate the actual length of the section of the Mississippi River that runs through the city. **Sample Response: about 11.5 mi**

20. The actual city covers about 58.7 mi². How many square inches is this on the map? **5.283 in.²**

21. There are about 3.6 mi² of inland water in the actual city. How many square inches of water is this on the map? **0.324 in.²**

RESEARCH

Exercise 22 checks that you can interpret the scale on a scale drawing.

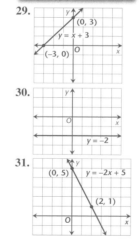

Reflecting ◀▶ on the Section

22. Find a floor plan. Some possible sources are books about architecture and magazines about homes. Use the scale on the floor plan to estimate the perimeter and the area of the actual floor. **Answers will vary. Check students' work to see whether they can interpret the scale on a scale drawing.**

Spiral ◀▶ Review

Solve each proportion. (Module 2, p. 132)

23. $\frac{x}{24} = \frac{0.5}{3}$ **4**

24. $\frac{x}{7} = \frac{5}{14}$ **2.5**

25. $\frac{n}{7} = \frac{32}{28}$ **8**

26. $\frac{n}{26} = \frac{\left(\frac{1}{4}\right)}{13}$ **$\frac{1}{2}$**

27. $\frac{24}{9} = \frac{52}{y}$ **19.5**

28. $\frac{0.125}{12} = \frac{m}{132}$ **1.375**

Graph each equation. (Module 3, p. 175)

29. $y = x + 3$

30. $y = -2$

31. $y = 5 - 2x$

Section 6
Extra Skill Practice

1. A 6 ft tall man is drawn 4 in. tall in a scale drawing. What is the scale? Answers will vary. They must be equivalent to $\frac{4\text{ in.}}{6\text{ ft}} = \frac{1\text{ in.}}{1.5\text{ ft}}$.

2. The dimensions of a room in a scale drawing are 8 cm by 5 cm. The scale is 2 cm to 1 m. Find the dimensions of the actual room. **4 m by 2.5 m**

The dimensions of some objects are given. Make a scale drawing of the top view, the front view, and the right-side view of each object. Include the scale. **3–4. Scales and views may vary. Check students' work. See margin.**

3. A rectangular prism is 27 ft long, 12 ft wide, and 36 ft high.

4. The base of a rectangular prism is 5 m long and 5 m wide. The height of the prism is 11 m.

The two polygons in each diagram are similar. Find the unknown perimeter or areas.

5. Perimeter = 30 in. **15 in.**   6. Area = 500 mm² **31.25 cm²** 7. Area = 405 ft² **6480 in.²**

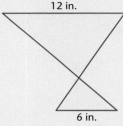

12 in.

6 in.

Perimeter = __?__

20 mm

5 cm

Area = __?__

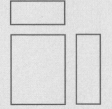

30 ft

120 in.

Area = __?__

Standardized Testing ◀▶ Multiple Choice

1. A door is 8 ft high. How high is the door in a scale drawing that uses the scale 1 in. to 2 ft? **C**

   Ⓐ 0.25 in.   Ⓑ 2 in.   Ⓒ 4 in.   Ⓓ 16 in.

2. ABCD and EFGH are similar parallelograms. If the perimeter of ABCD is 80 ft, the length of $\overline{AD}$ is 10 ft, and the length of the corresponding side $\overline{EH}$ is 5 ft, what is the perimeter of EFGH? **A**

   Ⓐ 40 ft   Ⓑ 20 ft   Ⓒ 15 ft   Ⓓ 30 ft

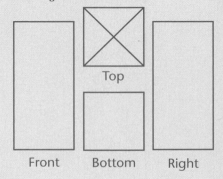

Module Project

Those students who wish to challenge themselves with a more complex building design can team with a partner. Both students should be held equally responsible for the final product.

Creating a Model Town

When architects and urban planners design housing developments and business districts, they draw plans and build models to show people how the buildings will look. For your module project, you and your classmates will draw plans for a model town and then build it.
The answers to all of the project questions will vary. Check students' work.

Sketching Nets One way to create a model for a building is to make a net that can be folded into the shape of the building.

1 Work as a class.

a. Brainstorm ideas for your town. Will you make houses, offices, stores, or some combination of buildings? How many styles of buildings will there be? You may want to look at books or magazines to help generate ideas.

b. Based on your ideas from part (a), decide which buildings will be included in your town and who will design and make each one. You will each make one building.

2 a. Sketch a view of your building that gives it a three-dimensional look.

b. Sketch a net for your building.

c. Label your sketches with the dimensions that the actual building would have. (*Hint*: Begin with dimensions of buildings you are familiar with.)

3 What polygons are used to create the floor, the walls, and the roof of your building?

Surface Area and Volume The surface area of a building determines how much siding, roofing, and flooring material is needed. The volume of a building determines what size heating and cooling systems should be installed.

Use your sketches from Question 2.

4 Find the surface area of your building.

5 Find the volume of your building.

SET UP

Work individually and as a class.

You will need:
- *graph paper (optional)*
- *ruler*
- *large sheets of sturdy paper*
- *colored pencils or markers*
- *scissors*
- *tape*

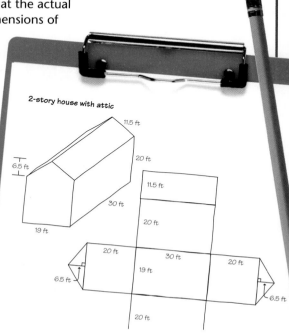

2-story house with attic

11.5 ft
20 ft
6.5 ft
11.5 ft
30 ft
19 ft
20 ft
20 ft
30 ft
20 ft
19 ft
6.5 ft
6.5 ft
20 ft

Scale Drawings You can use scale drawings to show details of the various parts of your building.

6 Use your sketch from Question 2. What actual dimensions will you use for the exterior doors and the windows of your building? Explain why you chose these dimensions.

7 **Discussion** Describe to another student the scale you would like to use for your building and discuss how each scale presented would affect the size of the final model.

You have made sketches and discussed scales to use for your models. To complete the project, you will build a three-dimensional model of your building and help to put together your class's model town.

8 Work as a class. Compare the scales you discussed in Question 7. Together choose a scale that you will all use to create the buildings for your model town.

9 Use the net you sketched in Question 2. On sturdy paper, make a net for your building using the scale from Question 8.

10 Add to your net features such as doors and windows using the scale from Question 8.

11 Use colored pencils or markers to add other details to your net.

12 Cut out your net and fold along the edges to form your building. Then tape the edges together.

13 Work as a class to arrange your buildings to form a model town. Use the same scale for the streets that you did for each building.

PROJECT NOTES
Question 9 You may want to help the class determine a scale that will accommodate the size of paper you have available, and that will fit in your classroom.

Question 10 Card stock such as old file folders can be used for smaller buildings. Be sure to have an ample supply of large, heavy sheets of paper available for the larger buildings.

Questions 11–12 Make sure students add color and all details to their buildings prior to folding them into three-dimensional figures.

Review and Assessment

MODULE 5

You will need: • *ruler* (Exs. 2, 21, and 23)

For Exercises 1 and 2, assume that the figure at the right is made of centimeter cubes. Also assume that there are no hidden cubes. (Sec. 1, Explors. 1 and 2)

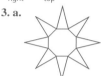

1. a. Find the surface area and the volume of the figure.
   surface area = 26 cm²; volume = 6 cm³
   b. Find the surface area and the volume of the figure without the green cubes. surface area = 18 cm²; volume = 4 cm³

2. Draw flat views of the entire figure from each of the following viewpoints: front, back, left, right, and top.

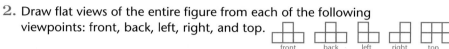

3. a. Sketch a net for an octagonal pyramid. (Sec. 2, Explor. 2)

   b. How many faces, edges, and vertices will the pyramid have?
   (Sec. 2, Explor. 2) 9 faces, 16 edges, 9 vertices

   3. a.

For Exercises 4 and 5, explain whether the triangles in each pair are congruent. If the triangles are congruent, write the relationship between them using symbols. (Sec. 2, Explor. 3) 4–5. See margin.

4.

5.

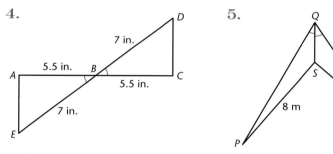

6. Beth wants to plant a rectangular garden in her backyard. If she uses the measurements shown will her garden be rectangular? Explain. (Sec. 3, Explor. 1) Since $7.5^2 + 4^2 = 56.25 + 16 = 72.25 = 8.5^2$, the two triangles will be right triangles, and the quadrilateral will be a rectangle.

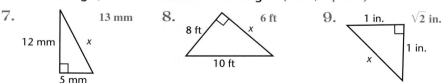

For each triangle, find the unknown side length. (Sec. 3, Explor. 2)

7.   13 mm
   12 mm   x
   5 mm

8.   6 ft
   8 ft   x
   10 ft

9.   1 in.   √2 in.
           1 in.
       x

Find the surface area and the volume of each figure. (Sec. 4, Explors. 1 and 2)

10.

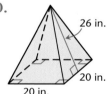

26 in.

20 in.

20 in.

S.A. = 1440 in.²; V = 3200 in.³

11.

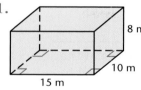

8 m

10 m

15 m

S.A. = 700 m²; V = 1200 m³

12.

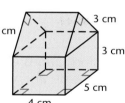

3 cm

4 cm

3 cm

5 cm

4 cm

S.A. = 114 cm²; V = 84 cm³

13. The volume of a cylinder is 51 cm³. What is the volume of a cone with the same base and height as the cylinder? (Sec. 4, Explor. 2) 17 cm³

For Exercises 14–17, use the diagram. Line *k* is parallel to line *n* and the measure of ∠3 is 105°. (Sec. 5, Explor. 1)

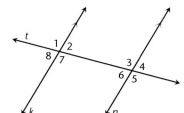

14. Identify and find the measure of the alternate interior angle to ∠3. ∠7; 105°

15. Identify and find the measure of the corresponding angle to ∠6. ∠8; 75°

16. Identify and find the measure of the alternate exterior angle to ∠8. ∠4; 75°

17. Find the measure of ∠5. Explain your method. 105°; Sample response: ∠3 and ∠5 are vertical angles, so m∠3 = m∠5 = 105°.

Use the diagram for Exercises 18–20. (Sec. 5, Explor. 2)

18. Which angle is a supplement of ∠UTQ? ∠RTQ

19. Which angle is a complement of ∠SQR? ∠SQT

20. Suppose m∠UPT = 40°. Find m∠PTR. 130°

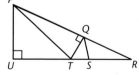

21. Use the scale $\frac{1}{2}$ in. to 1 ft. Make a scale drawing of a rectangular window that is 3 ft wide and 1.5 ft high. (Sec. 6, Explor. 1) Scale drawing should be $1\frac{1}{2}$ in. by $\frac{3}{4}$ in.

22. The scale on a map is 1 cm to 2 km. The perimeter of a lake on the map is 14 cm and its area on the map is 12 cm². Find the actual perimeter and area of the lake. (Sec. 6, Explor. 2) perimeter = 28 km; area = 48 km²

Reflecting ◀▶ on the Module

23. Sketch two rectangular prisms with different dimensions. Then make scale drawings of the figures from different views. Find the surface area and the volume of each figure. Answers will vary. Check students' work.

Assessment Options

TEACHER'S RESOURCE BOOK
• Module 5 Tests A and B
• Module 5 Standardized Test
• Module 5 Performance Assessment

TEST GENERATOR

Visualizing Change

Module 6 Overview

Students use graphs, tables, equations, and transformations to model changes in the world around them and to make predictions. Hands-on and visual models, as well as real-world applications, are used to build students' understanding of linear and quadratic functions, equation solving, exponential growth, and algorithms.

Module 6 Planner

Day 1: Section 1	Day 2: Section 1	Day 3: Section 1	Day 4: Section 2	Day 5: Section 2
Setting the Stage, *pp. 392–393* Exploration 1 *through Question 7, pp. 393–395*	Exploration 1 *from Question 8, pp. 395–396*	Exploration 2, *pp. 397–399* Key Concepts, *pp. 400–401*	Setting the Stage, *p. 406* Exploration 1, *pp. 407–409*	Exploration 2 *through Question 14, pp. 410–411*
Day 6: Section 2	**Day 7: E²**	**Day 8: Section 3**	**Day 9: Section 3**	**Day 10: Section 3**
Exploration 2 *from Question 15, pp. 411–412* Key Concepts, *pp. 413–414*	Work on Extended Exploration, *p. 419*	Setting the Stage, *p. 420* Exploration 1 *through Question 8, pp. 421–422*	Exploration 1 *from Question 9, pp. 422–423*	Exploration 2, *pp. 423–425* Key Concepts, *p. 426*
Day 11: Review and Assessment Mid-Module Quiz	**Day 12: Section 4** Setting the Stage, *pp. 432–433* Exploration 1, *pp. 433–435* Key Concepts, *p. 436*	**Day 13: Section 5** Setting the Stage, *p. 442* Exploration 1 *through Question 7, pp. 443–444*	**Day 14: Section 5** Exploration 1 *from Question 8, pp. 444–445*	**Day 15: Section 5** Exploration 2, *pp. 445–446* Key Concepts, *p. 447*
Day 16: Module Project Begin Module Project *pp. 452–453*	**Day 17: Review and Assessment** Review and Assessment *pp. 454–455*	**Day 18: Review and Assessment** Discuss Review and Assessment *pp. 454–455* Finish Module Project, *pp. 452–453*	**Day 19: Assessment** Module 6 Test	

Materials List

Section	Materials
1	• Labsheet 1A, water (or rice), clear plastic cup, metric ruler, clear container (1 per group), graph paper
2	• graph paper, graphing calculator (optional)
3	• a rectangular sheet of paper, calculator, graph paper, graphing calculator (optional)
4	• Labsheet 4A, graph paper
5	• graph paper, graphing calculator (optional)
Project	• Project Labsheet A, graph paper
Rev & Assess	• graph paper, graphing calculator (optional)

Module 6 Objectives

Section	Objectives	NCTM Standards 2000*
1	• Use a graph to model and interpret data. • Interpret coordinate graphs without scales or labels. • Use equations, tables, and graphs to identify functions. • Write equations for functions.	**1, 2, 3, 5, 6, 7, 8, 9, 10**
2	• Use equations, tables, and graphs to solve problems involving linear change. • Use the distributive property. • Solve equations with variables on both sides or that involve simplifying.	**1, 2, 3, 5, 6, 7, 8, 9, 10**
3	• Use equations and graphs to model exponential change. • Write an exponential equation to model a compound interest problem.	**1, 2, 3, 5, 6, 7, 8, 9, 10**
4	• Write an algorithm to describe a series of transformations. • Reflect geometric shapes across the x- or y-axis.	**1, 2, 3, 4, 5, 6, 7, 8, 9, 10**
5	• Use equations and graphs to model situations. • Use equations to predict the shapes of parabolas. • Recognize quadratic equations. • Simplify quadratic expressions.	**1, 2, 3, 4, 5, 6, 7, 8, 9, 10**

* See page T14.

Section ① Graphs and Functions

Section 1 Planner

Section Objectives

Exploration 1
- Use a graph to model and interpret data
- Interpret coordinate graphs without scales or labels

Exploration 2
- Use equations, tables, and graphs to identify functions
- Write equations for functions

Days for Section 1

First Day
Setting the Stage, *pp. 392–393*
Exploration 1 through Question 7, *pp. 393–395*

Second Day
Exploration 1 from Question 8, *pp. 395–396*

Third Day
Exploration 2, *pp. 397–399*
Key Concepts, *pp. 400–401*

Teaching Resources

Teacher's Resource Book
- Warm-Up
- Labsheet 1A
- Practice and Applications
- Study Guide
See page 391 for additional teaching resources.

Materials List

Exploration 1
- water
- clear plastic cup
- metric ruler
- clear container
- graph paper

Practice and Applications
- Labsheet 1A
- graph paper

Assessment Options

EMBEDDED ASSESSMENT
- Use a graph to model and interpret data
  Exercises 5, 8
- Interpret coordinate graphs without scales or labels
  Exercises 1–5
- Use equations, tables, and graphs to identify functions
  Exercises 14, 18
- Write equations for functions
  Exercises 10, 22

PERFORMANCE TASK/PORTFOLIO
- Exercise 6 on *p. 402 (open-ended)*
- Exercise 7 on *p. 402 (create your own)*
- Exercise 9 on *p. 402 (challenge)*
- Exercises 11–13 on *p. 403 (writing)*
- Exercise 25 on *p. 404 (earth science)*
- Exercise 26 on *p. 404 (discussion)*

QUIZZES/TESTS
- Section 1 Quick Quiz

TEST GENERATOR

Section 1 Overview

In this section, students will use tables, graphs, equations, and functions to model change. Students begin by matching a graph to the rain pattern described in Barbara Hale's poem *Sidewalk Measles.*

Exploration 1
In Exploration 1, students pour water into a container and measure the change in water level to model the change in a lake after a rainfall. Students record the results of their experiment on a graph. They then explore the relationship between the amount of water poured into a container and the water level inside it and make a conjecture about what container shapes produce linear graphs and what shapes produce nonlinear graphs.

Exploration 2
Students describe the shape of a graph for a given set of values and learn that some graphs model functions. They identify the input and output values for various functions and explain whether *y* is a function of *x* for a given set of (*x*, *y*) values. Students use equations to write rules for some functions. They learn to compare input and output values in tables and on graphs to tell whether an equation models a function.

390C

Guide for Assigning Homework

REGULAR SCHEDULING (45 MIN CLASS PERIOD)			EXERCISES TO NOTE		
Section/ P&A Pages	Core Assignment	Extended Assignment	Additional Practice/Review	Open-ended Problems	Extended Problems
1 pp. 401–404	**Day 1:** SR 27–32 **Day 2:** 1–8 **Day 3:** 10–24, ROS 26	SR 27–32 1–9 10–25, ROS 26	EP, p. 405	PA 6, 7	Challenge PA 9

Key: PA = Practice & Application; ROS = Reflecting on the Section; SR = Spiral Review; TB = Toolbox; EP = Extra Skill Practice; Ext = Extension; *more time

Math Background and Teaching Strategies

Classroom Notes

Bulletin board display ideas for this section include:

- student graphs from Exploration 1 with a sketch or photo of the corresponding container

- works of literature that can be modeled with a graph

- student graphs from P&A Exercise 6 or stories from P&A Exercise 7

Math Strands

Topic Spiraling and Integration

Exploration 1

In this exploration, students revisit graphs as a form of representation. They have had much exposure to this topic. In Module 1, students used scatterplots and fitted lines to make predictions. Scatterplots were used again in Module 4, to determine the formulas for circumference and area of a circle. In Module 3 students worked with rates and distances that produced linear and non-linear graphs. By graphing an equation, they were able to see how a graph can model an equation. Now students see how a graph can model a change described in a poem or one that occurs in an experiment. The *Setting the Stage* focuses on the change occurring in a graph and does not show a scale for either axis. In the exploration, students are expected to determine the scales for the graph of their data. For help with choosing a scale students are referred back to Module 1 where they first learned this skill. In addition to the experiment and poem, students also see how data relates to a graph by matching a table of information with a related graph.

Exploration 2

Though students may not have realized it, they have been working with many equations and graphs that are functions. In this exploration, the term function is formally defined. It is introduced through input and output values in a table and as the vertical line test on a graph. Students continue their exposure to both linear and non-linear equations and graphs as they practice determining whether an equation or a graph represents a function. Students will revisit functions in Section 5 of this module where they study quadratic functions and their graphs.

Section 2 Planner

Section Objectives

Exploration 1
• Use equations, tables, and graphs to solve problems involving linear change

Exploration 2
• Use the distributive property
• Solve equations with variables on both sides or that involve simplifying

Days for Section 2

First Day
Setting the Stage, *p. 406*
Exploration 1, *pp. 407–409*

Second Day
Exploration 2 through Question 14, *pp. 410–411*

Third Day
Exploration 2 from Question 15, *pp. 411–412*
Key Concepts, *pp. 413–414*

Teaching Resources

Teacher's Resource Book
• Warm-Up
• Practice and Applications
• Study Guide
See page 391 for additional teaching resources.

Materials List

Exploration 1
• graph paper
• graphing calculator (optional)

Practice and Applications
• graph paper
• graphing calculator (optional)

Extended Exploration
• graph paper

Assessment Options

EMBEDDED ASSESSMENT
• Use equations, tables, and graphs to solve problems involving linear change
 Exercises 6, 7
• Use the distributive property
 Exercises 10, 11, 12
• Solve equations with variables on both sides or that involve simplifying
 Exercises 20, 22, 24

PERFORMANCE TASK/PORTFOLIO
• Exercise 15 on *p. 416 (alternative method)*
• Exercise 16 on *p. 416 (writing)*
• Exercise 30 on *p. 417 (journal)*
• Exercises 1–3 on *p. 418 (open-ended)*
• Extended Exploration on *p. 419**

* indicates a problem solving task that can be assessed using the Assessment Scales

QUIZZES/TESTS
• Section 2 Quick Quiz

TEST GENERATOR

Section 2 Overview

In this section, students use equations, tables and graphs to model problems involving the growth of savings over time.

Exploration 1
Students begin the section by comparing the results of different savings plans. They record the results in a table and then plot the ordered pairs for the data on a coordinate grid. Since the savings functions are linear, students learn the meaning of linear equations. They will identify the slope and *y*-intercept of the line drawn through their data points, and will use these values to write an equation for the line. As they study other situations involving growth over time, students will model the situations with linear equations and will use the equations and their graphs to solve problems related to the situations.

Exploration 2
Students work with multi-step equations as they continue to model situations that involve saving money. They learn to solve multi-step equations with variables on both sides of the equation and to use the distributive property to simplify equations. A real life application in this exploration involves saving money in a savings bank certificate of deposit.

Guide for Assigning Homework

REGULAR SCHEDULING (45 MIN CLASS PERIOD)			EXERCISES TO NOTE		
Section/ P&A Pages	Core Assignment	Extended Assignment	Additional Practice/Review	Open-ended Problems	Extended Problems
2 pp. 414–417	**Day 1:** 1–8 **Day 2:** 16–19, SR 31–39 **Day 3:** 9–14, 20–28, ROS 30	1–8 16–19, SR 31–39 11–15, 19–25 odd, 26–29, ROS 30	EP, p. 418	ST, p. 418	E², p. 419

Key: PA = Practice & Application; ROS = Reflecting on the Section; SR = Spiral Review; TB = Toolbox; EP = Extra Skill Practice; Ext = Extension; *more time

Math Background and Teaching Strategies

Classroom Notes

Bulletin board display ideas for this section include:

- display of different types of savings plans with linear models
- student solutions to E²

Visitors might include:

- banker or financial advisor

Math Strands

Topic Spiraling and Integration

Exploration 1
By now, students should be familiar with the use of tables, equations, and graphs to represent a situation. This should allow students to focus on the introduction of new vocabulary. *Linear equation* is introduced to describe equations whose graphs are lines. The term is needed so that when students begin working with

exponential and quadratic equations later in this module, they will be able to distinguish among the three.

Students use the slope-intercept form of a linear equation, introduced in Module 4, to find the equation of a line from its graph. In addition, they are introduced to the solution of systems of equations by graphing two linear equations on the same axes and seeing that the intersection of the two lines is the solution of a related problem. In Section 3, the growth of a savings account that increases linearly will be contrasted with the exponential growth that results when interest is compounded.

Exploration 2
In this exploration, students use substitution to solve a system of equations that model two savings plans. Students should realize that when solving systems of equations by graphing, they often were unable

to determine the exact coordinates of the point of intersection. Thus, substitution may be a better method to use when exact answers are needed. Solving systems of equations by substitution also provides a meaningful context for learning how to solve equations with variables on both sides.

Solving multi-step equations is not new to students at this level. They had extensive experience solving equations in Book 2 and reviewed solving multi-step equations in Module 1. In Module 1, students also learned to simplify expressions by combining like terms. Now, they will simplify equations by getting all the variables on one side and combining like terms. They will also learn to use the distributive properties to rewrite expressions and to solve equations that require both simplifying using the distributive property and by combining like terms.

Section 3 Planner

Section Objectives

Exploration 1
- Use equations and graphs to model exponential change

Exploration 2
- Write an exponential equation to model a compound interest problem
- Use equations to model situations involving exponential growth

Days for Section 3

First Day
Setting the Stage, *p. 420*
Exploration 1 through Question 8, *pp. 421–422*

Second Day
Exploration 1 from Question 9, *pp. 422–423*

Third Day
Exploration 2, *pp. 423–425*
Key Concepts, *p. 426*

Teaching Resources

Teacher's Resource Book
- Warm-Up
- Practice and Applications
- Study Guide
See page 391 for additional teaching resources.

Materials List

Exploration 1
- a rectangular sheet of paper
- graph paper
- graphing calculator (optional)

Exploration 2
- calculator

Practice and Applications
- graph paper or a graphing calculator

Assessment Options

EMBEDDED ASSESSMENT
- Use equations and graphs to model exponential change
  Exercises 1, 3
- Write an exponential equation to model a compound interest problem
  Exercise 6
- Use equations to model situations involving exponential growth
  Exercise 7

PERFORMANCE TASK/PORTFOLIO
- Exercise 4 on *p. 427 (challenge)*
- Exercise 5 on *p. 428 (writing)*
- Exercise 8 on *p. 428 (open-ended)*
- Exercise 16 on *p. 429 (population growth)*
- Exercise 17 on *p. 429 (discussion)**
- Standardized Testing on *p. 431 (performance task)*

* *indicates a problem solving task that can be assessed using the Assessment Scales*

QUIZZES/TESTS
- Section 3 Quick Quiz
- Mid-Module Quiz

TEST GENERATOR

Section 3 Overview

In this section, a literature connection is used to introduce exponential change as students examine how Charlie might have eaten his birthday candy bar in *Charlie and the Chocolate Factory*.

Exploration 1
Students use paper folding to model the candy bar problem. They begin by folding a piece of paper in half and recording the number of layers and the area of one layer. Students continue folding the paper in half and recording the results. By writing the number of layers and the area of each layer as powers, students are introduced to exponential change. They then learn to write equations of the form $y = b^x$ to model the change in the number of folds and in the area of the layers. By graphing several equations in the form $y = b^x$, students see how the value of b affects the graph the equation.

Exploration 2
In the previous section, students examined the growth of money over time. In this section, they will see how the growth of money in a savings account that earns compound interest is an example of exponential growth. Students will model this type of savings growth with an equation of the form $y = ab^x$. They will use their equations to determine what the value of a savings account that earns a certain annual interest will be after a given number of years.

Guide for Assigning Homework

REGULAR SCHEDULING (45 MIN CLASS PERIOD)			EXERCISES TO NOTE		
Section/ P&A Pages	Core Assignment	Extended Assignment	Additional Practice/Review	Open-ended Problems	Extended Problems
3 pp. 427–430	**Day 1:** 3, SR 18–20 **Day 2:** 1–2, 5 **Day 3:** 6–12, ROS 17, 21	3–4, SR 18–20 1–2, 5 6–9, 13–16, ROS 17, 22–24	EP, p. 431	PA 8	PA Challenge 4 Career Connect 21 Ext 22–24

Key: PA = Practice & Application; ROS = Reflecting on the Section; SR = Spiral Review; TB = Toolbox; EP = Extra Skill Practice; Ext = Extension; *more time

Math Background and Teaching Strategies

Classroom Notes

Bulletin board display ideas for this section include:

• display of different types of savings plans with exponential models

Visitors might include:

• banker or financial advisor

Math Strands

Topic Spiraling and Integration

Exploration 1
Exploration 1 focuses on representing exponential growth with a table of values and then using the patterns in the table to develop an equation to represent the change that is occurring. Beginning with a hands-on activity allows students of all levels to take part in the exploration even though the concept of exponential growth is a more advanced topic. The paper folding activity gives students a visual representation of how the change is occurring. Students see the number of layers growing as the area of each layer decreases. Students are introduced to the basic equation $y = b^x$ and explore how the value of b affects the graph of the equation. Students are not expected to master writing exponential equations to model situations in this exploration. The topic will be extended in Exploration 2.

Exploration 2
Students contrast linear and exponential growth by comparing the increase in the price of a candy bar over a 50-year time period. The basic equation $y = b^x$ introduced in Exploration 1 is now expanded to $y = ab^x$ to account for starting values other than 1.

In Module 8 students will use exponential equations to generalize geometric sequences. At first, they may not recognize the connection between exponential change and multiplying by a factor to develop the next term of a sequence. To help make this connection the equation for the nth term of a geometric sequence, $t = ar^{n-1}$, can be related to the equation $y = ab^x$ where $r = b$, $n - 1 = x$ and $t = y$.

Section 4   Algorithms and Transformations

Section 4 Planner

Section Objectives

Exploration 1
- Write an algorithm to describe a series of transformations
- Reflect geometric shapes across the *x*- or *y*-axis

Days for Section 4

First Day
Setting the Stage, *pp. 432–433*
Exploration 1, *pp. 433–435*
Key Concepts, *p. 436*

Teaching Resources

Teacher's Resource Book
- Warm-Up
- Labsheet 4A
- Practice and Applications
- Study Guide

See page 391 for additional teaching resources.

Materials List

Exploration 1
- Labsheet 4A
- graph paper

Practice and Applications
- graph paper

Extra Skill Practice
- graph paper

Assessment Options

EMBEDDED ASSESSMENT
- Write an algorithm to describe a series of transformations
  Exercises 10, 11
- Reflect geometric shapes across the *x*- or *y*-axis
  Exercises 3, 4

PERFORMANCE TASK/PORTFOLIO
- Exercise 9 on *p. 438 (create your own)*
- Exercise 18 on *p. 440 (challenge)*
- Exercise 19 on *p. 440 (create your own)*
- Exercise 20 on *p. 440 (journal)*

QUIZZES/TESTS
- Section 4 Quick Quiz

TEST GENERATOR

Section 4 Overview

In this section, students begin by making a connection between coordinate graphing and computer simulation. They will see how algorithms can be used to move a figure by translation or reflection.

Exploration 1
Students are introduced to the use of animation to model movement that combines a series of transformations. By investigating the relationship between the coordinates of a figure and the coordinates of its image following a transformation, students discover how to write algebraic algorithms for translations and for reflections across the horizontal and vertical axes of the coordinate grid.

Guide for Assigning Homework

REGULAR SCHEDULING (45 MIN CLASS PERIOD)			EXERCISES TO NOTE		
Section/ P&A Pages	Core Assignment	Extended Assignment	Additional Practice/Review	Open-ended Problems	Extended Problems
4 pp. 437–440	**Day 1:** 1–11, 15–17, ROS 20, SR 21–28	3–7, 10–18, ROS 20, SR 21–28	EP, p. 441	PA 9, 19	PA Challenge 18

Key: PA = Practice & Application; ROS = Reflecting on the Section; SR = Spiral Review; TB = Toolbox; EP = Extra Skill Practice; Ext = Extension; *more time

Math Background and Teaching Strategies

Classroom Notes

Bulletin Board display ideas for this section include:

- student designs and algorithms from Practice and Applications Exercise 9

Visitors might include:

- computer animator

Math Strands

Topic Spiraling and Integration

Exploration 1

The focus of this lesson is transformational geometry. The concept of using an algorithm to move a figure on a coordinate plane was introduced in Module 2. Students were able to see how adding or subtracting constants from the coordinates of a figure could be used to translate the figure from one position to another and how multiplying or dividing the coordinates by a constant could be used to create a size transformation or dilation. In this exploration, students continue their study of algorithms and transformations, reviewing translations and dilations, while adding reflections. Students used algorithms to describe translations in Module 2, but now the terms *transformation* and *algorithm* will be formally introduced and students will write their own algorithms. Some algorithms require more than one step and often are a combination of translations and reflections.

Students are expected to understand the basic notion of rotation from their studies in Book 2. They do not have to create any rotation algorithms, but in the *Practice and Application Exercises* they are asked to try to produce a rotation image by a series of reflections. Rotations and rotational symmetry will be studied in depth in Section 2 of Module 8.

Working in a coordinate plane, allows students to practice graphing points and provides a review of integer operations as students apply algorithms to figures in various quadrants. Writing algorithms is another example of how algebra can be used to visualize and to model change, which is the theme of this module.

Section 5 · Exploring Quadratic Functions

Section 5 Planner

Section Objectives

Exploration 1
- Use equations and graphs to model events and objects
- Use equations to predict the shapes of parabolas

Exploration 2
- Recognize quadratic equations
- Simplify quadratic expressions

Days for Section 5

First Day
Setting the Stage, *p. 442*
Exploration 1 through Question 7,
pp. 443–444

Second Day
Exploration 1 from Question 8, *pp. 444–445*

Third Day
Exploration 2, *pp. 445–446*
Key Concepts, *p. 447*

Teaching Resources

Teacher's Resource Book
- Warm-Up
- Practice and Applications
- Study Guide
See page 391 for additional teaching resources.

Materials List

Exploration 1
- graph paper or a graphing calculator

Exploration 2
- graph paper or a graphing calculator

Practice and Applications
- graph paper or a graphing calculator

Extra Skill Practice
- graph paper

Assessment Options

EMBEDDED ASSESSMENT
- Use equations and graphs to model events and objects
  Exercise 9
- Use equations to predict the shapes of parabolas
  Exercise 5
- Recognize quadratic equations
  Exercises 11, 13
- Simplify quadratic expressions
  Exercise 13

PERFORMANCE TASK/PORTFOLIO
- Exercise 7 on *p. 448 (physics connection)*
- Exercise 16 on *p. 449 (challenge)*
- Exercise 17 on *p. 449 (journal)*
- Exercises 25–26 on *p. 450 (extension)*
- Standardized Testing on *p. 451 (free response)*

QUIZZES/TESTS
- Section 5 Quick Quiz
- Module Tests A and B
- Module Standardized Test
- Module Performance Assessment

TEST GENERATOR

Section 5 Overview

In this section, students will learn about parabolas and quadratic functions. Students will discover that various curves in the real world are examples of parabolas and can be modeled mathematically with a quadratic equation.

Exploration 1
Students begin by investigating the graph of an equation that approximates the curve formed by a main cable of the Golden Gate Bridge. As they do, they learn to identify the vertex and the line of symmetry of the parabola. Then, students use graph paper or graphing calculators to explore how the shape and direction of a parabola represented by an equation in the form $y = ax^2 + c$ is related to the graph of the parabola $y = x^2$.

Exploration 2
Students extend their study of quadratic equations to quadratic functions by examining an equation that models the path of a basketball after it is tossed. They look at the relationship between the dependent and independent variables on the graph and identify the equation as a quadratic function. Students then learn to distinguish between quadratic and other functions, simplifying when necessary to rewrite equations in the form $y = ax^2 + bx + c$. You may wish to review the distributive property, since students will be required to use it to simplify expressions in this exploration.

Guide for Assigning Homework

Regular Scheduling (45 min class period)			Exercises to Note		
Section/ P&A Pages	Core Assignment	Extended Assignment	Additional Practice/Review	Open-ended Problems	Extended Problems
5 pp. 448–450	**Day 1:** 1–4, SR 18–24 **Day 2:** 5–8 **Day 3:** 9–15, ROS 17	1–4, SR 18–24 5–8 9–16, Ros 17, 25–26	EP, p. 451 Review & Assessment, pp. 454–455		PA Challenge 16 Ext 25–26 Mod Proj, pp. 452–454

Key: PA = Practice & Application; ROS = Reflecting on the Section; SR = Spiral Review; TB = Toolbox; EP = Extra Skill Practice; Ext = Extension; *more time

Math Background and Teaching Strategies

Classroom Notes

Bulletin board display ideas for this section include:

- pictures of "real-world" parabolas such as fountains, bridges, etc.

- examples, explanations, and graphs of each type of equation studied in this module: linear, exponential, and quadratic

Math Strands

Spiraling and Integration

Exploration 1

Students' knowledge of non-linear equations is extended by introducing parabolas and their related equations. Parabolas whose equations have the form $y = ax^2$ are presented first. By varying the value of a and comparing the resulting graph to the graph of the parent equation $y = x^2$, students discover how the graph of a parabola is affected by the value of a. After

several comparisons, students develop generalizations about the graph of $y = ax^2$ when $a > 1$, $a < -1$, $0 < a < 1$, and $-1 < a < 0$. The goal is for students to be able to predict the shape and direction of the graph of an equation in comparison to the graph of $y = x^2$. Because students are only changing the value of a, the line of symmetry is always $x = 0$ and the vertex of the parabola is at $(0, 0)$. Students should notice that for negative values of a the vertex is the maximum point on the graph, whereas for positive values of a it is the minimum point.

Next, students observe how the graph of $y = x^2 + c$ where $c \neq 0$ differs from the graph of $y = x^2$. Using their observations, they then predict how the value of c affects the graph of the parabola. The line of symmetry is still $x = 0$, however students now see parabolas with a vertex other than $(0, 0)$. This is another application of translations on

a coordinate plane covered in Section 4 of this module. The exploration concludes with students predicting the graphs of equations of the form $y = ax^2 + c$ where $a \neq 1$ and $c \neq 0$, thus combining both scaling and translating the graph of $y = x^2$.

Exploration 2

The concept of a function was introduced in Section 1. In this exploration, students focus on quadratic functions and their relationship to parabolas. To determine if an equation models a quadratic function, students use the distributive property and combine like terms to see if it can be simplified to the form, $y = ax^2 + bx + c$. In the *Extension Exercises*, the vertex and axis of symmetry of a parabola are found by expressing its equation in the form $y - k = a(x - h)^2$. In the process, students are exposed to parabolas with vertices located on a line of symmetry other than the *y-axis*.

Module 6

OVERVIEW
Students use graphs, tables, equations, and transformations to model changes in the world around them and to make predictions. Hands-on and visual models, as well as real-world applications, are used to build students' understanding of linear and quadratic functions, equation solving, exponential growth, and algorithms.

PREREQUISITE SKILLS
Warm-Up Exercises for each section are provided in the *Teacher's Resource Book*. You can use these exercises to review skills and concepts students will need for each section. In addition, the Spiral Review exercises at the end of each section in the student edition provide practice on prerequisite skills.

MODULE DIAGNOSTIC TEST
The Module Diagnostic Test in the *Teacher's Resource Book* can be used to assess students' prior knowledge of skills and concepts that will be taught in each section of this module. You can use test results to help structure your teaching to meet the diverse needs of your classroom.

MODULE
6
Visualizing Change

390

Modeling Change in a Story

Leaves change color, caterpillars change into butterflies, and day changes into night. In this project, you will write a story that involves changes and use mathematics to model them.

More on the Module Project
See pp. 452–453.

See pp. 452–453.

CONNECTING
MATHEMATICS
The & Theme

MODULE
6 **SECTION OVERVIEW**

① Graphs and Functions

As you study rainfall data:
◆ Use tables and graphs to model changes in data
◆ Use equations, tables, and graphs to represent functions

② Linear Equations and Problem Solving

As you study different savings plans:
◆ Use linear equations, tables, and graphs to solve problems
◆ Simplify and solve equations
◆ Use the distributive property

③ Modeling Exponential Change

As you learn about compound interest:
◆ Use tables and equations to solve problems involving exponential growth

④ Algorithms and Transformations

As you model a gymnast's change in position:
◆ Use algorithms to transform geometric shapes
◆ Reflect geometric shapes

⑤ Exploring Quadratic Functions

As you model the paths of aircraft and the shapes of bridge cables:
◆ Explore the shape and symmetry of parabolas
◆ Recognize and simplify quadratic equations

INTERNET
Resources and practice at
classzone.com

391

Module Resources

TEACHER'S RESOURCE BOOK
Resources
• The *Math Gazette* (parent newsletter)
• Warm-Ups
• Labsheets
• Practice and Applications
• Study Guide

Assessment
• Section Quick Quizzes
• Mid-Module Quiz
• Module 6 Diagnostic Test
• Module 6 Tests A and B
• Module 6 Standardized Test
• Module 6 Performance Assessment
• Modules 5 and 6 Cumulative Test

SPANISH RESOURCES
• The *Math Gazette* (parent newsletter)
• Practice and Applications
• Assessment
• Spanish Glossary

STUDENT WORKBOOK

TECHNOLOGY BOOK

TECHNOLOGY RESOURCES
• @Home Tutor
• Test Generator
• Activity Generator
• Professional Development DVD
• Online Activities

Section 1 Graphs and Functions

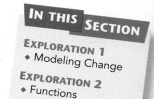

IN THIS SECTION

EXPLORATION 1
◆ Modeling Change

EXPLORATION 2
◆ Functions

Setting the Stage

Suppose you are asked to describe a rainfall. You might paint a picture, write a story, or compose a piece of music. Barbara M. Hales decided to write the poem shown below.

Sidewalk Measles

I saw the sidewalk catch the measles
When the rain came down today.
It started with a little blotching—
Quickly spread to heavy splotching,
Then as I continued watching
The rain-rash slowly dried away.

Think About It

1 Which graph below do you think best describes how the rainfall changes over time in the poem? C

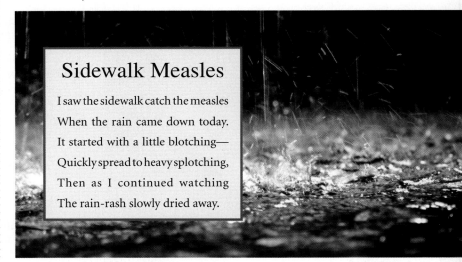

A.   B.   C.

2 **a.** How did the rainfall change in the poem? **It started slowly with scattered showers, then became heavy, and then slowly stopped.**
b. How was this change shown in the graph you chose in Question 1? **The graph starts at zero, climbs, reaches a peak, and then gradually drops off.**

3 What labels would you use for the horizontal and vertical axes of the graph you chose in Question 1? **Time; Amount of Rainfall**

▶ The world around you is constantly changing. A graph is one way to model change. Throughout this module you will choose and develop mathematical models that can help you visualize change.

Exploration 1

Modeling Change

SET UP *Work in a group of three. You will need: • water • clear plastic cup • metric ruler • clear container • graph paper*

GOAL

LEARN HOW TO...
◆ use tables and graphs to model changes in data

AS YOU...
◆ explore how the shape of a container affects changes in water level

▶ Rainfall can cause dramatic changes in the water level of lakes and rivers. For example, from 1963 to 1987, the water level in Utah's Great Salt Lake varied by as much as 20 ft. The surface area of the lake went from 950 mi^2 to 3,300 mi^2. These changes were due in part to the shape of the lake bed.

In this exploration, you will model rainfall on a lake by pouring water into a container. Each group in your class should choose a container with a different shape. As you add water to the container, your group will measure the change in water level.

4 **Discussion** Suppose you were to pour water into your group's container. How can you use a graph to show the change in water level inside the container? **Sample Response: Show the amount of water on the horizontal axis and the height of the water in the container on the vertical axis.**

TEACHING NOTES
The discussion in **Questions 2 and 3** of how these images and sounds can be represented in a graph provides a natural lead-in to the module theme of using mathematics to describe and visualize change. It also provides an introduction to the Module Project where students write a story that involves change and model the change mathematically.

Exploration 1

DEVELOPING MATH CONCEPTS
Question 4 is intended to make students think about what data would be displayed along each axis. To make this decision, students must recognize what things change when water is added to the container. They usually do not have trouble recognizing that the height of the water changes and that the water level can be measured in millimeters or centimeters. However, they are often unsure about what quantities or measurements to use for the other axis. You may need to ask leading questions to help them to recognize that this axis represents the amount of water that has been poured into the container.

Exploration 1 *continued*

CLASSROOM MANAGEMENT
To facilitate the experiment in **Question 6**, students should work at tables or move four desks together to create a work surface with the students seated around it.

ABOUT THE MATERIALS
Salad dressing bottles, flower vases, and condiment bottles can be used for this activity. It is best to use bottles with unusual shapes, but you should also include a right-circular cylinder and a shallow bowl. Each group needs water to use for filling their container. A pitcher or some other large container of water could be placed in the center of each group's work area for this purpose. Adding food coloring to the water will help students see the water level after each unit is added. You will also want to give each group paper towels for wiping up spills.

In **Step 1 of Question 6**, make sure each group marks their cup so that they pour about 50 mL of water into their bottle each time. If the "unit" they use is too large, they will not get a clear picture of the change and if it is too small, it will take too long to complete the experiment and graph the results.

TIPS FROM TEACHERS
In lieu of water, rice or dried split peas can be used for filling the containers.

394

---

5. a–b. Answers will vary. For narrower containers the water level will rise more drastically with each cup poured in.

5 a. Before you start your experiment, look at your group's container. How do you think the water level will change as water is poured into the container?

b. Use your prediction to sketch a graph of the water level as the container is filled.

6 Follow the steps below to perform the experiment. **Check students' work.**

Step 1 Mark your cup so that the same amount of water will be poured into the container each time. This amount will be called a "unit."

Step 2 Fill the cup with water up to the mark you made in Step 1. Pour the water into the container.

Step 3 Measure the water level to the nearest millimeter.

Step 4 Record the measurement in a table like the one shown.

Step 5 Repeat Steps 2–4 until the container is almost full. As you finish filling the container, you may need to estimate what fraction of a unit you use to completely fill it. Do not let the container overflow.

7 a. Use your table to make a graph that shows how the water level depends on the number of units of water in the container. Connect the data points with a smooth curve. **a–b. Answers will vary. Check students' work.**

b. Compare your graph from part (a) with the one you drew in Question 5. How accurate was your prediction?

▶ To get an idea of how something is changing, look at how one variable changes as the other variable increases by a fixed amount.

8 Try This as a Class Compare your results with other groups' results.

a. For which containers did the water level increase by the same amount each time water was added? **cylinders and prisms**

b. For which containers did the water level change by a different amount each time water was added? **irregularly shaped containers**

c. Which graphs are linear? **graphs for cylinders and prisms**

d. Which graphs are nonlinear? **graphs for irregularly shaped containers**

e. Suppose you repeated the experiment using the container shown at the right. Describe what you think your graph would look like. Explain your thinking. **The graph would be linear because the shape of the container is uniform.**

9 Try This as a Class Consider all groups' results.

a. For which groups did the water level in the container rise the fastest? **Answers will vary. Check students' work.**

b. How can you use your graphs to answer part (a)? **Graphs with a steep upward curve show the fastest rise.**

c. How does the shape of the container affect how fast the water level rises?

10 Two cylindrical containers are shown below. Equal amounts of water are poured into both containers.

Container A   Container B

a. For which container does the water level rise faster? **Container A**

b. A graph of the water level for Container A is shown. How would a graph of the water level for Container B compare with this graph? **Sample Response: The graph would be a line, but it would rise less steeply since the water level in Container B would rise more slowly than the water level in container A.**

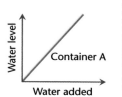

Water level

Container A

Water added

FOR◀HELP
with *choosing a scale*, see
MODULE 1, p. 51

9. c. Sample Response: In uniform containers the water level rises at the same rate. In irregularly shaped containers the water level will rise the fastest where the diameter is the smallest.

FOR◀HELP
with *linear and nonlinear graphs*, see
MODULE 3, p. 175

TIPS FROM TEACHERS
Question 7 Have students create graphs on overhead transparencies so it is easy to share the results in **Question 8**.

DEVELOPING MATH CONCEPTS
In **Question 9**, you may want to look at any rapid increases in the graphs and then point out containers that are similar for that corresponding section. For example, all containers with a narrow "neck" will probably all show a dramatic increase in the water height in one section of the graph. You could also do something similar for slow increases in the water height, showing how they correspond to parts of the containers that are wider.

TEACHING NOTES

To complete **Checkpoint Question 11**, students may look at the change in data values, examine rise or fall in the graphs, try to match the points given in the table with the points shown on the graph, or use some combination of these methods.

DEVELOPING MATH CONCEPTS

For **Question 12**, you may need to guide students by asking about the change in water level. For example, you might ask, "How quickly does the water level rise at the beginning?" or "Do you think each additional unit of water will give the same increase in water level?" (*It is rapid; The amount the water level rises is less each time.*)

✔ **QUESTION 11**

...checks that you can use tables and graphs to interpret data.

11. b. Table A: The graph starts at the origin and shows increase followed by decrease; Horizontal: Time (sec), vertical: Height (ft)
Table B: The graph starts above the origin and shows increasing growth over time; Horizontal: Time (days), vertical: Bacteria count
Table C: The graph starts at the origin and shows a steady rate of change; Horizontal: mi/hr, vertical: km/hr

---

11 ✔ CHECKPOINT

a. Match each table with one of the graphs below.
Table A: Graph 3   Table B: Graph 1   Table C: Graph 2

Table A: Height of a ball thrown in the air as time passes

Time (seconds)	0	0.5	1	1.5	2	2.5
Height (feet)	0	27	40	45	42	31

Table B: Bacteria growth in a heated swimming pool

Time (days)	0	0.5	1	1.5	2	2.5
Bacteria count	1500	2121	3000	4242	6000	8485

Table C: Speed conversion chart

mi/hr	0	10	20	30	40	50	60	70
km/hr	0	16	32	48	64	81	97	113

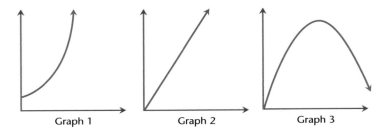

Graph 1   Graph 2   Graph 3

b. Explain why you chose that graph and tell what the labels on the horizontal and vertical axes should be.

12 On page 393, you read about the Great Salt Lake. Suppose a lake bed is approximately cone-shaped, as shown at the right. A long, steady rain causes the water level to rise. Sketch a graph that could model the water level over time.

HOMEWORK EXERCISES ▶ See Exs. 1–9 on pp. 401–402.

12.
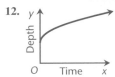

FUNCTIONS

GOAL

LEARN HOW TO...
- use tables, graphs, and equations to represent functions

AS YOU...
- compare different rainfall data

KEY TERM
- function

SET UP *Work with a partner.*

▶ In Exploration 1, you used a graph to show the relationship between the amount of water poured into a container and the water level inside the container.

13 Use the phrases *amount of water added* and *water level* to complete the following sentence. Explain your thinking.

In the experiment performed in Exploration 1, the __?__ depended on the __?__ . water level; amount of water added; The water level changed as a result of changes in the amount of water.

▶ Your graph in Question 7 represented a *function*. **A function is a relationship between input and output. For each input value, there is** *exactly* **one output value. Output is a function of input.**

14 a. Explain why the data you collected in your experiment represent a function. What is the input? the output?

b. Use the phrase *is a function of* to rewrite the completed statement from Question 13.

15 For five days, Mei recorded the data shown at the right. She concluded that the amount of rainfall for any given day is a function of the high temperature for that day.

a. How do you think Mei came to this conclusion? For each daily high temperature there is only one rainfall amount.

b. Suppose Mei recorded these data for a year. Do you think she would still say that daily rainfall is a function of daily high temperature? Why or why not?

c. In general, do you think that daily rainfall is a function of daily high temperature? Explain. Sample Response: No. Rainfall amounts are affected by more than daily high temperature.

14. There was only one water level for each amount of water added; the amount of water; the water level

15. b. No. It is likely that there would be different rainfall amounts for the same daily high temperature.

Daily high temperature (°F)	Amount of rainfall (in.)
81	0.4
75	0
79	0.5
80	1.2
74	0.5

Exploration 2

DEVELOPING MATH CONCEPTS
The study of functions is a central theme of mathematics. A function is a special kind of relationship between the elements of two sets, the domain (referred to in this exploration as the *input values*) and the range (or *output values*). Two ideas are fundamental to the understanding of functions. The first is that the output value paired with each input value is in some way dependent on the input value. This notion of dependence is introduced in **Question 13**, and reinforced throughout the exploration by the use of the terms input and output rather than domain and range. The second is that each input value has exactly one output value paired with it. This concept is introduced in **Question 14** and emphasized throughout the Exploration.

COMMON ERRORS
Students may have difficulty with **Question 15(a)**. Mei recognized that for each high temperature in the table there was exactly one rainfall amount and concluded that the amount of rainfall is a function of the daily high temperature. Some students will reverse the definition of function and conclude that since 0.5 occurs twice for the amount of rainfall, it cannot be a function of the high temperature. You can correct this misconception by asking questions such as "What values are the input values?" (*the high temperatures*) "What values are the output values?" (*the amount of rainfall*) and "Which values must have a unique number paired with them?" (*the input values or high temperatures*) or even more directed, "Does one temperature ever have two different amounts of rainfall listed?" (*No.*)

TEACHING NOTES
For students who have a hard time answering **Question 16(b)**, tell them to find the values of y in $y = 55x$ when $x = 1, 3, 6,$ and 8. Then compare the results with the data in the table in part (a).

▶ A function may be represented using a rule that relates one variable to another. A function rule is typically an equation that gives the output in terms of the input.

16 A driver is maintaining the same rate of travel during a long-distance trip on a highway. The table shows the total distances the driver travels for various amounts of driving time.

Time (hours)	1	3	6	8
Distance (miles)	55	165	330	440

a. Describe the relationship between the distance traveled and the number of hours traveled using the phrase *is a function of*. The distance traveled is a function of the number of hours traveled.

b. Let $x =$ the number of hours driven and let $y =$ the distance traveled in miles. Explain why the equation $y = 55x$ is a rule for the function in part (a). For each value of x in the table, $y = 55x$.

17 **Discussion** Tell whether y is a function of x. Explain your thinking. Sample Responses are given.

a. $x =$ the amount of time that the sky is cloudy
$y =$ the amount of rain that falls No. Not all clouds produce rain.

b. $x =$ the rate at which you read
$y =$ the time you take to read a book Yes. The time to read a book depends on the rate at which you read.

c. $x =$ the number of pounds of grapes purchased
$y =$ the cost of the grapes Yes. The cost depends on the number of pounds purchased.

d. $x =$ a person's height
$y =$ the foot length of someone with that height No. Two people can be the same height but have different foot lengths.

18 Suppose it starts raining steadily at noon. The rain falls for the rest of the afternoon at a rate of 0.2 inch per hour.

a. Let $y =$ the amount of rain that has fallen since noon. Let $x =$ the number of hours since noon. Explain why the value of y is a function of the value of x. The total amount of rainfall depends on the number of hours since noon.

b. Write an equation that represents this function. $y = 0.2x$

▶ You can use a table of values or a graph to tell whether an equation represents a function.

EXAMPLE

Given an equation relating x and y, you can tell whether y is a function of x by comparing input and output values in a table or a graph.

a. $y = x^2$ For every value of x, there is exactly one value of y. The equation represents a function.

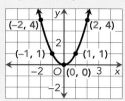

Input (x)	Output (y)
−2	4
−1	1
0	0
1	1
2	4

b. $x = y^2$ For some values of x, there are two different values of y. The equation does not represent a function.

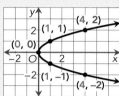

Input (x)	Output (y)
0	0
1	−1 and 1
4	−2 and 2

19 **Try This as a Class** Refer to the Example.

   a. How are the two graphs alike? How are they different?

   b. Use the table for each equation to find the value(s) of y when $x = 1$. Then use the graph of each equation. For $y = x^2$, $y = 1$ when $x = 1$; For $x = y^2$, $y = -1$ and 1 when $x = 1$.

   c. How can you use a table of values to tell whether an equation represents a function? How can you use a graph?

20 ✔ **CHECKPOINT** For each equation or graph, tell whether y is a function of x. Explain your thinking.

   a. $y = 7x$ **b.** $2 + x = y^2$

   c. 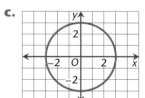   **d.**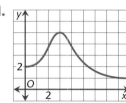

HOMEWORK EXERCISES ▶ See Exs. 10–26 on pp. 403–404.

---

19. a. Both graphs are the same shape; They are in different positions. One opens upward and the other opens to the right.

   c. If there is only one value of y for each value of x in a table, the equation represents a function. If for every value of x, there is at most one point on a graph with first coordinate x, the graph represents a function.

20. a. function; For every value of x there is a only one value of y.

   b. not a function; There are two values of y for some values of x.

   c. not a function; There are two values of y for some values of x.

✔ **QUESTION 20**

...checks that you can identify a function.

20. d. function; For every value of x there is only one value of y.

DEVELOPING MATH CONCEPTS

When discussing **Question 19**, have students slide a ruler across the graph while keeping the ruler parallel to the y-axis. They should notice that for a function, the ruler always intersects the curve in exactly one point, and if the ruler ever intersects the curve in more than one point, it is not a function. This is the *vertical line test*.

TEACHING NOTES

If students need more guidance determining if an equation represents a function, you may want to discuss the following examples before students begin **Checkpoint Question 20**.

CLASSROOM EXAMPLES

Make a table and draw a graph for each equation. Then tell whether y is a function of x by comparing input and output values.

  a. $y = |x|$ b. $x = |y|$

Answer:

a.
In (x)	Out (y)
−2	2
−1	1
0	0
1	1
2	2

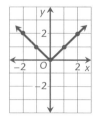

For every value of x, there is exactly one value of y. The equation models a function.

b.
In (x)	Out (y)
2	−2
1	−1
0	0
1	1
2	2

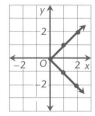

For some values of x, there are two different values of y. The equation does not model a function.

399

21. a. 11 gal; Sample Response: The table shows that with each minute the number of gallons in the tank increases by 4, so halfway between 2 and 3 in the table would be halfway between 9 and 13 gallons, which is 11 gallons.

b. Sample Response: During the first interval the car was most likely being driven at a steady rate. In the next 20 min the car used more gas so was probably being driven at a faster rate, perhaps on a highway. During the next interval the car may have been idling in a parking lot and was then turned off. In the next interval the car was not using any gas so it was parked and turned off. The final interval shows the car being driven at a steady rate as in the first interval.

Section 1
Key Concepts

Modeling Change (pp. 393–396)

You can use tables and graphs to model and analyze changes in data.

Example Suppose you measured the amount of gasoline in two different automobile tanks.

Car A The table shows that the number of gallons of gasoline in the tank increases by the same amount each minute as gasoline is pumped into the tank. The data points lie on a straight line.

Time (min)	Gallons in the tank
0	1
1	5
2	9
3	13

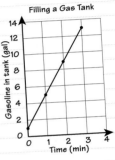

Filling a Gas Tank

Car B The table shows that the number of gallons of gasoline in the tank decreases by a different amount every 20 minutes while the car is being driven. The graph is always decreasing, but not in a straight line.

Time (min)	Gallons in the tank
0	14
20	13
40	11
60	10.5
80	10.5
100	9

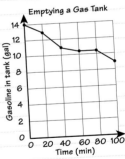

Emptying a Gas Tank

21 Key Concepts Question

a. How much gasoline is in Car A's tank after $2\frac{1}{2}$ min? Explain how you used either the table or the graph to find the answer.

b. Describe a situation that the graph for Car B might represent.

Section 1

Key Concepts

Functions (pp. 397–399)

A function is a relationship that pairs each input with exactly one output. You can use equations, tables, and graphs to represent functions.

Example A number y is 1 more than 3 times a number x.

Equation
$y = 3x + 1$

Table

x	y
−2	−5
−1	−2
0	1
1	4

Graph

22 Key Concepts Question Do the graphs and tables on page 400 represent functions? If so, list the input values and the corresponding output values. If not, explain why.

22. Yes. In both cases, the number of gallons in the tank is a function of time.

Input	Output
0	1
1	5
2	9
3	13

Input	Output
0	14
20	13
40	11
60	10.5
80	10.5
100	9

CLOSURE QUESTION

State the definition of a function and give an example.

Sample Response: A function is a rule that pairs each input value with exactly one output value. In the equation $y = x + 3$, y is a function of x, but in the equation $x = y^2$, y is not a function of x because for $x = 9$ there could be two y values 3, and −3.

Practice & Applications

SUGGESTED ASSIGNMENTS

Core Course
Day 1: Exs. 27–32
Day 2: Exs. 1–8
Day 3: Exs. 10–24, 26

Extended Course
Day 1: Exs. 27–32
Day 2: Exs. 1–9
Day 3: Exs. 10–26

Note: Extended Course assignments can be used to differentiate within the regular classroom. In classrooms where students are grouped homogeneously, the material might be covered in fewer days. In this case assignments may be combined.

ADDITIONAL PRACTICE

See the *Teacher's Resource Book* for additional practice and application exercises for this section.

Section 1

Practice & Application Exercises

Suppose water is steadily poured into each of the containers below. Which graph models the water level in each container over time?

1.
B

2.
C

3.
D

4.
A

A. **B.** **C.** **D.**

YOU WILL NEED

For Ex. 5:
◆ Labsheet 1A

For Exs. 6, 7, 25, and 29–32:
◆ graph paper

Practice & Applications

EXERCISE NOTES

Exercise 5 Since interpreting a graph or table in a physical context is so new to students, it is important to discuss the exercise and to give students a chance to share their approaches.

Writing Exercises 6 and 7 provide experience in the type of writing required for the Module Project. When discussing **Exercise 6**, talk about how more detail could be added for each part of the bike ride to explain what was happening and why. This will help students see how a story can be created from a basic outline of a situation. Brainstorming situations involving change will help get students started on **Exercise 7**.

---

5. The first graph matches the second table; the second graph matches the second description; The third graph matches the first table; The fourth graph matches the first description; The fifth graph matches the third description.

6. Sample Response:

The oldest surviving ▶ water clock is from Egypt, 14th century B.C.

8. the first graph; The water height does not increase with time (as shown in the third graph), nor will it decrease at a steady rate (as shown in the second graph) because the water clock is smaller at the base than at the top.

---

5. **Use Labsheet 1A.** You will match a verbal description or a table with each of the *Graphs Without Labels*.

6. **Open-ended** Sketch a graph that could model the following bike ride. You ride a bicycle for some time at a constant speed. Then you slow down for a stop sign, stop and look both ways, then speed up again.

7. **Create Your Own** Write a story or a poem that describes a change over time. Use a graph to illustrate your story or poem.
   Answers will vary. Check students' work.

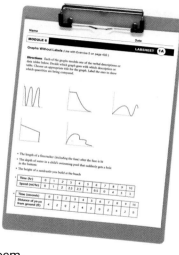

History In ancient times, people used containers filled with water to tell time. The water dripped out a hole in the base of the water clock at a nearly constant rate. People could tell the time by comparing the water level with hour marks on the container. Use this information for Exercises 8 and 9.

8. Which graph would you expect to model the change in water level inside the water clock shown above? Why?

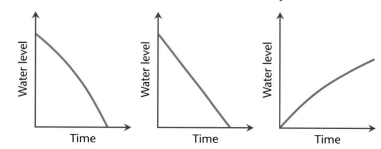

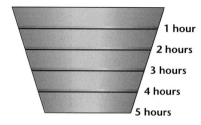

- 1 hour
- 2 hours
- 3 hours
- 4 hours
- 5 hours

9. **Challenge** An artist drew a sketch of the inside of a water clock to show that after one hour, the level is at the first hour mark, after two hours, the level is at the second hour mark, and so on. The artist makes the distances between the marks the same. Are the marks spaced correctly? Explain.
   No. The marks should be farther apart toward the bottom where the water clock is narrower.

10. Suppose you have $230 saved. You get a job that pays $25 a week. You decide to add all of your earnings to your savings.

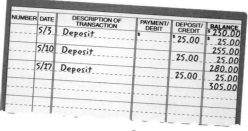

    a. Describe a function based on this situation. Each week the total amount in the savings account increases by $25.

    b. Identify the input and output.

    c. Write an equation to represent the function. $y = 25x + 230$

Writing For each pair of variables, tell whether *y* is a function of *x*. Explain your thinking.

11. *x* = the number of $12 concert tickets sold
y = the amount of money made from selling the tickets Yes. The amount of money made depends on the number of tickets sold.

12. *x* = the age of any given office building
y = the height of that office building No. The height of an office building does not depend on how old it is.

13. *x* = the time of year
y = the time at which the sun rises where you live Yes. In one location there is only one sunrise time for each day of the year.

For each equation or graph, tell whether *y* is a function of *x*.

14. $7x = y$ **15.** $x = 7$ **16.** $x^2 - 1 = y$ **17.** $2x = y^2$
function   not a function   function   not a function

18. 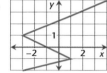 not a function **19.** 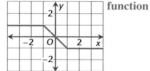 function

20. Geometry Connection

    a. Is the area of a square a function of its side length? Explain.
    Yes. Side lengths determine the area of a square.

    b. Is the side length of a square a function of its area? Explain.

For Exercises 21–23, a rule for a function is given. Write an equation to represent the function.

21. Divide a number by 5. $y = \frac{x}{5}$ **22.** Multiply a number by −1. $y = -1x$

23. Multiply a number by itself, then divide the result by 2. $y = \frac{x^2}{2}$

24. Home Involvement Make up a rule for a function like those in Exercises 21–23. Keep your rule secret. Have someone give you a number to use as the input. Tell the person the output for that number. The person should make a table of the input and output pairs. Have the person try to guess the rule. Answers will vary. Check students' work.

10. b. Input is the number of weeks and output is the total amount in the savings account.

20. b. Yes. The side length of a square is the positive square root of its area, so for each area, there is only one side length.

EXERCISE NOTES

For **Exercises 14–19,** have students give a short written explanation of why each relation is or is not a function. They might include a table of values or a graph for the equations in their explanations.

After students have completed **Exercise 20,** have them write algebraic equations for the geometric situations described in the exercise. Then ask how they could determine whether these equations represent functions. ($A = s^2$ and $s = \sqrt{A}$; Graph them and do a vertical line test.)

Practice & Applications

EXERCISE NOTES
Reflecting on the Section
Exercise 26 Throughout this exploration, students have seen various examples of quantities that change over time. However when it comes to thinking up their own example, some students may be stumped. Suggest they brainstorm about quantities that change over a period of 1 hr, 1 day, 1 week, 1 year, or even over a lifetime. Relating it to something that has changed (and can be measured) in their own lives may be helpful.

29. 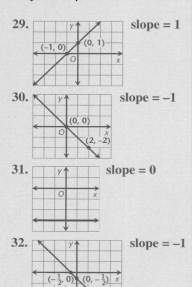 slope = 1

30. slope = –1

31. slope = 0

32. slope = –1

---

25. b. (0, 2.1), (1, 2.5), (2, 2.9), (3, 3.3), (4, 3.7), (5, 4.1), (6, 4.5); The values of x range from 0 to 6 since the river rose for 6 days. The values of y will be between 2 and 4.5 since the original height above the bank was 2.1 in. and it increased at a rate of 0.4 in. for 6 days.

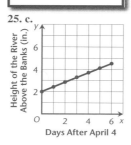

Discussion

Exercise 26 checks that you can identify and represent a function.

25. c.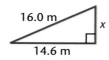

Height of the River Above the Banks (in.)

Days After April 4

---

25. **Earth Science** In 1993, heavy rains in the Midwest caused the Mississippi River to flood its banks. By April 4, the water had risen 2.1 in. above the banks of the river. It continued to rise at an average rate of 0.4 in. per day for the next six days.

a. Let y = the height of the river above the bank x days after April 4. Write an equation for y in terms of x. $y = 0.4x + 2.1$

b. Describe reasonable values for each of the variables in your equation. Explain your thinking.

c. Graph your equation.

d. Tell whether y is a function of x. Yes, y is a function of x.

Reflecting on the Section

26. In this section, you have seen how graphs and tables can be used to illustrate change. a–b. Answers will vary. Check students' work.

a. Describe a quantity that changes over time. Explain how you could use a table and graph to represent the change.

b. Is the change you described in part (a) a function? Explain.

Spiral Review

27. The perimeter of a rectangular garden is 136 m. Its area is 960 m². Find the perimeter and the area of a scale drawing of the garden with a scale of 1 cm to 2 m. (Module 5, p. 381)
Perimeter is 68 cm, area is 240 cm²

28. Find the value of x. Round to the nearest hundredth. (Module 5, p. 343) 6.55 m

16.0 m

14.6 m

x

Graph each equation. Give the slope of each line.
(Module 4, pp. 264–265) 29–32. See margin.

29. $y = x + 1$ 30. $y = -x$ 31. $y = -3$ 32. $y = -x - \dfrac{1}{2}$

Section 1

Extra Skill Practice

Match each container with a graph that shows the water level as a function of the amount of water in the container.

1. B
2. A
3. D
4. C

A.
B.
C.
D.

For each equation or graph, tell whether y is a function of x.

5. $2x = 2y$
   function

6. $y = x - 7$
   function

7. $2y = x^2$
   function

8. $2x = y^2$
   not a function

9. 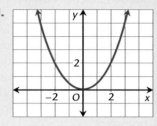 function

10. 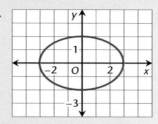 not a function

---

Extra Skill Practice

TEACHER NOTES
For each Exploration, the corresponding Extra Skill Practice Exercises are noted.

Exploration 1: Exs. 1–4
Exploration 2: Exs. 5–10

EXTRA HELP
Teacher's Resource Book
• Practice and Applications
• Study Guide

Technology Resources
• @Home Tutor
• Test Generator

ASSESSMENT
• Section 1 Quick Quiz
• Test Generator

Study Skills ◀▶ **Managing Your Time**

Whether you are working independently or in a group to complete a short-term activity or a long-term project, time management should be part of your preparation.

1. In Exploration 1, you worked in a group to conduct an experiment to explore how the shape of a container affects water level. Did your group finish the experiment in the available time? What strategies can you use in planning your time so that you will always finish group activities?

2. Before you begin working on the module project on pages 452–453, make a plan for how you will complete all of the steps so that you finish the entire project on time. Answers will vary.

1. Answers will vary. Check students' work. Set specific goals in the beginning and specify the time in which they need to be completed, appoint a group leader to make sure your project is on schedule.

Section 1 Graphs and Functions

405

Section ② Linear Equations and Problem Solving

IN THIS SECTION
EXPLORATION 1
♦ Linear Change
EXPLORATION 2
♦ Multi-Step Equations

Setting the Stage

A penny may not seem like very much, but you would be surprised at how quickly pennies add up.

Students at the Lovell J. Honiss School in Dumont, New Jersey, set a goal of filling two five-gallon jugs with pennies. Although they quickly met their goal, they continued to save pennies. In the end, they filled four jugs and raised over $1000 to help the homeless.

In Hartland, Michigan, students in the Hartland Consolidated Schools collected pennies for the Meals on Wheels program. They collected over $10,000, enough to fund the program for a year.

Think About It

1 a. About how may pennies does a five-gallon jug hold? How do you know? about 25,000 pennies; Four jugs held about $1000 or 100,000 pennies.

b. Suppose the Hartland students collected the pennies over 50 school days. On average, about how many pennies were collected each day? about 20,000 pennies

2. Answers will vary; Spread out in a single layer, the pennies would cover about 3900 ft² (including the space between the pennies).

2 Would the pennies collected at the Hartland Consolidated Schools cover your classroom floor? the gymnasium floor? Explain.

▶ In this section, you will use equations, tables, and graphs to model problems involving the growth of savings over time.

Exploration 1

Change

GOAL

LEARN HOW TO...
- use equations, tables, and graphs to solve problems

AS YOU...
- investigate different savings plans

KEY TERM
- linear equation

SET UP *Work with a partner. You will need: • graph paper • graphing calculator (optional)*

▶ **How quickly can you save $1000? It all depends on how much you start with, and how much you add to your savings over time.**

3 Discussion Read the savings plans described below. Without doing any calculations, tell which person you think will reach the $1000 goal first. Explain your thinking.

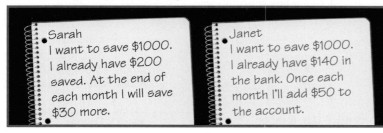

> Sarah
> I want to save $1000.
> I already have $200 saved. At the end of each month I will save $30 more.

> Janet
> I want to save $1000.
> I already have $140 in the bank. Once each month I'll add $50 to the account.

4 a. Copy and extend the table to show how much Sarah will save throughout the first year of her plan.

Sarah's Savings	
Number of months (*x*)	Amount saved (*y*)
0	200
1	230
...	...

b. Use your table to find the number of months it will take Sarah to save $1000. Describe your method. **See margin.**

5 a. Plot the ordered pairs (*x, y*) for the data in your table on a coordinate grid. What do you notice about the points? **a–c. See margin.**

b. Draw a line through the points on your graph. Extend the line and use it to find the number of months it will take Sarah to save $1000.

c. Discussion Find the point on the line whose *x*-coordinate is $6\frac{1}{2}$. Does the value of the *y*-coordinate of this point represent Sarah's savings after $6\frac{1}{2}$ months? Explain.

3. Sample Response: Janet; She starts with less but saves a greater amount each month.

4. a. 2, 260; 3, 290; 4, 320; 5, 350; 6, 380; 7, 410; 8, 440; 9, 470; 10, 500; 11, 530; 12, 560

Exploration 1

TEACHING NOTES
In **Question 3**, some students will say Sarah will save $1000 first because she starts with more money. Others will say Janet will save $1000 first because she saves more each month. Avoid a lengthy discussion of who is correct here. This is the question that is investigated in the remainder of Exploration 1. Use the difference of opinion to motivate the investigation that follows.

COMMON ERROR
Some students may have trouble interpreting the remainder in **Question 4(b)**. Some may answer $26\frac{2}{3}$ months, not recognizing that after 26 months Sarah has saved $980 and the next $30 isn't saved until the end of the 27th month, giving a total of $1010. Others will get the correct answer by rounding, which may lead to an error in **Question 7(a)**.

DEVELOPING MATH CONCEPTS
Question 5(c) It is important for students to understand that the line was drawn on the graph to help identify the trend in the savings data and to help make predictions. Since Sarah's deposits are made at monthly intervals, the total saved is discrete data, not continuous data as represented by the line. Only points on the graph corresponding to a whole number of months give actual amounts saved, so the *y*-coordinate for $6\frac{1}{2}$ months does not tell how much Sarah had saved.

4. b., 5. a–c. See Additional Answers beginning on page A1.

407

If students need more guidance using equations, tables, and graphs to analyze situations, you may want to discuss the following example before they begin **Checkpoint Question 9** on page 409.

CLASSROOM EXAMPLE

Glen has $56. He adds $24 to his savings at the end of each month. How much will he have after one year?

Answer:

Method 1: Use a linear equation.

$$\frac{\text{Savings after}}{x \text{ months}} = \frac{\text{starting}}{\text{amount}} + \frac{\$24 \text{ per}}{\text{month}} \cdot \frac{x}{\text{months}}$$

$$y = 56 + 24x$$
$$= 56 + 24(12) \quad \text{Substitute 12 for } x.$$
$$= 344 \quad \text{Solve the equation for } y.$$

Method 2: Use a table.

Glen's Savings	
Number of months	Amount saved
0	56
1	80
2	104
⋮	⋮
11	320
12	344

Method 3: Use a graph.

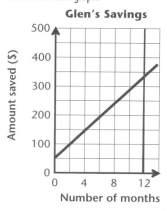

Glen's Savings

▶ The growth of Sarah's savings over time is an example of linear change. You can use a *linear equation* to represent linear change. A **linear equation** is an equation whose graph is a line. A linear equation whose graph is not a vertical line represents a function.

FOR HELP
with *slope-intercept form*, see
MODULE 4, p. 265

6 a. Find the slope *m* and the *y*-intercept *b* of the line you drew in Question 5(b). Use these values to write an equation for the line in slope-intercept form. slope = 30; y-intercept = 200; $y = 30x + 200$

b. Substitute values for *x* in the equation from part (a). Solve for *y*. Do the values you get match the values in your table? Yes

▶ You can use equations, tables, and graphs to model problems involving linear change.

EXAMPLE

Janet has $140. She adds $50 to her savings at the end of each month. When will she have $1000?

Method 1 Use a linear equation.

$$\frac{\text{Savings after}}{x \text{ months}} = \frac{\text{Starting}}{\text{amount}} + \frac{\$50 \text{ per}}{\text{month}} \cdot x \text{ months}$$

$$y = 140 + 50x$$
$$1000 = 140 + 50x$$

Substitute $1,000 for *y*. Solve the equation for *x*.

Method 2 Use a table.

Keep adding $50 to Janet's savings for each month until she reaches the $1000 goal.

Janet's Savings	
Number of months	Amount saved
0	140
1	190
2	240
…	…

Method 3 Use a graph.

Graph $y = 140 + 50x$ and $y = 1000$ on the same pair of axes.

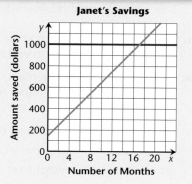

Janet's Savings

7 **Try This as a Class** Refer to the Example on page 408. You will use each model to find how long it will take Janet to save $1000.

    a. Solve the equation in the Example. How can you use the solution to find out when Janet will have saved $1000? *17.2; Round up to the next whole number 18.*

    b. Show how to use the table to find out how long it will take Janet to save $1000.

    c. Show how to use the graph to find out how long it will take Janet to save $1000.

    d. Which method do you prefer? Why? *Answers will vary.*

8 Plot the data for Janet's savings from the Example on page 408 on the same pair of axes as the graph you made in Question 5. What does the intersection of the two lines tell you? *See margin.*

9 ✔ **CHECKPOINT** The Hartland Consolidated students collected $10,000 in pennies. Suppose your class was given a gift of $650 and saved $175 each week. With your partner, use an equation, a table, or a graph to find out how many weeks it would take to save $10,000. Explain why you chose the model you did.
See margin.

10 **Discussion** Find a group in your class that chose a different model than you did for Question 9.

    a. Show the other group how you got your answer.
    See answer to Question 9.

    b. Compare the advantages and disadvantages of using an equation, a table, and a graph to model the growth of a savings plan. *See margin.*

7. b.

Number of months	Amount saved
0	140
1	190
⋮	⋮
17	990
18	1040

In month 18 the $50 she adds to her savings makes it more than $1000.

✔ **QUESTION 9**

...checks that you can model and solve a problem about linear change.

DIFFERENTIATED INSTRUCTION
Questions 8–10 For students who may have difficulty completing the graphs and tables at the rate of the rest of the class, use of a graphing calculator (or software) will allow them to participate in the discovery and discussions. By entering the equations and then using the TRACE feature students can find the coordinates of points on the two lines. This feature also shows (in a way that examining a static graph cannot) that the point where the two lines intersect is the point where the same amount has been saved with each plan. On the calculator, students can quickly view the equation, the table, and the graph.

7. c. The point where the graphs intersect is when she has saved $1000. When $y = 1000$, the x-coordinate is a little more than 17, showing she has saved at least $1000 in 18 months.

HOMEWORK EXERCISES ▶ See Exs. 1–8 on pp. 414–415.

Section 2 Linear Equations and Problem Solving

8., 9., and 10. b. See Additional Answers beginning on page A1.

Exploration 2

USING MANIPULATIVES

Algebra tiles can be used throughout Exploration 2 to help visual and kinesthetic learners understand the concepts. Algebra tiles are particularly useful for modeling the following: the equation in the **Example** on p. 410 and the solution of the equation in **Question 12**, the distributive property before **Question 15**, and the **Example** on page 411.

DEVELOPING MATH CONCEPTS

Students have had a great deal of experience solving equations that only have variables on one side of the equal sign. Based on this experience, their answer to **Question 12(a)** will probably be that they would subtract 140 from both sides of the equation. The result is the equation $60 + 30x = 50x$, which still has variables on both sides of the equals sign. You may need to follow this response with questions such as, "How do you know you can subtract 140 from both sides of the equation?" and "How can you get like terms combined?" The questions should lead students to the idea that the goal is to get all of the variables on one side of the equation and that this can be done by subtracting $30x$ from both sides.

DIFFERENTIATED INSTRUCTION

As an extension of **Checkpoint 13** ask students to solve the equation $x + 7 = 2x - x + 8$. You may want to show the graphs of the equations $y = x + 7$ and $y = 2x - x + 8$ to help students see that, because the lines are parallel and thus never intersect, there is no solution. Contrast this to $x + 7 = 2x - x + 7$ where every value of x is a solution since the graphs of $y = x + 7$ and $y = 2x - x + 7$ are the same line.

410

GOAL

LEARN HOW TO...
- ◆ solve equations that involve simplifying
- ◆ use the distributive property

AS YOU...
- ◆ model savings plans

KEY TERM
- ◆ distributive property

11. **Sample Response:** Make a table of input values and output values for each girl. Continue adding input values until a solution to the problem is reached.

12. a. Subtract or add one of the variable terms from both sides of the equation; When all the variable terms are on the same side of the equation it can be solved.

...checks that you can solve equations with variables on both sides.

Exploration 2

Multi-Step Equations

▶ On page 407, you read about two people who are each trying to save $1000. Sarah has $200 and saves another $30 each month. Janet is starting with $140 and saves an additional $50 each month.

11 **Discussion** In Question 8 on page 409, you used a graph to find when the two girls will have saved equal amounts of money. How could you use tables to solve this problem?

▶ You can also use an equation to find out when the girls will have the same amount.

EXAMPLE

For each plan, model the amount saved after x months.

Sarah's savings = 200 + 30x Janet's savings = 140 + 50x

Then write a new equation.

When will **Sarah's savings** equal **Janet's savings**?

Sarah's savings = Janet's savings

$200 + 30x = 140 + 50x$

To find out when the amounts saved are equal, solve the equation for x.

12 **Try This as a Class** The final equation in the Example has a variable on both sides of the equal sign.

a. What would be your first step in solving an equation like this one? Explain your thinking.

b. When will Sarah and Janet have the same amount?
    after 3 months of deposits

13 ✔ **CHECKPOINT** Solve each equation.

a. $18 + 3x = x + 24$ **b.** $9 + 2x = 12 + 5x$ **c.** $4x - 7 = 2 - 3x$ $\frac{9}{7}$
        3   -1

d. $5 - x = 25 + x$ **e.** $-12 + 7x = 3x + 8$ **f.** $-5x - 8 = -7x + 1$
        -10 5   4.5

▶ One way to save money is in a savings bank *certificate of deposit* (CD). You deposit an amount of money and agree not to take any money out for a certain amount of time. In return, the bank pays a higher than usual interest rate.

14 Suppose you deposit $1000 into a one-year CD. The expression $1000(1 + x)$ models the amount of money you will have after one year. What do you think x represents? the interest rate on the CD

▶ In Module 1 you learned the distributive property. Recall that all four of the following statements are true for all numbers a, b, and c.

$$a(b + c) = ab + ac \qquad\qquad ab + ac = a(b + c)$$
$$a(b - c) = ab - ac \qquad\qquad ab - ac = a(b - c)$$

15 a. Use the distributive property to rewrite the expression $1000(1 + x)$. $1000 + 1000x$

  b. Show that the expression in Question 14 and the expression you wrote in part (a) have the same value when $x = 0.04$.
  $1000(1 + 0.04) = 1000(1.04) = 1040$; $1000 + 1000(0.04) = 1000 + 40 = 1040$

  c. How much money will you have after one year at 4% interest? $1040

▶ You can use the distributive property to rewrite an expression involving parentheses.

EXAMPLE

Rewrite $5(3 - 2x)$ without parentheses.

$$5(3 - 2x) = 5(3) - 5(2x)$$
$$= 15 - 10x \qquad \text{Use the distributive property.}$$

16 a. In Module 1, you used the distributive property to combine like terms, such as $2x + 3x = (2 + 3)x = 5x$. Which version of the distributive property did you use? $ab + ac = a(b + c)$, which can also be written $ba + ca = (b + c)a$

  b. Which version of the distributive property is used in the Example above to rewrite an expression involving parentheses? $a(b - c) = ab - ac$

17 ✔ **CHECKPOINT** Use the distributive property to rewrite each expression without parentheses.

  a. $5(2x - 3)$ $10x - 15$ **b.** $-2(5 + x)$ $-10 - 2x$

  c. $3(6m + 7)$ $18m + 21$ **d.** $7(8m - 1)$ $56m - 7$

✔ **QUESTION 17**

…checks that you can use the distributive property.

DEVELOPING MATH CONCEPTS
Because students have not had much experience computing interest, you may need to lead them through **Question 14** by asking questions such as: What does the 1000 represent? (*the amount deposited*) What does the $1000x$ represent? (*the amount by which the deposit is increased*) Can x be a whole number? (*Probably not since the amount saved would be doubling, tripling and so on, and banks don't pay that much interest in a year.*) If x is a decimal less than 1, what does the decimal represent? (*the percent interest rate expressed by a decimal*)

TEACHING NOTES
The Classroom Example below can be used to debate or support the discussion in **Question 16**.

CLASSROOM EXAMPLE

Rewrite $10(3x - 4)$ without parentheses.

Answer: Write $3x - 4$ as an addition expression. Then use the distributive property.

$$10(3x - 4) = 10[3x + (-4)]$$
$$= 10(3x) + 10(-4)$$
$$= 30x + (-40)$$
$$= 30x - 40$$

TEACHER NOTES

If needed, the following example can be used before students begin **Checkpoint Question 20.**

CLASSROOM EXAMPLE

Eddy earns the same amount mowing lawns every week. Each week, he saves all but $15 of his earnings. If he has $330 after 12 weeks, how much does he earn each week?

Answer: Let x = the amount Eddy earns each week.

$$330 = 12(x - 15)$$
$$330 = 12x - 180$$
$$330 + 180 = 12x - 180 + 180$$
$$510 = 12x$$
$$42.50 = x$$

Eddy earns $42.50 each week.

COMMON ERRORS

When solving equations like the one in **Question 19**, students often make errors related to operations with integers. For example, when they use the distributive property to multiply -3 times $(3 - x)$, they erroneously get $-9 - 3x$ instead of $-9 + 3x$. This kind of error was investigated in **Question 18**. For students making this error, suggest they write out all the signs and operations as $(-3)(3) - (-3)(x)$ to get $-9 - (-3x)$ which can then be rewritten as $-9 + 3x$.

A second type of error occurs after students have completed steps similar to those shown below.

$$-3(x - 1) = 2(5 - x)$$
$$-3x + 3 = 10 - 2x$$
$$-3x = 7 - 2x$$

To get all the terms containing variables on the same side of the equation, they add $2x$ to both sides. However, when adding $-3x$ and $2x$ they get -5 instead of $-x$. Watch for and help students correct these types of errors.

---

18. a. Dennis; Steve used the distributive property incorrectly, dropping either the negative sign on the four or the minus sign before x.

b. Use the distributive property to simplify $-2(3 - x)$ or divide both sides of the equation by -2.

19. Sample Response: Use the distributive property to rewrite both sides of the equation. Next add $3x$ to both sides of the equation to get variable terms alone on one side of the equation. Finally, subtract 10 from both sides of the equation.

✔ **QUESTION 20**

...checks that you can use the distributive property to solve an equation.

▶ Sometimes you may want to use the distributive property to solve an equation.

EXAMPLE

Hector earns the same amount babysitting every week. Each week he saves all but $10 of his earnings. If he has $160 after 8 weeks, how much does he earn each week?

SAMPLE RESPONSE

Let x = the amount Hector earns each week. Then $x - 10$ = the amount he saves each week.

$$160 = 8(x - 10)$$
$$160 = 8x - 80 \quad \text{Use the distributive property.}$$
$$240 = 8x$$
$$30 = x$$

Hector earns $30 each week babysitting.

18 Two students tried to solve the equation $-4(2 - x) = 6$.

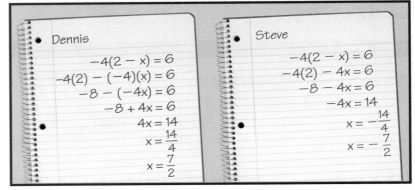

Dennis
$$-4(2 - x) = 6$$
$$-4(2) - (-4)(x) = 6$$
$$-8 - (-4x) = 6$$
$$-8 + 4x = 6$$
$$4x = 14$$
$$x = \frac{14}{4}$$
$$x = \frac{7}{2}$$

Steve
$$-4(2 - x) = 6$$
$$-4(2) - 4x = 6$$
$$-8 - 4x = 6$$
$$-4x = 14$$
$$x = -\frac{14}{4}$$
$$x = -\frac{7}{2}$$

a. Which student solved the equation correctly? What mistake did the other student make?

b. What would be your first step in solving $-2(3 - x) = 8$?

19 **Discussion** How would you solve $-3(x - 1) = 2(5 - x)$?

20 ✔ **CHECKPOINT** Solve each equation.

a. $4(x - 1) = 12$ **b.** $-2(3 - x) = 3x + 1$ **c.** $3(2x - 1) = x + 13$
  4   -7 $x = \frac{16}{5}$ or $3\frac{1}{5}$

HOMEWORK EXERCISES ▶ See Exs. 9–30 on pp. 415–417.

Section 2

Key Concepts

Modeling Linear Change (pp. 407–409)

When a quantity changes by the same amount at regular intervals, the quantity shows linear change. You can use a linear equation to model linear change. You can also use a table or a graph.

Example
Lynda borrowed **$175** from her parents. She pays them back **$10** a week. Her sister Maria borrowed **$200** and pays back **$15** a week. Who will finish paying off her loan first?

Write an equation for each person. Let y = the amount the person owes after x weeks.

Lynda
$$y = 175 - 10x$$

Maria
$$y = 200 - 15x$$

Number of weeks	Amount Lynda owes	Amount Maria owes
0	175	200
1	165	185
2	155	170
4	135	140
5	125	125
6	115	110
...	...	...
13	45	5
14	35	0

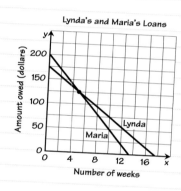

Lynda's and Maria's Loans

Maria only has to pay $5 in the 14th week.

After five weeks, they owe the same amount of money. After that, Maria is paying more per week than Lynda, so she will pay off her loan first.

21 **Key Concepts Question** In the Example above, how does the graph show when the sisters owe the same amount of money?
It is shown by the point of intersection of the two graphs.

Key Concepts

Key Term

linear equation

CLOSURE QUESTION
Define what is meant by *linear equation*.

Sample Response: When graphed, the solutions of the equation lie on a line. For example, $y = 2x + 8$ is a linear equation because its graph is a line.

Key Concepts *continued*

ABSENT STUDENTS

For students who were absent for all or part of this section, the blackline Study Guide for Section 2 may be used to present the ideas, concepts, and skills of Section 2.

Practice & Applications

SUGGESTED ASSIGNMENTS

Core Course

Day 1: Exs. 1–8
Day 2: Exs. 16–19, 31–39
Day 3: Exs. 9–14, 20–28, 30

Extended Course

Day 1: Exs. 1–8
Day 2: Exs. 16–19, 31–39
Day 3: Exs. 11–15, 19–25 odd, 26–30

Note: Extended Course assignments can be used to differentiate within the regular classroom. In classrooms where students are grouped homogeneously, the material might be covered in fewer days. In this case assignments may be combined.

ADDITIONAL PRACTICE

See the *Teacher's Resource Book* for additional practice and application exercises for this section.

Key Term

distributive property

22. Use the two equations given to write a new equation by setting the two expressions for y equal to each other; $175 - 10x = 200 - 15x$. Solve the new equation for x.

Section 2
Key Concepts

Solving Equations (pp. 410–412)

To solve some equations, you may need to use the distributive property and combine like terms.

Example

$$-3(1 + 4x) + 2x = 5x$$

Use the distributive property.

$$-3(1) + (-3)(4x) + 2x = 5x$$

$$-3 + (-12x) + 2x = 5x$$

Combine like terms.

$$-3 - 10x = 5x$$

$$-3 - 10x + 10x = 5x + 10x$$

Add 10x to both sides.

$$-3 = 15x$$

$$-\frac{3}{15} = \frac{15x}{15}$$

$$-\frac{1}{5} = x$$

22 Key Concepts Question Look back at the Example on page 413. Explain how to write and solve an equation to find out when the sisters owe the same amount of money.

Section 2
Practice & Application Exercises

1. The equation $y = 75x + 90$ models Bruce's savings after x weeks. Describe his savings plan in words. Bruce has $90 in his savings account and he deposits $75 each week without withdrawing any money.

Graph each pair of equations on the same pair of axes. Find the point where the graphs intersect and label its coordinates.

2. $y = 25x$ and $y = 20x + 10$ (2, 50) 3. $y = 10 - 2x$ and $y = 4 - x$ (6, −2)

4. $y = 18 - 3x$ and $y = 6$ (4, 6) 5. $y = 50 - 4x$ and $y = 20 + x$ (6, 26)

YOU WILL NEED

For Exs. 2–7, 17, 29, and 30:
◆ graph paper or graphing calculator (optional)

6. A school plans to rent a boat for a dolphin-watching trip. Rental company A charges a boat rental fee of $375 plus $125 per hour. Rental Company B charges a boat rental fee of $175 plus $150 per hour.

a. Use a table or graph. For how many hours will the total cost of renting a boat from Company A be $1500? **9 hr**

b. Use your answer to part (a). What would the cost of renting a boat from Company B for that number of hours be? **$1525**

c. Use your table or graph. For what number of hours will the boat rental cost be the same for both companies? **8 hr**

d. Explain why you could solve the equation $375 + 175x = 175 + 125x$ to answer part (c).

e. Solve the equation in part (d). Compare the result to your answer in part (c). **$375 + 125x = 175 + 150x$; $200 = 25x$; $x = 8$; The answers are the same.**

7. Suppose you have $5000 in savings. You start spending your savings at a rate of $150 per month. Your friend has $200 and adds $150 to his savings every month. Use a table or a graph to answer the questions below.

a. When do you run out of money? **at 34 months**

b. How much has your friend saved by that time? **$5300**

c. When will you and your friend have the same amount of money? **at 16 months**

d. How much money will you each have then? **$2600**

8. Look back at Exercise 7. Show how to write and solve equations to answer parts (a) and (b). **See margin.**

Use the distributive property to rewrite each expression without parentheses.

9. $-5(m + 12)$
$-5m - 60$

10. $3(1 + 8p)$
$3 + 24p$

11. $8(-5 - x)$
$-40 - 8x$

12. $10(0.5 - 0.5w)$
$5 - 5w$

13. $6(3x - 1)$
$18x - 6$

14. $(1 - 2t)2$
$2 - 4t$

---

6. d. The expressions $375 + 125x$ and $175 + 150x$ represent the total boat rental costs for the two companies for x hours. By setting the expressions equal, you can solve for x and find the number of hours for which the total boat rental cost is the same for both companies.

8. Equation for part (a):
$$5000 - 150x = 0$$
$$5000 - 150x + 150x = 0 + 150x$$
$$5000 = 150x$$
$$\frac{5000}{150} = \frac{150x}{150}$$
$$33\frac{1}{3} = x; 34 \text{ months}$$

Equation for part(b):
$$y = 200 + 150(34)$$
$$y = 200 + 5100$$
$$y = 5300; \$5300$$

Practice & Applications

DEVELOPING MATH CONCEPTS

Exercise 15 Since both methods always work, it is important to develop the idea of when each method might be the most efficient one to use. For example, Anne's method works nicely for the equation $160 = 8(x - 10)$ because 160 is evenly divisible by 8. However, students probably would not find it as convenient with the equation $150 = 8(x - 10)$ since they get a fraction when they divide.

EXERCISE NOTES

Exercise 16 offers a real world connection in which linear equations are used. When students attempt to write the equations for the two situations, they may be confused by the $3 and $8 charges. Make sure they understand that this is what it costs *each* time they park at Bay Beach.

DEVELOPING MATH CONCEPTS

Exercise 17 After students have completed their work, have them solve the equation $5x = 2x + 3$ and compare the solution with the x-coordinate of the point of intersection of the lines $y = 5x$ and $y = 2x + 3$. This should help students see how an equation like $5x = 2x + 3$ can be solved by graphing. This idea is further developed in **Exercise 29**.

17. b–c. See Additional Answers beginning on page A1.

416

15. **Alternative Method** Anne used a different method to solve the equation $160 = 8(x - 10)$ in the Example on page 412. She first divided both sides of the equation by 8. **Sample responses given.**

   a. Why do you think she did this? **to eliminate the multiplication required by the distributive property**

   b. What do you think she did next? **added 10 to both sides of the equation**

   c. Do you prefer her method or the method used in the Example? Explain. **Preferences will vary.**

16. It costs $3 to park at Bay Beach if you buy a special sticker for your car. A sticker costs $50 and can be used all summer. It costs $8 to park without a sticker.

   a. Write two equations that model your cost of parking at the beach n times, one if you have a sticker and one if you do not have a sticker. **Let c = the cost in dollars and n = the number of times you park; $c = 3n + 50$, $c = 8n$**

   b. **Writing** Under what circumstances would you save money by buying a sticker? Explain your thinking.

16. b. You would save money only if you parked at the beach more than 10 times in a summer because the cost of 10 tickets at $8 each is equal to the cost of 10 tickets at $3 each plus the initial $50 charge. After 10 times it would cost $5 more each time you parked than it would with the sticker.

17. a. Use an equation to find a common solution of $y = 5x$ and $y = 2x + 3$. Are there other common solutions? Explain.
   (1, 5); No; There is only one solution of the equation $5x = 2x + 3$.

   b. Graph the equations from part (a) on the same pair of axes. How can you use the graph to find a common solution of the two equations? **See margin.**

   c. Graph $y = 3x + 4$ and $y = 3x - 2$ on the same pair of axes. Do these equations have any common solutions? Explain. **See margin.**

Solve each equation.

18. $25x + 200 = 50x + 50$ **6**

19. $4t = -10t - 28$ **–2**

20. $3 = 2(m - 3)$ **$\frac{9}{2}$**

21. $-3 - 6h = 3(2h + 3)$ **–1**

22. $15m + 30 - 2m = 2m$ **$\frac{-30}{11}$**

23. $8(2x - 1) = 5(2x + 3)$ **$\frac{23}{6}$**

24. $2(5 - x) = -2x - 5 + x$ **15**

25. $5 - 3(1 - m) = 2(m - 5)$ **–12**

Geometry Connection For each diagram, use the given area to find the value of x.

26. Area = 25 m² **3 m**   27. Area = 24 ft² **5 ft**   28. Area = 35 cm² **3 cm**

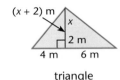

triangle

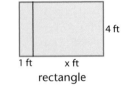

rectangle

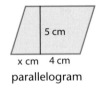

parallelogram

FOR ▶ HELP
with *using formulas from geometry*, see
TOOLBOX, p. 595

29. You can use graphs to solve equations like $3x + 8 = 2(x + 5)$.

  a. Graph $y = 3x + 8$ and $y = 2(x + 5)$ on the same pair of axes. Find the x-coordinate of the point where the graphs intersect.

  b. Check to see that the x-coordinate you found in part (a) is the solution of $3x + 8 = 2(x + 5)$. $3(2) + 8 = 6 + 8 = 14$; $2(2 + 5) = 2(7) = 14$

  c. Use graphs to solve $-5 = -3(-1 - x) + 7$. Check your solutions. **Check students' graphs; –5.**

29. a.

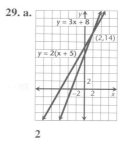

2

Reflecting ◀▶ on the Section

Write your response to Exercise 30 in your journal.

30. Suppose you have $100 in savings. How much money would you like to have saved in 10 years? Make a plan that involves linear change for achieving this savings goal. Describe your plan in words. Use an equation, a table, and a graph to model your plan.
Answers will vary. Check students' work.

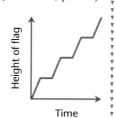

Journal

Exercise 30 checks that you can model change.

31. C; The graph shows the height of the flag increasing in stages with several pulls of a rope followed by brief rest periods.

Spiral ◀▶ Review

31. Suppose you raise a flag up a pole. Which of the graphs below best models this situation? Explain your choice(s). (Module 6, p. 400)

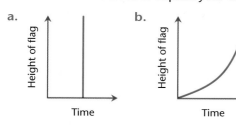

a.
Height of flag | Time

b.
Height of flag | Time

c.
Height of flag | Time

Write each rational number as a terminating or repeating decimal.
(Module 4, p. 277)

32. $\frac{3}{7}$ $0.\overline{428571}$ **33.** $\frac{6}{11}$ $0.\overline{54}$ **34.** $-2\frac{1}{5}$ -2.2 **35.** $\frac{5}{8}$ 0.625

Rewrite each product as a power. (Toolbox, p. 589)

36. $(5.2)(5.2)(5.2)(5.2)$ 5.2^4 **37.** $3 \cdot 3 \cdot 3 \cdot 3 \cdot 3 \cdot 3 \cdot 3 \cdot 3$ 3^8

38. $16 \cdot 16 \cdot 16 \cdot 16 \cdot 16$ 16^5 **39.** $\frac{3}{5} \cdot \frac{3}{5} \cdot \frac{3}{5} \cdot \frac{3}{5} \cdot \frac{3}{5} \cdot \frac{3}{5}$ $\left(\frac{3}{5}\right)^6$

EXERCISE NOTES

Exercise 29, parts(a) and (b) step students through the process of using graphs to solve $3x + 8 = 2(x + 5)$. Students should follow a similar process to complete **part(c)**.

1.
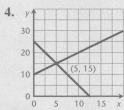

2.
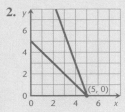

3.
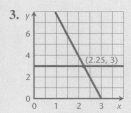

4.
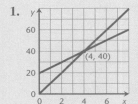

Section ② Extra Skill Practice

You will need: • *graph paper or graphing calculator (optional)* (Exs. 1–4)

Graph each pair of equations on the same pair of axes. Find the point where the graphs intersect and label its coordinates. **1–4. See margin.**

1. $y = 10x$ and $y = 5x + 20$
2. $y = 15 - 3x$ and $y = 5 - x$
3. $y = 12 - 4x$ and $y = 3$
4. $y = 25 - 2x$ and $y = 10 + x$

Solve each equation.

5. $3x - 4 = x + 10$ **7**
6. $6 + 2x = 5x + 9$ **–1**
7. $12 + x = -3 + 4x$ **5**
8. $7x + 4 = 2x - 11$ **–3**
9. $-3x - 2 = -9 - 4x$ **–7**
10. $-7x + 5 = 8x - 1$ $\frac{2}{5}$
11. $3x = 18 - 3x$ **3**
12. $14x + 6 = -2x - 2$ $-\frac{1}{2}$
13. $-5x - 9 = 3x + 17$ $-3\frac{1}{4}$

Use the distributive property to rewrite each expression without parentheses.

14. $5(x - 3)$ $5x - 15$
15. $-3(2 + 3x)$ $-6 - 9x$
16. $4(-1 - 6x)$ $-4 - 24x$
17. $(2x + 1)6$ $12x + 6$
18. $3(x - 3)$ $3x - 9$
19. $(7 - 4x)2$ $14 - 8x$
20. $x(x + 1)$ $x^2 + x$
21. $x(x + 4)$ $x^2 + 4x$
22. $(4x - 1)3$ $12x - 3$

Solve each equation.

23. $2(x - 1) = 3x + 4$ **–6**
24. $-w + 2(5w - 6) - 4w = -3(-w - 10)$ **21**
25. $3y + 5 + 2y = 5(2y + 1)$ **0**
26. $2 - 4(h - 4) = 10(2h - 3)$ **2**
27. $4k - 15(k - 2) = 17k + 9$ $\frac{3}{4}$
28. $8 + 5m(m - 3) = 12 - m(3 - 5m)$ $-\frac{1}{3}$
29. $6 - 2t = 3(2t + 4)$ $-\frac{3}{4}$
30. $3b(4 - 2b) - 6b = -b(6b + 7) + 104$ **8**

Standardized Testing ◀▶**Open-ended**

1. Describe a real-life situation that can be modeled by the equation $y = 5x + 30$. **Answers will vary. Check students' work.**

2. Write an expression that involves parentheses. Then use the distributive property to rewrite the expression without parentheses. **Answers will vary. Sample Response:** $2(12x + 4)$; $24x + 8$

3. Write an equation that can be solved by using the distributive property. Then solve your equation. **Answers will vary. Sample Response:** $5(2x - 1) = 75$; $x = 8$

FOR ASSESSMENT AND PORTFOLIOS

EXTENDED E2 EXPLORATION

Choosing the Right Plan

SET UP *You will need graph paper.*

The Situation See the *Teacher's Resource Book* for a sample solution for this Extended Exploration.

The Smith family is planning to subscribe to a cellular phone service. They have three payment plans from which to choose.

The Problem

The Smiths are not sure which plan they should choose. Evaluate each plan described at the right. Use mathematical models such as equations, tables, and graphs to make recommendations for choosing a plan.

Something to Think About

◆ What factors should the Smiths consider when choosing a payment plan?

◆ How can you model the three plans using equations, tables, and graphs?

Present Your Results

Write a letter to the Smith family explaining the advantages and disadvantages of each service plan. Give useful advice to the Smiths about choosing a plan. Include the mathematical models you used to come up with your recommendations.

PLAN A
$39.99
300 ANYTIME MINUTES
$.35 per additional minute

PLAN B
$69.99
1500 ANYTIME MINUTES
$.40 per additional minute

PLAN C
$99.99
2500 ANYTIME MINUTES
$.30 per additional minute

Extended Exploration

E² NOTES

Many students will be fairly familiar with cell phones and service plans through personal use or television advertisements. For those who are not, you may want to discuss what "anytime minutes" mean and ask students what happens when you use all of your "anytime minutes" during a month of service. (*Anytime refers to the idea that you are not restricted to weekends or evening times to use your phone; After you use your anytime minutes, you will have to pay extra for each minute used. This amount will be on top of the monthly charge.*)

Using an E²: Suggestions for managing and evaluating an Extended Exploration are available in the *Teacher's Resource Book* for Modules 1 and 2. See also pages T44–T45 in the *Teacher's Edition*.

Alternate E²: See the *Teacher's Resource Book* for Modules 5 and 6 for an alternate Extended Exploration that can be used after Module 6, Section 2.

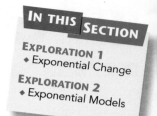

IN THIS SECTION

EXPLORATION 1
◆ Exponential Change

EXPLORATION 2
◆ Exponential Models

Section ③ Modeling Exponential Change

How Sweet It Is

Setting the Stage

In Roald Dahl's *Charlie and the Chocolate Factory*, Charlie Bucket's family is so poor that he only gets a chocolate bar once a year.

HAPPY BIRTHDAY CHARLIE

Only once a year, on his birthday, did Charlie Bucket ever get to taste a bit of chocolate. The whole family saved up their money for that special occasion, and when the great day arrived, Charlie was always presented with one small chocolate bar to eat all by himself.

...he would take a *tiny* nibble...

The next day, he would take another tiny nibble, and so on, and so on. And in this way, Charlie would make his ten-cent bar of birthday chocolate last him for more than a month.

Roald Dahl, *Charlie and the Chocolate Factory*

Think About It

Suppose on the first day, Charlie eats half the chocolate bar. The next day, he eats half the remaining chocolate bar, and continues to eat half the remaining chocolate each day after that.

1 Will Charlie eat the same amount of chocolate each day? Explain. No; Each day he eats half as much as he did the day before.

2 How long do you think the chocolate bar will last? Sample response: a few days; The pieces will soon become so small that he will not actually be able to divide them in half.

Exploration 1

Exponential CHANGE

Exploration 1

GOAL

LEARN HOW TO...
- model exponential change

AS YOU...
- use paper folding to model eating a chocolate bar

SET UP You will need: • *a rectangular sheet of paper* • *graph paper* • *graphing calculator (optional)*

▶ In Question 2, you estimated how long Charlie Bucket's chocolate bar would last if he ate half of the remaining chocolate each day. In this exploration, you will use paper folding to model this situation.

3 a. Fold a sheet of paper in half. With no folds there is one layer. After one fold there are two layers. **Check students' work.**

0 folds
1 layer
area = 1

1 fold
2 layers
area of a layer = **?**

b. If the area of the unfolded paper is one square unit, what is the area of each layer after you fold the paper once? $\frac{1}{2}$ **square unit**

c. Record the number of folds, the number of layers, and the area of each layer in a table like the one shown. **See margin.**

d. Fold your paper as many times as possible. Extend and fill in your table each time you fold the paper.
Check students' work.

Number of folds	Number of layers	Area of each layer
1	2	$\frac{1}{2}$
2	4	?
3	?	?
⋮	⋮	⋮

Section 3 Modeling Exponential Change **421**

Exploration 1

CLASSROOM MANAGEMENT
Students may work individually while completing Exploration 1. However, working with a partner will speed up the activity since one person can do the paper folding while the other student records the results. Working with a partner also allows students to discuss results if they get confused.

DIFFERENTIATED INSTRUCTION
As students make the folds and complete the table in **Question 3**, visual and kinesthetic learners may need to unfold the paper after each fold and count the number of regions the folds divide the paper into in order to determine the fraction for the area.

TIME MANAGEMENT
When students make their tables in **Question 3(c)**, warn them to leave enough space in order to add two more columns to the table later on. If they don't leave room, time may be wasted redoing the table in **Question 5**.

3. c.

Number of folds	Number of layers	Area of each layer
1	2	$\frac{1}{2}$
2	4	$\frac{1}{4}$
3	8	$\frac{1}{8}$
4	16	$\frac{1}{16}$
5	32	$\frac{1}{32}$
6	64	$\frac{1}{64}$
7	128	$\frac{1}{128}$

Exploration 1 continued

DEVELOPING MATH CONCEPTS

If students have difficulty writing the powers in **Question 5**, have them think back to how the amount of chocolate Charlie ate each day was found in **Question 1**. For Day 2 it was $\frac{1}{2} \cdot \frac{1}{2} = \left(\frac{1}{2}\right)^2 = \frac{1}{4}$. For Day 3 it was $\frac{1}{2} \cdot \frac{1}{2} \cdot \frac{1}{2} = \left(\frac{1}{2}\right)^3 = \frac{1}{8}$, and so on.

This should help students identify the powers of both $\frac{1}{2}$ and 2.

In **Question 8(b)**, students may need help determining what scale to use for the y-axis of their graph. If they do not use an interval that can be easily divided into smaller parts, they won't be able to plot the points accurately and draw the curve. Increments of $\frac{1}{16}$ work well.

ALTERNATIVE APPROACH

If graphing calculators are available, have students complete **Question 9** using a calculator. Otherwise you may wish to have students work in groups of three to complete the graphs. First they will need to agree on what scales to use on the axes and then each student can graph one of the equations. Having used the same scales, students can then compare the three graphs even though they are on separate sheets of paper. It is important however, that each student in a group use graph paper with the same size squares.

8. b–c. See Additional Answers beginning on page A1.

422

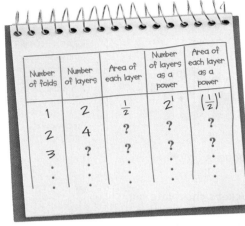

Number of folds	Number of layers	Area of each layer	Number of layers as a power	Area of each layer as a power
1	2	$\frac{1}{2}$	2^1	$\left(\frac{1}{2}\right)^1$
2	4	?	?	?
3	?	?	?	?
⋮	⋮	⋮	⋮	⋮

5. $2^2, \left(\frac{1}{2}\right)^2; \ldots 2^7, \left(\frac{1}{2}\right)^7$

7. b. $y = \left(\frac{1}{2}\right)^x$; when $x = 0$, the paper hasn't been folded, so there is 1 layer and the area y of each layer is 1.

8. a.

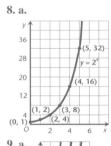

9. a.

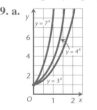

All three curves rise from left to right. The greater the base in the equation, the steeper the graph.

Module 6 Visualizing Change

For Questions 4–7, use your completed table from Question 3.

4 Suppose you could continue folding the paper.

  a. What would happen to the number of layers as the number of folds increased? It would increase, doubling at each stage.
  b. What would happen to the area of each layer? It would decrease, halving at each stage.

5 Add two columns to your table, as shown. Write the number of layers as a power of 2 and the area of each layer as a power of $\frac{1}{2}$.

6 Suppose you could fold the paper ten times. Predict how many layers there would be. Then predict the area of each layer. Explain your reasoning. 2^{10} or 1024 layers; area $= \left(\frac{1}{2}\right)^{10}$

▶ As you folded the paper, the number of layers and the area of each layer changed *exponentially*. You can use equations and graphs to model exponential change.

7 **Try This as a Class** Let x = the number of folds.

  a. Let y = the number of layers. Write an equation for y in terms of x. Explain why when $x = 0$, $y = 1$. $y = 2^x$; when $x = 0$, the paper hasn't been folded, so the number y of layers is 1.
  b. Let y = the area of each layer. Write an equation for y in terms of x. Explain why when $x = 0$, $y = 1$.
  c. How are your equations in parts (a) and (b) alike? How are they different? Both equations involve a variable exponent; In one the base is a whole number, in the other the base is a fraction.

8 **a.** Graph your equation from Question 7(a). Plot points for the number of folds and number of layers in your table. Plot (0, 1) as well. Connect the points with a smooth curve.

  b. Repeat part (a) for your equation from Question 7(b). See margin.

  c. How are the graphs in parts (a) and (b) alike? How are they different? Describe how each graph changes as x increases. See margin.

9 The *exponential equations* you have seen so far have all had the form $y = b^x$, where $b > 0$ and $x \geq 0$.

  a. To see how the value of b affects the graph of an equation in the form $y = b^x$, graph the equations $y = 3^x$, $y = 4^x$, and $y = 7^x$ for $x \geq 0$ on the same pair of axes. For each graph, include the point (0, 1). Describe the differences and the similarities in the curves.

b. How would you describe the graph of an equation in the form $y = b^x$, where $b > 1$ and $x \geq 0$? **The graph is a curve that passes through (0, 1) and rises from left to right.**

c. How is your graph of the equation $y = \left(\dfrac{1}{2}\right)^x$ from Question 8(b) different from the graphs in part (a)? **It fell from left to right.**

d. Why do you think the graphs are different? **The base in the expression b^x in one expression is less than 1.**

10 ✔ CHECKPOINT Look back at the excerpt from *Charlie and the Chocolate Factory* on page 420. What fraction of the original candy bar would Charlie have left after 1 month (30 days) if he eats half of what is left each day? $\left(\dfrac{1}{2}\right)^{30}$ or $\dfrac{1}{1{,}073{,}741{,}824}$

HOMEWORK EXERCISES ▶ See Exs. 1–5 on pp. 427–428.

Exploration 2

Exponential MODELS

SET UP | *Work with a partner. You will need a calculator.*

▶ **Much has changed since 1964, when *Charlie and the Chocolate Factory* was first published. The price of a candy bar is more than five times what it was then.**

11 In 1960, a candy bar cost about 10¢. Suppose this price is raised 5 times to reach 50¢. Work with your partner to find a way to change 10 to 50 in 5 steps using each method.

a. *Add* the same number at each step. Tell what number you added. Copy and complete the table for each step.

b. *Multiply* by the same number at each step. Use guess and check to find the number. Tell what number you multiplied by. Copy and complete the table for each step. **See margin.**

Step	Price
0	10¢
1	?
2	?
3	?
4	?
5	50¢

✔ QUESTION 10

...checks that you understand exponential change.

GOAL

LEARN HOW TO...
◆ write an equation to model compound interest
◆ use tables and equations to solve problems

AS YOU...
◆ model price changes and the growth of a savings account

KEY TERM
◆ exponential equation

11. a. Add 8¢;

Step	Price
0	10¢
1	18¢
2	26¢
3	34¢
4	42¢
5	50¢

Exploration 2

TEACHING NOTES

In **Exercise 11(a)**, students should find the exact amount that can be added at each step. In **part (b)** students may be frustrated at not being able to find the exact factor to multiply by. Ask them to get as close as possible. It is more important for students to see that the price must be multiplied by a number a little greater than 1 to maintain the original amount plus the percent of increase. This will also be true when students look at the growth factor in the upcoming exponential growth equations.

11. b. about 1.38;

Step	Price
0	10¢
1	14¢
2	19¢
3	26¢
4	36¢
5	50¢

TECHNOLOGY NOTE

For a related technology activity, see the *Technology Book.*

TEACHING NOTES

The example below can be used to reinforce the concepts presented in the example on this page.

CLASSROOM EXAMPLE

Suppose you deposit $1500 in an account that earns 6% annual interest. How much will you have in the account after 1 year?

Answer: After one year, you will have 100% of your deposit plus an additional 6% interest.

Initial deposit + Interest after 1 yr
(1.00)(1500) + (0.06)(1500)

You can use the distributive property to rewrite this expression.

$$(1.00)(1500) + (0.06)(1500) = (1.00 + 0.06)(1500)$$
$$= (1.06)(1500)$$
$$= 1590$$

After 1 year you will have $1590 in your account.

13. b. See Additional Answers beginning on page A1.

424

▶ **Savings can grow as quickly as prices if you deposit money in a savings account that earns interest. The amount of money increases exponentially, even if you do not make any more deposits.**

12 a. Suppose you deposit $1000 into an account that pays 8% annual interest. Find 8% of $1000 to determine the amount of interest you will earn in one year. $80

    b. What is the new total in your account at the end of one year? $1080

▶ **How much money will you have in a savings account after 10, 20, or 30 years? To find out, look for a pattern.**

EXAMPLE

Suppose you deposit $2000 into an account that earns 5% annual interest. After one year, you will have 100% of your deposit plus an additional 5% interest.

Initial deposit + Interest after one year
(1.00)(2000) + (0.05)(2000)

You can use the distributive property to rewrite this expression:

$$(1.00)(2000) + (0.05)(2000) = (1.00 + 0.05)(2000)$$

After one year, there will be $2100 in the account.
$$= (1.05)(2000)$$
$$= 2100$$

13 Refer to the situation described in the Example.

    a. Suppose you leave your money in the account for two years. How much money will you have at the end of the second year? Explain how you got your answer. $2205; Multiply $2100 by 1.05.

    b. Copy the table and complete it by continuing the pattern in the *Expression* column. See margin.

Year	Amount in account at beginning of year	Expression	Amount in account at end of year
1	$2000	1.05 · 2000	$2100
2	$2100	1.05 · 1.05 · 2000	?
3	?	?	?
4	?	?	?
5	?	?	?

    c. Discussion Describe the pattern in the *Expression* column. Each year, the expression is multiplied by another factor of 1.05. The number of times the factor appears is equal to the number of years.

424

14 a. At the end of two years, the amount of money in the account described in the Example is given by the expression $1.05 \cdot 1.05 \cdot 2000$. Rewrite this expression using exponents.

b. ▦ Calculator Use exponents to write an expression for the amount of money in your account at the end of 20 years. Use the ▣ y^x key to evaluate the expression.
$2000 \cdot 1.05^{20}; \$5306.60$

▶ **The growth of money in a savings account that earns annual interest is an example of an exponential function. You can represent an exponential function with an exponential equation in this form:**

starting amount

amount after x years → $y = a \cdot b^x$ → growth factor

15 Try This as a Class The equation $2923.08 = 1500 \cdot (1.1)^7$ gives the amount in an account after a certain number of years.

a. How much money was originally deposited into the account? $\$1500$

b. How many years was the money in the account? 7 years

c. How much money is in the account after this number of years? $\$2923.08$

d. What is the growth factor? What is the interest rate? $1.1; 10\%$

16 ✔ CHECKPOINT Suppose you deposit $\$4000$ in an account that earns 6% annual interest. Write an equation that models the amount y in the account after x years. How much will be in the account after each period of time? $y = 4000 \cdot (1.06)^x$

a. 1 year $\$4240$　　**b.** 12 years $\$8048.79$　**c.** 20 years $\$12,828.54$

17 Discussion Look back at Question 11 on page 423.

a. Suppose the price of a candy bar starts at $\$0.10$ and increases by $\$0.01$ each year. Write an equation for the price after x years. $y = 0.10 + 0.01x$

b. Suppose the price starts at $\$0.10$ and increases by 10% each year. Write an equation for the price after x years.
$y = 0.10 \cdot (1.10)^x$

c. Use your equations to copy and complete the table. Compare the predicted prices over time. See margin.

Price of candy bar	$.01 yearly increase	10% yearly increase
After 10 years	?	?
After 20 years	?	?
After 30 years	?	?
After 40 years	?	?

✔ QUESTION 16

...checks that you can write and use an exponential equation to solve problems.

▐ **HOMEWORK EXERCISES** ▶ See Exs. 6–17 on pp. 428–429.

COMMON ERROR
When students write the equation in **Question 16**, they may forget to add 1 to the interest rate, writing $y = 4000(0.06)^x$ instead of $y = 4000(1.06)^x$. This common error may also occur in **Question 17(b)**. Encouraging students to check the reasonableness of their answers may help them recognize this error. You can also refer students back to the candy bar pricing table in **Question 11(b)** to remind them of how they had to multiply by 1 to get the increased price.

17. c. See Additional Answers beginning on page A1.

Key Concepts

ABSENT STUDENTS

For students who were absent for all or part of this section, the blackline Study Guide for Section 3 may be used to present the ideas, concepts, and skills of Section 3.

CLOSURE QUESTION

Explain the meaning of y, a, b, and x in the exponential equation $y = a \cdot b^x$.

Sample Response: y is the amount after x time intervals, a is the starting amount, b is the rate of change, and x is the number of time intervals.

Key Term

exponential equation

Section 3
Key Concepts

Exponential Change (pp. 421–423)

Some exponential equations have the form $y = b^x$, where $b > 0$ and $x \geq 0$. You can use an equation in this form to model some types of exponential change.

Example Suppose a piece of paper has an area of 1 square unit. You fold the paper into thirds. Then you fold the paper into thirds again. You keep repeating this process.

Number of regions after x steps $= 3^x$

Area of each region after x steps $= \left(\frac{1}{3}\right)^x$

Step 0
Regions: 1
Area of each region: 1

Step 1
Regions: 3
Area of each region: $\frac{1}{3}$

Step 2
Regions: 9
Area of each region: $\frac{1}{9}$

Exponential Models (pp. 423–425)

When you deposit money into a savings account that earns annual interest, the amount of money in the account grows exponentially over time. You can model a relationship like this one with an exponential equation in the form $y = a \cdot b^x$.

starting amount

amount after x years $\quad y = a \cdot b^x \quad$ growth factor

Example Suppose you deposit $1800 into a savings account that earns 3% annual interest. To find out how much money you will have after 5 years, you can write an equation.

$$y = 1800 \cdot (1.03)^x$$

When $x = 5$, $y = 1800 \cdot (1.03)^5 \approx 2086.69$.

You will have about $2087 after 5 years.

18 Key Concepts Question In the Example above about the savings account, how is the number 1.03 related to the interest rate? Explain why you use 1.03 as a factor five times. **The interest rate is 0.03; 1.03 represents 100% of the initial amount deposited in the account plus 3% interest per year. 1.03 is used as a factor 5 times because the money was deposited for 5 years.**

Section 3

Practice & Application Exercises

YOU WILL NEED

For Ex. 16:
♦ graph paper or a graphing calculator

1. In the Example about folding paper into thirds on page 426, two equations are given. Match each equation with one of the graphs below. Explain your thinking.

A.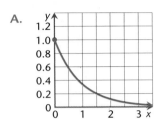

B.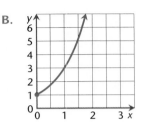

2. **Geometry Connection** In the diagram, the area of each regular hexagon is $\frac{3}{4}$ the area of the next larger hexagon. If the area of the outer hexagon is 1 square unit, what is the area of the smallest hexagon?

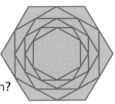

3. Suppose someone in your class starts a rumor. This student tells the rumor to two other students. Each of these students repeats the rumor to two other students. This pattern continues.

   a. Suppose it takes one minute to find two students and tell them the rumor. Copy and extend the table for the first ten minutes after the rumor starts. **See margin.**

Number of minutes	Number of new people hearing the rumor	Total number of people who have heard the rumor
0	1	1
1	2	3

   b. Write and solve an equation to find the **number of new people who *hear* the rumor** one hour after it was started. $y = 2^x$; When $x = 60$, $y = 2^{60}$.

   c. How is this problem like the paper folding activity in Exploration 1?

   d. **Visual Thinking** Show how you can use a tree diagram to model this situation. **See margin.**

4. **Challenge** Use the information in Exercise 3. Write an equation that models the **total number of people who *have heard* the rumor** after x minutes. $y = 2^{x+1} - 1$ or $y = 2 \cdot 2^x - 1$

Practice & Applications

SUGGESTED ASSIGNMENTS

Core Course
Day 1: Exs. 3, 18–20
Day 2: Exs. 1–2, 5
Day 3: Exs. 6–12, 17, 21

Extended Course
Day 1: Exs. 3–4, 18–20
Day 2: Exs. 1–2, 5
Day 3: Exs. 6–9, 13–17, 22–24*

Note: Extended Course assignments can be used to differentiate within the regular classroom. In classrooms where students are grouped homogeneously, the material might be covered in fewer days. In this case assignments may be combined.

* denotes Extension Exercises

1. A: Area of each region after x steps $= \left(\frac{1}{3}\right)^x$; B: Number of regions after x steps $= 3^x$; As x increases, $\left(\frac{1}{3}\right)^x$ decreases and 3^x increases.

2. $\left(\frac{3}{4}\right)^5 = \frac{243}{1024} \approx$ 0.24 square unit

3. c. Sample Response: It shows exponential growth with powers of 2.

ADDITIONAL PRACTICE
See the *Teacher's Resource Book* for additional practice and application exercises for this section.

EXERCISE NOTES
For **Exercise 1**, students should refer to the equations in the first example on p. 426.

DEVELOPING MATH CONCEPTS
In **Exercise 4**, most students will recognize that the total number of people is equal to the sum of $2^0 + 2^1 + 2^2 + ... + 2^{x-1} + 2^x$ where x is the number of minutes. This rule is difficult to use for large values of x, so encourage students to look for other patterns in their tables. Some students may recognize the pattern of one less than double the number of new people hearing the rumor. Help them to equate this to $2(2^x) - 1$.

3. a. and d. See Additional Answers beginning on page A1.

427

Developing Math Concepts

In **Exercise 6**, students must solve the equation $2000 = 500 \cdot 1.09^x$. They can do this by guess and check and the y^x key on their calculators. Encourage students to simplify the equation as much as possible (to $4 = 1.09^x$) before beginning this process.

5. **Writing** Jane graphed three equations on the same graphing calculator screen, but cannot tell which graph goes with each equation. Explain how she can tell just by looking at the graphs.

1st equation: $y = \left(\dfrac{1}{3}\right)^x$

2nd equation: $y = 4^x$

3rd equation: $y = \left(\dfrac{3}{2}\right)^x$

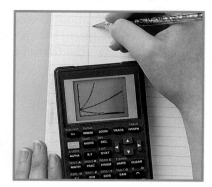

5. The graphs of $y = 4^x$ and $y = \left(\dfrac{3}{2}\right)^x$ rise from left to right, while the graph of $y = \left(\dfrac{1}{3}\right)^x$ decreases but remains positive. The graph of $y = 4^x$ has the steepest slope and the graph of $y = \left(\dfrac{3}{2}\right)^x$ has the next steepest slope. This is because for the same values of x, $y = 4^x$ gives greater values of y. The graph of $y = \left(\dfrac{1}{3}\right)^x$ decreases and approaches 0 or a horizontal line because as numbers less than 1 are raised to powers, they become smaller.

6. a. $y = 500 \cdot (1.09)^x$ where y represents the total money in the account and x represents the number of years.

   c. 17 years; Sample Response: I graphed my equation from part (a) and found the x value that had a y value of about 2000.

6. a. Suppose you deposit $500 into an account that earns 9% annual interest. Write an equation that shows the amount of money in the account after x years.

   b. How much money will be in the account after 10 years? **$1183.68**

   c. About how many years will it take for the amount of money in the account to reach $2000? How did you get your answer?

7. Write an equation in the form $y = a \cdot b^x$ to model each situation. Tell what the variables x and y represent.

   a. The student population of a school with 1200 students is predicted to grow at a rate of 4% each year. $y = 1200 \cdot (1.04)^x$ where y represents the enrollment and x represents the number of years.

   b. Marcia is training for a marathon. She runs 5 km this weekend. For the next several weeks, she will increase her distance by 10% each weekend. $y = 5 \cdot (1.1)^x$ where y represents the distance Maria runs each week and x represents the number of weeks.

8. **Open-ended** Describe a situation like the ones in Exercise 7. Write a word problem about the situation that you could use an exponential equation to solve. Give the solution of your problem. **Answers will vary. Check students' work.**

9. **Algebra Connection** Are the equations you wrote in Exercise 7 functions? Explain. **Yes; For every value of x there is only one value of y.**

Evaluate each expression for the given value of the variable.

10. $4 \cdot 3^x$; $x = 3$ **108** 11. $4 \cdot \left(\dfrac{1}{2}\right)^x$; $x = 4$ **$\dfrac{1}{4}$** 12. $100 \cdot 0.4^x$; $x = 2$ **16**

13. $\dfrac{1}{2} \cdot 2^x$; $x = 5$ **16** 14. $\dfrac{2}{3} \cdot 6^x$; $x = 3$ **144** 15. $5 \cdot \left(\dfrac{1}{3}\right)^x$; $x = 4$ **$\dfrac{5}{81}$**

16. **Population Growth** Exponential equations in the form $y = a \cdot b^x$ are often used to model population growth. For example, suppose the population of a town is 10,000 and is predicted to grow at a rate of 3% each year.

a. Write an equation to model the population y after x years.
   $y = 10{,}000 \cdot (1.03)^x$

b. Graph your equation. Your graph should show the town's population for the next 30 years.

c. In about how many years will the population double?
   about 24 years

d. Suppose the population of the town grows at a rate of 6% each year. Predict how many years it will take the population to double. Check your prediction by writing and graphing an equation.

Reflecting ◀▶ **on the Section**

Be prepared to discuss your response to Exercise 17 in class.

17. **Discussion** Suppose you win a $25,000 college scholarship on a TV quiz show. You are given two options for collecting your scholarship money. What are the advantages and disadvantages of each option? Which option would you choose? Why?

Discussion

Exercise 17 checks that you can use an exponential equation to model a problem situation.

16. b. about 12 years

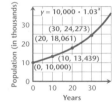

d. about 12 years

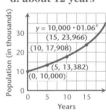

OPTION 1

You will receive $5000 each year for the next 5 years.

OPTION 2

A check for $25,000 is deposited into an account that earns 5% annual interest. You cannot withdraw money for 5 years.

The advantage of Option 1 over Option 2 is having the cash now. The disadvantage is that the total amount over 5 years is almost $7000 less; Answers will vary. Check students' work.

Spiral ◀▶ **Review**

Solve each equation. (Module 6, p. 414)

18. $13x + 15 = 185 - 4x$ 10

19. $-6 - 2p = -(3 - 4p)$ $-\frac{1}{2}$

20. After the translation $\left(x - 2,\ y + \dfrac{1}{2}\right)$, the image of a point is (5, 0). What are the coordinates of the original point? (Module 2, p. 87)
   $\left(7, -\dfrac{1}{2}\right)$

ALTERNATIVE APPROACH
If available, students can use graphing calculators to solve **Exercise 16**. Otherwise they can draw the graph for 5 or 6 years, and then use the y^x key on their calculators and guess and check to determine the number of years it will take for the population to double.

Practice & Applications

EXERCISE NOTES

In the Explorations, students modeled exponential growth. In the **Extension Exercises 22–24**, students learn how to use exponential equations to model exponential decay. In exponential growth, the growth factor is 1 plus the percent of increase. To represent the decay factor, the same principle is applied, but using subtraction instead of addition. Once the decay begins, an item is never at its whole value again, so the change is subtracted from 1, producing a decay factor of *1 minus the percent of decrease.*

Career ▪ Connection

Wildlife Veterinarian: William Karesh

As a wildlife veterinarian, William Karesh studies disease and nutrition. He may help a monkey with malaria or an elephant with an infected toe. Many infections are caused by bacteria that reproduce exponentially.

21. Suppose 2 bacteria infect an animal. In 20 min, each of these bacteria splits into 2 bacteria, so that there are 4 bacteria. In another 20 min, these 4 bacteria each split into 2 bacteria. This pattern continues over time.

    a. How many bacteria will there be after 2 hr? after 6 hr? How did you get your answers?

    b. How does exponential growth help explain what can happen if an infection is not treated quickly? **Sample Response: It shows how quickly the bacteria grow and so, how rapidly the infection worsens.**

21. a. 128 bacteria; 524,288 bacteria; Possible Answers: Write an equation, complete a table, or sketch a graph. Equation: $y = 2 \cdot 2^x$ where x represents the number of 20 min intervals that have passed.

Extension ▶ ▶

Exponential Decay

Most of the situations you modeled in this section involved *exponential growth.* You can also use an equation in the form $y = a \cdot b^x$ to model *exponential decay.* For example, suppose you pay $18,000 for a new car. You plan to sell the car in a few years, but know that the car will be worth less and less as time goes on. The value of the car is depreciating (losing value) at a rate of 12% a year.

Used car for sale

5 years old
1 owner, a/c, airbag
am/fm
very reliable
555-0173

22. About how much will your car be worth after 1 year? after 2 years? after 3 years? How did you get your answers?
    $15,840; $13,393.20; $12,266.50; Possible Answers: Make a table, write an equation.

23. Let y = the value of your car after x years. An equation for y in terms of x is $y = 18,000(0.88)^x$. The number 0.88 is the *decay factor.* How is the decay factor related to the rate of depreciation?
    The decay factor is the rate of depreciation subtracted from 1.

24. In Exploration 1, you found the area of each layer as you folded a sheet of paper. Was this an example of exponential growth or exponential decay? Explain. **exponential decay; The amount of area decreased by a decay factor of 0.5 with each fold.**

Section 3
Extra Skill Practice

Write an equation in the form $y = a \cdot b^x$ to model each situation. Tell what the variables x and y represent.

1. A baseball card worth $150 is projected to increase in value by 8% a year. $y = 150 \cdot (1.08)^x$ **where y represents the value of the baseball card and x represents the number of years.**

2. A TV station's local news program has 60,000 viewers. The managers of the station plan to increase viewership by 5% a month. $y = 60{,}000 \cdot (1.05)^x$ **where y represents the number of viewers and x represents the number of months from the onset of the manager's plan.**

3. A bakery produces 2000 loaves of bread on an average day. In order to meet demand for an upcoming holiday, the bakers want to increase production by 10% a day. $y = 2000 \cdot (1.10)^x$ **where y represents the value of the number of loaves of bread and x represents the number of days.**

Evaluate each expression for the given value of the variable.

4. $18 \cdot 4^x$; $x = 6$ 73,728

5. $\frac{3}{5} \cdot 5^x$; $x = 7$ 46,875

6. $0.35 \cdot 9^x$; $x = 4$ 2296.35

7. $\frac{4}{3} \cdot 3^x$; $x = 8$ 8748

8. $8 \cdot \left(\frac{1}{4}\right)^x$; $x = 6$ $\frac{1}{512} \approx 0.002$

9. $\frac{3}{2} \cdot \left(\frac{2}{3}\right)^x$; $x = 4$ $\frac{8}{27} \approx 0.3$

Write an equation to find out how much money you will have in each situation.

10. You deposit $2000 into an account for 1 year at 3% annual interest.

11. You deposit $200 into an account for 10 years at 3% annual interest.

12. You deposit $600 into an account for 4 years at 7% annual interest.

13. You deposit $1500 into an account for 8 years at 4% annual interest.

10. $y = 2000 \cdot (1.03)^1$, 2060
11. $y = 200 \cdot (1.03)^{10}$, 268.78
12. $y = 600 \cdot (1.07)^4$, 786.48
13. $y = 1500 \cdot (1.04)^8$, 2052.85

Standardized Testing ▶ Performance Task

1. A store is having a sale on sweaters. On the first day the price of a sweater is reduced by 20%. The price will be reduced another 20% each day until the sweater is sold. Gustav thinks that on the fifth day of the sale the sweater will be free. Is he right? Explain.

2. Carlos plans to deposit $1000 into one of two banks. For four years, he will leave any interest earned in the account, but make no other deposits or withdrawals. At the end of each year Bank A pays interest at a rate of 6% of the total amount in the account, while Bank B pays interest at a rate of 7% of the original amount deposited. Which bank should Carlos choose? Explain.

1. No. Each day the new price, not the original price, is being reduced 20%, so on the fifth day the price will be about 67% off the original price.

2. Bank B; The amount he will earn at Bank A is $y = 1000(1.06)^4 = \$1262.48$ and the amount he will earn at Bank B is $y = 1000 + 1000(0.07)(4) = \$1280$. He will make $17.52 more than at Bank A.

Setting the Stage

ABOUT THE THEME

Computer images can help artists create the sequence of movement in animated films, most of which are now computer generated. Students get a simplified introduction to animation by writing algorithms to represent the results of moving a figure on a coordinate grid.

GETTING STARTED

In preparation for working with algorithms, Module 6 Section 4 *Warm-Up* assesses student ability to follow a series of instructions to create the image of a point on a coordinate grid.

Section ④ Algorithms and Transformations

IN THIS SECTION

EXPLORATION 1
◆ Using Algorithms

Setting the Stage

Computer graphics can be used to model motion. For example, Olympic gymnasts in training are videotaped performing a floor routine or vault. A computer analyzes the tape and recreates the motion. Sometimes these tapes are broken down into stick figure sequences like the one below. Sports scientists study these sequences to help improve equipment and reduce injury among athletes.

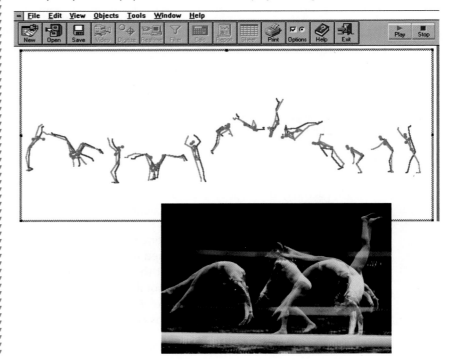

Think About It

Suppose the computer simulation on page 432 is shown in the first quadrant of a coordinate plane. You want to give instructions that will move the figure through the routine.

1 What information do you need to include in your instructions?
direction and type of movements

2 How can you use coordinates to describe changes in the gymnast's position?

▶ Movement of a figure on a computer screen can be created by assigning coordinates to points on the figure and giving instructions for moving each point. In this section you will explore how to represent movements using a series of instructions.

2. Put the figures on a coordinate grid. Choose a point on the original figure and determine the coordinates of the image. Determine how the coordinates of the original point and the image are related.

Exploration 1

Using Algorithms

SET UP You will need: • Labsheet 4A • graph paper

▶ In Module 2 you learned how to translate objects. You can use translations and other *transformations* to represent simple motions. A **transformation** is a change in an object's shape, size, or position.

3 The figures below show positions before and after a move.

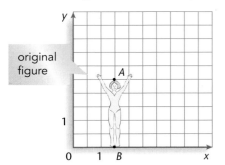

original figure

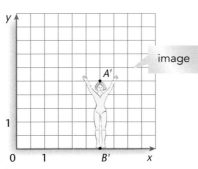

image

a. Are the image and the original figure congruent? Explain.
Yes; The two figures are the same shape and size.
b. How can you transform the original figure to get the image?
Sample Response: Translate it 1.5 units to the right.

GOAL

LEARN HOW TO...
♦ use algorithms to transform geometric shapes
♦ reflect geometric shapes

AS YOU...
♦ model a gymnast's change in position

KEY TERMS
♦ transformation
♦ algorithm
♦ reflection

FOR HELP
with *translations*, see
MODULE 2, p. 87

TEACHING NOTES

Question 1 You might want to have students speculate about how many points the computer must keep track of on the body. (*As a minimum, probably each foot, each knee, the hips, a point on the midriff, the shoulders, each elbow, each wrist, the hands, and the head. To keep track of the direction the gymnast is facing may require two points on each foot, the heel and toes, and two or three points on the head.*)

Question 2 Guide students to focus on what might be done to the coordinates of a point to describe how it moves from one position to the next. In particular, have students recall how they described translations in Module 2 by adding constants to the coordinates of the points.

Exploration 1

DEVELOPING MATH CONCEPTS

In discussing the definition of transformation, explain to students that a translation is a type of transformation, as is a reflection, a rotation, and an enlargement or reduction in size of an object. Transformation is the general term for all of these types of movements or any combinations of them.

Exploration 1 *continued*

TEACHING NOTES

The example below can be used prior to **Checkpoint 5** to further reinforce the concepts presented in the Example on this page.

CLASSROOM EXAMPLE

At the peak of a jump, a gymnast is 3 units to the right and 4 units higher than her starting position. After landing, the gymnast is 3 units to the right and 2 units lower than the peak.

Use an algorithm to create a model of the key positions on a coordinate plane.

Answer:

Step 1: Plot a point to show the gymnast's starting position.

Step 2: Translate the point 3 units to the right and 4 units up.

Step 3: Translate the point 3 units to the right and 2 units down.

Start: (x, y)
$(x', y') = (x + 3, y + 4)$
$(x'', y'') = (x' + 3, y' - 2)$

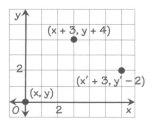

▶ Animation that models movement may combine a series of steps. You can use an *algorithm* to describe these steps. An **algorithm** is a step-by-step set of instructions you can follow to accomplish a goal.

The Example below shows an algorithm for creating a very simple representation of the key positions of a gymnast's jump.

EXAMPLE

Suppose a gymnast is videotaped jumping on a balance beam. At the peak of the jump, the gymnast is 2 units to the right and 1 unit higher than her starting position. After landing, she is 2 units to the right and 1 unit lower than when she was in the peak position.

Use an algorithm to create a simple representation of the gymnast's key positions in a coordinate plane.

SAMPLE RESPONSE

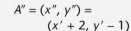

Step 1	**Step 2**	**Step 3**
Plot points to show the gymnast's starting position.	Translate each point 2 units to the right and 1 unit up.	Translate each point 2 units to the right and 1 unit down.
$A = (x, y)$	$A' = (x', y') =$ $(x + 2, y + 1)$	$A'' = (x'', y'') =$ $(x' + 2, y' - 1)$

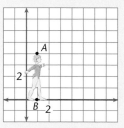 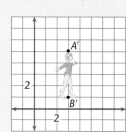 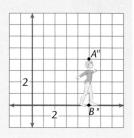

✔ **QUESTION 5**

...checks that you can use an algorithm to describe a series of transformations.

4 Give the coordinates of points *A*, *A'*, and *A''* in the Example.
$A(1, 4), A'(3, 5), A''(5, 4)$

5 ✔ **CHECKPOINT** Write an algorithm for moving a point from (0, 0) to (2, −3) and then to (2, 3). $(x', y') = (x + 2, y - 3);$ $(x'', y'') = (x', y' + 6)$

6 a. Write an algorithm that moves the gymnast in the Example directly from the starting position to the landing position.
$(x', y') = (x + 4, y)$

b. How is your algorithm different from the one in the Example? How is it similar? **It has only one step; The end result is the same.**

▶ Animation that models movement may be made up of different types of transformations. The Example below shows a **reflection**.

EXAMPLE

The triangle is *reflected* across the y-axis. We say that $\triangle A'B'C'$ is the reflection of $\triangle ABC$. Note that the triangles are congruent and the y-axis is the perpendicular bisector of every segment joining corresponding points on $\triangle ABC$ and $\triangle A'B'C'$.

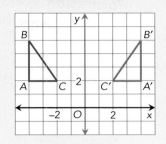

7 **Discussion** Look at the Example above. Compare the coordinates of points A and A'. Then compare the coordinates of points B and B' and the coordinates of points C and C'. Describe any patterns you see. **Sample Response: The y-coordinates are the same. The x-coordinates are opposites.**

8 **Try This as a Class** The vertices of $\triangle JKL$ are $J(1, -4)$, $K(5, -2)$, and $L(3, 0)$.

   a. Write an algorithm for reflecting $\triangle JKL$ across the y-axis of a coordinate plane. Then perform the steps of your algorithm.

   b. Compare $\triangle JKL$ and its reflection. Are the two figures congruent? How could you check? **Yes; You could fold the graph over the y-axis and the two triangles would fit over each other perfectly.**

9 **Use Labsheet 4A.** Sometimes there is more than one way to write an algorithm, depending on the order in which you perform the steps.

   a. Draw a figure on the blank grid to complete a *Sequence of Transformations*. Describe the steps that transform the original figure to its image.

   b. Compare your sequences with those of other students. Did everyone perform the same steps in the same order? **Probably not.**

10 ✔ **CHECKPOINT** In a coordinate plane, draw a triangle with vertices at points $M(-2, -4)$, $N(-2, -2)$, and $O(0, 0)$. Then write an algorithm for reflecting $\triangle MNO$ across the x-axis and then across the y-axis.

HOMEWORK EXERCISES ▶ See Exs. 1–20 on pp. 437–440.

8. a. $(x', y') = (-x, y)$

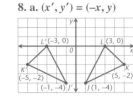

9. a. Answers will vary. Check students' work. Sample Responses:

Sequence 1:
$(x', y') = (x - 1, y)$,
$(x'', y'') = (x', -y')$
or $(x', y') = (x, -y)$,
$(x'', y'') = (x' - 1, y')$

Sequence 2:
$(x', y') = (-x, y)$,
$(x'', y'') = (-x', y')$

Sequence 3:
$(x', y') = (x + 5, y)$,
$(x'', y'') = (x', y' - 1)$ or
$(x', y') = (x, y - 1)$,
$(x'', y'') = (x' + 5, y')$

10. $(x', y') = (x, -y)$;
$(x'', y'') = (-x', y')$

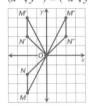

✔ **QUESTION 10**

...checks that you can write an algorithm for a reflection.

DEVELOPING MATH CONCEPTS
In **Question 7**, students should recognize that the x-coordinates of a point and its reflection in the y-axis are opposites and that the y-coordinates are the same. Make sure students understand that since the x-coordinates are opposites, the points are the same distances from the y-axis. That is, the reflecting line is the perpendicular bisector of the segment joining a point and its reflection. They will need to use this idea to reflect $\triangle MNO$ across the x-axis in **Question 10**.

TEACHING NOTES
The example below can be used after **Question 8** to show a reflection over the x-axis.

CLASSROOM EXAMPLE

Reflect the parallelogram across the x-axis.

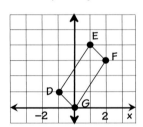

Answer: Parallelogram $D'E'F'G'$ is the reflection of parallelogram $DEFG$ across the x-axis. The parallelograms are congruent.

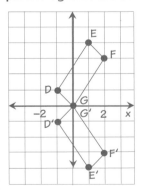

435

Key Concepts

CLOSURE QUESTION

Explain what is meant by a transformation of an object. Then name two kinds of transformations that can be described using algorithms.

Sample Response: A transformation is the change in an object's shape, size, or position; reflection and translation.

ABSENT STUDENTS

For students who were absent for all or part of this section, the blackline Study Guide for Section 4 may be used to present the ideas, concepts, and skills of Section 4.

Section 4
Key Concepts

Key Terms

transformation

algorithm

reflection

Transformation (p. 433)

A transformation is a change made to an object's shape, size, or position. Two types of transformations are translations and reflections.

Algorithms (p. 434)

An algorithm is a set of steps that you can follow to accomplish a goal.

Example Write an algorithm for the transformation shown.

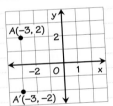

Step 1 Reflect each point across the y-axis.
$(x', y') = (-x, y)$

Step 2 Translate each point up 1 unit.
$(x'', y'') = (x', y' + 1)$

Step 3 Translate each point right 1 unit.
$(x''', y''') = (x'' + 1, y'')$

The algorithm $(x''', y''') = (-x + 1, y + 1)$ moves $\overline{AB}$ in the Example to its image $\overline{A'''B'''}$ in one step.

Reflection (p. 435)

A reflection is a transformation where a figure is flipped across a line such as the x-axis or the y-axis. The original figure and its reflection are congruent.

Example To reflect the point $(-3, 2)$ across the x-axis, multiply the y-coordinate by -1, or find the opposite of the y-coordinate. Then plot the new coordinates.

11 Key Concepts Question Write a two-step algorithm for the transformation shown.
Sample Response: $(x', y') = (x, -y)$;
$(x'', y'') = (x' + 1, y' + 2)$

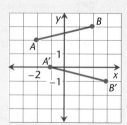

Section 4

Practice & Application Exercises

YOU WILL NEED

For Ex. 1–7, 9, 14–17, and 19:
♦ graph paper

For Exercises 1 and 2, sketch a stick figure in a coordinate plane. Label a point for each foot and a point for the head. Use algorithms to create simple models of the key positions of the head and each foot for the movement described. (If necessary, write a separate algorithm for each point.) Show the steps of your algorithms in a coordinate plane. **1–7. See margin.**

1. jumping up and down in place

2. standing in place and then doing a split

For each figure in Exercises 3–6:

a. **Copy the figure on graph paper.**

b. **Reflect the figure across the given axis or axes. Draw the reflection(s) in the same coordinate plane.**

3. the *y*-axis

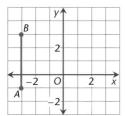

4. the *x*-axis

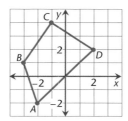

5. the *x*-axis, then the *y*-axis

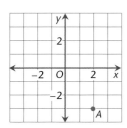

6. the *y*-axis, then the *x*-axis

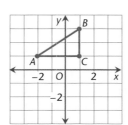

7. Copy the original figure from Exercise 6. Reflect the triangle across the *x*-axis and then across the *y*-axis. How does the final image compare to the final image in Exercise 6?

Practice & Applications

SUGGESTED ASSIGNMENTS

Core Course
Day 1: Exs. 1–11, 15–17, 20–28

Extended Course
Day 1: Exs. 3–7, 10–18, 20–28

Note: Extended Course assignments can be used to differentiate within the regular classroom. In classrooms where students are grouped homogeneously, the material might be covered in fewer days. In this case assignments may be combined.

ADDITIONAL PRACTICE
See the *Teacher's Resource Book* for additional practice and application exercises for this section.

1. **Sample Response:** $(x', y') = (x, y + 5)$; $(x'', y'') = (x', y' - 5)$

2–7. See Additional Answers beginning on page A1.

Practice & Applications

EXERCISE NOTES

For **Exercise 8**, there are many different algorithms that can be used to generate the designs. A sample response is given. Another correct algorithm is as follows:

Step 1: Produce first row using $(x', y') = (x + 2, y)$ twice.

Step 2: Produce succeeding rows using $(x'', y'') = (x', y' + 2)$ twice.

You may want to have students share different solutions to **Exercise 8** before they create their own design in **Exercise 9**.

DEVELOPING MATH CONCEPTS

In **Exercises 12–14**, many ideas regarding transformations are developed. **Exercises 12 and 13** expand on the idea of a rotation introduced informally in **Question 10** on page 435. **Exercise 14** develops ideas about reflecting across lines other than the axes. After students have completed these exercises, have them look back at **Exercise 13** and ask what reflecting lines can be used to transform △DEF to △D'E'F'. (*Reflect across the line y = x and then across the x-axis.*) Then ask if the result would be the same if they did the reflections in the opposite order. (*No; Reflecting across the line y = x and then across the x-axis is a 90° clockwise rotation about the origin. Reflecting across the x-axis and then across the line y = x is a 90° counterclockwise rotation about the origin.*)

8. Sample Response:
   Step 1: Produce first column using $(x', y') = (x, y + 2)$ twice.
   Step 2: Produce succeeding columns using $(x'', y'') = (x' + 2, y')$ twice.

10. Sample Response: $(x', y') = (x + 2, y - 1)$

11. $(x', y') = (x, -y)$; $(x'', y'') = (-x', y')$; $(x''', y''') = (x'', y'' + 2)$

Art The first and last steps in creating a design are shown.

8. Write an algorithm that can be used to create the design.

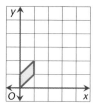 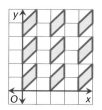

9. **Create Your Own** Sketch a repeating design and write an algorithm that can be used to create it. Answers will vary. Check students' work.

Write an algorithm that can be used to create each transformation.

10.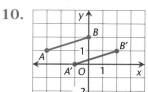

11.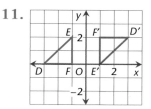

12. **Alternative Method** In the diagram at the right, △AB'C' was created by rotating △ABC 180° clockwise about the origin. Describe how to transform △ABC to △AB'C' using reflections. Reflect △ABC across both axes in either order.

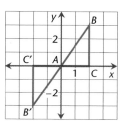

13. In the diagram at the right, △DE'F' was created by rotating △DEF 90° clockwise about the origin. Do you think it is possible to transform △DEF to △DE'F' using only reflections across the x- and y-axes? Explain. No; Sample Response: △DE'F' is on the same side of the y-axis as △DEF and is not the image of △DEF reflected across the x-axis.

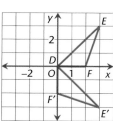

14. The diagram at the right shows a triangle and its reflection across the line y = x. Compare the coordinates of each point on the original figure with the coordinates of the corresponding point on the reflection. Write an algorithm for reflecting a figure across the line y = x. Draw a figure in a coordinate plane and use it to test your algorithm. $(x', y') = (y, x)$; Check students' work.

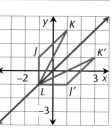

15. You can use an algorithm to model a change that involves stretching. The transformation shown is represented by the algorithm below.

Step 1 Multiply the *x*- and *y*-coordinates of each point by 2.

Step 2 Translate each point up 1 unit.

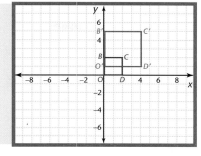

a. Draw square *OBCD* with coordinates *O*(0, 0), *B*(0, 2), *C*(2, 2) and *D*(2, 0). Translate the square up 1 unit. Then multiply each coordinate by 2. Draw the final image. **See margin.**

b. Compare your results from part (a) with the transformation shown. Does the order in which you perform the steps matter? **Yes**

16. Copy the figure below. Then use the algorithm to transform the figure. **See margin.**

Step 1 Multiply the *x*- and *y*-coordinates of each point by 3.

Step 2 Reflect each point over the *x*-axis.

Step 3 Translate each point up 12 units.

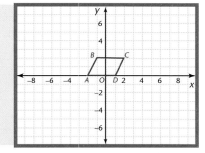

17. You already know how to stretch a figure using multiplication. You can also use multiplication to shrink a figure. Draw the figure below. Then use the algorithm to transform the figure. **See margin.**

Step 1 Multiply the *x*- and *y*-coordinates of each point by $\frac{1}{2}$.

Step 2 Translate each point to the left 1 unit.

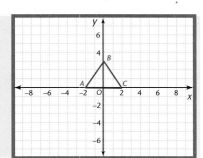

DEVELOPING MATH CONCEPTS

In **Exercises 15–17**, students *multiply* the coordinates by a constant to produce the image. This constant is often referred to as the scale factor. Therefore, since a scale factor refers to multiplication by a number, students are instructed to multiply by $\frac{1}{2}$ in **Exercise 17** instead of to divide by 2 even though they produce the same results.

15. a.

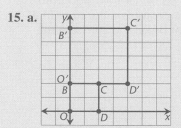

16.

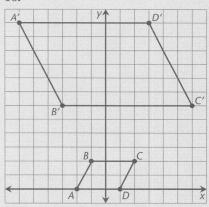

17.

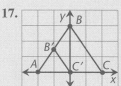

EXERCISE NOTES

To complete the work for **Exercise 19**, students will need to get together in groups of 3 to agree on a figure and an algorithm before completing the work at home. To compare, students will have to group together again the next class period. Alternatively, a student could design his or her own algorithm and then complete the steps in a different order and compare the results.

18. **Challenge** What value must you multiply each coordinate of the points on the original figure by to create the final image? $1\frac{1}{3}$

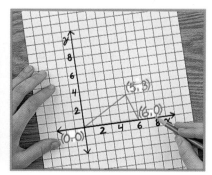

19. **Create Your Own** Work in a group of three. Agree on a figure to transform, and an algorithm with 3 or 4 steps. Each person should follow the steps in a different order. Compare your results.
Answers will vary. Check students' work.

Journal

Exercise 20 checks that you understand algorithms.

Reflecting ◀▶ on the Section

Write your response to Exercise 20 in your journal.

20. Write two different algorithms for the transformation shown.
Sample Response: $(x', y') = (x, -y)$; $(x'', y'') = (x' + 3, y')$ or $(x', y') = (-x, y)$; $(x'', y'') = (x', -y')$; $(x''', y''') = (x'' + 1, y'')$

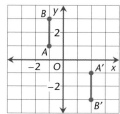

Spiral ◀▶ Review

Evaluate each expression when $x = 3$. (Module 6, p. 426)

21. 3^x 27

22. $2 \cdot \left(\frac{1}{4}\right)^x$ $\frac{1}{32} = 0.03125$

23. $(4x)^3$ 1728

24. In the diagram, line s is parallel to line t. Find each angle measure.
(Module 5, pp. 368–369) $m\angle 1 = m\angle 4 = 95°$; $m\angle 2 = m\angle 3 = 85°$

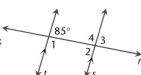

Mental Math Use mental math to find each value. (Module 3, p. 163)

25. $-\sqrt{144}$ –12

26. $\sqrt{0.0001}$ 0.01

27. $\sqrt{\frac{1}{81}}$ $\frac{1}{9}$

28. $-\sqrt{\frac{49}{225}}$ $-\frac{7}{15}$

Extra Skill Practice

Extra Skill Practice

TEACHER NOTES
All of the Exercises in the Extra Skill Practice correspond to Exploration 1.

EXTRA HELP
Teacher's Resource Book
- Practice and Applications
- Study Guide

Technology Resources
- @Home Tutor
- Test Generator

ASSESSMENT
- Section 4 Quick Quiz
- Test Generator

You will need: • *graph paper* (Exs. 7–9)

Write an algorithm for moving the point as specified.

1. from (0, 0) to (3, –3) $(x', y') = (x + 3, y – 3)$ 2. from (1, 4) to (3, 5) $(x', y') = (x + 2, y + 1)$

3. from (–2, 5) to (0, 7) and then to (2, 5) $(x', y') = (x + 2, y + 2); (x'', y'') = (–x' + 2, y' – 2)$

Explain how to perform the following reflection(s).

4. Reflect point (–1, 4) across the *y*-axis.   5. Reflect point (0, 3) across the *x*-axis.

6. Describe at least three different ways to transform point $A(2, 5)$
   to point $A'(2, –5)$. **Sample Response: Use $(x', y') = (x, y – 10)$; Reflect across the *x*-axis;
   Reflect across the *y*-axis then across the *x*-axis, then across the *y*-axis again.**

Sketch the original figure and the final image of the reflection(s).

7. Reflect across the *x*-axis.

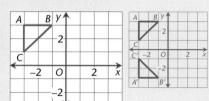

8. Reflect across the *y*-axis and
   then across the *x*-axis.

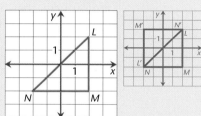

9. Write an algorithm that involves a reflection and a translation.
   Answers will vary. Check students' work.

Standardized Testing ▶Multiple Choice

1. △*ABC* is translated 8 units to the right and 5 units down. What are
   the coordinates of point *A* if the coordinates of point *A'* are (6, 7)? C

   Ⓐ (8, –5)   Ⓑ (11, –1)   Ⓒ (–2, 12)   Ⓓ (14, 2)

2. Which transformation cannot be represented by an algorithm that
   involves multiplication? C

   Ⓐ reflection over the *x*-axis   Ⓑ reflection over the *y*-axis

   Ⓒ a translation   Ⓓ stretching a figure

4. **Sample Response: Plot the point with the opposite *x*-coordinate and the same *y*-coordinate.**

5. **Sample Response: Plot the point with the same *x*-coordinate and the opposite *y*-coordinate.**

Setting the Stage

ABOUT THE THEME

Students work with equations of parabolas to explore how changing a value in a parent equation affects the graph of that equation.

GETTING STARTED

In Module 6 Section 5 *Warm-Up* students are asked to substitute values for *x* in a quadratic equation to find corresponding values for *y*. This helps assess whether students are prepared to graph the equations of parabolas, so that they can concentrate more on observing the differences among various graphs and making generalizations about the graphs.

DEVELOPING MATH CONCEPTS

In **Question 2**, make sure students understand that the graph itself is not a parabola, only the marked section is part of a parabola. Some students may need to make a sketch showing the curve and the line of symmetry. In the discussion, bring out the idea that one half of the curve is the reflection of the other side in the axis of symmetry. This can be modeled by folding a drawing along the line of symmetry and showing that the two halves coincide with each other.

2. Sample Response: An upward curve that reaches a peak and then points downward; Yes; The parabola has line symmetry with a vertical line drawn through the peak.

Section ⑤ Exploring Quadratic Functions

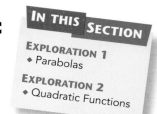

IN THIS SECTION

EXPLORATION 1
♦ Parabolas

EXPLORATION 2
♦ Quadratic Functions

It's All in the Curve

Setting the Stage

How does it feel to orbit Earth? Before NASA astronauts even leave the atmosphere, they have a chance to find out. Specially modified airplanes help astronauts get used to the near-weightless conditions they will experience in space. The airplanes zoom upward and back down, following part of a curve called a *parabola*. As the airplanes reach the top of the parabola, the astronauts feel weightless for a short period of time. For the KC-135 NASA used from 1995 to 2004, the feeling of weightlessness lasted 15-25 seconds.

Think About It

1 During a training flight aboard the KC-135, the astronauts usually flew along the curve of 40 parabolas. About how much time did they spend feeling weightless on a training flight?
800 to 1,000 sec, or about 13 to 17 min

2 The section of the curve where the astronauts felt weightless is part of a parabola. Describe it. Does it show symmetry? Explain.

▶ In this section, you will learn about objects and situations that can be modeled by parabolas.

Period of "weightlessness" 15–25 seconds

Altitude

Horizontal distance

Exploration 1

Parabolas

SET UP *Work in a group of four. You will need graph paper or a graphing calculator (optional).*

▶ A **parabola** is a type of curve. In the photos below, the main cable of the Golden Gate Bridge and the path of the water can be modeled with parabolas. You can represent a parabola with an equation.

GOAL

LEARN HOW TO...
♦ predict the shape of a parabola

AS YOU...
♦ use equations and graphs to model events and objects

KEY TERMS
♦ parabola
♦ line of symmetry
♦ vertex of a parabola

EXAMPLE

The graph of the equation $y = 0.0239x^2$ models the curve formed by a main cable on the Golden Gate Bridge.

The *y*-axis is the **line of symmetry** for this parabola because it divides the curve into two parts that are reflections of one another.

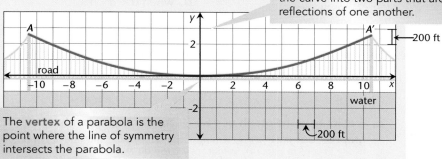

The **vertex** of a parabola is the point where the line of symmetry intersects the parabola.

3 Give the coordinates of the vertex of the parabola in the Example.
(0, 0)

Exploration 1

DEVELOPING MATH CONCEPTS

From this first example of a parabola, students may get the impression that the vertex is always at (0, 0) and that the axis of symmetry is always the *y*-axis. This will be true of many of the equations students investigate, so to avoid misconceptions, you may want to show the class the example below before moving on to **Question 5**. Since in this example, the line of symmetry is not the *y*-axis, the students will need to write the equation of the line as a way of identifying it. It would be appropriate at this time to discuss what the equation of the line is for the *y*-axis. ($x = 0$)

CLASSROOM EXAMPLE

Identify the coordinates of the vertex and the equation of the line of symmetry of the following parabola.

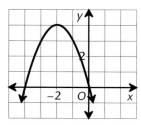

Answer: $x = -2$ is the line of symmetry since it divides the parabola into two parts which are reflections of one another. The vertex is at (–2, 4), the point where the line of symmetry intersects the parabola.

Exploration 1 *continued*

DEVELOPING MATH CONCEPTS

Since not all parabolas have the y-axis as their line of symmetry, it is important to generalize the ideas about symmetry that are developed in **Question 4**. If a point lies on a parabola, then there is another point on the opposite side of the *axis of symmetry* (not necessarily the y-axis) that also lies on the parabola and is the same distance from the axis of symmetry as the original point. Using the teaching notes for the Classroom Example on page 443 will help emphasize this point.

TEACHING NOTES

Question 5 Encourage students to describe the relationships between the graphs in terms of reflections and translations. For example, in **Question 5**, the graph of the equation $y = -x^2$ is the reflection of the graph of $y = x^2$ over the x-axis. In **Question 8**, the graphs are all translations of the graph of the equation $y = x^2$ up or down a given number of units equal to the value of c.

DEVELOPING MATH CONCEPTS

Question 7 Encourage students to think about the effect for positive values of a as stretching or compressing the graph of the equation $y = x^2$ parallel to the y-axis.

5. a.

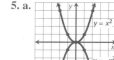

7. a. The graph of $y = ax^2$ is narrower than the graph of $y = x^2$.
   b. The graph of $y = ax^2$ is wider than the graph of $y = x^2$.
   c. The graph of $y = ax^2$ is narrower than the graph of $y = x^2$ and opens down instead of up.
   d. The graph of $y = ax^2$ is wider than the graph of $y = x^2$ and opens down instead of up.

6. a–d., 8. a. and c. See Additional Answers beginning on page A1.

4 **Discussion**

   a. Describe the relationship between the x-coordinates of points A and A' in the Example on page 443. **They are opposites.**

   b. Describe the relationship between the y-coordinates. **They are the same.**

   c. Are there other points with coordinates that have the same relationships? **Every point on one side of the y-axis has a corresponding point on the other side of the y-axis with an x-coordinate that is its opposite and a y-coordinate that is the same.**

▶ **All equations in the form $y = ax^2$, where $a \neq 0$, have graphs that are parabolas. The value of a determines the shape of the parabola.**

5 Use graph paper or a graphing calculator.

   a. Graph the equations $y = x^2$ and $y = -x^2$ on the same pair of axes.

   b. How are the graphs alike? **They have the same shape, vertex, and line of symmetry.**

   c. How are they different? **One opens up the other opens down.**

6 Each person in your group should use graph paper or a graphing calculator to graph one of the following sets of equations on the same pair of axes. How do you think the value of a affects the shape of the graph of an equation in the form $y = ax^2$?
a–d. See margin.

   a. $y = x^2$ $y = 2x^2$ $y = 3x^2$ $y = 4x^2$

   b. $y = x^2$ $y = -2x^2$ $y = -3x^2$ $y = -4x^2$

   c. $y = x^2$ $y = 0.25x^2$ $y = 0.07x^2$ $y = \frac{1}{3}x^2$

   d. $y = x^2$ $y = -0.25x^2$ $y = -0.07x^2$ $y = -\frac{1}{3}x^2$

7 **Try This as a Class** How does the graph of an equation in the form $y = ax^2$ compare with the graph of $y = x^2$ in each case?

   a. when $a > 1$ **b.** when $0 < a < 1$

   c. when $a < -1$ **d.** when $-1 < a < 0$

8 The graph of an equation in the form $y = ax^2 + c$ is also a parabola.
a, c. See margin.

   a. Graph the four equations below on the same pair of axes.

      $y = x^2 + 1$ $y = x^2 + 2$ $y = x^2 + 3$ $y = x^2 + 4$

   b. Predict how the graph of $y = x^2 + 5$ will compare with the graphs from part (a). **It will have the same shape and line of symmetry as the graphs in part (a), but its vertex will be (0, 5).**

   c. Predict how the graphs of $y = 0.5x^2 - 1$ and $y = 0.5x^2 - 2$ will compare with the graph of $y = 0.5x^2$. Then check your predictions by graphing all three equations on the same pair of axes.

9 ✔ CHECKPOINT

a. Predict how the graph of $y = -0.25x^2$ will compare with the graph of $y = x^2$. **The graph of $y = -0.25x^2$ is a wider parabola than the graph of $y = x^2$ and it opens down instead of up.**

b. Predict how the graph of $y = 2x^2 - 3$ will compare with the graph of $y = 2x^2$. **They have the same shape and axis of symmetry, but the vertex of $y = 2x^2 - 3$ is $(0, -3)$ instead of $(0, 0)$.**

c. Check your predictions by graphing all four equations on the same pair of axes. **See margin.**

| HOMEWORK EXERCISES ▶ See Exs. 1–8 on pp. 448–449.

✔ QUESTION 9

...checks that you can make predictions about parabolas.

Exploration 2

Quadratic Functions

GOAL

LEARN HOW TO...
- recognize quadratic equations
- simplify quadratic expressions

AS YOU...
- explore the physics of sports

KEY TERM
- quadratic function

| SET UP | *You will need graph paper or a graphing calculator.*

▶ One common place to "see" parabolas is at a sporting event such as a basketball game. When a ball is thrown, its path can be represented by a parabola.

EXAMPLE

The equation $y = -0.05x^2 + 0.7x + 5$ describes the path of a basketball after it is tossed.

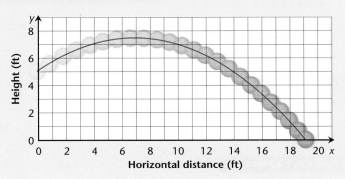

Exploration 2

TEACHING NOTES

So that students understand how the graph in the Example on this page was created from an equation, you can have the class work together to graph a similar example like the one below. It would be best displayed on an overhead projector for all to see.

CLASSROOM EXAMPLE

Suppose the equation $y = -0.1x^2 + 0.6x + 3$ describes the path of a basketball after it is tossed. Draw a graph of this equation.

Answer:

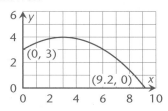

9. c.

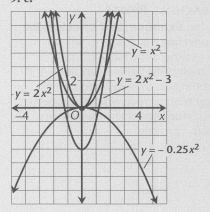

DEVELOPING MATH CONCEPTS

For **Question 11**, make sure students understand that when a function is used to describe a physical situation, only those values of the independent variable that make sense in the physical situation can be used as input values. At the beginning of the throw, the ball is held by a player (so *height* ≥ 0) and has not travelled any distance horizontally (so *distance* = 0). Since the distance the ball is thrown is measured from the spot where it was thrown independent of the direction of the throw, the horizontal distance cannot be negative. Similarly, since the ball cannot go below the playing surface, the height can never be negative and the throw ends when the ball hits the playing surface (*height* = 0). Thus, the only part of the parabola shown is for when the *horizontal distance* and *height* are both greater than or equal to 0.

TEACHING NOTES

In the **Example**, and **Checkpoint Question 15**, students will need to use the distributive properties of multiplication over addition and subtraction to rewrite equations. You may wish to review these properties with students to ensure they use them correctly.

---

10. a. The variable *x* represents the horizontal distance (in feet) that the ball is thrown and *y* represents the height (in feet) of the ball.
    b. No. Some players are taller than others and basketballs are thrown at different speeds and heights depending on the player and the play.

11. Sample Response: The point at which the parabola crosses the *y*-axis represents the height from which the ball was thrown. Distance thrown must be positive; therefore, no values of *y* that correspond to negative values of *x* are shown. Since the ball is thrown from about chest height, the height starts above 0 and since it eventually is caught or hits the floor, the parabola is completely on or above the *x*-axis. Negative *y*-values would mean the ball traveled below the floor.

✔ QUESTION 15

...checks that you can identify a quadratic function.

Refer to the Example on page 445 for Questions 10 and 11.

10 **a.** What do the variables *x* and *y* represent in the equation?

   b. Does the equation model every basketball throw? Explain.

   c. What was the maximum height the ball reached? *about 7.5 ft*

   d. When it hit the floor, how far was the ball from the person who tossed it? *about 19 ft*

11 Why do you think part of the parabola is missing?

▶ The equation and graph in the Example represent a *quadratic function*. A **quadratic function** can be represented by an equation in this form:

$$y = ax^2 + bx + c, \text{ where } a \neq 0$$

12 **Try This as a Class** Identify the values of *a*, *b*, and *c* in the equation $y = -0.05x^2 + 0.7x + 5$. *a = –0.05; b = 0.7, and c = 5*

13 In Exploration 1, you explored graphs of equations in the form $y = ax^2$. What were the values of *b* and *c* in these equations? *0*

14 **Discussion** Explain why the equation $y = 0x^2 + 5x + 3$ does *not* represent a quadratic function. What kind of function is it? *In the definition of a quadratic equation, a ≠ 0; a linear function*

▶ Sometimes it is difficult to tell if an equation represents a quadratic function. It may be helpful to rewrite the equation.

EXAMPLE

To see whether $y = 3(2x + 4) - x + 2x^2$ models a quadratic function, rewrite the equation in the form $y = ax^2 + bx + c$.

$$y = 3(2x + 4) - x + 2x^2 \quad \text{Use the distributive property.}$$
$$= 3(2x) + 3(4) - x + 2x^2$$
$$= 6x + 12 - x + 2x^2$$
$$= 2x^2 + 6x - x + 12 \quad \text{Regroup and combine like terms.}$$
$$= 2x^2 + 5x + 12$$

The equation represents a quadratic function where $a = 2$, $b = 5$, and $c = 12$.

15 ✔ **CHECKPOINT** Tell whether each equation represents a quadratic function.

   a. $y = 5x^2 - 3x$
   quadratic function

   b. $y = -2(2x^2 + 3x) + 1 + 4x^2$
   not a quadratic function

HOMEWORK EXERCISES ▶ See Exs. 9–17 on p. 449.

Section 5

Key Concepts

Key Concepts

Parabolas (pp. 443-445)

A parabola is a U-shaped curve. The vertex of a parabola is the point at which the line of symmetry intersects the curve. The graphs of equations in the form $y = ax^2$ where $a \neq 0$ are parabolas.

Example The graph of $y = -2x^2$ is narrower than the graph of $y = -0.5x^2$ because $|-2| > |-0.5|$. Both graphs are "upside-down" compared to the graph of $y = x^2$ because the coefficient of x^2 is negative.

x	$y = -0.5x^2$	$y = -2x^2$
-2	-2	-8
-1	-0.5	-2
0	0	0
1	-0.5	-2
2	-2	-8

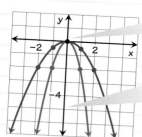

The vertex of each parabola is (0, 0).

The line of symmetry of each parabola is the y-axis.

To graph the parabola $y = ax^2 + c$, translate the graph of $y = ax^2$ up c units if $c > 0$ or down $|c|$ units if $c < 0$.

Quadratic Functions (pp. 445–446)

A quadratic function is represented by an equation in the form $y = ax^2 + bx + c$, where $a \neq 0$. Its graph is a parabola.

Example To see whether $y = 4x^2 - 2x - x^2 + 2x - 5$ represents a quadratic function, rewrite it in the form $y = ax^2 + bx + c$.

$$y = 4x^2 - 2x - x^2 + 2x - 5$$
$$= 4x^2 - x^2 - 2x + 2x - 5$$
$$= 3x^2 + 0x - 5 \quad \text{Combine like terms.}$$
$$= 3x^2 - 5$$

The equation represents a quadratic function where $a = 3$, $b = 0$, and $c = -5$.

Key Terms

parabola

vertex

line of symmetry

quadratic function

16 **Key Concepts Question** Tell whether each equation models a quadratic function. If so, sketch the graph of the function. Identify the vertex and the line of symmetry of the parabola.

a. $y = -x^2 + 4(x^2 - 3) - 3x^2$ **b.** $y = -2(x^2 + 1) + x^2$
not a quadratic function

16. b. quadratic
function
vertex: (0, −2)
line of symmetry:
x = 1

Section 5   Exploring Quadratic Functions   **447**

Key Concepts

ABSENT STUDENTS

For students who were absent for all or part of this section, the blackline Study Guide for Section 5 may be used to present the ideas, concepts, and skills of Section 5.

CLOSURE QUESTION

How does the value of a in the equation $y = ax^2$, affect the graph of the equation as compared to the graph of $y = x^2$?

Sample Response:

If $0 < a < 1$, then the graph is wider than the graph of $y = x^2$.

If $a > 1$, then the graph is narrower than the graph of $y = x^2$.

If $a < 0$, then the graph opens down, which is the opposite direction of the graph of $y = x^2$.

Practice & Applications

SUGGESTED ASSIGNMENTS

Core Course
Day 1: Exs. 1–4, 18–24
Day 2: Exs. 5–8
Day 3: Exs. 9–15, 17

Extended Course
Day 1: Exs. 1–4, 18–24
Day 2: Exs. 5–8
Day 3: Exs. 9–17, 25–26*

Note: Extended Course assignments can be used to differentiate within the regular classroom. In classrooms where students are grouped homogeneously, the material might be covered in fewer days. In this case assignments may be combined.

* denotes Extension Exercises

ADDITIONAL PRACTICE
See the *Teacher's Resource Book* for additional practice and application exercises for this section.

EXERCISE NOTES
Exercise 5 Ask students to make rough sketches of their predictions for **part (a)** before completing **part (b)**.

7. b–d. See Additional Answers beginning on page A1.

448

YOU WILL NEED

For Exs. 5, 7, and 18
♦ graph paper

For Exs. 9, 17, and 26:
♦ graph paper or graphing calculator (optional)

5. a. Answers may vary. Sample Response: The graph of $y = -2x^2$ will have the same vertex and axis of symmetry as the graph of $y = x^2$, but the parabola will be narrower and open downward. The graph of $y = -2x^2 + 3$ is the same as the graph of $y = -2x^2$ except that it is shifted up 3 units so its vertex is at $(0, 3)$ instead of $(0, 0)$.

b.

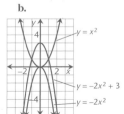

FOR ◄ HELP
with *reflections*, see
MODULE 6, p. 436

Section 5
Practice & Application Exercises

Match each equation with one of the parabolas at the right.

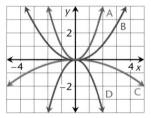

1. $y = 0.3x^2$ B

2. $y = x^2$ A

3. $y = -x^2$ D

4. $y = -0.08x^2$ C

5. a. Predict how the graphs of $y = -2x^2$ and $y = -2x^2 + 3$ will compare with the graph of $y = x^2$.

b. Check your prediction by graphing all three equations on the same pair of axes.

6. a. For each parabola give the coordinates of the vertex and the equation of the line of symmetry.

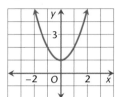 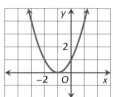

vertex: $(0, 1)$
line of symmetry: $x = 0$

vertex: $(-1, 0)$
line of symmetry: $x = -1$

b. Write an equation for the parabola on the left. $y = x^2 + 1$

7. Physics The observation deck of the Tower of the Americas in San Antonio, Texas, is 622 ft above the ground. You can use the formula $h = 622 - 16t^2$ to find the height h (in feet) of an object t seconds after it is dropped from the observation deck.

b–d. See margin.
a. Find the values of h for $t = 0, 1, 2, \dots, 7$.
622, 606, 558, 478, 366, 222, 46, −162

b. Use your answer to part (a) to plot eight ordered pairs (t, h). Connect the points with a smooth curve.

c. About how long does it take an object dropped from the observation deck to hit the ground? How do you know?

d. Reflect the curve you drew in part (b) across the y-axis. Does this part of the parabola make sense in this real-life situation? Explain.

e. Give the coordinates of the vertex of the parabola you drew in parts (b) and (d). $(0, 622)$

8. a. Use the graph in the Example on page 443 to estimate the height of point A above the road. Then use the equation $y = 0.0239x^2$ to make the same height estimate. (*Hint:* Use the scale on the x-axis to approximate the x-coordinate of A.) **Sample responses are given. about 500 ft; about 527 ft**

    b. About how high is point A above the water? **about 727 ft**

    c. Estimate the length of the main cable that stretches from point A′ to point A. **If the cables were tight lines, the length would be about 4300 ft (by the Pythagorean theorem).**

9. A ball is thrown upward with an initial speed of 32 ft/sec. The equation $h = -16t^2 + 32t + 4$ gives the height h (in feet) of the ball t seconds after it is thrown.

    a. Explain why this equation is a quadratic function. Identify the values of a, b, and c in the equation. **It is in the form $y = ax^2 + bx + c$ and $a \neq 0$; $a = -16, b = 32, c = 4$**

    b. Graph the equation. Show where the graph crosses the h-axis and about where the graph crosses the t-axis. Also draw the line of symmetry. **See margin.**

    c. How high does the ball go? **20 ft**

    d. After how many seconds does it begin to fall? **1 sec**

    e. To the nearest tenth of a second, how long does it stay in the air? **about 2.1 sec**

Rewrite each equation in the form $y = ax^2 + bx + c$. Tell whether the equation represents a quadratic function.

10. $y = 7x + 8 - 3x + 5$

11. $y = 3(x - 4)$

12. $y = 2(x^2 - 7) - 2x^2$

13. $y = 6x^2 - 2x - 3x^2$

14. $y - 3 = x^2 + 7x - 5$

15. $y + x^2 = x^2 - 2x + 5$

16. **Challenge** An ordered pair of numbers that make an equation true is a solution of the equation. Find a common solution for the equations $y = x^2 - 2$ and $y = -x^2 + 2$. **Possible answers: $(\sqrt{2}, 0), (-\sqrt{2}, 0)$**

Reflecting on the Section

Write your response to Exercise 17 in your journal.

17. You have explored linear, exponential, and quadratic functions. How can you tell from looking at an equation what type of function it represents? How can you tell from looking at a graph? Include examples in your explanation. **Sample Response: equation: $y = mx + b$, linear; $y = a^x$ where $a > 0$ and $a \neq 1$, exponential; $y = ax^2 + bx + c$ where $a \neq 0$, quadratic graph: line, linear; curve that increases from left to right or decreases from left to right, exponential; parabola, quadratic.**

10. $y = 4x + 13$; not a quadratic function

11. $y = 3x - 12$; not a quadratic function

12. $y = -14$; not a quadratic function

13. $y = 3x^2 - 2x$; quadratic function

14. $y = x^2 + 7x - 2$; quadratic function

15. $y = -2x + 5$; not a quadratic function

Journal

Exercise 17 checks that you can identify quadratic functions and graphs.

DEVELOPING MATH CONCEPTS

Exercise 9 Ask students to explain what the points where the curve crosses the axes represent and what input values are reasonable for t. (*The point where the graph intersects the vertical or h-axis corresponds to time $t = 0$, so the h-coordinate gives the initial height of the ball. The point where the graph intersects the horizontal or t-axis corresponds to a height of 0, so the t-coordinate gives the time when the ball returns and hits the ground. The only values of t that can be interpreted physically are the ones from 0 to the t-coordinate of the point where the graph crosses the horizontal axis.*)

COMMON ERROR

Exercise 16 Most students will find the common solution by graphing the equations and estimating the x-coordinate of the points where the curves intersect. Some may recognize that since the values of y in the common solution must be equal, the two expressions involving x are equal and that they can solve the equations as follows:

$$x^2 - 2 = -x^2 + 2$$
$$x^2 = -x^2 + 4$$
$$2x^2 = 4$$
$$x^2 = 2$$
$$x = \pm\sqrt{2}$$

Also, if they have not drawn the graphs of the equations, these students often forget the negative root.

9. b.
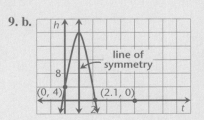

449

TEACHING NOTES

Extension Exercises 25 and 26

Ask students why writing the equation of a parabola in the form $y - k = a(x - h)^2$ might be more useful than writing it in the form of $y = ax^2 + bx + c$. *(They can tell from the equation that the vertex of a parabola is at point (h, k) and that the line y = h is the axis of symmetry. With this information, all they need to do is plot a couple more points to have a fairly accurate graph of the parabola.)*

18.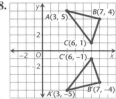

Spiral ◀▶ Review

18. The points $A(3, 5)$, $B(7, 4)$, and $C(6, 1)$ are vertices of a triangle. Draw $\triangle ABC$ and its image after a reflection across the x-axis. (Module 6, p. 436)

Find the complement of each angle. (Module 5, p. 369)

19. 16° 74°   20. 78° 12°   21. 31° 59°   22. 88° 2°

A survey is given to find out whether taxes should be used to build a playground. The survey is given to parents in the town. (Module 2, p. 132)

23. What is the population? What is the sample? taxpayers; parents

24. Is this a representative sample? Why or why not? No; Taxpayers who are not parents are not represented.

Extension ▶ ▶

Finding the Vertex

In this section you learned that all quadratic functions can be written in the form $y = ax^2 + bx + c$. All quadratic functions can also be written in the form $y - k = a(x - h)^2$, which is sometimes more useful.

25. The value of h is the x-coordinate and the value of k is the y-coordinate of the vertex of the parabola.

25. Study the equations and graphs below. What do the values of h and k tell you about the vertex of each parabola?

$y - 1 = (x - 2)^2$ $y - 3 = (x + 3)^2$ $y + 2 = (x + 4)^2$

$k = 1$ $h = 2$ $k = 3$ $h = -3$ $k = -2$ $h = -4$

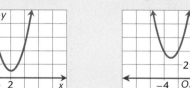

26. a. (2, −7)

b. (1, 2)

26. Make a prediction about the vertex of the graph of each equation. Then check your prediction by graphing the equation using graph paper or a graphing calculator. (*Hint:* Before graphing, rewrite the equation so that y is alone on one side of the equals sign.)

a. $y + 7 = (x - 2)^2$ b. $y - 2 = (x - 1)^2$ c. $y = (x + 3)^2$

c. (−3, 0)

Section ⑤
Extra Skill Practice

You will need: • *graph paper* (Exs. 1–6)

Predict how the graph of each equation will compare with the graph of $y = x^2$. Then check your prediction by graphing both equations on the same pair of axes. **1–6. See margin.**

1. $y = 5x^2$

2. $y = 0.1x^2$

3. $y = x^2 + 1$

4. $y = -x^2$

5. $y = -3x^2 - 2$

6. $y = -\dfrac{2}{3}x^2$

For each parabola give the coordinates of the vertex and the equation of the line of symmetry.

7. 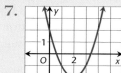 The vertex is at **(2, –2) and the line of symmetry is a vertical line through the point (2, –2).**

8. 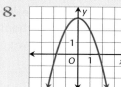 The vertex is at **(0, 3) and the line of symmetry is the y-axis.**

Rewrite each equation in the form $y = ax^2 + bx + c$. Tell whether the equation represents a quadratic function. **9–16. See margin.**

9. $y = 2x^2 + 7x - x^2$

10. $y = 3(x - 6) + 2(x + 1)$

11. $x^2 - 5x = 2(x^2 - 5) + y$

12. $y = 3(x + 4)$

13. $y - 2x^2 = 2(3 - x^2)$

14. $2 - 3(x + 7) = 1 - 2(x^2 + 3x) - y$

15. $y + 7 = x^2(2x - 5)$

16. $y + 8x^3 - 4 = -2(-2x^2 + x) - 4(x^3 + 9)$

Standardized Testing ◀▶ **Free Response**

1. Describe how the graphs of the following equations are the same and how they are different.

$y = x^2$ $\qquad y = \dfrac{1}{2}x^2$ $\qquad y = 2x^2$ $\qquad y = x^2 + 4$

2. Tell whether each equation represents a quadratic function.

a. $y = -5x^2 + 3x + 2 + 5(x^2 + 4)$ **not a quadratic function**

b. $y = 2(3x + 1) - 7x^2 + 4$ **quadratic function**

c. $y = 3x - 6x + 3x^2 + 4x + 5$ **quadratic function**

d. $y = 4x^2 + x - 4x^2 - 2$ **not a quadratic function**

1. Sample Response: All the graphs are parabolas that open up and have the same line of symmetry (the y-axis); the graphs of $y = x^2$, $y = \dfrac{1}{2}x^2$, and $y = 2x^2$ all have vertex (0, 0) but the graph of $y = x^2 + 4$ has vertex (0, 4).

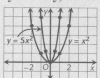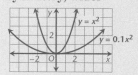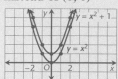

Module Project

PROJECT NOTES

Allow students to share their stories and graphs from **Questions 1 and 2** via small groups or through a bulletin board display of student work.

1. Sample Response: The seed is planted. After it sprouts, it grows rapidly for a period of time, then growth continues but at a gradually slower pace, until it appears to reach its maximum height.

2. Sample Response:

Jack's Height Above the Ground

height

time

the Module Project

Modeling Change in a Story

SET UP

You will need:
- *graph paper*
- *Project Labsheet A*

In this project you will experiment with using different mathematical models to describe changes. Then you will write a story using these mathematical models as illustrations.

Graphing Change Over Time Many stories involve change. You may be able to model the change with a graph. An example is the story of "Jack and the Beanstalk." In the story, a poor boy named Jack sells his family's cow for some magic beans. The beans sprout into a giant beanstalk that Jack climbs. He finds a wealthy giant at the top of the beanstalk, steals the giant's riches, and then chops down the beanstalk to protect himself from the giant. The graph shown models one change in the story. **1–2. See margin.**

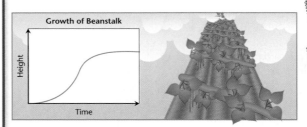

1 Describe in words the change modeled by the graph.

2 Draw a graph that could represent Jack's height above the ground, from the beginning to the end of the story. Give the graph a title and label the axes.

Linear Models Many stories involve travel. You can use equations, tables, and graphs to model changes in distance over time.

3 Suppose Brad leaves his house at 3:00 P.M. and heads west on his bike. His speed is 8 mi/hr. His friend John is 10 mi west of Brad's house. He starts walking toward Brad's house at 3:00 P.M. His speed is 4 mi/hr.

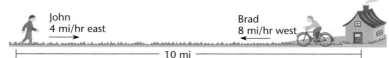

John
4 mi/hr east

Brad
8 mi/hr west

|← 10 mi →|

Time after 3:00 P.M. (hours)	Brad's distance from Brad's house (miles)	John's distance from Brad's house (miles)
0	0	10
0.25	2	9
0.50	?	?
0.75	?	?
1.00	?	?

John's speed is 4 mi/hr, so in 0.25 hr, he travels 1 mi and is 10 − 1 = 9 mi from Brad's house.

a. Copy and complete the table to model Brad's and John's distances from Brad's house. Then estimate when Brad and John will meet. *See margin.*

b. Let x = the number of hours after 3:00 P.M. and y = the distance from Brad's house. Use the table to write two equations, one that models Brad's distance from his house over time, and one that models John's distance from Brad's house over time. $y = 8x$ (Brad's distance) and $y = 10 - 4x$ (John's distance)

c. Graph your equations from part (b) on the same pair of axes. How does your graph show when John and Brad will meet? *See margin.*

d. Show how you can write and solve an equation to find out when John and Brad will meet. *See margin.*

4 Describe a situation that involves a change in distance over time like the one in Question 3. Explain how you could model the change. *Answers will vary. Check students' work.*

Algorithms for Change You know how to translate, stretch, and reflect figures in a coordinate plane. Each of these transformations can create a different visual effect that you can use to illustrate a story.

5 Use Project Labsheet A.

a. Imagine that the frames on the Project Labsheet are frames of film. Describe the visual effect of each transformation.

b. Follow the directions for the *Blank Film Frames* to create a visual effect using a series of transformations. *Check students' work.*

Illustrating a Story Any of the models you have experimented with can be used to represent change in a story. It all depends on the story.

6 Work with a partner to discuss possible story ideas. Each of you should write down at least three possible ideas. Each idea should involve a change that can be represented by at least one of the following. *6–8. Check students' work.*

- an equation, a table, or a graph
- transformations on a coordinate plane

7 a. On your own, choose the story idea that appeals to you. Write a draft of the story. Include the mathematical models you plan to use as illustrations.

b. Exchange drafts and models with a partner. Share helpful comments and suggestions for improvement.

8 Write the final draft of your story. Include your mathematical models.

5. a. Translation: The car is driving forward. Stretch: The motorcycle is moving toward me. Reflection: The wind is changing the direction of the sail.

PROJECT NOTES
Students who have difficulty thinking of original situations for **Question 4** may use the same setting and simply change the rates. To help with developing ideas, you can have the class brainstorm other settings. Some possibilities are given.

- Two hikers hike toward each other at different rates from opposite ends of a trail.

- Two planes leave an airport at the same time flying in opposite directions at different rates. When will they be a given number of miles apart?

- An accident happens a given distance from a hospital. An ambulance at the scene can travel to the hospital at 1 mi/min. A medical helicopter can fly from the hospital to the accident scene and back at 2 mi/min. Should the ambulance or the helicopter be used to transport a seriously injured person to the hospital?

3. a. and c–d. See Additional Answers beginning on page A1.

453

10. $y = 20{,}000 - 500x$; $15{,}000$

Years	Value ($)
0	20,000
1	19,500
2	19,000
3	18,500
4	18,000
5	17,500
6	17,000
7	16,500
8	16,000
9	15,500
10	15,000

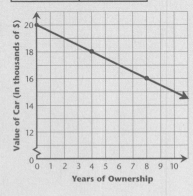

Value of Car (in thousands of $) — Years of Ownership

Review and Assessment

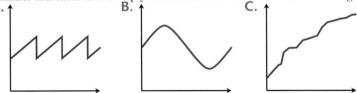

MODULE 6

You will need: • *graph paper* (Exs. 10, 23–26)
• *graph paper or graphing calculator (optional)* (Ex. 27)

Match each situation with a graph. Explain your thinking. (Sec. 1, Explor. 1)

1. the number of sunlight hours per day throughout the year B; The hours increase gradually to a maximum and then decrease gradually to a minimum.

2. your height from birth to age 18 C; Height increases at varying rates.

3. the length of the grass in your yard during the summer A; The length of the grass in the summer increases then sharply decreases each time it is cut and then begins to grow again.

A.   B.   C.

For each equation, tell whether *y* is a function of *x*. (Sec. 1, Explor. 2)

4. $y = 6x$ function   5. $x = 6y^2$ not a function 6. $2x = 2y$ function

7. $y = x^2 - 4$ function 8. $y = |x|$ function   9. $x = |y|$ not a function

10. Olivia Murk paid $20,000 for her car. Her car is losing value at the rate of $500 per year. Write an equation to model this situation. Then use your equation, a table, or a graph to determine what her car will be worth in 10 years. (Sec. 2, Explor. 1) See margin.

Solve each equation. (Sec. 2, Explor. 2)

11. $3x - 10 = 7 + 2x$ 17   12. $5(x - 2) = 10$ 4

13. $-4x - 7 = -2(x + 3)$ –0.5   14. $20 - (x - 5) = 3(3x + 5)$ 1

15. $7x - 2(x + 5) = 5(5x + 9)$ –2.75 16. $5 - 6x = -2(2x - 1) - 20$ 11.5

17. Joe starts walking at the rate of 3 ft/sec. His total distance traveled can be modeled by the equation $y = 3x$, where y = distance in feet and x = time in seconds. Ten seconds later, Lidia starts jogging at the rate of 5 ft/sec. Her total distance traveled can be modeled by the equation $y = 5(x - 10)$. When will Lidia's distance traveled equal Joe's? (Sec. 2, Explor. 2) at 25 sec

Evaluate each expression for the given value of the variable.
(Sec. 3, Explors. 1 and 2)

19. $\frac{9}{16}$

21. $\frac{1}{25}$

18. 10^x; $x = 4$ 19. $\left(\frac{3}{4}\right)^x$; $x = 2$ 20. $3 \cdot 2^x$; $x = 5$ 21. $5 \cdot \left(\frac{1}{5}\right)^x$; $x = 3$
   10,000   96

22. Irene Ehler deposits $100 in a savings account that earns 5% annual interest. Write an equation that models the amount of money y in the account after x years. Use your equation to determine how much money will be in the account after 25 years. (Sec. 3, Explor. 2) $y = 100 \cdot (1.05)^x$; $338.64

23. Use the triangle at the right. Write an algorithm for reflecting $\triangle ABC$ across the y-axis and then translating it up 3 units. Then draw the image. (Sec. 4, Explor. 1)
See margin.

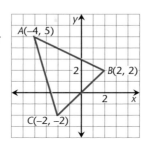

Make a sketch showing how you think the graphs of the given equations will compare with the graph of $y = x^2$. (Sec. 5, Explor. 1) 24–27. See margin.

24. $y = 2x^2$; $y = -2x^2$ 25. $y = 0.5x^2$; $y = 10x^2$ 26. $y = x^2 + 2$; $y = x^2 - 5$

27. A ball is thrown upward with an initial speed of 15 m/sec. The equation $h = -4.9t^2 + 15t + 1$ models the height h (in meters) of the ball t seconds after it is thrown. (Sec. 5, Explor. 2)

   a. Graph the equation and sketch the line of symmetry for the parabola.

   b. About how long does it take the ball to hit the ground?

   c. Give the approximate coordinates of the vertex of the parabola.

Rewrite each equation in the form $y = ax^2 + bx + c$. Tell whether the equation represents a quadratic function. (Sec. 5, Explor. 2)

28. $y = 5 - x^2$

29. $y + 7 = 2(x^2 - 3) + x$

30. $x^2 - 2x - y = x^2 + 7x + 4$

31. $x^2 + 4(x^2 - 2x) = -2(x - 3) + y + 3$

Reflecting ▶on the Module

32. **Writing** In this module you studied linear, exponential, and quadratic functions. Give an example of each type of equation. Describe a real-life situation that could be modeled by each type of equation.
Answers will vary. Check students' work.

28. $y = -x^2 + 5$;
    quadratic function

29. $y = 2x^2 + x - 13$;
    quadratic function

30. $y = -9x - 4$; not a
    quadratic function

31. $y = 5x^2 - 6x - 9$;
    quadratic function

Module 6   Review and Assessment   455

Assessment Options

TEACHER'S RESOURCE BOOK
• Module 6 Tests A and B
• Module 6 Standardized Test
• Module 6 Performance Assessment
• Modules 5 and 6 Cumulative Test

TEST GENERATOR

23. $(x', y') = (-x, y)$; $(x'', y'') = (x', y' + 3)$

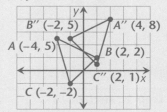

24.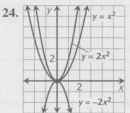

25.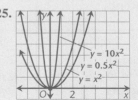

26.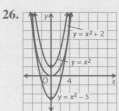

27. a.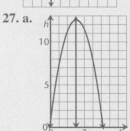

b. about 3.1 sec

c. (1.5, 12.5)

455

MODULE 7

The Algebra Connection

Module 7 Overview

Through the works of scientists, mathematicians, engineers, inventors, and artists, students see how the world is connected to algebra. In this module, students use algebra while applying rules of exponents, simplifying radical expressions, multiplying binomials, factoring quadratics, and solving inequalities.

Module 7 Planner

Day 1: Section 1	Day 2: Section 1	Day 3: Section 1	Day 4: Section 2	Day 5: Section 2
Setting the Stage, p. 458 Exploration 1, pp. 459–461	Exploration 2 *through* Question 20, pp. 461–462	Exploration 2 *from* Question 21, pp. 462–463 Key Concepts, p. 464	Setting the Stage, p. 470 Exploration 1 *through* Question 7, pp. 471–472	Exploration 1 *from* Question 8, pp. 472–473
Day 6: Section 2	**Day 7: E²**	**Day 8: Review and Assessment**	**Day 9: Section 3**	**Day 10: Section 3**
Exploration 2, pp. 474–476 Key Concepts, p. 477	Work on Extended Exploration, p. 481	Mid-Module Quiz	Setting the Stage, pp. 482–483 Exploration 1, pp. 483–485	Exploration 2, pp. 485–487
Day 11: Section 3	**Day 12: Module Project**	**Day 13: Section 4**	**Day 14: Section 4**	**Day 15: Section 4**
Exploration 3, pp. 487–488 Key Concepts, p. 489	Assign Module Project, pp. 512–513	Setting the Stage, p. 495 Exploration 1 *through* Question 13, pp. 496–499	Exploration 1 *from* Question 14, pp. 499–500	Exploration 2 *through* Question 28, pp. 501–503
Day 16: Section 4	**Day 17: Review and Assessment**	**Day 18: Review and Assessment**	**Day 19: Assessment**	**Day 20: Module Project**
Exploration 2 *from* Question 29, pp. 503–505 Key Concepts, pp. 506–507	Assign Review and Assessment, pp. 514–515	Discuss Review and Assessment, pp. 514–515	Module 7 Test	Present projects

Materials List

Section	Materials
1	• Labsheet 1A, scientific calculator
2	• calculator
4	• Labsheet 4A, algebra tiles
Rev & Assess	• algebra tiles

Module 7 Objectives

Section	Objectives	NCTM Standards 2000*
1	• Multiply and divide powers. • Simplify powers with zero and negative exponents. • Represent small numbers in scientific notation and in decimal notation.	1, 2, 4, 6, 7, 8, 9, 10
2	• Identify irrational numbers. • Simplify square roots. • Simplify radical expressions.	1, 2, 7, 8, 9, 10
3	• Write and graph inequalities. • Solve inequalities that involve one operation. • Solve inequalities that have more than one operation.	1, 2, 6, 7, 8, 9, 10
4	• Multiply binomials. • Factor quadratics.	1, 2, 3, 5, 6, 7, 8, 9, 10

* See page T14.

Section 1 Planner

Section Objectives

Exploration 1
- Multiply and divide powers

Exploration 2
- Simplify powers with zero and negative exponents
- Represent small numbers in scientific notation and in decimal notation

Days for Section 1

First Day
Setting the Stage, *p. 458*
Exploration 1, *pp. 459–461*

Second Day
Exploration 2 through Question 20
pp. 461–462

Third Day
Exploration 2 from Question 21, *pp. 462–463*
Key Concepts, *p. 464*

Teaching Resources

Teacher's Resource Book
- Warm-Up
- Labsheet 1A
- Practice and Applications
- Study Guide
See page 457 for additional teaching resources.

Materials List

Exploration 1
- calculator

Exploration 2
- Labsheet 1A
- calculator

Practice and Applications
- calculator

Assessment Options

EMBEDDED ASSESSMENT
- Multiply and divide powers
  Exercises 6, 10, 18, 20, 22
- Simplify powers with zero and negative exponents
  Exercises 30, 31, 34, 35
- Represent small numbers in scientific notation and in decimal notation
  Exercises 40, 44, 46, 48

PERFORMANCE TASK/PORTFOLIO
- Exercise 27 on *p. 466 (challenge)*
- Exercise 52 on *p. 467 (journal)*

QUIZZES/TESTS
- Section 1 Quick Quiz

TEST GENERATOR

Section 1 Overview

In this section, students will use exponents in products and quotients, with numbers and with variables, and to represent numbers in scientific notation.

Exploration 1
Using information about the giant star Betelgeuse, students learn to express the product of powers of 10 as one single base raised to a power. After working several numerical examples, the *product of powers property* is developed and then applied to numbers and algebraic expressions. Using the diameter of Betelgeuse and the diameter of the sun, students explore the relationship between the exponents of like bases in a quotient. From this and other examples, students work to develop the *quotient of powers property*.

Exploration 2
Students' interest is captured by pictures taken with different width fields of view to give students the impression of zooming in on a bee's eye by powers of 10. By comparing various ratios and applying the quotient property students discover that any non-zero number raised to the 0 power is 1. The idea of an exponent less than 1 also allows for the introduction of negative exponents and their use in representing small numbers in scientific notation.

Guide for Assigning Homework

Section/ P&A Pages	Core Assignment	Extended Assignment	Additional Practice/Review	Open-ended Problems	Extended Problems
REGULAR SCHEDULING (45 MIN CLASS PERIOD)			**EXERCISES TO NOTE**		
1 pp. 465–468	**Day 1:** 1–10, 15–24 **Day 2:** 30–38, SR 53–59 **Day 3:** 39–51, ROS 52, 60, 61	2–12 even, 13, 14–26 even, 27–29 30–38, SR 53–59 40–52 even, 62–70	EP, p. 469 TB, p. 589	PA 14	PA Challenge 27 Career Connection, 60, 61 Ext 62–70

Key: PA = Practice & Application; ROS = Reflecting on the Section; SR = Spiral Review; TB = Toolbox; EP = Extra Skill Practice; Ext = Extension; *more time

Math Background and Teaching Strategies

Classroom Notes

Bulletin board display ideas for this section include:

- copies of photos taken by the Hubble Space Telescope

- information about Edwin Hubble

Math Strands

Topic Spiraling and Integration

Exploration 1

Students evaluated expressions with exponents while working with area and volume formulas in Module 2 and exponential change and quadratic equations in Module 6. Building on their knowledge of exponents, students use a rate written in scientific notation, along with the commutative and associative properties of multiplication, to see how the product of two like bases can be written as one base raised to

a single power. Their observations are formalized and defined as the *product of powers property*. Students help complete the definition so that they learn how to generalize their observations with the algebraic statement: $b^m \cdot b^n = b^{m+n}$.

Using the star Betelgeuse, students write a ratio to compare its diameter to the diameter of the sun. Students simplify the ratio by dividing common factors out of the numerator and denominator to see how quotients can be written as a base raised to a single power. By completing an equation for dividing powers with the same base, students help to define the *quotient of powers property*.

During the lesson, both properties are first applied to numeric bases and then extended to include variable bases.

Exploration 2

Exploration 2 uses ratios and the quotient or powers property to show why $b^0 = 1$ when $b \neq 0$. Using a ratio also helps to explain why b cannot equal 0. You can easily relate it to Question 14 and show how in a ratio you would be dividing by 0 which is undefined. Since students have now seen exponents that are positive or zero, it provides a natural lead into the topic of negative exponents. The *quotient powers property* is used to show the relationship between a negative exponent and its fraction or whole number equivalent written without exponents.

In Module 3, scientific notation was used to represent large numbers. Now with the introduction of negative exponents, students are asked to apply their new skills to represent extremely small numbers in scientific notation.

456D

Section 2 Simplifying Radicals

Section 2 Planner

Section Objectives

Exploration 1
- Identify irrational numbers
- Simplify square roots

Exploration 2
- Simplify radical expressions

Days for Section 2

First Day
Setting the Stage, *p. 470*
Exploration 1 through Question 7,
pp. 471–472

Second Day
Exploration 1 from Question 8, *pp. 472–473*

Third Day
Exploration 2, *pp. 474–476*
Key Concepts, *p. 477*

Teaching Resources

Teacher's Resource Book
- Warm-Up
- Practice and Applications
- Study Guide
See page 457 for additional teaching resources.

Materials List

Setting the Stage
- calculator

Assessment Options

EMBEDDED ASSESSMENT
- Identify irrational numbers
  Exercises 1, 3(b)
- Simplify square roots
  Exercise 6
- Simplify radical expressions
  Exercises 8, 9

PERFORMANCE TASK/PORTFOLIO
- Exercise 4 on *p. 478*
- Exercise 12 on *p. 479*
- Exercise 13 on *p. 479 (journal)*
- Extended Exploration on *p. 481**

* indicates a problem-solving task that can be assessed using the Assessment Scales

QUIZZES/TESTS
- Section 2 Quick Quiz
- Mid-Module Quiz

TEST GENERATOR

Section 2 Overview

In this section, students will learn to represent radical expressions in simplest form. In the *Setting the Stage* students learn about the mathematician Brahmagupta, and use his formula for the area of a quadrilateral to obtain an approximate area and an exact area. Key terms *radical sign* and *radicand* are introduced in the *Setting the Stage*.

Exploration 1
The expression for the exact area of the quadrilateral from the *Setting the Stage* is used to introduce and help define the key term, *irrational number*. Students learn to simplify square roots and fractions that contain square roots in the numerators and denominators.

Exploration 2
In Exploration 2, students learn that Brahmagupta's formula is written in simplest radical form. They apply the *product property* to simplify radical expressions that contain numbers and variables. The cube root is introduced through the history of the development of the cube root symbol, $\sqrt[3]{}$, so a connection is made between the root and the index on the radical sign. Students conjecture about the meaning of an index of 4 and then simplify fourth root radical expressions.

Guide for Assigning Homework

Section/ P&A Pages	Core Assignment	Extended Assignment	Additional Practice/Review	Open-ended Problems	Extended Problems
REGULAR SCHEDULING (45 MIN CLASS PERIOD)			**EXERCISES TO NOTE**		
2 pp. 478–479	**Day 1:** 1–6 **Day 2:** 7–8, SR 14–20 **Day 3:** 9, 10, ROS 13	1–6 7–8, SR 14–20 9–12, ROS 13	EP, p. 480		PA Challenge 11 PA 12

Key: PA = Practice & Application; ROS = Reflecting on the Section; SR = Spiral Review; TB = Toolbox; EP = Extra Skill Practice; Ext = Extension; *more time

Math Background and Teaching Strategies

Classroom Notes

Bulletin board display ideas for this section include:

- history of various math symbols

- lists of perfect squares and cubes

Interest centers for this section might include:

- a guided activity on using the index key on a calculator to estimate third and fourth roots of a number

- compass and straightedge instructions for inscribing regular polygons in a circle

- special right triangle relationships that use radical expressions to represent side lengths. For example: for 30°-60°-90° triangles, the side lengths are x, $x\sqrt{3}$, and $2x$; for 45°-45°-90° triangles, the side lengths are x, x, and $x\sqrt{2}$.

Math Strands

Topic Spiraling and Integration

Exploration 1

Principal square roots and perfect squares were reviewed in Module 3. In that module, students also evaluated formulas in which the square root sign was a grouping symbol. Calculations with square roots that were not perfect squares were estimated to a given number of decimal places. In Module 7, the term *irrational* is defined using non-perfect square roots as examples. From this, students learn to use the radical sign to represent the exact value of a square root and to write it in simplest form. (A connection can be made to the use of π, which is also an irrational number, to express the exact circumference or area of a circle.)

Students apply the *product property* and *quotient property* to the radicand when possible as a strategy for simplifying a radical. The concept of rationalizing the denominator is also introduced as one of the methods for simplifying certain square root expressions.

Exploration 2

Exploration 2 extends Exploration 1 to include radical expressions with variables, cube roots, and other roots. The same principles for simplifying expressions are applied. Question 17 addresses the issue of negative values of a variable, however it is assumed for the remainder of the section that all variables are positive so as not to have to use absolute value signs. This exploration relies heavily on students' understanding of the *product of powers* and *quotient of powers properties* taught in Section 1 of this module.

Section 3   Graphing and Solving Inequalities

Section 3 Planner

Section Objectives

Exploration 1
• Write and graph inequalities

Exploration 2
• Solve inequalities that involve one operation

Exploration 3
• Solve inequalities that have more than one operation

Days for Section 3

First Day
Setting the Stage, *pp. 482–483*
Exploration 1, *pp. 483–485*

Second Day
Exploration 2, *pp. 485–487*

Third Day
Exploration 3, *pp. 487–488*
Key Concepts, *p. 489*

Teaching Resources

Teacher's Resource Book
• Warm-Up
• Practice and Applications
• Study Guide
See page 457 for additional teaching resources.

Assessment Options

EMBEDDED ASSESSMENT
• Write and graph inequalities
   Exercises 3, 4, 5
• Solve inequalities that involve one operation
   Exercises 11, 12, 13, 14
• Solve inequalities that have more than one operation
   Exercises 27, 29, 30, 31

PERFORMANCE TASK/PORTFOLIO
• Exercise 6 on *p. 490 (writing)*
• Exercise 35 on *p. 492 (create your own)*
• Exercise 38 on *p. 493 (journal)*

QUIZZES/TESTS
• Section 3 Quick Quiz

TEST GENERATOR

Section 3 Overview

In this section, students study how human factors engineers help design comfortable furniture. The explorations show how these engineers must solve linear inequalities to design seating for safety and comfort.

Exploration 1
Students begin by looking at how some of the guidelines for car seat use can be represented as inequalities. *Inequality* is defined and the graphs of inequalities are studied. The use of solid and open circles on the graphs of inequalities and their relation to the inequality signs are developed. By combining two inequalities, students learn to write and graph compound inequalities.

Exploration 2
In this exploration students learn to solve linear inequalities and graph the solutions on a number line. By investigating the properties used to solve inequalities, students discover which operations reverse an inequality. They also discuss how checking solutions of inequalities differs from checking solutions of equations.

Exploration 3
As students use human factors engineering techniques to design comfortable seating for a theater, they learn how to solve multi-step inequalities. Students write and solve inequalities, discussing as a class the order in which to perform inverse operations to solve an inequality.

Guide for Assigning Homework

Regular Scheduling (45 min class period)			Exercises to Note		
Section/ P&A Pages	Core Assignment	Extended Assignment	Additional Practice/Review	Open-ended Problems	Extended Problems
3 pp. 490–493	**Day 1:** 1–6, SR 39–44 **Day 2:** 7–20 **Day 3:** 22–36, ROS 38	1–6, SR 39–44 7, 11–21 24–37, ROS 38	EP, p. 494	PA 35	PA 21 Challenge PA 37

Key: PA = Practice & Application; ROS = Reflecting on the Section; SR = Spiral Review; TB = Toolbox; EP = Extra Skill Practice; Ext = Extension; ST = Standardized Testing

Math Background and Teaching Strategies

Classroom Notes

Bulletin board display ideas for this section include:

- various pictures of chairs gathered by students with the measure of the popliteal height noted

Visitors might include:

- a human factors engineer

Math Strands

Topic Spiraling and Integration

The three explorations in this section build upon each other, helping students move from simple to more complex concepts as they complete each exploration. The *Setting the Stage* begins with a graph that requires students to "think" in terms of inequalities. Each value of the dependent variable yields an inequality that describes how a given measure is related to the corresponding value of the independent variable. The intent of this graph and of the real-life examples in the exploration is to make students more aware of the ways in which our daily world is described by inequalities.

Exploration 1

Exploration 1 makes a connection between a real world description, an algebraic inequality, and a visual representation on a number line. The distinction between *greater* (or *less*) *than or equal to* and *greater* (or *less*) *than* are made in both the inequality statements and in the graphs. By examining situations that involve two inequalities joined by the conjunction "and" or "or", students learn how to read, write, and graph compound inequalities.

Exploration 2

Students began solving equations with rational numbers in Module 1 and continued to apply and build on this skill through Module 6. At this point they should be comfortable with the process of solving equations. This section uses that understanding to develop the various aspects of solving inequalities. The necessity of reversing an inequality to keep a statement true is approached by observing the results when operations are performed on a numeric inequality.

Exploration 3

Students continue to write and solve inequalities in this exploration. It is assumed students will use techniques applied with equations, along with the discoveries about solving inequalities made in Exploration 2. The applications in this exploration veer from the simpler representations in Exploration 1 to more in-depth real world problem-solving.

Section ④ Polynomials and Factoring

Section 4 Planner

Section Objectives

Exploration 1
• Multiply binomials

Exploration 2
• Factor quadratics

Days for Section 4

First Day
Setting the Stage, *p. 495*
Exploration 1 through Question 13,
pp. 496–499

Second Day
Exploration 1 from Question 14,
pp. 499–500

Third Day
Exploration 2 through Question 28,
pp. 501–503

Fourth Day
Exploration 2 from Question 29,
pp. 503–505
Key Concepts, *pp. 506–507*

Teaching Resources

Teacher's Resource Book
• Warm-Up
• Labsheet 4A
• Practice and Applications
• Study Guide
See page 457 for additional teaching
resources.

Materials List

Exploration 1
• Labsheet 4A
• algebra tiles

Exploration 2
• algebra tiles

Practice and Applications
• algebra tiles

Extra Skill Practice
• algebra tiles

Assessment Options

EMBEDDED ASSESSMENT
• Multiply binomials
   Exercises 2, 8, 15, 21
• Factor quadratics
   Exercises 31, 35, 42, 44

PERFORMANCE TASK/PORTFOLIO
• Exercise 47 on *p. 510 (journal)*

QUIZZES/TESTS
• Section 4 Quick Quiz
• Module Tests A and B
• Module Standardized Test
• Module Performance Assessment

TEST GENERATOR

Section 4 Overview

In this section, students work with
algebra tiles to multiply binomials and
factor quadratic expressions.

Exploration 1
This exploration begins with an
introduction to the key term
polynomial and the types of
polynomials. Students use algebra
tiles to model polynomials and then
to multiply two binomials. Students
progress from modeling with tiles to
representing a product with a table.
By the end of the exploration students
will find the product of two binomials
by using the distributive property.

Exploration 2
In this exploration students use
algebra tiles to represent polynomial
products. Using the tiles, they learn
to find the factors of a quadratic
expression. The exploration uses
algebra tiles throughout as students
develop their own explanations
about how to use the patterns they
have observed to help them factor a
polynomial.

Guide for Assigning Homework

REGULAR SCHEDULING (45 MIN CLASS PERIOD)			EXERCISES TO NOTE		
Section/ P&A Pages	Core Assignment	Extended Assignment	Additional Practice/Review	Open-ended Problems	Extended Problems
4 pp. 508–510	**Day 1:** 1–12 **Day 2:** 13–25 **Day 3:** 26–35 **Day 4:** 36–46, ROS 47, SR 48–51	1–12 13–25 26–35 36–46, ROS 47, SR 48–51	EP, p. 511 Review & Assessment, pp. 514–515		Mod Proj, pp. 512–513

Key: PA = Practice & Application; ROS = Reflecting on the Section; SR = Spiral Review; TB = Toolbox; EP = Extra Skill Practice; Ext = Extension; ST = Standardized Testing

Math Background and Teaching Strategies

Classroom Notes

Bulletin board displays for this section include:

• history of Leonardo da Vinci and his various artwork and inventions

Math Strands

Topic Spiraling and Integration

The material in this section is designed for students who have mastered most of the skills in Book 3 and are ready for more exposure to algebraic concepts. The lessons are taught using manipulatives in order for students to be able to move from concrete to abstract thinking at their own pace. This is the students' first exposure to multiplying and factoring polynomials. The ideas introduced here will be reviewed and extended in future math courses and treated in a more abstract fashion.

Exploration 1

Although Exploration 1 serves as a basis for factoring in Exploration 2, it can also be done as a stand alone unit. The exploration steps students through the process of finding the product of two binomials beginning with a concrete model (algebra tiles), then with an organized table, and finally by using the distributive property. Although the goal is for students to eventually be able to multiply using the distributive property, they should not be pushed through the process if they are not comfortable making the transition. Remember, this is an exposure lesson that allows students to learn how to use models and representations in algebra. In addition, it provides an opportunity for students to practice the skills learned in Section 1 of this module and to revisit the distributive property and integer operations.

Exploration 2

Exploration 2 is designed for students who made the progression from algebra tiles to the use of the distributive property in Exploration 1. Students will use algebra tiles, logical reasoning, and guess and check to find the factors of a polynomial. At first, students factor only polynomials in which the terms are added. During this exploration students discover patterns that they use to arrange tiles and find the factors of quadratics. Some students may be able to make the transition to factoring quadratic trinomials without the use of tiles, though it is not required. Further factoring of polynomials in this lesson requires the understanding of adding zeros in the form of positive and negative tiles. Students should find the work challenging and are not expected to master the concepts in this one exploration.

OVERVIEW
Through the work of scientists, mathematicians, engineers, inventors, and artists, students see how the world is connected to algebra. In this module, students use algebra while applying rules of exponents, simplifying radical expressions, multiplying binomials, factoring quadratics, and solving inequalities.

PREREQUISITE SKILLS
Warm-Up Exercises for each section are provided in the *Teacher's Resource Book*. You can use these exercises to review skills and concepts students will need for each section. In addition, the Spiral Review exercises at the end of each section in the student edition provide practice on prerequisite skills.

MODULE DIAGNOSTIC TEST
The Module Diagnostic Test in the *Teacher's Resource Book* can be used to assess students' prior knowledge of skills and concepts that will be taught in each section of this module. You can use test results to help structure your teaching to meet the diverse needs of your classroom.

MODULE 7 The Algebra Connection

The Module Project

Math and Careers

Mathematics appears in many places. In this module project you will conduct an interview with an individual who uses mathematics in his or her job. After gathering information about the person, the job, and the type of math used, you will present your findings to the class.

More on the Module Project
See pp. 512–513.

456

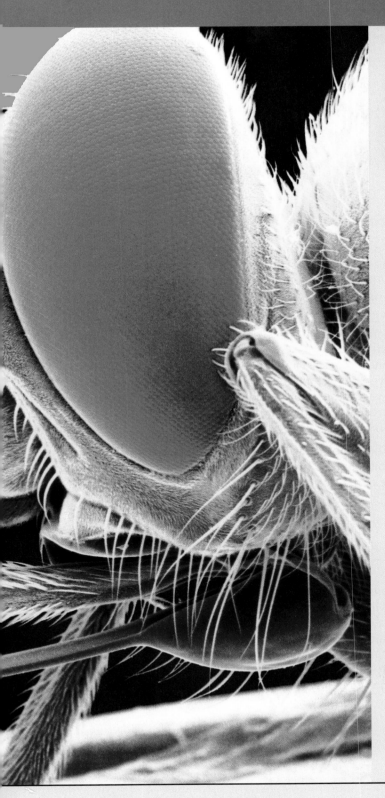

MODULE 7

SECTION OVERVIEW

1 Working with Exponents

As you read about the use of telescopes and microscopes:

◆ Multiply and divide powers
◆ Simplify powers with zero and negative exponents

2 Simplifying Radicals

As you study a mathematician's work:

◆ Identify irrational numbers
◆ Use the product and quotient properties of square roots to simplify square roots
◆ Simplify radical expressions

3 Graphing and Solving Inequalities

As you learn how engineers use data to design car seats, seat heights, and theater seating:

◆ Write and graph inequalities
◆ Solve simple inequalities
◆ Solve multi-step inequalities

4 Polynomials and Factoring

As you examine Leonardo da Vinci's work:

◆ Use algebra tiles to model binomials and their products
◆ Multiply binomials
◆ Use algebra tiles to factor quadratics

> **INTERNET**
> Resources and practice at
> **classzone.com**

 457

Module Resources

TEACHER'S RESOURCE BOOK
Resources
• The *Math Gazette* (parent newsletter)
• Warm-Ups
• Labsheets
• Practice and Applications
• Study Guide

Assessment
• Section Quick Quizzes
• Mid-Module Quiz
• Module 7 Diagnostic Test
• Module 7 Tests A and B
• Module 7 Standardized Test
• Module 7 Performance Assessment

SPANISH RESOURCES
• The *Math Gazette* (parent newsletter)
• Practice and Applications
• Assessment
• Spanish Glossary

STUDENT WORKBOOK

TECHNOLOGY BOOK

TECHNOLOGY RESOURCES
• @Home Tutor
• Test Generator
• Activity Generator
• Professional Development DVD
• Online Activities

IN THIS SECTION

EXPLORATION 1
♦ Properties of Exponents

EXPLORATION 2
♦ Zero and Negative Exponents

Big and Small

Setting the Stage

There is a lot in the universe that your eyes cannot see without help—objects as big as planets and stars and as small as blood cells and bacteria. The invention of the telescope and the microscope made these objects visible.

In 1924, Edwin Hubble was using a telescope to investigate the Andromeda Nebula, believed to be a gaseous cloud inside our own Milky Way Galaxy. Hubble calculated the distance to one of the stars in the nebula to be over 1,000,000 light-years, which placed it outside the Milky Way. (A light-year is the distance light travels in one year.) Scientists realized that the universe was much larger than they had presumed.

The Hubble Space Telescope, named for Edwin Hubble, orbits Earth 353 miles above its surface and has produced some of the clearest astronomical images ever recorded.

1. Answers will vary. Sample Response: A telescope in space doesn't have to see through Earth's atmosphere, which distorts images much as it makes stars appear to twinkle.

Think About It

1 Why do you think the Hubble Space Telescope provides clearer images of astronomical objects than telescopes located on Earth?

2 The Andromeda Nebula (now called the M31 Galaxy) is about 2,000,000 light-years away. The Hubble Space Telescope has identified a galaxy 10 times that distance from Earth. About how far from Earth is that galaxy? $20 \cdot 1{,}000{,}000 = 20{,}000{,}000$ light-years

▶ In this module, you will see how algebra is connected to the world around us and used in many walks of life.

Exploration 1

Properties of Exponents

GOAL

LEARN HOW TO...
- multiply and divide powers

AS YOU...
- work with astronomical distances

KEY TERMS
- product of powers property
- quotient of powers property

SET UP | *You will need a calculator.*

▶ In 1995, the Hubble Space Telescope sent an image of the giant star Betelgeuse (pronounced *beetle juice*) to Earth. This was the first detailed image of a star other than the sun. However, the image actually showed what the star looked like hundreds of years ago! The diagram explains why.

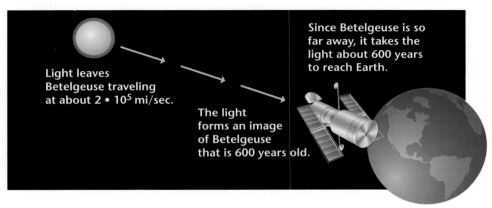

Light leaves Betelgeuse traveling at about $2 \cdot 10^5$ mi/sec.

The light forms an image of Betelgeuse that is 600 years old.

Since Betelgeuse is so far away, it takes the light about 600 years to reach Earth.

▶ How many miles is it from Betelgeuse to Earth? You can use the information in the diagram to find out.

3 You first need to convert the speed of light given in the diagram from miles per second to miles per year.

   a. Show that there are about $3 \cdot 10^7$ seconds in one year. **See margin.**

   b. Explain why the product of $2 \cdot 10^5$ and $3 \cdot 10^7$ approximates the speed of light in miles per year.

   c. Explain why the product in part (b) can be written as $6 \cdot (10^5 \cdot 10^7)$. **See margin.**

FOR▶HELP

with *powers*, see **TOOLBOX, p. 589**

3. b. $2 \cdot 10^5$ is the speed of light in mi/sec and there are about $3 \cdot 10^7$ seconds in a year. Multiplying mi/sec times sec/year results in mi/year.

Exploration 1

COMMON ERRORS

Question 3(c) Some students may not be able to explain why $(2 \cdot 10^5) \cdot (3 \cdot 10^7)$ can be written as $6 \cdot (10^5 \cdot 10^7)$. Give them a simpler problem to solve first. For example, have them compare $2 \cdot 3 \cdot 4 \cdot 5$ to $8 \cdot (3 \cdot 5)$.

3. a. and c. See Additional Answers beginning on page A1.

459

DEVELOPING MATH CONCEPTS
Questions 6 and 12 lead students to statements of two important properties. Check with students as they answer these questions to make sure they have the correct rules.

TEACHING NOTES
Question 7 asks students to apply the product of powers property to several exercises. Explain that the property works the same way for all bases, including variables, as long as the bases being multiplied are the same.

If students need more guidance interpreting and using the *product of powers property*, you may want to discuss the following Classroom Example before they complete **Checkpoint Question 7**.

CLASSROOM EXAMPLE

Use the *product of powers property* to write each product as a single power.

a. $3^6 \cdot 3^9$ b. $m^2 \cdot m^3$

Answer:
a. $3^6 \cdot 3^9 = 3^{6+9} = 3^{15}$
b. $m^2 \cdot m^3 = m^{2+3} = m^5$

---

10. b. See Additional Answers beginning on page A1.

✔ QUESTION 7

...checks that you can use the product of powers property to multiply powers.

FOR ◄HELP
with *scientific notation*, see
MODULE 3, p. 209

---

4 **a.** How many factors of 10 are in the product $10^5 \cdot 10^7$? 12

b. Use your answer from part (a) to write $6 \cdot (10^5 \cdot 10^7)$, the speed of light in miles per year, as $6 \cdot 10^k$ for some integer k.
$6 \cdot 10^{12}$

c. How is the exponent in 10^k related to the exponents in $10^5 \cdot 10^7$? $k = 5 + 7$; k is the sum of 5 and 7.

5 Write each product as a single power. Use a calculator to check each answer.

a. $10^2 \cdot 10^3$ 10^5 **b.** $3^6 \cdot 3^6$ 3^{12} **c.** $2^{10} \cdot 2^7$ 2^{17}

6 Complete this rule for multiplying powers with the same base: $b^m \cdot b^n = b^?$. This is the **product of powers property**.
$b^m \cdot b^n = b^{m+n}$

7 **✔ CHECKPOINT** Write each product as a single power.

a. $10^3 \cdot 10^4$ **b.** $5^9 \cdot 5^2$ **c.** $a \cdot a^7$ **d.** $b^5 \cdot b^8 \cdot b^2$
10^7 5^{11} a^8 b^{15}

8 It takes about 600 years for light from Betelgeuse to reach Earth.

a. Write 600 in scientific notation. $6 \cdot 10^2$

b. Use your answer from part (a), the speed of light in miles per year from Question 4, and the product of powers property to show that Betelgeuse is about $36 \cdot 10^{14}$ mi from Earth.
$(6 \cdot 10^2) \cdot (6 \cdot 10^{12}) = (6 \cdot 6) \cdot (10^2 \cdot 10^{12}) = 36 \cdot 10^{14}$

9 **a.** Explain why $36 \cdot 10^{14}$ is not in scientific notation.
36 is not between 1 and 10.
b. Use the product of powers rule to write $36 \cdot 10^{14}$ in scientific notation. (*Hint:* $36 = 3.6 \cdot 10^1$.)
$(3.6 \cdot 10^1) \cdot 10^{14} = 3.6 \cdot 10^1 \cdot 10^{14} = 3.6 \cdot 10^{15}$

10 Betelgeuse is huge, even for a star. You can use a *quotient of powers* to compare the sizes of Betelgeuse and the sun.

a. The diameter of Betelgeuse is roughly 10^9 mi. The diameter of the sun is roughly 10^6 mi. Write a fraction that represents the ratio of Betelgeuse's diameter to the sun's diameter. $\dfrac{10^9}{10^6}$

b. Rewrite the fraction showing all of the factors of 10 in the numerator and in the denominator. Then write the fraction as a single power of 10. (*Hint:* Look for factors that divide out.)
See margin.

c. How is the exponent of this single power of 10 related to the exponents of the powers in the numerator and denominator of the fraction you wrote in part (a)? $9 - 6 = 3$; It is the difference between the exponents.

d. The diameter of Betelgeuse is about how many times as great as the diameter of the sun? about $10^3 = 1000$ times

Module 7 The Algebra Connection

11 Write each quotient as a single power. Use a calculator to check each answer.

a. $\dfrac{10^6}{10^2}$ 10^4 b. $\dfrac{10^8}{10^3}$ 10^5 c. $\dfrac{6^7}{6^4}$ 6^3 d. $\dfrac{2^{13}}{2^5}$ 2^8

12 Complete this rule for dividing powers with the same base: $\dfrac{b^m}{b^n} = b^?$. This is the **quotient of powers property**. $\dfrac{b^m}{b^n} = b^{m-n}$

13 ✔ **CHECKPOINT** Write as a single power.

a. $\dfrac{10^{50}}{10^{30}}$ 10^{20} b. $\dfrac{5^{19}}{5^{14}}$ 5^5 c. $\dfrac{a^7}{a^2}$ a^5 d. $\dfrac{c^{11}}{c \cdot c^7}$ c^3

HOMEWORK EXERCISES ▶ See Exs. 1–28 on pp. 465–466.

Exploration 2

Zero and Negative Exponents

SET UP You will need: • calculator • Labsheet 1A

▶ Look at the images shown. As you go from one image to the next in the series, the width of the field of view decreases by a factor of 10.

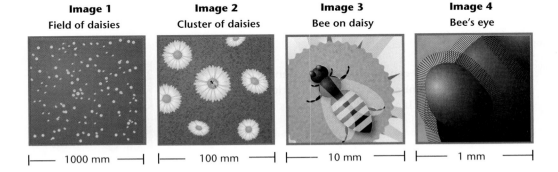

Image 1	**Image 2**	**Image 3**	**Image 4**
Field of daisies	Cluster of daisies	Bee on daisy	Bee's eye
⊢— 1000 mm —⊣	⊢— 100 mm —⊣	⊢— 10 mm —⊣	⊢— 1 mm —⊣

✔ **QUESTION 13**

...checks that you can use the quotient of powers property to divide powers.

GOAL

LEARN HOW TO...
- simplify powers with zero and negative exponents
- represent small numbers in scientific notation and in decimal notation

AS YOU...
- investigate dimensions of real-world objects

TEACHING NOTES

Question 19 You may have to do a few examples like the one below before students come to a conclusion in **part (c)**.

CLASSROOM EXAMPLE

Simplify $5^3 \div 5^4$ by using fractions and by using the quotient of powers property.

Answer:
$$\frac{5^3}{5^4} = \frac{5 \cdot 5 \cdot 5}{5 \cdot 5 \cdot 5 \cdot 5} = \frac{1}{5}$$

$$5^3 \div 5^4 = 5^{3-4} = 5^{-1}$$

---

21. a. It is a number between 1 and 10 multiplied by a power of 10.

▶ **In Exploration 1 you explored exponents greater than or equal to 1. An exponent may also be an integer less than 1.**

14 Written as a fraction, the ratio of the width of view of the first photo on page 461 to itself is $\frac{1000}{1000}$.

    a. Write the numerator and the denominator of the fraction as a power of 10. $\frac{10^3}{10^3}$

    b. Use the *quotient of powers property* to write the quotient in part (a) as a single power. 10^0

    c. Write the fraction $\frac{1000}{1000}$ in lowest terms. 1

15 Use a calculator to evaluate each power.

    a. 2^0 1   **b.** 9^0 1   **c.** 75^0 1   **d.** $(3.14)^0$ 1

16 Based on your results from Questions 14 and 15, what is the value of b^0 for any positive number b? 1

17 **Use Labsheet 1A** Follow the directions and answer the questions on the *Powers of 10* labsheet. **See margin.**

18 Let n be a positive integer. Complete this equation: $\frac{1}{10^n} = 10^?$. $-n$

19 **Try This as a Class** Use the expression $3^2 \div 3^4$.

    a. Write the division expression as a fraction. Then write the numerator and denominator as whole numbers without exponents. Write the fraction in lowest terms. $\frac{3^2}{3^4} = \frac{9}{81} = \frac{1}{9}$

    b. Use the quotient of powers property to write the quotient as a single power. $\frac{3^2}{3^4} = 3^{2-4} = 3^{-2}$

    c. Let b be any positive number and n be any positive integer. Complete this equation: $b^{-n} = \frac{1}{?}$ $\frac{1}{b^n}$

✔ **QUESTION 20**

...checks that you can simplify powers with zero and negative exponents.

---

20 ✔ **CHECKPOINT** Write each power as a whole number or a fraction without exponents.

    a. 6^0 1   **b.** 8^{-1} $\frac{1}{8}$ **c.** 3^{-4} $\frac{1}{81}$ **d.** 5^{-3} $\frac{1}{125}$

▶ **You can use negative exponents to write small numbers in scientific notation. For example, a red blood cell's diameter is $7.5 \cdot 10^{-3}$ mm.**

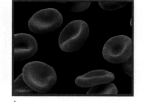

21 **a.** Explain why $7.5 \cdot 10^{-3}$ is in scientific notation.

    b. Evaluate $7.5 \cdot 10^{-3}$. Give the answer as a decimal. 0.0075

▲
This photograph shows a group of red blood cells.

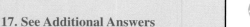

17. See Additional Answers beginning on page A1.

22 Use a calculator to write each number as a decimal.

   a. $9 \cdot 10^{-3}$ 0.009   **b.** $5.2 \cdot 10^{-1}$ 0.52   **c.** $4.26 \cdot 10^{-2}$ 0.0426

23 Look for a pattern in your answers to Questions 21 and 22. Explain how you can change a small number from scientific notation to decimal notation *without* using a calculator.

24 ✔ **CHECKPOINT** Write each number as a decimal without using a calculator.

   a. $2 \cdot 10^{-4}$
   0.0002

   b. $8.4 \cdot 10^{-5}$
   0.000084

   c. $6.31 \cdot 10^{-8}$
   0.0000000631

▶ **In Questions 21–24, you changed small numbers from scientific notation to decimal notation. You can also reverse this procedure.**

23. Move the decimal point to the left the number of places indicated by the exponent.

✔ QUESTION 24

...checks that you can change small numbers from scientific notation to decimal notation.

EXAMPLE

In 1996, scientists used an electron microscope to study a meterorite from Mars. The photograph shows tiny tube-shaped forms found inside the meteorite. A typical form is about 0.00000007 m long. Write this length in scientific notation.

SAMPLE RESPONSE

Decide how many places the decimal point in 0.00000007 must be moved to get a number that is at least 1 but less than 10.

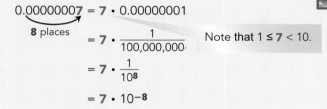

$$0.00000007 = 7 \cdot 0.00000001$$

8 places

$$= 7 \cdot \frac{1}{100,000,000}$$ Note that $1 \le 7 < 10$.

$$= 7 \cdot \frac{1}{10^8}$$

$$= 7 \cdot 10^{-8}$$

25 Describe a shortcut for writing 0.00000007 in scientific notation.

26 ✔ **CHECKPOINT** Write each number in scientific notation.

   a. 0.4
   4×10^{-1}

   b. 0.0089
   8.9×10^{-3}

   c. 0.00000123
   1.23×10^{-6}

25. Count the number of places from the decimal point to the right of 7. Then write the number as the product of 7 and 10 raised to the opposite of that number; $7 \cdot 10^{-8}$.

✔ QUESTION 26

...checks that you can change small numbers from decimal notation to scientific notation.

HOMEWORK EXERCISES ▶ See Exs. 29–52 on pp. 466–467.

Question 22 Be sure students know how to correctly enter a negative exponent into their calculators.

CLASSROOM MANAGEMENT
After students complete **Questions 22 and 23**, discuss as a class the patterns they noticed. Present the following Classroom Example and have students use their patterns to complete it without using a calculator. As a class, discuss which shortcuts work correctly. Then have students complete **Checkpoint 24** individually.

CLASSROOM EXAMPLE
Suppose a microorganism measures $1.6 \cdot 10^{-11}$ m. Write this as a decimal.

Answer: Move the decimal point to the left 11 places.

$$1.6 \cdot 10^{-11} = 0.000000000016$$

11 places

Key Concepts

CLOSURE QUESTIONS

How are the *product of powers property* and the *quotient of powers property* related?

How are zero and negative exponents used in writing scientific notation?

Sample Response: The product of powers property can be applied when two or more powers with the same base are being multiplied. The quotient of powers property can be applied when two powers with the same base are being divided.

Zero and negative exponents are sometimes used as the exponent of 10 when writing numbers in scientific notation.

ABSENT STUDENTS

For students who were absent for all or part of this section, the blackline Study Guide for Section 1 may be used to present the ideas, concepts, and skills of Section 1.

Key Terms

product of powers property

quotient of powers property

Product of Powers Property (pp. 459–460)
To multiply powers with the same base, add the exponents.

Examples $2^5 \cdot 2^3 = 2^{5+3} = 2^8$ $\qquad c^4 \cdot c^7 = c^{4+7} = c^{11}$

Quotient of Powers Property (pp. 460–461)
To divide powers with the same nonzero base, subtract the exponents.

Examples $\dfrac{3^{13}}{3^4} = 3^{13-4} = 3^9$ $\qquad \dfrac{y^8}{y^6} = y^{8-6} = y^2$

Zero and Negative Exponents (pp. 461–462)
If b is any positive number and n is any positive integer, then $b^0 = 1$ and $b^{-n} = \dfrac{1}{b^n}$.

Examples $5^0 = 1$ $\qquad 5^{-2} = \dfrac{1}{5^2} = \dfrac{1}{25}$

Scientific Notation with Small Numbers (pp. 462–463)
You can change small numbers in scientific notation to decimal notation. You can also change small numbers in decimal notation to scientific notation.

Examples

$3.8 \cdot 10^{-5} = 3.8 \cdot \dfrac{1}{10^5}$

$= 3.8 \cdot 0.00001$

$= 0.000038$ (5 places)

$0.000729 = 7.29 \cdot 0.0001$ (4 places)

$= 7.29 \cdot \dfrac{1}{10^4}$

$= 7.29 \cdot 10^{-4}$

Key Concepts Questions

27 Write b^7 as a product of two powers. Is there only one product that you can write? Explain. **Sample Response:** $b^1 \cdot b^6$; No, there are many ways to write 7 as a sum of two numbers.

28 Negative exponents are used to write small numbers in scientific notation. What precisely is a "small number" in this situation? any positive number less than 1

Section 1

Practice & Application Exercises

YOU WILL NEED

For Ex. 51:
- ♦ scientific calculator

Write each product as a single power.

1. $10^4 \cdot 10^2$ 10^6
2. $10^5 \cdot 10^8$ 10^{13}
3. $2^3 \cdot 2^6$ 2^9
4. $5^5 \cdot 5^5$ 5^{10}

5. $3^9 \cdot 3$ 3^{10}
6. $7^2 \cdot 7^6 \cdot 7^3$ 7^{11}
7. $a \cdot a^3$ a^4
8. $c^2 \cdot c^{10}$ c^{12}

9. $b^4 \cdot b^4$ b^8
10. $d^8 \cdot d^{12}$ d^{20}
11. $w^{60} \cdot w^{20}$ w^{80}
12. $t^5 \cdot t \cdot t^7$ t^{13}

Oceanography In his book *The Perfect Storm*, Sebastian Junger describes how the amount of energy in ocean waves depends on the wind speed.

Unfortunately for mariners, the total amount of wave energy in a storm doesn't [depend on the first power of] wind speed, but [on the] fourth power. The seas generated by a forty-knot wind aren't twice as violent as those from a twenty-knot wind, they're seventeen times as violent. A ship's crew watching the anemometer [an instrument that measures wind speed] climb even ten knots could well be [in great danger].

◀ As the anemometer spins in the wind, revolutions per minute are converted to miles per hour to calculate the wind speed.

13. The equation $h = 0.019s^2$ gives the height h (in feet) of waves caused by wind blowing at a speed of s knots. (One knot is slightly faster than 1 mi/hr.) The equation $E = 8h^2$ gives the energy E (in foot-pounds) in each square foot of a wave with height h.

   a. Write an equation that relates E and s. (*Hint:* First write $E = 8h^2$ as $E = 8 \cdot h \cdot h$. Then use the fact that $h = 0.019s^2$ to write another equation for E.) $E = 0.002888s^4$

   b. Junger says that wave energy depends on the fourth power of wind speed. Is this true? Explain. **Yes, in the equation s is raised to the 4th power.**

   c. What is the wave energy per square foot when the wind speed is 20 knots? when the wind speed is 40 knots? **462.08 foot-pounds; 7393.28 foot-pounds**

   d. Is the wave energy for a 40-knot wind about 17 times the wave energy for a 20-knot wind, as Junger states? **Yes, 7393.28 ÷ 17 = 434.899 which is close to 462.08. But it is actually 16 times the wave energy; 7393.28 ÷ 17 = 462.08.**

Practice & Applications

SUGGESTED ASSIGNMENTS

Core Course

Day 1: Exs. 1–10, 15–24
Day 2: Exs. 30–38, 53–59
Day 3: Exs. 39–52, 60, 61

Extended Course

Day 1: Exs. 2–12 even, 13, 14–26 even, 27–29
Day 2: Exs. 30–38, 53–59
Day 3: Exs. 40–52 even, 62–70*

Note: Extended Course assignments can be used to differentiate within the regular classroom. In classrooms where students are grouped homogeneously, the material might be covered in fewer days. In this case assignments may be combined.

* denotes Extension Exercises

ADDITIONAL PRACTICE

See the *Teacher's Resource Book* for additional practice and application exercises for this section.

COMMON ERROR

Exercises 1–12 Students may multiply bases or multiply exponents. If necessary, have them review the *product of powers property* in the *Key Concepts* on page 464. For students having difficulty remembering the property, encourage them to write out the powers of a sample problem to test themselves. For example, if they are not sure whether $2^3 \cdot 2^5 = 2^{15}$ or 2^8, Write out the factors of 2^3 as $2 \cdot 2 \cdot 2$ and 2^5 as $2 \cdot 2 \cdot 2 \cdot 2 \cdot 2$ and count the factors to get $2 \cdot 2 \cdot 2 \cdot 2 \cdot 2 \cdot 2 \cdot 2 \cdot 2$ which equals 2^8.

Practice & Applications

COMMON ERRORS

Exercises 15–26 Students will sometimes "cancel out" the bases leaving only the exponents. In this case or for other errors, have students write out the factors for both the numerator and the denominator, then separate factors into fractions equivalent to 1. Simplifying using this method may help students who need to concretely see why the result is the same as using the property. For

example, $\dfrac{a^5}{a^2} = \dfrac{a \cdot a \cdot a \cdot a \cdot a}{a \cdot a}$

$= \dfrac{a \cdot a \cdot 1 \cdot 1 \cdot a}{1 \cdot 1}$

$= a \cdot a \cdot a$

$= a^3.$

28. a. $\dfrac{1.16(1.44)^5}{1.16(1.44)^2} = 1.44^3$

29. No, if you substitute 0 for t in the formula, you get $w = 1.16(1.44)^0 = 1.16 \cdot 1$ or 1.16 lb, which is not a reasonable weight for a fish that is less than 5 mm long.

38. b. Sample Response: The earlier you begin saving, the less money you need to invest to reach a certain dollar amount.

14. Open-ended Junger says that even a 10-knot increase in wind speed can be very dangerous. For what intervals does a 10-knot increase in wind speed cause a great increase in wave energies? **See margin.**

Write each quotient as a single power.

15. $\dfrac{10^6}{10^4}$ 10^2

16. $\dfrac{10^9}{10^3}$ 10^6

17. $\dfrac{2^5}{2}$ 2^4

18. $\dfrac{3^{10}}{3^7}$ 3^3

19. $\dfrac{7^{15}}{7^6}$ 7^9

20. $\dfrac{5^3 \cdot 5^8}{5^2}$ 5^9

21. $\dfrac{a^5}{a^2}$ a^3

22. $\dfrac{b^6}{b^5}$ b^1

23. $\dfrac{c^{12}}{c^6}$ c^6

24. $\dfrac{d^7}{d}$ d^6

25. $\dfrac{u^{95}}{u^{52}}$ u^{43}

26. $\dfrac{v^{18}}{v^4 \cdot v^3}$ v^{11}

27. Challenge Write $\dfrac{a^5b^9}{ab^4}$ as the product of a power of a and a power of b. a^4b^5

Biology The average weight w (in pounds) of an Atlantic cod aged t years can be modeled by the equation $w = 1.16(1.44)^t$.

28. a. Find the ratio of the weight of a 5-year-old cod to the weight of a 2-year-old cod. Express this ratio as a power of 1.44.

b. A 5-year-old cod weighs how many times as much as a 2-year-old cod? **about 3 times as much**

29. A newly-hatched Atlantic cod is about 5 mm long. Does the given equation produce a reasonable weight for $t = 0$? Explain.

Write each power as a whole number or fraction without exponents.

30. 8^0 1

31. 3^{-2} $\dfrac{1}{9}$

32. 2^{-3} $\dfrac{1}{8}$

33. 5^{-1} $\dfrac{1}{5}$

Write each expression without using zero or negative exponents.

34. a^0 1

35. b^{-6} $\dfrac{1}{b^6}$

36. c^{-10} $\dfrac{1}{c^{10}}$

37. $4w^{-2}$ $\dfrac{4}{w^2}$

38. Personal Finance Many people invest in stocks as a way to save for retirement. Based on the history of stock prices, the amount A you need to invest in order to have D dollars after n years can be estimated using this equation:

$$A = D(1.105)^{-n}$$

a. How much money would you need to invest in stocks now to have $1,000,000 after 10 years? after 20 years? after 40 years? **about $368,449; about $135,755; about $18,429**

b. Writing Explain why your answers from part (a) show the importance of starting to save for retirement at an early age.

14. See Additional Answers beginning on page A1.

Write each number as a decimal.

39. $9 \cdot 10^{-1}$ 0.9   **40.** $3 \cdot 10^{-2}$ 0.03   **41.** $1.8 \cdot 10^{-4}$ 0.00018

42. $4.4 \cdot 10^{-7}$
0.00000044   **43.** $2.65 \cdot 10^{-6}$
0.00000265   **44.** $7.523 \cdot 10^{-8}$
0.00000007523

Write each number in scientific notation.

45. 0.3 $3 \cdot 10^{-1}$ **46.** 0.0087 $8.7 \cdot 10^{-3}$ **47.** 0.00025 $2.5 \cdot 10^{-4}$

48. 0.00001199
$1.199 \cdot 10^{-5}$ **49.** 0.000000006
$6 \cdot 10^{-9}$ **50.** 0.000000408
$4.08 \cdot 10^{-7}$

51. Probability Connection If you flip a coin n times, the theoretical probability of getting n heads is 2^{-n}.

a. Find the probability of getting 25 heads in 25 flips. Write your answer in scientific notation. $2^{-25} \approx 2.98 \cdot 10^{-8}$

b. Compare your answer from part (a) with the probability of winning a common type of state lottery (about $7.15 \cdot 10^{-8}$).
The probability of winning the state lottery is about 2.4 times greater than flipping 25 heads in 25 flips of a coin.

Reflecting ◀▶ **on the Section**

Write your response to Exercise 52 in your journal.

52. Write a quiz that covers the mathematical topics presented in this section. Include at least two questions for each topic. Then make an answer key for your quiz. **Answers will vary. Check students' work.**

> **Journal**
>
> Exercise 52 checks that you understand and can apply the mathematical ideas in this section.

Spiral ◀▶ **Review**

53. Give the slope and the y-intercept of the line with equation $y = -2x + 9$. (Module 4, p. 265) slope $= -2$ y-intercept $= 9$

54. Estimation Between which two consecutive integers does $\sqrt{60}$ lie? (Module 3, p. 163) 7 and 8

Solve each equation. (Module 1, p. 42)

55. $\frac{x}{3} = 4$ 12   **56.** $\frac{w}{13} + 2 = 7$ 65   **57.** $6 = \frac{t}{85}$ 510

Solve each equation. (Module 4, p. 277)

58. $-0.75s - 1.35 = 4.65$ –8   **59.** $14 = \frac{2}{3}n + 2$ 18

Practice & Applications

EXERCISE NOTES

The **Extension Exercises 62–70** further explore how the *product of powers* and *quotient of powers* properties apply to like bases with different signed exponents (one positive and one negative).

For students who need a concrete extension exercise, set up a center with some salt and rulers with millimeter marks. Ask students to estimate the width of a salt crystal, and to express the distance in centimeters. Assuming the salt crystal is a cube, what is its volume in cubic centimeters? What is the volume of your classroom in cubic centimeters? (You may want to provide the dimensions of the classroom.) How many salt crystals could fit in your classroom? Have students express all answers in scientific notation. When done, ask students to reflect on how the use of scientific notation affected the ease with which they could manipulate their numbers. (*Answers will vary.*)

62. See Additional Answers beginning on page A1.

Career Connection

Scientist: France Córdova

Dr. France Córdova was Chief Scientist at the National Aeronautics and Space Administration (NASA) from 1993–1996. She studied small, dense, rapidly spinning stars called *pulsars,* which result when a giant star undergoes a supernova explosion.

60. A pulsar's *mass density*—its mass per unit volume— is about 10^{11} kg/cm³. (A handful of material from a pulsar would weigh more than all the people on Earth combined!) The volume of a typical pulsar is about 10^{19} cm³. Find the mass of a pulsar with this volume. 10^{30} kg

61. Pulsars rotate very rapidly. The *period* of a pulsar is the time required for one rotation. The fastest-rotating pulsar known has a period of about 0.00156 sec. Write this period in scientific notation. $1.56 \cdot 10^{-3}$ sec

---

Extension ▶ ▶

Extending the Properties of Exponents

In this section, you applied the product and quotient of powers properties to expressions containing only positive exponents. Also, the quotient of powers property was applied only to quotients where the exponent in the numerator was greater than the exponent in the denominator. However, both properties work for any exponents.

Examples:

$$3^{-2} \cdot 3^7 = 3^{-2+7} = 3^5 \qquad \frac{5^8}{5^{11}} = 5^{8-11} = 5^{-3} \text{ or } \frac{1}{5^3}$$

62. Show that $3^{-2} \cdot 3^7 = 3^5$ and $\frac{5^8}{5^{11}} = 5^{-3}$ without using the product of powers and quotient of powers properties. (*Hint*: Write 3^{-2} and 5^{-3} using positive exponents.) See margin.

Write each product as a single power.

63. $2^{-1} \cdot 2^3$ 2^2 64. $10^9 \cdot 10^{-4}$ 10^5 65. $a^6 \cdot a^{-10}$ a^{-4} 66. $x^{-3} \cdot x^{-5}$ x^{-8}

Write each quotient as a single power.

67. $\frac{3^5}{3^7}$ 3^{-2} 68. $\frac{7^2}{7^{-12}}$ 7^{14} 69. $\frac{b^{-8}}{b^{-3}}$ b^{-5} 70. $\frac{y^{-2}}{y^{10}}$ y^{-12}

Section 1

Extra Skill Practice

Write each product as a single power.

1. $6^4 \cdot 6^3$ 6^7

2. $9^{10} \cdot 9^{17}$ 9^{27}

3. $11^{11} \cdot 11^{23}$ 11^{34}

4. $2^2 \cdot 2^{21} \cdot 2$ 2^{24}

5. $b^3 \cdot b^9$ b^{12}

6. $h^5 \cdot h^{19}$ h^{24}

7. $k^{33} \cdot k^{48}$ k^{81}

8. $n^7 \cdot n^8 \cdot n^9$ n^{24}

Write each quotient as a single power.

9. $\dfrac{10^{12}}{10^2}$ 10^{10}

10. $\dfrac{9^6}{9}$ 9^5

11. $\dfrac{8^{21}}{8^{19}}$ 8^2

12. $\dfrac{6^{15}}{6^4 \cdot 6^7}$ 6^4

13. $\dfrac{p^8}{p^5}$ p^3

14. $\dfrac{z^{57}}{z^{39}}$ z^{18}

15. $\dfrac{m^{82}}{m^{78}}$ m^4

16. $\dfrac{t^{26}}{t^7 \cdot t^{11}}$ t^8

Write each power as a number without exponents.

17. 24^0 1

18. 6^{-3} $\dfrac{1}{216}$

19. 11^{-2} $\dfrac{1}{121}$

20. 4^{-4} $\dfrac{1}{256}$

21. 13^{-1} $\dfrac{1}{13}$

Write each expression without using zero or negative exponents.

22. h^{-3} $\dfrac{1}{h^3}$

23. p^{-8} $\dfrac{1}{p^8}$

24. k^0 1

25. $3b^{-7}$ $\dfrac{3}{b^7}$

26. $12g^{-32}$ $\dfrac{12}{g^{32}}$

Write each number as a decimal.

27. $8 \cdot 10^{-3}$
0.008

28. $3.6 \cdot 10^{-4}$
0.00036

29. $6.14 \cdot 10^{-7}$
0.000000614

30. $1.271 \cdot 10^{-8}$
0.00000001271

Write each number in scientific notation.

31. 0.06
$6 \cdot 10^{-2}$

32. 0.000412
$4.12 \cdot 10^{-4}$

33. 0.000001013
$1.013 \cdot 10^{-6}$

34. 0.000000761
$7.61 \cdot 10^{-7}$

Standardized Testing ◀▶ Multiple Choice

1. Simplify $3^4 \cdot 3^5$. A

   (A) 3^9
   (B) 3^{20}
   (C) 9^9
   (D) 9^{20}

2. Simplify $\dfrac{2^{15}}{2^3}$. C

   (A) 5
   (B) 2^5
   (C) 2^{12}
   (D) 2^{18}

3. Simplify 8^{-2}. D

   (A) $\dfrac{1}{4}$
   (B) $\dfrac{1}{8}$
   (C) $\dfrac{1}{16}$
   (D) $\dfrac{1}{64}$

4. Which number is *not* in scientific notation? D

   (A) $4.3 \cdot 10^{-5}$
   (B) $1 \cdot 10^4$
   (C) $7.01 \cdot 10^{-8}$
   (D) $12 \cdot 10^{-3}$

Extra Skill Practice

TEACHER NOTES

For each Exploration, the corresponding Extra Skill Practice Exercises are noted.

Exploration 1: Exs. 1–16
Exploration 2: Exs. 17–34

EXTRA HELP

Teacher's Resource Book
• Practice and Applications
• Study Guide

Technology Resources
• @Home Tutor
• Test Generator

ASSESSMENT

• Section 1 Quick Quiz
• Test Generator

Setting the Stage

GETTING STARTED

Module 7 Section 2 *Warm-Up* assesses student facility with simplifying perfect squares. This prerequisite skill is necessary for simplifying square roots in Exploration 1 and radical expressions in Exploration 2.

ABOUT THE THEME

Students are introduced to the algebra used by the seventh century Hindu mathematician Brahmagupta in his discovery of a geometric formula for area of a quadrilateral inscribed in a circle.

To roughly verify that Brahmagupta's formula works, students can complete the following activity.

Use a compass to draw a circle on 1-cm grid paper, then use a ruler to draw a quadrilateral that is inscribed in the circle. After measuring the side lengths of the quadrilateral to the nearest tenth of a centimeter, use Brahmagupta's formula and a calculator to approximate the figure's area. Compare the area calculated with the total number of 1-cm squares in the interior of the quadrilateral. (For partial squares match pieces to count as full squares.) The results should be fairly close to the calculated area, allowing for measurement error. Drawing a rectangle and square will make checking the area easier as long as the circle is drawn with a whole number of centimeters as the radius.

TEACHING NOTES

As you discuss problems, answers, and examples, continue to use the key terms *radical sign* and *radicand* to help students develop their mathematical vocabulary.

Section 2 **Simplifying Radicals**

Brahmagupta's Discovery

KEY TERMS
♦ radical sign
♦ radicand

$A = bh$

$A = \frac{1}{2}(b_1 + b_2)h$

When all its vertices lie on a circle, a quadrilateral is *inscribed* in the circle.

Setting the Stage

The formulas shown at the left can be used to find the areas of parallelograms and trapezoids. But how do you find the area of a quadrilateral that is neither a parallelogram nor a trapezoid? Around 628 A.D., a Hindu mathematician named Brahmagupta discovered a formula for finding the area of a quadrilateral that is *inscribed* in a circle. His formula uses the principal square root of an expression involving the side lengths and perimeter of the quadrilateral.

The symbol $\sqrt{\ }$ is called a **radical sign**.

$$A = \sqrt{(s - a)(s - b)(s - c)(s - d)}$$

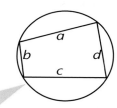

In this formula, *a*, *b*, *c*, and *d* represent the lengths of the sides of the quadrilateral, and *s* represents half of the perimeter of the quadrilateral.

$$s = \frac{a + b + c + d}{2}$$

Think About It

1 Find the area of the quadrilateral above if $a = 12$ mm, $b = 6$ mm, $c = 9$ mm, and $d = 7$ mm. Round to the nearest hundredth.
$A = 66.33$ mm²

2 Was the **radicand**, the value under the radical sign, a perfect square? Explain how you know. No, there is no whole number that when multiplied by itself equals 4440.

3 The value you obtained in Question 1 is the approximate area. How can you write the exact area of the quadrilateral?
Leave it in radical form $\sqrt{4400}$.

Exploration 1

Simplifying √Square Roots

SET UP *Work with a partner.*

▶ A square root like $\sqrt{4900}$, which equals 70, is a rational number because 70 is a perfect square. But a square root like $\sqrt{4400}$, which equals 66.332495. . . (whose digits neither terminate nor repeat), is an *irrational* number. An **irrational number** cannot be written as the quotient of two integers. When written as a decimal, an irrational number does not terminate or repeat.

4 Discussion Which of the following numbers are irrational? Explain how you know.

    a. $\sqrt{144}$ **b.** $\sqrt{10}$ **c.** $1.\overline{87}$ **d.** π
      rational; $\sqrt{144} = 12$ rational; It repeats.

▶ Many square roots can be *simplified*.

A square root is in **simplest form** if the following are true.
- There are no perfect square factors other than 1 in the radicand.
- There are no fractions in the radicand.
- There are no square roots in the denominator of a fraction.

Examples: $\sqrt{6}$ and $\dfrac{\sqrt{7}}{2}$

Nonexamples: $\sqrt{8}$, $\sqrt{\dfrac{25}{81}}$, and $\dfrac{5}{\sqrt{4}}$

FOR ◀HELP

with *square roots*, see
MODULE 3, p. 163

4. **b.** irrational; 10 is not a perfect square
   d. irrational; π never repeats and never ends.

5 a. Simplify $\sqrt{4}$. Simplify $\sqrt{25}$. Multiply the simplified answers.
    2; 5; 10
  b. Multiply 4 · 25. Find the principal square root of the result.
    100; 10
  c. How does $\sqrt{4} \cdot \sqrt{25}$ compare with $\sqrt{4 \cdot 25}$?
    They are both equal to 10.
  d. Choose any two perfect squares and use them in place of 4 and 25 in parts (a)–(c). What do you notice?
    Sample Response: $\sqrt{16} \cdot \sqrt{100} = 4 \cdot 10 = 40$
                    $\sqrt{16 \cdot 100} = \sqrt{1600} = 40$
          The expressions have the same value.

Exploration 1

TEACHER NOTES

Rational numbers were defined in Section 4 of Module 4. You may want to review the definition before introducing the key term *irrational number*. Students should also be familiar with *principal square root*, taught in Module 3, Section 1.

TIPS FROM TEACHERS

Have students create a list of perfect squares from 1 to 200 that they can keep in their math notebooks as reference when simplifying square roots and identifying irrational numbers.

Exploration 1 *continued*

TEACHING NOTES

Question 6(b) Students should separate 900 into factors that are perfect squares. Most students will choose 9 · 100. Ask if any students used other factor pairs (*25 · 36 or 4 · 225*). If so, compare the results, if not, have the class simplify the square root using these other factors and compare the results to their first answer. (*The results are the same. Their choice will depend upon which factors students find easier to identify as perfect squares.*) In **part (c)** have students try each problem and then have them share what factors they used.

If students need more guidance simplifying square roots, you may want to discuss the following Classroom Examples before they begin **Checkpoint Question 7.**

CLASSROOM EXAMPLES

Simplify $\sqrt{50}$.

Answer: $\sqrt{50} = \sqrt{25 \cdot 2}$
$= \sqrt{25} \cdot \sqrt{2}$
$= 5\sqrt{2}$

Simplify $\sqrt{18}$.

Answer: $\sqrt{18} = \sqrt{9 \cdot 2}$
$= \sqrt{9} \cdot \sqrt{2}$
$= 3\sqrt{2}$

Simplify $\sqrt{80}$.

Answer: $\sqrt{80} = \sqrt{16 \cdot 5}$
$= \sqrt{16} \cdot \sqrt{5}$
$= 4\sqrt{5}$

For **Question 8** the class can be broken into small groups with each group assigned one of the expressions. After testing several numbers, groups can report their conclusions to the whole class.

472

---

6. c. Sample Responses:

$\sqrt{25} \cdot \sqrt{100} =$
$5 \cdot 10 = 50$

$\sqrt{36} \cdot \sqrt{16} =$
$6 \cdot 4 = 24$

$\sqrt{36} \cdot \sqrt{9} =$
$6 \cdot 3 = 18$

▶ The **product property of square roots** states that for all positive numbers *a* and *b*,

$$\sqrt{a \cdot b} = \sqrt{a} \cdot \sqrt{b}.$$

6 **Try This as a Class**

a. Use the product property of square roots to simplify each of the following.

$\sqrt{64 \cdot 9}$ $\sqrt{81 \cdot 4 \cdot 36}$ $\sqrt{9 \cdot 49}$
$8 \cdot 3 = 24$ $9 \cdot 2 \cdot 6 = 108$ $3 \cdot 7 = 21$

b. How can you write 900 as the product of two perfect squares, each greater than 1? Use the result and the product property of squares to simplify $\sqrt{900}$. $900 = 9 \cdot 100$, so $\sqrt{900} = \sqrt{9} \cdot \sqrt{100} =$ $3 \cdot 10 = 30$

c. Write the radicand of each of the following as a product of perfect squares and then simplify.

$\sqrt{2500}$ $\sqrt{576}$ $\sqrt{324}$

▶ **Simplifying Irrational Numbers** The product property of square roots can be used to simplify square roots.

EXAMPLE

Simplify $\sqrt{45}$.

Think of perfect squares greater than 1. The first such number is 4, but 4 is not a factor of 45. The next is 9, and 9 is a factor of 45, so rewrite 45 as 9 · 5. Then use the product property of square roots.

SAMPLE RESPONSE

$$\sqrt{45} = \sqrt{9 \cdot 5}$$
$$= \sqrt{9} \cdot \sqrt{5}$$
$$= 3 \cdot \sqrt{5}$$

The radicand 5 can not be factored into perfect squares, so $\sqrt{5}$ is in simplest form.

In simplest form, $\sqrt{45} = 3\sqrt{5}$.

✔ **QUESTION 7**

...checks that you can simplify square roots.

7 ✔ **CHECKPOINT** Simplify each square root.

a. $\sqrt{75}$ $5\sqrt{3}$ **b.** $\sqrt{8}$ $2\sqrt{2}$ **c.** $\sqrt{216}$ $6\sqrt{6}$

8 **Try This As a Class** Replace the variables *a* and *b* using several different pairs of perfect squares. Simplify each expression. Which statements appear to be true?

a. $\sqrt{a} + \sqrt{b} = \sqrt{a + b}$ **b.** $\sqrt{a} - \sqrt{b} = \sqrt{a - b}$ **c.** $\sqrt{\dfrac{a}{b}} = \dfrac{\sqrt{a}}{\sqrt{b}}$

Check students' work. Students should determine that it appears that only the statement in part (c) is true.

Module 7   The Algebra Connection

9 **a.** Why is $\sqrt{\dfrac{25}{49}}$ not in simplest form? There is a fraction in the radicand.

  b. Show that $\sqrt{\dfrac{25}{49}} = \dfrac{\sqrt{25}}{\sqrt{49}}$. $\sqrt{\dfrac{25}{49}} = \sqrt{\left(\dfrac{5}{7}\right)^2} = \dfrac{5}{7}$ and $\dfrac{\sqrt{25}}{\sqrt{49}} = \dfrac{5}{7}$

▶ The **quotient property of square roots** states that for all positive numbers a and b,

$$\sqrt{\dfrac{a}{b}} = \dfrac{\sqrt{a}}{\sqrt{b}}.$$

10 ✔ **CHECKPOINT** Simplify each expression.

  a. $\sqrt{\dfrac{81}{4}}$ $\dfrac{9}{2}$

  b. $\sqrt{\dfrac{15}{16}}$ $\dfrac{\sqrt{15}}{4}$

  c. $\sqrt{\dfrac{7}{36}}$ $\dfrac{\sqrt{7}}{6}$

11 Why is $\dfrac{3}{\sqrt{2}}$ not in simplest form? There is a radical in the denominator of the fraction.

▶ To eliminate a square root in the denominator of a fraction, you can multiply the numerator and denominator of the fraction by a square root that will make the radicand in the denominator a perfect square.

12 Copy and replace each **?** with the correct number.

$$\dfrac{3}{\sqrt{2}} = \dfrac{3}{\sqrt{2}} \cdot \dfrac{?}{\sqrt{2}} = \dfrac{?}{\sqrt{2 \cdot ?}} = \dfrac{?}{\sqrt{?}} = \dfrac{?}{?} \quad \dfrac{3}{\sqrt{2}} \cdot \dfrac{\sqrt{2}}{\sqrt{2}} = \dfrac{3 \cdot \sqrt{2}}{\sqrt{2 \cdot 2}} = \dfrac{3\sqrt{2}}{\sqrt{4}} = \dfrac{3\sqrt{2}}{2}$$

13 What could you multiply the numerator and denominator of each fraction by to obtain an equivalent fraction that does not have a radical sign in its denominator?

  a. $\dfrac{3}{\sqrt{5}}$ $\sqrt{5}$

  b. $\dfrac{19}{\sqrt{10}}$ $\sqrt{10}$

  c. $\dfrac{2}{\sqrt{31}}$ $\sqrt{31}$

  d. $\dfrac{10}{\sqrt{15}}$ $\sqrt{5}$

14 ✔ **CHECKPOINT** Simplify each expression in Question 13.

15 A quadrilateral with sides a, b, c, and d is inscribed in a circle. Use Brahmagupta's formula to find the exact area. Be sure your answer is in simplest form.

  a. $a = 12$ mm
  $b = 6$ mm
  $c = 9$ mm
  $d = 7$ mm

  b. $a = 5$ in.
  $b = 1\dfrac{1}{2}$ in.
  $c = 5$ in.
  $d = 2\dfrac{1}{2}$ in.

| **HOMEWORK EXERCISES** | ▶ See Exs. 1–8 on p. 478. |

---

14. a. $\dfrac{3\sqrt{5}}{5}$

  b. $\dfrac{19\sqrt{10}}{10}$

  c. $\dfrac{2\sqrt{31}}{31}$

  d. $\dfrac{10\sqrt{15}}{15} = \dfrac{2\sqrt{15}}{3}$

✔ **QUESTION 10**

...checks that you can simplify a square root with a fractional radicand.

15. a. $s = 17$ mm
  $A = \sqrt{4400}$
  $A = \sqrt{4 \cdot 11 \cdot 100}$
  $A = 2 \cdot 10\sqrt{11}$
  $A = 20\sqrt{11}$ mm^2

  b. $s = 7$ in.
  $A = \sqrt{2 \cdot 5\dfrac{1}{2} \cdot 2 \cdot 4\dfrac{1}{2}}$
  $A = \sqrt{11 \cdot 9}$ or $\sqrt{99}$
  $A = 3\sqrt{11}$ in.^{2}

✔ **QUESTION 14**

...checks that you can simplify a fraction with a square root in the denominator.

DEVELOPING MATH CONCEPTS

Question 15(b) Depending on the order in which calculations are done in the radicand students will get different answers. If students multiply all 4 numbers to get 99, $\sqrt{99} = 3\sqrt{11}$. However, students noticing the factors of 2 occurring twice might first remove this perfect square leaving $2\sqrt{5.5 \cdot 4.5}$ or $2\sqrt{24.75}$. Students comparing results may wonder about the discrepancy. This would be an opportune time to show the equivalence. Had the product of the mixed numbers $5\dfrac{1}{2} \cdot 4\dfrac{1}{2}$ not been converted to decimals, then

$$2\sqrt{5\dfrac{1}{2} \cdot 4\dfrac{1}{2}} = 2\sqrt{\dfrac{11}{2} \cdot \dfrac{9}{2}} \text{ or } 2\sqrt{\dfrac{99}{4}} = \dfrac{3}{2} \cdot 2\sqrt{11}.$$

So $2\sqrt{5\dfrac{1}{2} \cdot 4\dfrac{1}{2}} = 3\sqrt{11}$.

Exploration 2

TEACHING NOTES

Question 17 When the radicand contains variables, it is not known whether the variable represents a number that is positive, negative, or zero. Therefore the square root of any number squared must be written as the absolute value of that number. Students will explore this concept by replacing *a* with both positive and negative integers. Be sure when students square –9 in **part (b)** that they perform the multiplication properly $(-9)^2 = -9 \cdot -9 = 81$ and not $-9^2 = -(9 \cdot 9) = -81$.

In this exploration all variables are assumed to be positive. This will eliminate the need for students to write absolute value signs when writing radical expressions in simplest form.

GOAL

LEARN HOW TO...
- simplify radical expressions

AS YOU...
- explore square roots, cube roots, and fourth roots

KEY TERMS
- radical expression
- cube root

17. e. For any number *a*, the principal square root of a^2 is the nonnegative number which when multiplied by itself gives a^2. That number is |a|.

Exploration 2

√Radical Expressions

SET UP *Work with a partner.*

▶ You can use other properties along with the product and quotient properties of square roots to simplify square roots. In some cases you can use the product of powers property that you learned in Section 1.

16 Use the fact that $5^3 = 5^2 \cdot 5$ to show that $\sqrt{5^3}$ is equal to $5\sqrt{5}$.
$\sqrt{5^3} = \sqrt{5^2 \cdot 5} = 5\sqrt{5}$

17 In Question 16, you used the fact that $\sqrt{5^2} = 5$. Suppose you want to simplify $\sqrt{a^2}$.

   a. Simplify $\sqrt{a^2}$ when $a = 9$, when $a = 7$, and when $a = 21$. 9; 7; 21

   b. Simplify $\sqrt{a^2}$ when $a = -9$, when $a = -7$, and when $a = -21$.
   9; 7; 21

   c. What do you notice about $\sqrt{a^2}$ when *a* is positive? It equals *a*.

   d. What do you notice about $\sqrt{a^2}$ when *a* is negative? It equals the opposite of *a*.

   e. Explain why $\sqrt{a^2} = |a|$ for all values for *a*.

▶ The product property of square roots can be used to simplify *radical expressions*. A **radical expression** is an expression that contains a radical with one or more variables in the radicand.

EXAMPLE

Simplify $\sqrt{16a^3}$. Assume *a* represents a positive number.

SAMPLE RESPONSE

$\sqrt{16a^3} = \sqrt{16 \cdot a^2 \cdot a}$ Rewrite $\sqrt{16a^3}$ as $\sqrt{16 \cdot a^2 \cdot a}$.

$\quad\quad\quad = \sqrt{16} \cdot \sqrt{a^2} \cdot \sqrt{a}$ Use the product property.

$\quad\quad\quad = 4 \cdot |a| \cdot \sqrt{a}$ Simplify perfect squares.

$\quad\quad\quad = 4 \cdot a \cdot \sqrt{a}$ Rewrite |a| as *a*.

In simplest form, $\sqrt{16a^3} = 4a\sqrt{a}$.

18 Discussion

a. In the example, why could you write $|a|$ as a?

b. Why was a^3 written as $a^2 \cdot a$? **To rewrite the product showing any perfect squares, a^2 is a perfect square.**

c. In simplifying $\sqrt{a^5}$, how would you rewrite a^5? **$a^4 \cdot a$ OR $a^2 \cdot a^2 \cdot a$**

d. Simplify $\sqrt{a^5}$. Assume a is a positive number. **$a^2\sqrt{a}$**

19 ✓ CHECKPOINT Simplify each radical expression. Use the product property of square roots when necessary. Assume all variables represent positive numbers.

a. $\sqrt{9x^8}$ **3x^4**

b. $\sqrt{36x^9}$ **6$x^4\sqrt{x}$**

c. $\sqrt{x^3y^{16}}$ **$xy^8\sqrt{x}$**

d. $\sqrt{y^{50}}$ **y^{25}**

20

a. Which of the radicands in Question 19 are perfect squares? **a and d**

b. Explain how you can tell if a radicand containing variables is a perfect square.

▶ Sometimes formulas contain a *cube root*. If $A = s^3$, then s is a **cube root** of A. Cube roots can be written with the symbol $\sqrt[3]{}$. For example, $\sqrt[3]{64}$ represents the cube root of 64.

In words	Using a radical symbol				Simplified
the cube root of 64	$\sqrt[3]{64}$	=	$\sqrt[3]{4 \cdot 4 \cdot 4}$	=	4

21 Why is $\sqrt[3]{64}$ equal to 4? **because $4^3 = 64$**

22 If $\sqrt[3]{n} = 5$, what is the value of n? **125**

23 Every positive number a has two square roots, $\sqrt{a}$ and $-\sqrt{a}$. For example, 8 and -8 are both square roots of 64.

a. Are 5 and -5 both cube roots of $\sqrt[3]{125}$? Why or why not?

b. What is $-\sqrt[3]{125}$? **-5**

c. What is $\sqrt[3]{-125}$? **-5**

24

a. What does $\sqrt[3]{-8}$ equal? **-2**

b. If $\sqrt[3]{n} = -3$, what is the value of n? **-27**

---

18. a. Because it was given that a is a positive number and the absolute value of a positive number is the number.

✓ **QUESTION 19**

...checks that you can simplify radical expressions.

20. b. The exponents are even and the coefficient is 1 or some other perfect square.

23. a. No; 5 is a cube root of 125 because $5^3 = 125$. -5 is not a cube root of 125 because $(-5)^3$ is not equal to 125.

TEACHING NOTES

If students need more guidance simplifying radical expressions, you may want to discuss the following Classroom Examples before they begin **Checkpoint Question 19**.

CLASSROOM EXAMPLES

Simplify each radical expression. Assume all variables represent positive numbers.

a. $\sqrt{m^6}$ **b.** $\sqrt{3m^7}$ **c.** $\sqrt{20m^{10}}$

Answers:

a. m^3

b. $m^3\sqrt{3m}$

c. $2m^5\sqrt{5}$

COMMON ERROR

Question 19(c) Some students may write the square root of y^{16} as y^4 instead of y^8. To alleviate this problem remind students to apply the *product property* they learned in Exploration 1 of this section. Ask them to restate the *product property* and to apply this rule when rewriting the variable parts of the radicand as perfect squares.

TEACHING NOTES

In **Questions 21 and 22**, make sure students understand that while the square of a negative number is always positive, the cube of a negative number is negative. So unlike square roots, they can find the cube root of a negative number. For example, $\sqrt[3]{-64} = -4$ because $(-4)^3 = -64$. In general, odd roots are defined for all numbers, whereas even roots are only defined for non-negative numbers.

Exploration 2 continued

Teaching Notes

In simplifying cube roots, students will need to be able to identify perfect cubes. Help students to develop a list of perfect cubes for reference or demonstrate how students can use prime factorization of a number to find factors that are repeated 3 times. For example in **Question 26(a)**, the prime factorization of $216 = 2 \cdot 2 \cdot 2 \cdot 3 \cdot 3 \cdot 3$, so the cube root of 216 is $2 \cdot 3$ or 6. This method of using prime factorization can also be applied for 4th roots in **Question 30**, except students will have to identify factors that are repeated 4 times instead of 3 times. Again be sure students apply the *product property* to the variable parts of the radicand.

28. a. $\sqrt[3]{5^4} = 5\sqrt[3]{5}$;

$(\sqrt[3]{5})^4 = \sqrt[3]{5} \cdot \sqrt[3]{5} \cdot \sqrt[3]{5} \cdot \sqrt[3]{5}$

$= \sqrt[3]{625}$

$= \sqrt[3]{125 \cdot 5}$

$= 5\sqrt[3]{5}$

---

25. $16 = 8 \cdot 2$ and 8 is a perfect cube you could apply the product property to $\sqrt[3]{16}$ to get $\sqrt[3]{16} = \sqrt[3]{8 \cdot 2} = \sqrt[3]{8} \cdot \sqrt[3]{2} = 2\sqrt[3]{2}$.

28. b. They are the same when simplified. $\sqrt[3]{5^4}$ only raises the radicand 5 to the 4th power where as in $(\sqrt[3]{5})^4$ the entire radical is raised to the 4th power.

▶ The product and quotient properties of square roots generalize to other radicals. For example, for all positive numbers a and b,

$$\sqrt[3]{ab} = \sqrt[3]{a} \cdot \sqrt[3]{b} \text{ and } \sqrt[3]{\frac{a}{b}} = \frac{\sqrt[3]{a}}{\sqrt[3]{b}}.$$

25 $2\sqrt[3]{2}$ is in simplest form, but $\sqrt[3]{16}$ is not. Explain why.

26 Use the product or quotient property shown above to simplify each expression.

  a. $\sqrt[3]{216}$ 6 **b.** Simplify $\sqrt[3]{48}$ $2\sqrt[3]{6}$ **c.** $\sqrt[3]{\frac{8}{27}}$ $\frac{2}{3}$

27 **Try This as a Class**

  a. n^6 is a perfect cube because $n^2 \cdot n^2 \cdot n^2$ or $(n^2)^3 = n^6$. Simplify $\sqrt[3]{n^6}$. n^2

  b. What is the next power of n that is a perfect cube? n^9

  c. Simplify $\sqrt[3]{n^8}$. $n^2\sqrt[3]{n^2}$

  d. Simplify $\sqrt[3]{4n^{12}m^9}$. $n^4m^3\sqrt[3]{4}$

28 Students in a class were asked to write *the cube root of five raised to the fourth power* in radical form. One student wrote $\sqrt[3]{5^4}$; the other wrote $\left(\sqrt[3]{5}\right)^4$.

  a. Simplify each expression. See margin.

  b. How are the expressions alike? How are they different?

29 **Discussion** The $\sqrt[3]{}$ symbol represents the third root (or cube root) of the radicand. What do you think $\sqrt[4]{64}$ represents?
  the 4th root of 64

30 Which of the following is the simplest form of $\sqrt[4]{64}$? $2\sqrt[4]{4}$

  $2\sqrt[4]{4}$ 　　　　 $4\sqrt[4]{2}$ 　　　　 4 　　　　 16

✔ **QUESTION 31**

...checks that you can simplify cube roots and fourth roots.

---

31 ✔ **CHECKPOINT**

  a. Simplify each expression.

  $\sqrt[3]{16}$ $2\sqrt[3]{2}$ 　　　 $\sqrt[3]{-24}$ $-2\sqrt[3]{3}$ 　　　 $\sqrt[4]{16}$ 2 　　　 $\sqrt[4]{32}$ $2\sqrt[4]{2}$

  b. Are any of the expressions in part (a) irrational? Explain how you can tell. Yes, $\sqrt[3]{16}$ and $\sqrt[4]{32}$ because when simplified each has a radical remaining.

■ **HOMEWORK EXERCISES** ▶ See Exs. 9–13 on p. 479.

Section 2 Key Concepts

Key Terms

Irrational Numbers (p. 471)

A number that cannot be written as the quotient of two integers is irrational. As a decimal, an irrational number will not terminate or repeat. For example, $\sqrt{4}$ is rational because $\sqrt{4} = 2$. $\sqrt{8}$ is irrational because the radicand 8 is not a perfect square.

irrational
radical sign
radicand

Simplifying Square Roots (pp. 471–475)

A square root is in simplest form if the following are true.
- There are no perfect square factors other than 1 in the radicand.
- There are no fractions in the radicand.
- There are no square roots in the denominator of a fraction.

**simplest form
(of a square
root)**

The product and quotient properties of square roots can be used to simplify radical expressions. A radical expression is an expression that contains a radical with one or more variables in the radicand.

**product
property of
square roots**

$$\sqrt{a \cdot b} = \sqrt{a} \cdot \sqrt{b} \qquad \sqrt{\frac{a}{b}} = \frac{\sqrt{a}}{\sqrt{b}}$$

**quotient
property of
square roots**

Examples

Simplify $\sqrt{8}$.　　　$\sqrt{8} = \sqrt{4} \cdot \sqrt{2} = 2\sqrt{2}$

Simplify $\sqrt{\dfrac{3}{4}}$.　　$\sqrt{\dfrac{3}{4}} = \dfrac{\sqrt{3}}{\sqrt{4}} = \dfrac{\sqrt{3}}{2}$

**radical
expression**

Cube Roots (p. 475)

If $A = s^3$, then s is a cube root of A. The cube root of a number can be represented using the symbol $\sqrt[3]{\ }$.

cube root

Examples
$4^3 = 64$, so $\sqrt[3]{64} = 4$

$\sqrt[3]{9m^5n^{15}} = \sqrt[3]{9m^3m^2n^{15}}$

> m^5 can be rewritten as $m^3 \cdot m^2$. m^3 and n^{15} are perfect cubes.

$= mn^5\sqrt[3]{9m^2}$

32 Key Concepts Question Show how to use the product and quotient properties of radicals to simplify each expression.

a. $\sqrt{\dfrac{13}{100}}$　$\dfrac{\sqrt{13}}{10}$

b. $\sqrt[3]{54n^7m^9}$
$\sqrt[3]{27 \cdot 2 \cdot n^6 \cdot n \cdot m^9} = 3n^2m^3\sqrt[3]{2n}$

Key Concepts

CLOSURE QUESTION
Find the square root, cube root, and fourth root of 729. How can you tell which, if any, of these roots are irrational?

Sample Response:

$\sqrt{729} = 27$

$\sqrt[3]{729} = 9$

$\sqrt[4]{729} = 3\sqrt[4]{9}$

The fourth root of 729 is irrational because a radicand remains in the simplified answer, so it is not a perfect fourth root.

ABSENT STUDENTS
For students who were absent for all or part of this section, the blackline Study Guide for Section 2 may be used to present the ideas, concepts, and skills of Section 2.

3. b. $0.\overline{12}$ repeats the same digits 121212...whereas 0.121121112 changes because the number of ones after each 2 increases by one as the pattern continues.

5. a. $A = \sqrt{9(1)(3)(5)} = 3\sqrt{15}$ cm²
b. $A = \sqrt{15(5)(5)(5)} = 25\sqrt{3}$ in.²

8. $\dfrac{50}{\sqrt{3}} \cdot \dfrac{\sqrt{3}}{\sqrt{3}} = \dfrac{50\sqrt{3}}{3}$;

$\sqrt{\dfrac{50}{3}} = \dfrac{5\sqrt{6}}{3}$; $\dfrac{\sqrt{50}}{3} = \dfrac{5\sqrt{2}}{3}$

Section 2
Practice & Application Exercises

1. Tell whether each number is *rational* or *irrational*.

    a. $\sqrt{17}$ **b.** $\dfrac{16}{3}$ **c.** $-14.\overline{14}$ **d.** $\sqrt{49}$
       irrational   rational   rational   rational

2. The number π is irrational. However, the rational numbers $\dfrac{22}{7}$ and 3.14 are often used to approximate π. Why do you think rational numbers are sometimes used in place of irrational numbers? **For ease in computations**

3. a. Suppose the digits of the decimal 0.12112111211112... continue to follow the same pattern forever. Write the next six digits. **111112**

    b. Why is $0.\overline{12}$ rational and 0.12112111211112... irrational, even though they both continue forever?

4. Jodie uses her calculator to find a decimal value for $\dfrac{8}{23}$. Her calculator displays 0.3478261, so she decides $\dfrac{8}{23}$ is an irrational number. Do you agree with her? Why or why not? **No, $\dfrac{8}{23}$ is the quotient of two integers.**

5. Around 75 A.D., Heron of Alexandra discovered the formula $A = \sqrt{s(s-a)(s-b)(s-c)}$ for finding the area of a triangle when only the lengths a, b, and c of the sides are known. In the formula, s represents one-half the perimeter of the triangle.

    a. Find the exact area of a triangle with side lengths 8 cm, 6 cm and 4 cm. Write your answer in simplest form.

    b. Find the exact area of an equilateral triangle with side length 10 in. Write your answer in simplest form.

    c. Use a calculator to find the approximate area of each triangle in parts (a) and (b). Round to the nearest tenth. **about 11.6 cm²; about 43.3 in.²**

6. Simplify.

    a. $\sqrt{60}$ $2\sqrt{15}$ **b.** $\sqrt{12}$ $2\sqrt{3}$ **c.** $\sqrt{484}$ 22   **d.** $\sqrt{\dfrac{5}{49}}$ $\dfrac{\sqrt{5}}{7}$

7. Which of the following are in simplest form? Explain.

    a. $\dfrac{\sqrt{3}}{50}$ yes   **b.** $\dfrac{50}{\sqrt{3}}$ no   **c.** $\sqrt{\dfrac{50}{3}}$ no   **d.** $\dfrac{\sqrt{50}}{3}$ no

8. Simplify the expressions in Exercise 7 that are not already written in simplest form.

For Exercises 9–11 assume all variables represent positive numbers.

9. Simplify each radical expression. Use the product and quotient properties of square roots when possible.

   a. $\sqrt{121x^6}$ $11x^3$ **b.** $\sqrt{y^{29}}$ $y^{14}\sqrt{y}$ **c.** $\sqrt{\dfrac{6}{m^{10}}}$ $\dfrac{\sqrt{6}}{m^5}$ **d.** $\dfrac{\sqrt{b^5}}{\sqrt{b^3}}$ b

10. Simplify each expression.

   a. $\sqrt[3]{40}$
   $2\sqrt[3]{5}$
   b. $\sqrt[3]{10n^{18}}$
   $n^6\sqrt[3]{10}$
   c. $\sqrt[4]{625}$
   5
   d. $\sqrt[4]{a^4b^6}$
   $ab\sqrt[4]{b^2}$

11. **Challenge** A radical expression is simplified to $9ab^3\sqrt[4]{ab^3}$. What was the original expression?

   $$\sqrt[4]{?} = 9ab^3\sqrt[4]{ab^3} \quad \sqrt[4]{6561a^5b^{15}}$$

12. Consider the expression $\sqrt[n]{64}$ where n is a positive integer. For which values of n is the expression rational? Name a value of n that makes the expression irrational. Explain your choices.

Reflecting ◀▶on the Section

Write your answer to Exercise 13 in your journal.

13. Two students are discussing whether the number represented by the expression $\sqrt[3]{n^2}$ is rational or irrational. The first student says it is always irrational, while the second says you cannot tell since it depends on the value of n. With whom do you agree? Justify your choice.

Spiral ◀▶Review

Rewrite each equation in the form $y = ax^2 + bx + c$. Tell whether the equation represents a quadratic function. (Module 6, p. 447)

14. $y = 3x^2 - 5x - x^2$
    $y = 2x^2 - 5x$; yes
15. $y = x(2x - 4)$
    $y = 2x^2 - 4x$; yes
16. $x(x + 2) = 16y + x^2$
    $y = \frac{1}{8}x$; no

Find each sum or difference. (Module 2, p. 100)

17. $-32\frac{1}{5} - \frac{3}{5}$ $-2\frac{4}{5}$
18. $-3\frac{1}{2} + \left(-3\frac{1}{8}\right)$ $-6\frac{5}{8}$
19. $-6\frac{2}{3} - \left(-3\frac{1}{4}\right)$ $-3\frac{5}{12}$

20. In the diagram $\triangle ABC \sim \triangle XYZ$. Find the length of $\overline{AB}$. (Module 3, p. 198) 21 mm

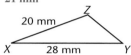

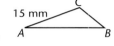

---

12. rational: 2, since $\sqrt[2]{64} = 8$; 3, since $\sqrt[3]{64} = 4$; 6, since $\sqrt[6]{64} = 2$
    sample value for irrational: $n = 4$; $\sqrt[4]{64} = \sqrt{8} \approx 2.828427...$

13. Sample Response: It depends on the number because if $n = 8$ then $\sqrt[3]{8^2} = \sqrt[3]{64} = 4$ which is rational, but if $n = 9$ then $\sqrt[3]{9^2} = \sqrt[3]{81} = 3\sqrt[3]{3}$ which is irrational.

Journal

Exercise 13 checks that you can simplify radical expressions and identify irrational numbers.

TEACHER NOTES
For each Exploration, the corresponding Extra Skill Practice Exercises are noted.

Exploration 1: Exs. 1–19
Exploration 2: Exs. 20–31

EXTRA HELP
Teacher's Resource Book
• Practice and Applications
• Study Guide

Technology Resources
• @Home Tutor
• Test Generator

ASSESSMENT
• Section 2 Quick Quiz
• Mid-Module Quiz
• Test Generator

10. Using the product property gives an expression equivalent to the original. The second expression does not use the property correctly and the third expression uses a sum which does not give an equivalent expression.

Section 2

Extra Skill Practice

Tell whether each number is *rational* or *irrational*.

1. $3.\overline{6}$ rational

2. $\frac{36}{11}$ rational

3. $\sqrt{3}$ irrational

4. 1.87 rational

5. $\sqrt{16}$ rational

6. -19 rational

7. $\sqrt{27}$ irrational

8. $\sqrt{35}$ irrational

9. $3.454454445\ldots$ irrational

10. Which expression(s) could be used to simplify $\sqrt{24}$? Explain. See margin.

$\sqrt{6} \cdot \sqrt{4}$ $\qquad$ $\sqrt{4} \cdot 6$ $\qquad$ $\sqrt{4} + \sqrt{4} + \sqrt{16}$

Simplify each expression. Assume all variables represent positive numbers.

11. $\sqrt{140}$ $2\sqrt{35}$

12. $\sqrt{44}$ $2\sqrt{11}$

13. $\sqrt{250}$ $5\sqrt{10}$

14. $\sqrt{28}$ $2\sqrt{7}$

15. $\sqrt{98}$ $7\sqrt{2}$

16. $\sqrt{320}$ $8\sqrt{5}$

17. $\sqrt{\frac{10}{81}}$ $\frac{\sqrt{10}}{9}$

18. $\sqrt{\frac{14}{9}}$ $\frac{\sqrt{14}}{3}$

19. $\sqrt{\frac{32}{81}}$ $\frac{4\sqrt{2}}{9}$

20. $\frac{11}{\sqrt{3}}$ $\frac{11\sqrt{3}}{3}$

21. $\frac{2}{\sqrt{5}}$ $\frac{2\sqrt{5}}{5}$

22. $\frac{\sqrt{9}}{25}$ $\frac{3}{25}$

23. $\frac{40}{\sqrt{2}}$ $20\sqrt{2}$

24. $\sqrt{49n^{10}}$ $7n^5$

25. $\sqrt{x^3 y^8}$ $xy^4\sqrt{x}$

26. $\sqrt[3]{343}$ 7

27. $\sqrt[3]{125}$ 5

28. $\sqrt[4]{48}$ $2\sqrt[4]{3}$

29. $\sqrt[4]{1296}$ 6

30. $\sqrt[3]{54n^5}$ $3n\sqrt[3]{2n^2}$

31. $\sqrt[3]{r^3 s^5 t^9}$ $rst^3\sqrt[3]{s^2}$

Standardized Testing ◆▶ Multiple Choice

1. Which of the following numbers is an irrational number? B

   (A) 40 $\qquad$ (B) $\sqrt{108}$ $\qquad$ (C) $\frac{29}{28}$ $\qquad$ (D) $3.\overline{51}$

2. Which expression is written in simplest form? D

   (A) $\sqrt{\frac{3}{5}}$ $\qquad$ (B) $3\sqrt{8}$ $\qquad$ (C) $\frac{\sqrt{4}}{9}$ $\qquad$ (D) $\frac{\sqrt{11}}{11}$

Extended Exploration

FOR ASSESSMENT AND PORTFOLIOS

Sum Fun!

7	5	8
6	4	7
9	7	10

The Situation See the *Teacher's Resource Book* for a sample solution for this Extended Exploration.

	5	3	6
2	7	5	8
1	6	4	7
4	9	7	10

Six numbers are chosen randomly and placed along the edge of a grid as shown. Corresponding numbers are then added to complete each box in the 3 × 3 grid.

A number is circled and all other numbers that share the same row and same column are crossed out. The process is repeated with the available numbers until only one number remains in each row and in each column. The sum of the circled numbers is 21.

Copy the grid and choose a different starting number to circle. Find the sum of the circled numbers. Repeat this several times.

The Problem

Find out what the sum of the circled numbers on any sum-generated grid will be before any numbers are circled.

Something to Think About

◆ What happens if different random numbers are chosen to generate the grid?

◆ If the grid is completed using variables for the six random numbers, what is the sum of the circled expressions? What if the variables are rearranged along the outside of the grid? How is the sum affected?

◆ Does the trick work with other size grids? Must the grids have an equal number of columns and rows or could a grid be 3 × 4?

Present Your Results

Explain why this puzzle works and how you could predict the sum for any size grid. Include an explanation of how you used algebra to solve this problem.

Extended Exploration

E² NOTES

This E² can be introduced by the teacher as a magic trick. Before class, seal a piece of paper with the number 21 written on it in an envelope. Begin the trick by displaying a copy of the 3 x 3 grid on the board or overhead. Hand the pre-made envelope to a student and ask them to safeguard it. Then ask a volunteer to come forward and circle one number, crossing out all other numbers in the same column or row. Repeat with a second volunteer. Finally have a third volunteer come forward and circle the only remaining number. Ask the class to find the sum the three circled numbers and report the sum. At this point ask the student with the envelope to open it and show the paper inside to the class. After the "oohs" and "aahhs", introduce the E² and instruct students that their assignment is to discover how and why this trick works.

Using an E²: Suggestions for managing and evaluating an Extended Exploration are available in the *Teacher's Resource Book* for Modules 1 and 2. See also pages T44–T45 in the *Teacher's Edition*.

Alternate E²: See the *Teacher's Resource Book* for Modules 7 and 8 for an alternate Extended Exploration that can be used after Module 7, Section 2.

Setting the Stage

GETTING STARTED

Before students write and solve inequalities they need to be able to write and solve equations. Module 7 Section 3 *Warm-Up* assesses students' ability to write and solve equations.

ABOUT THE THEME

Introduce the section by asking students if they have ever had to sit in a chair that they felt did not fit them very well. Some instances might include visiting an elementary school or children's section of a public library and finding chairs too short or riding in an airplane and finding your feet don't touch the floor of the airplane.

TEACHING NOTES

The graph in the *Setting the Stage* may differ from most graphs students have read. Give an example and explain to students how to interpret the graph. "My popliteal height is 15 in. Find the corresponding number on the vertical axis for women with a popliteal height of 15 in." (*It crosses at almost 30, ≈ 28*.) Ask, "What does this mean?" Help students to see that the 28% means 28% of female adults have a popliteal height *shorter* than 15 in. and therefore 72% have a popliteal height *equal to or longer* than 15 in. Students may be curious as to where their measures fit on the chart. Allow students to measure their popliteal heights (or encourage them to do so at home) and then compare their measurement to the graph results. Since the graph data is based on adults it may not accurately reflect student data, but students can at least get a rough idea of how they compare to adults.

Section ③ Graphing and Solving Inequalities

The Human Factor

◄◄ *Setting the Stage*

How high should the seat of a chair be so it is comfortable for most people? How can children ride safely and comfortably in a car? To get answers to questions like these, the person to call is a *human factors engineer*. These engineers make use of data about people—heights, weights, leg lengths, and so on. They use the information to help design buildings, furniture, tools, appliances, and cars that are comfortable for as many people as possible.

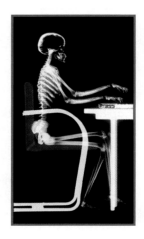

To decide how high to make the seat of a chair, for example, a human factors engineer would study the data below on *popliteal height*.

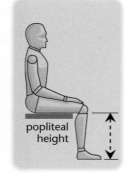

▲
Popliteal height is the distance from the floor to the underside of the knees when a person is seated.

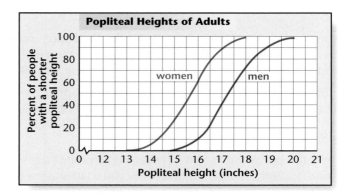

Think About It ‣

1 About what percent of adult women have a popliteal height less than 17 in.? about what percent of adult men? **about 90%; about 40%**

2 The popliteal height of 5% of women is less than how many inches? **about 14 in.**

3 Can you tell from the graph if any men have a popliteal height less than the number of inches you found in Question 2? Explain. **No; The percent is 0, but the number may not be.**

Exploration 1 ‣

Graphing
INEQUALITIES

GOAL

LEARN HOW TO...
◆ write and graph inequalities

AS YOU...
◆ study car seat safety for children

KEY TERM
◆ inequality

▶ Seats in cars are designed mainly for the safety and comfort of adults, therefore the National Highway Traffic Safety Administration (NHTSA) offers guiding principles for children riding in vehicles. Some of the principles can be represented using inequalities. An **inequality** is a mathematical sentence that compares two quantities using the symbols <, >, ≤, or ≥.

EXAMPLE

Infants up to age one weighing less than 20 lb should always be secured in a rear-facing safety seat in the back seat of a vehicle. Write and graph an inequality to describe the weight restriction.

SAMPLE RESPONSE

$w < 20$ where w is weight in pounds.

The open circle shows that 20 is not on the graph.

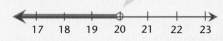

4 Discussion

a. In the inequality $w < 20$, what does the symbol < mean? **is less than**

b. How do you know that the graph does not include 20? How do you know that it includes values less than 17? **There is an open circle on 20; The heavy line covers numbers that are included, and the arrow indicates that all numbers less than 17 are included.**

TEACHING NOTES
As students complete **Discussion Question 4**, emphasize the features of inequality graphs: closed circle for *greater than or equal to* or for *less than or equal to*; open circle for *greater than* or for *less than*; solid arrow for a graph that continues beyond the values shown, and an equally spaced and labeled scale on the number line.

If needed, the example below can be used after **Question 4 or Question 5**.

CLASSROOM EXAMPLE

Write and graph an inequality to show that profits from the bake sale are expected to be greater than or equal to $45.

Answer: $p ≥ 45$, where p is the amount of profit in dollars.

The closed circle shows that 45 is included in the graph.

TEACHING NOTES

As you work through the Example in the text with students, graph the inequalities $w \geq 20$ and $w \leq 40$ on the same number line to show that the region where the graphs overlap is the line segment shown in the Example. Using two different color markers or drawing the graphs above and below the number line will make it easier for students to see the overlapping region.

If students need more guidance writing and graphing inequalities, the following Classroom Example can be discussed before students complete **Question 7**.

CLASSROOM EXAMPLE

The entry form for a poetry contest states that submitted poems must include at least 50 words and must not exceed 50 words. Write and graph an inequality to describe this fact.

Answer: $50 \leq w \leq 200$

---

5 According to NHTSA, an infant weighing 20 lb or more before age one should ride in a rear-facing safety seat rated for heavier infants.

 a. Write an inequality that describes the weight restriction in this situation. Use the symbol ≥ (read as *is greater than or equal to*).
 $w \geq 20$ where w is the weight of the infant in pounds

 b. The graph of the inequality from part (a) is shown below. Why is the circle filled in? **The solution includes 20.**

14 16 18 20 22 24

▶ Sometimes two inequalities are combined to form one inequality.

EXAMPLE

Children older than one year weighing from 20 lb to 40 lb may ride in a forward-facing safety seat in the back seat of a vehicle. Write and graph an inequality that describes this weight restriction.

SAMPLE RESPONSE

$w \geq 20$ represents a weight greater than or equal to 20 lb.
$w \leq 40$ represents a weight less than or equal to 40 lb. Together they can be written as $20 \leq w \leq 40$, where w is the weight in pounds.

You can read $20 \leq w \leq 40$ as "w is greater than or equal to 20 and less than or equal to 40."

> $20 \leq w \leq 40$ can also be read as "20 is less than or equal to w and w is less than or equal to 40."

15 20 25 30 35 40 45

6 Try This as a Class NHTSA recommends that children weighing over 40 lb use booster seats until they reach a height of 4 ft 9 in.

 a. Write and graph an inequality for the weights (in pounds) of children who should use booster seats. Write and graph an inequality for the heights (in inches) of children who should use booster seats.

 b. Explain why the two inequalities in part (a) should not be combined into one inequality.

6. b. The inequalities represent two different units of measure, pounds and inches, which cannot be represented on one number line.

7 The graph shows the percent of child safety seats that studies show are used incorrectly. Write an inequality represented by the graph.
$80 \leq c \leq 90$ where c is the percent of child safety seats

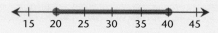

60% 70% 80% 90% 100%

6. a. $w > 40$ where w is the weight of the child in pounds;

$h < 57$ where h is the height of the child in inches

34 36 38 40 42 44   53 54 55 56 57 58

8 ✓ **CHECKPOINT** Write and graph each inequality.

a. n is less than or equal to 65. $n \le 65$

61   63   65   67

b. x is greater than -250. $x > -250$

-253 -250 -247

c. r is less than 16 but greater than 5. $5 < r < 16$

4   8   12   16

HOMEWORK EXERCISES ▸ See Exs. 1–6 on p. 490.

Exploration 2

Solving Simple Inequalities

▶ Some human factors engineers recommend that for comfort, the height of a chair seat should be less than or equal to the popliteal height of the person sitting in it plus 1.5 in. Adding 1.5 in. adjusts for the thickness of the soles and heels of the person's shoes.

9 a. Use h for the seat height and p for the popliteal height. Write an inequality for the recommended height of a chair seat. $h \le p + 1.5$

b. Substitute 15 for p in the inequality in part (a). A value of a variable that makes an inequality true is a **solution of the inequality**. Are 16.5 in. and 19 in. solutions of your new inequality? Why or why not?

c. A student claims that a 2 in. chair would be comfortable for a person with a 15 in. popliteal height because 2 is a solution of the inequality $h \le 15 + 1.5$. Is 2 a solution? Is it realistic?

10 **Try This as a Class** Suppose the seat height of a chair is 17 in.

a. Substitute 17 in. for the seat height in the inequality from Question 9(a). Write the new inequality. $17 \le p + 1.5$

b. People with what popliteal heights would be comfortable in such a chair? Explain how you found your answer.

c. Use the graph on page 482. About what percent of adult women would not be comfortable in the chair? About what percent of adult men would not be comfortable? about 40%, about 5%

10. b. people with popliteal heights greater than or equal to 15.5 in.; The seat height can be up to 1.5 in. less than 17 in., so $17 - 1.5 = 15.5$.

✓ **QUESTION 8**

...checks that you can write and graph an inequality.

GOAL

LEARN HOW TO...
◆ solve inequalites that involve one operation

AS YOU...
◆ study the seat heights of chairs

KEY TERMS
◆ solution of an inequality
◆ solve an inequality

9. b. $h \le 15 + 1.5$; 16.5 is a solution because 16.5 is equal to $15 + 1.5$. 19 is not a solution because 19 is not less than or equal to $15 + 1.5$.

c. Yes, it is a solution since $2 \le 15 + 1.5$, but a chair seat 2 in. off the ground would not be comfortable for sitting at a table. It might be comfortable as a beach chair where you could stretch your legs out straight in front of you.

Exploration 2

DEVELOPING MATH CONCEPTS
Explain to students that, unlike a linear equation, the solution of an inequality is a range of values rather than a single unique value. Make sure students understand the difference between solutions that are strictly *less than* or *greater than*, as opposed to ones which are *less than or equal to*, or *greater than or equal to*. These distinctions will be important when students begin checking their solutions to inequalities. Since the solution of an inequality is a range of values, it is usually impossible to check the solution by substituting *all* of the values back into the original inequality. The best that can be done is to substitute two or three values. If the solution has the form $x \ge a$, one of the values substituted back into the original inequality should be a and the others should be greater than a. Similarly, if the solution has the form $x \le a$, one of the values should be a and the others should be less than a. It is important that students understand that in these cases, the solution cannot be checked simply by substituting a back into the original inequality. These points should be discussed using specific examples in **Discussion Question 14** on page 486.

Exploration 2 *continued*

TEACHING NOTES

For **Question 11**, you may wish to tell some students to use two positive numbers, some to use two negative numbers, and some to use one positive and one negative number. This ensures that in discussing **Question 13** as a class, results using all possible types of inequalities will be available.

In **Discussion Question 14**, help students understand why using just 5 to check the first inequality in the Example is not a good idea. (*Since the inequality includes equal to, you may falsely believe a solution to be correct even if the inequality sign were facing the wrong direction.*) To make sure that they have the correct inequality, they should also substitute at least one value that is less than 5 back into the original inequality. It is also wise for students to check a number in the shaded portion of their graph to be sure the solution was graphed correctly.

In answering the second part of **Question 14**, students may state that an equation has only one answer. To dispute this claim, reintroduce an absolute equation such as $|n| = 3$ which has two solutions 3 and –3.

---

14. Sample Response: For the first inequality choose a number less than 5 and substitute it into the inequality $x - 7 \le -2$ to see if it makes a true statement. For the second inequality choose a number less than –3 and substitute it into $-6x > 18$ to see if it makes a true statement.; With an inequality you can not substitute all of the solutions into the inequality, so you substitute any of the values from the solution into the original inequality to see if it holds true. In an equation, you need to substitute each solution into the equation to check.

▶ In Question 10(c), you **solved the inequality** $17 \le p + 1.5$ by finding all of the solutions of the inequality. In Questions 11–13, you will investigate some of the operations used to solve inequalities.

11 Choose two different numbers (the numbers can both have the same sign, or they can have opposite signs). Write an inequality that compares the numbers. **Sample Response:** $8 > -2$

12 Perform each operation below to both sides of the original inequality you wrote in Question 11. Then write the correct inequality symbol between the two new numbers.

a. Add 5. $13 > 3$ **b.** Subtract 5. $3 > -7$ **c.** Multiply by 5. $40 > -10$

d. Divide by 5. $\frac{8}{5} > -\frac{2}{5}$ **e.** Add –2. $6 > -4$ **f.** Subtract –2. $10 > 0$

g. Multiply by –2. $-16 < 4$ **h.** Divide by –2. $-4 < 1$ **i.** Add $-\frac{1}{4}$. $7\frac{3}{4} > -2\frac{1}{4}$

j. Subtract $-\frac{1}{4}$. $8\frac{1}{4} > -1\frac{3}{4}$ **k.** Multiply by $-\frac{1}{4}$. $-2 < \frac{1}{2}$ **l.** Divide by $-\frac{1}{4}$. $-32 < 8$

13 Try This as a Class Look back at your results from Question 12. Tell how you think the operations described affect the inequality.

a. Adding or subtracting the same number on both sides It does not affect the inequality; Both sides increase or decrease by the same amount.

b. Multiplying or dividing both sides by the same nonzero number If the number is positive, it does not affect the inequality. If the number is negative, it reverses the inequality.

▶ The properties found in Question 13 can be used to solve inequalities.

EXAMPLE

Adding or subtracting the same number on both sides of an inequality does not affect the inequality.

$$x - 7 \le -2$$
$$x - 7 + 7 \le -2 + 7$$
$$x \le 5$$

Multiplying or dividing both sides of an inequality by a *negative* number **reverses the inequality**.

$$-6x > 18$$
$$\frac{-6x}{-6} < \frac{18}{-6}$$
$$x < -3$$

---

14 Discussion How would you check the solutions of the inequalities in the Example? How is this different than checking the solution of an equation?

15 ✔ **CHECKPOINT** Solve. Check and then graph each solution.

   a. $36 < x + 13$ **b.** $\frac{x}{3} \geq -2$ **c.** $-7x > -63$

✔ **QUESTION 15**

...checks that you can solve inequalities that involve one operation.

16 One manufacturer decided that the seat height of a non-adjustable chair should be at least 16 in. Using the inequality from Question 9(a), an inequality for the popliteal heights of the people who would be comfortable in a chair with a seat height of 16 in. is $16 \leq p + 1.5$.

   a. Solve $16 \leq p + 1.5$. People with what popliteal heights would be comfortable in the chair? $p \geq 14.5$; greater than or equal to 14.5 in.

   b. Use the graph on page 482. About what percent of adult women would not be comfortable in the chair? About what percent of adult men would not be comfortable? about 15%; 0%

   c. Why do you think the company decided on this seat height instead of a greater one? Sample Response: 85% – 100% of adults would be comfortable with this height.

HOMEWORK EXERCISES ▶ See Exs. 7–21 on p. 491.

Exploration 3

MULTI-STEP INEQUALITIES

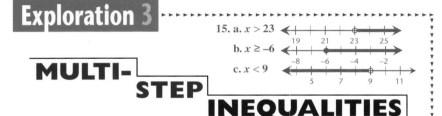

15. a. $x > 23$

   b. $x \geq -6$

   c. $x < 9$

GOAL

LEARN HOW TO...
◆ solve inequalities that have more than one operation

AS YOU...
◆ plan the arrangement of the seats in a theater

▶ In this exploration, you will use human factors engineering to design comfortable seating for a theater.

17 To provide comfortable seating, the width of a theater seat should be from 20 to 26 in. and the depth of each row should be from 34 to 42 in.

   a. What is the least area in square feet needed for a person to have a comfortable seat? What is the greatest area needed? (*Hint:* 1 ft² = 144 in.²) about 4.7 ft²; about 7.6 ft²

   b. What seat width and row depth would you recommend for each seat in a theater? Why? Answers will vary. Check students' work.

   c. Based on your recommendation, how many square feet would be needed for each seat in a theater? Multiply seat width by row depth (in inches) and divide by 144.

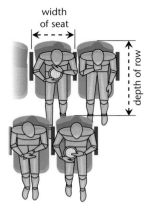

width of seat

depth of row

Section 3   Graphing and Solving Inequalities   **487**

TEACHING NOTES

If students need more guidance solving inequalities and graphing the solutions, the following Classroom Examples can be discussed before students complete **Checkpoint Question 15**.

CLASSROOM EXAMPLES

Solve the inequalities. Graph each solution.

a. $x + 4 \geq -3$ b. $-\frac{1}{3}x < 1$

Answers:

a. $x + 4 \geq -3$

     $x + 4 - 4 \geq -3 - 4$

         $x \geq -7$

Check:

    $-7 + 4 \overset{?}{\geq} -3$

       $-3 \geq -3$

    $-1 + 4 \overset{?}{\geq} -3$

        $3 \geq -3$

b. $-\frac{1}{3}x < 1$

   $(-3)\left(-\frac{1}{3}x\right) < (-3)(1)$

         $x > -3$ Note that the inequality is reversed.

Check:

    $-\frac{1}{3}(-1) \overset{?}{<} 1$

       $\frac{1}{3} < 1$

    $-\frac{1}{3}(6) \overset{?}{<} 1$

      $-2 < 1$

Exploration 3

COMMON ERRORS

Question 17 Students should be reminded that there are no partial seats in a theater, so answers referring to the number of seats should be whole numbers.

487

If students need more guidance solving multi-step inequalities and graphing the solutions, the following Classroom Example can be discussed before students complete **Checkpoint Question 20**.

CLASSROOM EXAMPLE

Use inverse operations to solve the inequality $12.2 - 4x \geq 13.8$. Then graph the solution.

Answer: $12.2 - 4x \geq 13.8$
$12.2 - 12.2 - 4x \geq 13.8 - 12.2$
$-4x \geq 1.6$
$\dfrac{-4x}{-4} \leq \dfrac{1.6}{-4}$
$x \leq -0.4$

COMMON ERRORS

Checkpoint Question 20 Students may fail to reverse the inequality when multiplying or dividing by a negative number. Encourage students to check their solutions by choosing numbers from their solution and substituting them into the original inequality.

---

18. a.

4 ft

48 ft

4 ft

36 ft

19. d. subtraction first and then division; To "undo" the operations done to the variable, work backwards from the order in which order of operations was performed.

QUESTION 20

...checks that you can solve inequalities that involve two operations.

---

18 A new theater will be 48 ft long and 36 ft wide. Two aisles are needed, one down the center of the theater and one between the front row and the screen. The aisles will be 4 ft wide.

  a. Make a sketch of the theater showing the locations and dimensions of the aisles.

  b. What is the total area of the theater? of the aisles?
  1728 ft²; 320 ft²

19 **Try This as a Class** The total area of the theater, t, must be greater than or equal to the area per seat times the number of seats, s, plus the area of the aisles, a. Use the area per seat that you recommended in Question 17(c).

  a. Write an inequality relating t, s, and a. $t \geq$ (area per seat)$s + a$

  b. Use your answers to Question 18(b) to write an inequality for the number of seats the theater can hold.
  $1728 \geq$ (area per seat)$s + 320$

  c. The inequality in part (b) uses both addition and multiplication. What are their inverse operations?
  subtraction, division

  d. In what order would you use the inverse operations to solve the inequality in part (b)? Why?

  e. About how many seats can the theater hold? Answers will vary based on area per seat selected. Check students' work.

20 ✔ **CHECKPOINT** Solve each inequality.

  a. $14 < 5x - 9$
  $x > 4.6$

  b. $-\dfrac{x}{2} - 3 \geq -2$
  $x \leq -2$

  c. $-3x + 17 > -4$
  $x < 7$

21 **a.** Use the aisle width and the theater width from Question 18 and the seat width you chose in Question 17(b) to write an inequality involving s, the number of seats. $36 \geq$ (seat width in feet)$s + 4$

  b. Suppose that, in each row, there will be the same number of seats on either side of the aisle. How many seats can you have in each row? $s \leq \dfrac{32}{\text{seat width in feet}}$

  c. Use the row depth you chose in Question 17(b). How many rows can you have? $r \leq \dfrac{44}{\text{row depth in feet}}$

  d. How many seats will fit in the theater? How does this compare with your answer to Question 19(e)? $s \cdot r$; Answers will vary. Check students' work.

22 **Discussion** Human factors engineers recommend that the rows of seats be staggered as in the diagram on page 487. How would this affect the number of seats you can have in the theater?
It would decrease the number of seats.

HOMEWORK EXERCISES ▶ See Exs. 22–38 on pp. 492–493.

Section 3

Key Concepts

Key Terms ▶▶▶▶▶▶▶▶▶▶▶▶▶▶▶▶▶▶▶▶▶▶

Inequalities (pp. 483–485)

The symbols <, >, ≤, and ≥ are used to write inequalities. Inequalities can be graphed on a number line.

inequality

Example A number is greater than or equal to –2 and less than 3.

$$-2 \leq x < 3$$

Solving Inequalities (pp. 485–488)

A value of a variable that makes an inequality true is a solution of the inequality. All the solutions together are called the solution of the inequality. When you find them, you are solving the inequality.

solution of an inequality

solve an inequality

Example

$$-3x + 2.5 < 11.8$$

$$-3x + 2.5 - 2.5 < 11.8 - 2.5$$

> Subtracting the same number does not affect the inequality.

$$-3x < 9.3$$

$$\frac{-3x}{-3} > \frac{9.3}{-3}$$

> Dividing by a *negative* number reverses the inequality.

$$x > -3.1$$

You can use inverse operations to solve inequalities. However, you must be sure to reverse the inequality symbol whenever you multiply or divide both sides by a negative number.

Key Concepts Questions

23 Explain why in the first Example above there is a closed circle on –2 and an open circle on 3. *x is greater than or equal to –2, so –2 is included in the solution, but x is less than 3, so 3 is not.*

24 **a.** Solve –2a – 3 = 5 and graph the solution. **See margin.**

   b. Solve –2a – 3 ≥ 5 and graph the solution. **See margin.**

   c. How is the solution of –2a – 3 ≥ 5 similar to the solution of –2a – 3 = 5? How is it different? *Both solutions include –4; The solution of the equation is –4 and the solution of the inequality is all numbers less than or equal to –4.*

Key Concepts

CLOSURE QUESTIONS

What is an inequality? When solving inequalities, what steps must be taken to be sure the inequality stays true throughout the process?

> *Sample Response:* An inequality is a mathematical sentence that compares two quantities using the symbols <, >, ≤, and ≥. Solving inequalities is much like solving equations in that whatever operations are performed to one side of the inequality must also be done to the opposite side. However, if you multiply or divide both sides by a negative number, you must remember to reverse the inequality for the statement to remain true.

ABSENT STUDENTS

For students who were absent for all or part of this section, the blackline Study Guide for Section 3 may be used to present the ideas, concepts, and skills of Section 3.

24. a. $a = -4$;

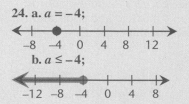

   b. $a \leq -4$;

Section ③
Practice & Application Exercises

Write an inequality to describe each situation. Then graph each inequality on a number line.

1. The price of the ticket for a concert was more than $25.
$p > 25$

2. The temperature today ranged from −10°F to 3°F.
$-10 \le t \le 3$

3. The elevation of the house was less than 50 ft above sea level.
$e < 50$

4. At a theater, people 55 years old and older pay a reduced admission price.
$p \ge 55$

5. Geometry Connection The graph of the inequality $a \ge 7$ is a *ray*, because it is a part of a line and has one endpoint. The graph of the inequality $2 \le b \le 6$ is a *segment*, because it is a part of a line and has two endpoints.

a. Graph each of the inequalities above on a number line and label the endpoints.

b. A segment has endpoints at −3 and 1. Write an inequality that has this segment as its graph. $-3 \le s \le 1$

c. A ray has an endpoint at 10 and includes points to the left on a number line. Write an inequality that has this ray as its graph.
$r \le 10$

6. Writing A student graphed the inequality $-2 < x \le 4$ as shown below. Explain what is wrong with the graph.

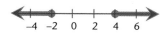

7. Is 6 a solution of the inequality $-8 + x < 2$? Explain. **Yes, when substituted for the variable, the left side equals -2 which is less than 2.**

Solve each inequality. Check and graph each solution.

8. $a + 17 < 37$ **9.** $8 + w \geq 10$ **10.** $-13 > b - 7$

11. $x - (-3) \leq 8$ **12.** $96 \leq 12n$ **13.** $-0.5z > -6.5$

14. $\dfrac{y}{2} < 2.5$ **15.** $-7 \geq \dfrac{q}{-1.5}$ **16.** $-\dfrac{2}{3}x < 6$

For Exercises 17–20, write and solve an inequality for each situation.

17. Seven more than a number is less than seven. $7 + n < 7;\ n < 0$

18. The opposite of a number is greater than or equal to five.
$-n \geq 5;\ n \leq -5$

19. A family needs to drive 95 miles in less than 1 hour and 45 minutes. What average speed must they drive? $1.75s \geq 95$; $s \geq 54.3$; at least 54.3 mi/hr

20. Building Codes The Uniform Building Code requires that there be at least 20 ft^2 of space for each person in a classroom. Suppose a classroom is 28 ft long and 18 ft wide. How many people can be in the classroom? $20p \leq 504$; $p \leq 25.2$; no more than 25 people

21. Theater Design Rows in a theater are often elevated so each person can look over the head of the person in front of him or her. Theater floors must either be sloped or have steps. Whether the floor can be sloped depends on the depth of the row d and the amount of rise r. A floor can only be sloped if $r \leq \dfrac{d}{8}$.

a. A rise of 5 in. will give the maximum visibility for the greatest number of people. How deep can the rows be if the floor is sloped and has a rise of 5 in.? **up to 40 in.**

b. Many theaters have 32-inch-deep rows. What is the maximum rise for a sloped floor? **4 in.**

c. A certain theater chain claims to give everyone an unobstructed view of the screen. Suppose the rise is 10.8 in. What is the minimum row depth for a sloped floor? **86.4 in.**

d. Why do you think the theaters in part (c) have stepped floors? **The rows would have to be so far apart that they would lose too much seating if they used a sloped floor.**

e. What are some advantages of a stepped floor? **See margin.**

f. What are some advantages of a sloped floor? **Sample Response: A sloped floor may be safer, since people may be less likely to trip in low light.**

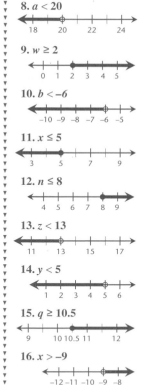

8. $a < 20$

9. $w \geq 2$

10. $b < -6$

11. $x \leq 5$

12. $n \leq 8$

13. $z < 13$

14. $y < 5$

15. $q \geq 10.5$

16. $x > -9$

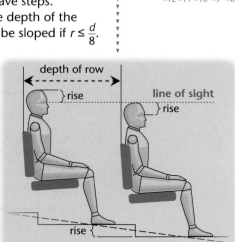

depth of row
rise
line of sight
rise
rise

Section 3   Graphing and Solving Inequalities   **491**

EXERCISE NOTES
Exercises 17–20 and 22–26 ask students to translate English sentences into mathematical statements. This can be difficult for any student, but especially for those whose primary language is one other than English, or those who are particularly challenged by decoding text in general. You may want to have these students pair with another student or adult who can read the sentence to them and help them to interpret it.

Exercise 20 Students may be curious about how this code applies to their classroom. If so, have students measure the classroom and determine the maximum number of people allowed.

21. e. Sample Response: More rows are possible with a stepped floor because of a higher rise and shorter row depth.

Practice & Applications

EXERCISE NOTES

For students having difficulty translating the sentences in **Exercises 22–26**, suggest the following. Copy the sentence, leaving a blank line above it. First underline all word groups that represent numbers. Then circle all word groups that indicate a mathematical operation such as add, multiply, subtract, or divide. Finally, box any word group that indicates an inequality symbol. Above each word or group of words, write the corresponding number, symbol, or operation. **Exercise 23** is shown as an example.

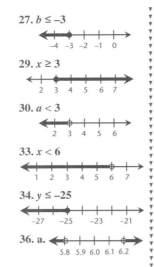

$$24 \quad - \quad \frac{1}{2} \cdot n$$

Twenty-four (minus) half (of) a number

$$\geq \quad 132$$

is greater than or equal to 132.

28. $z \leq -10.25$

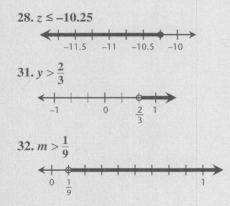

31. $y > \frac{2}{3}$

32. $m > \frac{1}{9}$

---

27. $b \leq -3$

29. $x \geq 3$

30. $a < 3$

33. $x < 6$

34. $y \leq -25$

36. a.

For Exercises 22–26, write and solve an inequality for each situation.

22. Two times a number minus 13 is less than 47. $2n - 13 < 47; n < 30$

23. Twenty-four minus half of a number is greater than or equal to 132. $24 - 0.5n \geq 132; n \leq -216$

24. The difference when 1.57 is subtracted from 3 times a number is less than or equal to 10.62. $3n - 1.57 \leq 10.62; n \leq 4.063$

25. Suppose you can rent a snowmobile for an initial fee of $25, plus $12.50 per hour. For how many hours can you rent a snowmobile and still spend less than $90? $12.50h + 25 < 90; h < 5.2;$ **less than 5.2 hr**

26. A landowner has 200 acres of land and wants to keep at least 20 acres. The rest will be divided and sold in 12-acre lots. How many of these lots can the land owner offer for sale? $200 - 12n \geq 20; n \leq 15;$ **at most 15 lots**

Solve each inequality. Check and graph each solution. 28, 31–32 See margin.

27. $-5b + 77 \geq 92$

28. $-8z + 9 \geq 93$

29. $-32 + (-41x) \leq -155$

30. $1.2a - 0.97 < 2.63$

31. $\frac{3}{4}y + \frac{11}{16} > \frac{19}{16}$

32. $\frac{8}{9} - \frac{1}{3}m < \frac{23}{27}$

33. $5.95 - 2.95x > -11.75$

34. $49y + 249 \leq -976$

35. Create Your Own For each graph, create three inequalities that when solved would produce the solution shown in the graph.

a.

Answers will vary. Sample Response: $x - 3 \geq 1, 12x \geq 48, -2x \leq -8$

b.

Answers will vary. Sample Response: $x + 5 < 4, 7x < -7, \frac{x}{2} < -\frac{1}{2}$

36. Riley's Factory produces energy bars for a sports company. The weight of each bar must be within a certain number of ounces or it is rejected. The graph below shows the range for the weights that are acceptable.

a. Make a graph that represents the weights that are rejected.

b. Complete the sentence: If a bar weighs ___?___ or ___?___ it is rejected. **less than 5.8 ounces; more than 6.2 ounces**

37. Challenge G-forces make a roller coaster thrilling, but extreme G-forces can make a rider pass out. A roller coaster designer can use the following inequality to keep the G-forces less than 3.5 G, a safe level according to one designer.

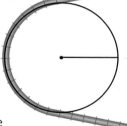

$$3.5\ G > \frac{[\text{speed of the car (in ft/sec)}]^2}{32.2 \times \text{radius of the curve (in feet)}}$$

The amount of G-force you feel depends on the car's speed and the curve of the track, which can be thought of as part of the circle.

a. If the speed of the car is 35 mi/hr, what is the minimum radius of the curve? Round to the nearest tenth. (*Hint:* 1 mi = 5280 ft)
23.4 ft

b. If the radius of the curve is 10 ft, what is the maximum speed in miles per hour? Round to the nearest tenth.
22.9 mi/hr

c. Do you think it is reasonable to design a roller coaster to go around a curve at 100 mi/hr? Explain. **Sample Response: No; The radius must be at least 191 ft.**

Reflecting on the Section

Write your response to Exercise 38 in your journal.

38. You can solve the inequality $\frac{x}{-2} < 5$ by multiplying both sides by −2.

$$\frac{x}{-2} < 5$$

$$-2 \cdot \frac{x}{-2} > -2 \cdot 5$$

$$x > -10$$

Explain why multiplying by x to solve the inequality $\frac{2}{x} < 5$ might lead to an error. **Assuming that x is not 0, x can be either positive or negative; When multiplying each side of the inequality by x to undo the fraction, you don't know whether to reverse the inequality or not.**

Journal

Exercise 38 checks that you understand how to solve inequalities.

Spiral Review

Use the diagram to find each angle measure. (Module 6, p. 438)

39. $m\angle 3$ 105°

40. $m\angle 5$ 105°

41. $m\angle 7$ 105°

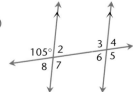

Solve each proportion. (Module 2, p. 132)

42. $\frac{x}{100} = \frac{3}{5}$ 60   **43.** $\frac{9}{h} = \frac{2}{3}$ 13.5   **44.** $\frac{1}{2} = \frac{x}{4.5}$ 2.25

Extra Skill Practice

TEACHER NOTES
For each Exploration, the corresponding Extra Skill Practice Exercises are noted.

Exploration 1: Exs. 1–4
Exploration 2: Exs. 5–16
Exploration 3: Exs. 17–31

EXTRA HELP
Teacher's Resource Book
• Practice and Applications
• Study Guide

Technology Resources
• @Home Tutor
• Test Generator

ASSESSMENT
• Section 3 Quick Quiz
• Test Generator

5. $x \le -2$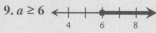

6. $x < 5$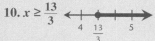

7. $a > \frac{1}{8}$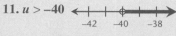

8. $c > -15$

9. $a \ge 6$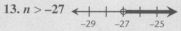

10. $x \ge \frac{13}{3}$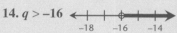

11. $u > -40$

12. $m \le 45$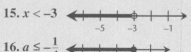

13. $n > -27$

14. $q > -16$

15. $x < -3$

16. $a \le -\frac{1}{4}$

Section ③
Extra Skill Practice

Write an inequality to describe each situation. Then graph each inequality on a number line.

1. The woman was at least 20 years old, but not yet 25. $20 \le w < 25$

2. The number of fish in the tank is always less than 10. $f < 10$

3. The price is $10 or more. $p \ge 10$

4. The number is greater than or equal to 2 and less than 7. $2 \le n < 7$

Solve each inequality. Check and graph each solution. 5–16. See margin.

5. $x + 4 \le 2$ 6. $-2 + x < 3$ 7. $16a > 2$ 8. $60 > -4c$

9. $a - 2 \ge 4$ 10. $x - \frac{4}{3} \ge 3$ 11. $-0.2u < 8$ 12. $15 \ge \frac{m}{3}$

13. $\frac{n}{-3} < 9$ 14. $-\frac{3}{4}q < 12$ 15. $\frac{x}{5} < -\frac{3}{5}$ 16. $\frac{3}{2} \le -6a$

Write and solve an inequality for each situation.

17. Five more than a number is greater than two. $5 + n > 2; n > -3$

18. Three minus twice a number is less than eight. $3 - 2n < 8; n > -2.5$

19. You will spend at least $10 if you buy a melon for $2.88 and 4 lb of grapes. What do grapes cost per pound? $2.88 + 4g \ge 10; g \ge 1.78$; at least $1.78

Solve each inequality. Check and graph each solution.

20. $3x - 5 \le 6$ $x \le \frac{11}{3}$ 21. $-4w - 18 \ge 2$ $w \le -5$ 22. $2 > 6 + 7c$ $c < -\frac{4}{7}$

23. $-36x + 15 < 24$ $x > -0.25$ 24. $14 \le -112a - 42$ $a \le -0.5$ 25. $4.5x + 0.8 > 3.5$ $x > 0.6$

26. $4.5 - 0.25x \ge 3.25$ $x \le 5$ 27. $7.8 - 2.3n < 3.2$ $n > 2$ 28. $\frac{a}{-2} + 7 < 8$ $a > -2$

29. $\frac{x}{3} - 1 < \frac{3}{4}$ $x < \frac{21}{4}$ 30. $\frac{7}{5} + \frac{y}{10} \le -\frac{2}{5}$ $y \le -18$ 31. $12 - \frac{1}{2}m \ge 3\frac{1}{4}$ $m \le 17\frac{1}{2}$

Standardized Testing ◀▶ Free Response

1. The edges of the base of a square pyramid are each 14 in. long. For what values of the height h will the volume of the pyramid be less than 5880 in.^{3}? less than 90 in.

2. A camera shop charges $12 to develop a roll of film plus $0.45 for each extra print. How many extra prints can Stephanie get if she has $20 to spend for photographs? 17 or fewer prints

Section 4 Polynomials and Factoring

IN THIS SECTION

EXPLORATION 1
◆ Multiplying Binomials

EXPLORATION 2
◆ Factoring Quadratics

The Art of Quadratics

Setting the Stage

Leonardo da Vinci, born on April 15, 1452, was a man of many talents. He was a famous artist, musician, mathematician, scientist, philosopher, writer, architect, sculptor, and inventor.

Da Vinci, like many other painters past and present, often used geometric shapes, ratios, and patterns in his paintings. *The Mona Lisa*, painted by Leonardo more than 450 years ago, is one of the world's most famous paintings.

◀ Leonardo da Vinci's painting entitled *The Mona Lisa*

Think About It

▶ **The width of the painting is 53 cm and the height is 77 cm. Suppose a frame of width *x* centimeters is placed around the painting as shown.**

▲ This chalk drawing is believed to be a self-portrait of Leonardo da Vinci in his later years of life.

1 Write an expression for the width of the painting when the frame is included. $53 + x + x$ or $53 + 2x$

2 Write an expression for the height of the painting when the frame is included. $77 + x + x$ or $77 + 2x$

3 **a.** What is the area of the painting without the frame? $4{,}081 \text{ cm}^2$

b. How might you express the area of the painting including the frame? $(53 + 2x)(77 + 2x)$ or $(77 + 2x)(53 + 2x)$

Setting the Stage

GETTING STARTED
In this section, students will use algebra tiles to multiply binomials and use their models to develop methods for multiplying without the tiles. It is essential that students be able to simplify the algebraic expressions presented in Module 7 Section 4 *Warm-Up*.

ABOUT THE THEME
Many students are familiar with Leonardo da Vinci's famous painting *The Mona Lisa*, but they may be surprised to find him in a lesson on mathematics. Leonardo used many math concepts to create his artwork and inventions. In this section students will use a different medium (algebra tiles) to model multiplication of binomials and factoring of quadratics. Leonardo's *The Mona Lisa* and catapult invention will set the stage for the explorations.

GOAL

LEARN HOW TO...
- multiply binomials

AS YOU...
- work with algebra tiles and find areas of various rectangles

KEY TERMS
- polynomial
- monomial
- term
- binomial
- trinomial

Exploration 1

Multiplying Binomials

SET UP   *Work with a partner. You will need:* • *Labsheet 4A*
  • *algebra tiles*

▶ In the *Setting the Stage*, you wrote *polynomial* expressions for the height and the width of the framed *Mona Lisa* painting. A **polynomial** is a *monomial* or a sum of monomials. The table shows some different types of polynomials.

	Examples
A **monomial** is a number or a variable or a product of a number and one or more variables. (Each monomial is a **term**.)	2 $3x^2$ $-st$
A **binomial** is a polynomial with exactly two terms.	$4x + 3$ $3t^2 + 2s$
A **trinomial** is a polynomial with exactly three terms.	$3x^2 + 2x + 1$ $25n + 4 - 17t$

4 a. Which type of polynomial did you use to represent the width of the painting, including the frame, in the *Setting the Stage*?
   binomial (when simplified)
b. Does the expression you wrote for the area of the framed painting have the form of a polynomial? Explain. No, it is not a sum, but a product of binomials.

▶ Algebra tiles can be used to model polynomials. When using algebra tiles, a negative or positive term can be identified by the color of the tile or by a negative or positive sign on the tile.

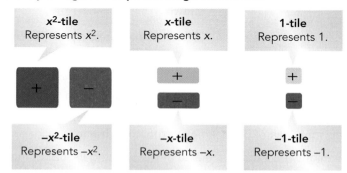

x^2-tile Represents x^2.	x-tile Represents x.	1-tile Represents 1.
$-x^2$-tile Represents $-x^2$.	$-x$-tile Represents $-x$.	-1-tile Represents -1.

6. a. Sample Response:

b. No, you could use
   a combination
   of positive and
   negative tiles to
   make each term.
   For example,
   $2x$ could be:

EXAMPLE

Write the polynomial represented by the group of algebra tiles.

Two x^2-tiles ⟶ $2x^2$

Two $-x$-tiles ⟶ $-2x$

One x-tile ⟶ x

One 1-tile ⟶ 1

The polynomial is:

$2x^2 + (-2x) + x + 1 = 2x^2 + (-x) + 1$

$= 2x^2 - x + 1$

5 Discussion Name the polynomial represented by each group of algebra tiles. Tell whether each polynomial is a *monomial, binomial,* or *trinomial*.

a.

$2x^2 + 3x + 1$; trinomial

b.

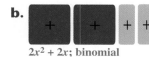

$2x^2 + 2x$; binomial

c.

$4x^2$; monomial

d.

$x^2 - 3x - 2$; trinomial

e.

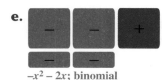

$-x^2 - 2x$; binomial

f.

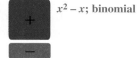

$x^2 - x$; binomial

6 a. Use algebra tiles to model the polynomial $x^2 + 2x + 3$.

b. Is there only one way to model $x^2 + 2x + 3$? Explain.

▶ The expression $(2x + 77)(2x + 53)$ represents the area of the framed *Mona Lisa* painting. Can $(2x + 77)(2x + 53)$ be expressed as a polynomial? If so, will it be a monomial, binomial, or trinomial? To answer these questions, let's first look at a simpler example.

TEACHING NOTES

In **Discussion Question 5**, students are expected to state the polynomial in simplest form as shown in the Example. In **part (e)** some students may prefer to list all the tiles present and then simplify the expression by combining like terms $(-2x^2 + x^2 + (-2) = -x^2 - 2x)$. Other students may visually group together tiles to form zero pairs before stating the polynomial that the model represents (one negative x^2-tile and one x^2-tile make zero, leaving $-x^2 + (-2x)$ or $-x^2 - 2$.

Exploration 1 *continued*

USING MANIPULATIVES

In **Question 7**, make sure students actually read and follow each step to create the model shown. As they work, ask them questions like "What part of your model represents the product rectangle?", "What part represents the binomial $x + 2$?", "Why are there only 2 one-tiles in the product?", "When do x-tiles appear in the product?", etc. to check students' understanding of the model.

DEVELOPING MATH CONCEPTS

Question 8 leads students to see that multiplication of binomials is commutative. Therefore, in setting up their models they may arrange the first binomial either horizontally or vertically. Note, however, that the terms of the binomials cannot be interchanged. To make this point you may want to use tiles to show that $(x + 2)(2x + 1)$ does not produce the same product rectangle as $(x + 1)(2x + 2)$.

TEACHING NOTES

If students need more guidance modelling products of binomials, discuss the following example before they begin **Question 9**.

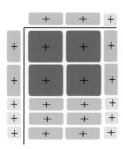
---

8. a.

Represents $x + 2$.

7 Complete each of the steps below to model the product $(x + 2)(2x + 1)$. **Check students' work.**

Step 1 Model each binomial with algebra tiles. Arrange the first binomial vertically and the second binomial horizontally as shown.

Step 2 The binomials define a rectangular region with width $(2x + 1)$ and height $(x + 2)$. Fill in the region with the appropriate tiles to form the *product rectangle*.

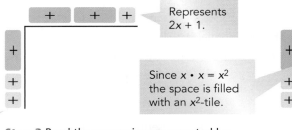

Represents $2x + 1$.

Since $x \cdot x = x^2$ the space is filled with an x^2-tile.

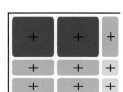

Step 3 Read the expression represented by the product rectangle, combining like terms if necessary. This model represents the expression $2x^2 + 5x + 2$. This is the product of the two binomials.

▶ The expression in Step 3 is written in *descending order of exponents*. The exponents of the variable decrease from left to right.

$$2x^2 + 5x + 2$$

x^2, then x^1, then x^0. (Think of 2 as $2x^0$ because $x^0 = 1$).

You should write polynomials in descending order of exponents.

8 **a.** Now rearrange the horizontal and the vertical binomials from Question 7 so the second binomial is vertical and the first binomial is horizontal and follow Steps 1–3 again.

b. Compare your answer to the one in Question 7. What does this tell you about multiplication of binomials? **It's commutative. The order does not affect the product.**

9 ✔ **CHECKPOINT** Use algebra tiles to find the product of the binomials.

a. $(x + 2)(x + 1)$
$x^2 + 3x + 2$

b. $(x + 3)(x + 4)$
$x^2 + 7x + 12$

c. $(x + 3)(2x + 5)$
$2x^2 + 11x + 15$

▶ You can use algebra tiles to multiply binomials where the terms are joined by subtraction. First rewrite all expressions involving subtraction as equivalent expressions involving addition. Then model the binomials with algebra tiles, using the red tiles to represent negative terms.

10 How would you write $(x + 2)(2x - 1)$ without subtraction signs?
Rewrite minus 1 as plus negative 1: $(x + 2)[2x + (-1)]$

11 Use Labsheet 4A. Follow the directions for *Multiplying Binomials* to find the product $(x + 2)(2x - 1)$. **See margin.**

12 Try This As a Class

a. Use algebra tiles to model $(x - 2)(x - 3)$.

b. In which situations does a negative tile appear in the product? **When multiplying a positive and a negative**

c. In which situations does a positive tile appear in the product? **When multiplying two positives or two negatives**

13 ✔ **CHECKPOINT** Use algebra tiles to find the product of the binomials. Combine like terms.

a. $(x - 2)(x - 1)$
$x^2 - 3x + 2$

b. $(2x - 1)(x + 3)$
$2x^2 + 5x - 3$

▶ The example below shows how you can multiply binomials using algebra tiles and a table.

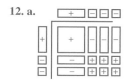
12. a.

✔ **QUESTION 13**

...checks that you can use algebra tiles to multiply binomials containing subtraction signs.

EXAMPLE

Multiply $(x - 2)(2x + 3)$.

Using Algebra Tiles

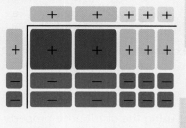

Using a Table

Write one of the binomials above the table.

	2x	+	3
x	$2x^2$		$3x$
+			
-2	$-4x$		-6

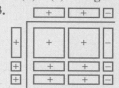
$x \cdot 3 = 3x$

Write the other binomial on the left side of the table.

The product is:
$2x^2 + 3x + (-4x) - 6 = 2x^2 + (-x) - 6$
$= 2x^2 - x - 6$

14 Discussion

a. Explain how the table was used to find the product. Compare this model to the algebra tile model. **See margin.**

b. Did you have to rewrite the product in descending order of exponents? Explain. **No; the term with the greatest exponent, x^2, is listed first, followed by x^1, followed by x^0.**

TEACHING NOTES
The following example can be used after **Discussion Question 14** to illustrate the use of a table for finding the product of two binomials.

CLASSROOM EXAMPLE

Use a table to multiply $(3x - 5)(2x - 4)$.

Answer: $6x^2 - 22x + 20$

	3x	+	(-5)
2x	$6x^2$		$-10x$
+			
-4	$-12x$		20

11. Answers for questions on Labsheet 4A:
1. $(x + 2)[2x + (-1)]$
2. $2x^2 + (-x)$; The last tile is negative because it is the product of the $+x$ tile in the factor on the left of the frame and the -1 tile in the factor above the frame and $(+) \cdot (-)$ is negative.
3.

4. $2x^2 + [4x + (-x)] + (-2) = 2x^2 + 3x - 2$

14. a. See Additional Answers beginning on page A1.

499

Exploration 1 *continued*

TEACHING NOTES

The example below can be used before assigning **Checkpoint Question 18.** Advanced students may not need to write down all the steps that are shown.

CLASSROOM EXAMPLE

Find the product $(x - 3)(3x + 4)$.

Answer: $(x - 3)(3x + 4)$
$= (x - 3)(3x) + (x - 3)(4)$
$= (x + (-3))(3x) + (x + (-3))(4)$
$= x(3x) + (-3)(3x) + x(4) + (-3)(4)$
$= 3x^2 + (-9x) + 4x + (-12)$
$= 3x^2 + (-5x) + (-12)$
$= 3x^2 - 5x - 12$

---

15. a.

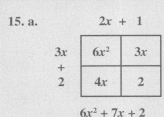

$6x^2 + 7x + 2$

b.

$-x^2 + 16$

c.

$x^2 - 9$

---

15 Find the product of each pair of binomials using a table. Show your work. **a–c. See margin.**

   a. $(3x + 2)(2x + 1)$ **b.** $(x + 4)(-x + 4)$ **c.** $(x + 3)(x - 3)$

16 Use algebra tiles to check your answers in Question 15.
   Check students' work.

17 a. Would it be easier to use algebra tiles or a table to find the product $(2x - 15)(3x + 20)$? Why? **A table; Sample Response: because you would have to arrange $15 \cdot 20 = 300$ tiles in the product rectangle**
   b. Find the product $(2x - 15)(3x + 20)$. Show your work.
   $6x^2 - 5x - 300$

▶ **You can also find a product of binomials by using the distributive property twice.**

FOR ◀ HELP
with *the distributive property,* see
MODULE 6, p. 411

EXAMPLE

Find the product $(10 - 2x)(6 - x)$.

> Rewrite all subtractions as additions.

$(10 - 2x)(6 - x) = (10 + (-2x))(6 + (-x))$

$\qquad = (10 + (-2x))6 + (10 + (-2x))(-x)$ Distributive property

$\qquad = 10(6) + (-2x)(6) + 10(-x) + (-2x)(-x)$ Distributive property

$\qquad = 60 + (-12x) + (-10x) + 2x^2$

$\qquad = 60 + (-22x) + 2x^2$ Combine like terms.

The product, in descending order of exponents, is
$2x^2 + (-22x) + 60$ or $2x^2 - 22x + 60$.

✔ QUESTION 18

...checks that you can use the distributive property to find the product of two binomials.

---

18 ✔ CHECKPOINT Find the product using the distributive property.
   a. $(x + 3)(3x + 2)$ **b.** $(4x - 3)(4x + 3)$ **c.** $(1 - 4x)(3 - 6x)$
   $3x^2 + 11x + 6$ $16x^2 - 9$ $24x^2 - 18x + 3$

19 a. Express the area of the *Mona Lisa* painting including the frame from Question 3(b) as a polynomial. $4x^2 + 260x + 4081$

   b. What type of polynomial is the product? **trinomial**

20 When is the product of two binomials a binomial? a trinomial? Explain. **The product of two binomials $ax + b$ and $cx + d$ is a binomial when $a = c$ and $b = -d$, or when $a = -b$ and $c = d$. Otherwise it is a trinomial.**

█ HOMEWORK EXERCISES ▶ See Exs. 1–25 on pp. 508–509.

Exploration 2

Factoring Quadratics

GOAL

LEARN HOW TO...
- factor quadratics

AS YOU...
- work with algebra tiles

KEY TERM
- factor

SET UP *Work with a partner. You will need algebra tiles.*

Leonardo's artwork includes sketches of various inventions such as a catapult, designed to throw projectiles great distances. The path that a projectile follows can be modeled by a quadratic equation.

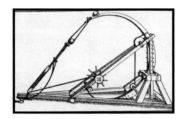

The expression $ax^2 + bx + c$ in the quadratic equation $y = ax^2 + bx + c$ is called a *quadratic polynomial* because the greatest exponent of the variable is 2. In a future course, you will learn that you may be able to solve a quadratic equation by factoring a quadratic polynomial.

▶ **In this exploration you will learn to *factor* quadratic polynomials.**

21 The product $x^2 + 4x + 3$ can be represented by the product rectangle of algebra tiles below.

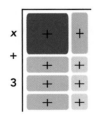

a. The height of the product rectangle is $x + 3$. Explain why.

b. Write the expression for the width of the product rectangle.
   $x + 1$

21. **a.** The vertical edge of the x^2 tile has a length of x and the vertical edges of the x-tiles arranged below the x^2-tile each have a length of 1. Since there are 3 x-tiles, their height is 3.

TEACHING NOTES
After students have read the introduction to Exploration 2 and completed **Question 20**, you may want to show how the factors of $x^2 + 4x + 3$ are related to the graph of the equation $y = x^2 + 4x + 3$. Begin by graphing the equation on a calculator and projecting it for students to see. Then, using a table or the trace key, have students note where the graph crosses the x-axis and compare the results to the factors. (*The x-coordinates are the opposites of the constants in the factors. Mathematically, this occurs because the x-coordinates of the points where the graph crosses the x-axis are the values of x for which y = 0. So, if $x^2 + 4x + 3 = (x + 5)(x - 2) = 0$ then one of these two factors must equal 0. For the first factor to equal 0, x must be –5 and for the second factor to equal 0, x must be 2.*) After factoring each expression in **Questions 22, 23, and 24**, advanced students may enjoy solving the related quadratic equation, predicting what the graph looks like and checking on the calculator. Remind students to build on what they learned about the vertex and axis of symmetry of parabolas in Module 6 *Visualizing Change*.

In this section, all factoring is done with algebra tiles. **Question 25** on page 503 begins developing the number sense ideas related to factoring by asking students to use the factor pairs of the constant to help them construct the product rectangle with their algebra tiles. Advanced students may begin to understand the relationships between the binomial factors and the factors of the constant and may want to try factoring without the tiles and check their results by multiplying or by using the tiles.

TEACHING NOTES

Question 22(b) Check that students apply the distributive property accurately.

In **Question 23**, point out that $(x + 2)(x + 2)$ can be written as $(x + 2)^2$.

---

24. b.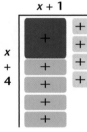
$(x + 1)$ and $(x + 4)$

▶ To **factor** a quadratic polynomial, or simply *quadratic,* you must find the factors whose product is the quadratic. For example, you know that

$$(x + 5)(x - 2) = x^2 + 3x - 10.$$

Then $x + 5$ and $x - 2$ are factors of $x^2 + 3x - 10$.

22 a. Look at your work from Question 21. What are the factors of $x^2 + 4x + 3$? $x + 1$ and $x + 3$

  b. Multiply the binomials in part (a) to check that they are the factors of $x^2 + 4x + 3$. $(x + 1)(x + 3) = x^2 + x + 3x + 3 = x^2 + 4x + 3$

23 Try This As a Class

  a. Use algebra tiles to model $x^2 + 4x + 4$. Check students' models.

  b. One student arranged the tiles used to model $x^2 + 4x + 4$ as shown. How can you tell that the student did *not* find the factors of $x^2 + 4x + 4$? The student did not produce a product rectangle.

  c. Experiment with arranging the algebra tiles until you complete a product rectangle. What are the height and width of your rectangle? Check students' models; $x + 2$ and $x + 2$

  d. What are the factors of $x^2 + 4x + 4$? $x + 2$ and $x + 2$

24 a. Use algebra tiles to model $x^2 + 5x + 4$. Check students' models.

  b. Arrange the tiles into a rectangle to find the factors of $x^2 + 5x + 4$. What are the factors?

  c. Check your answer in part (b) by multiplying the factors.
$(x + 1)(x + 4) = x^2 + 1x + 4x + 4 = x^2 + 5x + 4$

25 Consider your work from Questions 23 and 24.

a. The last term of each quadratic in Questions 23 and 24 is 4. Name all the factor pairs of 4. **1,4; 2, 2**

b. How do the factor pairs of 4 appear in the expressions for the length and width of each product rectangle? **They are the 1 tiles and appear in pairs that make 4, such as 2 and 2 or 1 and 4.**

c. **Discussion** If you were to factor $x^2 + 6x + 8$, what factor pairs do you think might appear in the expressions for the length and width of the product rectangle? Explain. **You could try 1 and 8 or 2 and 4 since 1 · 8 = 8 and 2 · 4 = 8.**

d. Use the factor pairs you found in part (c) and algebra tiles to help you factor $x^2 + 6x + 8$.

26 ✔ **CHECKPOINT** Use algebra tiles to factor each trinomial. Multiply the factors to check your answer.

a. $x^2 + 5x + 6$
$(x + 2)(x + 3)$

b. $x^2 + 7x + 6$
$(x + 6)(x + 1)$

27 **Try This as a Class** Look back at the quadratics you have factored so far. Suppose a quadratic is written in the form $x^2 + bx + c$ where b and c are positive.

a. Explain how you can use c to help find the factors of the quadratic. **The constant terms in the factors of the quadratic will be factors of c, so list the factors of c until you find a pair that works.**

b. Explain how the factors of c are related to b. **The two factors of c have a sum equal to b.**

28 Factor $x^2 + 10x + 9$ into two binomials by using 9's factor pairs. Check your answer by multiplying the binomials or by using algebra tiles. $(x + 9)(x + 1)$

▶ **Algebra tiles can also be used to factor quadratics of the form $x^2 + bx + c$ when either b or c is negative.**

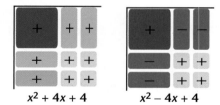

$x^2 + 4x + 4$ $x^2 - 4x + 4$

29 a. Use algebra tiles to represent $x^2 - 6x + 9$. **Check students' models.**

b. Arrange the tiles in a rectangle. What are the factors of $x^2 - 6x + 9$?

▶ **In some cases, tiles must be added to form a product rectangle for a quadratic.**

25. d.

$(x + 4)(x + 2)$

29. b.

$(x - 3)(x - 3)$

✔ **QUESTION 26**

...checks that you can factor a quadratic using algebra tiles.

TEACHING NOTES
Begin the discussion of the **Try This as a Class Question 27** by referring to **Question 26** where, in both cases, $c = 6$ but the values for b are different. Have students look at their answers to **Question 26**. Ask them how the value of b affected the factors of 6 that are used. Then have students find other trinomials that they factored in this exploration and compare the factors of c that were used and the value of b.

TIPS FROM TEACHERS

Model how to factor the expression in the **Example** by using overhead algebra tiles on an overhead projector and explaining your "thinking" out loud as you move tiles around and try different arrangements.

EXAMPLE

Use algebra tiles to factor $x^2 + x - 6$.

SAMPLE RESPONSE

First: Model the quadratic with algebra tiles.

Next: Arrange the tiles to form a rectangle. It helps to start with the x^2-tile in the upper left corner and the 1-tiles in the lower right. Remember that the edges of tiles that are lined up together must have the same edge length.

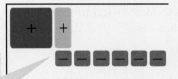

1 • 6 = 6, so try arranging the six –1-tiles in a 1 by 6 rectangle.

2 and 3 are also factors of 6, so try arranging the six –1-tiles in a 2 by 3 rectangle.

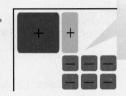

Then: Add the same number of tiles to the height and width so they fill in the spaces and form a rectangle.

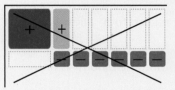

Not possible, because you cannot add the same number of x-tiles to the width as you do to the height when the 1-tiles are arranged in 1 row of 6.

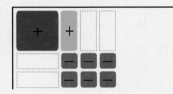

Two x-tiles and two –x-tiles can be added to form a rectangle, so factors of 2 and 3 will work.

---

30. a. to maintain the value of the original expression since $x + (-x) = 0$; You would have a different number of x tiles than the original expression had.

b. below the x^2-tile; If placed to the right of the existing x-tile, then the 1-tiles could not all be negatives.

---

 30 Discussion Refer to the Example above.

  a. Why do you have to add an equal number of x-tiles and –x-tiles? What would happen if you did not add an equal number of each?

  b. Where would you place the two –x-tiles? Why?

  c. How can you check that you have arranged the tiles correctly? Write the factors along the vertical and horizontal edges. Then multiply to check that they make the product rectangle.

  d. What are the factors of $x^2 + x - 6$? $x + 3$ and $x - 2$

31 Rafaela claims her model represents $x^2 + x - 6$. She has completed the rectangle by adding three x-tiles and three $-x$-tiles as shown below.

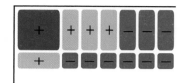

a. What two factors does her model represent? *x and x + 1*

b. Check Rafaela's solution by multiplying the two factors.
$x(x + 1) = x^2 + x$

c. What would you tell Rafaela to help her correctly use algebra tiles to factor polynomials?

32 Refer to the Example on the preceding page.

a. Could you have factored $x^2 + x - 6$ by arranging the 1-tiles in 6 rows of 1? Why or why not?

b. Could you have factored $x^2 + x - 6$ by arranging the 1-tiles in 3 rows of 2? Why or why not? *Yes, multiplication is commutative and 2 rows of 3 worked. 3 + (−2) = 1 and 3 · (−2) = −6*

33 **Try This as a Class** Use algebra tiles to factor $x^2 - 9x + 8$.

34 ✔ **CHECKPOINT** Use algebra tiles to factor each quadratic. Multiply the factors to check your answer.

a. $x^2 + 5x + 6$ **b.** $x^2 + 4x - 5$ **c.** $x^2 - 2x - 3$
  $(x + 2)(x + 3)$ $(x + 5)(x - 1)$ $(x - 3)(x + 1)$

35 Tyrell says that $x^2 - 4x + 5$ cannot be factored. Use what you have learned along with algebra tiles to prove whether or not he is right. *See margin.*

36 From your work with algebra tiles, you have seen that when the quadratic $x^2 + bx + c$ is factored into the product of two binomials $x + m$ and $x + n$, m and n are factors of c and $m + n = b$. What can you say about the signs of m and n in each of the following cases? Give examples to support your answers.

a. $b > 0$ and $c > 0$ *m and n are both positive.*

b. $b < 0$ and $c > 0$ *m and n are both negative.*

c. $c < 0$ ($b > 0$ or $b < 0$) *One of the two numbers must be negative and one positive.*

HOMEWORK EXERCISES ▶ See Exs. 26–47 on pp. 509–510.

---

31. c. Sample Response: Since the factors of 1 and 6 did not work, try 2 and 3. Always check your work by multiplying the factors and comparing the result to the product rectangle.

32. a. No, because you cannot add the same number of x-tiles to the width and height to complete the product rectangle. No factors of 6 sum to 1.

✔ **QUESTION 34**

...checks that you can factor quadratics using algebra tiles.

33.

$(x - 1)(x - 8)$

DEVELOPING MATH CONCEPTS
After students have completed **Questions 31–34**, refer back to **Question 31(a)** and ask students what Rafaela's product rectangle would look like if you used her two factors of x and $x + 1$. (*The product $x^2 + 1x$ would be 1 x^2-tile and 1 x-tile next to it.*) Ask "Can you factor this type of quadratic?" (*Yes, it factors to $x(x + 1)$. Adding zeros is not necessary.*) Ask how this type of quadratic is different from what they have been factoring. (*In this type of quadratic, there are no ones tiles.*) In this section all of the quadratics that factor use ones tiles and factor into two binomials. To make sure students understand that there are other cases where the factors of a quadratic are not both binomials, you may want to present a few problems like the following for them to try: $x^2 + 7x = x(x + 7)$; $2x^2 - 6x = 2x(x - 3)$

TEACHING NOTES
Question 32 Show students how to use tables to keep track of which arrangements of tiles they have tried. Encourage them to use this structure or some other form of organization when working **Questions 33–35**.

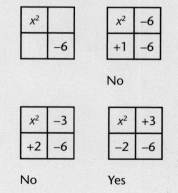

No

No   Yes

35. See Additional Answers beginning on page A1.

Key Concepts

CLOSURE QUESTION

Explain how to determine if the product of two binomials is a monomial, binomial, or trinomial.

Sample Response: First multiply the two binomials and simplify the product (combine any like terms). If there is only one term remaining, it is a monomial; two terms, a binomial; three terms, a trinomial. There could possibly be four terms and this would just be called a polynomial.

ABSENT STUDENTS

For students who were absent for all or part of this section, the blackline Study Guide for Section 4 may be used to present the ideas, concepts, and skills of Section 4.

Key Terms

monomial
term

polynomial
binomial
trinomial

Multiplying Binomials (pp. 496–500)

A monomial is a number or a variable or a product of a number and one or more variables. Each monomial is called a term.

A polynomial is a monomial or a sum of monomials. A binomial is a polynomial with exactly two terms. A trinomial is a polynomial with exactly three terms.

The product of two binomials can be found by using algebra tiles, a table, or the distributive property.

Example Multiply $(x + 2)(x - 3)$.

Represent each binomial with tiles, one as the height and one as the width. Then complete the product rectangle.

Using Algebra Tiles

Write one of the binomials on the left side of the table.

Using a Table

Write the other binomial above the table.

	x	+	2
x	x^2		2x
+			
−3	−3x		−6

$x^2 + (-3x) + 2x - 6 = x^2 - x - 6$

Using the Distributive Property

$$(x + 2)(x - 3) = (x + 2)(x + (-3))$$
$$= (x + 2)x + (x + 2)(-3)$$
$$= x^2 + 2x + (-3x) + (-6)$$
$$= x^2 + (-x) + (-6)$$
$$= x^2 - x - 6$$

The product $(x + 2)(x - 3)$ is equal to $x^2 - x - 6$.

x^2, $-x$, and -6 are each monomials, and $x^2 - x - 6$ is a trinomial.

37 Key Concepts Question

a. Multiply $(x - 5)(x - 4)$. $x^2 - 9x + 20$

b. Is the product in part (a) a monomial, binomial, or trinomial?
trinomial

Section 4

Key Concepts ►►►►►►►►►►►►►►►►►►►►►►►

Key Term

Factoring Quadratics (pp. 501–505)

To factor a quadratic, you need to find the factors whose product is the quadratic. In the example on page 506, $x - 3$ and $x + 2$ are the factors of the quadratic $x^2 - x - 6$. The factors of a quadratic can be found by using algebra tiles.

factor

Example Factor $x^2 - 9$.

Model $x^2 - 9$ with tiles. Arrange the x^2-tiles and the 1-tiles in opposite corners of the rectangle, so that you will be able to make a product rectangle.

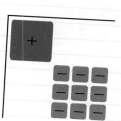

Add three x-tiles and three −x-tiles to complete the product rectangle.

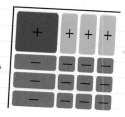

Adding an equal number of x-tiles and −x-tiles does not affect the product.

Then read the height and width of the product rectangle.
So, $x^2 - 9 = (x - 3)(x + 3)$.

38 Key Concepts Question

a. In the Example above the nine 1-tiles were arranged in 3 rows of 3. What other possible arrangement might have been tried if this arrangement had not worked? **1 row of 9 or 9 rows of 1**

b. Use the distributive property to show that the product $(x - 3)(x + 3)$ is equal to $x^2 - 9$.

c. Factor $x^2 - 16$. **$(x + 4)(x - 4)$**

38. b. $(x - 3)(x + 3)$ $\begin{aligned} &= (x - 3)x + (x - 3)^3 \\ &= x^2 - 3x + 3x - 9 \\ &= x^2 - 9 \end{aligned}$

$x^2 - 4$ and $x^2 - 4x$ are both binomials that can be factored. How are the product rectangles for these expressions different and how do their factors compare?

Sample Response: Both quadratics can be modeled using the same number of tiles. $x^2 - 4$ uses 1 x^2-tile and 4 one-tiles. $x^2 - 4x$ uses 1 x^2-tile and 4 x-tiles. To complete the product rectangle for $x^2 - 4$ you have to add zero in the form of 2 x-tiles and 2 negative x-tiles. This produces two binomial factors $(x - 2)$ and $(x + 2)$. The product rectangle for $x^2 - 4x$ is complete and produces two factors, the monomial factor x and the binomial factor $(x - 4)$.

Practice & Applications

ABOUT THE MATERIALS

Students will need algebra tiles for completing most of the practice and application exercises. If commercial algebra tiles are not available, a blackline master that can be copied and cut out to create sets of tiles is included in the *Activity Generator*. Pattern blocks or two-colored chips may also be used.

SUGGESTED ASSIGNMENTS

Core & Extended Courses

Day 1: Exs. 1–12
Day 2: Exs. 13–25
Day 3: Exs. 26–35
Day 4: Exs. 36–51

Note: Extended Course assignments can be used to differentiate within the regular classroom. In classrooms where students are grouped homogeneously, the material might be covered in fewer days. In this case assignments may be combined.

ADDITIONAL PRACTICE

See the *Teacher's Resource Book* for additional practice and application exercises for this section.

YOU WILL NEED

◆ algebra tiles

4. $4x^2 - 2x$
   binomial

Section ④

Practice & Application Exercises

Use algebra tiles to find the product of the binomials.

1. $(x + 1)(x + 2)$
   $x^2 + 3x + 2$

2. $(x + 4)(x + 4)$
   $x^2 + 8x + 16$

3. $(x + 2)(2x + 1)$
   $2x^2 + 5x + 2$

Name the polynomial represented by each group of tiles and tell whether it is a monomial, binomial, or trinomial.

4.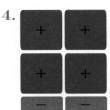

5.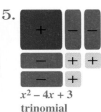
   $x^2 - 4x + 3$
   trinomial

6.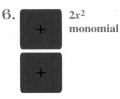
   $2x^2$
   monomial

Use algebra tiles to find the product of the binomials. Combine like terms.

7. $(x - 2)(x + 3)$ $x^2 + x - 6$

8. $(x + 2)(x - 1)$ $x^2 + x - 2$

9. $(x - 2)(x + 1)$ $x^2 - x - 2$

10. $(x + 4)(x - 4)$ $x^2 - 16$

11. $(x - 1)(x + 1)$ $x^2 - 1$

12. $(x + 3)(x - 4)$ $x^2 - x - 12$

Use a table to find the product of the binomials. Show your work.

13. $(x + 3)(x + 2)$ $x^2 + 5x + 6$

14. $(2x - 3)(x - 3)$ $2x^2 - 9x + 9$

15. $(-x - 3)(x + 3)$ $-x^2 - 6x - 9$

16. $(5x - 4)(-x + 6)$ $-5x^2 + 34x - 24$

17. $(2 - x)(4 - 2x)$ $2x^2 - 8x + 8$

18. $(-x - 5)(-x - 12)$ $x^2 + 17x + 60$

Use the distributive property to find the product of the binomials.

19. $(x + 5)(x + 8)$ $x^2 + 13x + 40$

20. $(x + 9)(x + 9)$ $x^2 + 18x + 81$

21. $(x + 12)(2x + 3)$ $2x^2 + 27x + 36$

22. $(9 + 5x)(4 - x)$ $-5x^2 + 11x + 36$

23. $(3 - 7x)(4 - 3x)$ $21x^2 - 37x + 12$

24. $(-x + 1)(6x - 23)$ $-6x^2 + 29x - 23$

25. A poster of Leonardo da Vinci's sketch of a woman is about one and a half times as high as it is wide. The sketch is to be placed in a 4 in. wide frame.

3x

2x

Not actual size

a. How many inches will the frame add to the poster's height? to its width? **8 in.; 8 in.**

b. Write the binomial that represents the height of the poster with the frame.
(3x + 8) in.

c. Write the binomial that represents the width of the poster with the frame.
(2x + 8) in.

d. What polynomial expression represents the total area of the poster and the frame? **6x² + 40x + 64 in.²**

Find the binomials whose product is represented by each product rectangle. Multiply the two binomials to check your answer.

26.

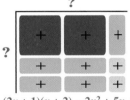

$(2x + 1)(x + 2) = 2x^2 + 5x + 2$

27.

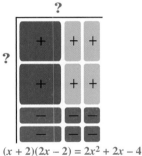

$(x + 2)(2x - 2) = 2x^2 + 2x - 4$

28.

$(x + 1)(x - 1) = x^2 - 1$

29.

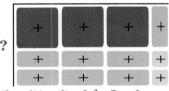

$(3x + 1)(x + 2) = 3x^2 + 7x + 2$

Use algebra tiles to factor each quadratic. Multiply the factors to check your answer.

30. $x^2 + 2x + 1$
$(x + 1)(x + 1)$

31. $x^2 + 5x + 6$
$(x + 2)(x + 3)$

32. $x^2 + 6x + 5$
$(x + 5)(x + 1)$

33. $x^2 + 4x + 3$
$(x + 3)(x + 1)$

34. $x^2 + 3x + 2$
$(x + 2)(x + 1)$

35. $x^2 + 8x + 7$
$(x + 7)(x + 1)$

Practice & Applications

EXERCISE NOTES

Exercises 40–45 Remind students that when adding zeros, they must add the same number of tiles to the width as they do to the height of the product rectangle. Just because tiles "fit" in the empty space does not mean their factors will make the correct product. Students should always check by multiplying the factors and comparing the products to the parts of the product rectangle.

37. Not possible; The only factors of 5 are 1 and 5 and this does not produce the correct product rectangle.

48. B and D are polygons. B appears to be regular because all 4 sides appear to be the same length and all 4 angles appear to have the same measure (90°).

49. $n \geq 8$

50. $y > -5$

51. $x \leq -2$

Journal

Exercise 47 checks that you understand how to use algebra tiles to represent a polynomial and its factors.

If possible, use algebra tiles to complete the product rectangle, and find the factors of the quadratic. Multiply the factors to check your answer. If the trinomial cannot be factored explain why.

36. $2x^2 - x - 3$ $(2x - 3)(x + 1)$

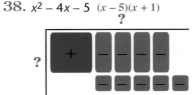

37. $x^2 + x - 5$

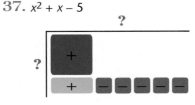

38. $x^2 - 4x - 5$ $(x - 5)(x + 1)$

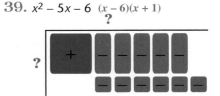

39. $x^2 - 5x - 6$ $(x - 6)(x + 1)$

Use algebra tiles to factor each quadratic. Multiply the factors to check your answers.

40. $x^2 + 3x - 4$
$(x + 4)(x - 1)$

41. $x^2 - 2x + 1$
$(x - 1)(x - 1)$

42. $x^2 - x - 6$
$(x - 3)(x + 2)$

43. $x^2 - 8x + 7$
$(x - 7)(x - 1)$

44. $x^2 - 5x + 4$
$(x - 4)(x - 1)$

45. $x^2 - 4$
$(x + 2)(x - 2)$

46. Use factor pairs of 10 to factor $x^2 + 7x + 10$ into two binomials. Check your answer by multiplying the binomials. $(x + 2)(x + 5)$

Reflecting ▶on the Section

Write your response to Exercise 47 in your journal.

47. Sketch algebra tiles arranged in a product rectangle. Explain the relationship between the polynomial that the product rectangle represents and the length and width of the product rectangle. Check student responses.

Spiral ◀▶Review

48. Which of these figures are polygons? Which appears to be a regular polygon? Explain your thinking. (Toolbox, p. 594)

A. B. C. D.

Solve each inequality. Check and graph each solution. (Module 7, p. 489)

49. $n - 3 \geq 5$

50. $55 > -11y$

51. $\frac{x}{2} - 6 \leq -7$

Section 4
Extra Skill Practice

You will need: • algebra tiles (Exs. 2–4 and 11–16)

1. Write the polynomial represented by the group of algebra tiles. Tell whether each polynomial is a monomial, binomial, or trinomial.

a. 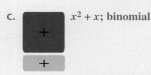 $x^2 - 2x + 1$; trinomial

b. 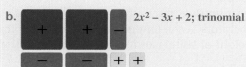 $2x^2 - 3x + 2$; trinomial

c. 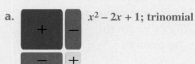 $x^2 + x$; binomial

d. 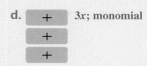 $3x$; monomial

Use algebra tiles to find the product of the binomials.

2. $(x + 3)(x + 1)$ $x^2 + 4x + 3$ 3. $(2x - 3)(x + 1)$ $2x^2 - x - 3$ 4. $(x - 3)(x - 2)$ $x^2 - 5x + 6$

Use a table to find the product of the binomials. Show your work.

5. $(-2x + 5)(x - 7)$
   $-2x^2 + 19x - 35$

6. $(x + 7)(x - 7)$
   $x^2 - 49$

7. $(3x + 5)(2x + 5)$
   $6x^2 + 25x + 25$

Use the distributive property to find the product of the binomials.

8. $(4x - 1)(3x + 2)$
   $12x^2 + 5x - 2$

9. $(1 - 6x)(3 + 9x)$
   $-54x^2 - 9x + 3$

10. $(3x + 2)(5x - 2)$
    $15x^2 + 24x - 12$

Use algebra tiles to factor the quadratic. Multiply the factors to check your answer.

11. $x^2 + 4x + 3$ $(x + 3)(x + 1)$ 12. $x^2 - x - 6$ $(x - 3)(x + 2)$ 13. $x^2 - 4$ $(x + 2)(x - 2)$

14. $x^2 + 6x + 5$ $(x + 1)(x + 1)$ 15. $x^2 - 3x + 2$ $(x - 2)(x - 1)$ 16. $x^2 - 2x - 3$ $(x - 3)(x + 1)$

Standardized Testing ◀▶ Open-ended

1. Find two trinomials that have $x + 3$ as a factor. Answers will vary. Sample Response: $x^2 + 6x + 9$; $2x^2 + 5x - 3$

2. Give a binomial that can be factored into two binomials. Answers will vary. Sample Response: $x^2 - 4 = (x - 2)(x + 2)$; $x^2 - 1 = (x + 1)(x - 1)$

Extra Skill Practice

TEACHER NOTES
For each Exploration, the corresponding Extra Skill Practice Exercises are noted.

Exploration 1: Exs. 1–10
Exploration 2: Exs. 11–16

EXTRA HELP
Teacher's Resource Book
• Practice and Applications for Section 4
• Study Guide
• Practice and Applications for Sections 1–4

Technology Resources
• @Home Tutor
• Test Generator

ASSESSMENT
• Section 4 Quick Quiz
• Test Generator

Module Project

Math and Careers

People who use mathematics in their occupations may be found in the most unusual places. Did you know that, to ensure load safety, elevator operators at the Empire State Building in New York City estimate the weight of visitors and their equipment as they enter the elevator?

In this project you will interview an individual who uses mathematics in his or her occupation and then present your findings to the class.
Answers to all questions will vary. Check students' work.

Getting Started

1 Choose a person and ask if he or she is willing to be interviewed.

2 Write 5 to 10 questions you would like answered.

- ◆ Questions should ask for specific information.

- ◆ Ask questions that will give background information such as the training and education required to perform the job.

- ◆ Ask questions about exactly how the person uses math in this occupation. In particular, ask whether he or she uses algebra.

3 Set up an appointment to visit with the individual, or conduct an email or phone interview.

Conducting the Interview

4 During the interview take careful notes. Be sure to record specific mathematics applications used by the individual.

5 If possible, obtain pictures of the individual performing his or her job.

PROJECT NOTES

A follow-up thank you note (and if possible a photo of the student with their project) would be appreciated by most interviewees.

Organizing Your Presentation

6 Look at the information you gathered. Which pieces of information are relevant to the presentation? Which pieces best show how mathematics is used in this occupation?

7 Choose one or more visual aids that will create a clear portrait of the work life of your interview subject. You may choose to create a poster, a bulletin board, or a computer slide show presentation, or use any other means to present your information to the class.

8 Think about how you will present your information. Discuss your ideas with a classmate. Based on the feedback from your classmate, make necessary changes to your presentation.

9 Prepare the final draft of your presentation.

Making Your Presentation

10 Share with the class what you learned about the individual you interviewed.

- Speak clearly and loudly enough for everyone to hear you.

- Use voice inflection to make your presentation interesting.

- Show pictures, charts, or other visual aids to draw attention to specific points you want to make.

- Be prepared to answer questions about the person you interviewed and his or her occupation.

Review and Assessment

You will need: • *algebra tiles* (Exs. 37–41)

Write each product or quotient as a single power. (Sec. 1, Explor. 1)

1. $10^8 \cdot 10^3$ 10^{11} 2. $a^4 \cdot a^5$ a^9 3. $\dfrac{2^{10}}{2^3}$ 2^7 4. $\dfrac{b^{23}}{b^{19}}$ b^4

Write each power as a whole number or fraction without exponents. (Sec. 1, Explor. 2)

5. 4^0 1   6. 11^{-2} $\frac{1}{121}$ 7. 3^{-3} $\frac{1}{27}$ 8. 2^{-6} $\frac{1}{64}$

Write each number in decimal notation. (Sec. 1, Explor. 2)

9. $5 \cdot 10^{-2}$ 0.05   10. $8.03 \cdot 10^{-4}$ 0.000803   11. $1.266 \cdot 10^{-7}$ 0.0000001266

12. Rock fragments ejected through the air or water from a volcano are called *tephra*. Geologists classify tephra by size according to a measurement called the *intermediate axis*. The classes of tephra according to the intermediate axis *a* are given in the table. Rewrite each inequality in the table so that the numbers in the inequality are expressed in scientific notation. (Sec. 1, Explor. 2) ash: $a < 2 \cdot 10^{-3}$; lapilli: $2 \cdot 10^{-3} \le a \le 6.4 \cdot 10^{-2}$; bombs: $a \ge 6.4 \cdot 10^{-2}$

Types of Tephra	
Name	**intermediate axis *a* (meters)**
ash	$a < 0.002$
lapilli	$0.002 \le a \le 0.064$
bombs	$a \ge 0.064$

Tell whether each number is *rational* or *irrational*. (Sec. 2, Explor. 1)

13. $\sqrt{75}$ irrational   14. $\sqrt{36}$ rational   15. $\sqrt{\dfrac{25}{9}}$ rational   16. $-0.\overline{12}$ rational

17. Show how to use the product property of square roots to simplify $\sqrt{108}$. (Sec. 2, Explor. 1) Sample Response: $\sqrt{108} = \sqrt{36 \cdot 3} = \sqrt{36} \cdot \sqrt{3} = 6\sqrt{3}$

Simplify each expression. Assume all variables represent positive numbers. (Sec. 2, Explor. 2)

18. $\sqrt{96}$ $4\sqrt{6}$ 19. $\sqrt{\dfrac{13}{64}}$ $\dfrac{\sqrt{13}}{8}$ 20. $\sqrt{500}$ $10\sqrt{5}$ 21. $\sqrt{\dfrac{17}{100}}$ $\dfrac{\sqrt{17}}{10}$

22. $\sqrt{\dfrac{8}{49}}$ $\dfrac{2\sqrt{2}}{7}$ 23. $\dfrac{5}{\sqrt{6}}$ $\dfrac{5\sqrt{6}}{6}$ 24. $\sqrt[3]{64}$ 4   25. $\sqrt{x^4 y^5}$ $x^2 y^2 \sqrt{y}$

Graph each inequality on a number line. (Sec. 3, Explor. 1)

26. $w > -10$ **27.** $1 < z \le 4$ **28.** $-2 < y \le 0$ **29.** $-3 \le v$

Solve each inequality. Check and graph each solution. (Sec. 3, Explors. 2 and 3)

30. $2a \le 10$ **31.** $-0.4n + 0.2 \le 1.6$ **32.** $\frac{n}{3} < -3$

33. A rectangular community garden is 100 m long by 70 m wide. The community will set aside 50 m² of the garden to plant trees. The rest of the garden space will be split into sections. The area of each section will be at least 20 m². Write and solve an inequality to find the number of sections the garden will contain. (Sec. 3, Explor. 3)
Sample Response: 6950 ≥ 20s; s ≤ 347.5; At most, the garden can contain 347 sections.

Use the distributive property to find the product of the binomials.
(Sec. 4, Explor. 1)

34. $(x + 4)(2x + 3)$ **35.** $(5 - x)(3 - 6x)$ **36.** $(10x - 2)(10x + 2)$
$2x^2 + 11x + 12$ $6x^2 - 33x + 15$ $100x^2 - 4$

Find the binomials whose product is represented by each product rectangle. Multiply the two binomials to check your answer.
(Sec. 4, Explor. 2)

37.
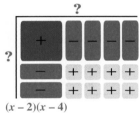
$(x - 2)(x - 4)$

38.
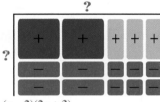
$(x - 2)(2x + 3)$

Use algebra tiles to factor each quadratic. Multiply the factors to check your answer. (Sec. 4, Explor. 2)

39. $x^2 + 5x + 4$ $(x + 1)(x + 4)$ **40.** $x^2 - 5x + 4$ $(x - 1)(x - 4)$ **41.** $x^2 - 3x - 4$ $(x + 1)(x - 4)$

Reflecting ◀▶ on the Module

42. According to the U.S. Department of Labor, math skills are one of the top ten skills employers would like their employees to have. Explain how some of the algebra skills learned in this module might be used at work. Describe a specific situation and give an example.
Answers will vary. Check students' work.

26.

27.

28.

29.

30. $a \le 5$

31. $n \ge -3.5$

32. $n < -9$

Module 7   Review and Assessment   **515**

Assessment Options

TEACHER'S RESOURCE BOOK
• Module 7 Tests A and B
• Module 7 Standardized Test
• Module 7 Performance Assessment

TEST GENERATOR

MATH-Thematical Mix

Module 8 Overview

Mathematics concepts are interwoven among the themes explored in previous modules. Students distinguish between sequences, find the measures of interior angles of polygons, explore rotational symmetry, classify quadrilaterals, explore geometric probabilities, and apply tangent, sine, and cosine ratios to right triangles.

Module 8 Planner

Day 1: Section 1	Day 2: Section 1	Day 3: Section 1	Day 4: Section 1	Day 5: E²
Setting the Stage, p. 518 Exploration 1 *through* Question 7, pp. 519–520	Exploration 1, p. 521	Exploration 2 *through* Question 16, pp. 522–523	Exploration 2 *from* Question 17, p. 524 Key Concepts, p. 525	Work on Extended Exploration, p. 531
Day 6: Section 2	**Day 7: Section 2**	**Day 8: Section 2**	**Day 9: Section 3**	**Day 10: Section 3**
Setting the Stage, p. 532 Exploration 1 *through* Question 6, p. 533	Exploration 1, p. 534	Exploration 2, pp. 535–536 Key Concepts, p. 537	Setting the Stage, p. 542 Exploration 1, pp. 543–546	Exploration 2, pp. 547–548 Key Concepts, pp. 549–550
Day 11: Review and Assessment	**Day 12: Section 4**	**Day 13: Section 4**	**Day 14: Section 5**	**Day 15: Section 5**
Mid-Module Quiz	Setting the Stage, pp. 554–555 Exploration 1 *through* Question 4, pp. 556–557	Exploration 1 *from* Question 5, p. 557 Key Concepts, p. 558	Setting the Stage, pp. 562–563 Exploration 1, pp. 563–566	Exploration 2, pp. 566–567 Key Concepts, p. 568
Day 16: Module Project	**Day 17: Module Project**	**Day 18: Review and Assessment**	**Day 19: Assessment**	
Begin Module Project, pp. 574–575	Finish Module Project, pp. 574–575	Review and Assessment, pp. 576–577	Module 8 Test	

Materials List

Section	Materials
1	• Labsheet 1A, grid paper, ruler, protractor
2	• Labsheets 2A–2C, ruler, scissors, plain white paper, protractor
3	• Labsheets 3A–3B, protractor, scissors, ruler, graph paper
4	• Labsheet 4A, metric ruler, graph paper
5	• Labsheet 5A, calculator, metric ruler, scissors, protractor, encyclopedia, drinking straw, string, weight (such as a washer), tape
Project	• graph paper, calculator

Module 8 Objectives

Section	Objectives	NCTM Standards 2000*
1	• Identify arithmetic and geometric sequences. • Write an equation for any term in a sequence. • Analyze sequences.	1, 2, 6, 7, 8, 9, 10
2	• Find the sum of the measures of interior angles of a polygon. • Describe rotational symmetry.	1, 2, 3, 4, 6, 7, 8, 9, 10
3	• Classify quadrilaterals. • Find the distance between points on a coordinate grid. • Find the midpoint of a segment on a coordinate grid.	3, 4, 6, 7, 8, 9, 10
4	• Find probabilities using areas.	1, 2, 3, 4, 5, 6, 7, 8, 9, 10
5	• Use the tangent ratio to find unknown side lengths in right triangles. • Use sine and cosine ratios to find unknown side lengths in right triangles.	1, 2, 3, 4, 6, 7, 8, 9, 10

* See page T14.

Section 1 Patterns and Sequences

Section 1 Planner

Section Objectives

Exploration 1
- Identify arithmetic and geometric sequences
- Write an equation for any term in a sequence

Exploration 2
- Analyze sequences

Days for Section 1

First Day
Setting the Stage, *p. 518*
Exploration 1 through Question 7,
  pp. 519–520

Second Day
Exploration 1, *p. 521*

Third Day
Exploration 2 through Question 16,
  pp. 522–523

Fourth Day
Exploration 2 from Question 17,
  p. 524
Key Concepts, *p. 525*

Teaching Resources

Teacher's Resource Book
- Warm-Up
- Labsheet 1A
- Practice and Applications
- Study Guide
See page 517 for additional teaching resources.

Materials List

Practice and Applications
- grid paper
- ruler
- protractor
- Labsheet 1A

Assessment Options

EMBEDDED ASSESSMENT
- Identify arithmetic and geometric sequences
    Exercises 1, 4
- Write an equation for any term in a sequence
    Exercise 11
- Analyze sequences
    Exercises 16, 19

PERFORMANCE TASK/PORTFOLIO
- Exercise 12 on *p. 526 (challenge)*
- Exercise 14 on *p. 527 (biology)*
- Exercise 15 on *p. 527 (writing)*
- Exercise 20 on *p. 528 (visual thinking)*
- Extended Exploration on *p. 531**

* indicates a problem-solving task that can be assessed using the Assessment Scales

QUIZZES/TESTS
- Section 1 Quick Quiz

TEST GENERATOR

Section 1 Overview

In this section, students will explore and analyze sequences based on a piece of literature.

Exploration 1
Students use a scenario from the story *Two of Everything* to organize information and write an arithmetic and a geometric sequence. These situations allow students to differentiate between the two types of sequences. Students are led to recognize that arithmetic sequences change at a constant rate while geometric sequences grow exponentially. Students will learn how a term and term number are related and write an equation for any term in a sequence.

Exploration 2
In this exploration, students explore sequences that are neither arithmetic nor geometric. The Fibonacci sequence is analyzed through a problem posed by the mathematician Leonardo Fibonacci. Students then examine other sequences. They identify the pattern of triangular numbers in a series of dots, and recognize the perfect squares inherent in a sequence of "growing triangles."

Guide for Assigning Homework

REGULAR SCHEDULING (45 MIN CLASS PERIOD)			EXERCISES TO NOTE		
Section/ P&A Pages	Core Assignment	Extended Assignment	Additional Practice/Review	Open-ended Problems	Extended Problems
1 pp. 526–529	**Day 1:** SR 21–26 **Day 2:** 1–11 **Day 3:** 13–14, 28–29 **Day 4:** 15–19, ROS 20	SR 21–26 1–12 13–14, 28–29 16–19, ROS 20, Ext 27	EP, p. 530	E², p. 531	Challenge PA 12 E², p. 531 Ext 27 Career Connection 28–29

Key: PA = Practice & Application; ROS = Reflecting on the Section; SR = Spiral Review; TB = Toolbox; EP = Extra Skill Practice; Ext = Extension; ST = Standardized Testing

Math Background and Teaching Strategies

Classroom Notes

Bulletin board displays for this section include:

• photographs showing examples of Fibonacci numbers in nature

Math Strands

Topic Spiraling and Integration

The study of patterns and sequences is foundational for algebraic reasoning. Students were introduced to the formal use of patterns in Module 1 of Book 1 and have applied the concepts throughout Books 2 and 3. Understanding the *Counting Principle* and combinatorics that were studied in Module 8 of Book 2 and again in Module 4 of Book 3 depends largely on a working knowledge of patterns and sequences.

Exploration 1

The focus of this exploration is the development of equations used to generalize arithmetic and geometric sequences. Understanding the difference between *term number* and *term* is essential for successful completion of this exploration. A *term number* is the ordinal number indicating the order in which an event occurs. If students are asked to find the *fourth* term, the term number is *4*. The *term* is the result of an event. Students are asked to use the *term number* to write an equation that will result in the *term* for any term number in the sequence. Students may need to see a variety of sequences in order to make the connections that will allow them to write an equation. A first step in finding an equation is identifying a sequence as arithmetic, geometric, or neither. In an arithmetic sequence each term changes by adding or subtracting a constant. A geometric sequence changes exponentially (doubling, tripling, halving, etc). The *Teaching Notes* in Section 1 offer strategies to help students discover patterns that will enable them to generalize sequences.

Exploration 2

Students examine sequences that are neither arithmetic nor geometric, but nevertheless follow a definite pattern. The Fibonacci problem asks students to create a model showing the total number of rabbit pairs over the first six months. Students should know that this is a hypothetical situation that does not occur in nature, however one that reveals a pattern found in many aspects of nature. (See the *Background Information* on page 523 for examples.) As students explore other sequences, they should be encouraged to search for patterns in other areas of mathematics and in their lives.

516D

Section 2 Polygons and Rotational Symmetry

Section 2 Planner

Section Objectives

Exploration 1
• Find the sum of the measures of the interior angles of a polygon

Exploration 2
• Describe rotational symmetry

Days for Section 2

First Day
Setting the Stage, *p. 532*
Exploration 1 through Question 6, *p. 533*

Second Day
Exploration 1, *p. 534*

Third Day
Exploration 2, *pp. 535–536*
Key Concepts, *p. 537*

Teaching Resources

Teacher's Resource Book
• Warm-Up
• Labsheets 2A, 2B, and 2C
• Practice and Applications
• Study Guide
See page 517 for additional teaching resources.

Materials List

Exploration 1
• Labsheets 2A–2B
• ruler
• scissors
• plain white paper

Exploration 2
• Labsheet 2C
• protractor

Practice and Applications
• protractor
• cardboard or thick paper
• scissors
• ruler

Assessment Options

EMBEDDED ASSESSMENT
• Find the sum of the measures of the interior angles of a polygon
  Exercises 1, 10
• Describe rotational symmetry
  Exercise 17(a)

PERFORMANCE TASK/PORTFOLIO
• Exercise 11 on *p. 538 (challenge)*
• Exercise 16 on *p. 539 (create your own)*
• Exercise 18 on *p. 540 (journal)*

QUIZZES/TESTS
• Section 2 Quick Quiz

TEST GENERATOR

Section 2 Overview

In this section, students will examine architectural designs and aspects of nature as they relate to polygons and symmetry.

Exploration 1
As students investigate which polygons can be used to create tile designs, they will learn the relationship between the number of sides of a polygon and the sum of the measures of its interior angles. Students explore the sum of the measures of the interior angles of a variety of polygons and identify a formula for determining the measure of one interior angle of a regular polygon.

Exploration 2
In this exploration, students identify architectural structures and objects in nature that have rotational symmetry. They use a protractor to find the rotational symmetries of a figure and use that knowledge to develop a method of determining the minimum rotational symmetry of a figure without the use of a protractor.

Guide for Assigning Homework

REGULAR SCHEDULING (45 MIN CLASS PERIOD)			EXERCISES TO NOTE		
Section/ P&A Pages	Core Assignment	Extended Assignment	Additional Practice/Review	Open-ended Problems	Extended Problems
2 pp. 538–540	**Day 1:** 1–4, SR 19–22 **Day 2:** 5–10, 12–13 **Day 3:** 14–17, ROS 18	1–4, SR 19–22 6–10 (even), 11–13 14–17, ROS 18	EP, p. 541	PA 13, 16	PA Challenge 11

Key: PA = Practice & Application; ROS = Reflecting on the Section; SR = Spiral Review; TB = Toolbox; EP = Extra Skill Practice; Ext = Extension; ST = Standardized Testing

Math Background and Teaching Strategies

Classroom Notes

Bulletin board displays for this section include:

- Photos of tilings and/or tessellations created by students

- Objects with rotational symmetry collected by students and/or pictures of objects with rotational symmetry

Visitors might include:

- A mason or brick-layer

Math Strands

Topic Spiraling and Integration

Students found the measures of special angles and the angles formed by intersecting lines in Module 5 and explored transformations and reflections in Module 6. The spatial skills developed in this section will help students classify quadrilaterals in Section 3 of this module.

Exploration 1

Students should notice that the polygons in the tilings shown in the text are all either squares or rectangles. Since the interior angles of squares and rectangles all measure 90°, the shapes fit together to create a tiling (or tessellation) with no gaps or overlaps. As students try to create tessellations with a regular hexagon and a regular pentagon, they re-discover the idea, first introduced in Module 8 of Book 2, that for a polygon to tessellate, the sum of the measures of the angles around any vertex in the tessellation must equal 360°. Students continue their investigation into which regular polygons will tessellate by building convex polygons, starting with a triangle and adding another triangle at each step. As they do, they discover that the sum of the measures of the interior angles of a convex polygon is $180(n - 2)$, where n is the number of sides of the polygon. They use this knowledge to find the measure of one interior angle of a regular polygon and to discover that for a regular polygon to tessellate, the measure of an interior angle must be a factor of 360°.

Exploration 2

In this exploration, ideas about tiling are used to investigate rotational symmetry. In a tessellation made with a regular polygon, the angles at a vertex of the tiling are all congruent and their measure is a factor of 360°. Similarly, for a figure to have rotational symmetry, the measures of the angles around a center point must be equal and have a sum of 360°. Students use this knowledge to develop a method for finding the minimum rotational symmetry of a figure without using a protractor. They also develop the ability to distinguish between objects that have rotational symmetry and those that do not, even if they appear to be symmetrical at first glance.

Section 3 Properties of Quadrilaterals

Section 3 Planner

Section Objectives

Exploration 1
• Classify quadrilaterals

Exploration 2
• Find the distance between points on a coordinate grid
• Find the midpoint of a segment on a coordinate grid

Days for Section 3

First Day
Setting the Stage, *p. 542*
Exploration 1, *pp. 543–546*

Second Day
Exploration 2, *pp. 547–548*
Key Concepts, *pp. 549–550*

Teaching Resources

Teacher's Resource Book
• Warm-Up
• Labsheets 3A and 3B
• Practice and Applications
• Study Guide
See page 517 for additional teaching resources.

Materials List

Exploration 1
• Labsheets 3A and 3B
• protractor
• scissors
• ruler

Exploration 2
• graph paper

Practice and Applications
• graph paper

Assessment Options

EMBEDDED ASSESSMENT
• Classify quadrilaterals
   Exercise 11
• Find the distance between points on a coordinate grid
   Exercise 12
• Find the midpoint of a segment on a coordinate grid
   Exercise 12

PERFORMANCE TASK/PORTFOLIO
• Exercises 6–9 on *p. 551 (open-ended)*
• Exercise 10 on *p. 551 (challenge)*
• Exercise 16 on *p. 552 (journal)*
• Standardized Testing 1–2 on *p. 553*

QUIZZES/TESTS
• Section 3 Quick Quiz
• Mid-Module Quiz

TEST GENERATOR

Section 3 Overview

In this section, students will classify quadrilaterals based on the properties of their angles and diagonals.

Exploration 1
Students create a chart comparing quadrilaterals in order to identify their properties. They will identify specific properties that distinguish certain quadrilaterals from others and recognize those properties that are shared by many quadrilaterals. Students are introduced to the terms *opposite angles* and *consecutive angles* and use them to explore angle properties. Student utilize what they have learned about perpendicular bisectors, and apply what they know about transversals, corresponding angles, alternate interior angles, and alternate exterior angles to justify properties.

Exploration 2
Students apply properties of parallelograms to quadrilaterals on a coordinate grid. For example, students find the slopes of the sides of a quadrilateral on a coordinate grid and use the slopes to determine whether the quadrilateral is a parallelogram.

Guide for Assigning Homework

REGULAR SCHEDULING (45 MIN CLASS PERIOD)			EXERCISES TO NOTE		
Section/ P&A Pages	Core Assignment	Extended Assignment	Additional Practice/Review	Open-ended Problems	Extended Problems
3 pp. 550–552	**Day 1:** 1–9, 11, SR 17–26 **Day 2:** 12, 14–15, ROS 16	1–11, SR 17–26 12–15, ROS 16	EP, p. 553	PA 6–9 ST 1–2	PA Challenge 10

Key: PA = Practice & Application; ROS = Reflecting on the Section; SR = Spiral Review; TB = Toolbox; EP = Extra Skill Practice; Ext = Extension; ST = Standardized Testing

Math Background and Teaching Strategies

Classroom Notes

Bulletin board display ideas for this section include:

• A collage of quadrilaterals, or pictures of objects shaped like quadrilaterals

• A polygon classification tree excluding the quadrilaterals (These can be added during the course of this section)

Math Strands

Topic Spiraling and Integration
Students classified quadrilaterals by the properties of their sides in Module 8 of Book 2. In this section, students are asked to classify quadrilaterals according to the properties of their sides, angles, and diagonals. Perpendicular bisectors were constructed in Module 3, and angles and transversals were explored in Module 5.

Exploration 1
Students distinguish between a variety of quadrilaterals based on specific properties. In this exploration, each type of quadrilateral is studied independently in order to recognize similarities and differences among the geometric figures. A classification tree can be used to help students recognize that although a rectangle, square, and rhombus have specific names they are all parallelograms. In Module 3, students explored and constructed perpendicular bisectors of chords. Students should recognize that a line can bisect a segment without being perpendicular to it. A compass or ruler can be used to determine whether segments bisect each other and a protractor can be used to determine if they are perpendicular. As students explore the premise that consecutive angles between two parallel sides of a quadrilateral are

supplementary, they will apply what they learned in Module 5 concerning angles and transversals. Since the two sides of the quadrilateral are parallel, properties of corresponding angles, alternate interior angles, and alternate exterior angles are relevant.

Exploration 2
Given a quadrilateral plotted on a coordinate grid, students use coordinates and properties of quadrilaterals to determine what type of quadrilateral is shown. Students use what they learned about slopes of lines in Module 4 to determine whether the opposite sides of a quadrilateral are parallel or the diagonals of a quadrilateral are perpendicular. They also use the Pythagorean Theorem from Module 5 to determine whether the opposite sides of a quadrilateral are the same length.

Section 4 Geometry and Probability

Section 4 Planner

Section Objectives

Exploration 1
- Find probabilities using areas

Days for Section 4

First Day
Setting the Stage, pp. 554–555
Exploration 1 through Question 4,
pp. 556–557

Second Day
Exploration 1 from Question 5, p. 557
Key Concepts, p. 558

Teaching Resources

Teacher's Resource Book
- Warm-Up
- Labsheet 4A
- Practice and Applications
- Study Guide
See page 517 for additional teaching resources.

Materials List

Exploration 1
- Labsheet 4A
- metric ruler

Practice and Applications
- graph paper

Assessment Options

EMBEDDED ASSESSMENT
- Find probabilities using areas
  Exercises 6, 7, 8

PERFORMANCE TASK/PORTFOLIO
- Exercise 2 on *p. 558 (visual thinking)*
- Exercise 10 on *p. 560 (journal)*

QUIZZES/TESTS
- Section 4 Quick Quiz

TEST GENERATOR

Section 4 Overview

In this section, students explore mathematical ideas that will enable them to determine the probability of a search team finding the sunken *Titanic*. On a map, students estimate the area of the region the team planned to search for the *Titanic* and the area of the part of the region that was not actually searched.

Exploration 1
As students compare their estimates from the *Setting the Stage,* they will discover how a geometric probability is determined. Using formulas for area, students find the probability of an object falling in a shaded region of a figure. The meaning of complementary events is developed by finding the probability of an object falling in the unshaded region of the same figure. Utilizing what they learn, students estimate the probability of finding the *Titanic* in the planned search region.

Guide for Assigning Homework

REGULAR SCHEDULING (45 MIN CLASS PERIOD)			EXERCISES TO NOTE		
Section/ P&A Pages	Core Assignment	Extended Assignment	Additional Practice/Review	Open-ended Problems	Extended Problems
4 pp. 558–560	**Day 1:** 1–8 **Day 2:** 9, ROS 10, SR 11–19	1–8 9, ROS 10, SR 11–19	EP, p. 561		

Key: PA = Practice & Application; ROS = Reflecting on the Section; SR = Spiral Review; TB = Toolbox; EP = Extra Skill Practice; Ext = Extension; ST = Standardized Testing

Math Background and Teaching Strategies

Classroom Notes

Bulletin board display ideas for this section include:

• a map of the Atlantic Ocean surrounded by pictures of the *Titanic*

Visitors might include:

• a search and rescue official

Math Strands

Topic Spiraling and Integration
Geometric probability is an extension of the probability concepts students explored in Modules 2 and 4.

Exploration 1
From Module 2 students should recall that the theoretical probability of an event is the ratio of the *number of outcomes that make up an event* to the *total number of possible outcomes*. Geometric probability is similar, but uses the areas of regions (or lengths of segments or volumes of objects) rather than numbers of outcomes. For example, the probability of an object landing in part of a given region is the ratio of the *area of the part* to the *area of the entire region*.

Differentiated Instruction

Since this section is developed around the concept of theoretical probability, some students may need a more tactile approach to internalize the concepts. Let these students conduct an experiment to find experimental probabilities. Provide student pairs with a 9″ × 12″ piece of colored construction paper and a square piece of different colored construction paper. Have them make a target by taping the square piece of paper on the rectangular piece so that it is entirely on the larger piece. Cut out twenty 1″ × 1″ pieces of plain paper. Direct students to hold a piece so that an edge of the paper is parallel to the construction paper and about 12 in. above it. Drop the small pieces individually so they flutter onto the target. If a piece misses the target completely or lands partially in each region, drop it again. Once all twenty pieces have been released, count the number on each color of paper to determine the experimental probability of a paper landing in each region of the target. Relate this to theoretical probability by measuring the area of each region and finding the ratio of the areas. Students can then compare the two probabilities and discuss their findings. You can also relate the way the pieces fluttered onto the target to the sinking of the *Titanic*. Discuss what happened to the falling paper if someone opened a door, walked by, sneezed, or did anything to cause the movement of the air to change.

516J

Section 5 — Tangent, Sine, and Cosine

Section 5 Planner

Section Objectives

Exploration 1
- Use the tangent ratio to find unknown side lengths in right triangles

Exploration 2
- Use sine and cosine ratios to find unknown side lengths in right triangles

Days for Section 5

First Day
Setting the Stage, *pp. 562–563*
Exploration 1, *pp. 563–566*

Second Day
Exploration 2, *pp. 566–567*
Key Concepts, *p. 568*

Materials List

Exploration 1
- protractor
- metric ruler
- scissors
- calculator

Exploration 2
- calculator

Practice and Applications
- calculator
- encyclopedia
- Labsheet 5A
- protractor
- drinking straw
- string
- weight (such as a washer)
- tape

Teaching Resources

Teacher's Resource Book
- Warm-Up
- Labsheet 5A
- Practice and Applications
- Study Guide

See page 517 for additional teaching resources.

Assessment Options

EMBEDDED ASSESSMENT
- Use the tangent ratio to find unknown side lengths in right triangles
  Exercises 4, 5, 7
- Use sine and cosine ratios to find unknown side lengths in right triangles
  Exercises 16, 17

PERFORMANCE TASK/PORTFOLIO
- Exercise 8 on *p. 569 (research)*
- Exercise 9 on *p. 570 (challenge)*
- Exercise 10 on *p. 570 (create your own)*
- Exercise 14 on *p. 570 (writing)*
- Exercise 19 on *p. 571 (challenge)*
- Exercise 22 on *p. 572 (journal)*

QUIZZES/TESTS
- Section 5 Quick Quiz
- Module Tests A and B
- Module Standardized Test
- Module Performance Assessment

TEST GENERATOR

Section 5 Overview

In this section, students will learn how to use the tangent, sine, and cosine ratios to find heights of objects. They examine the way an astrolabe is used to find the angle of elevation by identifying the complement of the angle determined by the astrolabe.

Exploration 1
As students investigate the ratio of the lengths of the sides of similar triangles, they will recognize that the ratios are the same for any similar right triangles. This leads to a study of the tangent ratio and how it can be used to find either the side opposite or the side adjacent to an acute angle of a right triangle.

Exploration 2
Students use what they learned in Exploration 1 to explore the sine and cosine ratios and compare them to the tangent ratio. They will notice that while the tangent ratio can be used to find only the adjacent and opposite sides of a right triangle, the sine and cosine ratios can be used to find the length of the hypotenuse as well. In both explorations, students use calculators to evaluate the sine, cosine, and tangent ratios in problem-solving settings.

Guide for Assigning Homework

REGULAR SCHEDULING (45 MIN CLASS PERIOD)			EXERCISES TO NOTE		
Section/ P&A Pages	**Core Assignment**	**Extended Assignment**	**Additional Practice/Review**	**Open-ended Problems**	**Extended Problems**
5 pp. 569–572	**Day 1:** 1–8, 10 SR 23–26 **Day 2:** 11–18, 20–21, ROS 22	1–10, SR 23–26 11–14, 16–21, ROS 22	EP, p. 573 Review & Assessment, pp. 576–577	PA 8, 14	PA Challenge 9, 19 Mod Proj, pp. 574–575

Key: PA = Practice & Application; ROS = Reflecting on the Section; SR = Spiral Review; TB = Toolbox; EP = Extra Skill Practice; Ext = Extension; ST = Standardized Testing

Math Background and Teaching Strategies

Classroom Notes

Students are asked to create their own astrolabes in Exercise 10 of the *Practice and Applications Exercises*. This can be done as a homework project or as a class project. You may choose to have your students make an astrolabe as part of the *Setting the Stage* for this section, then use them to find the height of their classroom or school building.

Math Strands

Topic Spiraling and Integration
In Module 5, students identified complements and supplements of angles and used the Pythagorean theorem to find missing side lengths in right triangles. In this section, complements are used to find the measures of missing angles in right triangles. Unlike the Pythagorean theorem, which expresses a relationship among the lengths of the sides of a right triangle, the *sine*, *cosine*, and *tangent* ratios that are introduced in this section express relationships between the side lengths and the measure of an acute angle of a right triangle. These ratios can be used to find missing side lengths in right triangles and are used extensively in later mathematics courses.

Exploration 1
In Module 3, students investigated the properties of similar figures and learned to apply the *angle-angle property* to determine if two triangles are similar. By comparing the ratios of the length of the side opposite one of the acute angles to the length of the side adjacent to the angle in similar right triangles, students discover that the ratio is the same no matter the size of the triangle. The ratio of the length of the side opposite an acute angle of a right triangle to the length of the side adjacent to the angle is known as the *tangent ratio*. Since the opposite and adjacent sides form the right angle the tangent ratio cannot be used to find the length of the hypotenuse.

Exploration 2
In this exploration, students explore the *sine* and *cosine* ratios and their relationship to the *tangent* ratio. Students verify the results obtained using these ratios by applying the Pythagorean theorem. They learn that either ratio results in the same measure. However, deciding which ratio to use to find a missing side length is dependent upon which side lengths and angle measures are known. Students will learn how to decide which ratio, *tangent*, *sine*, or *cosine*, to use for finding missing side lengths in right triangles.

Module 8

OVERVIEW

Mathematics concepts are interwoven among the themes explored in previous modules. Students distinguish between sequences, find the measures of interior angles of polygons, explore rotational symmetry, classify quadrilaterals, explore geometric probabilities, and apply tangent, sine, and cosine ratios to right triangles.

PREREQUISITE SKILLS

Warm-Up Exercises for each section are provided in the *Teacher's Resource Book*. You can use these exercises to review skills and concepts students will need for each section. In addition, the Spiral Review exercises at the end of each section in the student edition provide practice on prerequisite skills.

MODULE DIAGNOSTIC TEST

The Module Diagnostic Test in the *Teacher's Resource Book* can be used to assess students' prior knowledge of skills and concepts that will be taught in each section of this module. You can use test results to help structure your teaching to meet the diverse needs of your classroom.

MODULE 8

MATH Thematical MIX

516

MATHEMATICS
The & Theme

MODULE 8 • **SECTION OVERVIEW**

① Patterns and Sequences

As you revisit Amazing Feats and Facts:

- ◆ Identify and analyze arithmetic and geometric sequences
- ◆ Write an equation for a sequence

② Polygons and Rotational Symmetry

As you revisit Architects and Engineers:

- ◆ Find the sum of the measures of interior angles of a polygon
- ◆ Describe rotational symmetry

③ Properties of Quadrilaterals

As you revisit The Mystery of Blacktail Canyon:

- ◆ Classify quadrilaterals

④ Geometry and Probability

As you revisit At the Mall:

- ◆ Find probabilities using areas

⑤ Tangent, Sine, and Cosine

As you revisit Inventions:

- ◆ Use the tangent, sine, and cosine ratios to find unknown side lengths in right triangles

The Module Project
Looking for Patterns

Mathematics is filled with patterns and sequences. In this project you will use a visual pattern made up of borders on a grid to explore sequences and geometric probability. You will then create your own design that can be used to model a sequence.

More on the Module Project
See pp. 574–575.

INTERNET
Resources and practice at
classzone.com

517

Module Resources

TEACHER'S RESOURCE BOOK

Resources
- The *Math Gazette* (parent newsletter)
- Warm-Ups
- Labsheets
- Practice and Applications
- Study Guide

Assessment
- Section Quick Quizzes
- Mid-Module Quiz
- Module 8 Diagnostic Test
- Module 8 Tests A and B
- Module 8 Standardized Test
- Module 8 Performance Assessment
- Modules 7 and 8 Cumulative Test
- End-of-Year Test

SPANISH RESOURCES
- The *Math Gazette* (parent newsletter)
- Practice and Applications
- Assessment
- Spanish Glossary

STUDENT WORKBOOK

TECHNOLOGY BOOK

TECHNOLOGY RESOURCES
- @Home Tutor
- Test Generator
- Activity Generator
- Professional Development DVD
- Online Activities

If a copy of the book, *Two of Everything*, is available in your library (or an elementary school library) you might want to read it to the class prior to starting this section. Although it is a children's book, it is an engaging story about an elderly couple who find a magic pot that solves their problem of poverty. They also find how unnerving the magic pot can be when Mrs. Haktak falls in and TWO Mrs. Haktaks are pulled from the pot. The solution to their problem is accidental, albeit logical. Students of all ages enjoy the ensuing events and final outcome of the story.

This story serves as a catalyst for the study of patterns and sequences. The events in the story are used extensively throughout the first Exploration, helping students to recognize the structure of arithmetic and geometric sequences.

GETTING STARTED

Module 8, Section 1 *Warm-Up* assesses student facility with simple sequences. The *Warm-Up* checks that students can identify and extend a simple sequence mentally.

TEACHING NOTES

Question 2 Students may realize that since 51 is not a multiple of 2, it is not possible to put in any combination of purses that will produce 51 coins. Encourage students to try various combinations of purses placed in the pot. You might also ask if it is possible to pull 51 coins from the pot if you could alter the number of coins that were in the purses. (*No; Since the function is doubling, the result will always be an even number.*)

Section ① Patterns and Sequences

IN THIS SECTION

EXPLORATION 1
◆ Arithmetic and Geometric Sequences
EXPLORATION 2
◆ Exploring Sequences

Amazing Feats and Facts

Setting the Stage

In the story *Two of Everything* by Lily Toy Hong, Mr. Haktak, while out digging in his garden one spring day, finds a large pot buried there. As he carries the heavy pot home, his purse containing his last 5 gold coins falls to the ground. He picks up the purse, tosses it into the pot and takes the pot home to Mrs. Haktak.

As Mrs. Haktak leaned over to peer into the pot, her hairpin—the only one she owned—fell in. She felt around in the pot, and suddenly her eyes grew round with surprise. "Look!" she shouted. "I've pulled out TWO hairpins, exactly alike, and TWO purses, too!" Sure enough, the purses were identical, and so were the hairpins. Inside each purse were five gold coins!

Think About It

1 How many coins will Mrs. Haktak pull out of the pot if she puts in a purse containing 20 coins? 80 coins? **40 coins; 160 coins**

2 Considering the way the pot works, is it possible for Mrs. Haktak to pull 51 coins from the pot? Explain. **No. The pot doubles whatever is put into it, making the number of objects pulled out an even number. Twice any number is an even number. 51 is odd.**

+ Arithmetic +
and
× Geometric ×
Sequences

3 Suppose Mr. Haktak puts 1 purse containing 5 coins into the pot. When he reaches in, he pulls out 2 identical purses. The next time he puts in 2 identical purses and pulls out 4. But then he begins to fear that he will lose all of his money. So, the third time he puts only 3 purses into the pot. The fourth time he puts in 4 purses and so on.

a. How many purses will he take out of the pot after putting them into the pot the third time? **6 purses**

b. How many purses will he take out after the sixth time he puts purses into the pot? How do you know? **12; The sixth time he would put in 6 purses and pull out double that number.**

▶ **Describing Sequences** The number of purses pulled out of the pot each time is a *sequence*. A **sequence** is an ordered list of numbers or objects called **terms**.

You can use a table to organize the terms of a sequence.

EXAMPLE

To find each term after the first term of the sequence below, **add 4** to the **previous term**.

Term number	1	2	3	4	5	6
Term	3	7	11	15	19	23

+4 +4 +4 +4 +4

7 + 4 = 11

Exploration 1

TEACHING NOTES
Question 3 Encourage students to make an organized list of the result of what happens each time Mr. Haktak puts his bags of coins into the pot.

DEVELOPING MATH CONCEPTS
Some students may be confused by the mathematical language "term" and "term number" used in the **Example**. Refer them back to the organized list they made for Question 3. The term number is the ordinal used to show the sequence of events. The term number always increases by one. The term is the result that occurs at each numbered event and increases (or decreases) in increments that vary depending on the pattern of the sequence.

TEACHING NOTES
If another example is needed, discuss the following Classroom Example before students complete **Question 4**.

CLASSROOM EXAMPLE
Make a table to find the next three terms of the sequence 5, 11, 17, 23, ...
Answer:

Term number	1	2	3	4	5	6	7
Term	5	11	17	23	29	35	41

+6 +6 +6 +6 +6 +6

The next three terms in the sequence are 29, 35, 41.

TECHNOLOGY
For a related technology activity, see the *Technology Book*.

Exploration 1 *continued*

DEVELOPING MATH CONCEPTS

Question 4 Students may recognize the relationship between the term and the term number is $n \cdot 2$ or $2n$ where n is the term number. You may want to refer to this simple generalization when students are working through **Question 5(d)**.

In **Question 5**, students discover the equation for the *n*th term in an arithmetic sequence. By the time they get to **Question 6(c)**, students should be able to identify the four parts of the equation relating each term in the sequence to its term number. It may be helpful for students to see a chart that shows them how each term is generated.

term number	term	
1	2	2
2	7	2 + 5
3	12	2 + 5 + 5
4	17	2 + 5 + 5 + 5
5	22	2 + 5 + 5 + 5 + 5

You may want to use parentheses to show how each term is found by adding the constant 5 to the previous term. This model can help students see that the first term remains the same and that to get each successive term, 5 is added to the previous term. The number of times it is added is one less than the term number ($n - 1$). Encourage struggling students to make a chart similar to the one above as they answer **Question 7**.

4.

1	2	3	4	5	6
2	4	6	8	10	12

6. b.

7	8	9	10	11	12
32	37	42	47	52	57

520

FOR ◄ HELP

with *constants and variables*, see

MODULE 1, p. 42

6. c. Choices of variables may vary. $t = a + (n - 1)d$ where t = the term, a = the first term in the sequence, n = the term number and d = the difference between the terms.

✔ QUESTION 7

... checks that you can write and use an equation for an arithmetic sequence.

---

4 Make a table for the sequence you found in Question 3. The term numbers are the numbers of purses put in the pot, and the terms are the numbers of purses pulled out after each time purses are put in. See margin.

   a. How is each term in your sequence related to the previous one? Each term is two more than the previous term.

   b. Use the pattern in part (a) to predict how many purses Mr. Haktak will pull out of the pot after putting 10 purses in. 20 purses

▶ The sequences in the Example on page 519 and in Question 4 are *arithmetic sequences*. An **arithmetic sequence** is one in which each term after the first is found by adding a constant to the previous term. The constant may be positive or negative.

You can write an equation that uses the term number to find a term in an arithmetic sequence.

5 Look at the arithmetic sequence below.

Term number	1	2	3	4	5	6
Term	2	7	12	17	22	27

   a. What constant do you add to each term to obtain the next term? 5

   b. How many times did you add the constant from part (a) to the first term to get the second term? the third term? the fourth? one time; two times; three times

   c. What is the relationship between the number of times the constant was added and the *term number* for each term? It is one less than the term number.

   d. Write an equation that uses the term number n to find the *n*th term t of the sequence. $t = 2 + 5(n - 1)$

6 a. Use the equation you wrote in Question 5(d) to find the 12th term in the sequence. 57

   b. Check your answer from part (a) by extending the sequence. If your answer from part (a) is not correct, write an equation that will give you the correct result. See margin.

   c. Try This as a Class The equation you wrote is specific to this arithmetic sequence. How could you write it so it would apply to *any* arithmetic sequence?

7 **CHECKPOINT** Write an equation that uses the term number n to find the *n*th term t of each arithmetic sequence. Then find the 13th term.

   a. 5, 12, 19, 26, ...
      $t = 5 + 7(n - 1)$; 89

   b. 300, 289, 278, 267, ...
      $t = 300 - 11(n - 1)$; 168

▶ In the story, Mrs. Haktak wanted her fortune to grow more quickly. Every time she took purses out of the pot she put all the coins into one purse and put it back into the pot.

8 a. There were 5 coins in the first purse Mrs. Haktak put in the pot. How many coins did she have when she pulled purses out the first time? the second time? 10 coins; 20 coins

b. The process describes a sequence. The term numbers are the numbers of times she puts a single purse into the pot. The terms are the numbers of coins she has after pulling purses out each time. Make a table to show the first 6 terms in the sequence. See margin.

c. How is each term related to the preceding term? Each term is twice the previous term.

▶ The sequence in Question 8 is a *geometric sequence*. A **geometric sequence** is one in which each term after the first is found by multiplying the previous term by a non-zero constant.

You can write an equation that uses the term number to find a term in a geometric sequence.

9 Look at the geometric sequence in the table at the right.

a. What constant do you multiply each term by to obtain the next term? 2

b. By what power of the constant in part (a) can you multiply the first term to get the second term? the third? the fourth? the first power (2^1); the second (2^2); the third (2^3)

c. What is the relationship between the power of the constant and the term number? the power of the constant is 1 less than the term number

d. Write an equation that uses the term number n to find the nth term t of the geometric sequence. $t = 2 \cdot 2^{n-1}$

10 **Try This as a Class** Suppose the first term in a sequence is 2 and each successive term is found by multiplying the previous term by 3. Write an equation that can be used to find any term in the sequence. $t = 2 \cdot 3^{n-1}$

11 Rewrite your equation from Question 10 so that it could be used to find any term in *any* geometric sequence.

12 ✔ **CHECKPOINT** Identify each sequence as *arithmetic* or *geometric*. Then write an equation for the sequence.

a. 2, 9, 16, 23, ...
arithmetic (add 7);
$t = 2 + 7(n-1)$

b. $3x, 3x^2, 3x^3, 3x^4, ...$
geometric (multiply by x);
$t = 3x \cdot x^{n-1}$

| HOMEWORK EXERCISES | ▶ See Exs. 1–12 on p. 526. |

Term Number	Term
1	2
2	4
3	8
4	16
5	32
6	64

11. $t = a \cdot r^{n-1}$ or $t = ar^{n-1}$ where a = the first term in the sequence, r = the ratio or constant, n = the term number

✔ **QUESTION 12**

... checks that you can identify and write equations for arithmetic and geometric sequences.

TEACHING NOTES

Question 9 Students may recognize the sequence in the table as powers of 2. In this case, the exponent is directly related to the term number because the constant multiplier and the first term are the same.

DEVELOPING MATH CONCEPTS

Question 10 Using a chart, as was done for arithmetic sequences, can also help students understand the pattern in geometric sequences.

term number	term	
1	2	2
2	6	$2 \cdot 3$
3	18	$2 \cdot 3 \cdot 3$
4	54	$2 \cdot 3 \cdot 3 \cdot 3$
5	162	$2 \cdot 3 \cdot 3 \cdot 3 \cdot 3$

From this diagram students can see that the 2 is always present and is multiplied by a power of 3 to get each successive term in the sequence. The power used for each term is one less than the term number ($n - 1$). Again, parentheses may be used to help students see that each successive term is obtained by multiplying the previous term by 3.

8. b.

1	2	3	4	5	6
10	20	40	80	160	320

Exploration 2

TEACHING NOTES

Question 13 Students may need to work with a partner or in a small group to generate ideas for ways in which to model the Fibonacci rabbit problem. Once completed, students should share the diagrams they created to model the problem. Some students may try to draw the rabbits and others may use symbols. Discuss the advantages of each model. If no one uses a tree diagram that starts with the original rabbit pair you may want to share this model of the problem with the class.

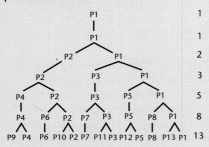

Note that totals are listed in the diagram even though students will not include them until they complete Question 14 on page 523.

Exploration 2

Exploring Sequences

GOAL

LEARN HOW TO...
- analyze sequences

AS YOU...
- explore the Fibonacci sequence

KEY TERM
- Fibonacci sequence

▶ **In Exploration 1 you explored arithmetic and geometric sequences. Some sequences are neither arithmetic nor geometric yet follow a definite pattern.**

His neighbors called him *Bigollone,* which means "the blockhead." His real name was Leonardo Fibonacci, and he was not a blockhead at all. He was a mathematician who loved to "play around" with numbers. In 1202 he published a book in which he introduced a fascinating mathematical problem.

Suppose two newborn rabbits, male and female, are put into a cage. How many rabbits will there be at the end of one year if this pair of rabbits produces another pair every month, and every new pair of rabbits produces another new pair every month? All rabbits must be two months old before they can produce more rabbits.

Here is what happens in the first three months after the first pair of newborn rabbits are put in the cage:

Start   Start with **1st pair** of newborn rabbits.

Month 1 **1st pair** are growing.

Month 2 **1st pair** are adults. They produce **2nd pair** of rabbits.

Month 3 **1st pair** produce **3rd pair** of rabbits.
             2nd pair are growing.

13 Solve Fibonacci's rabbit problem. Start by creating a model or diagram that shows the total number of rabbit pairs over the first six months of the year. Find a way to show newborn, growing, and adult rabbits. Answers may vary. Check students' work.

14 Use your model in Question 13 to help complete a table like the one shown. **See margin.**

Month	Number of rabbit pairs			Total number of rabbit pairs
	Newborn	Growing	Adult	
Start	1	0	0	1
1	0	1	?	?
2	?	?	?	?

15 The number pattern in the last column of the table you made in Question 14 is known as the **Fibonacci sequence**. The numbers in the sequence are sometimes called *Fibonacci numbers*.

Fibonacci sequence						
1	1	2	3	5	?	?
↓	↓	↓				
1st term	2nd term	3rd term				

a. How are any two consecutive terms in the Fibonacci sequence used to find the next term in the sequence? **Each term after the second term is the sum of the two previous consecutive terms.**

b. Use the pattern you found in part (a) to complete the table above. **8, 13**

c. What is the answer to the rabbit problem? Explain how you got your answer.

16 **Discussion** The sum of the first, second, and third terms in the Fibonacci sequence is one less than the fifth term of the sequence. The sum of the second, third, and fourth terms is 2 less than the sixth term. Find a similar relationship for sums of other terms in the sequence.

▶ **The Fibonacci sequence follows a pattern without using a constant as in arithmetic and geometric sequences. Other sequences may also follow patterns that do not use constants.**

15. c. 233;
Explanations will vary. The total numbers of pairs are terms of the Fibonacci sequence. The thirteenth term, which corresponds to the twelfth month or one year, is 233.

16. Answers may vary. Sample Response: The sum of the first, second, third, and fourth terms is 1 less than the sixth term; the sum of the first, second, third, fourth, and fifth terms is 1 less than the seventh term.

BACKGROUND INFORMATION
Leonardo Fibonacci's "claim to fame" came about quite by accident through the theoretical rabbit problem he posed in his book, *Liber Abaci.* His solution to this problem, which became known as the Fibonacci Sequence, or Fibonacci numbers, has had implications in other fields such as botany, art, biology, and music.

Occurrences of Fibonacci numbers can be found in the structure of certain plants such as the Sneeze wort plant and in the genealogy of a male bee. The use of Fibonacci numbers has influenced abstract art and the rhythmic structure of musical compositions. However, one of the most striking examples in nature is the occurrence of the Fibonacci numbers in phyllotaxy (the arrangement of leaves on a stem).

14. See Additional Answers beginning on page A1.

523

DEVELOPING MATH CONCEPTS

After students complete **Question 17**, you may want to use **Exercise 9** from the **Extra Skill Practice** to explore the fact that a sequence of growing squares also produces square numbers (or perfect squares). Using pattern blocks, challenge students to find other polygons that follow this pattern. Ask what they notice about polygons that follow the pattern. (*They are regular polygons.*)

TEACHING NOTES

Question 18 The figurate numbers shown in the sequence are neither arithmetic nor geometric, yet they follow a definite pattern. Ask students why the pattern shown is not arithmetic. (*It does not increase by adding a constant.*) Then ask why the sequence is not geometric. (*It does not increase by multiplying by a constant.*)

DIFFERENTIATED INSTRUCTION

Question 20 It may be helpful for students to work in pairs to make a chart showing how many bags of coins Mr. Haktak puts in the pot, how many he removes, and how many total he reserves.

step	bags in	bags out	total bags saved
1	1	2	0
2	2	4	1
3	3	6	3
4	4	8	6
5	5	10	10

Some students may need to use a manipulative to "act out" each step of the situation in order to make sense of the scenario.

---

18. a. Sample Responses: The difference between two consecutive terms increases by 1 with each successive set of terms (+2, then +3, then +4...). Each term is the sum of the term number and the previous term.

19. a. The numbers added to successive terms increase by 2 each time; 42, 56, 72

  b. The numbers added to successive terms decrease by consecutive powers of 2 each time: 276, 148, −108

✔ **QUESTION 19**

...checks that you can find patterns in sequences.

19. c. Each term is 1 less than twice the previous term; 97, 193, 385

  d. Each term is the opposite of twice the previous term; 96, −192, 384

---

17 Triangles are constructed as shown below. To create each successive triangle in the sequence, small congruent triangles are added to the previous triangle as shown.

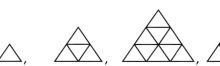

a. Write a rule to show how the number of small triangles in each term relates to the term number of this sequence.
$t = n^2$ where t = term and n = term number

b. What do you call the numbers in this sequence? **perfect squares**

18 **Try This as a Class** The arrays below represents the first four terms in the sequence of *triangular numbers*.

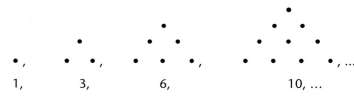

1,   3,   6,   10, …

a. Describe any patterns you notice in how the terms of the sequence are related to each other or in how the number of dots in each term is related to the term number.

b. Use the pattern you noticed in part (a) to find the next three terms in the sequence. **15, 21, 28**

19 ✔ **CHECKPOINT** Look for a pattern in each sequence. Then find the next three terms.

a. 2, 6, 12, 20, 30, …   **b.** 400, 396, 388, 372, 340, …

c. 4, 7, 13, 25, 49, …   **d.** −3, 6, −12, 24, −48, …

20 In Exploration 1 you saw how Mr. Haktak tried to conserve some of his money by setting some of the bags of money aside rather than putting them all into the pot.

a. How many total bags did he have set aside before using the pot the second time? the third time? the fourth time? the fifth time? the sixth time? **0; 1; 3; 6; 10**

b. How is the sequence created by the terms you recorded in part (a) related to the other sequences in this section?
Answers will vary. It has the same pattern as the triangular numbers (but with a different first term). The difference between two consecutive terms increases by 1 with each pair of successive terms.

HOMEWORK EXERCISES ▶ See Exs. 13–20 on pp. 527–528.

Section 1
Key Concepts

Arithmetic Sequences (pp. 519–520)

A sequence is an ordered list of numbers or objects called terms. An arithmetic sequence is one in which each term after the first is found by adding a constant to the previous term.

sequence

Example The sequence 1, 3, 5, 7, ... describes the number of triangles in each figure.

term

arithmetic sequence

Geometric Sequences (p. 520)

In a geometric sequence, each term after the first is found by multiplying the previous term by a nonzero constant.

Example The sequence 1, 5, 25, 125, ... describes the number of shaded squares in each figure.

geometric sequence

 , , , , ...

1,   5 ,   25 ,   125

Other Sequences (pp. 522–524)

In the Fibonacci sequence each term after the second is the sum of the two previous terms.

1, 1, 2, 3, 5, 8, 13, ...

Fibonacci sequence

In the following sequence, the differences of pairs of consecutive terms increase by 1.

1, 3, 6, 10, 15, 21, ...

Key Concepts Questions

21 Is the sequence 3, 8, 13, 18, 23, ... *arithmetic* or *geometric?* Explain. **arithmetic; The difference between each set of consecutive terms is 5.**

22 Write an equation that uses the term number n to find the nth term t of the sequence 1, 5, 25, 125.... $t = 5^{n-1}$

Section 1 Patterns and Sequences **525**

Key Concepts

CLOSURE QUESTIONS

How is the term number related to any term in an arithmetic and geometric sequence?

Sample Response: In an arithmetic sequence, to find any term, the constant difference is multiplied by one less than the term number. That product is added to the first term to obtain the term for that term number. In a geometric sequence, the exponent of the ratio is one less than the term number. This power is then multiplied by the first term to obtain the term for that term number.

ABSENT STUDENTS

For students who were absent for part or all of this section, the blackline Study Guide for Section 1 may be used to present the ideas, concepts, and skills of Section 1.

SUGGESTED ASSIGNMENTS

Core Course

Day 1: Exs. 21–26
Day 2: Exs. 1–11
Day 3: Exs. 13–14, 28–29
Day 4: Exs. 15–20

Extended Course

Day 1: Exs. 21–26
Day 2: Exs. 1–12
Day 3: Exs. 13–14, 28–29
Day 4: Exs. 16–20, 27*

Note: Extended Course assignments can be used to differentiate within the regular classroom. In classrooms where students are grouped homogeneously, the material might be covered in fewer days. In this case assignments may be combined.

* denotes Extension Exercise

ADDITIONAL PRACTICE

See the *Teacher's Resource Book* for additional practice and application exercises for this section.

YOU WILL NEED

For Exs. 21–22:
♦ grid paper
♦ ruler

For Exs. 23–24:
♦ protractor

For Ex. 27
♦ Labsheet 1A

1. geometric (multiply by $\frac{1}{2}$)

Section 1
Practice & Application Exercises

Identify each sequence as *arithmetic*, *geometric*, or *neither*.

1. $\frac{1}{2}$, $\frac{1}{4}$, $\frac{1}{8}$, $\frac{1}{16}$, ...

2. 4, 6, 9, 13, ...
neither

3. 94, 47, 23.5, 11.75, ...
geometric (multiply by 0.5)

4. –24, –13, –2, 9, ...
arithmetic (add 11)

5. 0.7, 1.1, 1.5, 1.9, ...
arithmetic (add 0.4)

6. 4, 9, 16, 25, ...
neither

Find the next three terms in each sequence.

7. 5, 6, 8, 11, ... 15, 20, 26

8. 128, 32, 8, 2, ... $\frac{1}{2}$, $\frac{1}{8}$, $\frac{1}{32}$

9. $10x$, $20x^2$, $40x^3$, $80x^4$, ...
$160x^5$, $320x^6$, $640x^7$

10. $\frac{1}{3}$, $\frac{3}{3}$, $\frac{5}{3}$, $\frac{7}{3}$, ... $\frac{9}{3}$, $\frac{11}{3}$, $\frac{13}{3}$

11. Write an equation that uses the term number n to find the nth term t of each sequence. Sequence 1: $t = 2n + 1$, or $n + (n + 1)$, or $2(n + 1) - 1$; Sequence 2: $t = 2 \cdot 3^{n-1}$

Sequence I

Term number	1	2	3	4	5	...	n
Term	3	5	7	9	11	...	t

12. a.

	1	2	3	4	5	6	7
	1	3	6	10	15	21	28

Sequence II

Term number	1	2	3	4	5	...	n
Term	2	6	18	54	162	...	t

12. **Challenge** At age 10, Carl Gauss, a future mathematician, was given a challenging problem by his teacher. The teacher expected the students in his class to struggle with the problem, but Carl solved the problem in a matter of seconds by finding a pattern.

The Problem: *Add the first one hundred positive integers.*

a. Make a table showing a sequence whose nth term t is the sum of the first n positive whole numbers.

b. Look for a pattern that relates a term to the product of its term number and the next term number. Each term is half of the product of its term number and the following term number.

c. Use the pattern in part (b) to write an equation for the sequence. $t = \dfrac{n(n+1)}{2}$

d. Solve Gauss's problem. The sum of the first one hundred positive integers is 5050.

13. Music Use the piano keyboard shown.

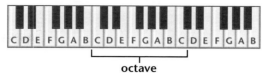

octave

a. How many *whole* black keys are there in an octave?
5 whole black keys

b. How many white keys are there in an octave? 8 white keys

c. What is the total number of keys in an octave? 13 keys

d. How are your answers to parts (a)–(c) related to the Fibonacci sequence? They are terms 5–7 of the Fibonacci sequence.

14. Biology A male bee is called a *drone* and has only a mother because it develops from an unfertilized egg. A female bee has a mother and a father because it develops from a fertilized egg.

a. The figure below shows the "family tree" of a drone. You read the tree from the bottom up. Copy the family tree and extend it to six generations back. See margin.

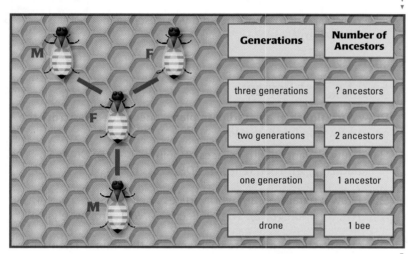

Generations	Number of Ancestors
three generations	? ancestors
two generations	2 ancestors
one generation	1 ancestor
drone	1 bee

b. Use your family tree to find the total number of bees in each generation. What pattern do you see? 1, 1, 2, 3, 5, 8, 13; the Fibonacci sequence

c. Without extending the diagram, find the total number of ancestors the drone would have eight generations back. Explain how you got your answer.

15. Writing Kanesha wrote a sequence using the rule *multiply the previous term by 2 and subtract 3.*

a. What is the fifth term of the sequence if the first term is 6? 51

b. Will each new term always be an odd number? Explain your thinking. Yes; Sample Response: Multiplying by 2 will give you an even number and subtracting 3 will make that number odd.

Practice & Applications

EXERCISE NOTES

Exercise 20 Students may find it helpful to draw the tiling and extend it to find the fourth and fifth terms in the sequence before trying to write an equation. Encourage students to apply the strategies learned in this section as they complete the exercise.

ALTERNATIVE APPROACH

Some students may need to physically build the tiling from **Exercise 20**. Have colored tiles available for those who require this aid.

22.

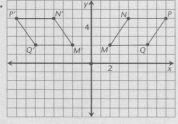

16. Add 0.5, then 1, then 1.5... to each successive term; 11.5, 14.5, 18

Visual THINKING

Exercise 20 checks that you understand sequences.

17. Add 3, then 3^2, then 3^3, 3^4... to each successive term; 364, 1093, 3280

18. Subtract 1, then 2, then 3...; –7, –13, –20

19. The terms are consecutive powers of 3, starting with 3^0; $3^5 = 243$, $3^6 = 729$, $3^7 = 2187$

20. b. Each successive term increases by 4 and can be described by the equation $t = 1 + (n - 1)4$ where t = term and n = term number.

21.

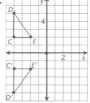

Describe the pattern in each sequence. Then use the pattern to write the next three terms of the sequence.

16. 4, 4.5, 5.5, 7, 9, ...

17. 1, 4, 13, 40, 121, ...

18. 8, 7, 5, 2, –2, ...

19. 1, 3, 9, 27, 81, ...

Reflecting ▶ on the Section

20. In the figure at the right, the tiling begins with a blue tile. The yellow tiles show the next set of tiles in the sequence. The red tiles are the third set of tiles in the sequence.

a. If this pattern continues, how many tiles will be needed for the tenth set of added tiles in the sequence? 37

b. Describe the pattern you found in words and with an equation.

c. What kind of sequence did you describe in part (b)? arithmetic

Spiral ▶ Review

Draw each figure in a coordinate plane, then reflect it across the given axis. (Module 6, p. 436)

21. Draw a triangle with vertices at points C(–4, 2), D(–4, 5), and E(–2, 2). Then reflect △CDE across the x-axis.

22. Draw a parallelogram with vertices at points M(2, 2), N(4, 5), P(8, 5), and Q(6, 2). Then reflect □MNPQ across the y-axis.
See margin.

Use a protractor to measure each angle in the figure. Then answer Exercises 23–26. (Module 5, p. 369)

23. What is the measure of an angle that is a complement of ∠CAD? 48° (based on m∠CAD = 42°)

24. What is the measure of an angle that is a supplement of ∠CEB? 123° (based on m∠CEB = 57°)

25. Name an angle that is a complement of ∠AEB. ∠BEC

26. Name an angle that is a supplement of ∠CBE. ∠ABE

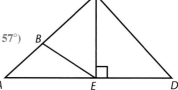

Extension ▶ ▶

The Koch Snowflake

Many objects in nature such as trees and snowflakes can be modeled by geometric shapes called *fractals*. The Koch snowflake is a fractal.

Use Labsheet 1A for Exercise 27.

27. **a.** Complete the third and fourth rows of the table. **See margin.**

   b. Describe the patterns in the sequences formed by the entries in the second and third columns. Then describe how each entry in the third column relates to entries in the other columns.

   c. Complete the last row in the table by writing an expression for the *n*th term of each sequence. **See table in part (a).**

Career Connection

Digital Artist: Junpei Sekino

When Junpei Sekino was 10 years old he won first prize for the junior division in a national printmaking contest in Japan. He now combines art and mathematics to create fractal art.
28–29. See margin.

28. Computers are often used to generate fractals and other patterns. Follow the steps below to get an idea of how computers are used to create patterns.

   First Draw a coordinate grid. Label the *x*-axis and the *y*-axis from 0 to 10.

   Next Evaluate the expression *xy* for all pairs (*x*, *y*) on the grid section you drew with *x* and *y* whole numbers. For example, for (2, 3), the value is 2 • 3 = 6.

   Then Plot and color the point for each coordinate on your grid using the following rules.

   - If *xy* is a multiple of 10, color the point green.
   - If *xy* is an odd number, color the point blue.
   - If *xy* is neither of these, color the point red.

29. What patterns do you see on your grid? What do you think would be the result if the numbers on the grid went to 100?

Junpei Sekino uses fractals to show the beautiful patterns in mathematics, as in his digital art, *Fractal Sphere,* below.

27 b. The number of line segments in each stage is multiplied by 4 to obtain the number of line segments in the next stage. The length of each segment in one stage is multiplied by $\frac{1}{3}$ to get the length of each segment in the next stage. To get the total perimeter at each stage, you multiply the entry in the "Number of segments" column by the entry in the "Length of each segment" column.

EXERCISE NOTES
Extension Exercise 27 Students should recognize the geometric sequences that appear in creating the fractal on *Labsheet 1A.* Fractal geometry is a growing area of interest with the increased power of computers. Fractal geometry is used in many movies to recreate mountains, clouds, or other natural features of the earth. For students who have an interest in learning more about fractals, a simple web search will provide them with links to many sites—some interactive—dealing with fractal geometry and its use in our world today. Students can then be encouraged to create their own fractal to share with the class.

The **Career Connection** offers one application of fractal geometry in the life of a digital artist.

28.

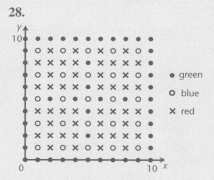

29. The outside edge is green dots. Inside the green dot edge, the following patterns occur from left to right; blue, red, blue, red, blue, red, blue, red, blue—rows 1, 3, 7 and 9; red, red, red, red, green, red, red, red, red—rows 2, 4, 6, and 8; blue, green, blue, green, blue, green, blue, green, blue—row 5; The pattern would repeat itself every 10 rows.

27. a. See Additional Answers beginning on page A1.

529

5. Multiply the previous term by $\frac{2}{3}$;
   $\frac{16}{162}, \frac{32}{486}, \frac{64}{1458}$

6. Subtract 5 from the previous term. $-6, -11, -16$

8. Sample Response: In both geometric and arithmetic sequences each term increases or decreases by a constant. Arithmetic sequences change more gradually since the constant is added to obtain each successive term. Geometric sequences change dramatically since the the term is multiplied by the constant to obtain each successive term.

Section 1

Extra Skill Practice

Write a rule for finding a term of each sequence. Then find the next three terms. 5–6 and 8. See margin.

1. $x, 1 + x, 2 + x, 3 + x, \ldots$
2. $64, 16, 4, 1, \ldots$
3. $4, -20, 100, -500, \ldots$

4. $24, 26, 30, 36, \ldots$
5. $\frac{1}{2}, \frac{2}{6}, \frac{4}{18}, \frac{8}{54}, \ldots$
6. $14, 9, 4, -1, \ldots$

7. Tell whether each of the sequences in Exercises 1–6 is *arithmetic*, *geometric*, or *neither*. 1: arithmetic; 2: geometric; 3: geometric; 4: neither; 5: geometric; 6: arithmetic

8. Describe the similarities and differences between arithmetic and geometric sequences.

9. Each of the following figures is made up of squares congruent to the first one in the sequence.

□, ⊞, ▦, ...
1, 4, 9, ...

1. Add 1 to the previous term; $4 + x, 5 + x, 6 + x$

2. Divide the previous term by 4; $\frac{1}{4}, \frac{1}{16}, \frac{1}{64}$

3. Multiply the previous term by -5; $2500, -12,500, 62,500$

4. Increase the difference between the two previous terms by 2; $44, 54, 66$

   a. What is the 10th term in the sequence? 100
   b. What is the nth term in the sequence? n^2

10. To what sequence is the sequence $3, 4, 7, 11, 18, \ldots$ related? Explain. It is related to the Fibonacci sequence because each successive term is found by adding the the two previous terms together.

Study Skills ◀▶ Test-Taking Strategies

There are many different types of test questions, including multiple choice, free response, open-ended, and performance task. The Standardized Testing feature in this book has provided practice with these types of questions. 1–2. See margin.

1. When you answer a multiple choice question, it is important to read all the choices before you decide which one is correct. Look back at Question 1 in the Standardized Testing feature on page 213. Explain why each choice is either correct or incorrect.

2. When you complete a performance task, it is important to show all your work. Look back at the performance task in the Standardized Testing feature on page 221. Describe the steps that you should show in your solution.

Changing SHAPE

The Situation See the *Teacher's Resource Book* for a sample solution for this Extended Exploration.

Some fractals can be constructed in surprising ways. Here are the first six steps for constructing a fractal called the *Sierpinski triangle* using circles.

The Problem

Find a method for determining the number of circles in each step. Then find the number of circles that would be needed for Steps 7–9.

Something to Think About

◆ How were the figures in each step created?

Present Your Results

Explain how you solved the problem and why your method worked. Use tables and drawings to support your explanation.

Extended Exploration

E² NOTES

The Extended Exploration provides students another opportunity to explore the patterns that evolve in fractals. One method of creating a Sierpinski triangle is offered here. If neither the Extension Exercise nor the Career Connection on page 529 were completed, students will need some background information about fractals. The definition given in the Extension Exercise on page 529 will suffice for completion of this E². Encourage students to use what they have learned about patterns as they contemplate the problem that is posed.

Using an E²: Suggestions for managing and evaluating an Extended Exploration are available in the *Teacher's Resource Book* for Modules 1 and 2. See also pages T44–T45 in the *Teacher's Edition*.

Section ② Polygons and Rotational Symmetry

ARCHITECTS and ENGINEERS

Setting the Stage

When designing houses or commercial properties, many architects take into account the natural environment around them. Landscape architects may design walkways and use plants to enhance a building's architecture or help draw the viewer's eye away from undesirable features. Architects may use nature's influence in the design or decoration of a building. Some examples are shown below.

Ceramic wall tile

Spiral staircase

Outdoor patio

Think About It

1 How is nature's influence evident in the tile design? **Answers will vary. Sample Response: The interior of the tiling resembles a flower.**

2 What item in nature might the architect of the spiral staircase have been thinking about when designing it? Explain. **Answers will vary. Sample Response: the shell of a chambered nautilus**

3 How does the patio design complement the geometry of the doors of the entryway? **Answers will vary. Sample Response: The two rectangular doors together form a square (note the shape of the doorway) as do pairs of nonsquare rectangular tiles on the patio floor.**

Exploration 1

Angles of POLYGONS

SET UP *Work with a partner. You will need:* • *Labsheets 2A and 2B*
• *ruler* • *scissors* • *plain white paper*

GOAL

LEARN HOW TO...
♦ find the sum of the measures of the interior angles of a polygon

AS YOU...
♦ look for patterns in polygons

▶ Many different patio designs can be made using pre-formed stones called *pavers*. The rectangle is considered one of the most basic shapes for pavers, although combinations of rectangular pavers can be used to create more complicated designs.

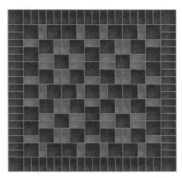

4 **Discussion** The pavers in both patio designs at the right fit together with no overlaps or gaps.

  a. Why do rectangles fit together so well?

  b. The patio designs shown use a combination of different size squares and rectangles that are not squares. Would it be possible to use only one size rectangle to build a design that fits together with no gaps or overlaps? If so, describe a design. If not, explain why not.

  c. Suppose you were to design a patio with pavers shaped like the polygons below. Do you think copies of either polygon would fit together without overlaps or gaps? Explain. Answers will vary.

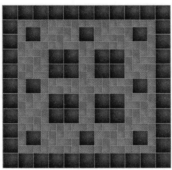

5 **Use Labsheet 2A.** Work with a partner to create two designs using *Pentagons and Hexagons*. Check students' work.

6 **a.** Which polygon from Labsheet 2A can be copied to fit together without gaps or overlaps? the hexagon

  b. Why do you think copies of one polygon fit together without gaps or overlaps and copies of the other polygon do not?
See margin.

4. a. Sample Response: All the corners are right angles so they fit with no gaps.
  b. Yes. Sample Response: Use congruent squares.

Exploration 1

TEACHING NOTES
Question 4 introduces the concept of tiling a plane with polygons. In **part (c)**, students are to make a prediction and justify it. At this time, it is important to accept any response. The activities that follow will test the hypothesis and help students make discoveries about the relationship between the angle measures a polygon and whether it can be used to create a *tessellation* (a tiling with no gaps or overlaps).

After completing **Question 6**, place overhead pattern blocks, tangram pieces, and/or other geometric shapes on the overhead projector and ask students to predict which ones will tessellate (fit together without gaps or overlaps). The reasoning students use will help you to assess whether they have developed the "spatial sense" to visually recognize the attributes they will explore in this exploration.

TIPS FROM TEACHERS
Question 5 You may want to reproduce **Labsheet 2A** on construction paper or card stock to make tracing easier.

DIFFERENTIATED INSTRUCTION
Question 5 Visual learners may benefit from using a different colored pencil to trace the outline of each polygon they create in **Labsheet 2A**. This will prevent confusion in distinguishing each polygon among all the lines drawn.

6. b. See Additional Answers beginning on page A1.

533

Exploration 1 *continued*

concave polygon

▶ The pentagons and hexagons you used to create your designs are examples of *convex* polygons. A polygon is convex if all its diagonals lie inside the polygon. A polygon that is not convex is *concave*. To decide whether copies of a convex polygon will fit together without gaps or overlaps, it helps to think about the *interior angles* of the polygon.

Use Labsheet 2B for Questions 7 and 8.

7 Follow the directions on the labsheet for finding *Patterns in Polygons*. You will explore the relationship between the number of sides of a convex polygon and the measure of its interior angles. See margin.

8 **Discussion**

a. How is the number of triangles in each polygon related to the number of sides of the polygon? It is 2 less than the number of sides.

b. How can you find the sum of the measures of the interior angles of any convex polygon? Multiply the number that is 2 less than the number of sides of the polygon by 180°.

9 ✔ **CHECKPOINT** Find the sum of the measures of the interior angles of each convex polygon.

a. heptagon (7-sided polygon) 900°

b. nonagon (9-sided polygon) 1260°

c. decagon (10-sided polygon) 1440°

10 The interior angles of a *regular polygon* are congruent.

a. What is the measure of one interior angle of a regular hexagon? 120°

b. What is the measure of one interior angle of a regular pentagon? 108°

11 Which of the following expressions could be used to find the measure of one interior angle of a regular polygon with *n* sides?

$$\frac{(n-2)180}{n} \qquad n(n-2)180 \qquad \frac{(n-2)}{180n} \qquad \frac{(n-2)180}{n}$$

12 Use what you know about the interior angles of convex polygons to explain what you observed about pentagons and hexagons in Question 6. (*Hint*: Find the sum of the angle measures where the polygons have a common vertex.)

HOMEWORK EXERCISES ▶ See Exs. 1–13 on pp. 538–539.

 Module 8 MATH-Thematical Mix

Exploration 2

Rotational Symmetry

SET UP *You will need: • Labsheet 2C • protractor*

Have you ever been drawn to the beauty of a flower or amazed by a starfish on the beach? Some people would claim that the object's symmetry is what caught your eye. So it's no wonder that many architects incorporate symmetry into their designs in hopes of catching the public's eye.

▶ **Fort Jefferson is on Garden Key off the Gulf Coast of Florida. Its design is based on *rotational symmetry*. A figure has rotational symmetry if it fits exactly on itself after being rotated less than 360° around a center point.**

Use Labsheet 2C with Questions 13–15.

13 Use the Fort Jefferson design and your protractor to find *Rotational Symmetries*.

▶ **The minimum rotational symmetry of a figure is the least angle measure, greater than 0° but less than 360°, that you could rotate a copy of an object for it to match with the original.**

14 What is the minimum rotational symmetry for the Fort Jefferson design? 60°

GOAL

LEARN HOW TO...
- ◆ describe rotational symmetry

AS YOU...
- ◆ discover patterns in nature and architecture

KEY TERMS
- ◆ rotational symmetry
- ◆ minimum rotational symmetry

13. Labsheet 2C
Answers:

$m\angle AOB = 60°$
$m\angle BOC = 60°$
$m\angle COD = 60°$
$m\angle DOE = 60°$
$m\angle EOF = 60°$
$m\angle FOA = 60°$

a. They are all the same.
b. point *B*: 60°
point *C*: 120°
point *D*: 180°
point *E*: 240°
point *F*: 300°

Exploration 2

TEACHING NOTES
Question 13 Draw attention to the fact that the named angles shown on the polygon ($\angle AOB$, $\angle BOC$, etc.) on **Labsheet 2C** are formed by drawing a segment from the center of the polygon to each of the labeled vertices. Students may want to pair up, overlay one labsheet on the other, and then physically rotate the polygon to observe how the angle of rotation is determined. Another option would be to have extra labsheets available for groups to cut out the polygon and physically rotate it on the page.

TEACHING NOTES

Question 15 Prompt students to answer **part (a)** by asking how many degrees are in a circle. (*360°*) If they were to rotate the design, how many times would they be able to turn it clockwise, making sure it matched after each turn, before returning to the starting position? (*5*) How could you use this information to get the minimum rotational symmetry of 72°? (*divide 360° by 5*)

The following Classroom Example may be used to bring closure to the class discussion in **Question 15**.

CLASSROOM EXAMPLE

The flower below has rotational symmetry. Find the minimum rotational symmetry and all of the rotational symmetries between 0° and 360°.

Answer:
Method 1:
Use a protractor to measure the angle formed by drawing a ray from the center of the flower to the tip of one petal and another ray from the center to the tip of an adjacent petal.
60°; 120°, 180°, 240°, 300°

Method 2:
There are 360° in a circle. Divide 360° by the number of congruent angles formed by the plant (6).
360° ÷ 6 = 60°; 60°, 120°, 180°, 240°, 300°

19. See Additional Answers beginning on page A1.

---

15. b. Sample Response: Add the minimum rotational symmetry together two times, three times, four times... until you have found all the rotational symmetries of the figure.

17. a. minimum: 60°; 120°, 180°, 240°, 300°
b. no rotational symmetry
c. minimum: 120°; 240°

18. Sample Response:

✔ **QUESTION 18**

...checks that you can use rotational symmetry to create shapes.

---

15 Try This as a Class

a. How could you find the minimum rotational symmetry of the Fort Jefferson design without using a protractor?
Divide 360 by the number of possible rotations.
b. How can you use the minimum rotational symmetry of a figure to find all its rotational symmetries?

16 Without using a protractor, find the minimum rotational symmetry of each flower on these iron gates.

a.  45°   **b.**  30°

17 Objects in nature may seem symmetrical, though they do not have perfect symmetry. Tell which figures appear to have rotational symmetry. For those that do, name all the rotational symmetries they appear to have.

a. 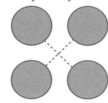   **b.**    **c.**

18 ✔ CHECKPOINT Sketch a shape that has rotational symmetries of 90°, 180°, and 270°.

19 At first glance the design below appears to have multiple rotational symmetries. Explain why it does not. Identify its only rotational symmetry. See margin.

◀ Folk-art designs like this one are a common outdoor sight in some areas of Pennsylvania.

HOMEWORK EXERCISES ▶ See Exs. 14–18 on pp. 539–540.

536

Section 2

Key Concepts

- **Key Terms**

Interior Angles of Polygons (pp. 533–534)

The sum of the measures of the interior angles of a convex polygon depends on the number of sides. The equation $S = 180°(n - 2)$ gives the sum S of the measures of the interior angles of a polygon with n sides.

Example

This is an 8-sided polygon, so
$S = 180°(8 - 2) = 1080°$.

In a regular 8-sided polygon each angle would measure 135° since $1080 ÷ 8 = 135$.

Rotational Symmetry (pp. 535–536)

An object has rotational symmetry if it fits exactly on itself after a rotation of less than 360° around a center point.

rotational symmetry

Example This figure has rotational symmetries of 90°, 180° and 270°. Its minimum rotational symmetry is 90°.

This figure does not have rotational symmetry.

minimum rotational symmetry

Key Concepts Questions

20 What is the sum of the measures of the interior angles of a 12-sided convex polygon? **1800°**

21 What is the minimum rotational symmetry of each figure?

a.   **72°**   b.   **30°**

Key Concepts

COMMON ERROR
Question 21(b) Some students may erroneously count all of the petals and calculate the minimum rotational symmetry as 15° rather than 30°. Encourage them to look closely at the picture and notice that only the petals in the foreground should be counted to determine the rotational symmetry.

CLOSURE QUESTION
Do all regular polygons have rotational symmetry? Explain.

Sample Response: Yes; If the polygon has an odd number of sides, the center of rotation is the point where the segments drawn from each vertex of the polygon to the midpoint of the opposite side intersect. If the polygon has an even number of sides, the center of rotation is the point where the diagonals drawn between vertices that are directly opposite each other intersect. The central angles formed by drawing rays from the center of rotation through adjacent vertices will all be congruent, and since the measure of the interior angles of a regular polygon are equal and its sides are congruent, when the polygon is rotated through each of the central angles, it will coincide with itself.

ABSENT STUDENTS
For students who were absent for part or all of this section, the blackline Study Guide for Section 2 may be used to present the ideas, concepts, and skills of Section 2.

ADDITIONAL PRACTICE
See the *Teacher's Resource Book* for additional practice and application exercises for this section.

EXERCISE NOTES
Exercises 5–8 Students should apply their knowledge about the sum of the measures of the interior angles of a polygon to find the unknown angle measure without measuring.

DEVELOPING MATH CONCEPTS
Exercises 9 and 10 Some students may try to measure the angles of the polygons with a protractor. In doing this, they may not end up with an exact answer. If they choose to employ this strategy, encourage them to check their answer using the formula $\frac{(n-2)180}{n}$, where n is the number of sides of the polygon.

Section ② Practice & Application Exercises

Find the sum of the measures of the interior angles of each polygon.

1.  1080°

2.  360°

3.  360°

4.  540°

Find the unknown angle measure in each polygon.

5.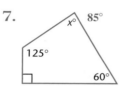

6.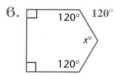

7.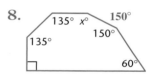

8.

Find the measure of one interior angle of each regular polygon. Round your answers to the nearest hundredth.

9. 128.57°

10. 140°

11. **Challenge** Look for a pattern in the sum of the measures of the *exterior angles* of a polygon.

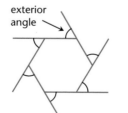

exterior angle

a. Draw several polygons with different numbers of sides. Draw one exterior angle at each vertex. **Check student' drawings.**

b. Find the sum of the measures of the exterior angles you sketched. Record your results in a table. What pattern do you notice? **Sample Response: triangle, quadrilateral, pentagon, hexagon, heptagon all have exterior angles whose sum is 360°.**

12. Patio designs such as the one shown at the right can be created from a paver stone in which a square is attached to a regular octagon. Use the measures of interior angles to explain why this paver shape can create a patio design with no gaps or overlaps.

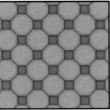

13. A *tessellation* is a repeating pattern of shapes that cover a plane with no gaps or overlaps.

  a. Draw and cut out a triangle or a quadrilateral. Trace around it several times to create a tessellation. **Check students' drawings.**

  b. On Labsheet 2A, you discovered that a regular hexagon could create a tessellation. Can a tessellation be made using any other regular polygons? Explain your thinking.

  c. This tessellation uses regular hexagons and equilateral triangles. List two other combinations of regular polygons that could be used to create a tessellation. Make a sketch of these new combinations of polygons.

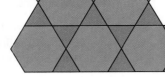

12. Sample Response: The measure of an interior angle of the octagon is 135°. The measure of an interior angle of a square is 90°. There are two 135° angles and one 90° angle at each vertex of the figure. 2(135) + 90 = 360°.

14. A figure has a minimum rotational symmetry of 30°. What other rotational symmetries does the figure have? **60°, 90°, 120°, 150°, 180°, 210°, 240°, 270°, 300°, 330°**

15. Japanese Family Crests In Japan, family crests are used to distinguish one family from another. Crests are typically carried on by a family's eldest son. Sometimes the patterns are modified by the younger males to show their heritage and differentiation. An example of a modified crest is shown below.

Original igeta	Igeta with a ring	Igeta with angular ring	Compounded igeta	Stacked igeta

◄ *Igeta* means "well crib" and refers to a framework that supports a well.

  a. What is the minimum rotational symmetry of the original igeta? **180°**

  b. Do the modified igetas have the same rotational symmetry as the original igeta? Explain. **All but the stacked igeta which does not have rotational symmetry**

16. Create Your Own Create 3 different designs that involve rotational symmetry. Use a different minimum rotational symmetry for each design. List all the rotational symmetries for each design. **Answers will vary. Check students' designs.**

13. b. Yes; a square and an equilateral triangle; They have interior angles whose measure is a factor of 360°.

  c. Sample Response: octagons and squares, triangles and squares; Check students' drawings.

EXERCISE NOTES
Exercise 13(c) Have pattern blocks or other geometric shapes available for students who require a concrete aid in visualizing the process of tiling with two or more polygons. They can then sketch or trace the polygons that form the resulting tessellation.

539

Practice & Applications

EXERCISE NOTES

Exercise 17 Remind students that objects in nature don't have exact rotational symmetry, however, some appear to be more symmetrical than others. They should look for those objects that visually appear to have rotational symmetry.

17. a. A: 72°; Divide 360° by 5; B: 180°; Divide 360° by 2; E: 20°; Divide 360° by 18; F: 60°; Divide 360° by 6.

18. Sample Response: If $600° = 180°(n - 2)$, then $n = 5\frac{1}{3}$, but n must be a whole number since it represents the number of sides of the polygon.

17. Use the objects shown.

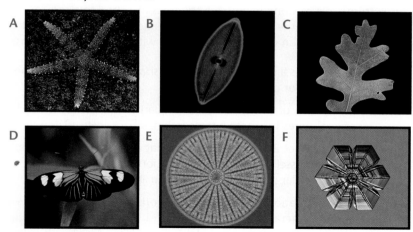

A   B   C

D   E   F

a. Tell which objects appear to have rotational symmetry. For each of these, find the minimum rotational symmetry and explain how you found your answer.

b. A figure has *line symmetry* if one half of the figure is the mirror image of the other half. Tell which objects appear to have line symmetry. **A, B, D, E, and F**

c. Make a Venn diagram that organizes the objects into these categories: objects that have line symmetry, objects that have rotational symmetry, objects that have both types of symmetry, and objects that have neither type of symmetry.

Journal

Exercise 18 checks that you understand the formula for finding the sum of the measures of the interior angles of a polygon.

Reflecting ◀▶ on the Section

Write your response to Exercise 18 in your journal.

18. Use the equation $S = 180°(n - 2)$ to explain why it is impossible to have an n-sided polygon for which the sum of the measures of the interior angles is 600°.

17. c.

> line symmetry — rotational & line symmetry — rotational symmetry
>
> D — A, B, E, F — C

Spiral ◀▶ Review

Multiply. Write each product in descending order of exponents. (Module 7, p. 506)

19. $(x + 5)(x - 10)$
$x^2 - 5x - 50$

20. $(2x - 4)(x - 7)$
$2x^2 - 18x + 28$

21. $(6x + 1)(6x - 1)$
$36x^2 - 1$

22. Evaluate $5 \cdot 10^x$ for $x = 4$.   (Module 3, p. 209) **50,000**

Section 2
Extra Skill Practice

Find the sum of the measures of the interior angles of each convex polygon.

1. a 100-sided polygon
17,640°

2. an 11-sided polygon
1620°

3. an 18-sided polygon
2880°

Find the unknown angle measure in each polygon.

4.

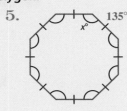

5.

Tell whether each figure appears to have rotational symmetry. If the figure has rotational symmetry, give the minimum rotational symmetry and tell what other rotational symmetries it has.

6.

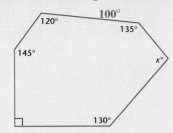

no rotational symmetry

7.

minimum:
90°; 180°, 270°

8.

no rotational symmetry

9.

no rotational symmetry

10.

minimum: 180°; none

11.

minimum: 120°; 240°

12.

no rotational symmetry

13.

minimum: 60°; 120°, 180°, 240°, 300°

Standardized Testing ◀▶ **Free Response**

1. Each measure below is the sum of the measures of the interior angles of a convex polygon. How many sides does each polygon have?

a. 360° 4 sides
b. 1800° 12 sides
c. 5940° 35 sides

2. A convex polygon has a minimum rotational symmetry of 45°. How many sides does the polygon have? 8 sides

Section 2 Polygons and Rotational Symmetry **541**

Extra Skill Practice

TEACHER NOTES
For each Exploration, the corresponding Extra Skills Practice Exercises are noted.

Exploration 1: Exs. 1–5
Exploration 2: Exs. 6–13

EXTRA HELP
Teacher's Resource Book
• Practice and Applications
• Study Guide

Technology Resources
• @Home Tutor
• Test Generator

ASSESSMENT
• Section 2 Quick Quiz
• Test Generator

Setting the Stage

ABOUT THE THEME

The methods Nageela used to study the properties of geometric figures in *The Mystery of Blacktail Canyon* provides the context for this section. The activities are designed to help students "unravel the mystery" of quadrilaterals by examining and comparing the most commonly used quadrilaterals. The section will build on students' knowledge of the basic properties of these polygons, expanding students' prior knowledge and leading them to classify each quadrilateral by more general characteristics.

GETTING STARTED

Module 8, Section 3 *Warm-Up* assesses whether students can find slopes of lines on a coordinate grid and determine whether those lines are parallel.

If students don't possess a working mathematical vocabulary of geometric terms, you may need to review terms such as perpendicular, parallel, diagonal, bisect, bisector, and congruent.

Section ③ Properties of Quadrilaterals

The Mystery of Blacktail Canyon

Setting the Stage

As the mystery at Blacktail Canyon unfolded, Nageela found broken pieces of pottery. By drawing chords and their perpendicular bisectors, she was able to locate the center of one of the circular pieces. Jim, suprised at how easily Nageela used mathematics, wondered if she could also unravel the mystery of quadrilaterals. "There are so many of them. How can I tell them apart?" Jim asked. Nageela told him that quadrilaterals have properties that distinguish them from each other. "Let me show you," she said. Nageela drew a rectangle, then added diagonal lines.

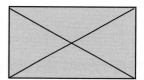

Think About It

1 Are the diagonals of the rectangle the same length? **Yes**

2 Are the diagonals of the rectangle perpendicular? Explain.
No; They do not intersect at right angles.

3 Do the diagonals bisect each other? Explain. **Yes; Each diagonal intersects the other at its midpoint.**

4 How do you think the diagonals of other rectangles compare to those of the one above? **Answers will vary.**

Exploration 1

Sides, Diagonals, and Angles

SET UP You will need: • ruler • Labsheets 3A and 3B • protractor • scissors

Use Labsheet 3A for Questions 5–7.

5 Follow the instructions on the labsheet for identifying *Characteristics of Quadrilaterals*. You'll use a protractor and ruler to make measurements. Then you'll mark right angles, sides with equal lengths, and parallel sides. **See margin.**

▶ *Quadrilaterals* can be classified according to their properties. Because different quadrilaterals can have the same properties, the quadrilaterals on Labsheet 3A may have more than one name.

6 a. A **parallelogram** is a quadrilateral that has two pairs of parallel sides. Identify all the parallelograms on the labsheet.
W, X, Y, Z

b. A **rectangle** is a quadrilateral that has four right angles. Identify all the rectangles on the labsheet. **W, Y**

c. A **rhombus** is a quadrilateral that has four congruent sides. Identify all the rhombuses on the labsheet. **W, X**

d. A **trapezoid** is a quadrilateral that has exactly one pair of parallel sides. Identify all the trapezoids on the labsheet. **V**

e. Use your results from parts (a)–(c) to give a definition for a **square**. Then identify all the squares on the labsheet.

7 Try This as a Class Complete the Venn diagram on Labsheet 3A. Decide on a category label for each oval. Then write the letter for each quadrilateral in the appropriate space on the Venn diagram. **See margin.**

8 ✔ CHECKPOINT List as many names as possible for each quadrilateral. Which name is most precise?

a.   **b.**   **c.**

LEARN HOW TO...
• classify quadrilaterals

AS YOU...
• investigate the properties of the sides, diagonals, and angles of quadrilaterals

KEY TERMS
• parallelogram
• rectangle
• rhombus
• trapezoid
• square
• kite
• opposite angles
• consecutive angles

6. e. Sample Response: A square is a parallelogram that is both a rectangle and a rhombus; W

8. a. parallelogram
   b. trapezoid
   c. rectangle; parallelogram; rectangle

✔ QUESTION 8

...checks that you can classify quadrilaterals.

Exploration 1

TEACHING NOTES
Question 5 A square, rectangle, and rhombus are all parallelograms, and a square is a rectangle as well as a rhombus. In this section each of these quadrilaterals are distinguished from each other to help students narrow the definition of each of them. Although a square fits the definition of a rhombus and a parallelogram, it has characteristics that makes it more specifically a "square".

DIFFERENTIATED INSTRUCTION
Second language learners may benefit from visual models to help them comprehend the vocabulary used in this section. Have visual diagrams available that specifically show examples of the following.

parallel || // =

perpendicular +

one pair ☆ ☆

two pair ✏✏ ✏✏

5.

7.

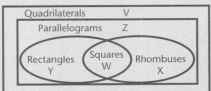

543

Exploration 1 *continued*

COMMON ERROR
Question 8 The quadrilaterals on **Labsheet 3A** have specific properties that are explored in this section. Students may believe that these are the only quadrilaterals that exist. After completing Question 8, they should be made aware that there are quadrilaterals, like the one in the example below, that do not possess any of the properties discovered on the labsheet.

CLASSROOM EXAMPLE

Classify the following quadrilateral based on its angle and/or diagonal properties.

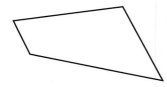

Answer:
It is a quadrilateral, but since it does not share any of the angle or diagonal properties of the quadrilaterals on the labsheet, it is not given a more specific name.

▶ In the *Setting the Stage* you explored the diagonals of a rectangle. Now you will compare the diagonals of other quadrilaterals and use that information to identify their properties.

A **kite** is a quadrilateral with two pairs of consecutive congruent sides, but opposite sides are not congruent.

9 a. On a piece of paper, draw a square, a parallelogram, a rhombus, a trapezoid, and a kite like the ones shown below. Check students' drawings.

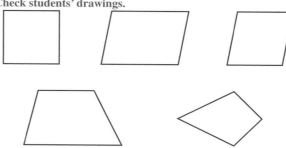

b. Draw the diagonals in each figure. Check students' drawings.

c. In which figure(s) are the diagonals congruent? the square

d. In which figure(s) do the diagonals bisect each other?
the square, the parallelogram, and the rhombus

e. In which figure(s) are the diagonals perpendicular?
the square, the kite, and the rhombus

f. Do any of the figures have diagonals that are perpendicular bisectors of each other? If so, which one(s)?
the square and the rhombus

FOR◀HELP
with perpendicular bisectors, see
MODULE 3, p. 198

Use Labsheet 3B for Questions 10–12.

10 a. Draw the diagonals of each quadrilateral in the *Properties of Quadrilaterals* table. Check students' work.

b. Use a ruler and a protractor to make measurements. In the *Diagonal Properties* column, record whether the diagonals are bisectors, are perpendicular, are neither, or are both.
See margin.

c. What generalization can you make about quadrilaterals whose diagonals are perpendicular bisectors? Both pairs of opposite sides are congruent.

11 a. Are there any quadrilaterals whose diagonals are congruent? If so, which ones? the square and the rectangle

b. What must be true about a parallelogram if its diagonals are congruent? Sample Response: It has four right angles.

10. b. See Additional Answers beginning on page A1.

▶ You have seen how quadrilaterals can be classified by their diagonals. Quadrilaterals can also be classified by the properties of their angles.

12 Use the following questions to complete the *Angle Properties* column in the *Properties of Quadrilaterals* table.

  a. How many of the quadrilaterals in the table have four congruent angles? Which quadrilaterals are they? **two; the rectangle and square**

  b. Which quadrilaterals have two pairs of congruent angles? Name the angle pairs that are congruent.

  c. Which quadrilateral has only one pair of congruent angles? **the kite**

  d. Is it possible to draw a quadrilateral, other than the one in part (c), that has only one pair of congruent angles? Explain.

◆ In a quadrilateral, angles whose vertices are the endpoints of the same diagonal are **opposite angles**.

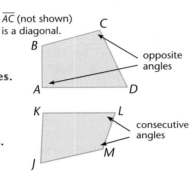

$\overline{AC}$ (not shown) is a diagonal.

opposite angles

◆ In a quadrilateral, angles whose vertices are the endpoints of the same side are **consecutive angles**.

consecutive angles

13 **Try This as a Class** Follow the steps below.

  ◆ Draw a quadrilateral with at least one pair of parallel sides and cut it out.

  ◆ Trace the quadrilateral onto a sheet of plain paper.

  ◆ Label the vertices of the original figure *A, B, C,* and *D* so that $\overline{BC}$ is parallel to $\overline{AD}$. Then label the corresponding vertices of the traced figure *A′, B′, C′,* and *D′*. **Sample Response: See margin.**

  a. Are ∠*C* and ∠*D* *opposite angles* or *consecutive angles*? **consecutive angles**

  b. Rotate the figure you cut out and position it so that ∠*C* and ∠*D′* have the same vertex and $\overline{CD}$ and $\overline{D′C′}$ overlap. **See margin.**

  c. What is the measure of the angle formed by ∠*C* and ∠*D′*? **180°**

  d. What other angles form an angle with the same measure as in part (c)? **∠*C′* and ∠*D,* ∠*C* and ∠*D,* ∠*A* and ∠*B′,* ∠*A′* and ∠*B,* ∠*A* and ∠*B***

  e. Will the measures of consecutive angles that are between parallel sides of a quadrilateral always have the same sum as those in parts (c) and (d)? Explain. **Yes; if you reproduce part (b) for any given quadrilateral with two parallel sides, the angles will form a straight angle.**

12. b. the rhombus (∠*S* ≅ ∠*Q* and ∠*R* ≅ ∠*T*); the parallelogram (∠*V* ≅ ∠*X* and ∠*U* ≅ ∠*W*); the square (∠*I,* ∠*J,* ∠*K,* and ∠*L* are all congruent.); the rectangle (∠*E,* ∠*F,* ∠*G,* and ∠*H* are all congruent.)

d. Yes; Sample Response: a trapezoid with two consecutive right angles

TEACHING NOTES

Question 13(d) Encourage students to rearrange their cutouts to find other angle pairs that are supplementary. Have them share what they found by placing their pieces on an overhead projector. Some students may have drawn parallelograms while others may have constructed trapezoids. If one or the other was not constructed, ask one or more students to do so. Then compare the result when the quadrilateral is a parallelogram and when it is a trapezoid. (The parallelogram has two sets of parallel sides, so the pieces fit together to create supplementary angles in more ways than the trapezoid.)

TEACHING NOTES

When referring to "consecutive angles between parallel sides" students should recognize the angles described are:

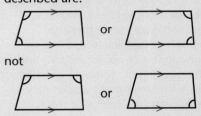

13. Sample Response and b. See Additional Answers beginning on page A1.

545

TEACHING NOTES

Question 15 Students can use the visual model in the Example that shows two transversals that make up a quadrilateral to justify their response to this question. They may notice that since $m\angle 3$ is greater than 90° and the measure of its consecutive angle along the parallel side is also greater than 90°, the two triangles cannot have a sum of 180°. Make sure students understand that the properties of alternate and corresponding angles between lines cut by a transversal only hold true when the lines are parallel.

For **Question 16**, draw two sets of parallel lines that intersect each other on the board or overhead. You may want to use colors to identify sets of angles as shown in the Example. Students should recognize that each of the lines drawn is a transversal and since there are two sets of parallel lines, there are multiple sets of corresponding and alternate angles. You may need to rotate the overhead transparency for students to "see" that this is true. Ask which pairs of angles correspond. (*multiple pairs exist*) Which pairs of angles are alternate interior angles? (*multiple pairs exist*) Lead students to use logical reasoning to show that opposite angles of the parallelogram created by the lines are congruent.

15. 180°; No; The angle properties between lines cut by a transversal only hold true when the lines are parallel.

16. See Additional Answers beginning on page A1.

---

14 **Use Labsheet 3B.** Find the sums of the measures of pairs of consecutive angles for the quadrilaterals in the table. Then tell which quadrilaterals in the table have the same diagonal and angle properties as a parallelogram. **rectangle, square, rhombus**

▶ **Transversals** You can use transversals to show why the angle properties of quadrilaterals hold true.

FOR ◀ HELP
with *transversals*,
see
MODULE 5, p. 368

EXAMPLE

Show that the consecutive angles between two parallel sides of a quadrilateral are supplementary.

Extend the sides of the quadrilateral to show the transversals.

$m\angle 2 = m\angle 4$ since they are corresponding angles.

Since $m\angle 2 + m\angle 3 = 180°$, then $m\angle 4 + m\angle 3 = 180°$.

So $\angle 3$ and $\angle 4$ are supplementary.

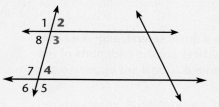

15 **Discussion** Will the consecutive angles between *nonparallel* sides of a quadrilateral be supplementary? Explain. **See margin.**

16 **Try This as a Class** Use transversals to show that opposite angles of a parallelogram are congruent. **See margin.**

✓ QUESTION 17

...checks that you can distinguish quadrilaterals by their properties.

17 **✓ CHECKPOINT** Use the table on Labsheet 3B to tell which quadrilateral is described. There may be more than one answer.

a. The diagonals bisect each other and are congruent. All angles are congruent. **square, rectangle**

b. The diagonals are perpendicular bisectors of each other. Opposite angles are congruent. **rhombus, square**

c. Consecutive angles are supplementary. The diagonals do not bisect each other and are not perpendicular. **trapezoid**

d. The diagonals are perpendicular to each other. One pair of opposite angles is congruent. **kite**

e. The diagonals are perpendicular bisectors of each other. All angles are congruent. **square**

HOMEWORK EXERCISES ▶ See Exs. 1–11 on pp. 550–551.

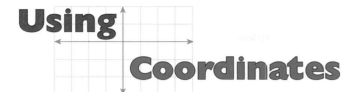

Exploration 2

Using Coordinates

SET UP Work in a group of four. You will need: • graph paper

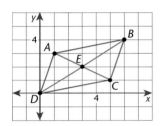

▶ When a quadrilateral is plotted on a coordinate grid, you can use coordinates and the properties of quadrilaterals to determine what type of quadrilateral it is.

18 Discussion Quadrilateral *ABCD* on the grid at the left appears to be a parallelogram. How can you show that a quadrilateral is a parallelogram? **Show that both pairs of opposite sides are parallel.**

19 One way to show that *ABCD* is a parallelogram is to use slopes to show that its opposite sides are parallel.

a. Have each person in your group find the slope of one of the segments $\overline{AB}$, $\overline{BC}$, $\overline{CD}$, and $\overline{DA}$.

b. Are the opposite sides of the quadrilateral parallel? Explain.
Yes; the slopes of the opposite sides are equal.

▶ If both pairs of opposite sides of a quadrilateral are congruent, then the quadrilateral is a parallelogram.

20 a. Try This as a Class Use the Pythagorean theorem to find the length of $\overline{CD}$. $\sqrt{26}$

b. Have each person in your group find the length of one of the segments $\overline{AB}$, $\overline{BC}$, and $\overline{DA}$. $AB = \sqrt{26}, BC = \sqrt{10}, DA = \sqrt{10}$

c. Is the quadrilateral a parallelogram? Explain. **Yes; the opposite sides are congruent.**

21 a. *E* is the midpoint of both diagonals of parallelogram *ABCD*. What are the coordinates of *E*? $(3, 2)$

b. How is the *x*-coordinate of *E* related to the *x*-coordinates of points *D* and *B*? of points *A* and *C*?

c. Answer part (b) for the *y*-coordinates of the points. **See margin.**

GOAL

LEARN HOW TO...
♦ find the distance between points on a coordinate grid
♦ find the midpoint of a segment on a coordinate grid

AS YOU...
♦ use coordinate geometry to identify quadrilaterals and explore their properties.

19. a. slope of $\overline{AB} = \frac{1}{5}$,
slope of $\overline{BC} = 3$,
slope of $\overline{CD} = \frac{1}{5}$,
slope of $\overline{DA} = 3$

FOR ◀ HELP

with *slopes of parallel lines*, see
MODULE 4, p. 263

FOR ◀ HELP

with the *Pythagorean theorem*, see
MODULE 5, p. 343

21. b. It is the mean of the *x*-coordinates of *D* and *B*:
$\frac{0+6}{2} = 3$; it is the mean of the *x*-coordinates of *A* and *C* (1 and 5): $\frac{1+5}{2} = 3$.

Section 3 Properties of Quadrilaterals **547**

Exploration 2

TEACHING NOTES
Question 19 Students use the fact that parallel lines have the same slope to determine that the opposite sides of the quadrilateral shown are parallel.

Question 20 In part (a), students use the Pythagorean theorem to find the length of a segment on a coordinate grid. For students who do not know how to apply the Pythagorean theorem in the coordinate plane, suggest that they place a bullet at (5, 0), label it point *F*, and use triangle *DFC* to find *CD*.

21. c. It is the mean of the *y*-coordinates of *D* and *B*:
$\frac{0+4}{2} = 2$; it is the mean of the *y*-coordinates of *A* and *C* (3 and 1): $\frac{3+1}{2} = 2$.

TEACHING NOTES

Question 25 For students to conclude that the diagonals are perpendicular, they need to know that the product of the slopes of perpendicular lines is –1.

24. b. Because all four sides are congruent, *PQRS* is a rhombus. Because both pairs of opposite sides are congruent, *PQRS* is a parallelogram.

25. a. Sample Response: The midpoint of $\overline{PR}$ is (4, 3). The midpoint of $\overline{SQ}$ is also (4, 3), so the lines intersect at their midpoints. That is, $\overline{PR}$ and $\overline{SQ}$ bisect each other.

26. a, b, d.

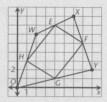

b. Quadrilateral *WXYO* is a parallelogram; the slopes of the opposite sides are equal.

---

22 **Try This as a Class** Based on the results in Question 21, how can you use the coordinates of the endpoints of a segment to find the coordinates of the midpoint of the segment?

✓ **QUESTION 23**

...checks that you can find the length and the midpoint of a segment on a coordinate grid.

23 ✓ **CHECKPOINT** The endpoints of $\overline{XY}$ are X(–2, –1) and Y(6, 5). (*Hint:* It may help to plot the points on a coordinate grid.)

   a. Find the length of $\overline{XY}$. **10 units**

   b. Find the coordinates of the midpoint of $\overline{XY}$. **(2, 2)**

▶ Coordinate geometry can also be used to verify the properties of quadrilaterals and to verify conjectures about figures.

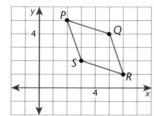

24 **a.** Have each member of your group find the length of one side of quadrilateral *PQRS*.

   b. Explain why quadrilateral *PQRS* is both a rhombus and a parallelogram. **See margin.**

FOR▶HELP
with *slopes of perpendicular lines,* see
MODULE 4, p. 268

25 Based on your discoveries in Exploration 1, the diagonals of quadrilateral *PQRS* should be perpendicular and bisect each other.

   a. Verify that the diagonals $\overline{PR}$ and $\overline{QS}$ bisect each other. **See margin.**

   b. Find the slope of each diagonal. **slope of $\overline{SQ}$ = 1, slope of $\overline{PR}$ = –1**

   c. Are the diagonals perpendicular? Why or why not? **Yes; the product of the slopes of the diagonals is –1.**

22. The *x*-coordinate of the midpoint is the mean of the *x*-coordinates of the endpoints, and the *y*-coordinate of the midpoint is the mean of the *y*-coordinates of the endpoints.

24. a. $PQ = \sqrt{10}$,
     $QR = \sqrt{10}$,
     $RS = \sqrt{10}$,
     $SP = \sqrt{10}$

26 **a.** Plot the points W(2, 6), X(6, 8), Y(8, 2), and O(0, 0) on a coordinate grid. **a, b, and d. See margin.**

   b. Draw segments $\overline{WX}$, $\overline{XY}$, $\overline{YO}$, and $\overline{OW}$. Is quadrilateral *WXYO* a special quadrilateral? Explain.

   c. Have each member of your group find the coordinates of the midpoint of one side of quadrilateral *WXYO*. Plot the midpoints on your graph. **E(4, 7), F(7, 5), G(4, 1), H(1, 3)**

   d. Draw segments to form a new quadrilateral *EFGH* where E, F, G, and H are the midpoints of $\overline{WX}$, $\overline{XY}$, $\overline{YO}$, and $\overline{OW}$ respectively.

   e. What type of quadrilateral is *EFGH*? Justify your answer. **parallelogram; the slopes of the opposite sides are equal; slope of $\overline{EF}$ = slope of $\overline{GH}$ = $-\frac{2}{3}$; slope of $\overline{FG}$ = slope of $\overline{EH}$ = $-\frac{4}{3}$**

HOMEWORK EXERCISES ▶ See Exs. 12–16 on pp. 551–552.

Section 3

Key Concepts

Key Terms

Properties of Quadrilaterals (pp. 543–546)

The chart shows some special types of quadrilaterals. Each quadrilateral belongs to the family of quadrilaterals linked to it above and has its same properties. So, for example, a square is also a rectangle, a parallelogram, and a quadrilateral. The chart and the Example identify some of the properties of quadrilaterals.

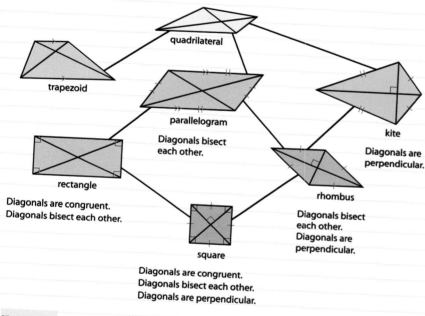

quadrilateral

trapezoid

parallelogram
Diagonals bisect each other.

kite
Diagonals are perpendicular.

rectangle
Diagonals are congruent.
Diagonals bisect each other.

rhombus
Diagonals bisect each other.
Diagonals are perpendicular.

square
Diagonals are congruent.
Diagonals bisect each other.
Diagonals are perpendicular.

parallelogram

rectangle

rhombus

trapezoid

square

kite

Example

Opposite angles of a parallelogram are congruent, and consecutive angles of a parallelogram are supplementary.

If both pairs of opposite sides of a quadrilateral are congruent, then the quadrilateral is a parallelogram.

opposite angles

consecutive angles

27 Key Concepts Question

a. What angle and diagonal properties do a rhombus and a parallelogram that is not a rhombus have in common?
Opposite angles are congruent and diagonals bisect each other.

b. What properties make them different? The diagonals of a rhombus are congruent and are perpendicular.

Key Concepts

CLOSURE QUESTION

What angle and diagonal properties can be used to distinguish a square from all other quadrilaterals?

Sample Response: A square is the only quadrilateral whose angles are all congruent AND whose diagonals are congruent AND are perpendicular bisectors of each other.

Key Concepts continued

ABSENT STUDENTS

For students who were absent for part or all of this section, the blackline Study Guide for Section 3 may be used to present the ideas, concepts, and skills of Section 3.

Practice & Applications

SUGGESTED ASSIGNMENTS

Core Course
Day 1: Exs. 1–9, 11, 17–26
Day 2: Exs. 12, 14–16

Extended Course
Day 1: Exs. 1–11, 17–26
Day 2: Exs. 12–16

Note: Extended Course assignments can be used to differentiate within the regular classroom. In classrooms where students are grouped homogeneously, the material might be covered in fewer days. In this case assignments may be combined.

ADDITIONAL PRACTICE

See the *Teacher's Resource Book* for additional practice and application exercises for this section.

Section 3
Key Concepts

Distance Between Points (pp. 547–548)

The Pythagorean theorem can be used to find the distance between two points on a coordinate grid.

Example Find the distance between points A(2, 5) and B(6, 2).

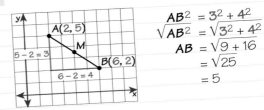

$$AB^2 = 3^2 + 4^2$$
$$\sqrt{AB^2} = \sqrt{3^2 + 4^2}$$
$$AB = \sqrt{9 + 16}$$
$$= \sqrt{25}$$
$$= 5$$

Midpoints of Segments (pp. 547–548)

The x-coordinate of the midpoint of a segment is the mean of the x-coordinates of the endpoints of the segment, and the y-coordinate is the mean of the y-coordinates of the endpoints.

Example The coordinates of the midpoint M of $\overline{AB}$ above are

$$\left(\frac{2+6}{2}, \frac{5+2}{2}\right) = \left(\frac{8}{2}, \frac{7}{2}\right) = \left(4, 3\frac{1}{2}\right).$$

28 Key Concepts Question Find the length and the coordinates of the midpoint of the segment with endpoints Y(9, 8) and Z(–3, 3). 13; $(3, 5\frac{1}{2})$

Section 3
Practice & Application Exercises

YOU WILL NEED

For Exs. 12 and 14:
♦ graph paper

2. True; If the diagonals bisect each other, they form two pairs of congruent triangles that can be used to show that the opposite sides are congruent, so that the quadrilateral is a parallelogram.

Tell whether each statement in Exercises 1–5 is *True* or *False*. Explain your answer. 1–5. Sample explanations are given.

1. The sum of the measures of the consecutive angles between two parallel sides of a quadrilateral is 180°. **True; This was shown in the Example on page 546.**

2. A quadrilateral whose diagonals bisect each other is a parallelogram.

3. A rhombus has congruent opposite angles. **True; A rhombus is a parallelogram and a parallelogram has opposite angles that are congruent.**

 Module 8 MATH-Thematical Mix

4. A square is the *only* quadrilateral whose diagonals are congruent.

5. If a quadrilateral has only one pair of congruent angles it *must* be a trapezoid. **False; A trapezoid may not have a pair of congruent angles. Also, a kite has only one pair of congruent angles.**

Open-ended **Draw and label a quadrilateral that fits each description.**
6, 8, and 11. See margin.

6. A quadrilateral with congruent opposite angles, neither of which have measure 90°.

7. A quadrilateral whose diagonals are perpendicular and bisect each other.

8. A quadrilateral with at least one pair of congruent sides and one diagonal that is a perpendicular bisector of the other diagonal.

9. A quadrilateral whose diagonals do not bisect each other and that has at least one pair of angles that are supplementary.

10. Challenge Use what you know about the properties of congruent triangles to show that the diagonals of rectangle *ABCD* at the right are congruent.

11. Draw a Venn diagram like the one below. Use the following quadrilaterals: rectangle, square, rhombus, parallelogram, kite, and trapezoid. Write the name of the quadrilateral in the most appropriate region.

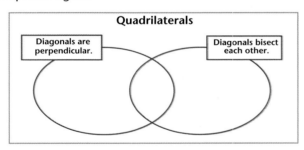

Quadrilaterals

Diagonals are perpendicular.

Diagonals bisect each other.

12. Find the length of the segment with the given endpoints. Then find the coordinates of the midpoint of the segment. (*Hint:* It may help to plot the points on a coordinate grid.)

a. (0, 3) and (0, −5) **b.** (8, 1) and (2, 9) **c.** (3, 5) and (−2, −7)
   8 units; (0, −1)   **10 units; (5, 5)**   **13 units; ($\frac{1}{2}$; −1)**

---

4. False; A rhombus and a rectangle that is not a square also have congruent diagonals.

7. Sample Response

9. Sample Response

FOR◀HELP
with *congruence properties*, see
MODULE 5, p. 330

10. $\overline{AB} \cong \overline{DC}$, $\overline{AD} \cong \overline{AD}$, and ∠*BAD* and ∠*CDA* are both right angles, so △*ABD* ≅ △*DCA* by SAS. Then $\overline{BD} \cong \overline{AC}$ because corresponding parts of congruent triangles are congruent.

EXERCISE NOTES

Exercises 4–5 Draw students' attention to the words in italics. They should understand that these qualifying terms have an effect on whether each statement is true or false.

Challenge Exercise 10 Students may notice that there are a number of congruent triangles in the rectangle. It may be helpful for them to draw the figure on their paper. Then, outline each of the two triangles they are comparing using a different color for each triangle. This will facilitate identification of each triangle.

6. Sample Response

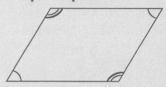

8. Sample Response

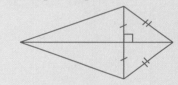

11. See Additional Answers beginning on page A1.

Practice & Applications

EXERCISE NOTES

Exercise 16 Throughout this section students have explored the diagonal and angle properties of quadrilaterals. They have used transversals to justify the opposite angle property of parallelograms. For this exercise, direct them to select a different property to justify using transversals.

15. b. Let $\overline{WY}$ and $\overline{XZ}$ intersect at point M. The coordinates of M are (2.5, 2.5). $WM = MY = \dfrac{\sqrt{26}}{2}$ and $WM = MY = \dfrac{\sqrt{26}}{2}$, so $\overline{WY}$ and $\overline{XZ}$ bisect each other.

c. slope of $\overline{WY} = -\dfrac{1}{5}$; slope of $\overline{XZ} = 5$; The product of the slopes is -1, so the diagonals are perpendicular.

14. a.

Journal

Exercise 16 checks that you can justify properties of quadrilaterals.

---

14. b. Sample Response: The slopes of $\overline{AB}$ and $\overline{DC}$ are both $-\dfrac{3}{2}$, and the slopes of $\overline{BC}$ and $\overline{AD}$ are both $\dfrac{2}{3}$. Then the slopes of the opposite sides are equal so $ABCD$ is a parallelogram. Also, $\overline{AB}$ and $\overline{BC}$ are perpendicular, so $\angle A$ is a right angle. Similarly, $\angle B$, $\angle C$, and $\angle D$ are right angles.

---

13. **Challenge** The coordinates of one endpoint of a segment are (6, 4) and the coordinates of the midpoint of the segment are $(1\tfrac{1}{2}, 5)$. What are the coordinates of the other endpoint? $(-3, 6)$

14. a. Plot the points $A(0, 0)$, $B(-2, 3)$, $C(4, 7)$, and $D(6, 4)$ on a coordinate grid.

    b. Show that $ABCD$ is a rectangle by first showing that $ABCD$ is a parallelogram, and then that each angle is a right angle.

15. Verify each statement for square $WXYZ$.
    b, c. See margin.
    a. The diagonals are congruent.
       $XY = WY = \sqrt{26}$
    b. The diagonals bisect each other.
    c. The diagonals are perpendicular.

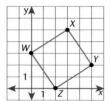

Reflecting ◀▶ on the Section

Write your response to Exercise 16 in your journal.

16. Give an example of how a transversal can be used to justify a property of a quadrilateral. Use a diagram to show your thinking.
    Answers will vary. Check students' work.

Spiral ◀▶ Review

Tell whether each equation represents a quadratic function. If so, rewrite the equation in the form $y = ax^2 + bx + c$. (Module 7, p. 447)

17. $y = 4(x - 3) + 7$ No

18. $y - 8x = 15x^2 + 3(2 - 5x)$
    Yes; $y = 15x^2 - 7x + 6$

For each right triangle find the unknown side length.
(Module 5, p. 343)

19.
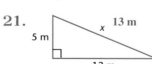

20.
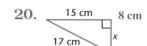

21.

22.
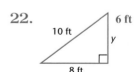

Write each expression without using zero or negative exponents. (Module 7, p. 464)

23. x^{-1} $\dfrac{1}{x}$

24. c^{-5} $\dfrac{1}{c^5}$

25. n^0 1

26. $3y^{-4}$ $\dfrac{3}{y^4}$

Section 3

Extra Skill Practice

List the angle properties for each of the quadrilaterals.

1. Opposite angles are congruent; consecutive angles are supplementary.

2.  Consecutive angles between parallel lines are supplementary.

List the diagonal properties for each of the quadrilaterals.

3. Diagonals bisect each other.

4. 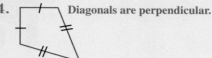 Diagonals are perpendicular.

Tell whether each statement is *True* or *False*. Explain your answer.

5. A rhombus has *all* the properties of a parallelogram. **True; a rhombus is a parallelogram.**

6. Opposite angles of a trapezoid *may* be congruent. **False; a trapezoid has only one set of parallel lines, so opposite angles will not be congruent.**

7. A kite has *some* of the diagonal properties of a rectangle. **See margin.**

8. A parallelogram has *at least* one pair of supplementary angles. **True; consecutive angles between parallel lines are supplementary.**

9. The opposite angles of *some* parallelograms are not congruent. **False; the opposite angles of all parallelograms are congruent.**

10. A square is the only quadrilateral whose diagonals are perpendicular bisectors of each other. **False. A rhombus that is not a square also has diagonals that are perpendicular bisectors of each other.**

11. Find the length of the segment with the given endpoints. Then find the coordinates of the midpoint of the segment.

    a. (–2, 5) and (4, 13) b. (3, –4) and (8, 8) c. (0, 7) and (8, –8)
       10; (1, 9)   **13; (5.5, 2)**   **17; $(4, -\frac{1}{2})$**

Standardized Testing ◀▶ Open-ended

1. Name a type of quadrilateral that always has the given properties.

   a. Both pairs of opposite angles are congruent.
      rectangle, square, parallelogram, rhombus
   b. Diagonals do not bisect each other. **trapezoid, kite**

   c. Diagonals are congruent and bisect each other. **rectangle, square, rhombus**

   d. Consecutive angles between parallel sides are supplementary. **trapezoid, parallelogram, rectangle, square, rhombus**

2. List the angle and diagonal properties of the quadrilateral at the right. **Opposite angles are congruent, and consecutive angles are supplementary; Diagonals are congruent and are perpendicular bisectors of each other.**

TEACHER NOTES

For each Exploration, the corresponding Extra Skills Practice Exercises are noted.

Exploration 1: Exs. 1–10
Exploration 2: Ex. 11

EXERCISE NOTES

Exercise 10 Students may answer that a square also has diagonals that are perpendicular bisectors of each other. Accept this response since the two quadrilaterals were distinguished from each other in this section, however, remind them that a square IS a rhombus.

EXTRA HELP

Teacher's Resource Book
• Practice and Applications
• Study Guide

Technology Resources
• @Home Tutor
• Test Generator

ASSESSMENT
• Section 3 Quick Quiz
• Mid-Module Quiz
• Test Generator

7. False; the diagonals of a kite are perpendicular, but the diagonals of a rectangle are not perpendicular (unless the rectangle is a square). The diagonals of a rhombus are not congruent and do not bisect each other, while the diagonals of a rectangle are congruent and bisect each other.

Most students have knowledge of the events surrounding the sinking of the *Titanic*. Although the location of the ship was reported when the iceberg was struck, many factors may have affected the exact spot where the ship came to rest on the ocean floor. Over the years, improvements in technology have made location of objects under water more accurate. With this technology, the *Titanic* was located and has been filmed. IMAX theaters across America take viewers on an underwater voyage to the remains of this extraordinary vessel. In this section, students will examine how geometric probability was used in search efforts to locate the sunken vessel.

GETTING STARTED

Module 8, Section 4 *Warm-Up* assesses that students can find the area of geometric figures. Calculating areas is an essential prerequisite skill for finding geometric probabilities.

CLASSROOM MANAGEMENT

Direct students to read the information on this page silently or in small groups. You might want to conduct a short classroom discussion to focus the students on the shipwreck and search operation rather than on the events leading up to the sinking of the *Titanic*.

Section ④ Geometry and Probability

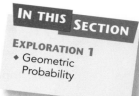

IN THIS SECTION

EXPLORATION 1
♦ Geometric Probability

Setting the Stage

Visit a mall in Providence, Rhode Island, the Ozarks of Missouri, or Edmonton, Alberta, and you could enjoy a movie in one of the many IMAX theaters across North America. Dome-shaped screens up to 8 stories high and 83 ft wide, along with 12,000 watts of digital sound give the viewer the sensation of being in scenes such as a *NASCAR* speedway race or an underwater expedition to the *Titanic* shipwreck.

The IMAX movie *Titanica* was filmed during a high-risk international expedition 12,500 ft beneath the surface of the Atlantic Ocean. The film crew was not the first to find the wreckage. Over the years, a number of different expeditions tried to find the *Titanic's* final resting place. One of the most challenging problems faced by searchers was locating the exact spot where the *Titanic* sank in 1912. The *Titanic* reported her position when she struck the iceberg. Another ship, the *Carpathia*, reported the location of the lifeboats it picked up some time later. Still, no one knew exactly where the *Titanic* lay.

The bow of the *Titanic* ▶ after nearly 80 years under water.

Think About It ▸▸

1 A team of searchers from the United States and France predicted that the *Titanic's* final resting place was likely to be in the region outlined with dashed lines on the map below. Estimate the area in square kilometers of this predicted shipwreck region. **about 320 km²**

2 In 1985, the French ship *Le Suroit* searched in the pink shaded region. Due to strong currents and other factors, *Le Suroit* could not search the entire predicted shipwreck region. Estimate how many square kilometers of the predicted shipwreck region *Le Suroit* covered in its search. **about 240 km²**

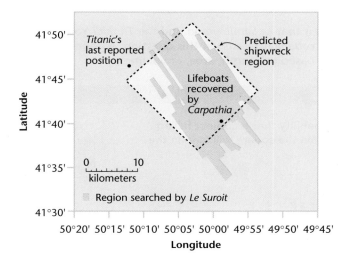

▶ Knowledge about historical events, ocean currents, and other conditions helped the people who eventually found the *Titanic* predict where the ship might be found. In this section, you will use mathematics to explore the probability of finding the *Titanic*.

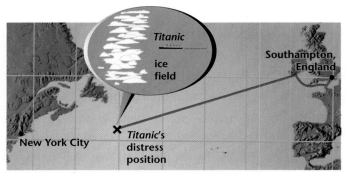

Students should make quick estimates of the areas in **Questions 1 and 2**. They will be asked to find more precise estimates later in the section.

You may want to review the concept of latitude and longitude, and have students locate the search area on a world map.

Exploration 1

DEVELOPING MATH CONCEPTS

Question 3(a) Students may believe that since the radius of the cut out circle is half of the radius of the original circle, the probability of landing in the blue region of the new figure will be half of the probability of landing in the blue region of the original figure. In Practice & Application Exercise 24 from Module 4 Section 1, students explored the relationship between the areas of circles when the radius is doubled. If they need a reminder, ask them to find the area of a circle with a radius of 6 cm. (≈ 113.1 cm²) Find the area of a circle whose radius is half of 6 cm. (≈ 28.27 cm²) Is the area of the circle with a radius of 3 cm half of the area of the circle with a radius of 6 cm? (*no*) What is the relationship between the areas? (*The area of the smaller circle is about one fourth of the area of the larger circle.*)

Returning to part (a), ask how much of the original blue circle was removed. (*about one fourth*) How much of the blue circle is remaining? (*about three fourths*) How do you expect the probabilities will be related? (*The probability of landing in the new blue region should be about three fourths of the probability of landing in the original blue region.*)

DEVELOPING MATH CONCEPTS

Reinforce the notation for probability by encouraging students to use the *P*(event) notation when recording their work and answers.

LEARN HOW TO...
- find probabilities using areas

AS YOU...
- examine the area where a shipwreck occurred

KEY TERMS
- geometric probability
- complementary events

3. b.

c. **Find the area of the original blue circle and subtract the area of the circle that was removed. Original circle: 3.14 ft² – removed circle: 0.785 ft² ≈ 2.355 ft²**

You write the probability of event A as *P*(A).

Exploration 1

Geometric Probability

SET UP *You will need:* • *Labsheet 4A* • *metric ruler*

▶ **How likely was it that *Le Suroit* would find the *Titanic*? You can use *geometric probability* to answer this question. A geometric probability is based on length, area, or volume.**

EXAMPLE

Find the probability that an object falling randomly within the square will land in the blue circle.

SAMPLE RESPONSE

$$P(\text{landing in the shaded circle}) = \frac{\text{area of circle}}{\text{area of square}} \approx \frac{3.14 \text{ ft}^2}{4 \text{ ft}^2} = 0.785$$

The probability of landing in the shaded circle is about 78.5%.

---

3 **Try This as a Class** Suppose a circle of radius 0.5 ft is removed from the blue circle in the Example above.

  a. How do you think this will affect the probability of landing in the blue region? **The probability will be less.**

  b. Make a sketch of the new figure.

  c. Explain how you could find the area of the new blue region.

  d. Find the probability that an object falling randomly on the new figure will land in the blue region. $\frac{2.355 \text{ ft}^2}{4 \text{ ft}^2} \approx 0.589$; **The probability is about 58.9%.**

  e. What is the probability that an object will *not* land in the blue region? **100% – 58.9% = 41.1%; The probability is about 41.1%, or 0.411.**

4 ✔ **CHECKPOINT** Find the probability that an object falling randomly on each figure will land in the blue region.

a.

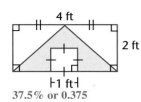

4 ft
2 ft
├1 ft┤

37.5% or 0.375

b.

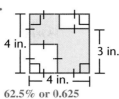

4 in.
3 in.
├─4 in.─┤

62.5% or 0.625

✔ **QUESTION 4**

...checks that you can find geometric probabilities.

▶ The events in parts (d) and (e) of Question 3 are *complementary events*. Two events are **complementary events** if one or the other must occur but they cannot both occur. In Question 3 the object cannot land both in the blue region and not in the blue region at the same time.

5 a. Find the probability that an object falling randomly on each figure in Question 4 will *not* land in the blue region. **part a: 0.625 or 62.5%; part b: 0.375 or 37.5%**

b. What do you notice about the sum of the probabilities of two complementary events? **The sum of the probabilities equals 1 (or 100%).**

6 Use your answers to Questions 1 and 2 on page 556. Assume the *Titanic* lay in the predicted shipwreck region.

a. Estimate the probability that the *Titanic* lay in the region *Le Suroit* searched. **about 0.75 or 75%**

b. Based on your answer to part (a), what is the probability that the *Titanic* did *not* lay in the region *Le Suroit* searched? **about 0.25 or 25%**

▲ *Le Suroit* used sonar to look for the *Titanic*.

7. a. about 100 km²
   b. about 70 km²
   c. about 0.70 or 70%

7 **Use Labsheet 4A.** Suppose you are on a ship that is *Searching for the Titanic.* Follow the directions on the labsheet to estimate the probability that the *Titanic* lies in your search region.

HOMEWORK EXERCISES ▶ See Exs. 1–10 on pp. 558–559.

TEACHING NOTES

If students need more guidance finding geometric probabilities, discuss the following Examples before they begin **Checkpoint 4**.

CLASSROOM EXAMPLES

Find the probability that an object falling randomly on the figure shown will land in the shaded triangle.

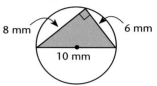

8 mm   6 mm
10 mm

Answer:

$$P(\text{landing in the shaded triangle}) = \frac{\text{area of the triangle}}{\text{area of the circle}}$$

$$= \frac{\frac{1}{2}(8)(6)}{\pi(5)^2}$$

$$\approx \frac{\frac{1}{2}(8)(6)}{(3.14)(25)}$$

$$= \frac{24}{78.5}$$

$$\approx 0.306$$

The probability of landing in the shaded triangle is about 30.6%.

Find the probability that an object falling randomly on the figure shown will not land in the shaded triangle.

Answer: 1.00 – 0.306 = 0.694

The probability of not landing in the shaded triangle is about 69.4%.

Question 4 Since these are multi-step problems, check to see that students clearly set up and label the area of the region they find in each step. In **part (a)**, the area of the large rectangle is 8 ft² and the area of the shaded section of the large triangle is the difference between the total area of the triangle and the area of the small square: 4 ft² – 1 ft² = 3 ft². The geometric probability that an object falling randomly lands in the blue region is $\frac{3}{8}$ or 0.375.

Key Concepts

CLOSURE QUESTION

In playing a game of darts, how can you find the probability that the dart will land in a specific section of the target?

Sample Response: Find the area of the entire target and the area of the region you wish to hit. Divide the area of the desired region by the area of the entire target.

ABSENT STUDENTS

For students who were absent for part or all of this section, the blackline Study Guide for Section 4 may be used to present the ideas, concepts, and skills of Section 4.

Practice & Applications

SUGGESTED ASSIGNMENTS

Core & Extended Courses

Day 1: Exs. 1–8
Day 2: Exs. 9–19

Note: Extended Course assignments can be used to differentiate within the regular classroom. In classrooms where students are grouped homogeneously, the material might be covered in fewer days. In this case assignments may be combined.

ADDITIONAL PRACTICE

See the *Teacher's Resource Book* for additional practice and application exercises for this section.

Section ④ Key Concepts

Key Terms

geometric probability

Geometric Probability (pp. 556–557)

Probabilities that are based on length, area, or volume are called geometric probabilities.

Example Suppose an object randomly falls onto the figure shown. What is the probability that the object will land in the orange region?

Total area of the figure = **4** in.²

Area of blue region = **1** in.²

1 in.

2 in.

Area of orange region = **3** in.²

The probability that the object will land in the orange region is $\frac{3}{4}$.

complementary events

Complementary Events (p. 557)

The sum of the probabilities of complementary events is 1.
P(the event occurs) = 1 − P(the event does not occur).

8 Key Concepts Question Use the Example above.

a. How was the probability of landing in the orange region found? **The area of the orange region is divided by the total area.**

b. What is the probability of landing in the blue region? **0.25 or 25%**

Section ④ Practice & Application Exercises

YOU WILL NEED

For Exs 14-16
◆ graph paper

1. Suppose the probability that event *A* will occur is 0.6. Find the probability that event *A* will *not* occur. **0.40 or 40%**

2. **Visual Thinking** A 12 in. by 14 in. rectangular cake is divided into 2 in. squares. If a piece is chosen at random, what is the probability that the piece is from the outside edge of the cake? **$\frac{11}{21}$ = 0.524 or 52.4%**

 558 **Module 8** MATH-Thematical Mix

Find the probability that an object falling randomly on each figure will land in the shaded area. Round your answers to the nearest hundredth.

3. $\frac{24}{49} \approx 0.49$ or 49%

4. 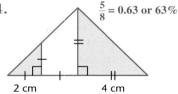 $\frac{5}{8} = 0.63$ or 63%

5 ft   5 ft   7 ft

7 ft

2 cm   4 cm

5. 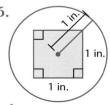 1 in.   1 in.   1 in.

$\frac{1}{\pi} \approx 0.32$ or 32%

6. 3 ft

6 ft

$1 - \frac{\pi}{4} \approx 0.22$ or 22%

7. Denise lost her ring while playing volleyball. Assume that the ring is equally likely to be anywhere in the entire region shown.

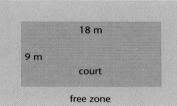

24 m

18 m

15 m   9 m

court

free zone

   a. Find the probability that Denise's ring is on the court. **0.45 or 45%**

   b. Find the probability that it is in the free zone. **0.55 or 55%**

8. **Social Studies** In the 1950s, there was a significant increase in the rat population in northern Borneo. In an attempt to control the rat population, cats were parachuted into the remote regions.

   a. Suppose the cats landed randomly on the rectangular field shown. Find the probability that a cat landed in the tan region. **0.46 or 46%**

24 m

18 m

8 m   8 m

   b. Find the probability that a cat landed in the green region. **0.54 or 54%**

9. *Barm brack* is a spongy cake served in Ireland. Traditionally, a ring is baked inside the cake. If the cake is divided into 10 equal-sized slices, find each probability.

   a. *P*(your slice contains the ring) **0.10 or 10%**

   b. *P*(your slice does not contain the ring) **0.90 or 90%**

Exercises 3–6 To ensure that students are applying area formulas for triangles, rectangles, and circles appropriately, ask them to show their work. This will allow you to accurately evaluate the entire problem-solving process they have used.

In **Exercise 9**, students should recognize that the sum of *P*(your slice contains the ring) and *P*(your slice does not contain the ring) should be 1 or 100%.

EXERCISE NOTES

Exercise 10 You may want to have students compare the methods they used to solve this problem. Some may have discovered that by using the problem-solving strategy of breaking the problem down into a simpler problem and finding the probability for just one rectangular section on the map, they can avoid having to compute all of the "inconvenient" areas on the entire map.

Journal

Exercise 10 checks that you can use geometric probability.

10. a. Sample Response: The print may be worn off at the fold making it hard to read. The fold may obstruct the view of a certain point or location on the map.

14.

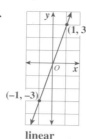

linear

15.

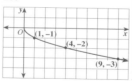

nonlinear

16.

linear

Reflecting ◀▶ on the Section

Write your answer to Exercise 10 in your journal.

10. Murphy's Law for Maps states: "If a place you're looking for can lie on the inconvenient parts of a map, it will." Suppose the inconvenient parts of a map are within 2 cm on either side of a fold of the map.

   a. Explain why it might be inconvenient if a place that you are looking for lies on the fold of a map.

   b. Find the total area of the map below. **774.4 cm²**

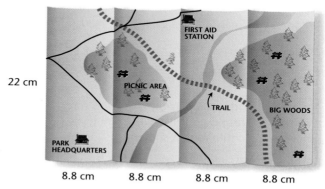

22 cm

PARK HEADQUARTERS PICNIC AREA FIRST AID STATION TRAIL BIG WOODS

8.8 cm   8.8 cm   8.8 cm   8.8 cm

   c. Find the probability that a place chosen randomly lies on an inconvenient part of the map. **0.34 or 34%**

Spiral ◀▶ Review

Tell whether each triangle is *acute, right,* or *obtuse.* (Module 5, p. 343)

11. **acute**
   12.4 cm
   9 cm
   10.3 cm

12. **obtuse**
   16 mm
   12 mm
   8 mm

13. **right**
   25 in.
   15 in.
   20 in.

Graph each equation. Tell whether the graph is *linear* or *nonlinear.* (Module 3, p. 175)

14. $y = 3x$ 15. $y = -\sqrt{x}$ 16. $y = -\frac{1}{2}x - 1$

Find the volume of each cylinder. Round your answers to the nearest hundredth. (Module 4, p. 238)

17. $r = 10$ mm
   $h = 6$ mm
   about 1884 mm³

18. $d = 4.6$ in.
   $h = 11.2$ in.
   about 186.04 in.³

19. $d = 9.2$ cm
   $h = 14$ cm
   about 930.19 cm³

Section 4

Extra Skill Practice

Suppose that during a storm, a hiker gets lost in the square region shown. Assume it is equally likely that he is anywhere in the region.

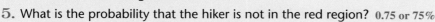

1. What is the probability that the hiker is in the white region? **0.50 or 50%**

2. What is the probability that the hiker is in the tan region? **0.25 or 25%**

3. What is the probability that the hiker is in the red region? **0.25 or 25%**

4. What is the probability that the hiker is not in the white region? **0.50 or 50%**

5. What is the probability that the hiker is not in the red region? **0.75 or 75%**

6. A dart thrown randomly lands on the rectangular target shown below. The score that the dart is assigned is the number of the region it lands in.

   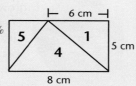

   a. What is the probability that the dart's score is less than 3? **0.375 or 37.5%**

   b. What is the probability that the dart's score is an even number? **0.50 or 50%**

7. Sketch a target that has a shaded region with a 60% chance of being hit when a dart thrown randomly lands on the target.
   Answers will vary. Check students' work.

Standardized Testing ◀▶ Multiple Choice

1. Which of the following could be the probabilities of complementary events? **D**

   Ⓐ 80% and 80% Ⓑ 1 and 0.1 Ⓒ $\frac{3}{8}$ and $-\frac{3}{8}$ Ⓓ 0.45 and 0.55

2. What is the probability that an object falling randomly onto the figure shown will land in the green region? **C**

   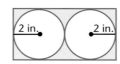

   Ⓐ $\frac{\pi}{3}$ Ⓑ $\frac{1}{3}$ Ⓒ $1 - \frac{\pi}{4}$ Ⓓ $\frac{\pi}{4}$

TEACHER NOTES
For each Exploration, the corresponding Extra Skills Practice Exercises are noted.

Exploration 1: Exs. 1–7

EXTRA HELP
Teacher's Resource Book
• Practice and Applications
• Study Guide

Technology Resources
• @Home Tutor
• Test Generator

ASSESSMENT
• Section 4 Quick Quiz
• Test Generator

ABOUT THE THEME

Ancient Greek and Roman cultures were highly sophisticated for their time. Their ideas were far more advanced than their technology. Hero, a Greek engineer, used steam, hot air, and air pressure in many devices—a precursor to the steam engine. He is also credited with inventing a machine that used the weight of a deposited coin to dispense water at the temple, an invention that has evolved into the coin operated machines of today. The Greeks are also believed to have invented the *astrolabe* (a device used to measure the position of stars). This instrument is the focus of the *Setting the Stage*.

GETTING STARTED

Module 8, Section 5 *Warm-Up* assesses student competence in solving equations and identifying complementary angles in a right triangle. These skills are utilized throughout the section.

TEACHING NOTES

Read the information on this page together as a class and hold a brief discussion about the way in which the astrolabe works. Students should realize that the weighted string hangs down over the protractor indicating the measure of angle *B*. When the protractor is pointed straight ahead a eye level, it measures 90° because the weighted string is pulled by gravity toward the ground.

INVENTIONS

Setting the Stage

Long ago, heights of objects were found indirectly by comparing their shadows with the shadows of objects whose heights were known. However, cloudy days and a growing interest in astrology and astronomy created a need for new measuring instruments. One of the first instruments designed for measuring the angle between a star and the horizon was the *astrolabe*, which many scholars believe was invented by the Greek mathematician Hypatia, one of the first notable female mathematicians.

A simple astrolabe can be constructed from a protractor, straw, and weighted string. By sighting the top of an object, the astrolabe can be used to find angle measures of a right triangle formed by the object, the person using the astrolabe, and the line of sight to the top of the object.

Astrolabes are used primarily for measuring the positions of stars, but they can also be used to find the heights of objects.

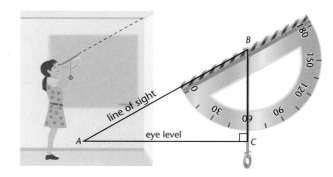

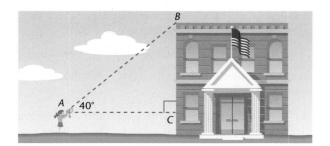

► Adriana uses an astrolabe to sight the top of her school. She finds that the measure of ∠B in the diagram is 50°.

Think About It

1 Adriana's astrolabe gives her the measure of ∠B. From that measure she calculates that the measure of ∠A, the angle of elevation, is 40°. How does she know that $m\angle A = 40°$?

2 What happens to the measure of the angle of elevation if Adriana steps closer to the building, but keeps her eye sighted on the top of the building? **It will increase.**

1. Her astrolabe shows that $m\angle B$ is 50°. Since ∠A and ∠B are complementary angles, $m\angle A$ is 40°.

Exploration 1

The **Tangent Ratio**

GOAL

LEARN HOW TO...
♦ use the tangent ratio to find unknown side lengths in right triangles

AS YOU...
♦ investigate heights of objects

KEY TERM
♦ tangent

SET UP *Work in a group. You will need:* • *protractor* • *metric ruler* • *scissors* • *calculator*

► **How can an astrolabe be used to find the heights of objects?** In this exploration, you will study a ratio that will help you answer this question.

3 Each person in your group should complete these steps:
Answers will vary. Check students' work.
Step 1 Draw a right triangle, △ABC, such that ∠C is the right angle and $m\angle A = 40°$. The triangles your group draws should be different sizes.

Step 2 Measure the lengths of sides $\overline{BC}$ and $\overline{AC}$ to the nearest tenth of a centimeter. Label $\overline{BC}$ and $\overline{AC}$ with their lengths.

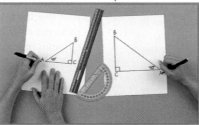

DEVELOPING MATH CONCEPTS

Question 1 Since the triangle formed is a right triangle, students may find the measure of angle *A* in more than one way. Some may use the fact that the sum of the angle measures in a triangle is 180°. Students can add the two known measures, 50° and 90° and subtract this sum from 180° to find the measure of ∠A. Other students may use what they know about complementary angles. Since the right angle measures 90°, the sum of the measures of the other two angles, ∠A and ∠B, must be 90° for a total of 180°. The complement of a 50° angle is a 40° angle. Make sure students recognize that the two acute angles in a right triangle are always complementary.

Exploration 1

TEACHING NOTES

Question 3 Students should be working in groups of 3 or 4. It is important for students to compare more than two triangles in order to make a generalization in Question 4.

COMMON ERROR

Question 3 Check that students are using a straightedge and a protractor to draw the angles in the triangle. If the 90° and 40° angles are not drawn carefully, the ratios students will be comparing in the following activities will not be accurate and could adversely affect the "discovery" students are expected to make.

563

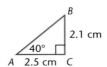

B
2.1 cm
40°
A   2.5 cm   C

4 **Discussion** Cut out your group's triangles and arrange them in order from smallest to largest. A sample triangle is shown.

  a. Are all the triangles similiar? How can you tell? **Yes; They have the same angle measures.**

  b. As *BC* increases from one triangle to the next, what happens to *AC* ? **It increases.**

  c. Find the ratio $\frac{BC}{AC}$ for each triangle. Write each ratio as a decimal rounded to the nearest hundredth. What do you notice? **The ratios are the same, about 0.84.**

  d. What seems to be true for any right triangle with a 40° angle? **The ratio of the length of the leg opposite the 40° angle to the length of the leg adjacent to the 40° angle is about 0.84.**

5 **Calculator** Enter this key sequence on a calculator: **TAN 4 0** . How does the number in the display compare with the ratios your group calculated in Question 4? **Rounded to the hundredths, it is the same, about 0.84.**

▶ **In a right triangle, the tangent of an acute angle is the ratio of the length of the leg opposite the angle to the length of the leg adjacent to the angle. The tangent of an angle A is written "tan A."**

$$\tan A = \frac{\text{opposite}}{\text{adjacent}}$$

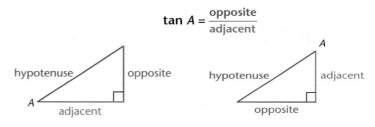

6 **Try This as a Class**

  a. In △ABC, which leg is opposite ∠B? **The leg labeled *b***

  b. Which leg is adjacent to ∠B? **The leg labeled *a***

  c. Write the tangent ratio for ∠B. $\tan B = \frac{b}{a}$

  d. Write the tangent ratio for ∠A. $\tan A = \frac{a}{b}$

  e. Why can't you write a tangent ratio for ∠C?

6. e. A right angle is not acute. The tangent of an angle of a right angle is defined for acute angles only. Note that in a right triangle, the side opposite the right angle is the hypotenuse, not a leg. Both legs are adjacent to the right angle.

7 Use the triangle shown to find each tangent rounded to the nearest hundredth. Check your answers with a calculator. (*Note*: Side lengths are approximate.)

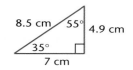

  a. tan 35° **0.7**

  b. tan 55° **about 11.1**

8 a. Copy the table. Then use a calculator to complete it.
0.176, 0.364, 0.577, 0.839, 1.192, 1.732, 2.747, 5.671, 57.290

Angle measure	10°	20°	30°	40°	50°	60°	70°	80°	89°
Tangent	?	?	?	?	?	?	?	?	?

b. What happens to the tangent as the angle measure increases?
It increases.

c. Discussion Try finding tan 90° on your calculator. What
happens? Why do you think this happens? **An error message
appears. The tangent of an angle of a right angle is defined for acute angles only.**

▶ You can use what you know about the tangent ratio to measure the
heights of objects indirectly.

9 Look back at the *Setting the Stage*. Suppose that, in addition
to the angle of elevation, Adriana knows her distance from the
school and the height of her eyes above ground.

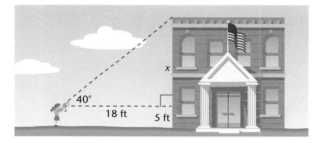

a. Write an equation relating tan 40° and *x*. $\tan 40° = \frac{x}{18}$

b. Find tan 40°. Use your answer to solve your equation for *x*.
about 0.839; 15.1

c. What is the height of the school? **about 20.1 ft**

10 Try This as a Class Use the triangle.

a. Write an equation relating tan 39°
and *x*. $\tan 39° = \frac{9}{x}$

b. How is your equation different
from the equation you wrote in
Question 9?

c. How can you solve this new type
of equation?

d. Find the value of *x*. **about 4.3**

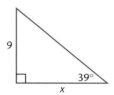

10. b. *x* is the
denominator. (*x*
is the length of a
side of a triangle,
so *x* is not zero.)

c. Multiply both
sides of the
equation by *x*,
then divide both
sides by 9. You
could also write
tan 39° as $\frac{\tan 39°}{1}$
and use cross
products to get
an equation that
could be solved
by dividing by
tan 39°.

Section 5 Tangent, Sine, and Cosine **565**

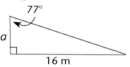

Exploration 2

DEVELOPING MATH CONCEPTS

Question 12 Make students aware of the fact that the tangent ratio excludes the hypotenuse in its calculation. Both the sine and cosine use the hypotenuse. Ask students when it would not be possible to use the tangent ratio to find the measure of a side. (*when you only know the length of the hypotenuse*) In this case either the sine or cosine ratio can be used.

DIFFERENTIATED INSTRUCTION

For those students who have trouble distinguishing between the two ratios, encourage them to make an association between the words sine/opposite and cosine/adjacent. Alphabetically, the words sine and opposite come after cosine and adjacent respectively. Since the hypotenuse is in the denominator of both ratios, this association should help students remember which side of the triangle belongs in the numerator of each ratio.

Just as was the case in Exploration 1, using colors to identify each side of the triangle may be helpful to those visual learners who need such assistance.

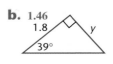

✔ **QUESTION 11**
...checks that you can use the tangent ratio to find unknown side lengths in right triangles.

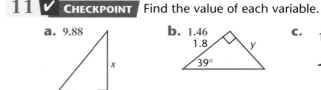

11 ✔ **CHECKPOINT** Find the value of each variable.

a. 9.88, 51°, 8, x

b. 1.46, 1.8, 39°, y

c. 18°, 3.69, 1.2, z

HOMEWORK EXERCISES ▶ See Exs. 1–10 on pp. 569–570.

GOAL

LEARN HOW TO...
◆ use the sine and cosine ratios to find unknown side lengths in right triangles

AS YOU...
◆ investigate right triangles

KEY TERMS
◆ sine
◆ cosine

Exploration 2

The Sine and Cosine Ratios

SET UP *You will need a calculator.*

▶ Like the tangent ratio, the **sine** and the **cosine** of an acute angle of a right triangle are ratios of side lengths. These ratios are defined below.

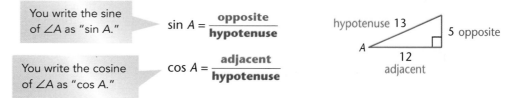

You write the sine of ∠A as "sin A."

$$\sin A = \frac{\text{opposite}}{\text{hypotenuse}}$$

You write the cosine of ∠A as "cos A."

$$\cos A = \frac{\text{adjacent}}{\text{hypotenuse}}$$

hypotenuse 13, 5 opposite, A, 12 adjacent

12 Use the triangle above to find each ratio.

a. sin A $\frac{5}{13}$

b. cos A $\frac{12}{13}$

13 a. Calculator In the right triangle above, $m\angle A \approx 22.6°$. On a calculator, enter **SIN** 2 2 · 6 to find sin A. Then enter **COS** 2 2 · 6 to find cos A.
sin A ≈ 0.38, cos A ≈ 0.92

b. Do your answers in part (a) agree (approximately) with your answers to Question 12? yes

14 **Try This as a Class** Use $\triangle ABC$ at the right.

   a. Write an equation relating cos B and x. $\cos 30° = \frac{x}{10}$

   b. Find cos 30°. Use your answer to solve your equation for x. Round your answer to the nearest hundredth of a centimeter.

   c. Show how you could find x using the sine ratio.

   d. Could you use the tangent ratio to find the value of x? Explain. **Yes; $\tan 30° = \frac{5}{x}$; $x \tan 30° = 5$, $x = \frac{5}{\tan 30°} \approx 8.66$ cm**

   e. Use the Pythagorean theorem to find the value of x. Round your answer to the nearest hundredth of a centimeter. How does the result compare with the value you found in part (b)?

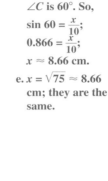

14. b. $0.866 \approx \frac{x}{10}$,
$x \approx 8.66$ cm
c. $\angle A$ and $\angle B$ are complementary angles, so the measure of $\angle C$ is 60°. So,
$\sin 60 = \frac{x}{10}$;
$0.866 = \frac{x}{10}$;
$x \approx 8.66$ cm.
e. $x = \sqrt{75} \approx 8.66$ cm; they are the same.

15 Assume you know the measure of $\angle M$ and the side lengths shown on each right triangle. Determine whether you could use the sine, the cosine, or the tangent of $\angle M$ to find the value of x.

   a. cosine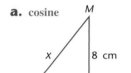

   b. 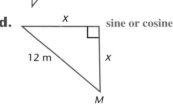 tangent

   c. sine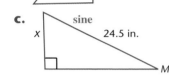

   d. 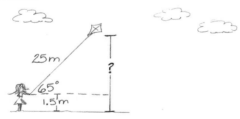 sine or cosine

16 ✔ **CHECKPOINT** While flying her kite at the park, Maureen let out all 25 m of her kite string. The measure of the angle of elevation of the kite was 65°. She made this sketch when she returned home.

How far above the ground was the kite flying? about 24.2 m

| HOMEWORK EXERCISES | ▶ See Exs. 11–22 on pp. 570–572.

✔ **QUESTION 16**

...checks that you can use the sine or cosine ratio to find unknown side lengths in a right triangle.

Section 5 Tangent, Sine, and Cosine **567**

TEACHING NOTES

Question 14(c) Students will need to use the measure of $\angle A$ to solve for x using the sine ratio. They should use complementary angles to determine that $m\angle A = 60°$. It may be helpful to have all three ratios posted on the board to help students build their equations quickly.

For **part (e)** you may need to do a quick review of the Pythagorean theorem. Students should set up and solve the equation $5^2 + x^2 = 10^2$ and compare the result to the answers found using the sine and cosine ratios.

If students need more guidance deciding whether to use the sine or cosine ratio, you may want to discuss the following Classroom Example before they begin **Question 15**.

CLASSROOM EXAMPLE

Find the value of x using the sine or the cosine ratio.

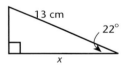

Answer: Use the cosine ratio, since

$$\cos 22° = \frac{\text{adjacent}}{\text{hypotenuse}}$$
$$0.92718 \approx \frac{x}{13}$$
$$0.92718 \cdot 13 \approx \frac{x}{13} \cdot \frac{13}{1}$$
$$12.05 \approx x$$

The value of x is about 12 cm.

COMMON ERROR

Question 16 Students may fail to add the 1.5 m to the side of the triangle to find the total distance from the kite to the ground.

Key Concepts

CLOSURE QUESTIONS

How does the tangent ratio compare to the sine and cosine ratios? In what situations would you use each ratio?

Sample Response: The tangent ratio compares the sides opposite and adjacent to the identified acute angle while the cosine and sine compare a side to the hypotenuse in a right triangle. The sine or cosine could be used to find the length of a side when one side or the hypotenuse and an angle measure are known, however the tangent ratio can only be used if a side other than the hypotenuse and an angle measure are known.

ABSENT STUDENTS

For students who were absent for part or all of this section, the blackline Study Guide for Section 5 may be used to present the ideas, concepts, and skills of Section 5.

Key Terms

tangent

sine

cosine

Section 5
Key Concepts

The Tangent Ratio (pp. 563–566)

In a right triangle, the tangent of an acute angle is the ratio of the length of the leg opposite the angle to the length of the leg adjacent to the angle. You can use the tangent ratio to find unknown side lengths in a right triangle.

Example You can use the tangent ratio to find the value of h in $\triangle ABC$.

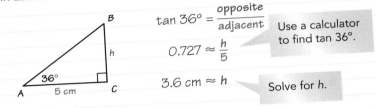

$$\tan 36° = \frac{\text{opposite}}{\text{adjacent}}$$

Use a calculator to find $\tan 36°$.

$$0.727 \approx \frac{h}{5}$$

$$3.6 \text{ cm} \approx h$$

Solve for h.

The Sine and Cosine Ratios (pp. 566–567)

In a right triangle, the sine of an acute angle is the ratio of the length of the leg opposite the angle to the length of the hypotenuse. The cosine is the ratio of the length of the leg adjacent to the angle to the length of the hypotenuse. Like the tangent ratio, the sine and cosine ratios can be used to find unknown side lengths in a right triangle.

Example Find the length of the hypotenuse $\overline{AB}$ in $\triangle ABC$ above.

$$\cos 36° = \frac{\text{adjacent}}{\text{hypotenuse}}$$

Use a calculator to find $\cos 36°$.

$$0.809 \approx \frac{5}{AB}$$

$$0.809 \cdot AB \approx 5$$

Solve for AB.

$$AB \approx \frac{5}{0.809}$$

$$AB \approx 6.2 \text{ cm}$$

17 **Key Concepts Question** Use $\triangle ABC$ in the Example above. Show how you can use the sine ratio to find AB. $\sin B = \frac{5}{x}$; $\sin 54° = \frac{5}{x}$; $0.809 = \frac{5}{x}$; $x \approx 6.2$ cm

Section 5

Practice & Application Exercises

YOU WILL NEED

For Exs 1–22:
♦ calculator

For Ex. 8:
♦ encyclopedia

For Ex. 10:
♦ Labsheet 5A
♦ protractor
♦ drinking straw
♦ string (8 in.)
♦ weight (such as a washer)
♦ tape

For Exercises 1–3, use the triangle to find the given tangent. Check each answer with a calculator. (*Note:* Side lengths are approximate.)

1. tan 45° **1**

2.6   3.7
2.6   45°
2.6

2. tan 65° **about 2.15**

19.2   65°   8.1
17.4

3. tan 28° **about 0.53**

28°
10   11.3
5.3

4. **Architecture** Mark uses an astrolabe to sight the top of the Sears Tower in Chicago.

Not drawn to scale

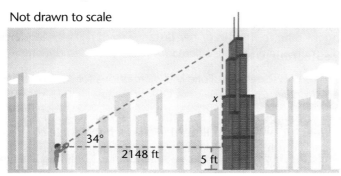

34°
2148 ft   5 ft   x

a. About how tall is the Sears Tower? **about 1454 ft**

b. Suppose Mark changes his position so that the angle of elevation is now 32°. About how far from the Sears Tower is he standing? **about 2319 ft**

Find the value of each variable. Round your answers to the nearest hundredth.

5.

173.21 yd
m
60°
100 yd

6.

12.08 ft
41°
x
10.5 ft

7.
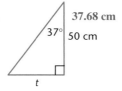
37.68 cm
37°   50 cm
t

8. **Research** Look up the height of a famous building in an encyclopedia or other source. Describe how a person could use this height and the tangent ratio to find his or her distance from the building. Include a diagram and sample calculation.
Answers will vary. Check students' work.

Practice & Applications

SUGGESTED ASSIGNMENTS

Core Course
Day 1: Exs. 1–8, 10, 23–26
Day 2: Exs. 11–18, 20–22

Extended Course
Day 1: Exs. 1–10, 23–26
Day 2: Exs. 11–14, 16–22

Note: Extended Course assignments can be used to differentiate within the regular classroom. In classrooms where students are grouped homogeneously, the material might be covered in fewer days. In this case assignments may be combined.

ADDITIONAL PRACTICE
See the *Teacher's Resource Book* for additional practice and application exercises for this section.

EXERCISE NOTES
Exercises 1–3 Encourage students to notice the relationships between the tangent ratio for a given angle and the length of the sides of the triangle. Help them make the connection to what they learned in Question 8. When an angle measure is greater than 45° the ratio is greater than 1, indicating that the length of the opposite side is longer than the length of the adjacent side. When the angle measure is less than 45° the ratio is less than 1 indicating that the length of the opposite side is shorter than the length of the adjacent side. When the angle measure is 45°, both sides are the same length.

Practice & Applications

EXERCISE NOTES

Exercise 10 If the astrolabes are made during class time, you may want students to work in pairs, helping each other follow the directions to construct their instruments.

Exercises 11–13 Encourage students to refer to the diagrams on pages 566 and 568 if they need help remembering which side belongs in the numerator of each of the ratios.

14. Sample Response: If one acute angle of a right triangle has measure 45°, then so does the other. For each 45° angle, the lengths of the opposite and adjacent legs are equal, so the sine and cosine of 45° are equal. In the diagram, the length of the hypotenuse is approximate.

$\sin 45° =$
$\dfrac{5}{7.07} \approx 0.7072$

$\cos 45° =$
$\dfrac{5}{7.1} \approx 0.7072$

9. Challenge The angle of depression from an airplane to the outskirts of a city measures 5.8°. The airplane is flying 6 mi above the ground at a speed of 200 mi/hr. How much time will elapse before the airplane begins passing over the city? about 17.7 min.

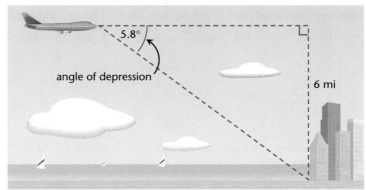

5.8°

angle of depression

6 mi

Not drawn to scale

10. Create Your Own

a. **Use Labsheet 5A.** Follow the directions for *Making an Astrolabe.* Check students' work.

b. Use your astrolabe to sight the top of objects such as buildings, trees, or lamp posts. Record in a sketch the angle of elevation and your horizontal distance from the object. Then use the tangent ratio to calculate the object's approximate height. Answers will vary. Check students' work.

For Exercises 11–13, use each right triangle to find the given sine or cosine. Check each answer with a calculator. (*Note:* Side lengths are approximate.)

11. $\sin 50°$ 0.77   **12.** $\sin 40°$ 0.64   **13.** $\cos 75°$ 0.26

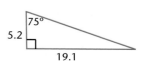

9.2   12
50°
7.7

77
40°
100   64

75°
5.2
19.1

14. Writing Benny used his calculator to find sin 45° and cos 45°. The calculator screen displayed the same answer for each. Benny is convinced he pressed a wrong key. Use a diagram to show him why sin 45° = cos 45°.

15. In Exploration 1 you used the tangent ratio to find the height of the building Adriana had sighted in her astrolabe. Explain why you cannot use the sine or cosine ratio to find the height of the building. **The length of the hypotenuse is unknown.**

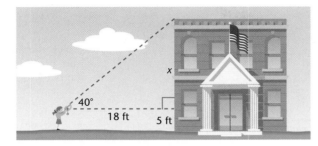

Find the value of each variable. Round your answers to the nearest hundredth.

16.
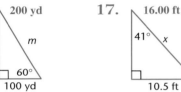
200 yd
m
60°
100 yd

17.
16.00 ft
41° x
10.5 ft

18.
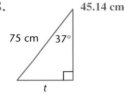
45.14 cm
75 cm 37°
t

19. Challenge The cosine of ∠B in a right triangle is 0.25.

    a. What is the approximate measure of ∠B? Make a sketch of the triangle and describe how you found the angle measure.

    b. Is this the only triangle for which cos B = 0.25? Explain how you know. **No; the ratio will be the same in any similar triangle.**

20. A painter places an extension ladder 7 ft from the base of a building so that it is at an angle of 65° with the ground.

    a. Make a sketch of the right triangle formed by the ladder, ground, and building. Include the angle measure and distance from the building.

    b. How far does the painter have the ladder extended? Round to the nearest tenth of a foot. **16.6 ft**

19. a. about 76°; Draw a right triangle in which the ratio of the lengths of one leg and the hypotenuse is 1 to 4. The cosine of the angle to which the leg is adjacent is 0.25. Measure the angle with a protractor.

B
4
1

20. a.

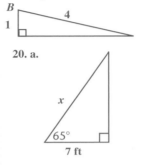
x
65°
7 ft

Practice & Applications

EXERCISE NOTES

Reflecting on the Section

Exercise 22 For students not sure how to begin the exercise, suggest they confirm that $\tan A = \frac{\sin A}{\cos A}$ by using some of the right triangle measures from this section. Then by replacing sine with the ratio $\frac{\text{opposite}}{\text{hypotenuse}}$ and cosine with the ratio $\frac{\text{adjacent}}{\text{hypotenuse}}$. They can then perform the division indicated by the fraction bar and use reciprocals to complete their proof.

26.

1st Flip	2nd Flip	3rd Flip	Outcome

HHH
HHT
HTH
HTT
THH
THT
TTH
TTT

---

21. Ramps and Angles An engineer designing a ramp often has to be concerned about the angle that the ramp makes with the ground. For example, the *American National Standards Institute* (ANSI) limits the possible angles for a wheelchair ramp like the one shown.

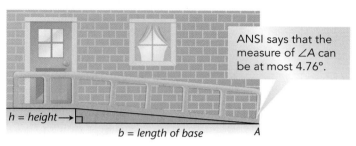

ANSI says that the measure of $\angle A$ can be at most 4.76°.

h = height →
b = length of base

a. Write an equation involving tangent that relates $\angle A$, h, and b. $\tan A = \frac{h}{b}$

b. Michelle is designing a wheelchair ramp that is supposed to reach a door 2 ft above the ground and have an angle of 4.76°. What should the length of the ramp's base be? **about 24 ft**

Journal

Exercise 22 checks that you understand and can apply the sine, cosine, and tangent ratios.

Reflecting ◀▶ on the Section

22. Use the definitions of sine, cosine, and tangent to show that $\tan A = \frac{\sin A}{\cos A}$ for any acute $\angle A$ in a right triangle. **Sample Response:** $\tan A = \frac{\text{opposite}}{\text{adjacent}}$;

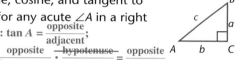

$$\frac{\sin A}{\cos A} = \frac{\text{opposite}}{\text{hypotenuse}} \div \frac{\text{adjacent}}{\text{hypotenuse}} = \frac{\text{opposite}}{\text{hypotenuse}} \cdot \frac{\text{hypotenuse}}{\text{adjacent}} = \frac{\text{opposite}}{\text{adjacent}}$$

Spiral ◀▶ Review

23. Write each expression as a single power. (Module 7, p. 464)

a. $3^5 \cdot 3^8$ $\quad 3^{13}$

b. $\frac{a^{22}}{a^{15}}$ $\quad a^7$

Describe the pattern in each sequence. Then use the pattern to find the next three terms of the sequence. (Module 8, p. 525)

24. 11, 22, 44, ...

25. $x + 2$, $2x + 3$, $3x + 4$, ...

24. Multiply the previous term by 2; 88, 176, 352

26. Make a tree diagram that shows all the possible outcomes when you flip a coin 3 times. (Module 2, p.115) **See margin.**

25. Add $x + 1$ to the previous term; $4x + 5$, $5x + 6$, $6x + 7$

Section 5

Extra Skill Practice

Use the triangle to find the given tangent. Check each answer with a calculator. (*Note: Side lengths are approximate.*)

1. $\tan 61°$ $\frac{74}{41} \approx 1.80$

41 m, 61°, 84.6 m, 74 m

2. $\tan 22°$ $\frac{2}{5} = 0.4$

22°, 5 in., 5.4 in., 2 in.

3. $\tan 67°$ $\frac{12}{5} = 2.75$

67°, 13 cm, 5 cm, 12 cm

4. For each triangle in Exercises 1–3, find the sine of the given angle. **0.87; 0.37; 0.92**

5. For each triangle in Exercises 1–3, find the cosine of the given angle. **0.48; 0.93; 0.38**

Find the value of each variable. Round your answers to the nearest hundredth.

6.
38.62 yd, x, 25°, 35 yd

7.
64.20 m, h, 44°, 62 m

8.
50.35 m, h, 44°, 70 m

9. A ramp must reach a door 3 ft off the ground. If the ramp's angle of elevation is 4°, find the length ℓ of the ramp to the nearest tenth of a foot. **43.0 ft**

3 ft, ℓ, 4°

---

1. Suppose $\angle A$ and $\angle B$ are two angles of a triangle. Which statement *cannot* be true? **B**

   Ⓐ $\angle A$ and $\angle B$ are complements.

   Ⓑ $\angle A$ and $\angle B$ are supplements.

   Ⓒ $m\angle A + m\angle B < 90°$

   Ⓓ $m\angle A + m\angle B > 90°$

2. What is the approximate value of y? **B**

   Ⓐ 21.72   Ⓑ 10.53

   Ⓒ 34.27   Ⓓ 39.19

   61°, y, 19

Extra Skill Practice

TEACHER NOTES

For each Exploration, the corresponding Extra Skills Practice Exercises are noted.

Exploration 1: Exs. 1–3, 7
Exploration 2: Exs. 4–6, 8, 9

EXTRA HELP

Teacher's Resource Book

• Practice and Applications for Section 5
• Study Guide
• Practice and Applications for Sections 1–5

Technology Resources

• @Home Tutor
• Test Generator

ASSESSMENT

• Section 5 Quick Quiz
• Test Generator

Module Project

PROJECT NOTES
Project Questions 2 and 3
To ensure accuracy, encourage students to help each other find strategies for counting the shaded squares.

Looking for Patterns

Sequences The sequence below was started by drawing an unshaded border and then a shaded border around a central shaded square. In each successive term, an additional unshaded and shaded border are added. The first two figures are shown.

SET UP

You will need:
- *graph paper*
- *calculator*

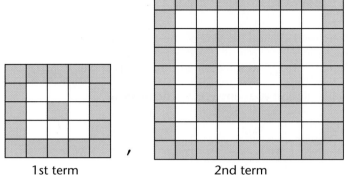

1st term   2nd term   , …

 1 Use graph paper to draw the next figure in the sequence. **See margin.**

2 How many squares the size of the central square are shaded in each term?

    a. the first term **17**   **b.** the second term **49** **c.** the third term **97**

3 Look at the pattern of shaded squares in each figure. Use it to find the number of shaded squares for the next two terms in the sequence. **The differences between pairs of consecutive terms increase by multiples of 16 beginning with 32; 161, 241.**

4 Is the sequence of the number of shaded squares arithmetic, geometric, or neither? Explain. **neither; Each term after the first is neither found by adding a constant to the previous term nor by multiplying the previous term by a constant.**

Rotational Symmetry

5 Does the geometric figure representing the first term have rotational symmetry? If so, name all its symmetries. **Yes; 90°, 180°, 270°**

6 Will any of the succeeding terms have rotational symmetry? How do you know? **Yes; They will all have the same rotational symmetries as the first term, because the basic shape is a square and the added shading each time is uniform along each of the 4 edges of the square.**

1. See Additional Answers beginning on page A1.

7. first term: 0.68 or 68%
   second term: 0.60 or 60%
   third term: 0.57 or 57%
   fourth term: 0.56 or 56%
   fifth term: 0.55 or 55%

Geometric Probability 9–10. See margin.

7 A computer randomly selects a point within the design of each geometric figure. For each of the first five terms, find the probability that the point selected is in a shaded region.

8 What happens to the probability as more borders are added? **It decreases. As the figure increases in size the probability decreases by a smaller amount with each consecutive term.**

9 Will the probability ever reach 0? ever reach 1? Explain. See margin.

10 Predict the geometric probability that the computer selects a point in the shaded region of the 20th term in the sequence. Explain your reasoning. See margin.

Designing Your Own Pattern 11–13. Answers will vary. Check students' work.

11 a. Design a sequence using a pattern of quadrilaterals. Begin with a figure that has rotational symmetry.

 b. Sketch the first three figures of your sequence.

 c. Is it possible for the first term of a sequence to have rotational symmetry, but for succeeding terms not to have rotational symmetry? Make a sketch to support your answer.

12 Explain two different ways that someone could find the next term in your sequence.

13 Explore geometric probability using your sequence. Write a summary of your findings.

In **Question 8**, students should have a deep enough understanding of probability to know that a probability of 0 means that an event will never occur or is impossible. A probability of 1 is a certain event.

As they predict the probability in **Question 9**, students should also recognize that if the probability of an event is 0.5 or 50%, then there is an equally likely chance of the event occurring or not occurring. Since there will always be more shaded than unshaded squares in the figures, the probability of selecting a shaded square may get closer to 0.5 but will never be 0.5 or less.

9. No, No; A probability of 0 indicates that there is no chance that a point selected will be in a shaded region. There will always be a chance that a point selected will be in a shaded region since there are shaded squares in each figure. A probability of 1 indicates that there is a certainty of selecting a point in a shaded region. There is always the possibility that a point selected is in an unshaded region since some of the squares in each figure are not shaded.

10. Sample Response: I think the probability will be around 53%. The probability seems to decrease as the figure increases in size, however it must always be greater than 50% since there are more shaded squares than unshaded squares in each figure.

TEACHER NOTES

Students should complete the Review and Assessment independently in preparation for the Module Test. Allow class time to discuss solutions and address any questions students may have.

During this time, you may want to allow students to work in groups to share methods for solving the problems and to quiz each other on the concepts covered in this module.

9. Possible answers: Use a protractor to measure all the angles and find their sum; Choose one vertex and draw segments to each of the other vertices to divide the polygon into 3 triangles. The sum of the measures of the angles in each triangle is 180°, so multiply 180° by 3.

12. parallelogram; both pairs of opposite angles are congruent, consecutive angles are supplementary, diagonals bisect each other

13. square; all angles are congruent, consecutive angles are supplementary, diagonals are congruent, diagonals bisect each other, diagonals are perpendicular

14. trapezoid; consecutive angles between parallel lines are supplementary, diagonals do not bisect, diagonals are not perpendicular, diagonals are not congruent, opposite angles are not congruent, one pair of congruent angles

---

Write a rule for finding a term of each sequence. Then find the next three terms. (Sec. 1, Explors. 1 and 2)

1. $\frac{1}{y}, \frac{1}{y^2}, \frac{1}{y^3}, \frac{1}{y^4}, \ldots$

2. $1, 10, 19, 28, \ldots$

3. $1, 0.5, 0.25, 0.125, \ldots$

4. $3, 8, 14, 21, 29, \ldots$

1. Multiply the previous term by $\frac{1}{y}$ (or divide by y); $\frac{1}{y^5}, \frac{1}{y^6}, \frac{1}{y^7}$

2. Add nine to the previous term; 37, 46, 55

3. Divide the previous term by 2 (or multiply by 0.5); 0.0625, 0.03125, 0.015625

4. Add 1 more than was added to the previous term; 38, 48, 59

5. geometric, multiply by –2

Tell whether each of the following sequences is *arithmetic*, *geometric*, or *neither*. (Sec. 1, Explors. 1 and 2)

5. $2, -4, 8, -16, \ldots$

6. $4, 11, 32, 95, \ldots$ neither

7. , $\ldots$

arithmetic, add 2

8. $1, 1, 2, 3, 5, \ldots$ neither

9. In this module you discovered the formula for finding the sum of the measures of the interior angles of a convex polygon. Suppose you cannot remember the formula. Describe a method for finding the sum of the interior angles of the polygon shown. (Sec. 2, Explor. 1) See margin.

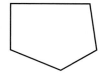

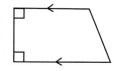

10. a. A carpenter designs and makes wooden tabletops. Find the minimum rotational symmetry of the design at the left. 60°

   b. List all the other rotational symmetries in the design. (Sec. 2, Explor. 2) 120°, 180°, 240°, 300°

11. A quadrilateral has congruent opposite angles and diagonals that bisect each other. Tell what types of quadrilateral it might be. Include sketches with your answer. (Sec. 3, Explor. 1) parallelogram, rectangle, square, rhombus; check students' drawings.

For each of the following quadrilaterals, name the quadrilateral, then list at least three of its diagonal or angle properties.
(Sec. 3, Explor. 1) 12–14. See margin.

12.

13.

14.

Find the length of the segment with the given endpoints. Then find the coordinates of the midpoint of the segment. (Sec. 3, Explor. 2)

15. (0, 4) and (0, 10)
6 units; (0, 7)

16. (1, 1) and (9, 7)
10 units; (5, 4)

17. (1, 2) and (–3, 5)
5 units; (–1, 3.5)

18. Verify that each statement is true for rectangle *ABCD*. **See margin.**

   a. The diagonals are congruent.

   b. The diagonals bisect each other.

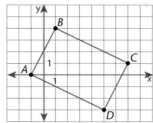

An object falls at random onto the figure shown. (Sec. 4, Explor. 1)

19. What is the probability that the object lands in the yellow region? **0.50 or 50%**

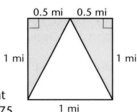

20. Alter the figure so that the probability that the object lands in the yellow region is 0.75.
See margin.

Find the value of each variable. Round your answers to the nearest hundredth. (Sec. 5, Explors. 1 and 2)

21. 9 yd   8.09 yd   26°   *u*

22. 20.26 in.   50°   17 in.   *y*

23. 5.45 mm   10 mm   *x*   33°

Reflecting ◄►on the Module

24. In this module, each section relates to the theme of a previous module. Some of the math concepts in this module relate to the math concepts of previous modules. **Answers will vary.**

   a. Choose two math concepts that relate to a math concept studied in an earlier module.

   b. Explain how the concepts are related.

EXERCISE NOTES
Exercise 16 If students are feeling frustrated by this problem, give them a hint. (*If the yellow region represents 50% of the entire figure, what percent of the figure does one of the congruent yellow triangles represent?*) This should provide students with the information that will lead them to divide the white triangle into two congruent triangles that are also congruent to the yellow triangles. By shading one of the triangles yellow, 75% of the figure will be yellow, making the probability of landing in a yellow region 0.75.

If a different mathematically accurate strategy is employed, accept it.

Assessment Options

TEACHER'S RESOURCE BOOK
• Module 8 Tests A and B
• Module 8 Standardized Test
• Module 8 Performance Assessment
• Modules 7 and 8 Cumulative Test
• End-of-Year Test

TEST GENERATOR

18. a–b. and 20. See Additional Answers beginning on page A1.

577

STUDENT RESOURCES

578

TOOLBOX

NUMBERS and OPERATIONS

Decimal Place Value

To compare two numbers in decimal form, first write each number using the same number of decimal places.

EXAMPLE

Replace each ? with >, <, or =.

a. 0.63 ? 0.8 **b. 0.02 ? 0.002**

SOLUTION **a.** 0.63 ? **0.80** — Rewrite **0.8** as **0.80.**

0.63 < 0.80

b. **0.020** ? 0.002 — Rewrite **0.02** as **0.020**.

0.020 > 0.002

EXAMPLE

Round each number to the nearest tenth.

a. 0.846 **b. 6.371**

SOLUTION Look at the digit in the hundredths place. Is it 5 or greater?

a. 0.846 — Not 5 or greater. Do not change. Drop the final digits.

0.8

b. 6.371 — Greater than 5. Add 1 to the tenths place. Drop the final digits.

6.4

Replace each ? with >, <, or =.

1. 0.4 ? 0.83 <
2. 0.65 ? 0.9 <
3. 0.750 ? 0.750 =
4. 0.163 ? 0.16 >
5. 0.12 ? 0.120 =
6. 0.8 ? 0.08 >
7. 0.5 ? 0.49 >
8. 0.3 ? 0.285 >
9. 0.1375 ? 0.18 <
10. 0.060 ? 0.06 =
11. 0.428 ? 0.73 <
12. 0.35 ? 0.25 >

Round each number to the nearest tenth.

13. 0.25 0.3
14. 0.81 0.8
15. 3.829 3.8
16. 1.657 1.7

Continued on next page

Round each number to the nearest hundredth.

17. 0.634 0.63   **18.** 7.852 7.85   **19.** 0.0499 0.05   **20.** 5.927 5.93

Round each number to the nearest thousandth.

21. 1.0375 1.038   **22.** 0.9932 0.993   **23.** 8.3096 8.310   **24.** 0.02405 0.024

Multiplying Whole Numbers and Decimals

To multiply by a number with more than one digit, you can break the number into parts.

EXAMPLE

Find each product.

   a. $425 \cdot 312$ b. $0.081 \cdot 0.02$

SOLUTION   a.

$$
\begin{array}{r}
425 \\
\times\ 312 \\
\hline
850 \\
4250 \\
127500 \\
\hline
132{,}600
\end{array}
$$

    850 ← Multiply 425 by 2 ones.
  4250 ← Multiply 425 by 1 ten.
127500 ← Multiply 425 by 3 hundreds.
132,600 ← Add the partial products.

  b.

$$
\begin{array}{r}
0.081 \\
\times\ 0.02 \\
\hline
0.00162
\end{array}
$$

   0.081 ← 3 decimal places
 × 0.02 ← 2 decimal places
0.00162 ← 5 decimal places in the product

Find each product.

1.
$$
\begin{array}{r} 62 \\ \times\ 21 \\ \hline 1302 \end{array}
$$

2.
$$
\begin{array}{r} 48 \\ \times\ 25 \\ \hline 1200 \end{array}
$$

3.
$$
\begin{array}{r} 263 \\ \times\ 109 \\ \hline 28{,}667 \end{array}
$$

4.
$$
\begin{array}{r} 3704 \\ \times\ 58 \\ \hline 214{,}832 \end{array}
$$

5.
$$
\begin{array}{r} 1696 \\ \times\ 43 \\ \hline 72{,}928 \end{array}
$$

6.
$$
\begin{array}{r} 75{,}080 \\ \times\ 243 \\ \hline 18{,}244{,}440 \end{array}
$$

7.
$$
\begin{array}{r} 1.8 \\ \times\ 3 \\ \hline 5.4 \end{array}
$$

8.
$$
\begin{array}{r} 5.7 \\ \times\ 2.2 \\ \hline 12.54 \end{array}
$$

9.
$$
\begin{array}{r} 9.07 \\ \times\ 5 \\ \hline 45.35 \end{array}
$$

10.
$$
\begin{array}{r} 4.61 \\ \times\ 1.7 \\ \hline 7.837 \end{array}
$$

11.
$$
\begin{array}{r} 8.95 \\ \times\ 2.36 \\ \hline 21.122 \end{array}
$$

12.
$$
\begin{array}{r} 92 \\ \times\ 4.73 \\ \hline 435.16 \end{array}
$$

13.
$$
\begin{array}{r} 0.06 \\ \times\ 0.03 \\ \hline 0.0018 \end{array}
$$

14.
$$
\begin{array}{r} 5.004 \\ \times\ 1.01 \\ \hline 5.05404 \end{array}
$$

15.
$$
\begin{array}{r} 0.048 \\ \times\ 0.04 \\ \hline 0.00192 \end{array}
$$

16.
$$
\begin{array}{r} 640.8 \\ \times\ 0.012 \\ \hline 7.6896 \end{array}
$$

Multiplying and Dividing by 10, 100, and 1000

To multiply by a power of 10, move the decimal point to the right.
To divide by a power of 10, move the decimal point to the left.
Use zeros as placeholders if necessary.

EXAMPLE

Find each product or quotient.

    a. 143.628 • 100   b. 0.057 ÷ 1000

SOLUTION   a. 143.628 • 100 = 143.628   Move the decimal point **two** places to the right.

             = 14,362.8

      b. 0.057 ÷ 1000 = 0000.057   Move the decimal point **three** places to the left. Add zeros as placeholders.

             = 0.000057

To convert from one metric measure to another, multiply or divide by a power of 10. Use the Table of Measures on page 601.

EXAMPLE

Complete the equation: 15 mm = _?_ cm

SOLUTION   10 mm = 1 cm

                15 mm = (15 ÷ 10) cm   Millimeters are a smaller unit than centimeters, so divide.

                15 mm = 1.5 cm

For Exercises 1–6, find each product or quotient.

1. 51.83 • 10 518.3   2. 9.8 • 100 980   3. 30.042 ÷ 10 3.0042

4. 0.067 • 1000 67   5. 29.4 ÷ 100 0.294   6. 0.056 • 10 0.56

7. To convert from kilometers to meters, should you *multiply* or *divide* by 1000? Multiply.

Complete each equation. Use the Table of Measures on page 601.

8. 68 cm = _?_ m 0.68   9. 13 km = _?_ m 13,000   10. 27 m = _?_ cm 2700

11. 3560 m = _?_ km 3.56 12. 4.8 m = _?_ mm 4800   13. 4540 mg = _?_ g 4.54

Dividing Whole Numbers and Decimals

When you divide, you may have to add zeros to the dividend. When dividing by a decimal, move both decimal points the same number of decimal places to the right, until the divisor is a whole number. Then follow the same rules as for dividing whole numbers.

EXAMPLE

Find the quotient 6)83. Round your answer to the nearest tenth.

SOLUTION

$$\begin{array}{r} 13.83 \\ 6\overline{)83.00} \\ \underline{6} \\ 23 \\ \underline{18} \\ 5\,0 \\ \underline{4\,8} \\ 20 \end{array}$$

To round to the nearest tenth, carry out the division to the hundredths place. Then round.

To the nearest tenth, the quotient is 13.8.

EXAMPLE

Find the quotient: 0.05)4.8

SOLUTION

0.05)4.80

Move the decimal point two places to the right. Write a zero.

Divide. ⟶
$$\begin{array}{r} 96 \\ 5\overline{)480} \\ \underline{45} \\ 30 \\ \underline{30} \\ 0 \end{array}$$

The quotient is 96.

Find each quotient. Round each answer to the nearest tenth.

1. 8)198   24.8
2. 15)265   17.7
3. 32)488   15.3

Find each quotient. Round each answer to the nearest hundredth.

4. 9)68   7.56
5. 16)851   53.19
6. 11)547   49.73

Find each quotient. If necessary, round each answer to the nearest tenth.

7. 1.8)25.2   14
8. 5.4)243   45
9. 6.4)54.4   8.5
10. 4.5)1180   262.2
11. 0.32)308   962.5
12. 0.027)26.136   968

Divisibility Rules

A number is divisible by another number if the remainder is zero when you divide the second number by the first. It is not possible to divide a number by zero. The table shows divisibility tests you can use to tell if a number is divisible by another number.

Divisible by	Test
2	The last digit is 0, 2, 4, 6, or 8.
3	The sum of the digits is divisible by 3.
4	The number formed by the last two digits is divisible by 4.
5	The last digit is 0 or 5.
6	The number is divisible by both 2 and 3.
8	The number formed by the last three digits is divisible by 8.
9	The sum of the digits is divisible by 9.
10	The last digit is 0.

EXAMPLE

Is 79,120 divisible by 8?

SOLUTION The number formed by the last three digits, 120, is divisible by 8.
Yes, 79,120 is divisible by 8.

EXAMPLE

Is 5742 divisible by 9?

SOLUTION The sum of the digits, 5 + 7 + 4 + 2 = 18, which is divisible by 9.
Yes, 5742 is divisible by 9.

EXAMPLE

Is 818 divisible by 6?

SOLUTION 818 is divisible by 2, because the last digit is 8. 818 is not divisible by 3, because 8 + 1 + 8 = 17, which is not divisible by 3.
No, 818 is not divisible by 6.

Test each number for divisibility.

1. Is 378 divisible by 4? No.
2. Is 657 divisible by 3? Yes.
3. Is 4695 divisible by 5? Yes.
4. Is 5934 divisible by 2? Yes.
5. Is 3511 divisible by 10? No.
6. Is 2178 divisible by 6? Yes.
7. Is 2043 divisible by 9? Yes.
8. Is 80,256 divisible by 8? Yes.

Toolbox 583

Finding Factors and Multiples

A common factor of two numbers is a number that is a factor of both numbers. For example, 4 is a common factor of 60 and 100, because $60 = 4 \cdot 15$ and $100 = 4 \cdot 25$.

The greatest common factor (GCF) of two numbers is the greatest number that is a common factor of the two numbers.

EXAMPLE

Find the GCF of 60 and 100.

SOLUTION   Write the prime factorizations of 60 and 100.

$$60 = 2 \cdot 2 \cdot 3 \cdot 5$$
$$100 = 2 \cdot 2 \cdot 5 \cdot 5$$

Circle the numbers that are in *both* factorizations.

Multiply the numbers you circled.
The GCF of 60 and 100 is $2 \cdot 2 \cdot 5 = 20$.

A common multiple of two numbers is a number that is a multiple of both numbers. For example, 72 is a common multiple of 12 and 9, because $12 \cdot 6 = 72$ and $9 \cdot 8 = 72$.

The least common multiple (LCM) of two numbers is the least number that is a common multiple of the numbers.

EXAMPLE

Find the LCM of 9 and 12.

SOLUTION   Find the GCF of 9 and 12.

$$9 = 3 \cdot 3$$
$$12 = 2 \cdot 2 \cdot 3$$

The GCF is 3.

Multiply the GCF by the numbers you did not circle.
The LCM of 9 and 12 is $3 \cdot 3 \cdot 2 \cdot 2 = 36$.

Find the GCF and the LCM of each pair of numbers.

1. 42, 60 6; 420
2. 24, 36 12; 72
3. 33, 110 11; 330
4. 80, 120 40; 240
5. 30, 90 30; 90
6. 125, 420 5; 10,500
7. 165, 315 15; 3465
8. 114, 138 6; 2622
9. 275, 495 55; 2475
10. 50, 98 2; 2450
11. 77, 81 1; 6237
12. 46, 69 23; 138

Finding Equivalent Fractions and Ratios

Fractions that name the same part of a whole are equivalent fractions.
A fraction is in lowest terms if the GCF of the numerator and the
denominator is 1.

EXAMPLE

a. Complete $\dfrac{48}{60} = \dfrac{?}{240}$.

b. Write $\dfrac{48}{60}$ in lowest terms.

SOLUTION

a. $\dfrac{48}{60} = \dfrac{48 \cdot 4}{60 \cdot 4} = \dfrac{192}{240}$ $60 \cdot 4 = 240$, so multiply by **4**.

b. $\dfrac{48}{60} = \dfrac{48 \div 12}{60 \div 12} = \dfrac{4}{5}$ The GCF of 48 and 60 is **12**, so divide by **12**.

A ratio is a comparison of two numbers using division. The ratio of
a and b, $b \neq 0$, can be written a to b, $a : b$, or $\dfrac{a}{b}$. To compare ratios,
first write them as fractions. Then compare the fractions.

EXAMPLE

Replace the ? with >, <, or =. $3 : 16 \underline{\ ?\ } 5 : 24$

SOLUTION   Write $3 : 16$ as $\dfrac{3}{16}$ and $5 : 24$ as $\dfrac{5}{24}$.

Then write the fractions using a common denominator.

$\dfrac{3}{16} = \dfrac{3 \cdot 3}{16 \cdot 3} = \dfrac{9}{48}$ and $\dfrac{5}{24} = \dfrac{5 \cdot 2}{24 \cdot 2} = \dfrac{10}{48}$ The LCM of 16 and 24, **48**, is the least common denominator.

Since $\dfrac{9}{48} < \dfrac{10}{48}$, $3 : 16 < 5 : 24$.

Replace each ? with the number that will make the fractions equivalent.

1. $\dfrac{2}{7} = \dfrac{?}{21}$ 6
2. $\dfrac{14}{15} = \dfrac{?}{60}$ 56
3. $\dfrac{12}{20} = \dfrac{?}{10}$ 6
4. $\dfrac{15}{45} = \dfrac{?}{9}$ 3

Write each fraction in lowest terms.

5. $\dfrac{9}{15}$ $\frac{3}{5}$
6. $\dfrac{4}{12}$ $\frac{1}{3}$
7. $\dfrac{18}{20}$ $\frac{9}{10}$
8. $\dfrac{6}{9}$ $\frac{2}{3}$

Replace each ? with >, <, or =.

9. $\dfrac{3}{10} \underline{\ ?\ } \dfrac{9}{30}$ =
10. $5 : 12 \underline{\ ?\ } 7 : 8$ <
11. 15 to 36 $\underline{\ ?\ }$ 1 to 27   >

Adding and Subtracting Fractions

To add or subtract fractions, write the fractions using a common denominator. Then add or subtract the numerators of these fractions.

EXAMPLE

Find the sum: $\dfrac{3}{8} + \dfrac{2}{5}$

> The least common denominator is 40. Write each fraction with a denominator of 40.

SOLUTION

$$\frac{3}{8} + \frac{2}{5} = \frac{15}{40} + \frac{16}{40}$$

> Add the numerators.

$$= \frac{15+16}{40}$$

$$= \frac{31}{40}$$

EXAMPLE

Find the difference: $\dfrac{11}{12} - \dfrac{2}{3}$

> The least common denominator is 12. Write $\dfrac{2}{3}$ as $\dfrac{8}{12}$.

SOLUTION

$$\frac{11}{12} - \frac{2}{3} = \frac{11}{12} - \frac{8}{12}$$

> Subtract the numerators.

$$= \frac{11-8}{12}$$

$$= \frac{3}{12}$$

> Write the answer in lowest terms.

$$= \frac{1}{4}$$

Find each sum or difference. Write each answer in lowest terms.

1. $\dfrac{1}{3} + \dfrac{1}{4}$ $\dfrac{7}{12}$

2. $\dfrac{3}{8} + \dfrac{3}{4}$ $1\dfrac{1}{8}$

3. $\dfrac{15}{16} - \dfrac{5}{8}$ $\dfrac{5}{16}$

4. $\dfrac{2}{7} + \dfrac{2}{3}$ $\dfrac{20}{21}$

5. $\dfrac{5}{8} - \dfrac{5}{9}$ $\dfrac{5}{72}$

6. $\dfrac{10}{11} - \dfrac{3}{4}$ $\dfrac{7}{44}$

7. $\dfrac{13}{20} - \dfrac{3}{10}$ $\dfrac{7}{20}$

8. $\dfrac{4}{15} + \dfrac{2}{5}$ $\dfrac{2}{3}$

9. $\dfrac{1}{6} + \dfrac{7}{12}$ $\dfrac{3}{4}$

10. $\dfrac{13}{18} - \dfrac{2}{9}$ $\dfrac{1}{2}$

11. $\dfrac{4}{7} - \dfrac{5}{11}$ $\dfrac{9}{77}$

12. $\dfrac{2}{7} + \dfrac{1}{6} + \dfrac{2}{21}$ $\dfrac{23}{42}$

13. $\dfrac{23}{24} - \dfrac{5}{12} - \dfrac{1}{8}$ $\dfrac{5}{12}$

14. $\dfrac{3}{2} + \dfrac{9}{5}$ $3\dfrac{3}{10}$

15. $\dfrac{1}{2} - \dfrac{1}{6} + \dfrac{5}{12}$ $\dfrac{3}{4}$

Multiplying and Dividing Fractions

To multiply two fractions, multiply the numerators and the denominators.

EXAMPLE

Find the product: $\dfrac{9}{10} \cdot \dfrac{2}{3}$

SOLUTION $\dfrac{9}{10} \cdot \dfrac{2}{3} = \dfrac{9 \cdot 2}{10 \cdot 3}$ Multiply the **numerators** and the **denominators**.

$= \dfrac{18}{30}$

$= \dfrac{3}{5}$ Write the answer in lowest terms.

To divide by a fraction, multiply by its reciprocal. Change mixed numbers to fractions before multiplying or dividing.

EXAMPLE

Find the quotient: $1\dfrac{5}{6} \div 2\dfrac{1}{3}$

SOLUTION $1\dfrac{5}{6} \div 2\dfrac{1}{3} = \dfrac{11}{6} \div \dfrac{7}{3}$ Write each mixed number as a fraction.

$= \dfrac{11}{6} \cdot \dfrac{3}{7}$ Multiply by the **reciprocal** of the second number.

$= \dfrac{33}{42}$

$= \dfrac{11}{14}$ Write the answer in lowest terms.

Find each product. Write each answer in lowest terms.

1. $\dfrac{4}{5} \cdot \dfrac{1}{3}$ $\tfrac{4}{15}$

2. $\dfrac{1}{14} \cdot \dfrac{2}{7}$ $\tfrac{1}{49}$

3. $\dfrac{1}{3} \cdot \dfrac{9}{10}$ $\tfrac{3}{10}$

4. $\dfrac{7}{12} \cdot \dfrac{8}{21}$ $\tfrac{2}{9}$

5. $\dfrac{3}{8} \cdot 16$ 6

6. $\dfrac{8}{15} \cdot 1\dfrac{1}{2}$ $\tfrac{4}{5}$

7. $1\dfrac{4}{5} \cdot 1\dfrac{2}{3}$ 3

8. $18 \cdot \dfrac{5}{6}$ 15

Find each quotient. Write each answer in lowest terms.

9. $\dfrac{1}{4} \div \dfrac{1}{2}$ $\tfrac{1}{2}$

10. $\dfrac{3}{10} \div \dfrac{2}{5}$ $\tfrac{3}{4}$

11. $\dfrac{1}{3} \div \dfrac{1}{8}$ $\tfrac{8}{3}$ or $2\tfrac{2}{3}$

12. $\dfrac{3}{10} \div \dfrac{6}{25}$ $\tfrac{5}{4}$ or $1\tfrac{1}{4}$

13. $6 \div \dfrac{4}{5}$ $\tfrac{15}{2}$ or $7\tfrac{1}{2}$

14. $\dfrac{3}{10} \div 3$ $\tfrac{1}{10}$

15. $1\dfrac{1}{2} \div \dfrac{1}{4}$ 6

16. $2\dfrac{2}{9} \div 1\dfrac{1}{4}$ $\tfrac{16}{9}$ or $1\tfrac{7}{9}$

Writing Fractions, Decimals, and Percents

You can write a fraction as a decimal or as a percent. Percent means "per hundred," so to write a fraction as a percent, start by finding an equivalent fraction with 100 as the denominator.

EXAMPLE

Write $\frac{2}{5}$ as a decimal and as a percent.

SOLUTION $\quad \frac{2}{5} = \frac{2 \cdot 20}{5 \cdot 20}$ Find an equivalent fraction with 100 as the denominator.

$$= \frac{40}{100}$$

$$\left. \begin{array}{l} = 0.40 \\ \\ = 40\% \end{array} \right\} \quad \frac{2}{5} = 0.40 = 40\%$$

EXAMPLE

Write 72% as a decimal and as a fraction in lowest terms.

SOLUTION $\quad 72\% = 0.72$

$$= \frac{72}{100}$$

$$= \frac{18}{25} \quad \text{Write the fraction in lowest terms.}$$

The chart shows some common percent, decimal, and fraction equivalents.

$1\% = 0.01 = \frac{1}{100}$	$33\frac{1}{3}\% = 0.\overline{3} = \frac{1}{3}$	$66\frac{2}{3}\% = 0.\overline{6} = \frac{2}{3}$
$10\% = 0.1 = \frac{1}{10}$	$40\% = 0.4 = \frac{2}{5}$	$75\% = 0.75 = \frac{3}{4}$
$20\% = 0.2 = \frac{1}{5}$	$50\% = 0.5 = \frac{1}{2}$	$80\% = 0.8 = \frac{4}{5}$
$25\% = 0.25 = \frac{1}{4}$	$60\% = 0.6 = \frac{3}{5}$	$100\% = 1$

Write each fraction as a decimal and as a percent.

1. $\frac{19}{20}$ $0.95; 95\%$
2. $\frac{4}{25}$ $0.16; 16\%$
3. $\frac{1}{1000}$ $0.001; 0.1\%$
4. $\frac{31}{50}$ $0.62; 62\%$

Write each percent as a decimal and as a fraction in lowest terms.

5. 80% $0.8; \frac{4}{5}$
6. 87.5% $0.875; \frac{7}{8}$
7. 64% $0.64; \frac{16}{25}$
8. 120% $1.2; \frac{6}{5}$ or $1\frac{1}{5}$

Write each decimal as a percent and as a fraction in lowest terms.

9. 0.48 $48\%; \frac{12}{25}$
10. 0.85 $85\%; \frac{17}{20}$
11. 0.125 $12.5\%; \frac{1}{8}$
12. 3.5 $350\%; \frac{7}{2}$ or $3\frac{1}{2}$

Using Order of Operations

When you evaluate an expression that contains more than one operation, perform the operations in the order shown below.

1. First do all work inside parentheses.
2. Then evaluate any powers.
3. Then do all multiplications and divisions in order from left to right.
4. Then do all additions and subtractions in order from left to right.

A power is the product when a number or an expression is used as a factor a given number of times. For example, $3 \cdot 3 \cdot 3 \cdot 3 \cdot 3$ is the fifth power of 3 and can be written as 3^5. In 3^5, 3 is the base and 5 is the exponent.

Sometimes multiplication is written with parentheses. For example, $3(4) = 3 \cdot 4$.

EXAMPLE

Find each answer.

   a. $2(11) + 20 \div (7 - 5)$ **b.** $5 \cdot 2^3 - 6$

SOLUTION

a. $2(11) + 20 \div (7 - 5) = 2(11) + 20 \div 2$ Do work inside parentheses first.

                 $= 22 + 10$ Do multiplication and division.

                 $= 32$ Add.

b. $5 \cdot 2^3 - 6 = 5 \cdot 8 - 6$ Evaluate the power first: $2^3 = 2 \cdot 2 \cdot 2 = 8$

             $= 40 - 6$ Multiply.

             $= 34$ Subtract.

Find each answer.

1. $4^2 - 1$ 15
2. $6(8 - 5)$ 18
3. $7 \cdot 2^3$ 56
4. $5 \cdot 6 - 17$ 13
5. $3 \cdot 10 \div 6$ 5
6. $(9 \div 3)^2$ 9
7. $9 \div 3^2$ 1
8. $15 + 42 \div 7 - 17$ 4
9. $15 + 2(11 - 4)$ 29
10. $4^2 + 5(2^3 - 3)$ 41
11. $2 \cdot 3^2 - 4(7 - 3)$ 2
12. $3(6 + 2) \div 4(9 - 7)$ 3

Comparing Integers

Integers are the numbers ... –3, –2, –1, 0, 1, 2, 3, ... To compare two integers, use a number line. The greater number is to the right of the lesser number on a horizontal number line.

EXAMPLE

Graph each pair of integers on a number line. Then replace each _?_ with > or <.

    a. –3 _?_ 2   b. 2 _?_ –3

SOLUTION

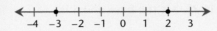

The greater number is always to the right of the lesser number.

Since 2 is to the right of –3, 2 is the greater number and –3 is the lesser number.

    a. –3 < 2   b. 2 > –3

EXAMPLE

Use a number line to write the integers 3, 5, and –2 in order from least to greatest.

SOLUTION   Graph each number on a number line.

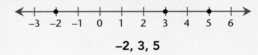

                    –2, 3, 5

Replace each _?_ with > or <.

  1. 4 _?_ –6 >   2. –3 _?_ –1 <   3. –5 _?_ 0 <

  4. –2 _?_ 4 <   5. 0 _?_ –7 >   6. –1 _?_ –4 >

  7. 5 _?_ 1 >   8. –8 _?_ 8 <   9. –4 _?_ 2 <

Use a number line to write each group of integers in order from least to greatest.

  10. –5, 1, –4 –5, –4, 1   11. 0, –3, 2 –3, 0, 2   12. –2, –4, –1 –4, –2, –1

  13. 3, 4, –5 –5, 3, 4   14. –3, 0, –6 –6, –3, 0   15. 2, –2, 6 –2, 2, 6

  16. 1, –1, 0, –2 –2, –1, 0, 1   17. 0, –4, –7, –2 –7, –4, –2, 0   18. 5, –3, 2, –6 –6, –3, 2, 5

Locating Points in a Coordinate Plane

You can use an ordered pair to describe the location of a point in a coordinate plane. The first number in an ordered pair is the **horizontal coordinate** and the second number is the **vertical coordinate**.

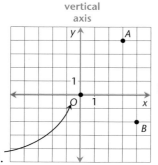

The coordinates of point A are (3, 4).

The coordinates of point B are (4, −2).

The origin is at (0, 0).

EXAMPLE

Graph each point.

a. (−5, −1)   b. (0, 3)

SOLUTION   a. From the origin, move **5 units left** and **1 unit down**.   b. From the origin, move **3 units up**.

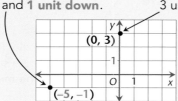

10–18.

Use the diagram at the right. Give the coordinates of each point.

1. A (−5, 2)   2. B (−3, −2)   3. C (−3, 1)

4. D (1, 4)   5. E (3, 0)   6. F (0, −2)

7. G (2, −4)   8. H (−2, 4)   9. K (−1, 1)

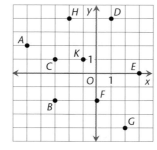

Graph each point in a coordinate plane. 10–18. See graph above.

10. (2, 3)   11. (4, −3)   12. (0, −5)

13. (−1, −2)   14. (−5, 2)   15. (−4, 0)

16. (1, −5)   17. (−1, 1)   18. (0, 0)

Toolbox 591

Measuring Angles

An angle is formed by two rays, called *sides* of the angle, with the same endpoint, called the *vertex*. Angles are measured in degrees. You use a protractor to measure an angle.

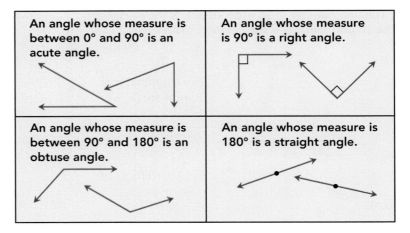

| An angle whose measure is between 0° and 90° is an acute angle. | An angle whose measure is 90° is a right angle. |
| An angle whose measure is between 90° and 180° is an obtuse angle. | An angle whose measure is 180° is a straight angle. |

EXAMPLE

Use a protractor to measure ∠S.

SOLUTION

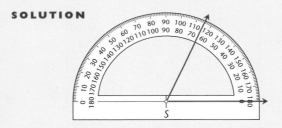

Step 1 Place the center mark of the protractor on the vertex.

Step 2 Place the 0° mark on one side of the angle.

Step 3 Read the number where the other side of the angle crosses the scale. Read the number on the bottom scale since you used its 0° mark.
The measure of ∠S is 65°.

Use a protractor to measure each angle. Then tell whether the angle is *acute, right, obtuse,* or *straight.*

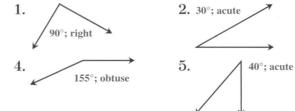

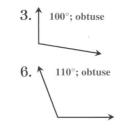

1. 90°; right
2. 30°; acute
3. 100°; obtuse
4. 155°; obtuse
5. 40°; acute
6. 110°; obtuse

Classifying Triangles

To classify a triangle, you can use the measures of its angles or the relationship between the lengths of its sides. The sum of the measures of the angles of a triangle is 180°.

An acute triangle has three acute angles.	A right triangle has one right angle.	An obtuse triangle has one obtuse angle.
A scalene triangle has no sides of equal length.	An isosceles triangle has at least two sides of equal length.	An equilateral triangle has three sides of equal length.

Sides marked alike
are equal in length.

Tell whether each triangle is *acute*, *right*, or *obtuse*.

1. 120° 28° 32° obtuse

2. right

3. 150° obtuse

4. acute 83° 60° 37°

Tell whether each triangle is *scalene*, *isosceles*, or *equilateral*.

5. 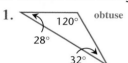 25 cm 14 cm 25 cm isosceles

6.  equilateral and isosceles

7. 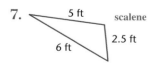 5 ft 2.5 ft 6 ft scalene

8. isosceles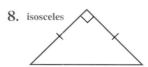

Identifying Polygons

A polygon is a closed plane figure formed by three or more segments that do not cross each other.

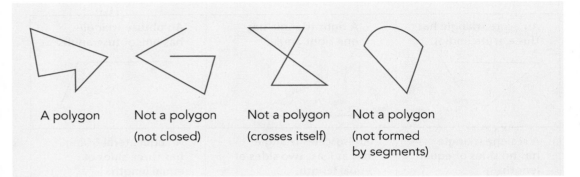

A polygon   Not a polygon (not closed)   Not a polygon (crosses itself)   Not a polygon (not formed by segments)

A regular polygon is a polygon with all sides of equal length and all angles of equal measure.

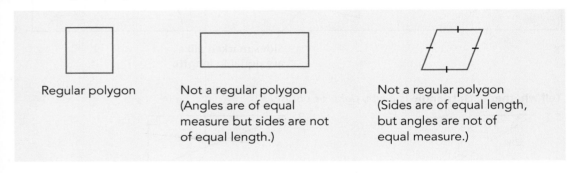

Regular polygon   Not a regular polygon (Angles are of equal measure but sides are not of equal length.)   Not a regular polygon (Sides are of equal length, but angles are not of equal measure.)

Which of these figures are polygons? Which appear to be regular polygons? Explain your thinking.

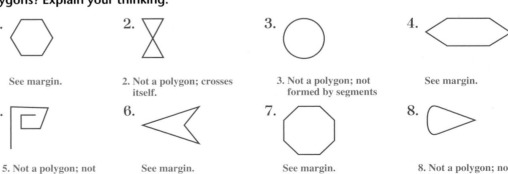

1.   See margin.

2. Not a polygon; crosses itself.

3. Not a polygon; not formed by segments

4.   See margin.

5. Not a polygon; not closed

6.   See margin.

7.   See margin.

8. Not a polygon; not formed by segments

Using Formulas from Geometry

To find the perimeter, area, or volume of a figure, use the
Table of Formulas on page 602.

EXAMPLE

Find the perimeter and the area of the rectangle.

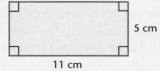

5 cm

11 cm

SOLUTION

$P = 2l + 2w$ ← Use the formula for the perimeter of a rectangle.
$= 2 \cdot 11 + 2 \cdot 5$ ← Substitute **11** for l and **5** for w.
$= 32$ ← Evaluate.

$A = lw$ ← Use the formula for the area of a rectangle.
$= 11 \cdot 5$ ← Substitute **11** for l and **5** for w.
$= 55$ ← Evaluate.

The perimeter is **32 cm**. The area is **55 cm²**.

EXAMPLE

Find the volume of the right rectangular prism.

4 in.

6 in.

8 in.

SOLUTION

$V = Bh$ ← Use the formula for the volume of a rectangular prism.
$= 48 \cdot 4$ ← $\begin{cases} B \text{ stands for the area of the base, which is } 8 \cdot 6 = 48. \\ \text{Substitute } 48 \text{ for } B \text{ and } 4 \text{ for } h. \end{cases}$
$= 192$ ← Evaluate.

The volume is **192 in.³**.

Find the perimeter and the area of each figure.

1. triangle $P = 16$ ft; $A = 12$ ft²

4 ft
5 ft 5 ft
6 ft

2. parallelogram $P = 58$ m; $A = 180$ m²

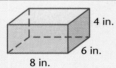

4 m 12 m
15 m

3. trapezoid $P = 80$ yd; $A = 360$ yd²

20 yd
5 yd 17 yd
28 yd

Find the volume of each right rectangular prism.

4.

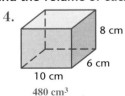

8 cm
6 cm
10 cm
480 cm³

5.

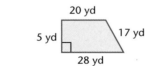

25 m
15 m 15 m
5625 m³

6.

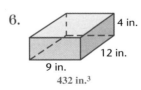

4 in.
12 in.
9 in.
432 in.³

Finding the Mean, Median, Mode, and Range

You can use different numbers to describe a data set.

Mean: The sum of the data items, divided by the number of data items.

Median: The middle number or the average of the two middle numbers when the data items are listed in order.

Mode: The most frequently occurring item, or items, in a data set. There may be more than one mode or no mode.

Range: The difference between the largest and the smallest data items.

EXAMPLE

Find the mean, the median, the mode, and the range of the data set.

14, 18, 19, 16, 14, 20, 12, 18, 14

SOLUTION

$$\text{Mean} = \frac{14 + 18 + 19 + 16 + 14 + 20 + 12 + 18 + 14}{9} \approx 16.1$$

There are **9** data items.

The mean is about 16.1.

Median: 12 14 14 14 **16** 18 18 19 20   List the numbers in order.

Find the **middle** number.

The median is 16.

Mode: 14 appears more often than any other number.

The mode is 14.

Range: The smallest number is 12. The largest number is 20. Subtract to find the range: 20 − 12 = 8.

The range is 8.

Find the mean, the median, the mode, and the range of each data set.

1. 29, 38, 32, 37, 29
mean: 33; median: 32; mode: 29; range: 9

2. 18, 14, 15, 16, 20, 17
mean: $16\frac{2}{3}$; median: 16.5; mode: none; range: 6

3. 3.6, 2.5, 4.2, 3.3, 5.4
mean: 3.8; median: 3.6; mode: none; range: 2.9

4. 34, 34, 34, 34, 34, 34, 34
mean: 34; median: 34; mode: 34; range: 0

5. 4, 1, 1, 0, 2, 3, 5, 2
mean: 2.25; median: 2; modes: 1 and 2; range: 5

6. 145, 95, 90, 120, 105, 85, 95
mean: 105; median: 95; mode: 95; range: 60

Use a **bar graph** to compare numbers of data items that are grouped into categories.

Votes for School Color

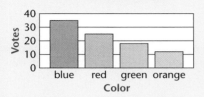

Use a **histogram** to compare numbers of data items that are grouped into numerical intervals.

Ages of Actors in a Play

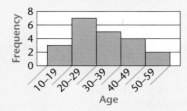

Use a **box-and-whisker plot** to show the median, the quartiles, and the extremes of a data set.

Ages of Actors in a Play

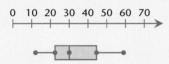

Use a **stem-and-leaf plot** to show each value in a data set and to group the values into intervals.

Ages of Actors in a Play

```
1 | 2  5  8
2 | 1  3  4  4  7  9
3 | 0  2  5  8  9
4 | 3  6  6  7
5 | 5  9
```
4 | 3 means 43 years old.

Use a **scatter plot** to show a relationship between two sets of data.

Corn Production

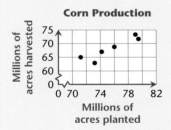

Use a **line graph** to show how data values change over time.

Corn Production

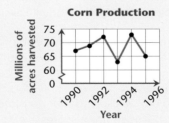

Use a **circle graph** to show the division of a whole into parts.

Votes for School Color

orange 13% blue 39%

green 20% red 28%

Using Self-Assessment Scales

One way to improve your problem solving skills is to use the Student Self-Assessment Scales on page 599. Use whichever scales apply to a problem you have solved to assess your work in mathematics.

EXAMPLE

PROBLEM Five people are hired to work at a new store. As they are introduced they shake hands exactly once. How many handshakes take place?

A STUDENT'S SOLUTION

Person A shakes 4 hands.

Person B shakes 3 more hands.

Person C shakes 2 more hands.

Person D shakes 1 more hand.

Person E has no more hands to shake.

There were ten total handshakes.

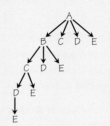

The problem was understood, the plan was to draw a diagram, a diagram was drawn, and the problem was solved. However, the solution was not verified. This solution scores a 4 on the Problem Solving Scale.

Mathematical vocabulary and symbols do not play a large role in this problem. The Mathematical Language Scale does not apply.

The representation chosen was helpful. The diagram shows why the answer is correct. This solution scores a 5 on the Representations Scale.

The problem was solved, but no patterns or generalizations were discussed. This solution scores a 1 on the Connections Scale.

The presentation of the problem shows there are 10 handshakes. A further explanation of why there are not more solutions would be helpful. This solution scores a 3 on the Presentation Scale.

Extended Exploration activities to which these scales can be applied are found on pages 71, 121, 191, 257, 362, 419, 481, and 531.

 Student Resources

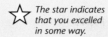

If your score is in the shaded area, explain why on the back of this sheet and stop.

☆ The star indicates that you excelled in some way.

Problem Solving

① I did not understand the problem well enough to get started or I did not show any work.

③ I understood the problem well enough to make a plan and to work toward a solution.

⑤ I made a plan, I used it to solve the problem, and I verified my solution.

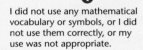

Mathematical Language

① I did not use any mathematical vocabulary or symbols, or I did not use them correctly, or my use was not appropriate.

③ I used appropriate mathematical language, but the way it was used was not always correct or other terms and symbols were needed.

⑤ I used mathematical language that was correct and appropriate to make my meaning clear.

Representations

① I did not use any representations such as equations, tables, graphs, or diagrams to help solve the problem or explain my solution.

③ I made appropriate representations to help solve the problem or help me explain my solution, but they were not always correct or other representations were needed.

⑤ I used appropriate and correct representations to solve the problem or explain my solution.

Connections

① I attempted or solved the problem and then stopped.

③ I found patterns and used them to extend the solution to other cases, or I recognized that this problem relates to other problems, mathematical ideas, or applications.

⑤ I extended the ideas in the solution to the general case, or I showed how this problem relates to other problems, mathematical ideas, or applications.

Presentation

① The presentation of my solution and reasoning is unclear to others.

③ The presentation of my solution and reasoning is clear in most places, but others may have trouble understanding parts of it.

⑤ The presentation of my solution and reasoning is clear and can be understood by others.

TABLE OF SYMBOLS

SYMBOL		Page	SYMBOL		Page
=	equals	3	$\overline{AB}$	segment AB	193
÷	divided by	4	AB	length of segment AB	193
%	percent	6	~	is similar to	194
×	times	6	◿ ◿	equal angle measures	194
≈	is approximately equal to	9	△ABC	triangle ABC	194
•	times	9	⌐	right angle	194
>	is greater than	30		equal side lengths	196
<	is less than	30	2 : 1	ratio of 2 to 1	203
−6	negative 6	30	≠	is not equal to	208
+	plus	34	...	and so on	273
$\frac{1}{4}$	1 divided by 4	34	$0.\overline{63}$	repeating bar—the digits 6 and 3 repeat	273
°	degrees	35	5!	5 factorial	289
( )	parentheses—a grouping symbol	40	≅	is congruent to	321
y^2	y used as a factor 2 times	40	[ ]	brackets—a grouping symbol	350
−	minus	43		parallel sides	367
(x, y)	ordered pair of numbers	51	3^{-4}	$\frac{1}{3^4}$	462
$-x$	the opposite of x	80	$\sqrt[3]{x}$	cube root of x	475
$\|x\|$	the absolute value of x	80	$\sqrt[4]{x}$	fourth root of x	476
A'	A prime—point A goes to point A' after a transformation	81	≥	is greater than or equal to	484
$\sqrt{x}$	positive, or principal, square root of x	159	≤	is less than or equal to	484
π	pi, a number approximately equal to 3.14	176	$P(A)$	the probability of event A	556
$\angle A$	angle A	193	tan A	tangent of angle A	564
$m\angle A$	the measure of angle A	193	sin A	sine of angle A	566
			cos A	cosine of angle A	566

TABLE OF MEASURES

Time

60 seconds (sec) = 1 minute (min)
60 minutes = 1 hour (hr)
24 hours = 1 day
7 days = 1 week
4 weeks (approx.) = 1 month

$$\left.\begin{array}{l} 365 \text{ days} \\ 52 \text{ weeks (approx.)} \\ 12 \text{ months} \end{array}\right\} = 1 \text{ year}$$

10 years = 1 decade
100 years = 1 century

METRIC

Length

10 millimeters (mm) = 1 centimeter (cm)

$$\left.\begin{array}{l} 100 \text{ cm} \\ 1000 \text{ mm} \end{array}\right\} = 1 \text{ meter (m)}$$

1000 m = 1 kilometer (km)

Area

100 square millimeters = 1 square centimeter
(mm^2) (cm^2)
10,000 cm^2 = 1 square meter (m^2)
10,000 m^2 = 1 hectare (ha)

Volume

1000 cubic millimeters = 1 cubic centimeter
(mm^3) (cm^3)
1,000,000 cm^3 = 1 cubic meter (m^3)

Liquid Capacity

1000 milliliters (mL) = 1 liter (L)
1000 L = 1 kiloliter (kL)

Mass

1000 milligrams (mg) = 1 gram (g)
1000 g = 1 kilogram (kg)
1000 kg = 1 metric ton (t)

Temperature — Degrees Celsius (°C)

0°C = freezing point of water
37°C = normal body temperature
100°C = boiling point of water

UNITED STATES CUSTOMARY

Length

12 inches (in.) = 1 foot (ft)

$$\left.\begin{array}{l} 36 \text{ in.} \\ 3 \text{ ft} \end{array}\right\} = 1 \text{ yard (yd)}$$

$$\left.\begin{array}{l} 5280 \text{ ft} \\ 1760 \text{ yd} \end{array}\right\} = 1 \text{ mile (mi)}$$

Area

144 square inches (in.^{2}) = 1 square foot (ft^2)
9 ft^2 = 1 square yard (yd^2)

$$\left.\begin{array}{l} 43{,}560 \text{ ft}^2 \\ 4840 \text{ yd}^2 \end{array}\right\} = 1 \text{ acre (A)}$$

Volume

1728 cubic inches (in.^{3}) = 1 cubic foot (ft^3)
27 ft^3 = 1 cubic yard (yd^3)

Liquid Capacity

8 fluid ounces (fl oz) = 1 cup (c)
2 c = 1 pint (pt)
2 pt = 1 quart (qt)
4 qt = 1 gallon (gal)

Weight

16 ounces (oz) = 1 pound (lb)
2000 lb = 1 ton (t)

Temperature — Degrees Fahrenheit (°F)

32°F = freezing point of water
98.6°F = normal body temperature
212°F = boiling point of water

TABLE OF FORMULAS

RECTANGLE

Area = lw

Perimeter = $2l + 2w$

PARALLELOGRAM

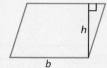

Area = bh

TRIANGLE

Area = $\frac{1}{2}bh$

CIRCLE

Circumference = πd, or $2\pi r$

Area = πr^2

TRAPEZOID

Area = $\frac{1}{2}(b_1 + b_2)h$

PRISM

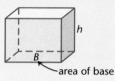

area of base

Surface Area =
sum of areas of faces

CYLINDER

Volume = $\pi r^2 h$

Surface Area = $2\pi r^2 + 2\pi rh$

PYRAMID

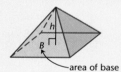

area of base

Volume = $\frac{1}{3} Bh$

Surface Area =
sum of areas of faces

CONE

Volume = $\frac{1}{3} \pi r^2 h$

POWERS

$b^0 = 1$ $b^{-n} = \frac{1}{b^n}$

$b^m \cdot b^n = b^{m+n}$

$\frac{b^m}{b^n} = b^{m-n}$

DISTANCE

Distance = rate $\cdot$ time

$d = rt$

PYTHAGOREAN THEOREM

$a^2 + b^2 = c^2$

GLOSSARY

A ▸

absolute value (p. 80) A number's distance from 0 on a number line.

acute angle (p. 592) An angle whose measure is greater than 0° but less than 90°.

acute triangle (p. 593) A triangle that has three acute angles.

algorithm (p. 434) A step-by-step set of instructions you can follow to accomplish a goal.

alternate exterior angles (p. 366) When two lines are cut by a transversal, these angles are outside of the two lines and are on opposite sides of the transversal.

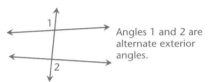

Angles 1 and 2 are alternate exterior angles.

alternate interior angles (p. 366) When two lines are cut by a transversal, these angles are between the two lines and are on opposite sides of the transversal.

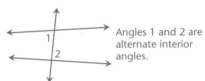

Angles 1 and 2 are alternate interior angles.

angle (p. 592) A figure formed by two rays, called sides, with the same endpoint, called the vertex.

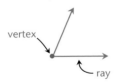

vertex

ray

angle bisector (p. 327) A ray that divides an angle into two congruent angles is an angle bisector of the angle.

arc (p. 322) A part of a circle.

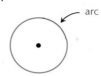

arc

area (p. 232) The area of a plane figure is the number of square units of surface area the figure covers.

arithmetic sequence (p. 520) A sequence in which each term after the first is found by adding a constant to the previous term.

B ▸

base (p. 589) *See* exponent.

base of a space figure (pp. 234, 325) *See* prism, cylinder, pyramid, *and* cone.

biased question (p. 124) A question that produces responses that do not accurately reflect the opinions of the people surveyed.

binomial (p. 496) A polynomial with exactly two terms.

box-and-whisker plot (p. 18) A plot that shows how data are distributed by dividing the data into 4 groups. The *box* contains about the middle 50% of the data values. The two *whiskers* each contain about 25% of the data values.

Average January Temperature in 50 U.S. Cities

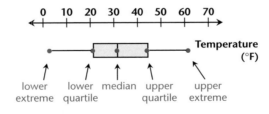

Temperature (°F)

lower extreme · lower quartile · median · upper quartile · upper extreme

C ▸

center (p. 197) *See* circle.

certain event (p. 110) An event that is sure to occur. It has a probability of 1.

chord (p. 196) A segment that has both endpoints on a given circle. *See also* circle.

circle (p. 197) The set of all points in a plane that are a given distance from a point called the center of the circle.

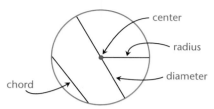

circle graph (p. 5) A graph that shows the division of a whole into parts, each represented by a sector.

circumference (p. 231) The distance around a circle.

coefficient (p. 40) The numerical factor of a term.

combination (p. 289) A selection of items in which order is not important.

complement (p. 366) One angle is the complement of a second angle if the two angles are complementary angles.

complementary angles (p. 366) Two angles whose measures have a sum of 90°.

complementary events (p. 557) Two events where one or the other must occur but they cannot both occur.

concave (p. 534) A polygon that is not convex is concave. *See also* polygon.

cone (p. 354) A space figure with one curved base and a vertex.

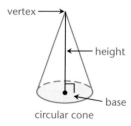

circular cone

congruent (p. 321) Having the same shape and size.

consecutive angles (p. 545) Angles in a quadrilateral whose vertices are the endpoints of the same side.

constant (p. 33) A quantity that does not change.

convex (p. 534) A polygon is convex when all of its diagonals lie in the interior of the polygon. *See also* polygon.

coordinate grid or plane (p. 591) A grid with a horizontal axis and a vertical axis that intersect at a point called the *origin* with coordinates (0, 0). Each point on the grid is identified by an ordered pair of coordinates that give the point's location left or right of the vertical axis and up or down from the horizontal axis.

corresponding angles (p. 362) When two lines are cut by a transversal, these angles are in the same position with respect to the two lines and the transversal.

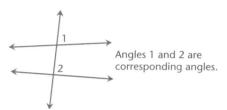

Angles 1 and 2 are corresponding angles.

corresponding parts (p. 193) When two figures are similar, for each angle or side on one figure there is a similar angle or side on the other figure. The corresponding angles have the same measure. The corresponding sides are in proportion.

cosine (p. 566) In a right triangle, the cosine of an acute angle A is the ratio of the length of the leg adjacent to angle A to the length of the hypotenuse; $\cos A = \dfrac{\text{adjacent}}{\text{hypotenuse}}$. *See also* tangent.

counting principle (p. 286) The total number of ways a sequence of decisions can be made is the product of the number of choices for each decision.

cross products (p. 128) Equal products formed from a pair of equivalent ratios by multiplying the numerator of each fraction by the denominator of the other fraction.

cube (p. 169) A prism with six square faces.

cube root (p. 475) If $A = s^3$, then s is a cube root of A. Cube roots can be written with the symbol $\sqrt[3]{\ }$.

cylinder (p. 235) A space figure that has a curved surface and two parallel, congruent bases.

circular cylinder

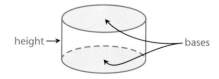

decimal notation (p. 205) A number is in decimal notation when it is written as a decimal, without using any powers. *See also* scientific notation.

dependent events (p. 110) Events for which the probability of one is affected by whether or not the other event occurs.

diameter (p. 197) A segment whose endpoints are on a given circle and that passes through the center of the circle. The length of a diameter is called *the* diameter. *See also* circle.

distributive property (pp. 40, 411) For all numbers a, b, and c: $a(b + c) = ab + ac$ and $ab + ac = a(b + c)$.

edge of a space figure (p. 325) A segment where two faces of a space figure meet. *See also* prism *and* pyramid.

equally likely (p. 106) Two outcomes that have the same chance of happening are equally likely.

equation (p. 33) A mathematical sentence stating that two quantities or expressions are equal.

equilateral triangle (p. 593) A triangle that has three sides of equal length.

equivalent rates (p. 4) Equivalent rates are equal rates that may be expressed using different units. For example $\frac{8 \text{ oz}}{25¢}$ and $\frac{2 \text{ lb}}{\$1}$ are equivalent rates.

evaluate (p. 37) To find the value of an expression for given values of the variables.

event (p. 106) A set of outcomes of an experiment.

experiment (p. 106) An activity whose results can be observed and recorded.

experimental probability (p. 107) A probability determined by repeating an experiment a number of times and observing the results. It is the ratio of the number of times an event occurs to the number of times the experiment is done.

exponent (p. 589) A raised number that tells the power of the base.

$$2^3 = 2 \cdot 2 \cdot 2 = 8$$

exponent — ; 8 is the 3rd power of 2. base

exponential equation (p. 425) An equation of the form $y = a \cdot b^x$, where a is the starting amount, b is the growth factor, and y is the amount after x units of time.

face of a space figure (pp. 234, 325) A flat surface of a space figure. *See also* prism *and* pyramid.

factor a polynomial (p. 502) Find the factors whose product is the polynomial.

fair game (p. 119) A game in which every player has an equal chance of winning.

Fibonacci sequence (p. 523) The sequence 1, 1, 2, 3, 5, 8, 13, ... Each term after the second is the sum of the two previous terms.

fitted line (p. 55) A line drawn on a scatter plot to show a pattern in the data. *See also* scatter plot.

flat view (p. 314) A view of an object straight on from any side.

frequency (p. 5) The number of items in a category or numerical interval.

frequency table (p. 5) A table that shows the frequency of items in each category or numerical interval.

function (p. 397) A relationship that pairs each input value with exactly one output value.

geometric probability (p. 556) A probability based on length, area, or volume.

geometric sequence (p. 520) A sequence in which each term after the first is found by multiplying the previous term by a nonzero constant.

greatest common factor (GCF) (p. 584) The greatest number that is a factor of each of two or more numbers.

growth factor (p. 425) *See* exponential equation.

half-life (p. 204) The amount of time it takes for a radioactive substance to reduce to half of its original amount.

histogram (p. 7) A graph that shows the frequencies of numerical values that fall within intervals of equal width.

hypotenuse (p. 340) In a right triangle, the side opposite the right angle. *See also* right triangle.

image (p. 81) The figure that results from a transformation.

impossible event (p. 110) An event that cannot occur. It has a probability of 0.

included angle (p. 328) An angle of a polygon whose vertex is the shared point of two sides of the polygon.

independent events (p. 110) Events for which the probability of one is not affected by whether or not the other event occurs.

inequality (p. 483) A mathematical sentence that compares two quantities using the symbols >, <, ≥, or ≤.

integer (pp. 79, 590) Any number in the set of numbers ... –3, –2, –1, 0, 1, 2, 3, ...

interval (p. 51) The step between grid lines on a scale.

inverse operations (p. 36) Operations that undo each other, like addition and subtraction or multiplication and division.

irrational number (p. 471) A number that cannot be written as the quotient of two integers.

isosceles triangle (p. 593) A triangle that has at least two sides of equal length.

K ▸▸▸▸▸▸▸▸▸▸▸▸▸▸▸▸▸▸▸▸▸▸▸▸▸▸▸▸▸▸▸▸▸▸

kite (p. 544) A quadrilateral with two pairs of consecutive congruent sides, but opposite sides are not congruent.

L ▸▸▸▸▸▸▸▸▸▸▸▸▸▸▸▸▸▸▸▸▸▸▸▸▸▸▸▸▸▸▸▸▸▸

leaf (p. 16) *See* stem-and-leaf plot.

least common denominator (p. 585) The least common multiple of the denominators of two or more fractions.

least common multiple (LCM) (p. 584) The least number that is a multiple of each of two or more numbers.

legs (p. 340) In a right triangle, the sides adjacent to the right angle. *See also* right triangle.

like terms (p. 40) Terms of an expression that have identical variable parts.

line symmetry (p. 540) When one half of a figure is the mirror image of the other half, the figure has line symmetry.

line of symmetry (p. 443) A line that divides a figure into two parts that are reflections of each other. *See also* parabola.

linear (p. 174) When the graph of an equation is a straight line, the equation and its graph are linear.

linear equation (pp. 84, 408) An equation whose graph is a straight line.

lower extreme (p. 18) The least data value in a data set. *See also* box-and-whisker plot.

lower quartile (p. 18) The median of the data in the lower half of a data set. *See also* box-and-whisker plot.

lowest terms (p. 585) A fraction is in lowest terms when the greatest common factor of the numerator and the denominator is 1.

M ▸▸▸▸▸▸▸▸▸▸▸▸▸▸▸▸▸▸▸▸▸▸▸▸▸▸▸▸▸▸▸▸▸▸

mean (p. 596) The sum of the data in a numerical data set divided by the number of data items.

median (p. 596) When the data in a data set are ordered in numerical order, the median is the middle number or the mean of the two middle numbers.

midpoint (p. 547) The point of a segment that divides it into two congruent segments.

minimum rotational symmetry (p. 535) The smallest number of degrees a figure can be rotated and fit exactly on itself. *See also* rotational symmetry.

mode (p. 596) The most frequently occurring item, or items, in a data set. A data set can have no mode.

monomial (p. 496) A number or a variable or a product of a number and one or more variables.

N ▸▸▸▸▸▸▸▸▸▸▸▸▸▸▸▸▸▸▸▸▸▸▸▸▸▸▸▸▸▸▸▸▸▸

negative correlation (p. 54) The relationship between two variables when one variable tends to decrease as the other increases.

net (p. 324) A two-dimensional pattern that can be folded into a space figure.

prism   prism net

"nice" fraction (p. 127) A fraction that can easily be converted to a decimal or a percent or that makes computations easier.

nonlinear (p. 174) When the graph of an equation is not a straight line, the equation and its graph are nonlinear.

obtuse angle (p. 592) An angle whose measure is between 90° and 180°.

obtuse triangle (p. 593) A triangle that has one obtuse angle.

opposite (p. 80) A number and its opposite are the same distance from 0 on a number line but on opposite sides. The opposite of 3 is –3.

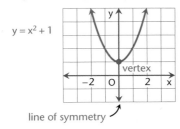

opposite angles (p. 545) Angles in a quadrilateral whose vertices are the endpoints of the same diagonal.

order of operations (p. 589) The correct order in which to perform mathematical operations in an expression: operations inside grouping symbols first, exponents next, then multiplication or division from left to right, and finally addition or subtraction from left to right.

outcome (p. 106) The result of an experiment.

P

parabola (p. 443) The graph of a quadratic function.

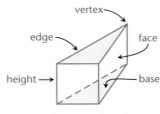
$y = x^2 + 1$
vertex
line of symmetry

parallelogram (p. 543) A quadrilateral that has two pairs of parallel sides.

percent (p. 588) Percent means "per hundred" or "out of one hundred."

percent of change (p. 142) The percent by which an amount increases or decreases from its original amount.

percent of decrease (p. 141) The ratio of the amount of decrease to the original amount.

percent of increase (p. 142) The ratio of the amount of increase to the original amount.

perfect square (p. 159) A number whose principal square root is a whole number.

permutation (p. 287) An arrangement of a group of items in which order is important.

perpendicular bisector (p. 196) A segment, line, or ray that forms a right angle with a segment and divides the segment in half.

polygon (p. 594) A closed plane figure formed by three or more segments that do not cross each other.

convex   concave   regular

polyhedron (p. 234) A 3-dimensional object made up of flat surfaces, or faces, that are polygons.

polynomial (p. 496) A monomial or a sum of monomials.

population (p. 125) The entire group being studied.

positive correlation (p. 54) The relationship between two variables when one variable tends to increase as the other increases.

power (p. 589) *See* exponent.

principal square root (p. 159) The positive square root.

prism (p. 234) A polyhedron in which two of the faces, the bases, are congruent and parallel. The other faces are parallelograms. In a *right* prism, the other faces are rectangles.

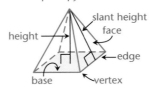
vertex
edge
face
height
base

right triangular prism

probability (p. 107) A number from 0 to 1 that tells how likely it is that an event will happen.

product of powers property (p. 460) To multiply powers with the same base, add the exponents: $b^m \cdot b^n = b^{m+n}$.

product property of square roots (p. 472) For all positive numbers a and b, $\sqrt{a \cdot b} = \sqrt{a} \cdot \sqrt{b}$.

proportion (p. 128) A statement that two ratios are equal.

pyramid (p. 325) A space figure with one base that can be any polygon. The other faces are triangles that meet at a common vertex.

square pyramid
slant height
face
height
edge
base   vertex

Pythagorean theorem (p. 340) In a right triangle, the square of·the length of the hypotenuse is equal to the sum of the squares of the lengths of the legs.

Q ▸

quadrant (p. 79) The four parts of a coordinate grid divided by the axes.

quadratic function (p. 446) A function that can be represented by an equation in the form $y = ax^2 + bx + c$, where $a \neq 0$.

quadrilateral (p. 543) A polygon with four sides.

quotient of powers property (p. 460) To divide powers with the same nonzero base, subtract the exponents: $\frac{b^m}{b^n} = b^{m-n}$.

quotient property of square roots (p. 473) For all positive numbers a and b, $\sqrt{\frac{a}{b}} = \frac{\sqrt{a}}{\sqrt{b}}$.

R ▸

radical expression (p. 474) An expression that contains a radical with one or more variables in the radicand.

radical sign (p. 470) The symbol $\sqrt{\ }$.

radicand (p. 470) The value under a radical sign.

radius (plural: radii) (p. 197) A segment whose endpoints are the center and any point on a given circle. The length of a radius is called *the* radius. *See also* circle.

range (p. 596) The difference between the greatest data value and the least data value in a data set.

rate (p. 6) A ratio that compares two quantities measured in different units.

ratio (p. 585) The quotient you get when one number is divided by a second number not equal to zero.

rational number (p. 272) A number that can be written in the form $\frac{a}{b}$, where a and b are integers and $b \neq 0$.

reciprocals (p. 587) Two numbers whose product is 1.

rectangle (p. 543) A quadrilateral that has four right angles.

reflection (p. 435) A transformation where a figure is flipped across a line such as the *x*-axis or the *y*-axis.

regular polygon (p. 594) A polygon with all sides of equal length and all angles of equal measure. *See also* polygon.

regular pyramid (p. 351) A pyramid with a base that is a regular polygon and whose faces are congruent isosceles triangles.

repeating decimal (p. 272) A decimal that contains a digit or a group of digits that repeats forever.

representative sample (p. 125) A sample whose characteristics are similar to those of the entire population.

rhombus (p. 543) A quadrilateral that has four sides of equal length.

right angle (p. 592) An angle whose measure is 90°.

right triangle (p. 593) A triangle that has one right angle.

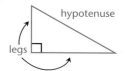

rise (p. 182) *See* slope.

rotation (p. 535) A turn of a figure about a fixed point, the center of rotation, a certain number of degrees either clockwise or counterclockwise.

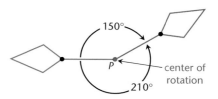

rotational symmetry (p. 535) When a figure fits exactly on itself after being rotated less than 360° around a center point, the figure has rotational symmetry.

The minimum rotational symmetry is 72°

run (p. 182) *See* slope.

S ▸

sample (p. 125) A small group from the population.

scale of a drawing (p. 375) The ratio of a length on a drawing to a corresponding length on the actual object.

scale on a graph (p. 57) The numbers written along an axis of a graph.

scalene triangle (p. 593) A triangle that has no sides of equal length.

scatter plot (p. 52) A graph that compares two sets of data. It can be used to look for relationships between data sets.

Average Temperature in 50 U.S. Cities

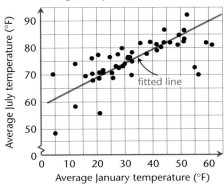

scientific notation (p. 205) A number is in scientific notation when it is written as the product of a number that is at least one but less than 10 and a power of ten.

$$\text{decimal notation} \longrightarrow 5263.4 = 5.2634 \cdot 10^3 \longleftarrow \text{scientific notation}$$

sector (p. 5) A wedge-shaped region in a circle bounded by two radii and an arc. Can be used to refer to part of a circle graph.

sequence (p. 519) An ordered list of numbers or objects.

side-side-side rule (p. 323) If the sides of one triangle have the same lengths as the sides of another triangle, the triangles are congruent.

similar (p. 193) Figures that have the same shape, but not necessarily the same size.

simplest form of a square root (p. 471) A square root is in simplest form if the following are true: There are no perfect square factors other than 1, there are no fractions in the radicand, and there are no square roots in the denominator of a fraction.

sine (p. 566) In a right triangle, the sine of an acute angle A is the ratio of the length of the leg opposite angle A to the length of the hypotenuse; $\sin A = \dfrac{\text{opposite}}{\text{hypotenuse}}$. *See also* tangent.

slant height (p. 351) The height of a triangular face of a pyramid. In a regular pyramid, the slant heights are all the same length. *See also* pyramid.

slope (p. 182) The ratio of the vertical change to the horizontal change along a line. Slope is a measure of a line's steepness.

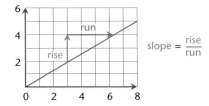

$$\text{slope} = \frac{\text{rise}}{\text{run}}$$

slope-intercept form (p. 262) An equation of a line in the form $y = mx + b$, where m is the slope and b is the y-intercept.

solution of an equation (pp. 35, 173) A value of a variable that makes an equation true. Also an ordered pair of numbers that make an equation with two variables true.

solution of an inequality (p. 485) A value of a variable that makes an inequality true is a solution of the inequality. All the solutions together are called the solution of the inequality.

solve an equation (p. 35) Find all the solutions of an equation.

solve an inequality (p. 486) Find all the solutions of an inequality.

sphere (p. 237) A 3-dimensional figure made up of a set of points that are an equal distance from a given point, called the center.

square (p. 543) A quadrilateral that has four right angles and four sides of equal length.

square root (p. 159) If $s^2 = n$, then s is a square root of n. For example, 5 and -5 are square roots of 25.

stem (p. 16) *See* stem-and-leaf plot.

stem-and-leaf plot (p. 16) A display of data where each number is represented by a *stem* (the left-most digits) and a *leaf* (the right-most digits).

straight angle (p. 592) An angle whose measure is 180°.

supplement (p. 365) One angle is the supplement of a second angle if the two angles are supplementary angles.

supplementary angles (p. 365) Two angles whose measures have a sum of 180°.

surface area (p. 247) The combined area of a figure's outer surfaces.

T ►

tangent (p. 564) In a right triangle, the tangent of an acute angle is the ratio of the length of the leg opposite the acute angle to the length of the leg adjacent to the angle.

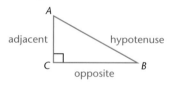

$$\tan A = \frac{\text{opposite}}{\text{adjacent}}$$

term of an expression (p. 39) The parts of an expression that are added together are called terms.

term number (p. 519) A number indicating the position of a term in a sequence.

term of a polynomial (p. 496) A monomial.

term of a sequence (p. 519) A number or object in a sequence.

terminating decimal (p. 272) A decimal that contains a finite number of digits.

tessellation (p. 539) A covering of a plane with polygons that has no gaps or overlaps.

tetrahedron (p. 325) A pyramid with four triangular faces, including the base.

theoretical probability (p. 109) The ratio of the number of outcomes that make up the event to the total number of possible outcomes if all the outcomes are equally likely. Theoretical probability can be determined without actually doing an experiment.

transformation (p. 433) A change in an object's shape, size, or position. *See also* reflection, rotation, and translation.

translation (p. 81) A transformation that moves each point of a figure the same distance in the same direction.

transversal (p. 366) A line that intersects two or more lines in a plane at separate points.

trapezoid (p. 543) A quadrilateral that has exactly one pair of parallel sides, called *bases*.

The perpendicular distance between bases of a trapezoid is the height.

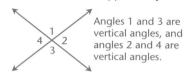

tree diagram (p. 111) A diagram that can be used to show all the possible outcomes of an experiment.

triangle inequality (p. 324) The sum of the lengths of any two sides of a triangle is greater than the length of the third side.

trinomial (p. 496) A polynomial with exactly three terms.

U ►

unit rate (p. 7) A ratio that compares a quantity to one unit of another quantity.

unlike terms (p. 40) Terms that do not have identical variable parts.

upper extreme (p. 18) The greatest data value in a data set. *See also* box-and-whisker plot.

upper quartile (p. 18) The median of the data in the upper half of a data set. *See also* box-and-whisker plot.

V ►

variable (p. 33) A quantity, usually represented by a letter, that is unknown or that changes.

Venn diagram (p. 215) A diagram used to model relationships among groups.

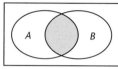

A and B   A or B

vertex of a parabola (p. 443) The point where a parabola intersects its line of symmetry. *See also* parabola.

vertex of a plane figure (p. 592) A point where sides of a figure, such as an angle or a polygon, come together. *See also* angle.

vertex of a space figure (plural: vertices) (p. 325) A point where three or more edges of a space figure meet. *See also* prism *and* pyramid.

vertical angles (p. 367) Angles that have the same vertex and whose sides are opposite rays.

Angles 1 and 3 are vertical angles, and angles 2 and 4 are vertical angles.

Y ►

y-intercept (p. 262) The *y*-coordinate of the point where a line crosses the *y*-axis.

INDEX

Complementary events, 557–561

Complete graph, 294

Concave polygon, 534

Cone, 354
  surface area of, 360
  volume of, 354, 356, 358, 361

Congruent figures, 321, 330

Congruent triangles, 322–323, 328–329, 330, 332, 336

Conjecture
  making, 202
  Questions in explorations throughout the book ask the student to make conjectures. See also Logical reasoning; Pattern(s); Prediction

Connections, *See* Algebra Connections; Applications; Career Connections; Geometry Connections; Interdisciplinary Connections; Language Arts Connections; Multicultural Connections; Theme, module

Connections scale, 599

Consecutive angles, 545–546, 549, 550, 553

Constant, 33, 42

Construction
  angle bisector, 327
  circle, 197
  regular hexagon, 333
  triangle, 322

Context-based multiple choice questions, strategies for answering, xxxii–xxxiv

Convenience sampling, 137

Convex polygon(s), 534

Cooperative learning, *See also* Discussion; Games; Projects
  activities, *Throughout. See for example,* 5, 50, 64, 79, 106, 123, 140, 150, 158, 161, 181, 184
  Try this as a class exercises, *Throughout. See for example,* 16, 19, 34, 36, 37, 40, 41, 51, 54, 65, 79, 80, 93

Coordinate plane, 80, 591
  distance between points on, 547–548, 550–553
  midpoint of a segment on, 548, 550–553
  quadrants of, 80

Coordinates, of a point, 591

Corresponding angles, 193, 198, 367, 368

Corresponding sides, 193, 198

Cosine ratio, 566–568, 571–573

Counting principle, 286–287, 289, 291, 293–294, 296
  probability and, 297–303

Create Your Own, exercises, 382, 402, 438, 440, 492, 539, 570

Critical thinking, *Students are required to apply critical thinking skills throughout the explorations. See also Logical reasoning; Pattern(s); Prediction*

Cross products, 128, 132, 376

Cross section, 310

Cube
  edge of, 162
  face of, 162
  length, area, and volume relationships, 161–162, 167
  sketching, 312

Cube root(s), 475–477, 479–480

Cylinder, 235, 238
  surface area of, 246–256
    volume and, 248–251, 253–256
  volume of, 235–238, 241–244

D ▸

Data, interpreting, exercises, 62, 117, 188, 267

Data analysis
  and, or, and *not* statements and, 216–221
  correlation and, 53–62
  finding mean, median, mode, and range, 596
  fitted lines and, 55–62
  prediction from surveys and samples, 125–136

Data collection
  from an experiment, 106, 114
  from an interview, 512–513
  from a survey, 123–124

Data displays, *See also* Graphs; Tables
  bar graph, 149, 597
  box-and-whisker plot, 18–20, 23, 25–31, 597
  choosing, 21–23, 28, 29, 31, 302, 597
  circle graph, 5, 6–7, 9, 12, 14, 597
  double bar graph, 146
  histogram, 7–8, 10, 13, 14, 597

line graph, 258, 597
scatter plot, 22, 50–52, 56, 597
stem-and-leaf plot, 16–18, 23–24, 29, 31, 597
Venn diagram, 215–221

Decimal(s)
  comparing, 579–580
  dividing, 582
  equations with, 207–209, 211–213
  fractions, percents and, 123–136, 138, 588
    common equivalents, 588
  multiplying, 580–581
  negative exponents and, 462–464, 466–469
  place value, 579–580
  rounding, 579–580

Decimal notation, scientific notation and, 205–207, 209, 210–213

Decrease, percent of, 141

Dependent events, 109–110, 115, 118, 119, 120

Depression, angle of, 570

Diagonal properties, of quadrilaterals, 542, 544, 546, 549–551, 553

Diameter
  of a circle, 197
  circumference and, 231–232, 238, 239–240, 242, 244

Dimensional analysis
  area and radius, 232, 242
  circumference and diameter, 231
  circumference and radius, 242
  cylinder height and volume, 243
  cylinder radius and volume, 243
  length, area, and volume, 161–167
  perimeter and area, 64–65, 378–381, 383–385
  surface area and volume of cubic figures, 312–313, 316–317, 320
  surface area and volume of a cylinder, 248–251, 253–256

Discrete mathematics, *See* Combinations; Counting principle; Logical reasoning; Permutations; Probability; Sequence; Tree diagram

Discussion, *Throughout. See for example,* 3, 4, 5, 7, 17, 19, 20, 22, 29, 33, 35, 36, 40

617

Proportion, 128, 132
   cross products and, 128, 132
   equivalent fraction method for
     solving, 134
   percent and, 125–132,
     134–136, 138
   scale and, 375–385
   similar figures and, 193–195,
     198–201, 203
   undoing method for solving,
     134
Proportional reasoning, *See*
   also Dimensional analysis
   finding percents, 125–132,
     134–136, 138
   length, area, and volume,
     161–167
   scale drawing and, 374–378,
     380–385, 387
   similar figures and, 193–195,
     198–201, 203
Protractor
   steps for measuring angles with,
     592
   using, 6–7, 12, 14, 193,
     322–324, 327–329, 338, 363,
     365, 543, 563
Pyramid(s), 325
   constructing, 324
   nets for, 324–326, 328–329,
     331, 333–336
   regular, 351, 355
   slant height of, 342, 351–352,
     355
   surface area of, 350–352, 355,
     357, 359, 361
   volume of, 353, 356, 358–359,
     361
Pythagorean theorem,
   340–347
   to find distance on a coordinate
     plane, 547–548, 550–553

Q ▸ ▸ ▸ ▸ ▸ ▸ ▸ ▸ ▸ ▸ ▸ ▸ ▸ ▸ ▸ ▸ ▸

Quadrant(s), in a coordinate
   plane, 80
Quadratic function(s),
   442–451
Quadratic polynomial(s), 501
   factoring, 501–505, 507,
     509–511
Quadrilateral(s), *See also*
   specific quadrilaterals
   angles of, 543–546, 549–553
   classifying, 543–544, 549, 551
   diagonals of, 542, 544, 546,
     549–553

inscribed, 470
   sides of, 543, 547–549,
     551–553
Quartile
   lower, 18, 23
   upper, 18, 23
Quotient of powers property,
   461
   using, 460–469
**Quotient property of square
   roots,** 473
   using, 473, 476–480

R ▸ ▸ ▸ ▸ ▸ ▸ ▸ ▸ ▸ ▸ ▸ ▸ ▸ ▸ ▸ ▸ ▸

Radical(s), 470–480
Radical expression(s),
   474–480
Radicand, 470
Radius (radii), 197
   circumference and, 232, 238,
     239–240, 242, 244
Random sampling, 137
Range, 596
   stem-and-leaf plots and, 16–17,
     31
Rate(s), *See also* Ratio(s), 3–4,
   9–11, 14
   distance and, 182
   equivalent, 4, 9, 10–11, 14
   unit, 4, 9–11, 14
Ratio(s), *See also* Proportion;
   Rate(s), 585
   cosine, 566–568, 571–573
   equivalent, 376, 585
   fractions, decimals, percents
     and, 123–136, 138
   probability and, 107, 109,
     299–303
   scale and, 375–385
   for similar figures, 193–195,
     198–201, 203
   sine, 566–568, 571–573
   slope, 182–184, 186–188, 190,
     259–269
   surface area and volume,
     248–251, 253–256
   tangent, 563–566, 568–573
Rational number(s), *See also*
   Fraction(s); Mixed number(s),
   271–282
   dividing, 275–282
   multiplying, 275–282
   repeating decimals, 272–273,
     277, 278, 281, 282
   terminating decimals, 272–273,
     277, 278, 282

Reasoning, *See* Logical
   reasoning; Pattern(s);
   Proportional reasoning
Rectangle, 543
   area of, 595
   diagonals and angles of, 542
   perimeter of, 595
Rectangular prism, *See*
   Prism(s)
Reflection, 435–438, 441
Regular polygon, 594
Regular pyramid, *See also*
   Pyramid(s), 351, 355
Repeating decimal(s),
   272–273, 277, 278, 281,
   282
   writing as fractions, 281
Representations scale, 599
Representative sample,
   125–126, 130–131, 132, 136,
   137
Research, 13, 29, 61, 147, 220,
   253, 345, 384, 569
Reviews, *See* Assessment; Spiral
   Review; Toolbox
Rhombus, 543
Right angle, 592
Right triangle(s), 192, 593
   cosine ratio and, 566–568,
     571–573
   hypotenuse of, 340
   legs of, 340
   Pythagorean theorem and,
     340–347
   relationship among side lengths
     of, 337–347
   sine ratio and, 566–568,
     571–573
   tangent ratio and, 563–566,
     568–573
   three-four-five, 337–338
Rise, slope and, 182
Rotation, 438
Rotational symmetry,
   535–537, 539–541
   minimum, 535–537,
     539–541
Rounding, decimals,
   579–580
Rubric, scoring, xxix–xxx,
   xxxv–xxxvi
Rules
   divisibility, 583
   of thumb, 34, 35, 44, 59
Run, slope and, 182

CREDITS

ACKNOWLEDGMENTS

392 "Sidewalk Measles" by Barbara M. Hales, from *The Sky Is Full of Song,* selected by Lee Bennett Hopkins. Reprinted by permission of Barbara M. Hales. **518** *Two of Everything* by Lily Toy Hong. Text and illustrations copyright © 1993 by Lily Toy Hong. Excerpt and cover image reprinted by permission of Albert Whitman & Company. All rights reserved.

Littell/Houghton Mifflin Co.; **325** © Jochen Helle/age fotostock; **328** RMIP/Richard Haynes/McDougal Littell/Houghton Mifflin Co.; **337** © Richard Nowitz/Getty Images; **338** RMIP/Richard Haynes/McDougal Littell/Houghton Mifflin Co.; **340** © Paul Hardy/Corbis; **345** © Charles O. Cecil/Alamy; **348** *right* © Bryan & Cherry Alexander/Photo Researchers, Inc.; *left* © Chris Rainier/Corbis; **349** © Mary Steinbacher/Alamy; **352** © National Anthropological Archives, Smithsonian Institution (41,887); **354** © National Anthropological Archives, Smithsonian Institution (41,886-Z); **357** © Alison Wright/Corbis; **358** *right* © Eric Martin/Alamy; *bottom, bottom left* Courtesy of Christa McAuliffe Planetarium; **362** *all* School Division, Houghton Mifflin Company; **363** © qaphotos.com/Alamy; **364** RMIP/Richard Haynes/McDougal Littell/Houghton Mifflin Co.; **372** Courtesy of Wendy Lathrop; **374** © Steve Hall/Hedrich Blessing; **377** © Simon Jarratt/Corbis; **386** School Division, Houghton Mifflin Company; **387** RMIP/Richard Haynes/McDougal Littell/Houghton Mifflin Co.; **390–391** © Firefly Productions/Corbis; **392** © Andrew Chin/Shutterstock; **393** School Division, Houghton Mifflin Company; **394** *both* RMIP/Richard Haynes/McDougal Littell/Houghton Mifflin Co.; **396** © Jim Wark/Index Stock Imagery; **402** © SSPL/The Image Works; **404** © Dynamic Graphics Group/Creatas/Alamy; **406** © Joel Sartore/Getty Images; **407** RMIP/Richard Haynes/McDougal Littell/Houghton Mifflin Co.; **409** RMIP/Richard Haynes/McDougal Littell/Houghton Mifflin Co.; **410** RMIP/Richard Haynes/McDougal Littell/Houghton Mifflin Co.; **415** © Craig Tuttle/Corbis; **417** © Michelle D. Bridwell/PhotoEdit; **428** *both* RMIP/Richard Haynes/McDougal Littell/Houghton Mifflin Co.; **429** © Richard Laird/Getty Images; **430** *top* Courtesy of William Karesh; *bottom* © Tomislav Stajduhar/Shutterstock; **432** © Duomo/Corbis; **437** RMIP/Richard Haynes/McDougal Littell/Houghton Mifflin Co.; **440** *both* RMIP/Richard Haynes/McDougal Littell/Houghton Mifflin Co.; **442** NASA; **443** *left* © Thinkstock/Corbis; *right* © Justin Pumfrey/Getty Images; **448** © James Davis Photography/Alamy; **449** © Neil Rabinowitz/Corbis; **456–457** © BSIP/Photo Researchers, Inc.; **458** © Time & Life Pictures/Getty Images; **462** © Andrew Syred/Getty Images; **463** NASA; **465** © Philippe Giraud/Corbis; **466** © Hans Leijnse/Foto Natura/Minden Pictures; **468** Courtesy of France Córdova; **478** RMIP/Richard Haynes/McDougal Littell/Houghton Mifflin Co.; **482** © Digital Vision/Getty Images; **490** *top left* © Daniel Dempster Photography/Alamy; *top right* © Alan Kearney/Getty Images; *center left* © Caroline von Tumpling-Manning/Getty Images; *center right* © Gary Conner/PhotoEdit; **495** *right Self-Portrait* (ca. 1512), Leonardo da Vinci © Bettmann/Corbis; *bottom left Mona Lisa,* Leonardo da Vinci © Stuart Gregory/Getty Images; **501** *Ballista That Threw Two Stones,* Leonardo da Vinci © Bettmann/Corbis; **509** *Head of a Woman,* Leonardo da Vinci. Charcoal on paper. © British Museum, London, UK/ Alinari/The Bridgeman Art Library; **512** © Bob Daemmrich/The Image Works;

513 RMIP/Richard Haynes/McDougal Littell/Houghton Mifflin Co.; **516–517** © Josh Westrich/zefa/Corbis; **522** © PhotoDisc; **529** *both* Courtesy of Junpei Sekino; **532** *left* © Gary James Calder/Shutterstock; *center* © Don Hammond/Design Pics/Corbis; *right* © Tim Street-Porter/Beateworks/Corbis; **535** *left* © Barbara Strnadova/Photo Researchers, Inc.; *center* © Bob Krist/Corbis; *right* © Ronald Weir/Albaimages/Alamy; **536** *top left* © AA World Travel Library/Alamy; *top right* © Ingo Jezierski/Corbis; *center left* © Visuals Unlimited/Corbis; *center* © Roland Birke/OKAPIA/Photo Researchers, Inc.; *center right* © M.I. Walker/Photo Researchers, Inc.; *bottom* © SuperStock, Inc.; **538** *all* © PhotoDisc; **540** *top left* © Andrew G. Wood/Photo Researchers, Inc.; *top center* © John Burbidge/Photo Researchers, Inc.; *top right* © Rod Planck/Photo Researchers, Inc.; *left* © Richard Cummins/SuperStock; *center* © M.I. Walker/Photo Researchers, Inc.; *right* © Visuals Unlimited/Corbis; **542** © George H. H. Huey/Corbis; **554** *bottom right* © Ralph White/Corbis; *center* © The Mariner's Museum/Corbis; **557** © Emory Kristof/National Geographic Image Collection; **562** *center* © Bridgeman Art Library; *bottom* © Werner Forman/Art Resource, NY; **563** RMIP/Richard Haynes/McDougal Littell/Houghton Mifflin Co.; **571** © John Arsenault/Getty Images; **575** RMIP/Richard Haynes/McDougal Littell/Houghton Mifflin Co.

ILLUSTRATION

34 Robin Storesund/McDougal Littell/Houghton Mifflin Co.; **39** Jeremy Spiegel/McDougal Littell/Houghton Mifflin Co.; **68, 112, 117** Robin Storesund/McDougal Littell/Houghton Mifflin Co.; **156, 157, 158** Chris Costello/McDougal Littell/Houghton Mifflin Co.; **161, 192, 221, 223** Betsy James/McDougal Littell/Houghton Mifflin Co.; **230, 274, 275, 345** Robin Storesund/McDougal Littell/Houghton Mifflin Co.; **370** Magellan Geographix; **372** Robin Storesund/McDougal Littell/Houghton Mifflin Co.; **374, 380** Courtesy of Ross Barney Architects; **419** Robin Storesund/McDougal Littell/Houghton Mifflin Co.; **432** Courtesy of Vicon Motion Systems, Inc., Centennial, CO; **461, 527, 533, 539, 560** Robin Storesund/McDougal Littell/Houghton Mifflin Co.

All other illustrations by McDougal Littell/Houghton Mifflin Co. or School Division/Houghton Mifflin Co.

SELECTED ANSWERS

MODULE 1

Section 1, Practice and Application (p. 10)
1. miles and hours; 60 mi/hr **3.** 480,000 **5.** not equivalent **9. a.** about 99 kicks/min **b.** At about 119 kicks/min, this rate is greater than Constance Constable's. **11.** Sample Response: The unit price given for cinnamon is $0.99 per ounce. What is the cost of 6 oz? Answer: $5.94 **13. a.** about 29,523,810 mi/month **b.** about 971,178 mi/day **c.** about 40,466 mi/hr **d.** Sample Response; miles per hour; It is more common to measure speed in miles per hour. **15.** 8
17. a.   Source of China's 2004 GDP

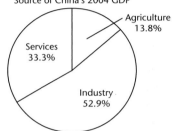

b.   Source of India's 2004 GDP

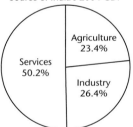

c.   Source of Pakistan's 2004 GDP

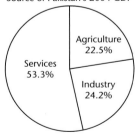

19. The sum of the percents is only 90%.
21.

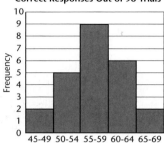

Spiral Review (p. 13)
25. mean: about 9.84, median: 9.8, modes: 9.8 and 10; range: 0.4 **26.** $\frac{2}{5}$ **27.** $\frac{4}{5}$ **28.** $\frac{1}{5}$ **29.** $\frac{7}{20}$

Extra Skill Practice (p. 14)
1. not equivalent **3.** 10%; The circle graph represents 100%; 100% − (60% + 30%) = 10% **5.** 1200 Cal
7.

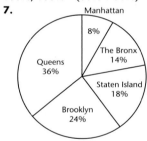

Standardized Testing (p. 14)
1. C **2.** B

Section 2, Practice and Application (p. 24)
1. a.

Age when Awarded Grammy for Best Female Vocal
Performance

Country		Pop
	1	
4	1	
4	2	3 3 3 3 5
7 5 4 3 3 3 1	3	0 0 0 0 2 3
8	4	1
6	5	
	6	
4	7	

5 | 3 | represents | 2 | 3 represents
an age of 35.   an age of 23.

b. Sample Response: Ages of country winners are much more spread out than pop winners, although the greatest numbers of winners for both pop and country are in their 30s. **3. a.** Class A: 54, Class B: 45 **b.** Class A: 100, Class B: 100 **c.** Class A: 65, Class B: 70 **d.** Class A: 95, Class B: 85 **7. a.** lower extreme = 1, upper extreme = 40; the range of the data. You know Elvis had at least one hit make it to #1 and at least one make it only to #40 on the charts. **b.** 16 **c.** about 50% **9. a.** These are the data values that range from the line inside the box (the median) to the end of the upper whisker (the upper extreme). **b.** Answers will vary. Sample Response: Elvis because more than $\frac{1}{2}$ of his hits stayed at #1 for 4 or more weeks, whereas the Beatles had less than 25% of their #1 hits stay for 4 weeks or longer. The median is greater for Elvis, and for the Beatles, the median is equal to Elvis's lower quartile value showing that only about 50% of the Beatles' hits were at #1 for 2 weeks or more while about 75% of Elvis's hits were at #1 for 2 weeks or more.

11. a–b.

Number of Times a Composer's Work
Was Performed by American Orchestras

Spiral Review (p. 30)
19. 288 **20.** about 0.92 **21.** about 0.06 **22.** $5.25
23. 3 and 5 only **24.** none **25.** 2 only **26.** 3 only
27. > **28.** > **29.** >

Career Connection (p. 30)
31. Sample Response: 230, 350, 490 (any score below the median which is about 510)

Extra Skill Practice (p. 31)
1. a.   Ages of Academy Award Winners

Actors		Actresses
6	2	1 5 5 6 8 9
9 8 7 7 6 5 2 1	3	1 3 3 3 3 4 5 5 8 9
7 6 5 5 3 3 2 0	4	1 2 5 9 9
7 4 2 2	5	
1 0	6	1
6	7	4
	8	0

| 2 | 5 represents | 4 | 2 represents
an age of 52.   an age of 42.

b. With the exception of a few actresses, the actresses were mainly in their 20s, 30s or 40s when receiving an Academy Award. For men, the awards were earned at slightly older ages, mainly 30s, 40s and 50s. Only one actor was in his 20s as compared to six actresses.
c. Actor: mean = 44.75, median 43, modes = 37, 43, 45, 52.

Actress: mean = 39.125, median = 34.5, mode = 33.

Sample Response: For actors, there are too many modes to be a good representation of the data. The mean is a good representation of the actors' ages. For the actresses, the mean is a bit high, probably due to the two ages of 74 and 80; therefore, the mode or the median is a better representation. There were four actresses at age 33 and four others were within 2 yrs of that age when they won, so I would choose the mode. **3.** Sample Response: Very unusual; Among the actors and actresses listed, she is the only person in her 80s to receive an Academy Award, and only 1 of 3 actresses over the age of 49. **5.** bar graph; A bar graph compares data items grouped into categories. **7.** circle graph; A circle graph shows the division of a whole into parts.

Standardized Testing (p. 31)
1. D **2.** A

Section 3, Practice and Application (p. 44)

1. A **3.** Let t = total distance of the trip, d = number of days; $\frac{t}{50}$ = d **5.** Let c = beginning length of cord, f = finished length of the bracelet; $c = 8f$ **7. a.** 30°F, 60°F, 230°F **b.** 32°F, 59°F, 212°F **c.** 15°C **9. a.** 25 **b.** 1260 **c.** 3.5 **d.** 23 **e.** 156 **f.** 45 **11.** A **13.** Answers will vary. **17.** $17x + 1$ **19.** $17w + 3$ **21.** not possible, unlike terms **23.** $15y^2 + 7x$ **25. a.** $P = 2l + 2w$ **b.** 26 in. **c.** 7 cm **d.** 4.5 m **27.** triangle: 12 yd, square: 9 yd

Spiral Review (p. 47)

30. Sample Response: a bar graph; The data fall into categories. **31.** Sample Response: a circle graph; The data are given in percentages. **32. a.** Sample Response: mi/hr; The speed of a car is usually given in mi/hr. **b.** 750 mi/hr

Extra Skill Practice (p. 48)

1. Let t = total amount of hamburger used in pounds and c = the number of campers; $t = 0.25c + 5$ **3.** Let r = rent and a = area of the apartment; $r = 0.9a$ **5.** 31 **7.** 208 **9.** 148 **11.** $5y$ **13.** $10t - 4$ **15.** $36r - 18rd$ **17.** no like terms **19.** $7 + w + w^2$

Standardized Testing (p. 48)

1. D **2.** A

Section 4, Practice and Application (p. 57)

1. a. 92 yr, 6.5 hr **b.** 6 yr, just under 5.5 hr **5.** negative correlation **7.** Plot A: straight-line pattern; Plot B: curved pattern **9.** negative correlation **11.** positive correlation **13.** negative correlation **17.** Answers will vary.

Spiral Review (p. 61)

19. 16 **20.** 16 **21.** 24 **22.** 7.85 **23.** 36 cm² **24.** 36 m² **25.** 96 mm² **26. a.** True; The upper extreme for linebackers is 245. **b.** True; The median for the defensive linemen is 285 lb. **c.** False; The upper extreme for the linebackers is about 245 lb and the lower extreme for the defensive linemen is about 270 lb. **d.** True; The upper whisker of the offensive linemen contains 25% of the data values and it begins at the same value as the upper extreme of the defensive linemen plot.

Extra Skill Practice (p. 62)

1. 52 miles; 2002 **3. a–b.** Sample Response: I chose a horizontal scale of 40 to 90 because the temperatures range from 51° to 77°. I chose a vertical scale of 0 to 35 because the cups of cocoa sold range from 4 to 31.

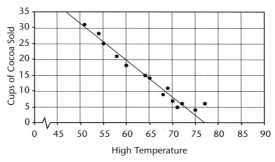

Cocoa Sales for Two Weeks

c. 3 pots

Standardized Testing (p. 62)

1. approximately 7 through 22; approximately 35 through 62 **2.** curved pattern; The data decreases, then levels off, then increases. This creates a curve.

Section 5, Practice and Application (p. 68)

1. 2042 **3. a.** Sample Response: Weigh 4 rocks on each side. Take the heavier side, divide it in half, and weigh 2 rocks on each side. Take the heavier side, divide it in half and weigh 1 rock on each side. **b.** 3 weighings **5. a.**

Rectangles with Perimeter 28 Units														
Length	0	1	2	3	4	5	6	7	8	9	10	11	12	13	14
Width	14	13	12	11	10	9	8	7	6	5	4	3	2	1	0
Area	0	13	24	33	40	45	48	49	48	45	40	33	24	13	0

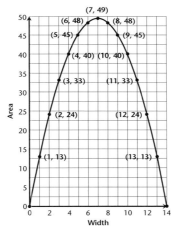

b. The length and width of the rectangle with the greatest area is 7 units and the area is 49 square units.

Spiral Review (p. 69)

7. a. area: 6320 sq mi **b.** area: 19,750 sq mi **c.** It is about in the middle. Sample Response: Yes; I would expect the average width to be about 33 mi which would make the area of this lake about 13,000 sq. mi. **8. a.** perimeter: 822 mi **b.** perimeter: 890 mi **c.** The actual perimeter is greater than either of the two that were calculated. The shoreline must have many inlets.

Extra Skill Practice (p. 70)

1. Sample Response: Measure two $3\frac{1}{2}$ pt pots of water then remove three $1\frac{1}{2}$ pt pots of water.

3.

Rectangles with Area of 48 Square Units									
Length	1	2	3	4	6	8	12	16	24	48
Width	48	24	16	12	8	6	4	3	2	1
Perimeter	98	52	38	32	28	28	32	38	52	98

5. about 7 units; Sample Response: I used the graph to find the least perimeter.

Standardized Testing (p. 70)

1.

Polygon	A	B	C	D	E	F	G	H	I
Area (A)	1	$1\frac{1}{2}$	2	$3\frac{1}{2}$	4	4	6	$6\frac{1}{2}$	8
Number of dots on perimeter (P)	4	5	6	7	8	6	10	9	8
Number of dots inside (I)	0	0	0	1	1	2	2	3	5

2. $A = \frac{P}{2} + I - 1$

Review & Assessment (pp. 74–75)

1. 2064 **2.** 10,800

3. a.

Ages of Airplanes by Company

Company A		Company B
9 6 5 3 2	0	1 2 3 3 5 6 7 7 8 9
9 8 7 7 7 5 5 3 2	1	2 4 6 6 6 9
6 1 0 0	2	0 5

2 | 1 represents an age | 1 | 4 represents an age
   of 12 years.   of 14 years.

3. b. Sample Response: Most of the planes owned by Company A are older than the planes owned by Company B. **c.** Company A: mean: about 14.2, median: 16, mode: 17; Company B: mean: 10.5, median: 8.5, mode: 16

4. a. Company A: lower extreme = 2
Company B: lower extreme = 1
b. Company A: upper extreme = 26
Company B: upper extreme = 25
c. Company A: lower quartile = 9
Company B: lower quartile = 5
d. Company A: upper quartile = 19
Company B: upper quartile = 16

5. Company B. The median for Company B is below 10, so more than 50% of the planes are under 10 years old.

6. histogram **7. a.** $t = 0.50a + 0.25c$ **b.** $2.00 **8. a.** $5\frac{1}{3}$

b. 7 **c.** 24 **d.** 9 **9. a.** not possible **b.** $8y$ **c.** $t + 4$ **d.** $3m + 6$

10. a.

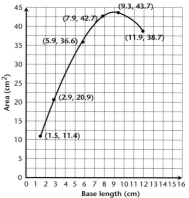

Right Triangles with Perimeter 32 cm

b. about 9 cm

MODULE 2

Section 1, Practice and Application (p. 88)

1. –31 **3.** –8 **5.** –100 **7.** 15 **9.** –74 **11.** 47 **13.** $8\frac{1}{2}$
15. 7, –7 **17.** –2 **19.** 5 **21.** 22 **23.** –2 **27.** 31
29. 0 **31.** 12 **33. a.** $P'(5, -2)$, $Q'(5, -1)$, $R'(4, 0)$, $S'(3, -1)$, $T'(3, -2)$ **35. a.** –1, 1; 1, –1 **b.** 2, 6; –2, –6
c. –4, –6; 4, 6 **37.** –320 **39.** –56 **41.** 7 **43.** 8
45. –192 **47.** 4 **49.** 84 **51.** 42
53. $15(5) + 4(-2) + 1(0)$; 67

Spiral Review (p. 90)

56. $1\frac{1}{2}$ **57.** $\frac{7}{10}$ **58.** 1 **59.** $\frac{30}{49}$ **60.** 6 **61.** 8 **62.** 56
63. 33 **64.** 28 **65.** 96

Extension (p. 90)

67. 6, –10 **69.** –2, 2

Extra Skill Practice (p. 91)

1. 4 **3.** –195 **5.** –512 **7.** 1 **9.** 29 **11.** $3\frac{3}{4}$ **13.** –77
15. 6 **17.** 250 **19.** –42 **21.** –6 **23.** 18 **25.** 42

27. 4 **29.** –4 **31.** –16 **33.** –26

Standardized Testing (p. 91)
1. a. Sample Response: –7, 5 **b.** None. Two numbers with sums of 0 are opposites. The product of opposites is always less than or equal to 0. **c.** Sample Response: 10 and –5 **2.** Sample Response: $A(-3, 2)$, $B(3, 2)$, $C(3, -2)$, $D(-3, -2)$; $A'(-7, 8)$, $B'(-1, 8)$, $C'(-1, 4)$, $D'(-7, 4)$

Section 2, Practice and Application (p. 101)
1. $\frac{59}{72}$ **3.** $\frac{1}{14}$ **5.** $-\frac{1}{2}$ **7.** –1 **9. a.** yes **b.** Use one piece from the $\frac{1}{2}$ yd remnant, two pieces from the $\frac{7}{8}$ yd remnant, and one piece from the $\frac{5}{8}$ yd remnant; $\frac{1}{8}$ yd;
$\frac{1}{8}$ yd; $\frac{1}{4}$ yd **11.** –1 **13.** $-\frac{2}{15}$ **15.** $-\frac{9}{14}$ **17.** $-\frac{11}{42}$
19. $-\frac{53}{60}$ **21. a.** $\frac{1}{2} - \frac{1}{4} + \frac{1}{8} - \frac{1}{16} + \frac{1}{32}$;
$\frac{1}{2} - \frac{1}{4} + \frac{1}{8} - \frac{1}{16} + \frac{1}{32} - \frac{1}{64}$ **b.** $\frac{1}{4}, \frac{3}{8}, \frac{5}{16}, \frac{11}{32}, \frac{21}{64}$
c. Sample response: positive; The fraction to be subtracted will be smaller than the value of the twenty-ninth
expression. **23.** –8 **25.** $6\frac{3}{8}$ **27.** $5\frac{8}{9}$ **29.** $\frac{3}{8}$ **31.** –7
33. 3 **35.** $-\frac{3}{4}$

Spiral Review (p. 103)
39. –13 **40.** 96 **41.** –9 **42.** –112 **43.** lower
extreme = 10; upper extreme = 45; median = 20

Extra Skill Practice (p. 104)
1. $-2\frac{9}{10}$ **3.** $1\frac{1}{8}$ **5.** $-\frac{2}{3}$ **7.** $2\frac{1}{10}$ **9.** $-3\frac{1}{9}$ **11.** $3\frac{1}{8}$
13. a. $4\frac{2}{3}$ in. by $6\frac{2}{3}$ in. **b.** Possible answers: $4\frac{2}{3}$ in. by
$13\frac{1}{3}$ in. or $9\frac{1}{3}$ in. by $6\frac{2}{3}$ in.

Standardized Testing (p. 104)
1. D **2.** A **3.** A

Section 3, Practice and Application (p. 115)
1. 1, 2, 3, 4, 5, 6 **3. a.** 1, 3, 5 **b.** 4, 6 **5.** No; while
landing on each sector is equally likely, the number of
sectors for each outcome are not equal. **7.** 4 sectors are
labeled with vowels and 4 are labeled with consonants,
so the spinner is just as likely to stop on a vowel as a
consonant. **9.** Results will vary. **11.** Answers will vary.
(Theoretically, 4 occurs most often, then 5 and 3.)
13. Results will vary. **15.** Answers will vary. You can tell
which player won most often by comparing the probabilities. The player with the greater probability won
most often.

17. a. $\frac{1}{4}$ **b.** $\frac{1}{8}$ **c.** $\frac{1}{8}$ **d.** $\frac{1}{2}$

19. 0;

21. 1;

23. equally likely **25.** equally likely **27. a.** $\frac{1}{5}; \frac{4}{5}$ **b.** $\frac{3}{19}$

c. $\frac{4}{19}$ **d.** dependent on; The outcome of the first draw
affects the probability of drawing a blue ball on the
second draw.
31. a.

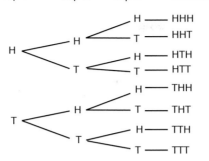

| Flip 1 | Flip 2 | Flip 3 | Outcomes |

b. 8 outcomes **c.** Yes; The outcomes on each flip are
equally likely.

Spiral Review (p. 119)
34. $-\frac{2}{3}$ **35.** $-3\frac{7}{8}$ **36.** $5\frac{7}{30}$ **37.** $-6\frac{2}{3}$ **38.** $2x + 1$
39. n^2 **40.** $8s + 4st$ **41.** acute **42.** obtuse
43. straight **44.** obtuse

Extra Skill Practice (p. 120)
1. $\frac{7}{15}$ **3.** $\frac{1}{8}$ **5.** $\frac{5}{8}$ **7. a.** golden: $\frac{2}{5}$; green: $\frac{7}{25}$; not
green: $\frac{18}{25}$ **b.** red: $\frac{6}{23}$, green: $\frac{7}{23}$ **c.** The events are
independent if the first apple is replaced before the second apple is taken. If the first apple is not replaced, the
events are dependent.

Standardized Testing (p. 120)
1.

2. $\frac{1}{4}, \frac{1}{8}, \frac{1}{16}, \frac{1}{2^{49}}$

Section 4, Practice and Application (p. 133)
1. $\frac{2}{5}$; 0.4 **3.** $\frac{23}{20}$; 1.15 **5.** $\frac{4}{5}$; 80% **7.** 0.19; 19% **9.** 0.65;
65% **11.** not biased **13. a.** middle school students
b. sixth grade students **c.** No; Sample Response: Sixth
graders are not representative of the entire school.
17. about $66, nice fraction; about $64, using multiples
of 10% **19. a.** Estimates will vary: about 540; 541
b. Estimates will vary: about 180; 180 **21.** 33.6
23. 211 **25.** 21 **27.** Woodfield Mall: about 64%;
The Galleria: about 57%; Tysons Corner Center:
about 52% **29.** 0.45 **31.** 1% **33.** 200 **35.** 20
37. a. about 46% **b.** about 10% **c.** about 19%

39. a. Sample Response: Would you be more likely to eat at a new Italian or a new Chinese restaurant in the mall? **b.** people who visit the mall **c.** Sample Response: every 5th person entering the mall

Spiral Review (p. 137)
42. 24 m **43.** 19.2 **44.** 377.8 **45.** 2.4 **46.** 1.8 **47.** 0.062 **48.** 30 **49.** 150 **51.** Random sampling; Each person in the population has an equally likely chance of being chosen and represented.

Extra Skill Practice (p. 138)
1. Sample Response: biased; "How do you feel about a grocery store being built in this town?" **3.** not biased **5.** about 1275 **7.** about 18,500 **9.** about $26 **11.** about 567 **13.** 6 **15.** 8690 **17.** 66 **19.** 50 **21.** 40 **23.** 1862 **25.** 2032

Study Skills (p. 138)
2. Answers will vary. Sample response: At a store with items on sale for 50%, 25%, or 20% off. **3.** Answers will vary.

Section 5, Practice and Application (p. 144)
1. Sample Response: Change 69% to the "nice" fraction $\frac{2}{3}$, then find $\frac{2}{3}$ of 60. Find 10% of $60 and then multiply by 7. **3.** about 48; 52.8 **5.** about 120; 107.55 **7.** Hard Hats USA **9.** about 1000, 964; about 650, 656; about 900, 923; about 500, 533; about 200, 226. **11. a.** about a 3.1% increase **b.** 0% increase **13.** Sample Response: Movies about 9.9 billion, sports about 15.5 billion. **15. a.** 300% increase **b.** 55% decrease **c.** 108% increase **d.** 59% decrease

Spiral Review (p. 147)
18. 1456 **19.** 9.7 **20.** 639.1 **21.** 61 **22.** 300.2 **23.** 332.5 **24.** GCF 5; LCM 30 **25.** GCF 4, LCM 48 **26.** GCF 7, LCM 147 **27.** < **28.** < **29.** = **30.** >

Extension (p. 148)
31. about 43%; 30%

Career Connection (p. 148)
33. about 178%

Extra Skill Practice (p. 149)
1. about 170; 187 **3.** about 3.5; 3.36 **5.** about 64; 60.8 **7.** about 9% **9.** about 19% **11.** about 99.4% **13.** about 95% decrease

Standardized Testing (p. 149)
Sample Response: Rosa is correct. New York only had a 1.3% increase in population while North Carolina had a 7.5% increase.

Review & Assessment (pp. 152)
1. 70 **2.** −15 **3.** 17 **4.** −37 **5.** −90 **6.** 192 **7.** −9 **8.** 12 **9.** −14 **10.** 0 **11.** −50 **12.** −5 and 5

13. Sample Response: The opposite of a number is the integer you add to that number to get a sum of 0; −2 and 2, −7 and 7, −0.34 and 0.34.

14.

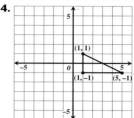

15. $-\frac{11}{24}$ **16.** $-1\frac{7}{15}$ **17.** $-2\frac{14}{15}$ **18.** $6\frac{1}{2}$

19.

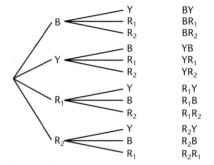

20. $\frac{1}{6}$ **21.** $\frac{13}{25}$ **22.** Yes; Should students have access to the Internet? **23. a.** representative; This group should have the same characteristics as the rest of the population. **b.** not representative; Students in grades 5–7 are not represented. **24. a.** about 525 **b.** about 770 **25. a.** 500 New England youths; Sample Response: No; the sample is too small and only from one region of the country. **b.** 450 youths **26.** about 50%: the markup is $153 and $\frac{153}{322} \approx \frac{1}{2}$ = 50%. **27.** about $44.50; 30% $\approx \frac{1}{3}$ and $\frac{1}{3}$ of $66 = $22, so $66.50 − $22 = $44.50. **28. a.** 41% **b.** 64% **c.** 86%

MODULE 3

Section 1, Practice and Application (p. 164)
1. 10 **3.** 60 **5.** $\frac{2}{5}$ **7. a.** $93\frac{1}{2}$ in.^{2} **b.** $9\frac{1}{2}$ in. × $9\frac{1}{2}$ in. **9.** about 6.2 **11.** about 3.5 **15.** $\frac{1}{10}$ **17.** −900; exact **19.** about −5.7; estimate **21.** about 31.6; estimate **23.** length of side ≈ 97.5 yd; perimeter of plot ≈ 390 yd **25.** $c = 10a + 3000$ where c represents the cooling capacity and a represents the floor area

27. a.

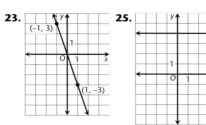

cooling capacity: 7320 Btu/hr   cooling capacity: 5160 Btu/hr

b. No; Sample Response: 7320 is only about 1.5 • 5160 so she needs about 1.5 times the cooling capacity for the larger room.

Spiral Review (p. 166)

30.

Amounts Raised by Students at a Charity Dance Marathon (dollars)

31. 4 or –4 **32.** 11 or –11 **33.** –19 **34.** 6
35. a. $A(-2, -2)$, $B(-2, 1)$, $C(1, 1)$, $D(2, -1)$
b. $A'(0, -2)$, $B'(0, 1)$, $C'(3, 1)$, $D'(4, -1)$

Extra Skill Practice (p. 167)

1. 700 **3.** $\frac{1}{10}$ **5.** 0.06 **7.** 0.02 **9.** about 7.1 **11.** about
11.7 **13.** about 6.6 **15.** about 5.7 **17.** about 5.3;
estimate **19.** 2.5; exact **21.** about 2.2; estimate
23. 0.8; exact **25.** 8 cm^3

Study Skills (p. 167)

1.–4. Answers will vary.

Section 2, Practice and Application (p. 176)

1. 15 **3.** 3 **5.** 3 **7.** The operations were done in order from left to right instead of doing the division and then the addition. **9.** The 5 in the numerator was divided by 5 but the 3 was not. The numerator should have been evaluated before dividing by 5. **11.** about 1.6
13. a. about 39.5 **b.** Sample Response: No. The Lake of the Ozarks isn't even close to a circle. It is very long and skinny, so the ratio shouldn't be very close to 1.
15. –23 **17.** –0.1 **19.** 7.5 **21. a.** 11.75 mi/hr;
$d = 11.75h$ **b.** 6 mi/hr; $d = 6h$

c.

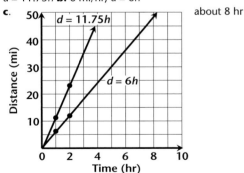

about 8 hr

23.

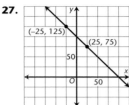

25.

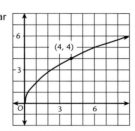

27.

29. $y = 4$
31. nonlinear

33. a.

Radius r (cm)	Volume V (cm^3)
1	4
2	34
3	113
5	524
10	4189
20	33,510

b.

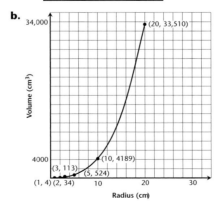

c. about 1150 cm^3

Spiral Review (p. 178)

35. about 2.8 **36.** about 3.3 **37.** about 3.9 **38.** about 0.4 **39.** A(–2, –3), B(0, –1), C(1, 0), M(–2, 2), N(1, –1) **40.** $0.14/oz **41.** 0.29 mi/hr **42.** $74.67/hr

Extra Skill Practice (p. 179)

1. 4 **3.** 0.47 **5.** 1 **7.** 5 **9.** –6

11.

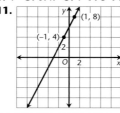

13.

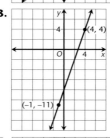

15.

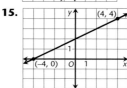

17. $y = -2x + 12$; $y = 3x - 8$; $y = 0.5x + 2$

19.

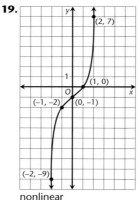

nonlinear

Standardized Testing (p. 179)

1. A **2.** C **3.** B

Section 3, Practice and Application (p. 187)

1. 5 **3.** $\frac{1}{2}$ or 0.5 **5. a.** the blue line; Sample Response: Since the blue line is steeper than the red line, it represents a faster walking rate. **b.** Segura's walking

rate = 16 km/hr or about 0.27 km/min; Petersen's walking rate = 12 km/hr or 0.2 km/min **c.** Segura: $d = 0.27t$ where d = distance (km) and t = time (min) or $d = 16t$ where d = distance (km) and t = time (hr) Petersen: $d = 0.2t$ where d = distance (km) and t = time (min) or $d = 12t$ where d = distance (km) and t = time (hr) **9.** A; slope = 0.75, (0, –10) is on the line. **11.** about 1.9; Sample Response: I divided the height of each woman at age 18 by her height at age 2. All of the answers rounded to 1.9, so the average is about 1.9. **13.** 160.1 cm

Spiral Review (p. 189)

15. $10\frac{2}{3}$ **16.** 12 **17.** $\frac{3}{4}$ **18.** 12 **19.** multiply by 8; $x = 136$ **20.** 13.5 **21.** 26.55 **22.** 0.068 **23.** 55 boxes **24.** Possible answers: 3 round and 16 rectangular, 6 round and 12 rectangular, 9 round and 8 rectangular, 12 round and 4 rectangular **25.** dollars and pairs of socks; $5/pair **26.** dollars and oranges; $0.27/orange

Extra Skill Practice (p. 190)

1. $\frac{3}{2}$ or 1.5 **3.** $\frac{1}{3}$ **5.** slope $= \frac{160 - 110}{90 - 60} = \frac{5}{3}$

Standardized Testing (p. 190)

Answers will vary. Sample Response: Two people hiked up a trail to a mountain lake, a distance of 8 km. They both left the trailhead at the same time, the more experienced hiker averaging 1.5 km/hr and the other averaging $\frac{1}{3}$ km/hr. The faster hiker reached the lake in $5\frac{1}{3}$ hr. However, after hiking 12 hr, the novice hiker was only half way to the lake and decided to pitch camp and continue on in the morning.
vertical axis: distance from trailhead in kilometers
horizontal axis: time in hours
The red line represents the faster hiker, so it is steeper than the green line which represents the slower hiker.

Section 4, Practice and Application (p. 199)

1. $\frac{5}{3.3}$ **3. a.** 65° **b.** 7.26 cm **c.** about 7.58 cm **5.** $\triangle LMN \sim \triangle PQN$ **7.** $\triangle QRS \sim \triangle UPT$ **9.** Sample Response: Because the corresponding angles of trapezoids $MNQR$ and $NLPQ$ have the same measures. **11.** $\frac{PQ}{QR} = \frac{0.8}{1.4} \approx 0.57$ and $\frac{LP}{NQ} = \frac{2.5}{2.8} \approx 0.89$. Since the ratios are not equal, the trapezoids are not similar. **15.** Use the folded paper to show that the angles of each smaller triangle have the same measures as the angles of the larger triangles.

17. Yes; Sample Response: The corresponding angles of the parallelograms have the same measure, and the corresponding sides are in proportion, so the parallelograms are similar.

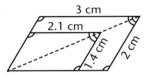

19. Answers will vary.

Spiral Review (p. 202)

20.

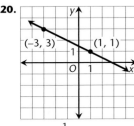

slope = $-\frac{1}{2}$

21.

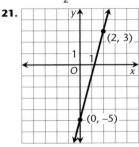

slope = 4

22. $33\frac{1}{3}$% decrease **23.** 37.5% increase **24.** about 34% decrease **25.** 360 **26.** 4 **27.** 249,000 **28.** 0.7 **29.** 753,000 **30.** 987,000 **31.** 16 **32.** 10,180,000

Extension (p. 202)

33. Answers will vary.

Extra Skill Practice (p. 203)

1. $\frac{3}{8}$ or $\frac{8}{3}$ **3. a.** 90° **b.** 12 **c.** 40 **5.** Use the proportion $\frac{BA}{ED} = \frac{AC}{DC}$. Substitute the known distances and solve for x: $\frac{x}{15} = \frac{40}{20}$; CE is not needed.

Standardized Testing (p. 203)
1. a. $\overline{PC}$ and $\overline{PD}$ **b.** any two of $\angle CPA$, $\angle CPB$, $\angle DPA$, and $\angle DPB$ **2.** Sample Response:

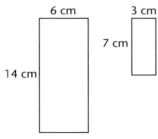

Section 5, Practice and Application (p. 210)

1. 4,500,000,000 yr **3.** 186,000 mi/sec **5.** A and B are in scientific notation. The numbers are written as a product of a number that is greater than or equal to 1 and less than 10 and a power of 10. C is not in scientific notation because 82.1 is greater than 10, and D is not in scientific notation because 2^{10} is not a power of 10.
7. Large Cloud of Magellan: $9.7 \cdot 10^{17}$ mi
  Small Cloud of Magellan: $1.1 \cdot 10^{18}$ mi
  Ursa Minor dwarf: $1.4 \cdot 10^{18}$ mi
  Draco dwarf: $1.5 \cdot 10^{18}$ mi
  Sculptor dwarf: $1.6 \cdot 10^{18}$ mi
  Fornax dwarf: $2.5 \cdot 10^{18}$ mi
  Leo II dwarf: $4.4 \cdot 10^{18}$ mi
  Leo I dwarf: $4.4 \cdot 10^{18}$ mi
  Barnard's Galaxy: $1.0 \cdot 10^{19}$ mi
9. a. $3.795 \cdot 10^{3}$ **b.** 3.795 km and 11.033 km
11. 5 **13.** 2.4 **15.** 24 **17.** 0 **19.** 1.02 **21.** 11 in.

23. size $8\frac{1}{2}$ or 9

Spiral Review (p. 212)
27. about 3.0 m **28.** −1 **29.** 17 **30.** 90 **31.** 6 **32.** 0
33. 12 **34.** −13 **35.** 6 **36.** about 80 **37.** about 95

Extra Skill Practice (p. 213)
1. $5.18 \cdot 10^{6}$ **3.** $2.89 \cdot 10^{7}$ **5.** $3.629 \cdot 10^{11}$
7. 350,000,000 **9.** 810,000
11. 480,000,000,000,000 **13.** 47,600
15. 60,000,000,000 **17.** 132.84 **19.** 1.1
21. 67.07 **23.** 71.97 **25.** 301.5 **27.** 1.33 **29.** 3.20

Standardized Testing (p. 213)
1. D **2.** B

Section 6, Practice and Application (p. 218)
1. exclusive or **3.** Marion Jones, Florence Griffith Joyner, and Renate Stecher **5.** 17 **7.** 42 students **9.** About 62% of the students acted in *Hello Dolly*, so she was only off by 2%.

11.

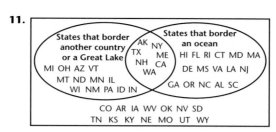

Spiral Review (p. 220)

15. 83 **16.** 0.6 **17.** 15.43

18. a.

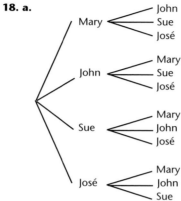

b. $\frac{1}{6}$ **19.** equilateral and isosceles **20.** scalene

21. isosceles

Extra Skill Practice (p. 221)

1. moose, raccoon, skunk, deer **3.** 7 animals **5.** in the blue part of the oval labeled "Mammals"

Standardized Testing (p. 221)

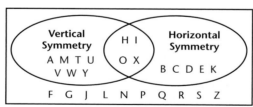

Review and Assessment (p. 226)

1. 0.3; mental math; exact **2.** about 126.5; calculator; estimate **3.** about –9.8; calculator; estimate **4.** $\frac{2}{9}$; mental math; exact **5.** No; Sample Response: He is comparing linear dimensions. Since the radius and height of the large can are twice those of the small can, the volume is 8 times greater. **6.** 3 **7.** $\frac{2}{3}$ **8.** $\frac{2}{9}$

9. linear

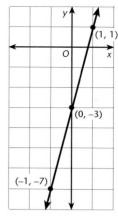

10. linear

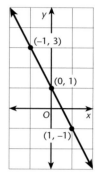

11. nonlinear

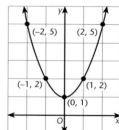

12. linear

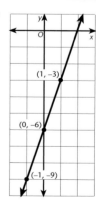

13. $\frac{1}{2}$ **14.** 2 **15.** 1 **16. a.** I **b.** 6780 **17.** about 30 ft
18. about 22 cm or $8\frac{5}{8}$ in. **19.** $5.25 \cdot 10^7$
20. $7.62 \cdot 10^5$ **21.** 6950 ft **22.** 700 yr
24.

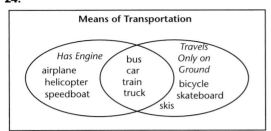

Means of Transportation

Has Engine
airplane
helicopter
speedboat

bus
car
train
truck

Travels Only on Ground
bicycle
skateboard
skis

25. airplane, helicopter, speedboat, bus, car, train, truck **26.** bus, car, train, truck **27.** Sample Response: raft (neither), motorcycle (both)

MODULE 4

Section 1, Practice and Application (p. 239)
1. a. 24π m **b.** 10π ft **c.** 1.1π cm **3. a.** smallest bicycle: about 2.39 in.; largest bicycle: about 31.4 ft **b.** smallest bicycle: about 2.39 in.; largest bicycle: about 31.4 ft **c.** about 68 **d.** about 2135.2 ft **5. a.** 64π ft² **b.** 900π cm² **c.** 1.96π m² **7. a.** about 95 ft² **b.** about 190 ft² **c.** about 34.54 ft **d.** about 18.84 ft **e.** about $\frac{1}{6}$
11. 54π in.³ or about 169.56 in.³ **13.** 40π cm³ or about 125.6 cm³ **15.** 1690π cm³ or about 5306.6 cm³
17. 1274 cm³ **19. a.** 16 and 17 **b.** 15
21. a. about 6400 ft³, about 6620 ft³ **b.** 275.625 in.³
c. about 41,503; Multiply the volume of the large popcorn box by $12^3 = 1728$ to convert it to in.³. Then divide that volume by the volume of the regular size box to get an estimate. **23. a.** 267,946.67 in.³
b. 555.37 m³ **c.** 4.19 ft³

Spiral Review (p. 243)
27.

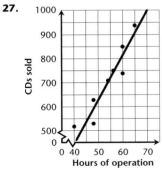

28. 0.01175 **29.** 2 **30.** $1.0\overline{3}$ **31.** $8.36\overline{7}$ **32.** 44
33. 27 **34.** 33 **35.** 15

Extra Skill Practice (p. 244)
1. 30π cm **3.** 12π ft **5.** 16π in.² **7.** 3120.28 mm³
9. 192 mm³ **11. a.** 1471.29 in.³ **b.** 0.24 mm³

Standardized Testing (p. 244)
1. Sample Response: Both use the formula $V = Bh$. The base of a prism is a polygon, so the area of its base, B, will always be exact. The base of a cylinder is a circle, so the formula for the area of its base is $B = \pi r^2$ and will only be exact when left in terms of π. **2.** Sample Response: A cereal box has a length of 10 in., a width of 3 in., and a height of 14 in. What is the volume of the cereal box? Answer: 420 in.³

Section 2, Practice and Application (p. 252)
1. 113.04 cm² **3.** 452.16 in.² **5.** 103.56 m² **7.** about 30 in.² **9. a.** about 1282 frames **b.** about 15,384 light detectors **11.** about 0.84 **13.** water chestnuts, olives, chili peppers **15.** Answers will vary.

Spiral Review (p. 254)
20. about 20 **21.** about 700 **22.** about 560

23.

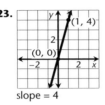

slope = 4

24.

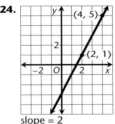

slope = 2

25.

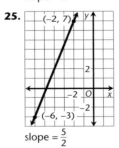

slope = $\frac{5}{2}$

26.

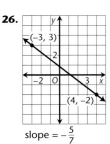

slope $= -\dfrac{5}{7}$

27. a. $A = 24$ in.^{2} **b.** $A = 26$ m^2

Extension (p. 255)

29. Sample Response: radius: 0.6 cm; height: 1.2 cm

Extra Skill Practice (p. 256)

1. 251.2 in.^{2} **3.** 3523.08 cm^2 **5.** 90.432 m^2 **7.** $2.\overline{3}$
9. $1.7\overline{3}$ **11.** 1.5 **13.** The cylinder with a radius of 2.5 in.
and a height of 3 in.; The ratio of surface area to volume
is lowest.

Study Skills (p. 256)

1. Sample Response: The two formulas are alike in that
they both use π, r, and h. They are different in that the
formula for surface area ($2\pi r^2 + 2\pi rh$) uses both multiplication and addition and has an answer in square
units, while the formula for volume ($\pi r^2 h$) uses only
multiplication and has an answer in cubic units.

2. Sample Response: The lines both intersect the y-axis
at 2 and appear to be equally steep, although the first
line slopes up to the right while the second slopes down
to the right.

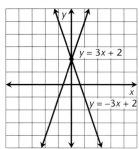

3. Answers will vary.

Section 3, Practice and Application (p. 265)

1. $-\dfrac{3}{5}$ **3.** $\dfrac{1}{3}$ **5.** 0 **7.** $-\dfrac{9}{7}$

9. Accept reasonable estimates.

Kemp's Ridley Turtle Nests (1970–1995)	
Time Period	Rate of Change (number of turtle nests/year)
1970–1975	−350
1975–1980	−75
1980–1985	−50
1985–1990	65
1990–1995	200

11. Sample Response: 1985; The number of nests began
to increase in 1985. **13.** slope: 2; y-intercept: 0 **15.** It
got worse; The line shows a decrease in pH which means
that the acidity of the rain increased. **17.** about 4.58;
Sample Response: I assumed the trend would continue,
so I solved the equation $y = -0.005x + 5.43$ for $x = 170$.
19. $y = 2x + 4$ **21.** $y = -5$

23. a.

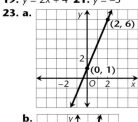

b.

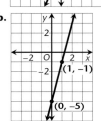

c.

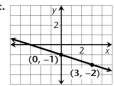

25.

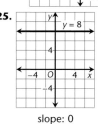

slope: 0

27.

slope: undefined

Spiral Review (p. 268)
30. 351.68 in.^{2} **31.** 55% **32.** 4.5 **33.** 7 · 10^2
34. 2.593 · 10^3 **35.** 1.01 · 10^5

Extra Skill Practice (p. 269)
1. 3 **3.** $-\frac{1}{3}$ **5.** 0 **7.** line B **9.** line A **11.** $y = 2x - 3$
13. $y = 1$ **15.** $y = -x + 5$

Standardized Testing (p. 269)
1–4. Sample responses are given. **1.** $y = -5x + 4$
2. $y = 3x - 2$ **3.** $y = 2$ **4.** $y = -3x + 7$

Section 4, Practice and Application (p. 278)
1. a. $\frac{1}{5}$ **b.** $\frac{1}{6} + \frac{1}{10} = \frac{8}{30} = \frac{4}{15}$ **c.** $\frac{1}{2} + \frac{1}{3} + \frac{1}{12} = \frac{11}{12}$
3. a. $\frac{-4}{1}$ **b.** $\frac{4}{1}$ **c.** $\frac{1}{4}$ **d.** $\frac{17}{7}$ **7.** $-14.\overline{14}, -\sqrt{4}, -1, 5.33, \frac{16}{3},$
$5\frac{4}{9}, 14.1$ **9.** -8 **11.** $-\frac{6}{5}$ or $-1\frac{1}{5}$ **13.** -12 **15.** -9
17. -0.5 **19.** -2.5 **21.** $-\frac{25}{3}$ or $-8\frac{1}{3}$ **23.** 22 ft
27. a. 100°C **b.** -4°F

c.
$$F = \frac{9}{5}C + 32$$
$$F - 32 = \frac{9}{5}C$$
$$\frac{5}{9}(F - 32) = C$$
$$\frac{5}{9}F - \frac{5}{9} \cdot 32 = C$$
$$\frac{5}{9}F - \frac{160}{9} = C$$
$$\frac{5}{9}F - 17\frac{7}{9} = C$$

29. a. about 2464 cm^2 **b.** about 4158 cm^2

Spiral Review (p. 280)
31. 3.57 **32.** 14.92 **33.** 0.89 **34.** yes **35.** no **36.** no
37. no **38.** 8.84 **39.** 59.84 **40.** 121.67 **41.** 20.2

Extension (p. 281)
43. $\frac{2}{9}$ **45.** $\frac{53}{90}$ (multiply by 10)

Extra Skill Practice (p. 282)
1. $\frac{137}{100}$ **3.** $\frac{1}{8}$ **5.** 1.75 **7.** $0.5\overline{3}$ **9.** $-0.\overline{3}, -\frac{3}{10}, \frac{1}{3}, 0.35, \frac{2}{5}$
11. > **13.** = **15.** -1.1 **17.** $-\frac{5}{4}$ **19.** -15 **21.** -3
23. -1.5 **25.** -5 **27.** 8

Standardized Testing (p. 282)
1. Answers will vary. Sample responses are given. Kelly saves $\frac{3}{5}$ of all the money she earns. How much must she earn to save $30? **2.** Answers will vary. Sample

responses are given. Moses purchased a $12 single CD and a half-priced boxed set. The total cost was $40. What was the regular price of the boxed set?

Section 5, Practice and Application (p. 293)
1. a.

Exterior Color	Interior Color	Combination
white	black	white, black
	gray	white, gray
red	black	red, black
	gray	red, gray
navy blue	black	navy blue, black
	gray	navy blue, gray
forest green	black	forest green, black
	gray	forest green, gray
tan	black	tan, black
	gray	tan, gray
maroon	black	maroon, black
	gray	maroon, gray

b. 12 ways

3. a.

Entrée	Vegetable	Dessert	Combination
spaghetti	corn	apple pie	spaghetti, corn, apple pie
		cherry pie	spaghetti, corn, cherry pie
		pecan pie	spaghetti, corn, pecan pie
	squash	apple pie	spaghetti, squash, apple pie
		cherry pie	spaghetti, squash, cherry pie
		pecan pie	spaghetti, squash, pecan pie
chicken	corn	apple pie	chicken, corn, apple pie
		cherry pie	chicken, corn, cherry pie
		pecan pie	chicken, corn, pecan pie
	squash	apple pie	chicken, squash, apple pie
		cherry pie	chicken, squash, cherry pie
		pecan pie	chicken, squash, pecan pie
roast beef	corn	apple pie	roast beef, corn, apple pie
		cherry pie	roast beef, corn, cherry pie
		pecan pie	roast beef, corn, pecan pie
	squash	apple pie	roast beef, squash, apple pie
		cherry pie	roast beef, squash, cherry pie
		pecan pie	roast beef, squash, pecan pie

b. 18 dinners

5. 2 **7.** 24 **9.** 5040 **11.** 40,320 orders **13.** 6 combinations **15. a.** 5 **b.** 10 **c.** 10 **d.** 16

Spiral Review (p. 295)

20. $\frac{3}{4}$ **21.** $\frac{3}{2}$ **22.** 2 **23.** $\frac{1}{2}$ **24.** $\frac{2}{3}$

Extension (p. 295)
27. 70 ways

Extra Skill Practice (p. 296)
1. 144 ways **3.** 30 ways **5.** 24 ways **7.** 2^{10} or 1024 ways **9.** 40,320 ways

Standardized Testing (p. 296)
1. 3 ways; combinations problem; The order in which she selects her sketches is not important. **2.** 6 ways; permutations problem; The order in which she hangs her sketches is important.

Section 6, Practice and Application (p. 301)
1. HHH, HHT, HTH, HTT, THH, THT, TTH, TTT

3. $\frac{7}{8}$ = 0.875 **5. a.** 3.315312 · 10^{10}

b. MATH4YOU: $\dfrac{1}{26 \cdot 25 \cdot 24 \cdot 23 \cdot 10 \cdot 22 \cdot 21 \cdot 20}$

$= \dfrac{1}{3.315312 \cdot 10^{10}}$

MATH: $\dfrac{1 \cdot 1 \cdot 1 \cdot 1 \cdot 10 \cdot 22 \cdot 21 \cdot 20}{26 \cdot 25 \cdot 24 \cdot 23 \cdot 10 \cdot 22 \cdot 21 \cdot 20} = \dfrac{1}{358,800}$

A license plate on which the first four letters spell MATH is about 92,400 times more likely than the license plate MATH4YOU. **c.** 80,318,101,760 or $26^7 \cdot 10$ license plates; MATH4YOU: $\dfrac{1}{26^7 \cdot 10}$; MATH as first four

letters: $\dfrac{1 \cdot 1 \cdot 1 \cdot 1 \cdot 10 \cdot 26^3}{26^7 \cdot 10} = \dfrac{1}{456,976}$. A license plate

on which the first four letters spell MATH is 175,760 times more likely than the license plate MATH4YOU.

7. a. 15,625 keys **b.** $\dfrac{1}{15,625}$

Spiral Review (p. 302)
12. 6 combinations
13. a.

Science Test Scores

Stem	Leaf
4	1 8
5	2 3 9
6	1 4 6 8
7	0 2 5 5 7 8
8	1 1 1 5 6 7
9	3 4 6 8 9

7 | 2 = 72

b. Science Test Scores

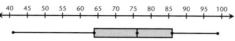

40 45 50 55 60 65 70 75 80 85 90 95 100

c. median: 76, mode: 81 **d.** Either the stem-and-leaf plot or the box-and-whisker plot could be used to find

the median, but only the stem-and-leaf plot could be used to find the mode.

Extra Skill Practice (p. 303)
1. $\frac{1}{100}$ = 0.01 **3.** $\frac{64}{125}$ = 0.512 **5.** $\frac{999}{1000}$ = 0.999
7. $\frac{1}{7776}$ ≈ 0.00013 **9.** $\frac{5}{54}$ ≈ 0.093 **11.** $\frac{3125}{7776}$ ≈ 0.40

Standardized Testing (p. 303)
1. $\frac{1}{16}$ = 0.0625 **2. a.** $\frac{1}{1296}$ ≈ 0.00077 **b.** $\frac{625}{1296}$ ≈ 0.48

Review and Assessment (p. 306)
1. 21.81 ft **2.** the box **3. a.** 9 times greater **b.** 27 times greater **4.** 131.88 cm² **5.** 100.48 in.² **6.** 127.17 ft²
7. 0.8 **8.** 0.7 **9.** $0.8\overline{3}$ **10.** The can in Ex. 8; It has the lowest ratio of surface area to volume.

11. slope: $-\frac{1}{4}$; y-intercept: 2; $y = -\frac{1}{4}x + 2$ **12.** slope: 3; y-intercept: –1; $y = 3x - 1$ **13.** slope: 0; y-intercept: –2; $y = -2$ **14.** Sample Response: The run of a vertical line is always 0. To calculate the slope division by zero is necessary. Since division by zero is undefined, the slope must also be undefined. **15.** Sample Response: $y = mx$ and $y = mx + b$. (Students may substitute any numbers for m and b in the equations as long as the slope (m) is the same in both equations.) They are parallel because the slope is the same in both equations. **16. a.** $0.\overline{45}$
b. –3.25 **c.** 0.875 **17.** $-\frac{3}{4}, -\frac{8}{11}, -0.72, -0.7, \frac{5}{7}, 0.72,$
$0.7\overline{2}, 0.\overline{72}, \frac{3}{4}$ **18.** –2 **19.** –12 **20.** –9 **21. a.** 6 uniforms
b. 120 ways **c.** Armand and Cathy, Armand and Ishana, Armand and Jim, Armand and Susan, Cathy and Ishana, Cathy and Jim, Cathy and Susan, Ishana and Jim, Ishana and Susan, Jim and Susan. **22. a.** 10^4 or 10,000 passwords **b.** $\frac{9}{100}$ = 0.09

MODULE 5

Section 1, Practice and Application (p. 317)

1. Sample Response:

3. 4 prisms: 1 · 1 · 12; 1 · 2 · 6; 1 · 3 · 4; 2 · 2 · 3
5.

Figure before removing cubes: S.A. = 24 unit²,
V = 8 unit³; Figure after removing cubes:
S.A. = 24 unit², V = 7 unit³

7. a.

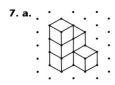

b. Sample Responses:

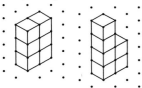

9. front view

11.

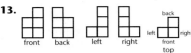

13.

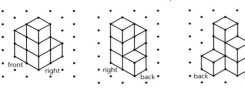

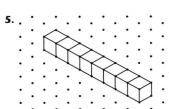

Spiral Reveiw (p. 319)

16. a. $\frac{1}{3}$ or about 0.33 **b.** $\frac{2}{3}$ or about 0.67 **17.** 6

18. 3 **19.** 12 **20.** 7.5 **21.** 3.2 **22.** 5.6 **23.** $\frac{13}{24}$

24. $-\frac{7}{20}$ **25.** $-1\frac{7}{9}$

Extra Skills Practice (p. 320)

1. Sample Response: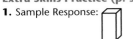

3.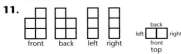

5.

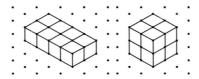

7.

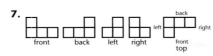

9.

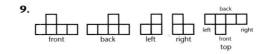

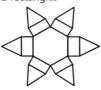

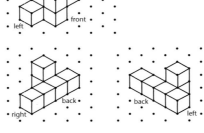

Section 2, Practice and Application (p. 332)

1. No; The sum of the lengths of segments k and m is less than the length of segment n, so the segments will not form a triangle. **3.** Yes; The sum of the lengths of segments x and w is greater than the length of segment y, so these three segments will form a triangle. **5.** Yes **7.** Yes **9.** Yes **11** similar: 1 and 3, 2 and 5, 4, 6, and 7; congruent: 2 and 5, 4 and 6; For similar triangles, check the type of triangle and the angle measures. For congruent triangles, use the side-side-side or side-angle-side rule. $\triangle GHK \cong \triangle EFD$, $\triangle STV \cong \triangle QPR$ **15. a–c.** Answers will vary. **17.** 16 edges **19. a.** triangles and rectangles **b.** Sample sketch:

c. 13 faces, 24 edges, 13 vertices **21.** D **23.** C

Spiral Review (p. 335)

30.

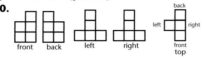

31. –30 **32.** 1 **33.** –20 **34.** –0.5 **35.** 2 **36.** –0.$\overline{3}$
37. 45 **38.** 15 **39.** 30

Extra Skill Practice (p. 336)

1. No **3.** Yes
5. a. Sample Response:

7. Congruent; Two sides and the included angle of $\triangle PQR$ are congruent to two sides and the included angle of $\triangle NML$.

Standardized Testing (p. 336)

Number of sides on the base of each pyramid	Number of faces on the new polyhedron	Number of edges on the new polyhedron	Number of vertices on the new polyhedron
3	6	9	5
4	8	12	6
5	10	15	7
100	200	300	102

Section 3, Practice and Application (p. 344)

1. right **3.** acute **5.** acute **7.** Sample Response: Yes; the square root of the sum of the squares of the legs is about 20.81, which is close to 21. Allowing for measurement errors, the angle is probably a right angle.
9. 14.70 mm **11.** 8 cm **13.** 12 mm **15.** No; the diagonal of the door opening is only about 12.81 ft.
17. a. Yes; 9 in.:12 in. = 3:4 **b.** 75 in. **c.** Answers will vary.

Spiral Review (p. 346)

22. 7.5 **23.** 12.2 **24.** 3.5 **25.** 362.67 cm^2 **26.** $\frac{7}{12}$
27. $\frac{4}{11}$

Extra Skill Practice (p. 347)

1. obtuse **3.** acute **5.** 8.31 in. **7.** 10 cm **9.** No; $3^2 + 3^2 \neq 5^2$ **11.** No; $6^2 + 6^2 \neq 10^2$

Standardized Testing (p. 347)

1. Possible answers are given. **a.** acute: $6 < x < 7.5$ right: $x = 7.5$ obtuse: $7.5 < x < 10.5$

b. acute: $5.5 < x < \sqrt{34.25}$ right: $x = \sqrt{34.25}$
obtuse: $\sqrt{34.25} < x < 7.5$
2. 48 ft^2

Section 4, Practice and Application (p. 357)

1. 54 m^2 **3.** 1249.21 in.^{2} **5.** 175 cm^2 **9.** 4 in.^{3}
11. 4.67 m^3 **13.** 3014.4 mm^3 **15. a.** a cylinder and a cone **b.** 339.88 ft^3 **17.** S.A. = 240 in.^{2}, V = 264 in.^{3}

Spiral Review (p. 359)

22. not congruent; Corresponding sides $\overline{PR}$ and $\overline{DF}$ are not congruent. **23.** congruent; SAS **24** $y = 3x + 2$
25. $y = -4x + 5$

Extension (p. 360)

27. Labsheet 4D answers are given. **a.** $2\pi r$ **b.** the circumference of the partial circle **c.** the radius of the partial circle

Extra Skill Practice (p. 361)

1. 520 m^2 **3.** 75 cm^2 **5.** 0.75 ft^3 **7.** S.A. is about 730.35 ft^2, V = 1342.69 ft^3

Standardized Testing (p. 361)

1. Sample response:

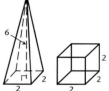

2. Sample responses are given.
a.

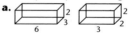

b.

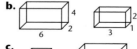

c.

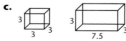

Section 5, Practice and Application (p. 369)

1. 120° **3.** 90° **5.** 135° **7.** 60° **9.** 27° **11.** 42° **13.** 78°
15. 54° **17.** ∠CED **19.** ∠DCE **21.** ∠8 **23.** ∠1
25. 150° **27.** 30° **29.** $m\angle 1 = 110°$; $m\angle 2 = 70°$; $m\angle 3 = 110°$; $m\angle 4 = 70°$; $m\angle 5 = 110°$; $m\angle 6 = 70°$
31. 180° **33.** x = 125; y = 125; (3x – 250) and x are the measures of alternate exterior angles, and since lines m and n are parallel, the measures of alternate exterior angles are equal. Thus, 3x – 250 = x. Solving 3x – 250 = x for x gives x = 125. y and x are the measures of corresponding angles, and since the measures of corresponding angles are equal, y = x = 125.
35. y + 45 = 90; y = 45°

 Selected Answers

Spiral Review (p. 372)
38. 301.44 m^3 **39.** 8.37 ft^3 **40.** 192 in.^{3} **41.** 28 in. = $2\frac{1}{3}$ ft **42.** 1.5 mi = 7920 ft **43.** 3 yd = 108 in.
44. 36 mm = 3.6 cm **45.** 248 cm = 2.48 m
46. 2.6 km = 2600 m

Career Connection (p. 372)
47. a. Since the alternate interior angles formed by the transversal $\overline{CB}$ are congruent, the lines are parallel.
b. 60°

Extra Skill Practice (p. 373)
1. 78° **3.** 28° **5.** 82° **7.** 32° **9.** Yes, it intersects lines m and n at different points. **11.** ∠1 and ∠3, ∠2 and ∠4, ∠5 and ∠7, ∠6 and ∠8 **13.** ∠1 and ∠5, ∠4 and ∠8 **15.** 50° **17.** 50°

Standardized Testing (p. 373)
1. C **2.** B

Section 6, Practice and Application (p. 382)

1. Based on measurements of $1\frac{5}{16}$ in. by $\frac{13}{16}$ in., the new scale drawing should be a $2\frac{5}{8}$ in. by $1\frac{5}{8}$ in. rectangle.

3. Scale may vary. Sample Response:

Scale: 5 mm = 1 mm
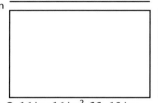

5. Answers will vary. **9.** 16 in.; 16 in.^{2} **11.** 12 in.; 9 in.^{2} **13.** 58.3 mm^2 **15.** 2338.28 yd^2 **19.** Sample Response: about 11.5 mi **21.** 0.324 in.^{2}

Spiral Review (p. 384)

23. 4 **24.** 2.5 **25.** 8 **26.** $\frac{1}{2}$ **27.** 19.5 **28.** 1.375

29.
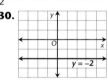

30.
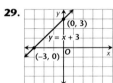

31.
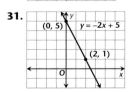

Extra Skill Practice (p. 385)
1. Answers will vary. They must be equivalent to $\frac{4 \text{ in.}}{6 \text{ ft}} = \frac{1 \text{ in.}}{1.5 \text{ ft}}$. **3.** Scale and views may vary. Sample Response: Scale: $\frac{1}{4}$ in. = 12 ft

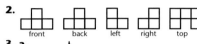

5. 15 in. **7.** 6480 in.^{2}

Standardized Testing (p. 385)
1. C **2.** A

Review and Assessment (p. 388)
1. a. surface area = 26 cm^2; volume = 6 cm^3 **b.** surface area = 18 cm^2; volume = 4 cm^3

2.

front back left right top

3. a.

b. 9 faces, 16 edges, 9 vertices **4.** △ABE ≅ △CBD because two sides and the included angle of △ABE are congruent to two sides and the included angle of △CBD (SAS). **5.** Two sides of △PQS are congruent to two sides of △RQS, but the included angles are not congruent, so the triangles are not congruent.
6. Since $7.5^2 + 4^2 = 56.25 + 16 = 72.25 = 8.5^2$, the two triangles will be right triangles, and the quadrilateral will be a rectangle. **7.** 13 mm **8.** 6 ft **9.** $\sqrt{2}$ in.
10. S.A. = 1440 in.^{2}; V = 3200 in.^{3} **11.** S.A. = 700 m^2; V = 1200 m^3 **12.** S.A. = 114 cm^2; V = 84 cm^3
13. 17 cm^3 **14.** ∠7; 105° **15.** ∠8; 75° **16.** ∠4; 75°
17. 105°; Sample response: ∠3 and ∠5 are vertical angles, so $m\angle 3 = m\angle 5 = 105°$. **18.** ∠RTQ **19.** ∠SQT
20. 130° **21.** Scale drawing should be $1\frac{1}{2}$ in. by $\frac{3}{4}$ in.
22. perimeter = 28 km; area = 48 km^2

MODULE 6

Section 1, Practice and Application (p. 401)
1. B **3.** D **5.** The first graph matches the second table; the second graph matches the second description; The third graph matches the first table; The fourth graph matches the first description; The fifth graph matches the third description. **7.** Answers will vary.

11. Yes. The amount of money made depends on the number of tickets sold. **13.** Yes. In one location there is only one sunrise time for each day of the year. **15.** not a function **17.** not a function **19.** function **21.** $y = \frac{x}{5}$

23. $y = \frac{x^2}{2}$ **25. a.** $y = 0.4x + 2.1$ **b.** (0, 2.1), (1, 2.5), (2, 2.9), (3, 3.3), (4, 3.7), (5, 4.1), (6, 4.5); The values of x range from 0 to 6 since the river rose for 6 days. The values of y will be between 2 and 4.5 since the original height above the bank was 2.1 in. and it increased at a rate of 0.4 in. for 6 days. **c.**

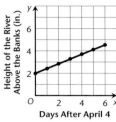

Height of the River Above the Banks (in.)
Days After April 4

d. Yes, y is a function of x.

Spiral Review (p. 404)
27. Perimeter is 68 cm, area is 240 cm² **28.** 6.55 m
29.

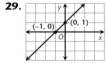

slope = 1
(−1, 0) (0, 1)

30.

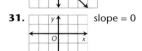

slope = −1
(0, 0)
(2, −2)

31.

slope = 0
y
O x

32.

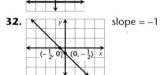

slope = −1
$\left(-\frac{1}{2}, 0\right)$ $\left(0, -\frac{1}{2}\right)$ x

Extra Skill Practice (p. 405)
1. B **3.** D **5.** function **7.** function **9.** function

Study Skills (p. 405)
1. Answers will vary. Set specific goals in the beginning and specify the time in which they need to be completed, appoint a group leader to make sure your project is on schedule. **2.** Answers will vary.

Section 2, Practice and Application (p. 414)
1. Bruce has $90 in his savings account and he deposits $75 each week without withdrawing any money.
3. (6, −2) **5.** (6, 26) **7. a.** at 34 months **b.** $5300

c. at 16 months **d.** $2600 **9.** $-5m - 60$ **11.** $-40 - 8x$
13. $18x - 6$ **15. a.** to eliminate the multiplication required by the distributive property **b.** added 10 to both sides of the equation **c.** Preferences will vary.
17. a. (1, 5); No; There is only one solution of the equation $5x = 2x + 3$.
b.

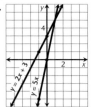

$y = 2x + 3$
$y = 5x$

Find the point of intersection of the two graphs.
c.

$y = 3x + 4$
$y = 3x - 2$

No; The graphs are parallel lines and do not intersect. **19.** -2 **21.** -1 **23.** $\frac{23}{6}$ **25.** -12 **27.** 5 ft

29. a.

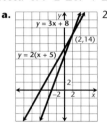

$y = 3x + 8$
(2,14)
$y = 2(x + 5)$

b. $3(2) + 8 = 6 + 8 = 14$; $2(2 + 5) = 2(7) = 14$ **c.** -5

Spiral Review (p. 417)
31. C; The graph shows the height of the flag increasing in stages with several pulls of a rope followed by brief rest periods. **32.** $0.\overline{428571}$ **33.** $0.5\overline{4}$ **34.** -2.2
35. 0.625 **36.** 5.2^4 **37.** 3^8 **38.** 16^5 **39.** $\left(\frac{3}{5}\right)^6$

Extra Skill Practice (p. 418)
1.

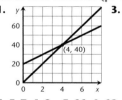

(4, 40)

3.

(2.25, 3)

5. 7 **7.** 5 **9.** -7 **11.** 3 **13.** $-3\frac{1}{4}$ **15.** $-6 - 9x$
17. $12x + 6$ **19.** $14 - 8x$ **21.** $x^2 + 4x$ **23.** -6
25. 0 **27.** $\frac{3}{4}$ **29.** $-\frac{3}{4}$

Standardized Testing (p. 418)
1. Answers will vary. **2.** Answers will vary. Sample Response: $2(12x + 4)$; $24x + 8$ **3.** Answers will vary. Sample Response: $5(2x - 1) = 75$; $x = 8$

Section 3, Practice and Application (p. 427)
1. A: Area of each region after x steps $= \left(\frac{1}{3}\right)^x$; B: Number of regions after x steps $= 3^x$; As x increases, $\left(\frac{1}{3}\right)^x$ decreases and 3^x increases.

3. a.

Number of minutes	Number of new people hearing the rumor	Total number of people who have heard the rumor
0	1	1
1	2	3
2	4	7
3	8	15
4	16	31
5	32	63
6	64	127
7	128	255
8	256	511
9	512	1023
10	1024	2047

b. $y = 2^x$; When $x = 60$, $y = 2^{60}$. **c.** Sample Response: It shows exponential growth with powers of 2.
3. d.

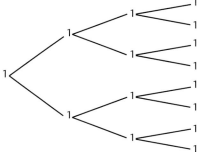

0 min   1 min   2 min   3 min   …

7. a. $y = 1200 \cdot (1.04)^x$ where y represents the enrollment and x represents the number of years.
b. $y = 5 \cdot (1.1)^x$ where y represents the distance Maria runs each week and x represents the number of weeks.
9. Yes; For every value of x there is only one value of y.
11. $\frac{1}{4}$ **13.** 16 **15.** $\frac{5}{81}$

Spiral Review (p. 429)
18. 10 **19.** $-\frac{1}{2}$ **20.** $\left(7, -\frac{1}{2}\right)$

Career Connection (p. 430)
21. a. 128 bacteria; 524,288 bacteria; Possible Answers: Write an equation, complete a table, or sketch a graph. Equation: $y = 2 \cdot 2^x$ where x represents the number of 20 min intervals that have passed. **b.** Sample Response: It shows how quickly the bacteria grow and so, how rapidly the infection worsens.

Extension (p. 430)
23. The decay factor is the rate of depreciation subtracted from 1.

Extra Skill Practice (p. 431)
1. $y = 150 \cdot (1.08)^x$ where y represents the value of the baseball card and x represents the number of years.
3. $y = 2000 \cdot (1.10)^x$ where y represents the value of the number of loaves of bread and x represents the number of days. **5.** 46,875 **7.** 8748 **9.** $\frac{8}{27} \approx 0.3$
11. $y = 200 \cdot (1.03)^{10}$, $268.78
13. $y = 1500 \cdot (1.04)^8$, $2052.85

Standardized Testing (p. 431)
1. No. Each day the new price, not the original price, is being reduced 20%, so on the fifth day the price will be about 67% off the original price. **2.** Bank B; The amount he will earn at Bank A is $y = 1000(1.06)^4 = 1262.48$ and the amount he will earn at Bank B is $y = 1000 + 1000(0.07)(4) = 1280$. He will make $17.52 more than at Bank A.

Section 4, Practice and Application (p. 437)
1. Sample Response: $(x', y') = (x, y + 5)$; $(x'', y'') = (x', y' - 5)$

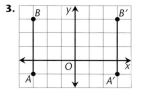 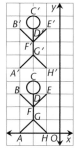

3.

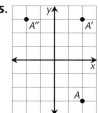

5.

7.

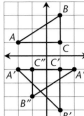

It is the same.

9. Answers will vary. **11.** $(x', y') = (x, -y)$; $(x'', y'') = (-x', y')$; $(x''', y''') = (x'', y'' + 2)$ **13.** No; Sample Response: $\triangle DE'F'$ is on the same side of the y-axis as $\triangle DEF$ and is not the image of $\triangle DEF$ reflected across the x-axis.

15. a.

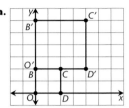

b. Yes

17.

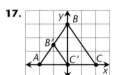

19. Answers will vary.

Spiral Review (p. 440)

21. 27 **22.** $\frac{1}{32} = 0.03125$ **23.** 1728 **24.** $m\angle 1 = m\angle 4 = 95°$; $m\angle 2 = m\angle 3 = 85°$ **25.** −12

26. 0.01 **27.** $\frac{1}{9}$ **28.** $-\frac{7}{15}$

Extra Skill Practice (p. 441)

1. $(x', y') = (x + 3, y - 3)$ **3.** $(x', y') = (x + 2, y + 2)$; $(x'', y'') = (-x' + 2, y' - 2)$ **5.** Sample Response: Plot the point with the same x-coordinate and the opposite y-coordinate.

7.

9. Answers will vary.

Standardized Testing (p. 441)

1. C **2.** C

Section 5, Practice and Application (p. 448)

1. B **3.** D **5. a.** Answers may vary. Sample Response: The graph of $y = -2x^2$ will have the same vertex and axis of symmetry as the graph of $y = x^2$, but the parabola will be narrower and open downward. The graph of $y = -2x^2 + 3$ is the same as the graph of $y = -2x^2$ except that it is shifted up 3 units so its vertex is at $(0, 3)$ instead of $(0, 0)$.

b.

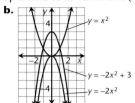

7. a. 622, 606, 558, 478, 366, 222, 46, −162

b.

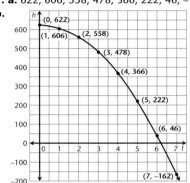

c. about 6.25 sec; The graph crosses the x-axis at about $x = 6.25$.

d.

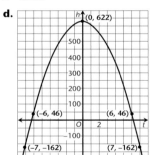

No; When the object is dropped, $t = 0$. Negative time values do not make sense in this situation.

e. $(0, 622)$ **9. a.** It is in the form $y = ax^2 + bx + c$ and $a \neq 0$; $a = -16$, $b = 32$, $c = 4$

9. b.

line of symmetry

c. 20 ft **d.** 1 sec **e.** about 2.1 sec **11.** $y = 3x - 12$; not a quadratic function **13.** $y = 3x^2 - 2x$; quadratic function **15.** $y = -2x + 5$; not a quadratic function

Spiral Review (p. 450)

18.

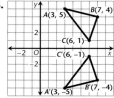

19. 74° **20.** 12° **21.** 59° **22.** 2° **23.** taxpayers; parents **24.** No; Taxpayers who are not parents are not represented.

Extension (p. 450)

25. The value of h is the x-coordinate and the value of k is the y-coordinate of the vertex of the parabola.

Extra Skill Practice (p. 451)

1. same vertex and axis of symmetry, narrower

3. same shape and axis of symmetry, vertex (0, 1) instead of (0, 0)

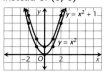

5. same axis of symmetry, narrower, vertex at (0, –2) instead of (0, 0), opens in opposite direction

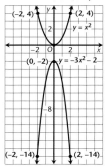

7. The vertex is at (2, –2) and the line of symmetry is a vertical line through the point (2, –2). **9.** $y = x^2 + 7x$; quadratic function **11.** $y = -x^2 - 5x + 10$; quadratic function **13.** $y = 6$; not a quadratic function **15.** $y = 2x^3 - 5x^2 - 7$; not a quadratic function

Standardized Testing (p. 451)

1. Sample Response: All the graphs are parabolas that open up and have the same line of symmetry (the y-axis); the graphs of $y = x^2$, $y = \frac{1}{2}x^2$, and $y = 2x^2$ all have vertex (0, 0) but the graph of $y = x^2 + 4$ has vertex (0, 4). **2. a.** not a quadratic function **b.** quadratic function **c.** quadratic function **d.** not a quadratic function

Review and Assessment (p. 454)

1. B; The hours increase gradually to a maximum and then decrease gradually to a minimum. **2.** C; Height increases at varying rates. **3.** A; The length of the grass in the summer increases then sharply decreases each time it is cut and then begins to grow again.
4. function **5.** not a function **6.** function **7.** function
8. function **9.** not a function
10. $y = 20{,}000 - 500x$; \$15,000

Years	Value (\$)
0	20,000
1	19,500
2	19,000
3	18,500
4	18,000
5	17,500
6	17,000
7	16,500
8	16,000
9	15,500
10	15,000

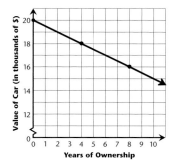

11. 17 **12.** 4 **13.** –0.5 **14.** 1 **15.** –2.75 **16.** 11.5

17. at 25 sec **18.** 10,000 **19.** $\frac{9}{16}$ **20.** 96 **21.** $\frac{1}{25}$
22. $y = 100 \cdot (1.05)^x$; \$338.64

23. $(x', y') = (-x, y)$; $(x'', y'') = (x', y' + 3)$

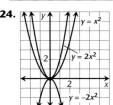

24.

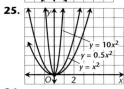

25.

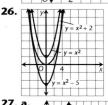

26.

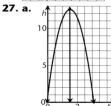

27. a.

b. about 3.1 sec **c.** (1.5, 12.5) **28.** $y = -x^2 + 5$; quadratic function **29.** $y = 2x^2 + x - 13$; quadratic function **30.** $y = -9x - 4$; not a quadratic function **31.** $y = 5x^2 - 6x - 9$; quadratic function

MODULE 7

Section 1, Practice and Application (p. 465)
1. 10^6 **3.** 2^9 **5.** 3^{10} **7.** a^4 **9.** b^8 **11.** w^{80}
13. a. $E = 0.002888s^4$ **b.** Yes, in the equation s is raised to the 4th power. **c.** 462.08 foot-pounds; 7393.28 foot-pounds **d.** Yes, $7393.28 \div 17 = 434.899$ which is close to 462.08. But it is actually 16 times the wave energy; $7393.28 \div 17 = 462.08$. **15.** 10^2
17. 2^4 **19.** 7^9 **21.** a^3 **23.** c^6 **25.** u^{43}

29. No, if you substitute 0 for t in the formula, you get $w = 1.16(1.44)^0 = 1.16 \cdot 1$ or 1.16 lb, which is not a reasonable weight for a fish that is less than 5 mm long.
31. $\frac{1}{9}$ **33.** $\frac{1}{5}$ **35.** $\frac{1}{b^6}$ **37.** $\frac{4}{w^2}$ **39.** 0.9 **41.** 0.00018
43. 0.00000265 **45.** $3 \cdot 10^{-1}$ **47.** $2.5 \cdot 10^{-4}$
49. $6 \cdot 10^{-9}$ **51. a.** $2^{-25} \approx 2.98 \cdot 10^{-8}$ **b.** The probability of winning the state lottery is about 2.4 times greater than flipping 25 heads in 25 flips of a coin.

Spiral Review (p. 467)
53. slope = -2, y-intercept = 9 **54.** 7 and 8 **55.** 12
56. 65 **57.** 510 **58.** -8 **59.** 18

Career Connection (p. 468)
61. $1.56 \cdot 10^{-3}$ sec

Extension (p. 468)
63. 2^2 **65.** a^{-4} **67.** 3^{-2} **69.** b^{-5}

Extra Skill Practice (p. 469)
1. 6^7 **3.** 11^{34} **5.** b^{12} **7.** k^{81} **9.** 10^{10} **11.** 8^2 **13.** p^3
15. m^4 **17.** 1 **19.** $\frac{1}{121}$ **21.** $\frac{1}{13}$ **23.** $\frac{1}{p^8}$ **25.** $\frac{3}{b^7}$
27. 0.008 **29.** 0.000000614 **31.** $6 \cdot 10^{-2}$
33. $1.013 \cdot 10^{-6}$

Standardized Testing (p. 469)
1. A **2.** C **3.** D **4.** D

Section 2, Practice and Application (p. 478)
1. a. irrational **b.** rational **c.** rational **d.** rational
3. a. 111112 **b.** $0.\overline{12}$ repeats the same digits 121212... where as 0.121121112 changes because the number of ones after each 2 increases by one as the pattern continues. **5. a.** $A = \sqrt{9(1)(3)(5)} = 3\sqrt{15}$ cm^2
b. $A = \sqrt{15(5)(5)(5)} = 25\sqrt{3}$ in.^{2} **c.** about 11.6 cm^2; about 43.3 in.^{2} **7. a.** yes **b.** no **c.** no **d.** no
9. a. $11x^3$ **b.** $y^{14}\sqrt{y}$ **c.** $\frac{\sqrt{6}}{m^5}$ **d.** b

Spiral Review (p. 479)
14. $y = 2x^2 - 5x$; yes **15.** $y = 2x^2 - 4x$; yes
16. $y = \frac{1}{8}x$; no **17.** $-2\frac{4}{5}$ **18.** $-6\frac{5}{8}$ **19.** $-3\frac{5}{12}$ **20.** 21 mm

Extra Skill Practice (p. 480)
1. rational **3.** irrational **5.** rational **7.** irrational
9. irrational **11.** $2\sqrt{35}$ **13.** $5\sqrt{10}$ **15.** $7\sqrt{2}$ **17.** $\frac{\sqrt{10}}{9}$
19. $\frac{4\sqrt{2}}{9}$ **21.** $\frac{2\sqrt{5}}{5}$ **23.** $20\sqrt{2}$ **25.** $xy^4\sqrt{x}$ **27.** 5 **29.** 6
31. $rst^3\sqrt[3]{s^2}$

Standardized Testing (p. 480)
1. B **2.** D

Section 3, Practice and Application (p. 490)

1. $p > 25$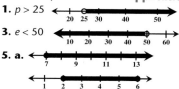

3. $e < 50$

5. a.

b. $-3 \le s \le 1$ **c.** $r \le 10$ **7.** Yes, when substituted for the variable, the left side equals –2 which is less than 2.

9. $w \ge 2$

11. $x \le 5$

13. $z < 13$

15. $q \ge 10.5$

17. $7 + n < 7$; $n < 0$ **19.** $1.75s \ge 95$; $s \ge 54.3$; at least 54.3 mi/hr **21. a.** up to 40 in. **b.** 4 in. **c.** 86.4 in. **d.** The rows would have to be so far apart that they would lose too much seating if they used a sloped floor. **e.** Sample Response: More rows are possible with a stepped floor because of a higher rise and shorter row depth. **f.** Sample Response: A sloped floor may be safer, since people may be less likely to trip in low light. **23.** $24 - 0.5n \ge 132$; $n \le -216$ **25.** $12.50h + 25 < 90$; $h < 5.2$; less than 5.2 hr

27. $b \le -3$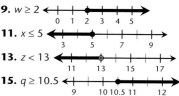

29. $x \ge 3$

31. $y > \frac{2}{3}$

33. $x < 6$

35. a. Answers will vary. Sample Response: $x - 3 \ge 1$, $12x \ge 48$, $-2x \le -8$ **b.** Answers will vary. Sample Response: $x + 5 < 4$, $7x < -7$, $\frac{x}{2} < -\frac{1}{2}$

Spiral Review (p. 493)
39. 105° **40.** 105° **41.** 105° **42.** 60 **43.** 13.5
44. 2.25

Extra Skill Practice (p. 494)
1. $20 \le w < 25$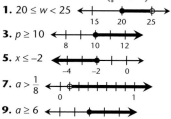

3. $p \ge 10$

5. $x \le -2$

7. $a > \frac{1}{8}$

9. $a \ge 6$

11. $u > -40$

13. $n > -27$

15. $x < -3$

17. $5 + n > 2$; $n > -3$ **19.** $2.88 + 4g \ge 10$; $g \ge 1.78$; at least $1.78 **21.** $w \le -5$ **23.** $x > -0.25$ **25.** $x > 0.6$
27. $n > 2$ **29.** $x < \frac{21}{4}$ **31.** $m \le 17\frac{1}{2}$

Standardized Testing (p. 494)
1. less than 90 in. **2.** 17 or fewer prints

Section 4, Practice and Application (p. 508)
1. $x^2 + 3x + 2$ **3.** $2x^2 + 5x + 2$ **5.** $x^2 - 4x + 3$ trinomial
7. $x^2 + x - 6$ **9.** $x^2 - x - 2$ **11.** $x^2 - 1$ **13.** $x^2 + 5x + 6$
15. $-x^2 - 6x - 9$ **17.** $2x^2 - 8x + 8$ **19.** $x^2 + 13x + 40$
21. $2x^2 + 27x + 36$ **23.** $21x^2 - 37x + 12$ **25. a.** 8 in.;
8 in. **b.** $(3x + 8)$ in. **c.** $(2x + 8)$ in. **d.** $6x^2 + 40x + 64$ in.^{2}
27. $(x + 2)(2x - 2) = 2x^2 + 2x - 4$ **29.** $(3x + 1)(x + 2) = 3x^2 + 7x + 2$ **31.** $(x + 2)(x + 3)$ **33.** $(x + 3)(x + 1)$
35. $(x + 7)(x + 1)$ **37.** Not possible; The only factors of 5 are 1 and 5 and this does not produce the correct product rectangle. **39.** $(x - 6)(x + 1)$ **41.** $(x - 1)(x - 1)$
43. $(x - 7)(x - 1)$ **45.** $(x + 2)(x - 2)$

Spiral Review (p. 510)
48. B and D are polygons. B appears to be regular because all 4 sides appear to be the same length and all 4 angles appear to have the same measure (90°).

49. $n \ge 8$

50. $y > -5$

51. $x \le -2$

Extra Skill Practice (p. 511)
1. a. $x^2 - 2x + 1$; trinomial **b.** $2x^2 - 3x + 2$; trinomial
c. $x^2 + x$; binomial **d.** $3x$; monomial **3.** $2x^2 - x - 3$
5. $-2x^2 + 19x - 35$ **7.** $6x^2 + 25x + 25$ **9.** $-54x^2 - 9x + 3$
11. $(x + 3)(x + 1)$ **13.** $(x + 2)(x - 2)$ **15.** $(x - 2)(x - 1)$

Standardized Testing (p. 511)
1. Answers will vary. Sample Response: $x^2 + 6x + 9$; $2x^2 + 5x - 3$ **2.** Answers will vary. Sample Response: $x^2 - 4 = (x - 2)(x + 2)$; $x^2 - 1 = (x + 1)(x - 1)$

Review and Assessment (p. 514)
1. 10^{11} **2.** a^9 **3.** 2^7 **4.** b^4 **5.** 1 **6.** $\frac{1}{121}$ **7.** $\frac{1}{27}$ **8.** $\frac{1}{64}$
9. 0.05 **10.** 0.000803 **11.** 0.0000001266
12. ash: $a < 2 \cdot 10^{-3}$; lapilli: $2 \cdot 10^{-3} \le a \le 6.4 \cdot 10^{-2}$; bombs: $a \ge 6.4 \cdot 10^{-2}$ **13.** irrational **14.** rational
15. rational **16.** rational **17.** Sample Response:
$\sqrt{108} = \sqrt{36 \cdot 3} = \sqrt{36} \cdot \sqrt{3} = 6\sqrt{3}$ **18.** $4\sqrt{6}$ **19.** $\frac{\sqrt{13}}{8}$
20. $10\sqrt{5}$ **21.** $\frac{\sqrt{17}}{10}$ **22.** $\frac{2\sqrt{2}}{7}$ **23.** $\frac{5\sqrt{6}}{6}$ **24.** 4 **25.** $x^2 y^2 \sqrt{y}$

26.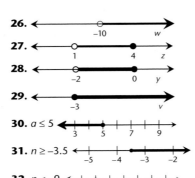

27. (number line: open circle at 1, closed circle at 4, z)

28. (number line: open circle at -2, closed circle at 0, y)

29. (number line: closed circle at -3, v)

30. $a \le 5$ (number line: 3, 5, 7, 9)

31. $n \ge -3.5$ (number line: -5, -4, -3, -2)

32. $n < -9$ (number line: -9, -7, -5)

33. Sample Response: $6950 \ge 20s$; $s \le 347.5$;
At most, the garden can contain 347 sections.
34. $2x^2 + 11x + 12$ **35.** $6x^2 - 33x + 15$ **36.** $100x^2 - 4$
37. $(x - 2)(x - 4)$ **38.** $(x - 2)(2x + 3)$ **39.** $(x + 1)(x + 4)$
40. $(x - 1)(x - 4)$ **41.** $(x + 1)(x - 4)$

MODULE 8

Section 1, Practice and Application (p. 526)

1. geometric (multiply by $\frac{1}{2}$) **3.** geometric (multiply by 0.5) **5.** arithmetic (add 0.4) **7.** 15, 20, 26 **9.** $160x^5$, $320x^6$, $640x^7$ **11.** Sequence 1: $t = 2n + 1$, or $n + (n + 1)$, or $2(n + 1) - 1$; Sequence 2: $t = 2 \cdot 3^{n-1}$
13. a. 5 whole black keys **b.** 8 white keys **c.** 13 keys
d. They are terms 5–7 of the Fibonacci sequence.
15. a. 51 **b.** Yes; Sample Response: Multiplying by 2 will give you an even number and subtracting 3 will make that number odd. **17.** Add 3, then 3^2, then 3^3, 3^4... to each successive term; 364, 1093, 3280 **19.** The terms are consecutive powers of 3, starting with 3^0; $3^5 = 243$, $3^6 = 729$, $3^7 = 2187$

Spiral Review (p. 528)

21.

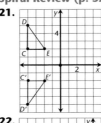

22.

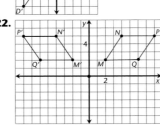

23. 48° (based on $m\angle CAD = 42°$) **24.** 123° (based on $m\angle CEB = 57°$) **25.** $\angle BEC$ **26.** $\angle ABE$

Extension (p. 529)

27. a.

Steps	Number of segments	Length of each segment	Total perimeter at this stage
(triangle)	3	1 unit	3 units
(star)	12	$\frac{1}{3}$ unit	$\frac{12}{3} = 4$ units
(snowflake)	48	$\frac{1}{9}$ unit	$\frac{48}{9}$ units
(snowflake)	192	$\frac{1}{27}$ unit	$\frac{192}{27}$ units
⋮	⋮	⋮	⋮
n	$3 \cdot 4^{n-1}$	$\frac{1}{3^{n-1}}$	$\frac{3 \cdot 4^{n-1}}{3^{n-1}}$

b. The number of line segments in each stage is multiplied by 4 to obtain the number of line segments in the next stage. The length of each segment in one stage is multiplied by $\frac{1}{3}$ to get the length of each segment in the next stage. To get the total perimeter at each stage, you multiply the entry in the "Number of segments" column by the entry in the "Length of each segment" column.
c. See table in part (a).

Career Connection (p. 529)

29. The outside edge is green dots. Inside the green dot edge, the following patterns occur from left to right; blue, red, blue, red, blue, red, blue, red, blue—rows 1, 3, 7 and 9; red, red, red, red, green, red, red, red, red—rows 2, 4, 6, and 8; blue, green, blue, green, blue, green, blue, green, blue—row 5; The pattern would repeat itself every 10 rows.

Extra Skill Practice (p. 530)

1. Add 1 to the previous term; $4 + x$, $5 + x$, $6 + x$
3. Multiply the previous term by -5; 2500, $-12{,}500$, 62,500 **5.** Multiply the previous term by $\frac{2}{3}$; $\frac{16}{162}$, $\frac{32}{486}$, $\frac{64}{1458}$ **7.** 1: arithmetic; 2: geometric; 3: geometric; 4: neither; 5: geometric; 6: arithmetic **9. a.** 100 **b.** n^2

Study Skills (p. 530)

1. Sample Response: Choices A and C are not correct because they are not in scientific notation. Choice B is not correct because 16.6 is not between 1 and 10. Choice D is correct because it is in scientific notation.
2. Sample Response: Draw a rectangle. Inside the rectangle, draw two intersecting ovals. Put letters with no vertical or horizontal symmetry in the rectangle outside the ovals. Put letters with only horizontal symmetry in one oval and letters with only vertical symmetry in the other oval. Put letters with both horizontal and vertical symmetry in the intersection of the ovals.

Section 2, Practice and Application (p. 538)

1. 1080° **3.** 360° **5.** 65° **7.** 85° **9.** 128.57°
13. b. Yes; a square and an equilateral triangle; They have interior angles whose measure is a factor of 360°.
c. Sample Response: octagons and squares, triangles and squares. **15. a.** 180° **b.** All but the stacked igeta which does not have rotational symmetry. **17. a.** A: 72°; Divide 360° by 5; B: 180°; Divide 360° by 2; E: 20°; Divide 360° by 18; F: 60°; Divide 360° by 6 **b.** A, B, D, E, and F

c.

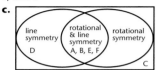

Spiral Review (p. 540)

19. $x^2 - 5x - 50$ **20.** $2x^2 - 18x + 28$ **21.** $36x^2 - 1$
22. 50,000

Extra Skill Practice (p. 541)

1. 17,640° **3.** 2880° **5.** 135° **7.** minimum: 90°; 180°, 270° **9.** no rotational symmetry **11.** minimum: 120°; 240° **13.** minimum: 60°; 120°, 180°, 240°, 300°

Standardized Testing (p. 541)

1. a. 4 sides **b.** 12 sides **c.** 35 sides **2.** 8 sides

Section 3, Practice and Application (p. 550)

1. True; This was shown in the Example on page 546.
3. True; A rhombus is a parallelogram and a parallelogram has opposite angles that are congruent.
5. False; A trapezoid may not have a pair of congruent angles. Also, a kite has only one pair of congruent angles.
7. Sample Response

9. Sample Response

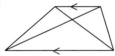

11.

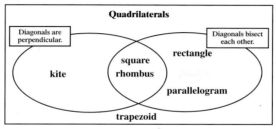

15. a. $XY = WY = \sqrt{26}$ **b.** Let $\overline{WY}$ and $\overline{XZ}$ intersect at point M. The coordinates of M are (2.5, 2.5). $WM = MY = \dfrac{\sqrt{26}}{2}$ and $WM = MY = \dfrac{\sqrt{26}}{2}$, so $\overline{WY}$ and $\overline{XZ}$ bisect each other. **c.** slope of $\overline{WY} = -\dfrac{1}{5}$; slope of $\overline{XZ} = 5$; The product of the slopes is –1, so the diagonals are perpendicular.

Spiral Review (p. 552)

17. No **18.** Yes; $y = 15x^2 - 7x + 6$ **19.** 12 mm
20. 8 cm **21.** 13 m **22.** 6 ft **23.** $\dfrac{1}{x}$ **24.** $\dfrac{1}{c^5}$ **25.** 1 **26.** $\dfrac{3}{y^4}$

Extra Skill Practice (p. 553)

1. Opposite angles are congruent; consecutive angles are supplementary. **3.** Diagonals bisect each other.
5. True; a rhombus is a parallelogram. **7.** False; the diagonals of a kite are perpendicular, but the diagonals of a rectangle are not perpendicular (unless the rectangle is a square). The diagonals of a rhombus are not congruent and do not bisect each other, while the diagonals of a rectangle are congruent and bisect each other.
9. False; the opposite angles of all parallelograms are congruent. **11. a.** 10; (1, 9) **b.** 13; (5.5, 2)
c. 17; $\left(4, -\dfrac{1}{2}\right)$

Standardized Testing (p. 553)

1. a. rectangle, square, parallelogram, rhombus
b. trapezoid, kite **c.** rectangle, square, rhombus
d. trapezoid, parallelogram, rectangle, square, rhombus **2.** Opposite angles are congruent, and consecutive angles are supplementary; Diagonals are congruent and are perpendicular bisectors of each other.

Section 4, Practice and Application (p. 558)

1. 0.40 or 40% **3.** $\dfrac{24}{49} \approx 0.49$ or 49% **5.** $\dfrac{1}{\pi} \approx 0.32$ or 32% **7. a.** 0.45 or 45% **b.** 0.55 or 55% **9. a.** 0.10 or 10% **b.** 0.90 or 90%

Spiral Review (p. 560)

11. acute **12.** obtuse **13.** right

14.

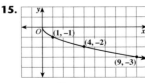

linear

15.

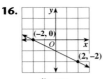

nonlinear

16.

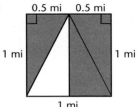

linear

17. about 1884 mm^3 **18.** about 186.04 in.^{3} **19.** about 930.19 cm^3

Extra Skill Practice (p. 561)
1. 0.50 or 50% **3.** 0.25 or 25% **5.** 0.75 or 75%
7. Answers will vary.

Standardized Testing (p. 561)
1. D **2.** C

Section 5, Practice and Application (p. 569)
1. 1 **3.** about 0.53 **5.** 173.21 yd **7.** 37.68 cm
11. 0.77 **13.** 0.26 **15.** The length of the hypotenuse
is unknown. **17.** 16.00 ft **21. a.** $\tan A = \frac{h}{b}$
b. about 24 ft

Spiral Review (p. 572)
23. a. 3^{13} **b.** a^7 **24.** Multiply the previous term by 2;
88, 176, 352 **25.** Add $x + 1$ to the previous term;
$4x + 5$, $5x + 6$, $6x + 7$

26.

1st Flip	2nd Flip	3rd Flip	Outcome
		H	HHH
	H	T	HHT
H		H	HTH
	T	T	HTT
		H	THH
	H	T	THT
T		H	TTH
	T	T	TTT

Extra Skill Practice (p. 573)
1. $\frac{74}{41} \approx 1.80$ **3.** $\frac{12}{5} = 2.75$ **5.** 0.48; 0.93; 0.38
7. 64.20 m **9.** 43.0 ft

Standardized Testing (p. 573)
1. B **2.** B

Review and Assessment (p. 576)
1. Multiply the previous term by $\frac{1}{y}$ (or divide by y);
$\frac{1}{y^5}, \frac{1}{y^6}, \frac{1}{y^7}$ **2.** Add nine to the previous term; 37, 46, 55
3. Divide the previous term by 2 (or multiply by 0.5);
0.0625, 0.03125, 0.015625 **4.** Add 1 more than was
added to the previous term; 38, 48, 59 **5.** geometric,
multiply by –2 **6.** neither **7.** arithmetic, add 2
8. neither **9.** Possible answers: Use a protractor to
measure all the angles and find their sum; Choose one
vertex and draw segments to each of the other vertices
to divide the polygon into 3 triangles. The sum of the
measures of the angles in each triangle is 180°, so
multiply 180° by 3. **10. a.** 60° **b.** 120°, 180°, 240°,
300° **11.** parallelogram, rectangle, square,
rhombus. **12.** parallelogram; both pairs of opposite
angles are congruent, consecutive angles are
supplementary, diagonals bisect each other **13.** square;
all angles are congruent, consecutive angles are supplementary, diagonals are congruent, diagonals bisect each
other, diagonals are perpendicular **14.** trapezoid; consecutive angles between parallel lines are supplementary,
diagonals do not bisect, diagonals are not perpendicular,
diagonals are not congruent, opposite angles are not
congruent, one pair of congruent angles
15. 6 units; (0, 7) **16.** 10 units; (5, 4) **17.** 5 units;
(–1, 3.5) **18. a.** $AB = \sqrt{2^2 + 4^2} = \sqrt{16 + 4} = \sqrt{20}$
and $BC = \sqrt{6^2 + 3^2} = \sqrt{36 + 9} = \sqrt{45}$, so $AC =$
$\sqrt{20 + 45} = \sqrt{65}$. Because $ABCD$ is a rectangle
and therefore a parallelogram, $CD = AB = \sqrt{20}$ and
$AD = BC = \sqrt{65}$. Then $BD = \sqrt{20 + 45} = \sqrt{65}$.
b. The midpoint of $\overline{AC}$ is $\left(\frac{-1 + 7}{2}, \frac{0 + 1}{2}\right) = \left(3, \frac{1}{2}\right)$. The midpoint of $\overline{BD}$ is $\left(\frac{1 + 5}{2}, 4 + \left(\frac{-3}{2}\right)\right) = \left(3, \frac{1}{2}\right)$. So, the diagonals
bisect each other. **19.** 0.50 or 50%
20. Sample Response:

0.5 mi   0.5 mi

1 mi   1 mi

1 mi

21. 8.09 yd **22.** 20.26 in. **23.** 5.45 mm

TOOLBOX ANSWERS

NUMBERS AND OPERATIONS

Decimal Place Value (p. 579)
1. < **2.** < **3.** = **4.** > **5.** = **6.** > **7.** > **8.** > **9.** <
10. = **11.** < **12.** > **13.** 0.3 **14.** 0.8 **15.** 3.8
16. 1.7 **17.** 0.63 **18.** 7.85 **19.** 0.05 **20.** 5.93
21. 1.038 **22.** 0.993 **23.** 8.310 **24.** 0.024

Multiplying Whole Numbers and Decimals (p. 580)
1. 1302 **2.** 1200 **3.** 28,667 **4.** 214,832 **5.** 72,928
6. 18,244,440 **7.** 5.4 **8.** 12.54 **9.** 45.35 **10.** 7.837
11. 21.122 **12.** 435.16 **13.** 0.0018 **14.** 5.05404
15. 0.00192 **16.** 7.6896

Multiplying and Dividing by 10, 100, and 1000 (p. 581)
1. 518.3 **2.** 980 **3.** 3.0042 **4.** 67 **5.** 0.294
6. 0.56 **7.** Multiply **8.** 0.68 **9.** 13,000
10. 2700 **11.** 3.56 **12.** 4800 **13.** 4.54

Dividing Whole Numbers and Decimals (p. 582)
1. 24.8 **2.** 17.7 **3.** 15.3 **4.** 7.56 **5.** 53.19 **6.** 49.73
7. 14 **8.** 45 **9.** 8.5 **10.** 262.2 **11.** 962.5 **12.** 968

Divisibility Rules (p. 583)
1. No **2.** Yes **3.** Yes **4.** Yes **5.** No **6.** Yes **7.** Yes **8.** Yes

Finding Factors and Multiples (p. 584)
1. 6; 420 **2.** 12; 72 **3.** 11; 330 **4.** 40; 240 **5.** 30; 90
6. 5; 10,500 **7.** 15; 3465 **8.** 6; 2622 **9.** 55; 2475
10. 2; 2450 **11.** 1; 6237 **12.** 23; 138

Finding Equivalent Fractions and Ratios (p. 585)
1. 6 **2.** 56 **3.** 6 **4.** 3 **5.** $\frac{3}{5}$ **6.** $\frac{1}{3}$ **7.** $\frac{9}{10}$ **8.** $\frac{2}{3}$ **9.** =
10. < **11.** >

Adding and Subtracting Fractions (p. 586)
1. $\frac{7}{12}$ **2.** $1\frac{1}{8}$ **3.** $\frac{5}{16}$ **4.** $\frac{20}{21}$ **5.** $\frac{5}{72}$ **6.** $\frac{7}{44}$ **7.** $\frac{7}{20}$ **8.** $\frac{2}{3}$ **9.** $\frac{3}{4}$
10. $\frac{1}{2}$ **11.** $\frac{9}{77}$ **12.** $\frac{23}{42}$ **13.** $\frac{5}{12}$ **14.** $3\frac{3}{10}$ **15.** $\frac{3}{4}$

Multiplying and Dividing Fractions (p. 587)
1. $\frac{4}{5}$ **2.** $\frac{1}{49}$ **3.** $\frac{3}{10}$ **4.** $\frac{2}{9}$ **5.** 6 **6.** $\frac{4}{5}$ **7.** 3 **8.** 15 **9.** $\frac{1}{2}$
10. $\frac{3}{4}$ **11.** $\frac{8}{3}$ or $2\frac{2}{3}$ **12.** $\frac{5}{4}$ or $1\frac{1}{4}$ **13.** $\frac{15}{2}$ or $7\frac{1}{2}$ **14.** $\frac{1}{10}$
15. 6 **16.** $\frac{16}{9}$ or $1\frac{7}{9}$

Writing Fractions, Decimals, and Percents (p. 588)
1. 0.95; 95% **2.** 0.16; 16% **3.** 0.001; 0.1%
4. 0.62; 62% **5.** 0.8; $\frac{4}{5}$ **6.** 0.875; $\frac{7}{8}$ **7.** 0.64; $\frac{16}{25}$
8. 1.2; $\frac{6}{5}$ or $1\frac{1}{5}$ **9.** 48%; $\frac{12}{25}$ **10.** 85%; $\frac{17}{20}$
11. 12.5%; $\frac{1}{8}$ **12.** 350%; $\frac{7}{2}$ or $3\frac{1}{2}$

Using Order of Operations (p. 589)
1. 15 **2.** 18 **3.** 56 **4.** 13 **5.** 5 **6.** 9 **7.** 1 **8.** 4 **9.** 29
10. 41 **11.** 2 **12.** 3

Comparing Integers (p. 590)
1. > **2.** < **3.** < **4.** < **5.** > **6.** > **7.** > **8.** < **9.** <
10. −5, −4, 1 **11.** −3, 0, 2 **12.** −4, −2, −1 **13.** −5, 3, 4
14. −6, −3, 0 **15.** −2, 2, 6 **16.** −2, −1, 0, 1
17. −7, −4, −2, 0 **18.** −6, −3, 2, 5

GEOMETRY AND MEASUREMENT

Locating Points in a Coordinate Plane (p. 591)
1. (−5, 2) **2.** (−3, −2) **3.** (−3, 1) **4.** (1, 4) **5.** (3, 0)
6. (0, −2) **7.** (2, −4) **8.** (−2, 4) **9.** (−1, 1)
10–18.

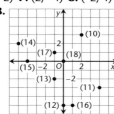

Measuring Angles (p. 592)
1. 90°; right **2.** 30°; acute **3.** 100°; obtuse
4. 155°; obtuse **5.** 40°; acute **6.** 110°; obtuse

Classifying Triangles (p. 593)
1. obtuse **2.** right **3.** obtuse **4.** acute **5.** isosceles
6. equilateral and isosceles **7.** scalene **8.** isosceles

Identifying Polygons (p. 594)
1. Regular polygon; closed, formed by 6 segments that do not cross each other; angles appear to be of equal measure, sides appear to be of equal length. **2.** Not a polygon; crosses itself. **3.** Not a polygon; not formed by segments **4.** Polygon; closed, formed by 6 segments that do not cross each other. **5.** Not a polygon; not closed

Selected Answers SA27

6. Polygon; closed, formed by 4 segments that do not cross each other. **7.** Regular polygon; closed, formed by 8 segments that do not cross each other; angles appear to be of equal measure, sides appear to be of equal length. **8.** Not a polygon; not formed by segments

Using Formulas from Geometry (p. 595)
1. $P = 16$ ft; $A = 12$ ft^2 **2.** $P = 58$ m; $A = 180$ m^2
3. $P = 80$ yd; $A = 360$ yd^2 **4.** 480 cm^3 **5.** 5625 m^3
6. 432 in.^{3}

DATA ANALYSIS

Finding the Mean, Median, Mode, and Range (p. 596)
1. mean: 33; median: 32; mode: 29; range: 9 **2.** mean: $16\frac{2}{3}$; median: 16.5; mode: none; range: 6 **3.** mean: 3.8; median: 3.6; mode: none; range: 2.9 **4.** mean: 34; median: 34; mode: 34; range: 0 **5.** mean: 2.25; median: 2; modes: 1 and 2; range: 5
6. mean: 105; median: 95; mode: 95; range: 60

ADDITIONAL ANSWERS

Managing Extended Explorations (Teacher's Edition, pp. T44–T45)

1. *How might you introduce the* A Special Number E^2?

Students are used to recognizing the meaning of a digit in terms of its place value. They may have trouble identifying the digit with another property as well, so you may want to begin by asking students whether there is a 2-digit number in which the first digit tells you how many 0s there are in the number, and the second digit tells you how many 1s there are in the number. The first digit cannot be 0 because the number would then be a 1-digit number. The first digit cannot be 1 because the other digit would have to be 0, meaning that there are no 1s in the number. There is, then, no such 2-digit number.

2. *What approaches do you think might work best?*

The best approach to the problem might be to look for a pattern. For example, how does any one digit in the number affect the others? One way to begin is to consider the special 4-digit number, 1210, described in the E^2. Encourage students to determine whether there is another 4-digit number that fits the same description. (They should find that 2020 works, as well.) Although the 10-digit situation is much more complicated, the same approach will be helpful.

6. *Read, assess, and grade the students' sample work.*

Matt's solution

Matt's solution would score at Level 4 on the *Problem Solving Scale*. He understood the problem well enough to make a plan and find a solution. He verified that the number he found was a solution, but not the only solution.

This E^2 does not provide an opportunity for students to use much mathematical vocabulary, so their solutions should not be scored on the *Mathematical Language Scale*.

Matt's solution would score at Level 3 on the *Representations Scale*. He used patterns of addition expressions to represent possible solutions, but left room for confusion between the number of digits and the position of a digit in the number. For instance, there could be confusion about whether the sum that lead to his solution represents the number 6,211,000,000 or the number 6,210,001,000. His solution would have been clearer had he put the information in a clearly-labeled table.

Matt's solution would score at Level 2 on the *Connections Scale*. He essentially found a solution to the problem, and then stopped. He made no effort to determine whether there are other solutions to the problem. However, he did recognize that the sum of the digits of a 10-digit number must equal 10, which was instrumental to his solution method.

Matt's explanation of his work (as far as it went) was clear but fell short of the mark at the end. He realized that continuing on the path he started would be troublesome, so he quit. It is clear that Matt was aware that while his problem solving method might succeed in finding another

solution or determining that no other solution exists, his method was too cumbersome to be reasonable. Matt's solution would score at Level 2 on the *Presentation Scale*.

Matt's solution would be considered a **Developing Response**. He is higher on the *Problem Solving Scale* than shown on the Developing Response Profile, but is on target with the *Representations Scale* and lower on the *Connections* and *Presentation Scales*. He needs to work on being able to generalize and extend his results and to be sure that his reasoning is clear.

Linda's solution

Linda's solution would score at Level 5 on the *Problem Solving Scale*. She made a plan and used it to verify her solution. She established that the 10-digit number she found was the only one possible.

Linda's solution should not be scored on the *Mathematical Language Scale*.

Linda's solution would score at Level 5 on the *Representations Scale*. The patterns she created were appropriate and correct representations, and she used them to solve the problem and to explain her solution. Each pattern clearly represented a 10-digit number, with blanks representing digits yet to be determined. In the first part of Linda's solution, the blanks helped to emphasize that if you begin with the assumption that there are nine 0s, you would end up not having enough digits left to include nine 0s.

Linda recognized, as Matt did, that the sum of the digits in the 10-digit number must equal 10. This was fundamental to her solution. She used the sum of the digits and the effect of the first digit (the number of 0s in the 10-digit number) to identify the correct solution. She also extended her results to explain why there is only one solution. Linda's solution would score at Level 4 on the *Connections Scale*.

Linda's method was mathematically correct and successful, but her lack of consistency in wording might be confusing to some. For example, Linda used different expressions to refer to the same digit: *one 6* and *1 six*. Her answer was difficult to read because of her writing style. Linda's solution would score at Level 3 on the *Presentation Scale*.

Linda's solution would be considered an **Excellent Response**. She is on target on the *Problem Solving, Representations* and *Connections Scales* on the Excellent Response Profile. She is lower on the *Presentation Scale*. She needs to work on her language and writing skills.

Practicing Test-Taking Skills (p. xxxvii), (Teacher's Edition, p. T73)

1. Gym A: $y = 45x + 75$, gym B: $y = 60x$;

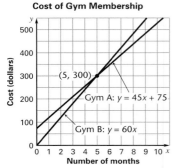

Cost of Gym Membership

(5, 300); the point of intersection represents when the costs of the gyms are the same; I would choose gym B if I were going to join for 4 months or less. I would choose gym A if I were going to join for 6 months or more. If I were joining for 5 months, it wouldn't matter which gym I chose since the costs are equal. **2.** Answers may vary. *Sample Response:* a rotation 90° counterclockwise about the origin, a reflection in the y-axis, and a translation 2 units down; The original coordinates of triangle ABC are $A(-4, 3)$, $B(-4, 0)$, and $C(0, 0)$. After the rotation, the new coordinates are $A(-3, -4)$, $B(0, -4)$, and $C(0, 0)$. After the reflection, the new coordinates are $A(3, -4)$, $B(0, -4)$, and $C(0, 0)$. After the translation, the new coordinates are $A'(3, -6)$, $B'(0, -6)$, and $C'(0, -2)$. **3.** the savings bond; between 23 and 24 years; The equation $y = 50 \cdot 1.03^x$ models the amount of money y in the savings account after x years. After 20 years, the balance will be $50 \cdot 1.03^{20} \approx \$90.31$. Try 23 years: $y = 50 \cdot 1.03^{23} \approx \$98.68$. For 24 years: $y = 50 \cdot 1.03^{24} \approx \$101.64$. So, the balance will equal $100 between 23 years and 24 years from now.

4.

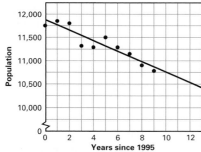

Town Population

negative correlation; about 10,500; *Sample Response:* I drew a fitted line and then looked to see where the line had an x-value of 12. The corresponding y-value at that point is about 10,500.

5.

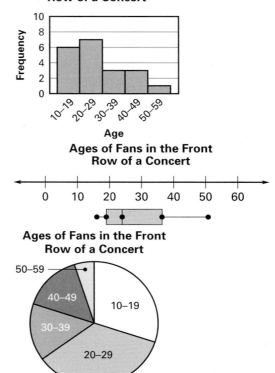

Ages of Fans in the Front Row of a Concert

Ages of Fans in the Front Row of a Concert

Ages of Fans in the Front Row of a Concert

the box-and-whisker plot, because the median can be read from the graph; the stem-and-leaf plot, because you can see all of the data and it is ordered; the circle graph or the histogram, because both of these graphs contain numerical intervals.

MODULE I

Section 1, Exploration 2 (pp. 5–8)

12. a.

Adults Who Used the Internet at Home in 2003				
Age group	Number	Percent of all adults who used the Internet at home	Angle measure of sector	Percent of total measure (360°)
18 to 24	16,438,000	13%	47°	13%
25 to 34	23,951,000	19%	68°	19%
35 to 44	29,391,000	23%	83°	23%
45 to 54	27,563,000	22%	79°	22%
55 and over	28,413,000	23%	83°	23%
Total	125,756,000	100%	360°	100%

The percents in steps 1 and 3 are either the same or close to the same.

b. Sample Response: First find the percent of each frequency. Then multiply each percent by 360 to find the number of degrees for each sector of the circle graph. Using a protractor, divide a circle into sectors that have the calculated number of degrees.

18. a. Frequency of Internet Use per Month

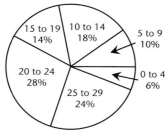

Each sector gives the percentage of students who fall within particular intervals of Internet usage.

19.

Internet Access by Students at School	
Times per Day	Frequency
0-4	1
5-9	3
10-14	4
15-19	6
20-24	8
25-29	5
30-34	2
34-39	1

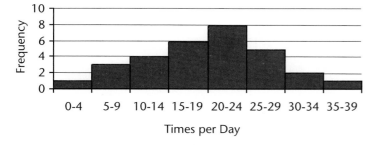

Internet Access by Students at School	
Times per Day	Frequency
0-9	4
10-19	10
20-29	13
30-39	3

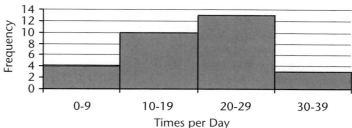

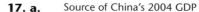

24. a. Weekly High Temperatures

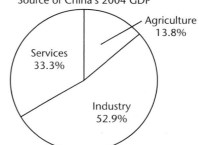

Section 1, Practice and Application (pp. 12–13)

17. a. Source of China's 2004 GDP

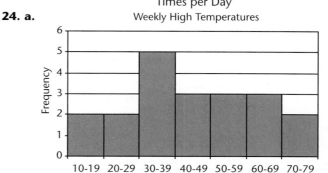

b. Source of India's 2004 GDP

c. Source of Pakistan's 2004 GDP

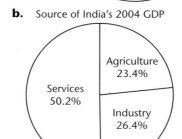

20. a.

Correct Responses	Frequency
48–49	2
50–51	3
52–53	0
54–55	5
56–57	2
58–59	4
60–61	3
62–63	3
64–65	1
66–67	1

b.

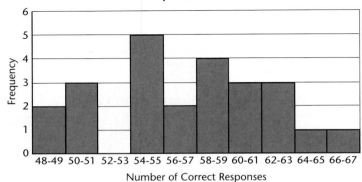

Correct Responses Out of 96 Trials

21.

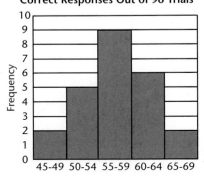

Correct Responses Out of 96 Trials

22. c.

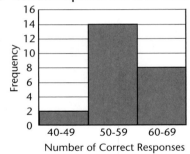

Correct Responses Out of 96 Trials

23. The frequencies of the 50-51 and 52-53 intervals, for example, could be added to find the number of responses that fall within the interval 50-53. However, we can't expand that interval to 50-54 because we can't tell how many responses within the 54-55 interval were 54 and how many were 55.

Section 1, Extra Skill Practice (p. 14)

6.

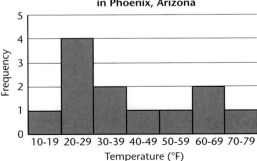

Record Low Temperatures in Phoenix, Arizona

Section 2, Setting the Stage (p. 15)

2. Answers will vary. Sample Response: the median, because the median represents the middle of the data and since there is not much of a range in the data, the middle would be close to the age of most of the artists.

3. Answers will vary. Sample Response: I think there are a lot of top pop musicians today that become famous while they are teenagers, and so I think the mean, median, and mode would be lower now than it was in the 1900s.

Section 2, Exploration 1 (p. 17)

7. Top 20 Artists Ages at First #1 Hit Single

Country Artists		Pop Artists
	1	3 4 8
9 8 8 8 7 7 7 4 4 1	**2**	0 0 1 1 1 1 2 5 5 5 6 6 6 9 9 9
6 4 3 2 1 0 0 0 0	**3**	1
2	**4**	

2 | 4 | represents an age of 42. | 3 | 1 represents an age of 31.

8. a. The pop artists were younger than the country artists were at their first #1 single. Pop artists were generally in their 20s, while half of the country artists were 30 or older. **b.** range among country artists: 21, range among pop artists: 18; There is a slightly wider range of ages for country artists than for pop artists.

Section 2, Exploration 2 (pp. 19–20)

12.

Lower Extreme	7
Lower Quartile	9
Median	10
Upper Quartile	15
Upper Extreme	26

ADDITIONAL ANSWERS

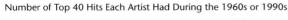

Number of Top 40 Hits Each Artist Had During the 1960s or 1990s

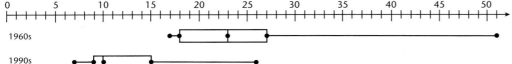

15. a.

	1960s	1990s
Lower Extreme	27	42
Lower Quartile	35	45
Median	39	48.5
Upper Quartile	49	51
Upper Extreme	53	61

Ages of Winners of the Academy Award
for Best Original Song

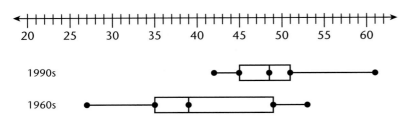

Section 2, Exploration 3 (p. 22)

22. a. No, individual values are needed to find the information in Question 21. **b.** Yes, the stem-and-leaf plot gives individual values that can be used to find all of the information in Question 21. **c.** No, the histogram gives a visual comparison of the data by intervals, but individual values cannot be read from the graph.

Section 2, Practice and Application (pp. 24–28)

1. a. Age when Awarded Grammy for Best Female
Vocal Performance

Country		Pop
	4 | 1	
	4 | 2	3 3 3 3 5
7 5 4 3 3 3 1 | 3	0 0 0 0 2 3
	8 | 4	1
	6 | 5	
	| 6	
	4 | 7	

5 \| 3 \| represents
an age of 35.

\| 2 \| 3 represents
an age of 23.

10. a. Number of Weeks at the #1 Position
on the Chart (Mariah Carey)

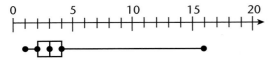

11. a–b. Number of Times a Composer's Work
Was Performed by American Orchestras

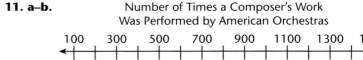

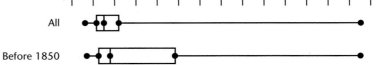

14. a. Lengths of Iris Petals (cm)

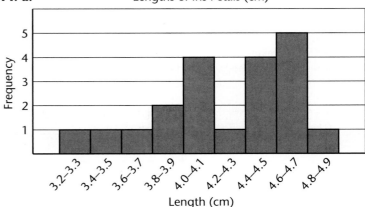

The histogram shows the frequencies within intervals.

b. Iris Petal Widths

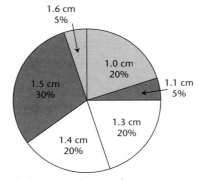

The circle graph shows what percentage a part is of a whole.

c. Lengths and Widths of Iris Petals (cm)

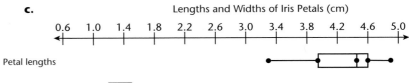

The box-and-whisker plots show the medians of the data.

Section 2, Extra Skill Practice (p. 31)

1. a.

Ages of Academy Award Winners

Actors		Actresses
6	2	1 5 5 6 8 9
9 8 7 7 6 5 2 1	3	1 3 3 3 3 4 5 5 8 9
7 6 5 5 3 3 2 0	4	1 2 5 9 9
7 4 2 2	5	
1 0	6	1
6	7	4
	8	0

$2|5$ represents an age of 52. $4|2$ represents an age of 42.

c. Actor: mean = 44.75, median 43, modes = 37, 43, 45, 52
Actress: mean = 39.125, median = 34.5, mode = 33 Sample Response:
For actors, there are too many modes to be a good representation of
the data. The mean is a good representation of the actors' ages. For the
actresses, the mean is a bit high, probably due to the two ages of 74
and 80; therefore, the mode or the median is a better representation.
There were four actresses at age 33 and four others were within 2 yrs of
that age when they won, so I would choose the mode.

2.

Ages of Academy Award Winners

Best Actor Ages

Best Actress Ages

Section 3, Exploration 1 (p. 34)

6. 1. _The number of hours a college student should plan to_ **spend each**
week studying outside of class (is equal to) 3 (times) _the number of hours_
spent in class.
$s = 3c$

2. _The number of pounds of gravel you should add to a home aquarium_
(is equal to) about 1.5 (times) _the number of gallons of water in the_
aquarium.
$g = 1.5w$

3. _The outdoor temperature_ (is equal to) _the number of times a cricket_
chirps in fifteen seconds (plus) _39._
$t = c + 39$

4. _A dog's "human" age_ (is equal to) _4_ (times) _the dog's age_
(plus) _15._
$a = 4d + 15$

5. _The temperature in degrees Fahrenheit_ (is equal to) _the_ (sum) _of 2_ (times)
the temperature in degrees Celsius (plus) _30._
$f = 2c + 30$

6. _The distance in nautical miles to the beginning of an airplane's_
descent (is equal to) _the plane's altitude in feet_ (divided by) _300._

$d = \dfrac{a}{300}$

Section 4, Practice and Application (pp. 58–60)

4. a–b.

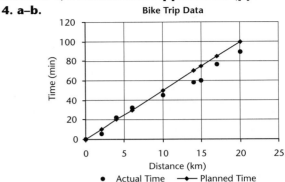

Bike Trip Data

16. a.

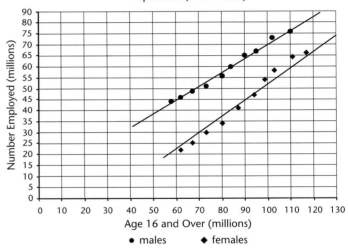

Employment Status of United States Civilian Population (1960–2005)

Section 4, Extra Skill Practice (p. 62)

3. a–b. Sample Response: I chose a horizontal scale of 40 to 90 because
the temperatures range from 51° to 77°. I chose a vertical scale of 0 to
35 because the cups of cocoa sold range from 4 to 31.

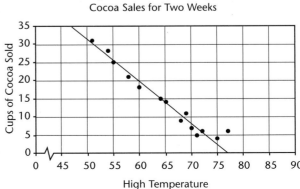

Cocoa Sales for Two Weeks

Section 5, Exploration 1 (p. 65)

4. c. Polygons will vary; a sample is shown. Check students' drawings to see that perimeters are greater than 28 units.

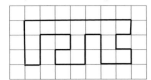

Perimeter = 32   Area = 15

7., 9. a.

Rectangles with Area of 24 Square Units								
Length	6	4	3	8	12	2	1	24
Width	4	6	8	3	2	12	24	1
Perimeter	20	20	22	22	28	28	50	50

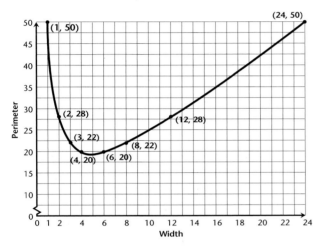

Section 5, Practice and Application (p. 68)

2. a. Possible Answers: One 12-person tent, two 6-person tents, and one 2-person tent; One 12-person tent and seven 2-person tents; One 12-person tent, two 5-person tents, and two 2-person tents; One 12-person tent, one 6-person tent, and four 2-person tents **b.** Possible Answers: Four 6-person tents and one 2-person tent; Three 6-person tents and four 2-person tents; Two 6-person tents and seven 2-person tents; One 6-person tent and four 5-person tents; One 6-person tent, two 5-person tents, and five 2-person tents; One 6-person tent and ten 2-person tents; Thirteen 2-person tents; Two 6-person tents, two 5-person tents and two 2-person tents. **c.** Possible Answers: One 12-person tent, two 5-person tents, and two 2-person tents; One 6-person tent and four 5-person tents; One 6-person tent, two 5-person tents, and five 2-person tents; Two 6-person tents, two 5-person tents, and two 2-person tents.

4. a.

Rectangles with Area of 30 Square Units								
Length	1	2	3	5	6	10	15	30
Width	30	15	10	6	5	3	2	1
Perimeter	62	34	26	22	22	26	34	62

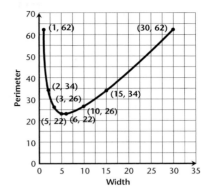

5. a.

Rectangles with Perimeter 28 Units															
Length	0	1	2	3	4	5	6	7	8	9	10	11	12	13	14
Width	14	13	12	11	10	9	8	7	6	5	4	3	2	1	0
Area	0	13	24	33	40	45	48	49	48	45	40	33	24	13	0

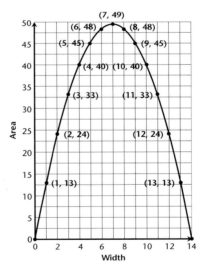

Section 5, Extra Skill Practice (p. 70)

3.

Rectangles with Area of 48 Square Units								
Length	1	2	3	4	6	8	12	16	24	48
Width	48	24	16	12	8	6	4	3	2	1
Perimeter	98	52	38	32	28	28	32	38	52	98

4.

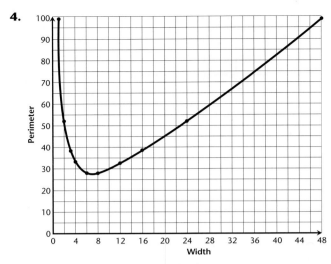

MODULE 2

Section 1, Exploration 3 (p. 83)

23. a.

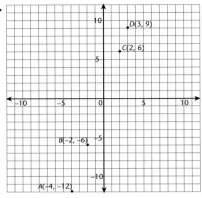

Standardized Testing (p. 70)

1.

Polygon	A	B	C	D	E	F	G	H	I
Area (A)	1	$1\frac{1}{2}$	2	$3\frac{1}{2}$	4	4	6	$6\frac{1}{2}$	8
Number of dots on perimeter (P)	4	5	6	7	8	6	10	9	8
Number of dots inside (I)	0	0	0	1	1	2	2	3	5

Review and Assessment (pp. 74–75)

3. a.

Ages of Airplanes by Company

Company A		Company B
9 6 5 3 2	0	1 2 3 3 5 6 7 7 8 9
9 8 7 7 7 5 5 3 2	1	2 4 6 6 6 9
6 1 0 0	2	0 5

2|1 represents an age of 12 years |1|4 represents an age of 14 years

10. a.

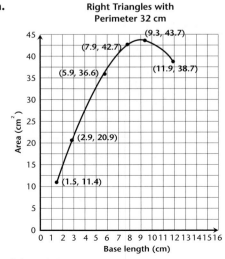

Section 3, Exploration 3 (pp. 112–113)

23. a., d.

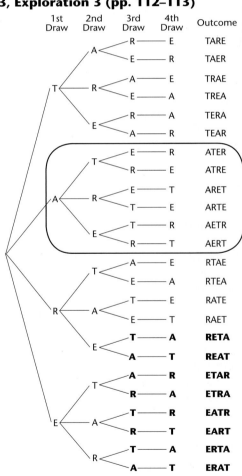

A8   **Additional Answers**

28. a.

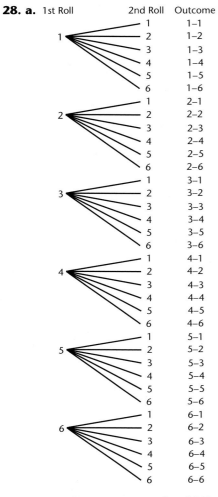

Section 3, Key Concepts (p. 115)

30. a.

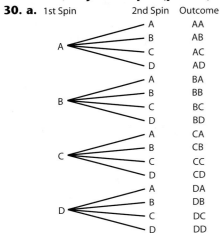

Section 3, Practice and Application (p. 119)

28. a.

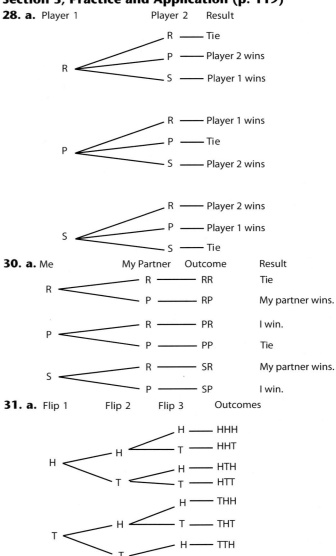

30. a.

31. a.

Section 3, Extra Skill Practice (p. 120)

8. a.

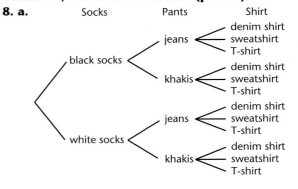

MODULE 3

Section 1, Exploration 2 (pp. 161–162)

11. b. Sample Response: Since the length, width, and height of the larger room are twice the length, width, and height of the smaller room, Jim says the larger room is twice the size of the smaller one. Some students may agree with Jim. Others may disagree because the area of the floor of the larger room (10 ft · 10 ft = 100 ft²) is 4 times the area of the floor of the smaller room (5 ft · 5 ft = 25 ft²). Still others may disagree because the volume of the larger room (10 ft · 10 ft · 10 ft = 1000 ft³) is 8 times the volume of the smaller room (5 ft · 5 ft · 5 ft = 125 ft³). Do not insist on or explain the correct answer at this point.

12.

Cube Measurements			
Length of an edge	1 cm	2 cm	3 cm
Perimeter of a face	4 cm	8 cm	12 cm
Area of a face	1 cm²	4 cm²	9 cm²
Volume of the cube	1 cm³	8 cm³	27 cm³

Section 1, Practice and Application (p. 166)

30. Amounts Raised by Students at a Charity Dance Marathon (dollars)

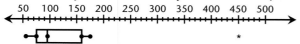

Section 2, Exploration 2 (p. 174)

16. a.

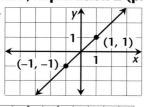

b.

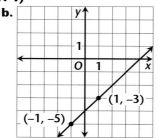

c.

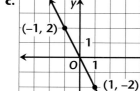

17.

Skid Distance on a Dry, Concrete Road		
Skid distance *d* (ft)	Speed *s* (mi/hr)	(*d*, *s*)
1	5	(1, 5)
7	13	(7, 13)
33	28	(33, 28)
57	37	(57, 37)
95	**48**	**(95, 48)**
129	**56**	**(129, 56)**
154	**61**	**(154, 61)**

18. a.

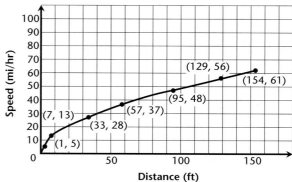

19. a.

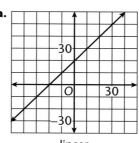

linear

b.

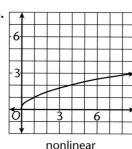

nonlinear

c.

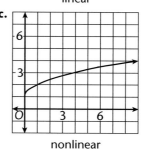

nonlinear

Section 2, Practice and Application (pp. 176–178)

8. The operations were done in order from left to right instead of doing both multiplications and then subtracting the products. **9.** The 5 in the numerator was divided by 5 but the 3 was not. The numerator should have been evaluated before dividing by 5. **10.** $\sqrt{4}$ was added to $\sqrt{9}$ instead of finding $\sqrt{13}$.

24.

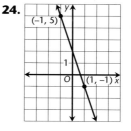

25.

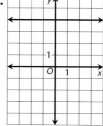

26.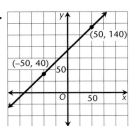

27.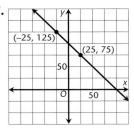

30. linear

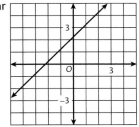

31. nonlinear

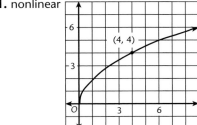

32. nonlinear

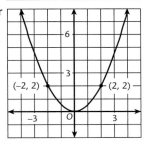

33. b.

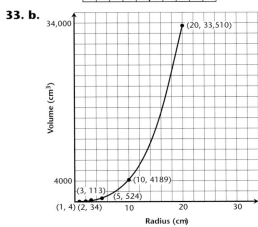

34. a.

Length of skid (ft)	Approximate speed of car (mi/hr)
1	$2\sqrt{5.1} \approx 4.5$
5	10
15	17.3
35	26.5
55	33.2
75	38.7
100	44.7
150	54.8

Section 2, Extra Skill Practice (p. 179)

12.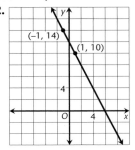

13.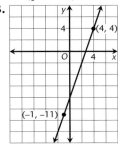

14.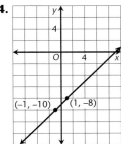

15.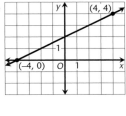

18.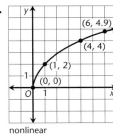

nonlinear

19.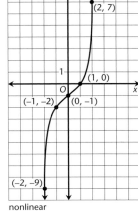

nonlinear

20.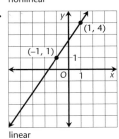

linear

Section 3, Exploration 1 (p. 181)

4. a. Sample Responses:

Blue Line

Time (min)	Distance (m)	Rate (m/min)
10	1000	100
20	2000	100
30	3000	100
40	4000	100

Red Line

Time (min)	Distance (m)	Rate (m/min)
15	1000	66.7
30	2000	66.7
45	3000	66.7
60	4000	66.7

Section 3, Exploration 2 (pp. 184–185)

12.

Name	Foot length (cm)	Height (cm)
Adult 1	29.0	178.0
Adult 2	30.0	177.0
Adult 3	29.5	175.0
Adult 4	29.0	175.0
Adult 5	30.0	178.0
Adult 6	28.0	172.5
Adult 7	26.5	164.5
Adult 8	27.0	165.5
Adult 9	27.0	169.0
Adult 10	26.5	160.0
Student 1	24.5	161.0
Student 2	28.0	178.0
Student 3	27.0	174.0
Student 4	24.0	161.0
Student 5	25.0	169.0
Student 6	24.5	168.0
Student 7	25.0	165.5
Student 8	26.0	166.0

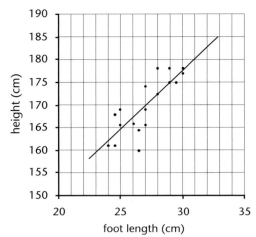

15. a. Sample Responses:

Foot length (cm)	Height (cm) (Fitted line prediction)	Height (cm) (Equation prediction)	Difference
24 cm	162 cm	60 cm	102 cm
26 cm	167 cm	65 cm	102 cm
28 cm	172.5 cm	70 cm	102.5 cm
30 cm	177.5 cm	75 cm	102.5 cm

Section 3, Practice and Application (pp. 187–188)

5. c. Segura: $d = 0.27t$ where d = distance (km) and t = time (min) or $d = 16t$ where d = distance (km) and t = time (hr); Petersen: $d = 0.2t$ where d = distance (km) and t = time (min) or $d = 12t$ where d = distance (km) and t = time (hr)

6. d.

Sarah Kane's Earnings

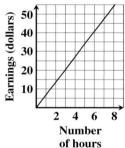

slope: 6.75

12. d. Sample Response:

Height at age 2	Height at age 18 (Fitted line prediction)	Height at age 18 (Equation prediction)	Difference
81	155	137.7	17.3
84	160	142.8	17.2
87	165	147.9	17.1
88	167	149.6	17.4
91	172	154.7	17.3

The average of the differences is about 17.3.

Section 4, Exploration 1 (p. 194)

6. a. Answers for the lengths of the sides of △DEF and the ratios of the corresponding sides will vary. Sample responses are given.

△ABC	△DEF	Ratio of the lengths of the corresponding sides
AB = 4.0 cm	DE = 8.0 cm	$\frac{AB}{DE} = \frac{1}{2}$
BC = 3.1 cm	EF = 6.2 cm	$\frac{BC}{EF} = \frac{1}{2}$
AC = 3.1 cm	DF = 6.2 cm	$\frac{AC}{DF} = \frac{1}{2}$

b.

△ABC	△DEF
m∠A = 50°	m∠D = 50°
m∠B = 50°	m∠E = 50°
m∠C = 80°	m∠F = 80°

c. Sample Response: Added the two known angle measures and subtracted the sum from 180° to find the measure of the third angle.
d. △ABC ~ △DEF because the corresponding angles have the same measure and the ratios of the lengths of the corresponding sides are all equal. **8.** Answers will vary. Sample Response: No. The angles in these rectangles are all right angles, so corresponding angles have the same measures, but the rectangles are not similar.

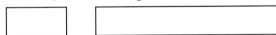

Section 4, Practice and Application (p. 201)

17. Yes; Sample Response: The corresponding angles of the parallelograms have the same measure, and the corresponding sides are in proportion, so the parallelograms are similar.

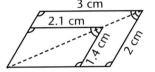

Section 5, Setting the Stage (p. 204)

3.

Decay Pattern of Carbon-14		
Number of years	Number of half-lives	Fraction remaining of the original amount of carbon -14
0	0	all
5,730	1	$\frac{1}{2}$
11,460	2	$\frac{1}{2}$ of $\frac{1}{2} = \frac{1}{4}$
17,190	3	$\frac{1}{2}$ of $\frac{1}{4} = \frac{1}{8}$
22,920	4	$\frac{1}{2}$ of $\frac{1}{8} = \frac{1}{16}$
28,650	5	$\frac{1}{2}$ of $\frac{1}{16} = \frac{1}{32}$

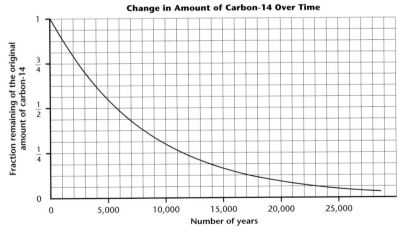

Section 5, Exploration 2 (p. 208)

14. Step 1: Substitute 152 for h in the formula.

Step 2: Subtract 61.41 from both sides of the equation to undo the addition.

Step 3: Simplify and use the commutative property to regroup terms.

Step 4: Simplify.

Step 5: Divide both sides of the equation by 2.38 to undo the multiplication.

Step 6: Simplify.

16. a.
$$100(152) = 100(61.41 + 2.38f)$$
$$15200 = 6141 + 238f$$
$$15200 - 6141 = 6141 + 238f - 6141$$
$$9059 = 238f$$
$$\frac{9059}{238} = \frac{238f}{238}$$
$$38.06 \approx f$$

b.
$$10(9.7) = 10(3 + 2.7x)$$ The first power of 10 since the
$$97 = 30 + 27x$$ least decimal place was tenths.
$$97 - 30 = 30 + 27x - 30$$
$$67 = 27x$$
$$\frac{67}{27} = \frac{27x}{27}$$
$$2.48 \approx x$$

Section 5, Practice and Application (p. 210)

7. Large Cloud of Magellan: $9.7 \cdot 10^{17}$ mi
Small Cloud of Magellan: $1.1 \cdot 10^{18}$ mi
Ursa Minor dwarf: $1.4 \cdot 10^{18}$ mi
Draco dwarf: $1.5 \cdot 10^{18}$ mi
Sculptor dwarf: $1.6 \cdot 10^{18}$ mi
Fornax dwarf: $2.5 \cdot 10^{18}$ mi
Leo II dwarf: $4.4 \cdot 10^{18}$ mi
Leo I dwarf: $4.4 \cdot 10^{18}$ mi
Barnard's Galaxy: $1.0 \cdot 10^{19}$ mi

Section 6, Exploration 1 (pp. 215–217)

3.

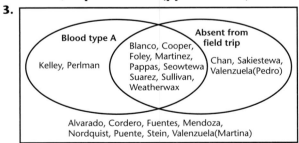

7.

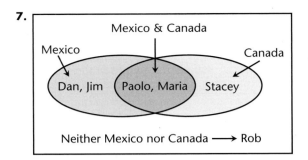

Section 6, Practice and Application (p. 219)

10.

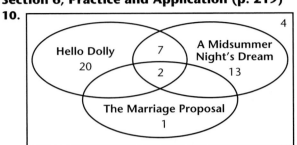

11.

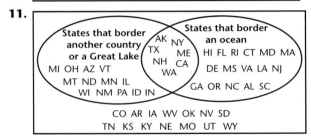

Section 6, Extra Skill Practice (p. 221)

6.

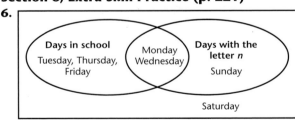

Section 6, Standardized Testing (p. 221)

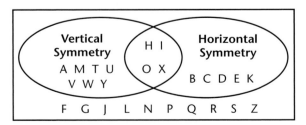

Module Project (pp. 222–225)

1. Dr. Ashilaka is an expert on cliff dwellings and is giving a lecture and tour of Anasazi cliff dwellings. His daughter, Nageela, helps her paralyzed father by being his "eyes and legs."; They hope to discover a previously undiscovered Anasazi site where a local boy found pottery.

3. Uncle LeVerle, science teacher, who seemed quite interested in the topic; Gloria Blanco, art teacher; Teresa Seowtewa, social studies teacher, took notes for her class; Ms. Weatherwax, principal, a serious art collector who doesn't know anything about Anasazi pottery; Perry Martinez, mathematics teacher, has never shown an interest in archeology **14.**

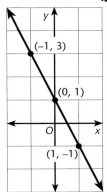

16. Answers will vary depending on which Clues Handout Set is used. In each case, the two suspects each have access to the closet, both have cuts on their heads, and both know the area well; the person who is exonerated does not know the area well and cannot be the thief. Sample Responses: **(1)** Using Clues Handout Set #1 and information from the *Mystery of Blacktail Canyon:* **Either Alice Weatherwax or Perry Martinez is the thief**; Teresa Seowtewa cannot be the thief. **(2)** Using Clues Handout Set #2 and information from the ***Mystery of Blacktail Canyon***: **Either Perry Martinez or Teresa Seowtewa is the thief**; Alice Weatherwax cannot be the thief. **(3)** Using Clues Handout Set #3 and information from the *Mystery of Blacktail Canyon:* **Either Teresa Seowtewa or Alice Weatherwax is the thief**; Perry Martinez cannot be the thief. **17.** Answers will vary depending on which Clues Handout Set and corresponding Interview Transcripts are used. In each case, the final suspect has the right blood type and height, was not on the field trip, and knows the area well, and another witness' statement indicates that the suspect lied during his or her interview with the police. Sample Responses: **(1)** Using Clues Set #1 and Martinez 113-2 and Weatherwax 111-7 transcripts: **Alice Weatherwax is the thief**; another witness' statement indicated that she lied about the rain during the conference she was attending; Perry Martinez was at the rodeo all day and cannot be the thief. **(2)** Using Clues Set #2 and Martinez 222-2 and Seowtewa 112-4 transcripts: **Perry Martinez is the thief**; another witness' statement indicated that he lied about the rain during the rodeo; Teresa Seowtewa was at the library all day and cannot be the thief. **(3)** Using Clues Set #3 and Seowtewa 333-4 and Weatherwax 223-7 transcripts: **Teresa Seowtewa is the thief**; another witness' statement indicated that she lied about the rain at lunchtime; Alice Weatherwax was at a conference in Crownpoint all day and cannot be the thief.

Review and Assessment (pp. 226–227)

10. linear

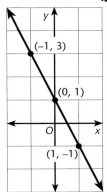

11. nonlinear

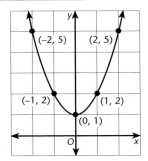

12. linear

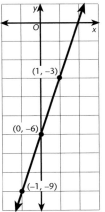

24.

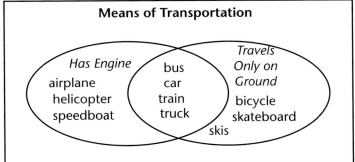

MODULE 4

Section 1, Exploration 2 (p. 237)

21. b. The lengths of the diameters will vary. A sample is given.

Sphere	Volume (fraction of the original sphere)	Length of Diameter (cm)
1	1	6 cm
2	$\frac{1}{2}$	4.8 cm
3	$\frac{1}{4}$	3.8 cm
4	$\frac{1}{8}$	3 cm

Section 2, Extension (p. 255)

28. a.

The Efficiency of Cylindrical Containers Whose Height is Twice the Radius			
Container Name	Height h	Radius r	Efficiency $\frac{3}{r}$
A	2	1	3
B	6	3	1
C	12	6	0.5
D	18	9	0.33
E	24	12	0.25

Section 3, Exploration 1 (p. 259)

5.

Rise	Run	Slope	Slant	increasing/decreasing
3.1	5	0.62	up	increasing
−4.1	5	−0.82	down	decreasing
0.3	5	0.06	up	increasing
1.7	5	0.34	up	increasing
−3	5	−0.6	down	decreasing
−2.3	5	−0.46	down	decreasing
−0.9	5	−0.18	down	decreasing

Section 3, Exploration 2 (p. 261)

14. a.

Expected DVD player Sales	Expected VCR sales
800 + 160(3) = 1280	600 − 120(3) = 240
800 + 160(4) = 1440	600 − 120(4) = 120
800 + 160(5) = 1600	600 − 120(5) = 0

b.

Expected DVD Player Sales

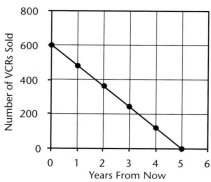

Expected VCR Sales

The points lie on a straight line.

Section 3, Practice and Application (pp. 266–268)

9. Accept reasonable estimates.

Kemp's Ridley Turtle Nests (1970–1995)	
Time Period	Rate of Change (number of turtle nests/year)
1970–1975	−350
1975–1980	−75
1980–1985	−50
1985–1990	65
1990–1995	200

26.

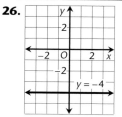

slope: 0

27.

slope: undefined

28.

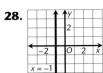

slope: undefined

Section 5, Exploration 1 (p. 286)

4. a.

Choices for position 1	Choices for position 2	Choices for position 3	Symbol

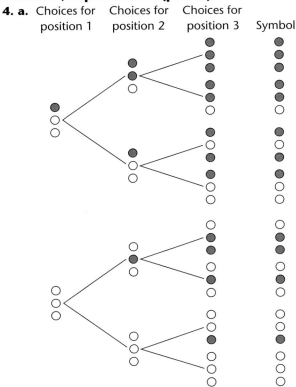

Section 5, Exploration 2 (p. 288)

10. a.

Position of 1st dot	Position of 2nd dot	Positions chosen
4	1	4, 1
	2	4, 2
	5	4, 5
5	1	5, 1
	2	5, 2
	4	5, 4

12 paths

Section 5, Practice and Application (pp. 293–294)

1. a.

Exterior Color	Interior Color	Combination
white	black	white, black
	gray	white, gray
red	black	red, black
	gray	red, gray
navy blue	black	navy blue, black
	gray	navy blue, gray
forest green	black	forest green, black
	gray	forest green, gray
tan	black	tan, black
	gray	tan, gray
maroon	black	maroon, black
	gray	maroon, gray

3. a.

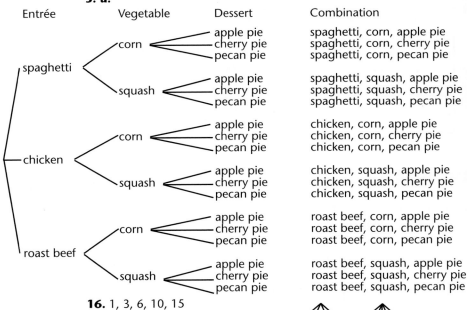

Entrée	Vegetable	Dessert	Combination
spaghetti	corn	apple pie	spaghetti, corn, apple pie
		cherry pie	spaghetti, corn, cherry pie
		pecan pie	spaghetti, corn, pecan pie
	squash	apple pie	spaghetti, squash, apple pie
		cherry pie	spaghetti, squash, cherry pie
		pecan pie	spaghetti, squash, pecan pie
chicken	corn	apple pie	chicken, corn, apple pie
		cherry pie	chicken, corn, cherry pie
		pecan pie	chicken, corn, pecan pie
	squash	apple pie	chicken, squash, apple pie
		cherry pie	chicken, squash, cherry pie
		pecan pie	chicken, squash, pecan pie
roast beef	corn	apple pie	roast beef, corn, apple pie
		cherry pie	roast beef, corn, cherry pie
		pecan pie	roast beef, corn, pecan pie
	squash	apple pie	roast beef, squash, apple pie
		cherry pie	roast beef, squash, cherry pie
		pecan pie	roast beef, squash, pecan pie

16. 1, 3, 6, 10, 15

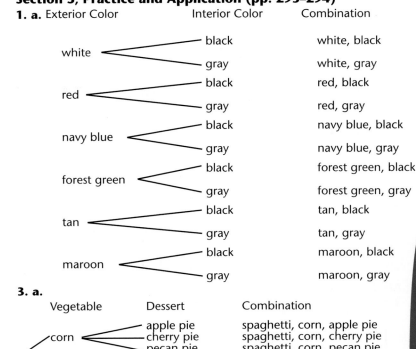

Section 6, Exploration 1 (p. 299)

9. a. $\frac{11{,}703{,}240}{12{,}960{,}000} = \frac{23{,}509}{36{,}000} \approx 0.90$;

$$\left(\frac{\cancel{60} \cdot 59 \cdot \cancel{58} \cdot \cancel{57}}{\cancel{60} \cdot 60 \cdot \cancel{60} \cdot \cancel{60}} = \frac{1 \cdot 59 \cdot 29 \cdot 19}{1 \cdot 60 \cdot 30 \cdot 20} = \frac{32{,}509}{36{,}000} \right)$$

Section 6, Practice and Application (pp. 301–302)

5. b. MATH4YOU: $\dfrac{1}{26 \cdot 25 \cdot 24 \cdot 23 \cdot 10 \cdot 22 \cdot 21 \cdot 20} = \dfrac{1}{3.315312 \cdot 10^{10}}$

MATH: $\dfrac{1 \cdot 1 \cdot 1 \cdot 1 \cdot 10 \cdot 22 \cdot 21 \cdot 20}{26 \cdot 25 \cdot 24 \cdot 23 \cdot 10 \cdot 22 \cdot 21 \cdot 20} = \dfrac{1}{358,800}$

A license plate on which the first four letters spell MATH is about 92,400 times more likely than the license plate MATH4YOU.

c. 80,318,101,760 or $26^7 \cdot 10$ license plates

MATH4YOU: $\dfrac{1}{26^7 \cdot 10}$;

MATH as first four letters: $\dfrac{1 \cdot 1 \cdot 1 \cdot 1 \cdot 10 \cdot 26^3}{26^7 \cdot 10} = \dfrac{1}{456,976}$

A license plate on which the first four letters spell MATH is 175,760 times more likely than the license plate MATH4YOU.

13. b.   Science Test Scores

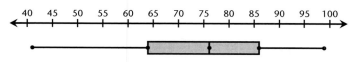

Module Project (p. 304)

1.

Cylinder diameter (in.)	Number of cylinders needed	Volume of each cylinder (in.³)	Combined volume of all cylinders (in.³)
3	3	84.78	254.34
2	4	37.68	150.72
1.5	5	21.195	105.975
1	7	9.42	65.94

MODULE 5

Section 1, Exploration 1 (p. 311)

4. Sample responses are given.

a. **b.** It shows the prism from a different side.

c.

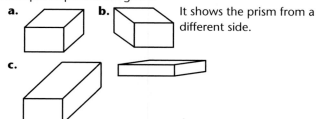

Section 1, Exploration 2 (p. 314)

15. b.

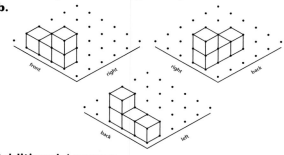

Section 1, Key Concepts (p. 316)

23.

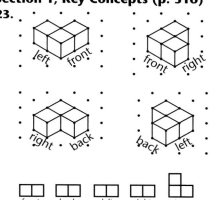

Section 1, Practice and Application (p. 317)

2. d.

Figure	# of cubes	Surface area	Volume
a	8	24 unit²	8 unit³
b	16	40 unit²	16 unit³
c	24	56 unit²	24 unit³

When you multiply one of the dimensions by n the volume (or number of cubes) is also multiplied by n.

5. Figure before removing cubes: S.A. = 24 unit², V = 8 unit³; Figure after removing cubes: S.A. = 24 unit², V = 7 unit³

6. Figure before removing cubes: S.A. = 36 unit², V = 12 unit³; Figure after removing cubes: S.A. = 30 unit², V = 8 unit³

Section 1, Extra Skill Practice (p. 320)

5.

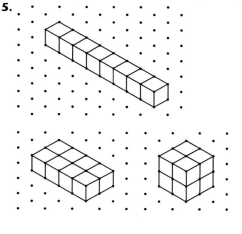

6.

Prism	Cubes	Surface Area	Volume
3 × 1 × 1	3	14	3
4 × 1 × 1	4	14	4
2 × 1 × 2	4	16	4
8 × 1 × 1	8	34	8
4 × 2 × 1	8	30	8
2 × 2 × 2	8	24	8

The number of cubes and the volume are equal to the product of the dimensions of the prism.

7.

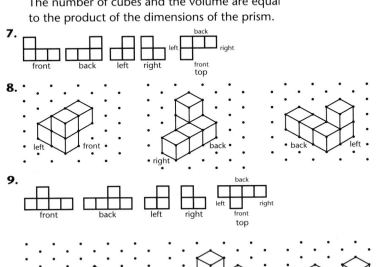

8.

9.

Section 2, Exploration 2 (p. 326)
20. a.

Figure	Number of faces	Number of vertices	Number of edges
tetrahedron	4	4	6
modified mansard-roof house	10	12	20
rectangular prism	6	8	12

Figure	Number of faces	Number of vertices	Number of edges
peaked-roof house	9	9	16
Sample response: triangular prism	5	6	9
Sample response: square pyramid	5	5	8

Section 2, Practice and Application (p. 332)
11. similar: 1 and 3, 2 and 5, 4, 6, and 7; congruent: 2 and 5, 4 and 6; For similar triangles, check the type of triangle and the angle measures. For congruent triangles, use the side-side-side or side-angle-side rule.

$\triangle GHK \cong \triangle EFD$, $\triangle STV \cong \triangle QPR$

Section 2, Standardized Testing (p. 336)

Number of sides on the base of each pyramid	Number of faces on the new polyhedron	Number of edges on the new polyhedron	Number of vertices on the new polyhedron
3	6	9	5
4	8	12	6
5	10	15	7
100	200	300	102

Section 4, Exploration 2 (p. 353)
12.

Block Prisms				Block Pyramids				Volume Ratio
	h	B	Bh		h	B	V	$V:Bh$
	1	1	1		1	1	1	$1 \div 1 = 1.000$
	2	4	8		2	4	5	$5 \div 8 = 0.625$
	3	9	27		3	9	14	$14 \div 27 = 0.519$
	4	16	64		4	16	30	$30 \div 64 = 0.469$
	5	25	125		5	25	55	$55 \div 125 = 0.44$
	6	36	216		6	36	91	$91 \div 216 = 0.421$
	7	49	343		7	49	140	$140 \div 343 = 0.408$
	8	64	512		8	64	204	$204 \div 512 = 0.398$
	9	81	729		9	81	285	$285 \div 729 = 0.391$
	10	100	1000		10	100	385	$385 \div 1000 = 0.385$

Section 4, Practice and Application (p. 357)
7. b. Possible answers:

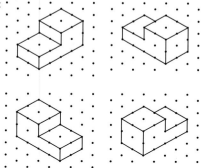

8. b.

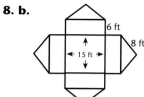

6 ft
8 ft
15 ft

Section 5, Exploration 1 (p. 367)
13. a. ∠5 and ∠6 are supplementary, so $m\angle 5 = 180° - m\angle 6 = 180° - 56° = 124°$. **b.** Lines p and q are parallel and ∠2 and ∠6 are alternate interior angles, so $m\angle 2 = m\angle 6 = 56°$. **c.** Lines p and q are parallel and ∠8 and ∠6 are corresponding angles, so $m\angle 8 = m\angle 6 = 56°$. **14. a.** alternate interior angles: ∠4 and ∠8, ∠3 and ∠7; alternate exterior angles: ∠1 and ∠5, ∠2 and ∠6; vertical angles: ∠1 and ∠3,

∠2 and ∠8, ∠5 and ∠7, ∠4 and ∠6; corresponding angles: ∠1 and ∠7, ∠2 and ∠4, ∠3 and ∠5, ∠8 and ∠6

Section 6, Exploration 1 (p. 377)
6. a.

Actual length (inches)	12	18	24	30	36
Length on drawing (in.)	$\frac{1}{8}$	$\frac{3}{16}$	$\frac{1}{4}$	$\frac{5}{16}$	$\frac{3}{8}$

Actual length (inches)	42	48	120	144	384	480
Length on drawing (in.)	$\frac{7}{16}$	$\frac{1}{2}$	$1\frac{1}{4}$	$1\frac{1}{2}$	4	5

Section 6, Exploration 2 (p. 379)
15. a. $\dfrac{\text{area } \triangle DEF}{\text{area } \triangle ABC} = \left(\dfrac{150 \text{ cm}}{3\text{m}}\right)^2 = \left(\dfrac{50 \text{ cm}}{1 \text{ m}}\right)^2 = \dfrac{2500 \text{ cm}^2}{1 \text{ m}^2}$ or

$\dfrac{\text{area } \triangle DEF}{\text{area } \triangle ABC} = \left(\dfrac{150 \text{ cm}}{3 \text{ m}}\right)^2 = \left(\dfrac{150 \text{ cm}}{300 \text{ cm}}\right)^2 = \left(\dfrac{1 \text{ cm}}{2 \text{ cm}}\right)^2 = \dfrac{1}{4}$

Section 6, Practice and Application (p. 382)
3. Sample Response: Scale: 5 mm = 1 mm

4. Sample Response: Scale: 1 in. = 24 ft

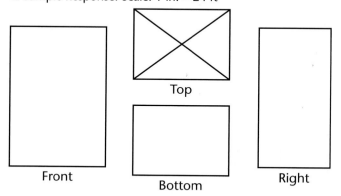

Front
Top
Bottom
Right

MODULE 6

Section 2, Exploration 1 (pp. 407–409)
4. b. 27 months; Sample Response: After 12 months, she still needs $440 and $\dfrac{440}{30} = 14\frac{2}{3}$, so it will take $15 + 12 = 27$ months.

A20 Additional Answers

5. a, b.

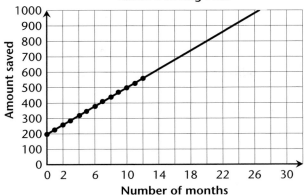

Sarah's Saving Plan

a. See graph; The points lie on a line. **b.** See graph; 27 months
c. No; Sarah deposits the money at the end of each month.

8.

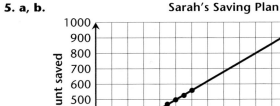

Savings Plan

The point where the lines intersect shows when Sarah and Janet had the same amount of money in the bank.

9. Possible answers: Use the equation $y = 650 + 175x$. If $y = 10,000$ then $x \approx 53.4$; 54 weeks.

Number of Weeks	Amount of Savings ($)
0	0
1	825
2	1000
3	1175
4	1350
. . .	. . .
54	10,100

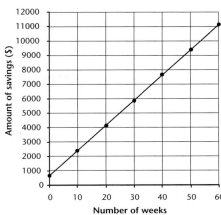

School Savings

Explanations may vary. Check students' work.

10. b. Sample responses are given. Equation: It requires less time and effort than a table or graph, but it only provides data values when numbers are substituted into the equation. Table: It gives additional information that may be helpful, but may have to be carried out really far to display that information. Graph: It gives a visual interpretation, but may be difficult to determine exact coordinates if they are not integers.

Section 2, Practice and Application (p. 416)

17. b.

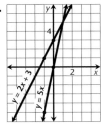

Find the point of intersection of the two graphs.

c.

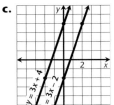

No; The graphs are parallel lines and do not intersect.

Section 3, Exploration 1 (p. 422)

8. b.

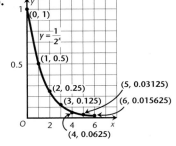

c. They are both curves; The graph of $y = 2^x$ increases rapidly and becomes very steep. The graph of $y = \left(\frac{1}{2}\right)^x$ decreases and flattens out gradually, getting closer and closer to the x-axis.

Section 3, Exploration 2 (pp. 424–425)

13. b.

Year	Amount in account at beginning of year	Expression	Amount in account at end of year
1	$2000	1.05 · 2000	$2100
2	$2100	1.05 · 1.05 · 2000	$2205
3	$2205	1.05 · 1.05 · 1.05 · 2000	$2315.25
4	$2315.25	1.05 · 1.05 · 1.05 · 1.05 · 2000	$2431.01
5	$2431.01	1.05 · 1.05 · 1.05 · 1.05 · 1.05 · 2000	$2552.56

17. c.

Price of candy bar	$0.01 yearly increase	10% yearly increase
After 10 years	$0.20	$0.26
After 20 years	$0.30	$0.67
After 30 years	$0.40	$1.74
After 40 years	$0.50	$4.53

Sample response: For 10 years, the prices are not significantly different. After that, the price increases much more rapidly for the 10% increase than for the $0.01 increase.

Section 3, Practice and Application (p. 427)

3. a.

Number of minutes	Number of new people hearing the rumor	Total number of people who have heard the rumor
0	1	1
1	2	3
2	4	7
3	8	15
4	16	31
5	32	63
6	64	127
7	128	255
8	256	511
9	512	1023
10	1024	2047

d.

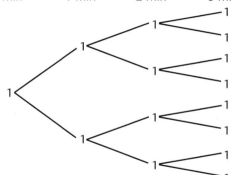

Section 4, Practice and Application (p. 437)

2. Sample Response: head $(x', y') = (x, y - 1)$; left foot $(x, y) = (x + 1, y)$; right foot $(x, y) = (x - 1, y)$

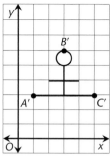

3.

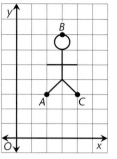

4.

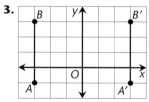

5.

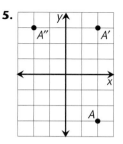

6.

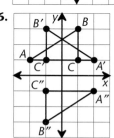

7. 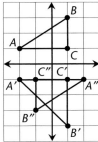 It is the same.

Section 5, Exploration 1 (p. 444)

6. Sample Response: I think it determines whether the parabola opens up or down, and how wide or narrow the parabola is.

a.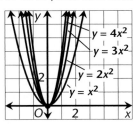

b.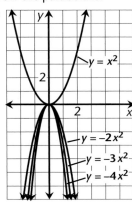

c.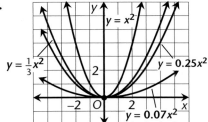

d.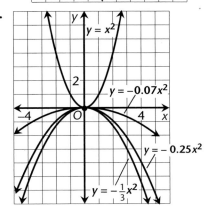

8. a.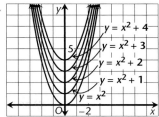

c. They will have the same shape and line of symmetry. Their vertices will be $(0, -1)$ and $(0, -2)$.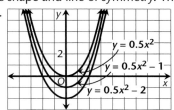

Section 5, Practice and Application (p. 448)

7. b.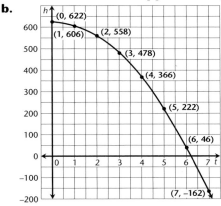

c. about 6.25 sec; The graph crosses the x-axis at about $x = 6.25$.

d. 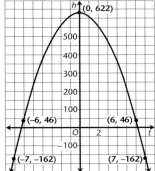 No; When the object is dropped, $t = 0$. Negative time values do not make sense in this situation.

Section 5, Extra Skill Practice (p. 451)

4. same shape, vertex, and axis of symmetry, but opens in opposite direction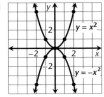

5. same axis of symmetry, narrower, vertex at (0, –2) instead of (0, 0), opens in opposite direction

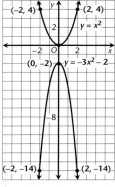

6. same vertex and axis of symmetry, wider, and opens in opposite direction

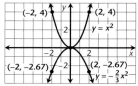

9. $y = x^2 + 7x$; quadratic function **10.** $y = 5x - 16$; not a quadratic function **11.** $y = -x^2 - 5x + 10$; quadratic function **12.** $y = 3x + 12$; not a quadratic function **13.** $y = 6$; not a quadratic function **14.** $y = -2x^2 - 3x + 20$; quadratic function **15.** $y = 2x^3 - 5x^2 - 7$; not a quadratic function **16.** $y = -12x^3 + 4x^2 - 2x - 32$; not a quadratic function

Module Project (p. 453)

3. a. See table below; between 3:45 P.M. and 4:00 P.M.

Time after 3:00 P.M. (hours)	Brad's distance from Brad's house (miles)	John's distance from Brad's house (miles)
0	0	10
0.25	2	9
0.50	4	8
0.75	6	7
1.00	8	6

c. See graph below. The point where the lines intersect indicates when Brad and John will meet.

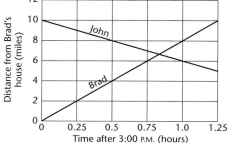

d. $8x = 10 - 4x$
$12x = 10$
$x = \dfrac{5}{6}$; after $\dfrac{5}{6}$ hr or 50 min; They will meet at 3:50 P.M.

MODULE 7

Section 1, Exploration 1 (pp. 459–460)

3. a. $\dfrac{60 \text{ sec}}{1 \text{ min}} \cdot \dfrac{60 \text{ min}}{1 \text{ hr}} \cdot \dfrac{24 \text{ hr}}{1 \text{ day}} \cdot \dfrac{365 \text{ days}}{1 \text{ year}} = \dfrac{31{,}536{,}000 \text{ sec}}{1 \text{ yr}} \approx$
$3 \cdot 10^7$ sec/year

c. $(2 \cdot 10^5) \cdot (3 \cdot 10^7) = 2 \cdot (10^5 \cdot (3 \cdot 10^7))$ Associative property
$ = 2 \cdot ((10^5 \cdot 3) \cdot 10^7)$ Associative property
$ = 2 \cdot ((3 \cdot 10^5) \cdot 10^7)$ Commutative property
$ = 2 \cdot (3 \cdot (10^5 \cdot 10^7))$ Associative property
$ = (2 \cdot 3) \cdot (10^5 \cdot 10^7)$ Associative property
$ = 6 \cdot (10^5 \cdot 10^7)$

10. b. $\dfrac{10 \cdot 10 \cdot 10 \cdot 10 \cdot 10 \cdot 10 \cdot 10 \cdot 10 \cdot 10}{10 \cdot 10 \cdot 10 \cdot 10 \cdot 10 \cdot 10} = 10^3$

Section 1, Exploration 2 (p. 462)

17. a.–h. The exponents in the Quotient column decrease by 1. The denominator in the Simplified ratio column is multiplied by 10, so the exponent in the Simplified ratio using exponents column increases by 1.

Ratio of fields of view	Ratio using exponents	Simplified ratio	Simplified ratio using exponents	Ratio expressed as a single power
$\dfrac{1000}{1000}$	$\dfrac{10^3}{10^3}$	$\dfrac{1}{1} = 1$		10^0
$\dfrac{100}{1000}$	$\dfrac{10^2}{10^3}$	$\dfrac{1}{10}$	$\dfrac{1}{10^1}$	10^{-1}
$\dfrac{10}{1000}$	$\dfrac{10^1}{10^3}$	$\dfrac{1}{100}$	$\dfrac{1}{10^2}$	10^{-2}
$\dfrac{1}{1000}$	$\dfrac{10^0}{10^3}$	$\dfrac{1}{1000}$	$\dfrac{1}{10^3}$	10^{-3}
$\dfrac{0.1}{1000}$	$\dfrac{10^{-1}}{10^3}$	$\dfrac{1}{10{,}000}$	$\dfrac{1}{10^4}$	10^{-4}
$\dfrac{0.01}{1000}$	$\dfrac{10^{-2}}{10^3}$	$\dfrac{1}{100{,}000}$	$\dfrac{1}{10^5}$	10^{-5}
$\dfrac{0.001}{1000}$	$\dfrac{10^{-3}}{10^3}$	$\dfrac{1}{1{,}000{,}000}$	$\dfrac{1}{10^6}$	10^{-6}
$\dfrac{0.0001}{1000}$	$\dfrac{10^{-4}}{10^3}$	$\dfrac{1}{10{,}000{,}000}$	$\dfrac{1}{10^7}$	10^{-7}

Section 1, Practice and Application (pp. 466–468)

14. Answers will vary. Sample response:

Change in wind speed in knots	Change in wave energy in foot-pounds
From 0 to 10	≈29
From 20 to 30	≈1877
From 50 to 60	≈19,378

The more severe the wind the greater the increase in wave energy for a 10-knot increase in wind speed.

62. $3^{-2} = \dfrac{1}{3^2}$ so $3^{-2} \cdot 3^7 = \dfrac{1}{3^2} \cdot 3^7 = \dfrac{3^7}{3^2} = \dfrac{\overset{1}{\cancel{3}} \cdot \overset{1}{\cancel{3}} \cdot 3 \cdot 3 \cdot 3 \cdot 3 \cdot 3}{\underset{1}{\cancel{3}} \cdot \underset{1}{\cancel{3}}} = 3^5$

$\dfrac{5^8}{5^{11}} = \dfrac{\overset{1}{\cancel{5^8}}}{\underset{1}{\cancel{5^8}} \cdot 5 \cdot 5 \cdot 5} = \dfrac{1}{5^3}$

Section 4, Exploration 1 (p. 499)

14. a. Each term arranged vertically is multiplied by each term arranged horizontally and the product is written in the cell of the table corresponding to the terms that were multiplied. The table model is a shortened version of the tile model in which expressions replace combinations of tiles. For example, you can write "3" instead of using 3 tiles or "–2x" instead of using 2 negative x-tiles.

Section 4, Exploration 2 (p. 505)

35. Sample Response: Tyrell is correct. The only factors of 5 are 5 and 1, and when arranged in 1 row of 5 or 5 rows of 1 there is no way to add the same number of x-tiles to the width and to the length. For example:

◄ These cannot be 5 positive tiles.

MODULE 8

Section 1, Exploration 2 (p. 523)

14.

Month	Number of Rabbit Pairs			Total Number of Rabbit Pairs
	Newborn	Growing	Adult	
Start	1	0	0	1
1	0	1	0	1
2	1	0	1	2
3	1	1	1	3
4	2	1	2	5
5	3	2	3	8
6	5	3	5	13

Section 1, Extension (p. 529)

27. a.

Steps	Number of segments	Length of each segment	Total perimeter at this stage
(triangle)	3	1 unit	3 units
(star)	12	$\dfrac{1}{3}$ unit	$\dfrac{12}{3} = 4$ units
(figure)	48	$\dfrac{1}{9}$ unit	$\dfrac{48}{9}$ units
(figure)	192	$\dfrac{1}{27}$ unit	$\dfrac{192}{27}$ units
⋮	⋮	⋮	⋮
n	$3 \cdot 4^{n-1}$	$\dfrac{1}{3^{n-1}}$	$\dfrac{3 \cdot 4^{n-1}}{3^{n-1}}$

Section 1, Study Skills (p. 530)

1. Sample Response: Choices A and C are not correct because they are not in scientific notation. Choice B is not correct because 16.6 is not between 1 and 10. Choice D is correct because it is in scientific notation. **2.** Sample Response: Draw a rectangle. Inside the rectangle, draw two intersecting ovals. Put letters with no vertical or horizontal symmetry in the rectangle outside the ovals. Put letters with only horizontal symmetry in one oval and letters with only vertical symmetry in the other oval. Put letters with both horizontal and vertical symmetry in the intersection of the ovals.

Section 2, Exploration 1 (pp. 533–534)

6. b. When placing the edges of hexagons together the gaps left form angles with the same measure as the angles of a regular hexagon and can be filled with another hexagon. When placing the edges of pentagons together around another pentagon, gaps that form acute angles are left between the pieces making it impossible to fill with another pentagon.

7.

Polygon	Number of sides	Number of triangles	Sum of measures of interior angles	Sample figure for parts (a), (b), (d), and (f)
triangle	3	1	180°	
quadrilateral	4	2	360°	
pentagon	5	3	540°	
hexagon	6	4	720°	

Section 2, Exploration 2 (p. 536)

19. Sample Response: The design in the center would change if the figure was rotated. There are also shapes between the points of the star that are mirror images of each other and would prevent the rotated figure from being congruent to the original figure; 180°

Section 3, Exploration 1 (pp. 544–546)

10. b.

Quadrilateral	Diagonal Properties
rectangle	bisectors
square	both
trapezoid	neither
rhombus	both
parallelogram	bisectors
kite	perpendicular

13. Sample Response:

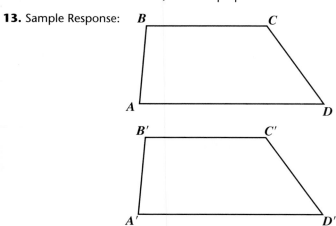

b.

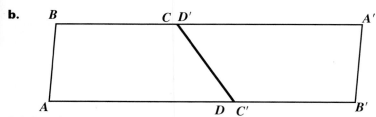

16. Sample Response:

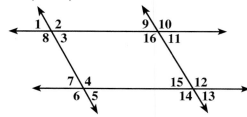

$m\angle2 = m\angle4$, corresponding angles
$m\angle2 = m\angle16$, alternate interior angles
so $m\angle4 = m\angle16$, substitution

Section 3, Practice and Application (p. 551)

11.

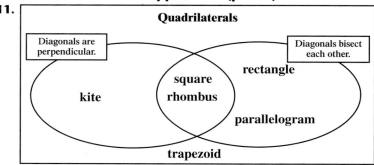

Module Project (p. 574)

1.

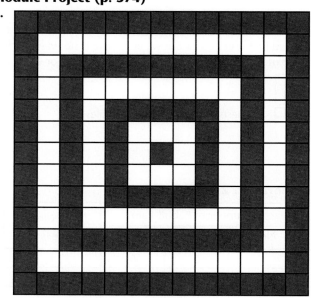

Review and Assessment (p. 577)

18. a. $AB = \sqrt{2^2 + 4^2} = \sqrt{16 + 4} = \sqrt{20}$ and $BC = \sqrt{6^2 + 3^2} = \sqrt{36 + 9} = \sqrt{45}$, so $AC = \sqrt{20 + 45} = \sqrt{65}$. Because $ABCD$ is a rectangle and therefore a parallelogram, $CD = AB = \sqrt{20}$ and $AD = BC = \sqrt{65}$. Then $BD = \sqrt{20 + 45} = \sqrt{65}$. **b.** The midpoint of $\overline{AC}$ is $\left(\frac{-1 + 7}{2} + \frac{0 + 1}{2}\right) = \left(3, \frac{1}{2}\right)$. The midpoint of $\overline{BD}$ is $\left(\frac{1 + 5}{2}, 4 + \left(\frac{-3}{2}\right)\right) = \left(3, \frac{1}{2}\right)$. So, the diagonals bisect each other. **20.** Sample Response:

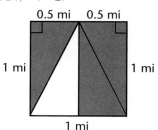